Peter Jenkins

Calgary, Alberta

January 25, 1971

ENGINEERING MECHANICS
Dynamics

PRENTICE-HALL, INTERNATIONAL, INC., *London*
PRENTICE-HALL OF AUSTRALIA, PTY, LTD., *Sydney*
PRENTICE-HALL OF CANADA, LTD., *Toronto*
PRENTICE-HALL OF INDIA (PRIVATE) LTD., *New Delhi*
PRENTICE-HALL OF JAPAN, INC., *Tokyo*

second edition

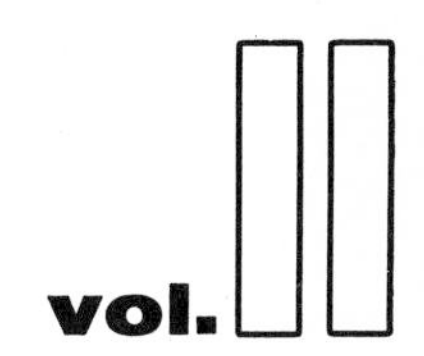

ENGINEERING MECHANICS

Dynamics

IRVING H. SHAMES

Professor and Head
Division of Interdisciplinary Studies
State University of New York at Buffalo

PRENTICE-HALL, INC., ENGLEWOOD CLIFFS, NEW JERSEY

PRENTICE-HALL
SERIES IN ENGINEERING SCIENCE

Hall and Ibele: ENGINEERING THERMODYNAMICS
Li: ENGINEERING ANALYSIS
Shames: ENGINEERING MECHANICS: STATICS
Shames: ENGINEERING MECHANICS: DYNAMICS
Shames: ENGINEERING MECHANICS: STATICS AND DYNAMICS
Shames: MECHANICS OF DEFORMABLE SOLIDS

Library of Congress Catalog Card Number 66–10092

Printed in the United States of America C–27923

Current printing (last digit):
10 9 8 7 6 5 4

PREFACE
to the Second Edition

The opening paragraph from the first edition applies to the second edition and, accordingly, I now quote: "This book is a vector treatment of mechanics. I have endeavored to write a fundamental and rigorous text designed to give the student a background that will enable him to deal with the novel and challenging situations confronting present-day engineers. At the same time, I have tried to present material that will help the student develop a reasonable facility for discharging the more routine but ever-present problems in mechanics and, by including in this first course certain introductory and common material for other ensuing courses in mechanics, I have attempted to present a broader perspective of the usual undergraduate aspects of the subjects."

My primary effort in preparing the second edition has been directed toward increasing the pedogogical effectiveness of the treatment while still maintaining the level and degree of rigor of the first edition. Toward this end I have instituted the following changes:

1. The material on kinematics (Chapter 11 in the first edition) has been redistributed so as to occupy Chapters 11 and 15 of the text. This allows for a more gradual buildup in the difficulty and degree of sophistication of the presentation. Also, this new arrangement decreases the delay time between the presentation of certain kinematical concepts and the full application of these concepts to general dynamical problems.

2. Much of the material on vibrations (formerly part of Chapter 12) has been moved to Chapter 20 so as to take full advantage of concurrent course work in differential equations. However, enough material on vibrations has been presented in Chapter 12 (Dynamics of Particles) to avoid giving the student the impression that vibrations of lumped systems is something apart from ordinary particle dynamics.

3. Except for the deletion of the chapter on mechanics of deformable media, readers familiar with the first edition will find the ordering of the material outside of kinematics and vibrations unchanged. However, most of the text has been rewritten with the goal of achieving greater clarity and greater continuity.

4. Many new sample problems have been added to better illustrate the use of the theory and to convey information on problems of topical interest. A similar buildup in the homework problems has been undertaken in this edition so as to provide a wide range of problems varying

from simple ones to those that are complex. Listed among the homework, problems are suggested projects making use of digital and analog computers for students interested and knowledgeable in these techniques. An asterisk has been used to identify particularly challenging problems and projects.

5. The asterisk has also been used in the new edition to identify sections that might easily be deleted with little or no loss in continuity. Also, I have used smaller type to set off material which, due to its advanced or specialized nature, might be reserved for the particularly interested student as extra-credit work or merely as suitable extra reading. It is hoped that these devices will be helpful to the instructor in developing his course.

6. By expanded use of footnotes and by closure sections in each chapter, I have attempted to convey a view of mechanics that will securely link the subject matter presented to other engineering sciences to be studied later and to more advanced studies of mechanics itself.

The following is a more detailed description of the contents of the text and will further illustrate some of the changes made in the second edition.

We begin by computing time derivatives of a vector in the presence of a single reference using Cartesian coordinates, cylindrical coordinates, and path coordinates. We are then able to present the kinematics of a particle in the presence of a single reference. The concept of relative motion is next presented but is restricted, in this edition, until Chapter 15 to references that are translating relative to each other. We are able to carefully define, at this time, what is meant by the motion of a particle "relative to a point." In Chapter 12 we then examine the dynamics of a particle for rectilinear translation, for central force motion, and for certain applications to curvilinear motions. The concept of vibration is set forth and made ready for more careful study later in Chapter 20. The chapter closes with an examination of a system of particles and, using the center of mass concept, we are able, at this time, to better understand the particle concept that we have been using so often. In Chapters 13 and 14, respectively, the powerful methods of energy and momentum are employed on particles and systems of particles. At the end of Chapter 14, in the interest of continuity, I have examined the application of the equation $\boldsymbol{M} = \dot{\boldsymbol{H}}$ for simple, rigid-body, plane-motion problems of the type studied in earlier physics courses. Here we employ kinematical formulations of rigid bodies as given in earlier course work and show how the moment of inertia appears. These simple problems then set the stage for the remainder of the text by motivating the need for a careful study of the kinematics of a rigid body in Chapter 15 and the study of the inertia tensor in Chapter 16. Accordingly in Chapter 15 we present Chasle's theorem for a rigid body and, with this, are now able to extend the relative motion relations, introduced in Chapter 11, to cover the general case of references moving arbitrarily relative to each other. We are thus able in this chapter to wind up our efforts in particle dynamics and simultaneously to form the basis for a careful treatment of rigid-body dynamics. In Chapter 16 the material on the inertia tensor is so arranged that the use of tensor notation is made optional. A new section has been added for finding principal moments of inertia and the directions of the principal axes using the Lagrange multiplier approach. We are now ready, in Chapter 17, to examine carefully the equation $\boldsymbol{M} = \dot{\boldsymbol{H}}$ as applied to a rigid body. In particular, the very useful Euler equations are presented. At this time, the instructor has the option of making extensive use of Euler's equations and $\boldsymbol{M} = \dot{\boldsymbol{H}}$ to problems involving simple, pure rotation and plane motions before going to the more general three-dimensional motions. Alternatively, he can proceed from the more general problems, designed to give a grasp of the general equations, to challenging specialized problems of rotation and plane motion. (My own preference is the latter.) In Chapter 18, we consider energy methods for rigid bodies. Utilizing the material in both Chapters 17 and 18, we examine in Chapter 19 the special case of the motion of a rigid body about a fixed point. We explain the need for Euler angles and, with them, present material of topical interest in gyrodynamics. In small print, we have a somewhat shortened revision, from the first edition, of the interesting dynamics of the spinning top. This chapter has been considerably reworked to provide a more practical presentation. Finally, in Chapter 20 we continue the work on vibrations begun in Chapter 11. My decision to delete Chapter 21 of the first edition (the chapter on deformable media) is motivated by the feeling that such material is best studied in depth in courses on fluid mechanics.

I wish to express my gratitude to Dr. M. Morduchow of the Polytechnic Institute of Brooklyn and to Dr. Y. King Liu of the University of Michigan who, acting as reviewers for the publisher, have made numerous helpful comments and suggestions. My thanks go to Dr. C. K. Chu of Columbia University for the helpful and encouraging comments he has conveyed to me. Drs. H. Reismann and F. Cozzarelli, my colleagues at Buffalo, generously have made available to me short projects involving the use of the analog and the digital computer. I am indebted to them. Also, I am indebted to my other colleagues at Buffalo who have been a constant source of encouragement to me. To the many professors around the country who have kindly taken the time to write to me concerning many aspects of the first edition, I extend my sincere thanks. Their letters have been a strong impetus toward my continuing efforts to further develop this text. Finally, I wish to express my profound gratitude to Dr. E. A. Trabant for his long unwavering interest and confidence in my work. He has brought me to a place where I have been able to continue my writing efforts in an exciting and stimulating atmosphere.

I. H. Shames

CONTENTS

11

Kinematics of a Particle—Simple Relative Motion 301

11.1 Introduction *301*

Part A. General Notions 302

11.2 Differentiation of a Vector with Respect to Time *302*
11.3 General Notions for Integration of a Vector with Respect to time *305*

Part B. Evaluation of Derivatives 307

11.4 Introductory Remark *307*
11.5 Rectangular Components *307*
11.6 Velocity and Acceleration in Terms of Path Variables *308*
11.7 Cylindrical Coordinates *313*

Part C. Simple Kinematic Relations and Applications 318

11.8 Simple Relative Motion *318*
11.9 Forces Acting on a Body Having Known Motion *320*
11.10 Closure *324*

12

Particle Dynamics 337

Part A. Rectilinear Translation 337

12.1 Introduction *337*
12.2 Force is Constant *337*
12.3 Force is a Function of Time *339*
12.4 Force is a Function of Speed *340*
12.5 Force is a Function of Position *342*
12.6 Note on Other Cases *348*
12.7 Rectilinear Motion of Several Interacting Particles *349*
12.8 D'Alembert's Principle *349*

Part B Central-Force Motion 351

12.9 Introduction *351*
12.10 General Central-Force Motion *352*
12.11 Gravitational Central-Force Motion *354*
12.12 General Two-Body Problem *356*
12.13 Applications to Space Mechanics *357*

Part C. Special Topics 366

12.14 Introduction *366*
12.15 Introduction to Ballistics of Shells *366*
12.16 Remarks Concerning Motion of Charged Particles *373*
12.17 Motion of Charged Particles *376*

Part D. A System of Particles 381

12.18 The General Motion of a System of Particles *381*
12.19 Closure *384*

13

Energy Methods 398

Part A. Analysis for a Single Particle 398

13.1 Introduction *398*
13.2 Power Considerations *402*
13.3 Conservative Force Fields *405*
13.4 Conservation of Mechanical Energy *407*
13.5 Alternate Form of Work-Energy Equation *410*

Part B. Systems of Particles 411

13.6 Work-Energy Equations *411*
13.7 Kinetic-Energy Expression Based on Center of Mass *414*
13.8 Work-Kinetic Energy Expressions Based on Center of Mass *417*
13.9 Closure *422*

14

Methods of Momentum 439

Part A. Linear Momentum 439

14.1 Impulse and Momentum Relations for a Particle *439*
14.2 Linear Momentum Considerations for a System of Particles *443*
14.3 Conservation of Linear Momentum—Impact of Particles *447*
14.4 Collision of a Particle with a Massive Rigid Body *452*
14.5 A Note on Energy Loss *456*

Part B. Moment of Momentum 457

14.6 Moment of Momentum Equation for a Single Particle *457*
14.7 Moment of Momentum Equation for a System of Particles *459*
14.8 Angular Impulse: Conservation of Moment of Momentum *466*
14.9 Closure *467*

15

Kinematics of Rigid Bodies: Relative Motion 485

15.1 Introduction *485*
15.2 Translation and Rotation of Rigid Bodies *486*
15.3 Chasle's Theorem *487*
15.4 Derivative of a Vector Fixed in a Moving Reference *488*
15.5 Application of the Fixed Vector Concept *493*
15.6 General Relationship Between Derivatives of a Vector for Different References *500*
15.7 The Relationship Between Velocities of a Particle for Different References *502*
15.8 The Acceleration of a Particle for Different References *506*
15.9 Forces on a Particle Having a Known Motion *516*
15.10 The Coriolis Force *518*
15.11 Closure *521*

16

The Inertia Tensor 541

16.1 Introduction *541*
16.2 Formal Definition of Inertia Quantities *542*
16.3 The Relation of Mass Inertia Terms to Area Inertia Terms *545*
16.4 Translation of Coordinate Axes *546*
16.5 Transformation Properties of the Inertia Terms *548*
16.6 Tensor Notation for Transformations *552*
16.7 The Inertia Ellipsoid and Principal Moments of Inertia *554*
16.8 Computation of Principal Moments of Inertia *557*
16.9 Closure *558*

17

Dynamics of Rigid Bodies 565

17.1 Introduction *565*
17.2 Moment of Momentum for a Rigid Body *566*
17.3 Euler's Equations of Motion *570*
17.4 Application of Euler's Equation *572*
17.5 Balancing *585*
17.6 Simplifications of Euler's Equations *589*
17.7 D'Alembert's Principle for Rigid Bodies *599*
17.8 Necessary and Sufficient Conditions for Equilibrium of a Rigid Body *604*
17.9 Closure *604*

18

Energy Considerations for Rigid Bodies 620

18.1 Kinetic Energy of a Rigid Body *620*
18.2 Kinetic Energy of a Body in Pure Rotation *622*
18.3 Energy Formulations for Conservative Systems *626*
18.4 Work-Energy Relations *634*
18.5 Closure *639*

19

Motion of a Body about a Fixed Point 652

19.1 Introduction *652*
19.2 Euler Angles *653*
19.3 Equations of Motion *656*
19.4 Euler's Equation *665*
19.5 Torque-free Motion *666*
19.6 Symmetric Spinning Top under the Action of Gravity *673*
19.7 An Examination of Expected Nutation Velocity of the Top *675*
19.8 The Precession and Spin of the Top *677*
19.9 Closure *678*

20

Vibrations 685

20.1 Introduction *685*
20.2 Free Vibration *685*
20.3 Torsional Vibration *690*
20.4 Examples of Other Free-Oscillating Motions *694*
20.5 Energy Methods *697*
20.6 Linear Restoring Force and a Force Varying Sinusoidally with Time *699*
20.7 Linear Restoring Force with Viscous Damping *703*
20.8 Linear Restoring Force, Viscous Damping, and a Harmonic Disturbance *706*
20.9 Oscillatory Systems with Multi-degrees of Freedom *711*
20.10 Electric Circuit Analogue for a Mechanical System *715*
20.11 Closure *717*

Appendixes i

I Review of Conic Sections i

II Work—Kinetic Energy Relation iv

III Proof that Infinitesimal Rotations Are Vectors vi

IV General Proof of Chasle's Theorem vii

V Table of Properties of Various Homogeneous Solids ix

Selected Answers to Problems xi

Index xix

ENGINEERING MECHANICS
Dynamics

11

Kinematics of a Particle—Simple Relative Motion

11.1 Introduction

Kinematics is that phase of mechanics concerned with the study of the motion of particles and rigid bodies, with no consideration of what has caused the motion. We can consider kinematics as the geometry of motion. Once it is mastered, we can smoothly proceed to the relations between the factors causing the motion and the motion itself. This area of study is called *dynamics*. Dynamics can be conveniently separated into the following divisions, all of which we will study in this text:

1. Dynamics of a single particle. (You will remember from our chapters on statics that a particle is an idealization having no volume but having mass.)
2. Dynamics of a system of particles. This follows division 1 logically and forms the basis for the motion of continuous media such as fluid flow and rigid-body motion.
3. Dynamics of a rigid body. A large portion of this text concerns itself with this important part of mechanics.
4. Dynamics of a system of rigid bodies.

5. Dynamics of a continuous deformable medium. One of the most important cases of this is, of course, the fluid.

It is clear from our opening statements that the particle plays a vital role in the study of dynamics. What is the connection between the particle, which is a completely hypothetical concept, and the finite bodies encountered in physical problems? Briefly it is this: In many problems, the size and shape of a body are not relevant in the discussion of certain aspects of its motion; only the mass of the object is significant for such computations. For example, in towing a truck up a hill, as shown in Fig. 11.1, we would only be concerned with the mass of the truck and not its shape or size (if we neglect forces from the wind, etc.).* The truck may just as well be considered a particle in computing the necessary towing force. Other situations were pointed out in Chapter 1, and you are urged to review that material.

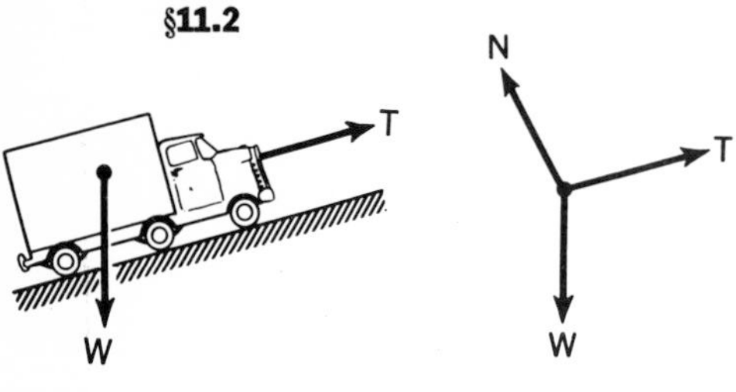

Fig. 11.1

We may present this relationship more precisely in the following manner. As will be learned in the next chapter (Section 12.18), the equation of motion of the center of mass of any body can be formed by:

1. concentrating the entire mass at the mass center of the body,
2. applying the total resultant force acting on the body to this hypothetical particle.

When the motion of the mass center characterizes all we need to know of the motion of the body, we employ the particle concept (i.e., we find the motion of the mass center). Thus, if all points of a body have at any time t the same velocity (this is called *translatory motion*), we need only know the motion of the mass center to fully characterize the motion. (This was the case for the truck, where the inertia of the tires was neglected.) If, additionally, the size of a body is small compared to its trajectory (as in planetary motion, for example), the motion of the center of mass is all that may be needed, and so again we may use the particle concept for such bodies.

PART A. General Notions

11.2 Differentiation of a Vector with Respect to Time

In the study of statics, we dealt with vector quantities. We found it convenient to incorporate the directional nature of these quantities in a certain notation and set of operations. In most cases these operations could be degenerated to the familiar algebraic operations on scalars. We called the totality of these very useful formulations vector algebra. It is once again necessary to expand our thinking from scalars to vectors—this time for the operation of differentiation and integration with respect to any scalar variable t (such as time).

For scalars, we are concerned only with the variation in magnitude of some

* We are neglecting the rotational effects of the wheels also.

quantity which is changing with time. The scalar definition of the derivative, then, is given as:

$$\frac{df(t)}{dt} = \lim_{\Delta t \to 0} \left[\frac{f(t + \Delta t) - f(t)}{\Delta t} \right] \qquad 11.1$$

This leads to another function of time, which may be differentiated in this manner, and the process may be repeated again and again, for suitable functions, to give higher derivatives.

In the case of a vector, the variation in time may be a change in magnitude or may be a *change in direction* or both. A vector that varies in this way is sometimes indicated as $\boldsymbol{F}(t)$. The formal definition of the derivative of a vector $\boldsymbol{F}$ with respect to time has the same form as above:

$$\frac{d\boldsymbol{F}}{dt} = \lim_{\Delta t \to 0} \left[\frac{\boldsymbol{F}(t + \Delta t) - \boldsymbol{F}(t)}{\Delta t} \right] \qquad 11.2$$

If $\boldsymbol{F}$ has no change in direction during the time interval, this operation differs little from the scalar case. However, when this is not the situation, we find, for the derivative of $\boldsymbol{F}$, a new vector having a magnitude as well as a direction that is different from $\boldsymbol{F}$ itself. It is this directional consideration which can be somewhat troublesome.

Let us consider the rate of change of the position vector of a particle with respect to time; this rate is defined as the *velocity vector*, $\boldsymbol{V}$, of the particle. Following the definition given by Eq. 11.2, we have:

$$\frac{d\boldsymbol{r}}{dt} = \lim_{\Delta t \to 0} \left[\frac{\boldsymbol{r}(t + \Delta t) - \boldsymbol{r}(t)}{\Delta t} \right] \qquad 11.3$$

The position vectors given in the bracket are shown in Fig. 11.2. The subtraction of these two vectors gives rise to the vector $\Delta \boldsymbol{r}$, which is shown as a chord connecting two points along the trajectory of the particle. Hence we can say:

$$\frac{d\boldsymbol{r}}{dt} = \lim_{\Delta t \to 0} \frac{\Delta \boldsymbol{r}}{\Delta t} = \lim_{\Delta t \to 0} \frac{\Delta \boldsymbol{r}}{\Delta s} \frac{\Delta s}{\Delta t}$$

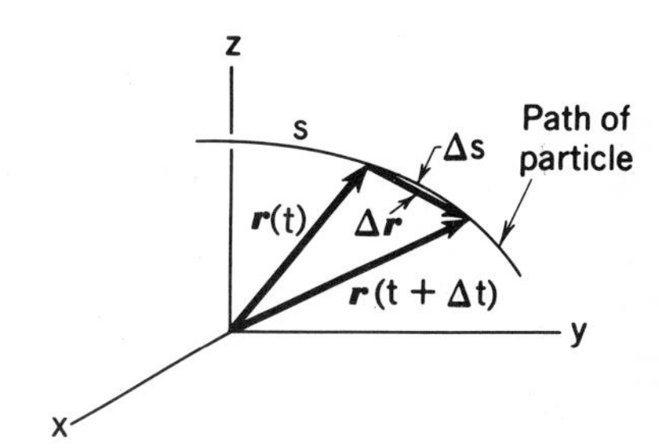

Fig. 11.2

As Δt goes to zero, the direction of $\Delta \boldsymbol{r}$ approaches tangency to the trajectory at position $\boldsymbol{r}(t)$ and approaches Δs in magnitude. Thus in the limit, $\Delta \boldsymbol{r}/\Delta s$ becomes a unit vector $\boldsymbol{\varepsilon}_t$ tangent to the trajectory. We then can say for the above equation:

$$\frac{d\boldsymbol{r}}{dt} = \boldsymbol{V} = \frac{ds}{dt} \boldsymbol{\varepsilon}_t \qquad 11.4$$

Therefore, $d\boldsymbol{r}/dt$ leads to a vector having a magnitude equal to the speed of the particle and a direction tangent to the trajectory. Keep in mind that there can be any angle between the position vector and the velocity vector. Students seem to want to limit this angle to 90°, which actually restricts you to a circular path.

Let us now consider the differentiation of vectors undergoing certain algebraic operations that were presented in Chapter 2 on statics. Examine first the sum of two vectors, $\boldsymbol{A}(t)$ and $\boldsymbol{B}(t)$. The derivative of this sum can be carried out by the following three steps:

$$(1)\quad \frac{d(\boldsymbol{A}+\boldsymbol{B})}{dt} = \lim_{\Delta t\to 0}\left[\frac{\boldsymbol{A}(t+\Delta t)+\boldsymbol{B}(t+\Delta t)-\boldsymbol{A}(t)-\boldsymbol{B}(t)}{\Delta t}\right]$$

$$(2)\quad = \lim_{\Delta t\to 0}\left[\frac{\boldsymbol{A}(t+\Delta t)-\boldsymbol{A}(t)}{\Delta t}\right] + \lim_{\Delta t\to 0}\left[\frac{\boldsymbol{B}(t+\Delta t)-\boldsymbol{B}(t)}{\Delta t}\right]$$

$$(3)\quad = \frac{d\boldsymbol{A}}{dt}+\frac{d\boldsymbol{B}}{dt} \tag{11.5}$$

In step 2 we have used the condition that the limit of the sum is equal to the sum of the limits. This and other theories concerning the limits may be carried over from the scalar theory of real variables, since each vector function is expressible in terms of three scalar functions. The taking of the derivative of the sum of vectors is, therefore, a *distributive* operation.

Consider next the derivative of the dot product of the vectors $\boldsymbol{A}$ and $\boldsymbol{B}$. Using our theorems on limits, we have:

$$\frac{d}{dt}(\boldsymbol{A}\cdot\boldsymbol{B}) = \lim_{\Delta t\to 0}\left[\frac{\boldsymbol{A}(t+\Delta t)\cdot\boldsymbol{B}(t+\Delta t)-\boldsymbol{A}(t)\cdot\boldsymbol{B}(t)}{\Delta t}\right]$$

Adding and subtracting $\boldsymbol{A}(t+\Delta t)\cdot\boldsymbol{B}(t)$ in the numerator, we have:

$$\frac{d}{dt}(\boldsymbol{A}\cdot\boldsymbol{B}) = \lim_{\Delta t\to 0}\left[\frac{\boldsymbol{A}(t+\Delta t)\cdot\boldsymbol{B}(t+\Delta t)-\boldsymbol{A}(t+\Delta t)\cdot\boldsymbol{B}(t)+\boldsymbol{A}(t+\Delta t)\cdot\boldsymbol{B}(t)-\boldsymbol{A}(t)\cdot\boldsymbol{B}(t)}{\Delta t}\right]$$

Rearranging the numerator, we get:

$$\frac{d}{dt}(\boldsymbol{A}\cdot\boldsymbol{B}) = \lim_{\Delta t\to 0}\left[\frac{\boldsymbol{A}(t+\Delta t)\cdot[\boldsymbol{B}(t+\Delta t)-\boldsymbol{B}(t)]+[\boldsymbol{A}(t+\Delta t)-\boldsymbol{A}(t)]\cdot\boldsymbol{B}(t)}{\Delta t}\right]$$

Thus taking the limit, we write:

$$\frac{d(\boldsymbol{A}\cdot\boldsymbol{B})}{dt} = \boldsymbol{A}\cdot\frac{d\boldsymbol{B}}{dt}+\frac{d\boldsymbol{A}}{dt}\cdot\boldsymbol{B} \tag{11.6}$$

It may similarly be shown for the derivative of the cross product that:

$$\frac{d}{dt}(\boldsymbol{A}\times\boldsymbol{B}) = \boldsymbol{A}\times\frac{d\boldsymbol{B}}{dt}+\frac{d\boldsymbol{A}}{dt}\times\boldsymbol{B}$$

Finally, consider the derivative of the product of a scalar function of time and a vector function of time. It will be left as an exercise to show that:

$$\frac{d}{dt}[f(t)\boldsymbol{A}(t)] = f\frac{d\boldsymbol{A}}{dt}+\frac{df}{dt}\boldsymbol{A}$$

Thus in differentiating the various types of products involving vectors, we proceed in a manner analogous to the differentiation of the product of scalars that we learned in elementary calculus.

Directing our attention to mechanics, we have already indicated that:

$$\boldsymbol{V} = \frac{d\boldsymbol{r}}{dt} \tag{11.7}$$

The acceleration vector of a particle can then be given as

$$\boldsymbol{a} = \frac{d\boldsymbol{V}}{dt} = \frac{d^2\boldsymbol{r}}{dt^2} \tag{11.8}$$

The differentiation and integration of vectors $\boldsymbol{r}$, $\boldsymbol{V}$, and $\boldsymbol{a}$ will concern us throughout the text.

11.3 General Notions for Integration of a Vector with Respect to Time

Let us now consider the integration of a vector. We have shown above that for the vector $\boldsymbol{A}(t)$ we can generally find a vector $\boldsymbol{B}(t)$ by the process of differentiation, as we defined it earlier. That is:

$$\boldsymbol{B}(t) = \frac{d\boldsymbol{A}(t)}{dt} \tag{11.9}$$

We can, on the other hand, proceed in the reverse order. That is, for a suitable vector $\boldsymbol{B}(t)$, we can determine the vector $\boldsymbol{A}(t)$ up to a constant vector. In other words, $\boldsymbol{A}(t)$ is said to be the integral of $\boldsymbol{B}(t)$ and, without the constant of integration, is given mathematically as:

$$\boldsymbol{A}(t) = \int \boldsymbol{B}(t)\, dt \tag{11.10}$$

Let us suppose now that we have a second relation:

$$\boldsymbol{B}(t)' = \frac{d\boldsymbol{A}(t)'}{dt} \tag{11.11}$$

We can say, assuming $\boldsymbol{B}(t)'$ is a suitable function, that:

$$\boldsymbol{A}(t)' = \int \boldsymbol{B}(t)'\, dt \tag{11.12}$$

Furthermore, using the distributive rule of differentiation, we may form the relation:

$$\frac{d}{dt}(\boldsymbol{A} + \boldsymbol{A}') = \frac{d\boldsymbol{A}}{dt} + \frac{d\boldsymbol{A}'}{dt} = \boldsymbol{B} + \boldsymbol{B}' \tag{11.13}$$

The definition of integration then stipulates for the above equation that:

$$\boldsymbol{A} + \boldsymbol{A}' = \int (\boldsymbol{B} + \boldsymbol{B}')\, dt$$

Replacing the left side of the above equation, using Eqs. 11.10 and 11.12, we have:

$$\int \boldsymbol{B}\, dt + \int \boldsymbol{B}'\, dt = \int (\boldsymbol{B}' + \boldsymbol{B})\, dt \tag{11.14}$$

Thus it follows from the distributive nature of differentiation that the operation of integration must also be distributive.

Now consider the product of $f(t)$, a scalar function of time, and $\boldsymbol{C}$, a constant vector. We know that in differentiating, *only* the function $f(t)$ is involved. Thus:

$$\frac{d[f(t)\,\boldsymbol{C}]}{dt} = \boldsymbol{C}\frac{df(t)}{dt} = \boldsymbol{C}g(t) \tag{11.15}$$

Since $\boldsymbol{C}$ is not affected during differentiation, it must not be affected during an integration. Thus in integrating $\boldsymbol{C}$, a constant vector, times $g(t)$, a scalar function of time, we may extract $\boldsymbol{C}$ from under the integral sign and proceed with the integration by methods of scalar calculus:

$$\int \boldsymbol{C}g(t)\,dt = \boldsymbol{C}\int g(t)\,dt \tag{11.16}$$

Similarly, if we have a scalar constant C times a variable vector $\boldsymbol{A}(t)$, we can say:

$$\int C\boldsymbol{A}(t)\,dt = C\int \boldsymbol{A}(t)\,dt \tag{11.17}$$

We can further demonstrate that with a constant vector $\boldsymbol{C}$ we can perform the following steps:

$$\int \boldsymbol{C}\cdot\boldsymbol{V}(t)\,dt = \boldsymbol{C}\cdot\int \boldsymbol{V}(t)\,dt$$

$$\int \boldsymbol{C}\times\boldsymbol{V}(t)\,dt = \boldsymbol{C}\times\int \boldsymbol{V}(t)\,dt$$

How can we proceed to evaluate the integral of a vector which is a function of time? Using $\boldsymbol{a}(t)$ to demonstrate the steps, we can, by employing the distributive rule, resolve $\boldsymbol{a}(t)$ into rectangular components and replace the single integration by three integrations as follows:

$$\int \boldsymbol{a}(t)\,dt = \int a_x(t)\boldsymbol{i}\,dt + \int a_y(t)\boldsymbol{j}\,dt + \int a_z(t)\,\boldsymbol{k}\,dt$$

Employing the rule in Eq. 11.16, where constant vectors are extracted from the integral sign, we then have:

$$\int \boldsymbol{a}(t)\,dt = \boldsymbol{i}\int a_x(t)\,dt + \boldsymbol{j}\int a_y(t)\,dt + \boldsymbol{k}\int a_z(t)\,dt$$

Thus the integration of the vector has been replaced by three scalar integrations of the type you have studied in calculus classes. These are indefinite integrations and so we get three constants of integration from the three integrations. Thus we have:

$$\int \boldsymbol{a}\,dt = (V_x + C_1)\boldsymbol{i} + (V_y + C_2)\boldsymbol{j} + (V_z + C_3)\,\boldsymbol{k}$$

$$\therefore \int \boldsymbol{a}\,dt = \boldsymbol{V} + \boldsymbol{C} \tag{11.18}$$

The vector $\boldsymbol{C}$ is hence a constant vector of integration. The indefinite integration of $\boldsymbol{V}(t)$ in the same manner can be given as follows:

$$\int \boldsymbol{V}\,dt = \boldsymbol{r} + \boldsymbol{D} \tag{11.19}$$

where $\boldsymbol{D}$ is another arbitrary constant vector of integration.

If we are integrating between limits t_1 and t_2, we can show, using the fundamental theorem of the calculus, that the following relation is valid:

$$\int_{t_1}^{t_2} \boldsymbol{B}(t)\,dt = \boldsymbol{A}(t_2) - \boldsymbol{A}(t_1) \tag{11.20}$$

provided that $d\boldsymbol{A}/dt = \boldsymbol{B}$.

These operations of differentiation and integration of vectors will suffice for the remainder of the text and, indeed, for most situations in mechanics. We shall now proceed with the study of kinematics.

PART B. Evaluation of Derivatives

11.4 Introductory Remark

As you well know from statics, we can express a vector in many ways. For instance, we may use rectangular components, or, as we will shortly explain, we may use cylindrical components. In evaluating derivatives of vectors with respect to time, we must proceed in accordance with the manner in which the vector has been expressed. In Part B of this chapter we will accordingly examine certain differentiation processes that are used extensively in mechanics. Other differentiation processes will be examined later at appropriate times.

We have already carried out a derivative operation in Section 11.2 directly on the vector $\boldsymbol{r}$. You will see in Section 11.6 that the approach used gives the derivative in terms of so-called *path variables*. This approach will be one of several that we will now examine with some care.

11.5 Rectangular Components

Consider first the case where the position vector $\boldsymbol{r}$ of a moving particle is expressed in terms of rectangular components in the following manner:

$$\boldsymbol{r}(t) = x(t)\boldsymbol{i} + y(t)\boldsymbol{j} + z(t)\boldsymbol{k} \tag{11.21}$$

where $x(t)$, $y(t)$, and $z(t)$ are scalar functions of time. The unit vectors $\boldsymbol{i}$, $\boldsymbol{j}$, and $\boldsymbol{k}$ are fixed in magnitude and direction at all times and so we can get $d\boldsymbol{r}/dt$ in the following straightforward manner:

$$\frac{d\boldsymbol{r}}{dt} = \boldsymbol{V}(t) = \dot{x}(t)\boldsymbol{i} + \dot{y}(t)\boldsymbol{j} + \dot{z}(t)\boldsymbol{k} \tag{11.22}$$

A second differentiation with respect to time gives us the acceleration as follows:

$$\frac{d^2\boldsymbol{r}}{dt^2} = \boldsymbol{a} = \ddot{x}(t)\boldsymbol{i} + \ddot{y}(t)\boldsymbol{j} + \ddot{z}(t)\boldsymbol{k} \tag{11.23}$$

By such a procedure, note that we have formulated velocity and acceleration in terms of components parallel to the coordinate axes.

We do not always know the variation of the position vector with time in the form 11.21. Furthermore, it may be that the components of velocity and acceleration that we desire are not those parallel to a fixed Cartesian reference. The evaluation of $\boldsymbol{V}$ and $\boldsymbol{a}$ for certain other circumstances will be considered in the following sections.

11.6 Velocity and Acceleration in Terms of Path Variables

We have formulated velocity and acceleration for the case where the rectangular coordinates of a particle are known as functions of time. We now explore another approach, in which the formulations are carried out in terms of the path variables of the particle, i.e., in terms of geometrical parameters of the path, and the speed and the rate of change of speed of the particle along the path. These results are particularly useful when a particle moves along a path that we know a priori (such as the case of a roller coaster).

As a matter of fact, in Section 11.2 (Eq. 11.4) we expressed the velocity vector in terms of path variables in the following form:

$$\boldsymbol{V} = \frac{ds}{dt}\boldsymbol{\varepsilon}_t \tag{11.24}$$

where ds/dt represents the speed along the path and $\boldsymbol{\varepsilon}_t = d\boldsymbol{r}/ds$ is the unit vector tangent to the path (and hence collinear with the velocity vector). The acceleration becomes:

$$\frac{d\boldsymbol{V}}{dt} = \boldsymbol{a} = \frac{d^2s}{dt^2}\boldsymbol{\varepsilon}_t + \frac{ds}{dt}\frac{d\boldsymbol{\varepsilon}_t}{dt} \tag{11.25}$$

It will be helpful to replace $d\boldsymbol{\varepsilon}_t/dt$ in the last expression by $(d\boldsymbol{\epsilon}_t/ds)(ds/dt)$, in which we have used the chain rule of differentiation. We then have:

$$\boldsymbol{a} = \frac{d^2s}{dt^2}\boldsymbol{\varepsilon}_t + \left(\frac{ds}{dt}\right)^2\frac{d\boldsymbol{\varepsilon}_t}{ds} \tag{11.26}$$

Before proceeding further, let us consider two positions that are Δs apart along the path of the particle as shown in Fig. 11.3. If Δs is small enough, the unit vectors $\boldsymbol{\varepsilon}_t(s)$ and $\boldsymbol{\varepsilon}_t(s + \Delta s)$ may be considered as intersecting, thus forming a plane. If $\Delta s \to 0$, these unit vectors then form a *limiting plane*, which we shall call the *osculating plane*. The plane will have an orientation that depends on the position s on the path of the particle. The osculating plane at $\boldsymbol{r}(t)$ is illustrated in Fig. 11.3. Having defined the osculating plane, let us continue discussion of Eq. 11.26.

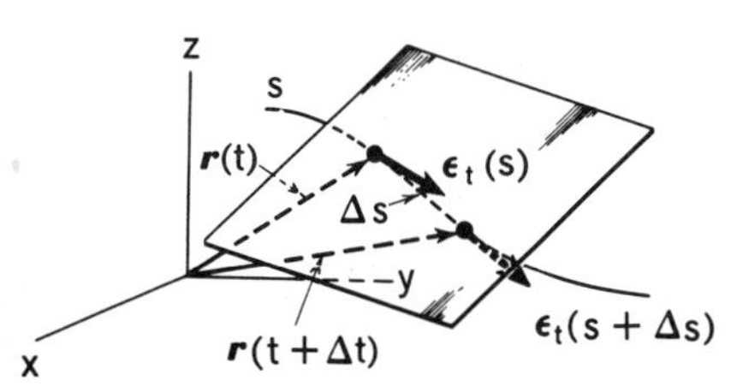

Fig. 11.3

Since we have not formally carried out the differentiation of a vector with respect to a spatial coordinate, we will carry out the derivative $d\boldsymbol{\varepsilon}_t/ds$ needed in Eq. 11.26 from the basic definition. Thus:

$$\frac{d\boldsymbol{\varepsilon}_t}{ds} = \lim_{\Delta s \to 0}\left[\frac{\boldsymbol{\varepsilon}_t(s + \Delta s) - \boldsymbol{\varepsilon}_t(s)}{\Delta s}\right] = \lim_{\Delta s \to 0}\frac{\Delta\boldsymbol{\varepsilon}_t}{\Delta s} \tag{11.27}$$

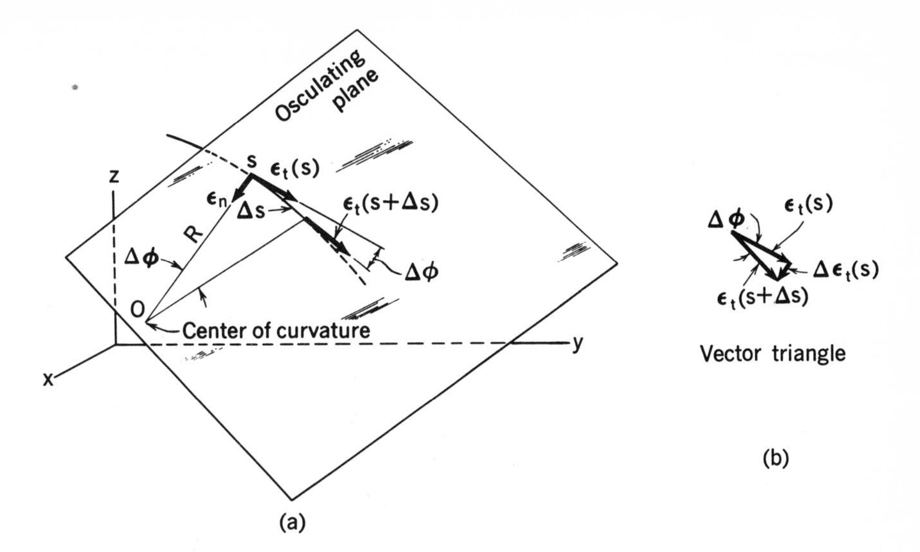

Fig. 11.4

The vectors $\boldsymbol{\varepsilon}_t(s + \Delta s)$ and $\boldsymbol{\varepsilon}_t(s)$ are shown in Fig. 11.4(a) along the path and are also shown with $\Delta\boldsymbol{\varepsilon}_t$ as a vector triangle in Fig. 11.4(b). When $\Delta s \to 0$, all these vectors will be in the osculating plane at position s. Furthermore, the normals to vectors $\boldsymbol{\varepsilon}_t(s)$ and $\boldsymbol{\varepsilon}_t(s + \Delta s)$ taken in the plane of these vectors intersect in the limit at a point O, the *center of curvature* for position s of the curve. Point O clearly is in the osculating plane associated with position s of the curve. The distance between O and s is the *radius of curvature* R for the curve at s. Finally, the direction of $\Delta\boldsymbol{\varepsilon}_t$ becomes, in the limit, normal to the path and is in the osculating plane directed toward the center of curvature. The unit vector $\boldsymbol{\varepsilon}_n$ in this direction is called the *principal normal vector*.

With the limiting direction of $\Delta\boldsymbol{\varepsilon}_t$ established, we next evaluate the magnitude of $\Delta\boldsymbol{\varepsilon}_t$ as an approximate value that becomes correct as $\Delta s \to 0$. Observing the vector triangle we can accordingly say:

$$|\Delta\boldsymbol{\varepsilon}_t| \approx |\boldsymbol{\varepsilon}_t|\,\Delta\phi = \Delta\phi$$

Next, we note that the lines from the center of curvature to the points s and $s + \Delta s$ along the trajectory form the same angle $\Delta\phi$ as is between the vectors $\boldsymbol{\varepsilon}_t(s)$ and $\boldsymbol{\varepsilon}_t(s + \Delta s)$ in the vector triangle, and so we can say:

$$\Delta\phi \approx \frac{\Delta s}{R}$$

Hence we have:

$$|\Delta\boldsymbol{\varepsilon}_t| \approx \frac{\Delta s}{R}$$

We thus have the direction and magnitude of $\Delta\boldsymbol{\varepsilon}_t$ established in an approximate manner, and we can write:

$$\Delta\boldsymbol{\varepsilon}_t \approx \frac{\Delta s}{R}\,\boldsymbol{\varepsilon}_n$$

If we use this result in the limiting process (where it becomes exact), the evaluation of $d\boldsymbol{\varepsilon}_t/ds$ becomes:

$$\frac{d\boldsymbol{\varepsilon}_t}{ds} = \lim_{\Delta s \to 0} \frac{\Delta \boldsymbol{\varepsilon}_t}{\Delta s} = \lim_{\Delta s \to 0} \left[\frac{(\Delta s/R)\,\boldsymbol{\varepsilon}_n}{\Delta s} \right] = \frac{\boldsymbol{\varepsilon}_n}{R} \qquad \textbf{11.28}$$

When we substitute Eq. 11.28 into Eq. 11.26, the acceleration vector becomes:

$$\boldsymbol{a} = \frac{d^2s}{dt^2}\boldsymbol{\varepsilon}_t + \frac{(ds/dt)^2}{R}\boldsymbol{\varepsilon}_n \qquad \textbf{11.29}$$

We thus have two components of acceleration: *one component in a direction tangent to the path, and one component in the osculating plane at right angles to the path and pointing toward the center of curvature.* These components are of great importance in certain problems.

For the special case of a *plane curve* we learned in analytic geometry that the radius of curvature R is given by the relation:

$$R = \frac{\left[1 + \left(\frac{dy}{dx}\right)^2\right]^{3/2}}{\left|\frac{d^2y}{dx^2}\right|} \qquad \textbf{11.30}$$

Furthermore, in the case of a plane curve the osculating plane at every point clearly must correspond to the plane of the curve, and the computation of unit vectors $\boldsymbol{\varepsilon}_n$ and $\boldsymbol{\varepsilon}_t$ is quite simple, as will be illustrated in Example 11.2.

How do we get the principal normal vector $\boldsymbol{\varepsilon}_n$, the radius of curvature, and the direction of the osculating plane for a three-dimensional curve? One procedure is to evaluate $\boldsymbol{\varepsilon}_t$ as a function of s and then differentiate this vector with respect to s. Accordingly, Eq. 11.28 indicates that we can determine $\boldsymbol{\varepsilon}_n$ as well as R in this way. We establish the direction of the osculating plane by taking the cross product of $\boldsymbol{\varepsilon}_n \times \boldsymbol{\varepsilon}_t$, to get a unit vector normal to the osculating plane. This vector is called the *binormal* vector.

Quite often for three-dimensional curves the path is given parametrically as follows:

$$x = x(\tau)$$
$$y = y(\tau)$$
$$z = z(\tau)$$

where τ is any parameter. Thus we have:

$$\boldsymbol{\varepsilon}_t = \frac{d\boldsymbol{r}}{ds} = \frac{dx}{ds}\boldsymbol{i} + \frac{dy}{ds}\boldsymbol{j} + \frac{dz}{ds}\boldsymbol{k} = \left(\frac{dx}{d\tau}\boldsymbol{i} + \frac{dy}{d\tau}\boldsymbol{j} + \frac{dz}{d\tau}\boldsymbol{k}\right)\frac{d\tau}{ds}$$

where we have used the chain rule to reach the last form. Since $|\boldsymbol{\varepsilon}_t| = 1$ we can see from the above equation that:

$$\frac{d\tau}{ds} = \frac{1}{\sqrt{\left(\frac{dx}{d\tau}\right)^2 + \left(\frac{dy}{d\tau}\right)^2 + \left(\frac{dz}{d\tau}\right)^2}}$$

Accordingly we can compute $\boldsymbol{\varepsilon}_t$ as follows:

$$\boldsymbol{\varepsilon}_t = \frac{1}{\sqrt{\left(\frac{dx}{d\tau}\right)^2 + \left(\frac{dy}{d\tau}\right)^2 + \left(\frac{dz}{d\tau}\right)^2}}\left(\frac{dx}{d\tau}\boldsymbol{i} + \frac{dy}{d\tau}\boldsymbol{j} + \frac{dz}{d\tau}\boldsymbol{k}\right) \qquad \textbf{11.31}$$

To get $\boldsymbol{\varepsilon}_n$ is now a straightforward process. Employing Eq. 11.28 and replacing $d\tau/ds$ we have:

$$\boldsymbol{\varepsilon}_n = R\frac{d\boldsymbol{\varepsilon}_t}{ds} = R\frac{d\boldsymbol{\varepsilon}_t/d\tau}{ds/d\tau} = \frac{R}{\sqrt{\left(\frac{dx}{d\tau}\right)^2 + \left(\frac{dy}{d\tau}\right)^2 + \left(\frac{dz}{d\tau}\right)^2}}\frac{d\boldsymbol{\varepsilon}_t}{d\tau} \qquad \textbf{11.32}$$

Employing Eq. 11.31 we can then get $\boldsymbol{\varepsilon}_n$ in terms of τ and R. Taking the magnitude of both sides then gives R in terms of τ. Thus the essential geometric quantities can be determined in terms of τ. We shall illustrate the use of the above formulations in Example 11.3.

EXAMPLE 11.1

A particle is moving along a circular path in the xy plane (Fig. 11.5). When it crosses the x axis, it has an acceleration along the path of 5 ft/sec², and is moving with the speed of 20 ft/sec in the negative y direction. What is the total acceleration of the particle?

Clearly the osculating plane must be the plane of the path. Hence R is 2 ft, as is shown in the diagram. We need simply to employ Eq. 11.29 for the desired result. Thus:

$$\boldsymbol{a} = 5\boldsymbol{\varepsilon}_t + \frac{20^2}{2}\boldsymbol{\varepsilon}_n$$

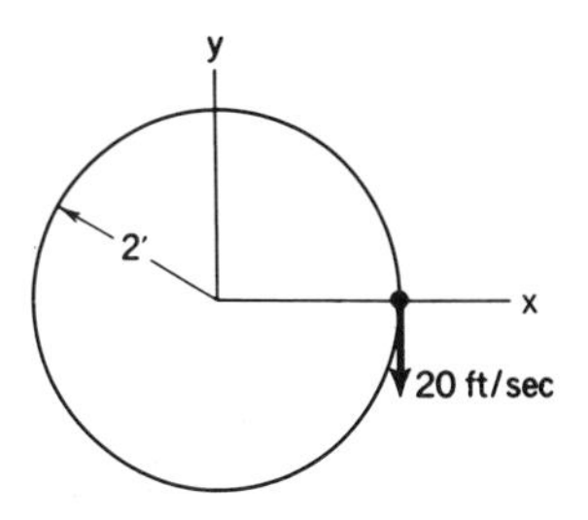

Fig. 11.5

For the xy reference, the acceleration is:

$$\boldsymbol{a} = -5\boldsymbol{j} - 200\boldsymbol{i}$$

EXAMPLE 11.2

A particle is moving along a parabolic path (Fig. 11.6) given as $y = 2\sqrt{x}$. At position A, it has a speed of 10 ft/sec and it has a rate of change of speed of 10 ft/sec² along the path. What is the acceleration vector of the particle at this position?

We first find $\boldsymbol{\varepsilon}_t$ by noting from the diagram that:

$$\boldsymbol{\varepsilon}_t = \cos\alpha\boldsymbol{i} + \sin\alpha\boldsymbol{j} \qquad \textbf{(a)}$$

where

$$\tan\alpha = \frac{dy}{dx} = \frac{1}{\sqrt{x}} \qquad \textbf{(b)}$$

At the position of interest we have:

$$\tan\alpha = \tfrac{1}{2}, \qquad \therefore \alpha = 26.6°$$

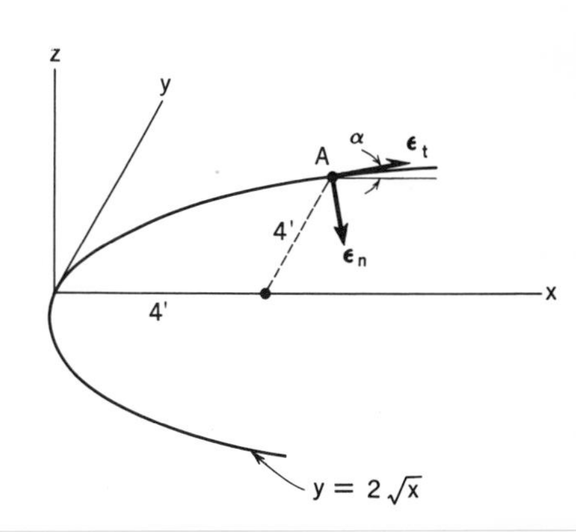

Fig. 11.6

Hence

$$\boldsymbol{\varepsilon}_t = 0.895\boldsymbol{i} + 0.447\boldsymbol{j} \qquad \textbf{(c)}$$

As for $\boldsymbol{\varepsilon}_n$ we see from the diagram that:

$$\boldsymbol{\varepsilon}_n = \sin\alpha\boldsymbol{i} - \cos\alpha\boldsymbol{j}$$

$$\therefore \boldsymbol{\varepsilon}_n = 0.447\boldsymbol{i} - 0.895\boldsymbol{j} \qquad \textbf{(d)}$$

Next, employing Eq. 11.30, we can find R. We shall need the following results for this step:

$$\frac{dy}{dx} = x^{-1/2} \qquad \textbf{(e)}$$

$$\frac{d^2y}{dx^2} = -\frac{1}{2}\,x^{-3/2} \tag{f}$$

Substituting Eqs. (e) and (f) into Eq. 11.30 we have for R:

$$R = \frac{[1 + (x^{-1/2})^2]^{3/2}}{\frac{1}{2}x^{-3/2}} \tag{g}$$

At the position of interest we get:

$$R = \frac{[1 + (\frac{1}{2})^2]^{3/2}}{(\frac{1}{2})(\frac{1}{8})} = 22.4 \text{ ft} \tag{h}$$

We can now give the desired acceleration vector. Thus, from Eq. 11.29 we have:

$$\boldsymbol{a} = 10(0.895\boldsymbol{i} + 0.447\boldsymbol{j}) + \frac{100}{22.4}(0.447\boldsymbol{i} - 0.895\boldsymbol{j})$$

$$\boldsymbol{a} = 10.95\boldsymbol{i} + 0.47\boldsymbol{j} \text{ ft/sec}^2 \tag{i}$$

EXAMPLE 11.3

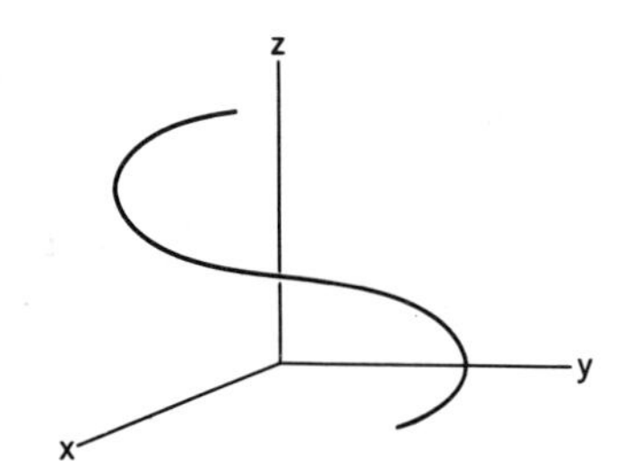

Fig. 11.7

A particle is made to move along a spiral path, as is shown in Fig. 11.7. The equations representing the *path* can be given parameterically in terms of the variable τ in the following manner:

$$x_p = A \sin \eta\tau$$

$$y_p = A \cos \eta\tau \qquad (A, \eta, C \text{ are known constants}) \tag{a}$$

$$z_p = C\tau$$

where the subscript p is to remind the reader that these relations refer to a fixed path. When the particle is at the xy plane ($z = 0$), it has a speed of V_0 ft/sec and a rate of change of speed of N ft/sec². What is the acceleration of the particle at this position?

To answer this, we must ascertain $\boldsymbol{\varepsilon}_t$, $\boldsymbol{\varepsilon}_n$, and R of the path. To get $\boldsymbol{\varepsilon}_t$ we employ Eq. 11.31. Thus:

$$\boldsymbol{\varepsilon}_t = \frac{2}{\sqrt{A^2\eta^2 + C^2}}[A\eta(\cos\eta\tau\boldsymbol{i} - \sin\eta\tau\boldsymbol{j}) + C\boldsymbol{k}] \tag{b}$$

For $\boldsymbol{\varepsilon}_n$ we have from Eq. 11.32:

$$\boldsymbol{\varepsilon}_n = \frac{R}{(A^2\eta^2 + C^2)^{1/2}}\frac{d\boldsymbol{\varepsilon}_t}{d\tau} \tag{c}$$

We can now employ Eq. (b) to find $d\boldsymbol{\varepsilon}_t/d\tau$:

$$\frac{d\boldsymbol{\varepsilon}_t}{d\tau} = -\frac{A\eta^2}{(A^2\eta^2 + C^2)^{1/2}}(\sin \eta\tau\boldsymbol{i} + \cos \eta\tau\boldsymbol{j}) \tag{d}$$

When we substitute this relation for $d\boldsymbol{\varepsilon}_t/d\tau$ in Eq. (c), the principal normal vector $\boldsymbol{\varepsilon}_n$ becomes:

$$\boldsymbol{\varepsilon}_n = -\frac{RA\eta^2}{A^2\eta^2 + C^2}(\sin \eta\tau\boldsymbol{i} + \cos \eta\tau\boldsymbol{j}) \tag{e}$$

If we take the magnitude of each side, we can solve for R:

$$R = \frac{A^2\eta^2 + C^2}{A\eta^2} \qquad \text{(f)}$$

We now have $\boldsymbol{\varepsilon}_t$ and $\boldsymbol{\varepsilon}_n$ at any point of the path in terms of the parameter τ. As the particle goes through the xy plane, this means that the z coordinate of the particle is zero and z_p of the path corresponding to the position of the particle is zero. When we note Eq. (a) it is clear, therefore, that τ must be zero for this position. Thus $\boldsymbol{\varepsilon}_n$ and $\boldsymbol{\varepsilon}_t$ for the point of interest on the path are:

$$\boldsymbol{\varepsilon}_t = \frac{1}{(A^2\eta^2 + C^2)^{1/2}}(A\eta\boldsymbol{i} + C\boldsymbol{k}) \qquad \text{(g)}$$

$$\boldsymbol{\varepsilon}_n = -\frac{RA\eta^2}{A^2\eta^2 + C^2}\boldsymbol{j} = -\boldsymbol{j} \qquad \text{(h)}$$

We can now express the acceleration vector of the particle moving along the path at this point by using Eq. 11.29. Thus:

$$\boldsymbol{a} = \frac{N}{(A^2\eta^2 + C^2)^{1/2}}(A\eta\boldsymbol{i} + C\boldsymbol{k}) - \frac{V_0{}^2A\eta^2}{A^2\eta^2 + C^2}\boldsymbol{j} \qquad \text{(i)}$$

The orientation of the osculating plane can be found by taking the cross product of $\boldsymbol{\varepsilon}_t$ and $\boldsymbol{\varepsilon}_n$.

11.7 Cylindrical Coordinates

The final method we will consider for evaluating the velocity and acceleration of a particle brings us back to considering coordinates of the particle as time functions, as we did at the outset of this study. This time we shall employ cylindrical coordinates, and we shall evaluate velocity and acceleration in components having certain directions that are associated with the cylindrical coordinates of the particles. Thus particle P in Fig. 11.8 is located by specifying cylindrical coordinates ϕ, $\bar{r}$ and z*. The transformation equations between Cartesian and cylindrical coordinates are seen to be:

$$x = \bar{r}\cos\phi, \qquad \bar{r} = (x^2 + y^2)^{1/2}$$

$$y = \bar{r}\sin\phi, \qquad \phi = \tan^{-1}\frac{y}{x} \qquad \textbf{11.33}$$

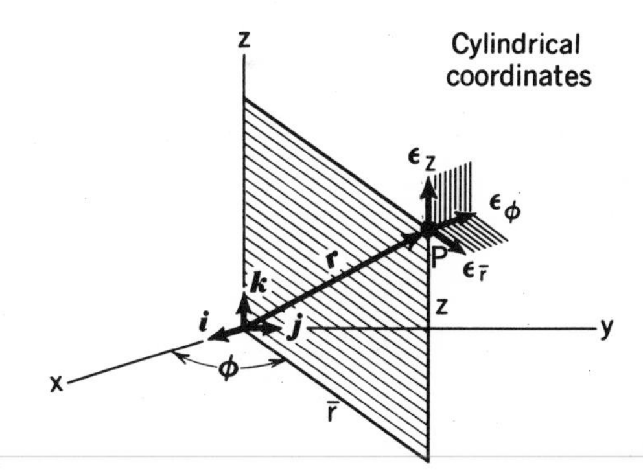

Fig. 11.8

Unit vectors are associated with these coordinates and are given as:

$\boldsymbol{\varepsilon}_z$, which is parallel to the z axis and, for practical purposes, is the same as $\boldsymbol{k}$. It is helpful to consider this as the *axial direction*.

$\boldsymbol{\varepsilon}_{\bar{r}}$, which is normal to the z axis, pointing out from the axis, and is identified as the *radial direction* from z.

* The author has used the notation $\bar{r}$ to distinguish it from r, which, according to previous definitions in statics, is the magnitude of $\boldsymbol{r}$, the position vector.

$\boldsymbol{\varepsilon}_\phi$, which is normal to the plane formed by $\boldsymbol{\varepsilon}_{\bar{r}}$ and $\boldsymbol{\varepsilon}_z$ and has a sense in accordance with the right-hand screw rule for the permutation z, $\bar{r}$, ϕ. We call this the *transverse direction.*

It *will be noted that* $\boldsymbol{\varepsilon}_{\bar{r}}$ *and* $\boldsymbol{\varepsilon}_\phi$ *will change direction as the particle moves relative to the xyz reference.* Thus, these unit vectors are generally *functions of time,* while $\boldsymbol{\varepsilon}_z$ is a constant vector.

Using previously developed concepts, we can express the velocity and acceleration of the particle relative to the xyz reference *in terms of components always in the transverse, radial, and axial directions and can use cylindrical coordinates exclusively in the process.* This information is most useful, for instance, in turbomachine studies, where, if we take the z axis as the axis of rotation, the axial components of fluid acceleration are used for thrust computation while the transverse components are important for torque considerations. It is these components that are meaningful for such computations and not components parallel to some xyz reference.

The position vector $\boldsymbol{r}$ of the particle determines the direction of the unit vectors $\boldsymbol{\varepsilon}_{\bar{r}}$ and $\boldsymbol{\varepsilon}_\phi$ at any time t, and it can be expressed as:

$$\boldsymbol{r} = \bar{r}\boldsymbol{\varepsilon}_{\bar{r}} + z\boldsymbol{\varepsilon}_z \tag{11.34}$$

To get the desired velocity, we differentiate $\boldsymbol{r}$ with respect to time:

$$\frac{d\boldsymbol{r}}{dt} = \boldsymbol{V} = \bar{r}\dot{\boldsymbol{\varepsilon}}_{\bar{r}} + \dot{\bar{r}}\boldsymbol{\varepsilon}_{\bar{r}} + \dot{z}\boldsymbol{\varepsilon}_z$$

Our task here is to evaluate $\dot{\boldsymbol{\varepsilon}}_{\bar{r}}$. On consulting Fig. 11.8 it should be clear that changes in direction of $\boldsymbol{\varepsilon}_{\bar{r}}$ occur only when the ϕ coordinate of the particle changes. Hence, remembering that the magnitude of $\boldsymbol{\varepsilon}_{\bar{r}}$ is always constant, we have for $\dot{\boldsymbol{\varepsilon}}_{\bar{r}}$:

$$\frac{d\boldsymbol{\varepsilon}_{\bar{r}}}{dt} = \frac{d\boldsymbol{\varepsilon}_{\bar{r}}}{d\phi}\dot{\phi} \tag{11.35}$$

To evaluate $d\boldsymbol{\varepsilon}_{\bar{r}}/d\phi$, we have shown in Fig. 11.9(a) the vector $\boldsymbol{\varepsilon}_{\bar{r}}$ for a given $\bar{r}$ and z at positions corresponding to ϕ and $\phi + \Delta\phi$. In Fig. 11.9(b), furthermore,

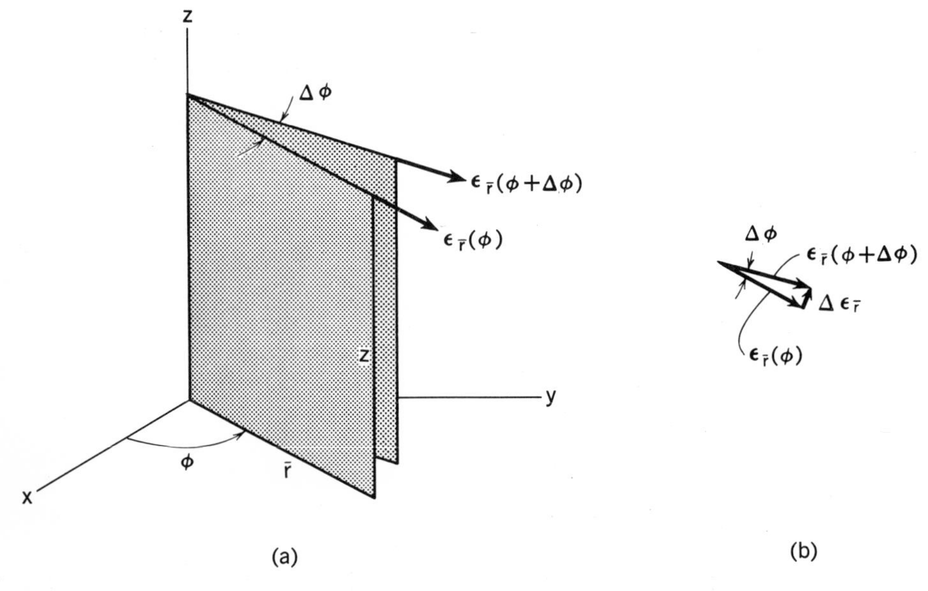

Fig. 11.9

we have formed a vector triangle from these vectors and in this way we have shown the vector $\Delta\boldsymbol{\varepsilon}_{\bar{r}}$, i.e., the change in $\boldsymbol{\varepsilon}_{\bar{r}}$ during a change in coordinate ϕ. We now express Eq. 11.35 in the following approximate manner:

$$\frac{d\boldsymbol{\varepsilon}_{\bar{r}}}{dt} \approx \frac{\Delta\boldsymbol{\varepsilon}_{\bar{r}}}{\Delta\phi}\dot{\phi}$$

As $\Delta\phi \rightarrow 0$ we see, on consulting Fig. 11.9, that the direction of $\Delta\boldsymbol{\varepsilon}_{\bar{r}}$ approaches that of the unit vector $\boldsymbol{\varepsilon}_{\phi}$ and the magnitude of $\Delta\boldsymbol{\varepsilon}_{\bar{r}}$ approaches the value $\Delta\phi$. In the limit all the previously made approximations become exact statements and we accordingly have

$$\frac{d\boldsymbol{\varepsilon}_{\bar{r}}}{dt} = \dot{\phi}\boldsymbol{\varepsilon}_{\phi} \qquad \textbf{11.36}$$

The velocity of particle P is, then:

$$\boxed{\boldsymbol{V} = \dot{\bar{r}}\boldsymbol{\varepsilon}_{\bar{r}} + \bar{r}\dot{\phi}\boldsymbol{\varepsilon}_{\phi} + \dot{z}\boldsymbol{\varepsilon}_{z}} \qquad \textbf{11.37}$$

To get the acceleration relative to xyz in terms of cylindrical coordinates and radial, transverse, and axial components, we simply take the time derivative of the above velocity vector:

$$\boldsymbol{a} = \frac{d\boldsymbol{V}}{dt} = \ddot{\bar{r}}\boldsymbol{\varepsilon}_{\bar{r}} + \dot{\bar{r}}\dot{\boldsymbol{\varepsilon}}_{\bar{r}} + \dot{\bar{r}}\dot{\phi}\boldsymbol{\varepsilon}_{\phi} + \bar{r}\ddot{\phi}\boldsymbol{\varepsilon}_{\phi} + \bar{r}\dot{\phi}\dot{\boldsymbol{\varepsilon}}_{\phi} + \ddot{z}\boldsymbol{\varepsilon}_{z} \qquad \textbf{11.38}$$

We must next evaluate $\dot{\boldsymbol{\varepsilon}}_{\phi}$. Like $\boldsymbol{\varepsilon}_{\bar{r}}$, the vector $\boldsymbol{\varepsilon}_{\phi}$ can vary only when a change in the coordinate ϕ causes a change in direction of this vector as has been shown in Fig. 11.10(a). The vectors $\boldsymbol{\varepsilon}_{\phi}(\phi)$ and $\boldsymbol{\varepsilon}_{\phi}(\phi + \Delta\phi)$ have been shown in a vector triangle in Fig. 11.10(b) and here we have shown $\Delta\boldsymbol{\varepsilon}_{\phi}$, the change of the vector $\boldsymbol{\varepsilon}_{\phi}$ as a result of the change in coordinate ϕ. We may then say:

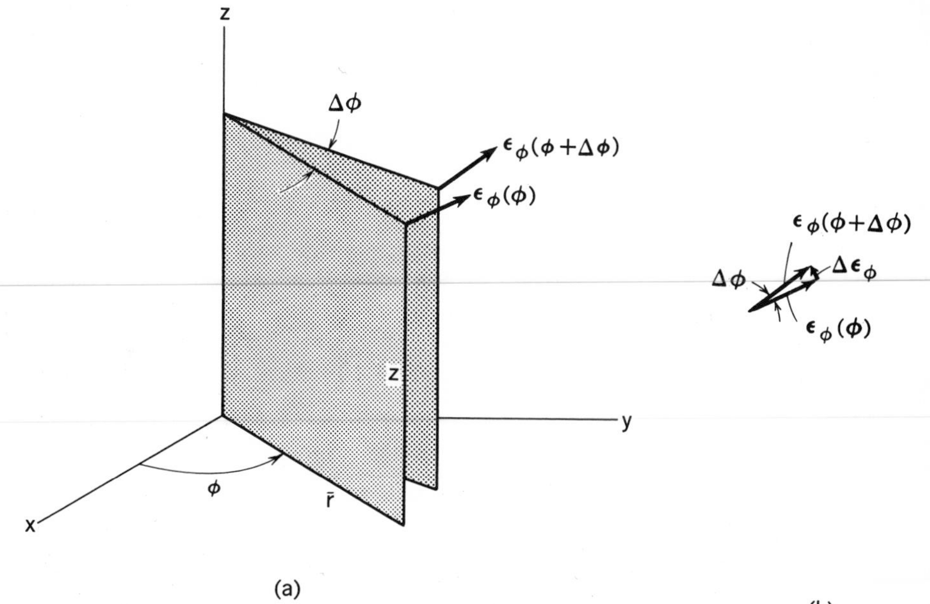

Fig. 11.10

$$\frac{d\boldsymbol{\varepsilon}_\phi}{dt} = \frac{d\boldsymbol{\varepsilon}_\phi}{d\phi}\dot{\phi} \approx \frac{\Delta\boldsymbol{\varepsilon}_\phi}{\Delta\phi}\dot{\phi} \tag{11.39}$$

As $\Delta\phi \to 0$ the direction of $\Delta\boldsymbol{\varepsilon}_\phi$ becomes that of $-\boldsymbol{\varepsilon}_{\bar{r}}$ and the magnitude clearly approaches $\Delta\phi$. In the limit we then get:

$$\dot{\boldsymbol{\varepsilon}}_\phi = -\dot{\phi}\boldsymbol{\varepsilon}_{\bar{r}} \tag{11.40}$$

Using Eqs. 11.36 and 11.40, we find that Eq. 11.38 now becomes:

$$\boldsymbol{a} = \ddot{\bar{r}}\boldsymbol{\varepsilon}_{\bar{r}} + \dot{\bar{r}}\dot{\phi}\boldsymbol{\varepsilon}_\phi + \dot{\bar{r}}\dot{\phi}\boldsymbol{\varepsilon}_\phi + \bar{r}\ddot{\phi}\boldsymbol{\varepsilon}_\phi - \bar{r}\dot{\phi}^2\boldsymbol{\varepsilon}_{\bar{r}} + \ddot{z}\boldsymbol{\varepsilon}_z$$

Collecting components, we write:

$$\boxed{\boldsymbol{a} = (\ddot{\bar{r}} - \bar{r}\dot{\phi}^2)\boldsymbol{\varepsilon}_{\bar{r}} + (\bar{r}\ddot{\phi} + 2\dot{\bar{r}}\dot{\phi})\boldsymbol{\varepsilon}_\phi + \ddot{z}\boldsymbol{\varepsilon}_z} \tag{11.41}$$

Thus we have accomplished the desired task. A similar procedure may be followed to reach corresponding formulations for spherical coordinates. By now you should be able to produce the above equations readily and should by no means attempt to memorize them.

For motion in a circle in xy plane, note that $\dot{\bar{r}} = \dot{z} = 0$, and $\bar{r} = r$, and so we can get the following simplifications:

$$\boldsymbol{V} = r\dot{\phi}\boldsymbol{\varepsilon}_\phi \qquad \text{(a)}$$

$$\boldsymbol{a} = r\ddot{\phi}\boldsymbol{\varepsilon}_\phi - r\dot{\phi}^2\boldsymbol{\varepsilon}_r \qquad \text{(b)} \quad \mathbf{11.42}$$

Furthermore, the unit vector $\boldsymbol{\varepsilon}_\phi$ is tangent to the path, and the unit vector $\boldsymbol{\varepsilon}_r$ is normal to the path and pointing away from the center of curvature. Therefore, when we compare these results with those stemming from considerations of path variables (Section 11.6), it is clear that for circular motion in the xy coordinate plane of a right-hand triad:

$$|r\ddot{\phi}| = \left|\frac{d^2s}{dt^2}\right| \qquad \boldsymbol{\varepsilon}_\phi = \boldsymbol{\varepsilon}_t \quad \text{(for counterclockwise motion as seen from } +z)^*$$

$$|r\dot{\phi}^2| = \left|\frac{V^2}{r}\right| \qquad \boldsymbol{\varepsilon}_\phi = -\boldsymbol{\varepsilon}_t \quad \text{(for clockwise motion as seen from } +z)$$

$$\boldsymbol{\varepsilon}_r = -\boldsymbol{\varepsilon}_n \tag{11.43}$$

Thus Eqs. 11.42(b) and 11.29 are equally useful for quickly expressing the acceleration of a particle moving in a simple circular path. You probably remember these formulae from earlier physics courses and may want to use them in the ensuing work of this chapter.

EXAMPLE 11.4

The motion of a particle relative to the xyz reference (Fig. 11.11) can be expressed as follows:

* The sense of $\boldsymbol{\varepsilon}_t$ is that of the velocity of the particle, whereas the sense of $\boldsymbol{\varepsilon}_\phi$ is determined by the reference xyz. It is for this reason that a multiplicity of relations between these unit vectors exists.

$$x = 6t, \qquad y = 10t, \qquad z = t^3 + 10$$

Express the position, velocity, and acceleration of the particle, using cylindrical coordinates with components in the axial, transverse, and radial directions.

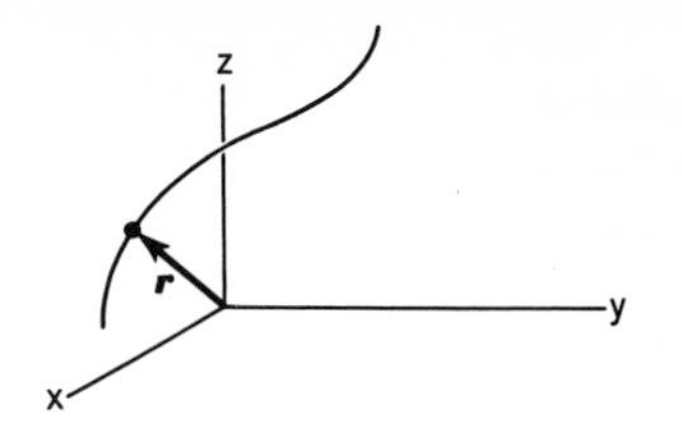

Fig. 11.11

The cylindrical coordinates for the particle as functions of time can be given from the transformation equations (Eqs. 11.33) as:

$$\bar{r} = (36t^2 + 100t^2)^{1/2} = 11.66t$$

$$\phi = \tan^{-1}\frac{10t}{6t} = \tan^{-1}\frac{5}{3}$$

$$\dot{\phi} = 0$$

$$z = t^3 + 10 \qquad \textbf{(a)}$$

The position vector $\boldsymbol{r}$ can then be given as:

$$\boldsymbol{r} = 11.66t\boldsymbol{\varepsilon}_{\bar{r}} + (t^3 + 10)\boldsymbol{\varepsilon}_z \qquad \textbf{(b)}$$

where the direction of $\boldsymbol{\varepsilon}_{\bar{r}}$ must be such that $\tan^{-1}\phi = \frac{5}{3}$. The velocity and acceleration vectors are found by differentiating Eq. (b):

$$\boldsymbol{V} = 11.66\boldsymbol{\varepsilon}_{\bar{r}} + 11.66t\dot{\boldsymbol{\varepsilon}}_{\bar{r}} + 3t^2\boldsymbol{\varepsilon}_z$$

$$= 11.66\boldsymbol{\varepsilon}_{\bar{r}} + 11.66t\dot{\phi}\boldsymbol{\varepsilon}_\phi + 3t^2\boldsymbol{\varepsilon}_z$$

Noting that $\dot{\phi} = 0$ we get:

$$\boldsymbol{V} = 11.66\boldsymbol{\varepsilon}_{\bar{r}} + 3t^2\boldsymbol{\varepsilon}_z$$

$$\boldsymbol{a} = 11.66\dot{\boldsymbol{\varepsilon}}_{\bar{r}} + 6t\boldsymbol{\varepsilon}_z = 11.66\dot{\phi}\boldsymbol{\varepsilon}_\phi + 6t\boldsymbol{\varepsilon}_z = 6t\boldsymbol{\varepsilon}_z$$

EXAMPLE 11.5

Shown in Fig. 11.12 is a wheel rotating at time t with an angular speed ω of 5 rad/sec. At this instant, the wheel also has a rate of change of angular speed of 2 rad/sec². A body B is moving along a spoke at this instant with a speed of 10 ft/sec relative to the spoke* and is increasing in its speed at the rate of 5 ft/sec². These data are given when the spoke, on which B is moving, is vertical and when B is 2 ft from the center of the wheel as has been shown in the diagram. What are the velocity and acceleration of B at this instant relative to the fixed reference xyz?

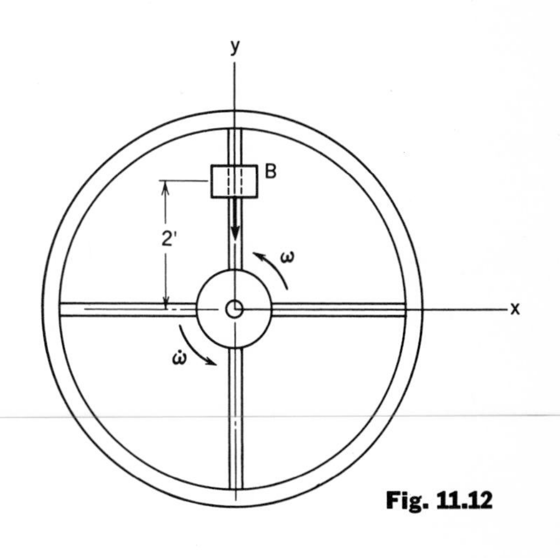

Fig. 11.12

We may make good use of cylindrical coordinates for this problem. Thus we can say:

$$\bar{r} = 2 \text{ ft}, \qquad \dot{\phi} = 5 \text{ rad/sec}$$

$$\dot{\bar{r}} = -10 \text{ ft/sec}, \qquad \ddot{\phi} = 2 \text{ rad/sec}^2$$

$$\ddot{\bar{r}} = -5 \text{ ft/sec}^2, \qquad \dot{z} = \ddot{z} = 0 \qquad \textbf{(a)}$$

We then have for the velocity:

$$\boldsymbol{V} = (-10)\boldsymbol{\varepsilon}_{\bar{r}} + (2)(5)\boldsymbol{\varepsilon}_\phi$$

$$\therefore\ \boldsymbol{V} = -10\boldsymbol{\varepsilon}_{\bar{r}} + 10\boldsymbol{\varepsilon}_\phi \text{ ft/sec} \qquad \textbf{(b)}$$

---

* That is, if you placed yourself on the spoke and observed body B, you would say that it has a speed of 10 ft/sec.

And for the acceleration we have:

$$a = [-5 - (2)(25)]\varepsilon_{\bar{r}} + [(2)(2) + 2(-10)(5)]\varepsilon_{\phi}$$

$$\therefore\ a = -55\varepsilon_{\bar{r}} - 96\varepsilon_{\phi}\ \text{ft/sec}^2 \quad \textbf{(c)}$$

We have thus determined the motion in terms of radial and transverse components.

PART C. Simple Kinematical Relations and Applications

11.8 Simple Relative Motion

Up to now we have considered only a single reference in our kinematical considerations. There are times when two or more references may be profitably employed in describing the motion of a particle. We will consider in this section a very simple case that will fulfill our needs in the early portion of the text.

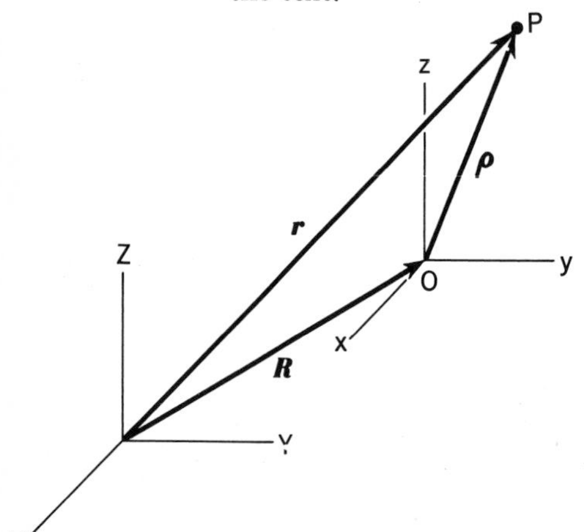

Fig. 11.13

Shown in Fig. 11.13 are a pair of references xyz and XYZ moving relative to each other in such a way that corresponding axes always remain parallel. We call such motion *translation.* The velocity of any particle P depends on the reference from which the motion is observed. More precisely we say that the velocity of particle P relative to reference XYZ is the time rate of change of the position vector $\boldsymbol{r}$ for this reference, where this rate of change is viewed from the XYZ reference. This may be stated mathematically as:

$$V_{XYZ} = \left(\frac{d\boldsymbol{r}}{dt}\right)_{XYZ} \qquad \textbf{11.44}$$

Similarly for the velocity of particle P as seen from reference xyz we have:

$$V_{xyz} = \left(\frac{d\boldsymbol{\varrho}}{dt}\right)_{xyz} \qquad \textbf{11.45}$$

where we now use position vector $\boldsymbol{\varrho}$ and view the change from the xyz reference (see Fig. 11.13). By the same token, $(d\boldsymbol{R}/dt)_{XYZ}$ is the velocity of the origin of the xyz reference as seen from XYZ. Since all points of the xyz reference have the same velocity relative to XYZ at any time t for this case, we can say that $(d\boldsymbol{R}/dt)_{XYZ}$ is the velocity of reference xyz as seen from XYZ.

From Fig. 11.13 we can relate position vectors $\boldsymbol{\varrho}$ and $\boldsymbol{r}$ by the following equation:

$$\boldsymbol{r} = \boldsymbol{R} + \boldsymbol{\varrho} \qquad \textbf{11.46}$$

Now take the time rate of change of these vectors as seen from XYZ. We get:

$$\left(\frac{d\mathbf{r}}{dt}\right)_{XYZ} = \left(\frac{d\mathbf{R}}{dt}\right)_{XYZ} + \left(\frac{d\boldsymbol{\varrho}}{dt}\right)_{XYZ} \qquad \textbf{11.47}$$

The term on the left side of the above equation is $\boldsymbol{V}_{XYZ}$ as indicated earlier, and we shall use the notation $\dot{\boldsymbol{R}}$ for the first term on the right side of the equation. We thus have:

$$(\boldsymbol{V})_{XYZ} = \dot{\boldsymbol{R}} + \left(\frac{d\boldsymbol{\varrho}}{dt}\right)_{XYZ} \qquad \textbf{11.48}$$

Solving for $(d\boldsymbol{\varrho}/dt)_{XYZ}$,

$$\left(\frac{d\boldsymbol{\varrho}}{dt}\right)_{XYZ} = \boldsymbol{V}_{XYZ} - \dot{\boldsymbol{R}} \qquad \textbf{11.49}$$

we see that it represents the *difference* between the velocity of P as seen from XYZ and the velocity of O as seen from XYZ. Suppose now there were yet a third reference $\eta\xi\zeta$ *translating* relative to XYZ. Then viewing P and O from this new reference would clearly generate an equal change of velocity for both points over those velocities observed from XYZ. Thus the *difference* between the velocities of P and O as viewed now from $\eta\xi\zeta$ would be *unchanged*. Indeed this difference is the same when viewed from *any* translatory reference; accordingly, $d\boldsymbol{\varrho}/dt$ is the same for all translatory references including the reference xyz itself. For that case, we have $(d\boldsymbol{\varrho}/dt)_{xyz}$ which can be expressed as $\boldsymbol{V}_{xyz}$, and which represents the velocity of the particle relative to the reference xyz. Accordingly, we can write Eq. 11.48 as follows:

$$\boldsymbol{V}_{XYZ} = \dot{\boldsymbol{R}} + \boldsymbol{V}_{xyz} \qquad \textbf{11.50}$$

We may show, by the same reasoning furthermore, that the acceleration of particle P is related to references XYZ and xyz as follows:

$$\boldsymbol{a}_{XYZ} = \ddot{\boldsymbol{R}} + \boldsymbol{a}_{xyz} \qquad \textbf{11.51}$$

It must be kept clearly in mind that the equations which we have developed apply only to references which are *translatory* relative to each other. In Chapter 15 we will consider references which have arbitrary motion relative to each other. Since a reference is a rigid system, we shall need to examine at that time the kinematics of rigid bodies in order to develop these general considerations of relative motion. The equations presented here will then be special cases.

How can we make use of multireferences? In many problems the motion of a particle is known relative to a given rigid body, and the motion of this body is known relative to the ground or other convenient reference. We can then fix a reference xyz to the body, and if the body is in translation relative to the ground we can then employ the relations presented in this section to give the motion of the particle relative to the ground.

If, in the ensuing chapters, we talk about the "motion of particles relative to a point," such as for example the center of mass of the system, then it will be understood that this motion is relative to a hypothetical reference moving with the center of mass in a translatory manner as seen from the reference of the problem.

We illustrate these remarks in the following example.

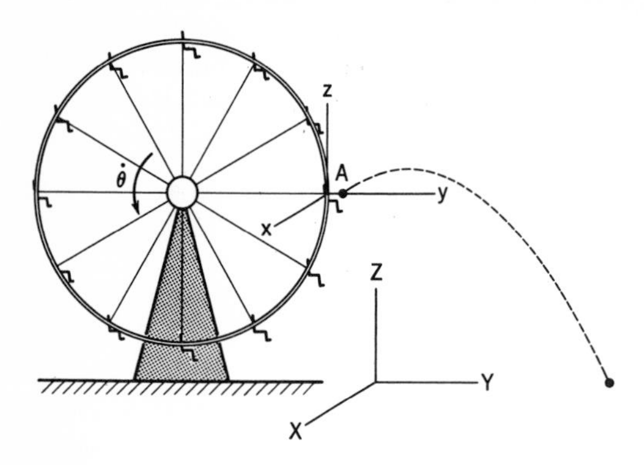

Fig. 11.14

EXAMPLE 11.6

Shown in Fig. 11.14 is a ferris wheel rotating at the instant of interest with an angular speed $\dot{\theta}$ of 0.5 rad/sec and increasing its angular speed at the rate of 0.1 rad/sec². A ball is thrown from the ground to an occupant at A. The ball arrives at the instant of interest with a speed relative to the ground given as:

$$\boldsymbol{V}_{XYZ} = -10\boldsymbol{j} - 2\boldsymbol{k} \text{ ft/sec} \quad \textbf{(a)}$$

What are the velocity and the acceleration of the ball relative to the occupant at seat A provided that this seat is not "swinging"? The radius of the wheel is 20 ft.

The fact that the seat is not "swinging" implies that it is translating relative to the ground reference XYZ. Accordingly we attach a reference xyz fixed to the seat as shown in the diagram. We can then employ Eq. 11.50. Thus:

$$\boldsymbol{V}_{XYZ} = -10\boldsymbol{j} - 2\boldsymbol{k} = \dot{\boldsymbol{R}} + \boldsymbol{V}_{xyz} \quad \textbf{(b)}$$

Clearly, $\boldsymbol{V}_{xyz}$ is the desired result, and $\dot{\boldsymbol{R}}$ is the velocity of the seat A (or the origin of xyz) relative to XYZ. Since the origin of xyz is performing simple circular motion, we get:

$$\dot{\boldsymbol{R}} = (20)(\dot{\theta})\boldsymbol{k} = 10\boldsymbol{k} \text{ ft/sec} \quad \textbf{(c)}$$

Substituting for $\dot{\boldsymbol{R}}$ in Eq. (b) we then get for $\boldsymbol{V}_{xyz}$:

$$\boldsymbol{V}_{xyz} = -10\boldsymbol{j} - 12\boldsymbol{k} \text{ ft/sec} \quad \textbf{(d)}$$

This velocity is what the occupant of seat A must react to.

To get the acceleration of the ball relative to the occupant of seat A we now employ Eq. 11.51 as follows:

$$\boldsymbol{a}_{XYZ} = -g\boldsymbol{k} = \ddot{\boldsymbol{R}} + \boldsymbol{a}_{xyz} \quad \textbf{(e)}$$

where $\boldsymbol{a}_{xyz}$ is now the desired unknown. To get $\ddot{\boldsymbol{R}}$ we employ Eq. 11.42(b) for simple circular motion. Thus:

$$\ddot{\boldsymbol{R}} = (20)(\ddot{\theta})\boldsymbol{k} - (20)(\dot{\theta})^2\boldsymbol{j}$$

$$\therefore \ddot{\boldsymbol{R}} = 2\boldsymbol{k} - 5\boldsymbol{j} \text{ ft/sec}^2 \quad \textbf{(f)}$$

Substituting into Eq. (e) and solving for $\boldsymbol{a}_{xyz}$, we obtain:

$$\begin{aligned}\boldsymbol{a}_{xyz} &= -2\boldsymbol{k} + 5\boldsymbol{j} - 32.2\boldsymbol{k} \\ &= 5\boldsymbol{j} - 34.2\boldsymbol{k} \text{ ft/sec}^2 \quad \textbf{(g)}\end{aligned}$$

11.9 Forces Acting on a Body Having Known Motion

The computation of forces on a particle having known motion is actually a province of dynamics. However, since the major part of the analysis is kinematical in nature, we have included this undertaking in this chapter. The procedure to follow in computing $\boldsymbol{F}$ for such cases is simply to evaluate $\boldsymbol{a}$ relative to an *inertial reference** using whatever

* You will recall from Section 1.10 of Statics that an inertial reference is one that translates with uniform speed relative to the so-called fixed stars. For such references Newton's law may be applied in its simple form.

coordinate system that is most desirable. The resulting three scalar equations from Newton's law then permit the direct computation of $\boldsymbol{F}$ as components in that particular coordinate system. We now illustrate this procedure in the following examples.

EXAMPLE 11.7

A truck moving down a 10° incline is shown in Fig. 11.15(a). The driver strongly applies his brakes to avoid a collision and the truck decelerates at the steady rate of 3 ft/sec². If the coefficient of friction μ_s between the load W and the truck trailer is 0.3, will the load slide or remain stationary relative to the truck trailer? The weight of W is 1000 lb.

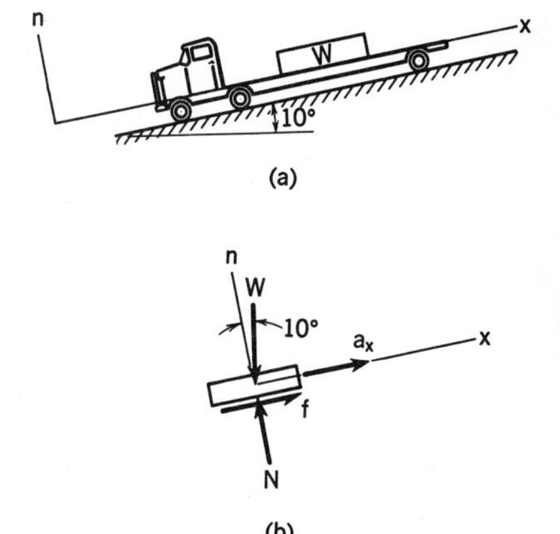

Fig. 11.15

Let us assume that the load does not slide and accordingly has a known deceleration relative to the ground of 3 ft/sec². The free-body diagram of the load is accordingly shown in Fig. 11.15(b) with an acceleration component a_x which is known. We can accordingly solve for f, the friction force required for no slipping, by using a component of Newton's law in the x direction. Thus:

$$-W \sin 10° + f = \frac{W}{g} a_x \qquad \text{(a)}$$

Inserting known values for W, g, and a_x, we can solve for f in the following manner:

$$f = \frac{1000}{32.2}(3) + (1000)(0.1739) = 267.1 \text{ lb} \qquad \text{(b)}$$

We must now compare this force with the largest attainable force from coulomb friction. Accordingly, using Newton's law in the direction n normal to the incline we have:

$$-W \cos 10° + N = 0$$

$$\therefore N = 984 \text{ lb} \qquad \text{(c)}$$

The maximum friction force attainable is:

$$f_{\max} = \mu_s N = (0.3)(984) = 295 \text{ lb}$$

Clearly there will be no slipping for the data given.

EXAMPLE 11.8

In Fig. 11.16(a) is shown a portion of a roller coaster that one finds in an amusement park. The portion of the track shown is coplanar. The curve from A to the right is that of a parabola given as:

$$(y - 100)^2 = 10x \qquad \text{(a)}$$

If the train of cars is moving at a speed of 20 ft/sec when the front car is 60 ft above the ground, what is the total normal force exerted by a 150-lb occupant of the front car on the seat and floor of the car?

Here we find it most convenient to use path coordinates. Since we require only the force F normal

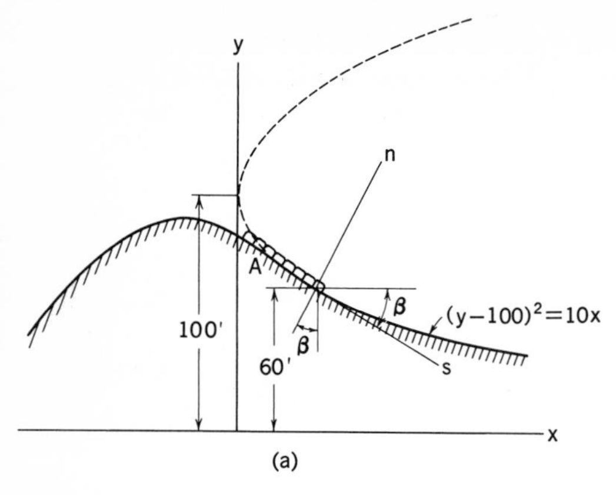

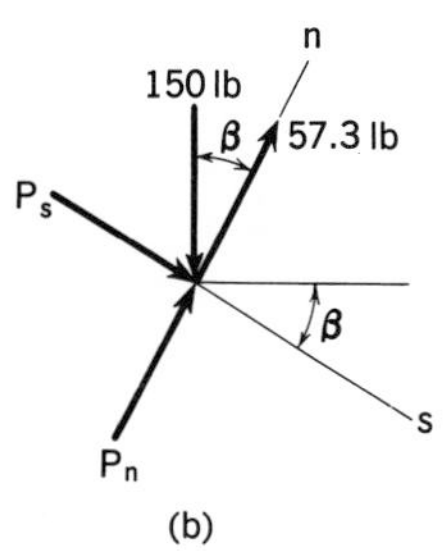

Fig. 11.16

to the path, we need only be concerned with a_n in Eq. 11.29. Thus we have:

$$a_n = \frac{(ds/dt)^2}{R} = \frac{20^2}{R} \tag{b}$$

We can compute R from analytic geometry as follows:

$$R = \frac{[1 + (dy/dx)^2]^{3/2}}{\left|\dfrac{d^2y}{dx^2}\right|} \tag{c}$$

wherein from Eq. (a) we have:

$$\frac{dy}{dx} = \frac{5}{(y - 100)} \tag{d}$$

$$\frac{d^2y}{dx^2} = -\frac{25}{(y - 100)^3} \tag{e}$$

Substituting into Eq. (c) we have:

$$R = \frac{\left[1 + \left(\dfrac{5}{y - 100}\right)^2\right]^{3/2}}{\dfrac{25}{(y - 100)^3}}$$

At the position of interest we get:

$$R = \frac{\left[1 + \dfrac{25}{1600}\right]^{3/2}}{\left(\dfrac{25}{64{,}000}\right)} = 262 \text{ ft} \tag{f}$$

Accordingly, we now have for F_n as required by Newton's law:

$$F_n = \frac{W}{g_0} a_n = \left(\frac{150}{g_0}\right)\left(\frac{400}{262}\right) = 7.11 \text{ lb} \tag{g}$$

Note that F_n is the total force component normal to the trajectory needed by the occupant for maintaining his motion on the given trajectory. This force component comes from the action of gravity and the forces from the seat and floor of the car. These forces have been shown in Fig. 11.16(b), where P_n and P_s are the force components from the car acting on the occupant. The resultant of this force system must accordingly have a component along n equal to 56.9 lb. Thus:

$$-150 \cos \beta + P_n = 7.11 \tag{h}$$

To get β note that:

$$\beta = \tan^{-1}\left(\frac{dy}{dx}\right)_{y=60} = \tan^{-1}\left(\frac{5}{-40}\right) = -7.14° \tag{i}$$

Hence we get the desired result for the reaction to P_n from Eq. (h):

$$-P_n = 150 \cos \beta + 7.11 = 148.5 + 7.11$$

$$\therefore\ P_n = -155.6 \text{ lb} \tag{j}$$

EXAMPLE 11.9

Shown in Fig. 11.17(a) is a device called a *flyball governor* used to regulate the speed of such devices as steam engines and turbines. As the governor is made to rotate through a system of gears by the device to be controlled, the balls will attain a configuration given by the angle θ, which is dependent on both the angular speed ω of the governor and the force P acting on the bearing at A. The up and down motion of the bearing at A in response to change in ω is then used to open or close a valve so as to regulate the speed of the device.

The following data are given for the flyball governor:

$$l = 1 \text{ ft}$$

$$D = 2 \text{ in.}$$

$$\omega = 300 \text{ rpm}$$

$$\theta = 45°$$

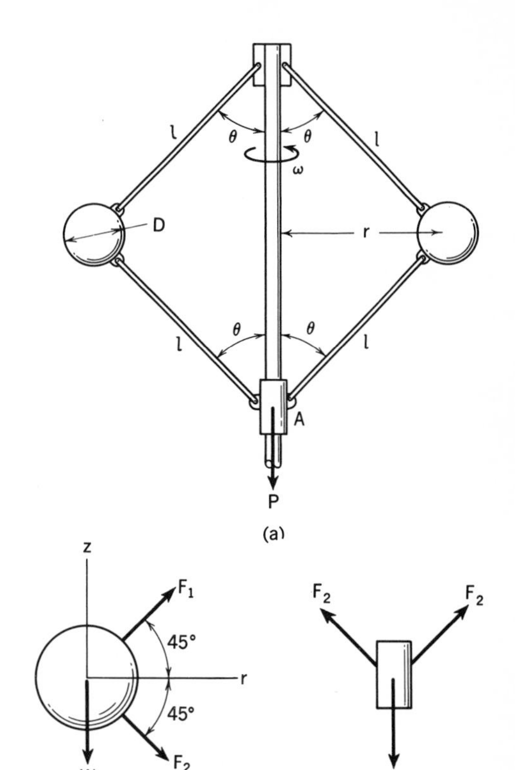

Fig. 11.17

What is the force P acting on bearing A if each ball weighs 2 lb and we neglect the weight of all other moving members of the system?

Each ball undergoes simple circular motion for a fixed θ. Using cylindrical coordinates in expressing Newton's law, we have, for the free-body diagram of Fig. 11.17(b):

$$(-F_1 - F_2)(0.707)\boldsymbol{\varepsilon}_{\bar{r}} + [(F_1 - F_2)(0.707) - W]\boldsymbol{\varepsilon}_z = -\frac{W}{g} r\omega^2\boldsymbol{\varepsilon}_{\bar{r}} \qquad \textbf{(a)}$$

The scalar equations are:

$$-(F_1 + F_2)(0.707) = -\frac{W}{g} r\omega^2$$

$$= -\frac{2}{32.2}(0.707)\left[\frac{(300)(2\pi)}{60}\right]^2$$

$$= -43.3$$

$$(F_1 - F_2)(0.0707) - 2 = 0 \qquad \textbf{(b)}$$

Solving these equations simultaneously, we get:

$$F_1 = 32.0 \text{ lb}$$

$$F_2 = 29.2 \text{ lb}$$

Now, using a free-body diagram of the bearing A wherein we have neglected friction as shown in Fig. 11.17(c), we can say from equilibrium considerations:

$$P = 2F_2(0.707) = 41.2 \text{ lb}$$

EXAMPLE 11.10

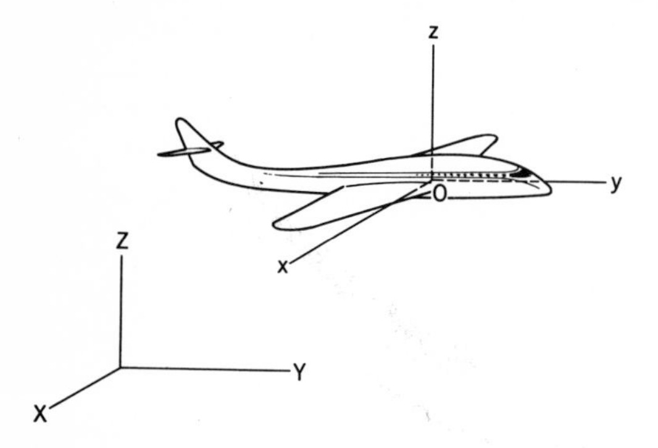

Fig. 11.18

Shown in Fig. 11.18 is a jet airliner flying at speed of 600 mph in a translatory manner relative to the ground reference XYZ. At the instant of interest, a downwind causes the plane to accelerate downward at a rate of 50 miles/hour/sec. While this is happening the pilot cuts back on the throttle so that the plane is decelerating in the Y direction at the rate of 30 miles/hour/sec. Thus the plane has an acceleration given as:

$$\boldsymbol{a} = -50\boldsymbol{k} - 30\boldsymbol{j} \qquad \textbf{(a)}$$

while maintaining a translatory attitude. While this is happening, the stewardess is placing a plate on the tray of a passenger. In steady flight or on the ground, she would start this maneuver by giving the plate a translatory acceleration of 16.1 ft/sec^2 downward toward the tray. If the plate weighs $\frac{1}{2}$ lb, this would require her to exert a force of $\frac{1}{4}$ lb upward on the plate. What force must she now exert to start the same maneuver?

We must find the acceleration of the plate relative to reference XYZ, which may be taken in the problem to be an inertial reference. It will be convenient in this undertaking to fix a reference xyz, having the same unit vectors as reference XYZ, to the airplane at any convenient location (see Fig. 11.18). We can then say for the motion of the plate relative to xyz:

$$\boldsymbol{a}_{xyz} = -16.1\boldsymbol{k} \qquad \textbf{(b)}$$

The acceleration of O, the origin of xyz relative to XYZ, is:

$$\ddot{\boldsymbol{R}} = -50\boldsymbol{k} - 30\boldsymbol{j} \qquad \textbf{(c)}$$

Since the references are translating relative to each other, we may employ Eq. 11.51 to get $\boldsymbol{a}_{XYZ}$, the acceleration of the plate relative to inertial space. Thus:

$$\boldsymbol{a}_{XYZ} = (-50\boldsymbol{k} - 30\boldsymbol{j})\left(\frac{5280}{3600}\right) + (-16.1\boldsymbol{k})$$

$$= -44\boldsymbol{j} - 89.5\boldsymbol{k} \text{ ft/sec}^2$$

We can now employ Newton's law in the form:

$$\boldsymbol{F} = m\boldsymbol{a}_{XYZ} \qquad \textbf{(d)}$$

Thus, denoting the force exerted by the stewardess as $\boldsymbol{F}_s$, we have:

$$\boldsymbol{F}_s - \frac{1}{2}\boldsymbol{k} = \left(\frac{\frac{1}{2}}{g}\right)(-44\boldsymbol{j} - 89.5\boldsymbol{k}) \qquad \textbf{(e)}$$

Solving for $\boldsymbol{F}_s$, we get:

$$\boldsymbol{F}_s = -0.684\boldsymbol{j} - 0.890\boldsymbol{k} \text{ lb} \qquad \textbf{(f)}$$

Obviously, the stewardess must perform quite differently to accomplish the same task under these circumstances.

11.10 Closure

In this chapter we have presented, first, general comments on differentiation and integration of vectors. We then carried out differentiations in a variety of ways. In the first case the vector $\boldsymbol{r}$ was expressed in terms of rectangular scalar components and the fixed unit vectors $\boldsymbol{i}$, $\boldsymbol{j}$, and $\boldsymbol{k}$. The procedure for finding $\dot{\boldsymbol{r}}$ and $\ddot{\boldsymbol{r}}$ in terms of rectangular scalar components was straightforward, involving only the familiar differentiation operations of scalar calculus. We next considered the kinematics of a particle moving along some given path. Here we obtained $\dot{\boldsymbol{r}}$ and $\ddot{\boldsymbol{r}}$ in terms of speeds and rates of changes of speeds of the particle along the path with component directions no longer fixed in space but instead related at each point along the path to the geometry of the path. For this reason we brought in certain concepts of differential geometry such as the osculating plane, the normal vector, etc. As can be seen from Example 11.3, the carrying out of such problems for three-dimensional curves is by no means an easy matter. Finally, we computed $\dot{\boldsymbol{r}}$ and $\ddot{\boldsymbol{r}}$ in terms of cylindrical coordinates with component directions always in the radial, transverse, and axial directions. Clearly, the radial and transverse directions are not fixed in space and change as the particle moves about.

In carrying out various derivatives of unit vectors which are not fixed in space, such as $\boldsymbol{\varepsilon}_{\bar{r}}$ and $\boldsymbol{\varepsilon}_{\phi}$, we went through a simple limiting process in arriving at the desired results. You should be able now to think through these limiting processes to arrive at the simple derivatives of unit vectors that you will need in the early part of the text. Later, in a continuation of kinematics, we present simple straightforward formal procedures for this purpose.

We next investigated the relations between velocities and accelerations of a particle, as seen from different references, which are translating relative to each other. We called such motions simple relative motion. Later, when we undertake rigid-body motion, we shall consider the case involving references moving arbitrarily relative to each other.

At the close of this chapter we computed the force on a particle at some instant of time when the acceleration of the particle was available from kinematical considerations. It is vital to remember here that we must measure $\boldsymbol{a}$ relative to an *inertial reference* when we employ Newton's law in the form $\boldsymbol{F} = m\boldsymbol{a}$. We may find it convenient at times to employ two references in this connection where one reference is the inertial reference needed for the proper acceleration vector. At this time, however, we are equipped only to handle references translating relative to each other.

In the next chapter we shall examine the inverse of the problem undertaken at the end of this chapter. We will then be given the forces (rather than the accelerations), and we will be asked to solve for the motion of the system (rather than the forces). This will prove to be a more difficult task, since we shall have to carry out integrations or solve differential equations. In setting up such problems, we shall have ample opportunity to employ the kinematics presented in this chapter.

PROBLEMS

The bracketed numbers [11.3] etc. indicate how far along in the chapter one should be before most profitably doing the problem. It is to be cautioned however that the problems are not necessarily directly related only to the indicated section. They may cover anything preceding that Section.

1. [11.2] Show that $(d/dt)(\boldsymbol{A} \times \boldsymbol{B}) = \boldsymbol{A} \times (d\boldsymbol{B}/dt) + (d\boldsymbol{A}/dt) \times \boldsymbol{B}$.

2. [11.2] The vector $\boldsymbol{A}(t)$ is given as $16t^2\boldsymbol{i} + 10t\boldsymbol{j} - 16\boldsymbol{k}$. What is the derivative of $20t^2\boldsymbol{A}$ with respect to time?

3. [11.2] The vector $\boldsymbol{B}$ is known to be $6\boldsymbol{i} + 3\boldsymbol{j}$. What is the derivative of the dot product of $\boldsymbol{B}$ and $\boldsymbol{A}(t)$ of the last problem? What is the derivative of the cross product of $\boldsymbol{B} \times \boldsymbol{A}$?

4. [11.2] The following vectors are functions of time:

$$\boldsymbol{C}(t) = 10t\boldsymbol{i} - (2t^3 + 3)\boldsymbol{j}$$

$$\boldsymbol{D}(t) = -3t^2\boldsymbol{i} + 6\boldsymbol{k}$$

What is the time derivative of the sum of these vectors? Determine the derivative of the dot and cross products of these vectors.

5. [11.2] Give the time derivative of:

$$[\ddot{\boldsymbol{A}}\cdot\boldsymbol{A}]\dot{\boldsymbol{A}} + \frac{\boldsymbol{C}}{\boldsymbol{A}\cdot\boldsymbol{B}}$$

6. [11.2] The kinetic energy of a particle will later be shown to be $\frac{1}{2}mV^2$. Show that this expression is the same as $\frac{1}{2}m\boldsymbol{V}\cdot(d\boldsymbol{r}/dt)$. Show furthermore that $(d/dt)(\frac{1}{2}mV^2)$ can be given as $m\boldsymbol{V}\cdot\boldsymbol{a}$.

7. [11.2] A particle has an acceleration $\boldsymbol{a}$ given as:

$$\boldsymbol{a} = \boldsymbol{B}t^2 \text{ ft/sec}^2$$

where $\boldsymbol{B}$ is a constant vector. If the velocity at $t = 2$ sec is known to be $6\boldsymbol{j}$ ft/sec and the velocity at $t = 3$ sec is known to be $5\boldsymbol{i} + 3\boldsymbol{k}$ ft/sec, what is the velocity at $t = 10$ sec?

8. [11.3] Integrate the vector $\boldsymbol{C} = 16t^2\boldsymbol{i} + \ln t\boldsymbol{j} + 10\boldsymbol{k}$. to form vector $\boldsymbol{D}$. If $\boldsymbol{D}$ is $20\boldsymbol{i} + 10\boldsymbol{j} - 5\boldsymbol{k}$ when $t = 10$ sec, what is the vector of integration?

9. [11.3] Given the following vectors:

$$\boldsymbol{A} = 6t^2\boldsymbol{i} + 3 \sin t\boldsymbol{j}$$

$$\boldsymbol{B} = 10\boldsymbol{i} + 4t\boldsymbol{k}$$

What is the integral $\boldsymbol{A} + \boldsymbol{B}$?

10. [11.3] Given the following vectors:

$$\boldsymbol{A} = 10\boldsymbol{i} + 3\boldsymbol{j} + 6\boldsymbol{k}$$

$$\boldsymbol{B} = \sin 3t\boldsymbol{i} + \sinh 2t\boldsymbol{j} + 10\boldsymbol{k}$$

Compute:

$$\int \boldsymbol{A}\cdot\boldsymbol{B}\, dt; \qquad \int \boldsymbol{B} \times \boldsymbol{A}\, dt.$$

11. [11.3] Integrate the vector $6t^2\boldsymbol{i} + 4t\boldsymbol{k}$ between the limits $t = 2$ to $t = 4$. Give the result as a single vector.

12. [11.3] Integrate the vector

$$\boldsymbol{A} = (13 + 6t^2)\boldsymbol{j} + 16\boldsymbol{k}$$

from the time $t = 3$ seconds to the time $t = 5$ seconds. What is the derivative of $\boldsymbol{A}$ at $t = 10$ seconds?

13. [11.3] A particle at position (3, 4, 6) at time $t_0 = 1$ sec is given a constant acceleration having the value $6\boldsymbol{i} + 3\boldsymbol{j}$ ft/sec^2. If the velocity at the time t_0 is $16\boldsymbol{i} + 20\boldsymbol{j} + 5\boldsymbol{k}$ ft/sec, what is the velocity of the particle 20 seconds later? Also give the position of the particle.

14. [11.3] A particle having a position vector $\boldsymbol{r} = 5\boldsymbol{i} + 6\boldsymbol{j} + \boldsymbol{k}$ ft initially, has an acceleration imposed on it given as:

$$\boldsymbol{a} = 6t\boldsymbol{i} + 5t^2\boldsymbol{j} + 10\boldsymbol{k} \text{ ft/sec}^2$$

If it has zero velocity initially, what are the acceleration, velocity, and position of the particle when $t = 10$ seconds?

15. [11.3] The velocity of a particle is known at times $t_1 = 2$ sec and $t_2 = 5$ sec to be respectively:

$$V(t_1) = 16\boldsymbol{i} + 3\boldsymbol{j} + 18\boldsymbol{k} \text{ ft/sec}$$
$$V(t_2) = -5\boldsymbol{i} + 16\boldsymbol{j} \text{ ft/sec}$$

If the acceleration vector is known to have the form:

$$\boldsymbol{a} = \alpha t\boldsymbol{i} + \beta\left(\frac{1}{t}\right)\boldsymbol{j} + \gamma \ln t\boldsymbol{k}$$

where α, β, and γ are constants, what is the acceleration of the particle at times t_1 and t_2?

16. [11.3] The position of a particle at times $t = 10$ sec, $t = 5$ sec, and $t = 2$ sec is known to be respectively:

$$\boldsymbol{r}(10) = 10\boldsymbol{i} + 5\boldsymbol{j} - 10\boldsymbol{k} \text{ ft}$$
$$\boldsymbol{r}(5) = 3\boldsymbol{i} + 2\boldsymbol{j} + 5\boldsymbol{k} \text{ ft}$$
$$\boldsymbol{r}(2) = 8\boldsymbol{i} - 20\boldsymbol{j} + 10\boldsymbol{k} \text{ ft}$$

What is the acceleration of the particle at time $t = 5$ sec if the acceleration vector has the form:

$$\boldsymbol{a} = C_1 t\boldsymbol{i} + C_2 t^2\boldsymbol{j} + C_3 \ln t\boldsymbol{k}$$

where C_1, C_2, and C_3 are constants. Hint: Reduce work by eliminating one of the integration vectors from the three vector equations thereby reducing the number of equations to work with to two vector equations.

17. [11.3] Shown in Fig. 11.19 is a highly idealized diagram of an *accelerometer*, a device for measuring the acceleration component of motion along a certain direction—in this case the indicated x direction. A mass B is constrained in the accelerometer case so that it can only move against linear springs in the x direction. When the accelerometer case accelerates in this direction, the mass assumes a displaced position, shown dashed, at a distance δ. This configuration is such that the force in the springs gives the mass B the acceleration corresponding to that of the accelerometer case. The shift δ of the mass in the case is picked up by an electrical sensor device and is plotted as a function of time. The damping fluid present eliminates extraneous oscillations of the mass. If a plot of a_x versus time has the form shown in Fig. 11.20, what is the speed of the body after 50 seconds? The acceleration is measured in g's—i.e., in units of 32.2 ft/sec^2. Assume body starts from rest at $x = 0$.

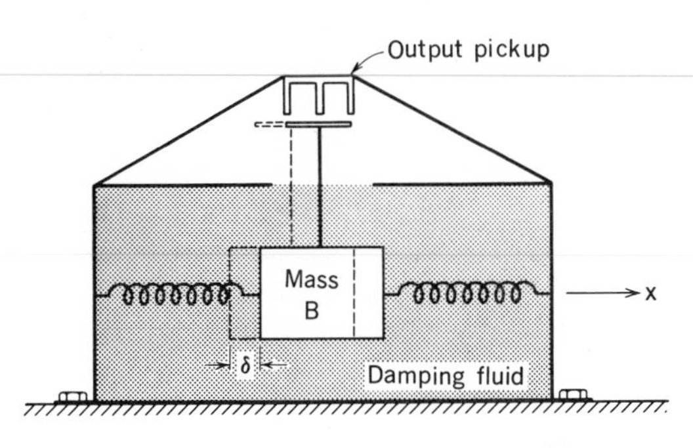

Fig. 11.19

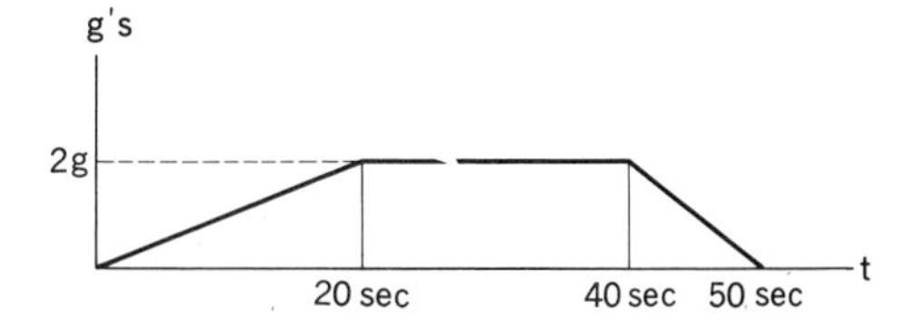

Fig. 11.20

18. [11.3] A *stabilized reference platform* is a device which, by the proper use of gyroscopes (to be studied later), retains a fixed orientation in inertial space no matter where the container of the platform is moved or how it is positioned. In Fig. 11.21 we have shown the earth and a reference XYZ which moves with the earth but which remains fixed in direction in space relative to the stars. The earth rotates in the reference one revolution per day. At various positions around the earth's surface is shown a stabilized reference platform. As indicated in the diagram, this platform retains at all times a fixed orientation relative to XYZ.

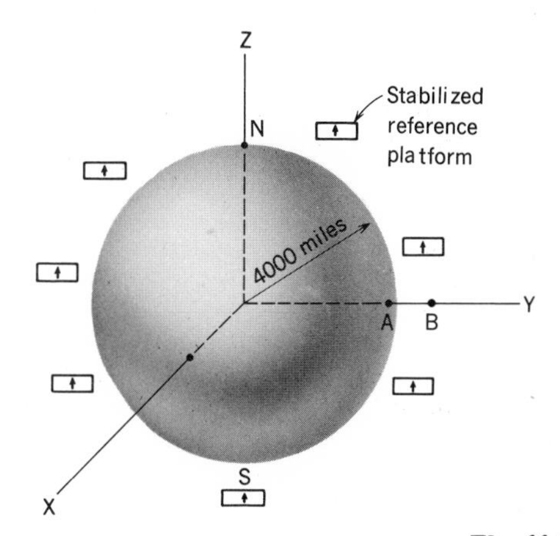

Fig. 11.21

For the problem at hand, a stabilized platform has three orthogonal accelerometers (see previous problem) oriented in the X, Y, and Z directions and is mounted in a space vehicle. What is the initial acceleration of the platform when it is at the equator at A with $X = Z = 0$ at the instant before firing ($t = 0$)? Find the velocity and position of the space vehicle after 18 seconds, if superposed on its initial terrestrial acceleration there are the following three given acceleration components telemetered back from the accelerometers:

$$a_X = 0.6t \text{ g}$$

$$a_Y = 0.5t^2 \text{ g}$$

$$a_Z = 0.3t \text{ g}$$

Hint: Recall from physics that $r\omega^2$ is the acceleration of a particle moving in a circular path such that its position vector r rotates at the rate of ω rad/sec.

19. [11.3] In the previous problem what is the displacement vector between the position where point A on the earth is after 80 seconds and the position of the space vehicle?

20. [11.3] In Fig. 11.21, suppose a body B is stationary in inertial space at position $Y =$ 4100 miles. If this body is released at the instant point A of the earth is at the Y axis and this body accelerates with an average value of 30 ft/sec^2, how far would you have to walk from A to get to the point of impact? (Later we shall examine the case of body B being dropped from a position in space which rotates with the earth—i.e., from a position which is always directly above A. Some very surprising results occur for this case.)

21. [11.5] The position vector of a particle is given as

$$\boldsymbol{r} = 6t\boldsymbol{i} + (5t + 10)\boldsymbol{j} + 6t^2\boldsymbol{k}$$

What is the acceleration of the particle at $t = 3$ sec? What distance has been traveled by the particle during this time? Hint: Note that $dr = \sqrt{dx^2 + dy^2 + dz^2}$ in second half of problem.

22. [11.5] A particle moves along a plane circular path of radius a (see Fig. 11.22). The position OA is given as a function of time as follows:

$$\theta = 6 \sin 5t$$

What are the rectangular components of velocity and acceleration for the particle at time t?

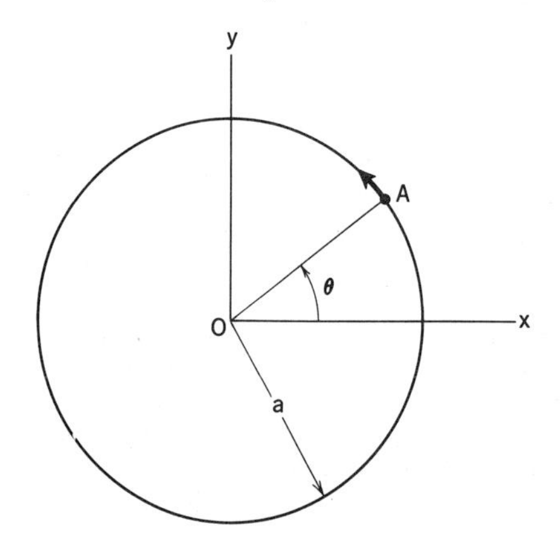

Fig. 11.22

23. [11.5] Pins A and B must always remain in the slot of member C which moves to the right at a constant speed of 6 ft/sec (Fig. 11.23). Furthermore, the pins cannot leave the indicated path which is an ellipse. What is the speed at which the particles approach each other and the rate of change of speed toward each other when the slot is at $x = 5$ ft?

24. [11.5] In the previous problem what is the acceleration vector for pin B if the member C is accelerating at the rate of 10 ft/sec^2 at the instant of interest?

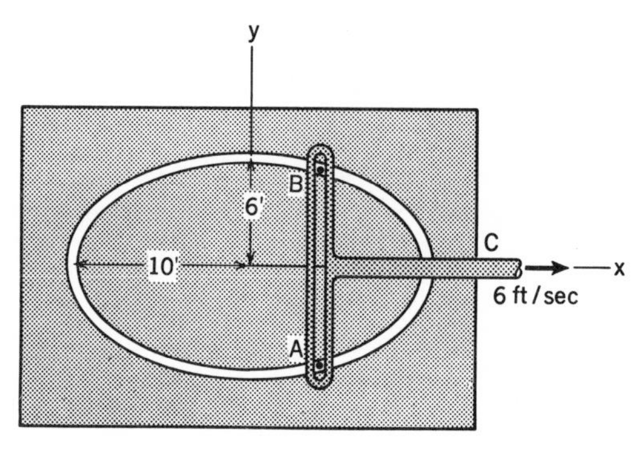

Fig. 11.23

25. [11.5] A pin is confined to slide in a circular slot of radius 6 ft (Fig. 11.24). It must also slide in a straight slot which moves to the right at a constant speed, V, of 3 ft/sec while maintaining a constant angle of 30° with the horizontal. What are the velocity and acceleration of the pin A at the instant shown? Hint: Set up equations for pin on circular path and on straight line path (latter a function of time). Solve simultaneously for x, y, $\dot{x}$, $\dot{y}$, $\ddot{x}$ and $\ddot{y}$.

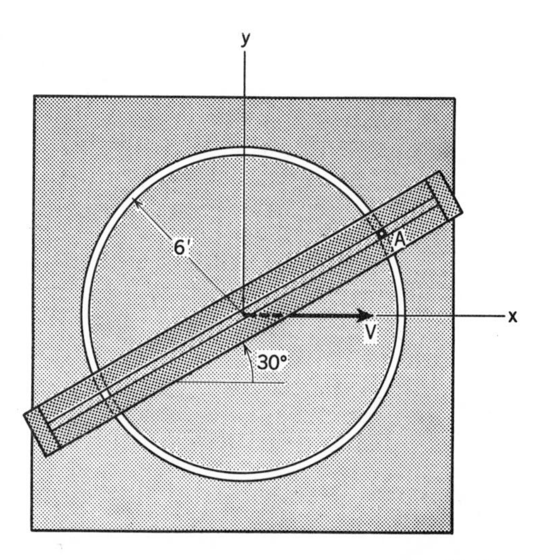

Fig. 11.24

26. [11.5] If the straight slot in the previous problem has a velocity V given as:

$$V = 5t$$

to the right such that at $t = 0$ the slot is as shown in Fig. 11.24, what are the rectangular components velocity and the acceleration of pin A at $t = 1$ sec?

27. [11.5] Particles A and B are confined to always be in a circular groove (see Fig. 11.25) of radius 5 ft. At the same time, these particles must also be in a slot which has the shape of a parabola. The slot is shown dotted at time $t = 0$. If the slot moves to the right at a constant speed of 3 ft/sec, what are the speed and rate of change of speed of particles toward each other at $t = 1$ sec? See hint in Prob. 25.

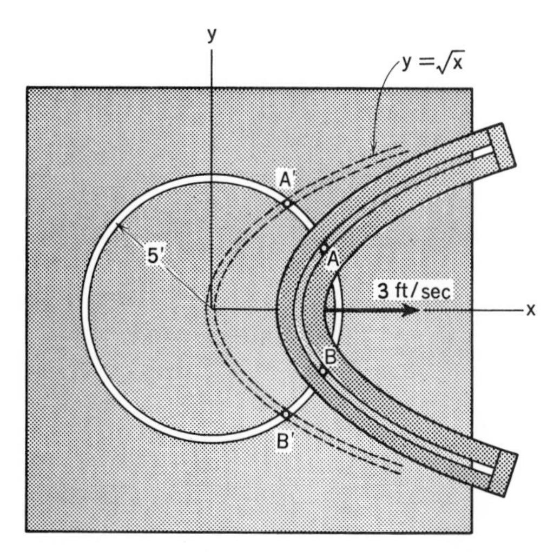

Fig. 11.25

28. [11.5] In the previous problem, the parabolic path moves to the right at a speed given as $3t$ ft/sec. What are the rectangular components of the speed and acceleration of particle A at $t = 1$ sec?

29. [11.6] A particle moves with a constant speed of 5 ft/sec along the path shown in Fig. 11.26. Compute the acceleration at points 1, 2, and 3.

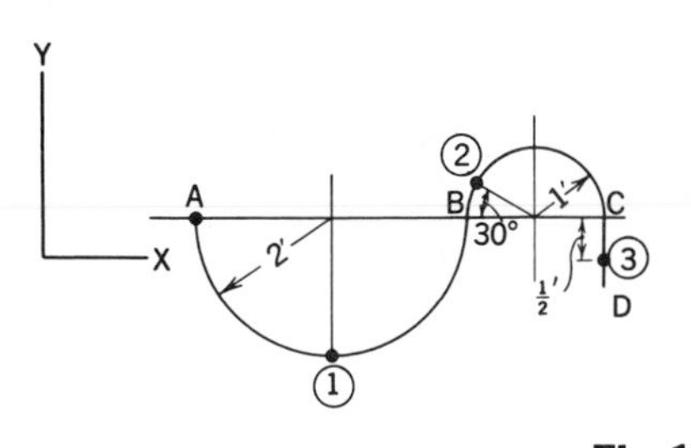

Fig. 11.26

30. [11.6] If, in the above problem, the speed is 5 ft/sec only at point A, and it increases 5 ft/sec for each foot traveled, compute the acceleration at points 1, 2, and 3.

31. [11.6] A particle moves with a constant speed of 10 ft/sec along the path shown in Fig. 11.27. What is the acceleration at position $x =$ 5 ft?

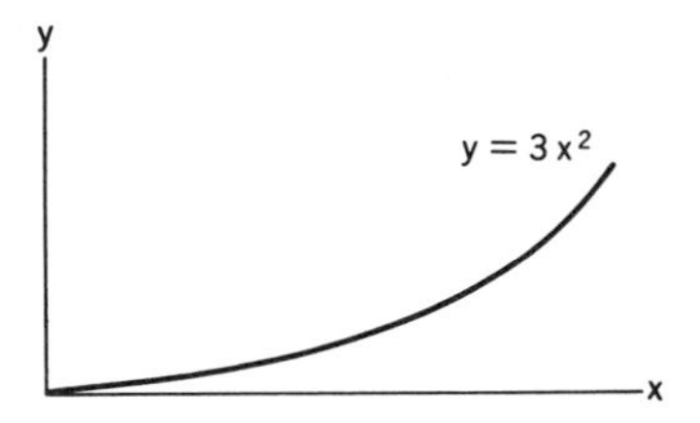

Fig. 11.27

32. [11.6] A particle moves along a sinusoidal path shown in Fig. 11.28. If it has a speed of 10 ft/sec and a rate of change of speed of 5 ft/sec^2 at A, what is the *magnitude* of the acceleration? What is the magnitude and direction of the acceleration of the particle at B, if it has a speed of 20 ft/sec and a rate of change of speed of 3 ft/sec^2 at this point?

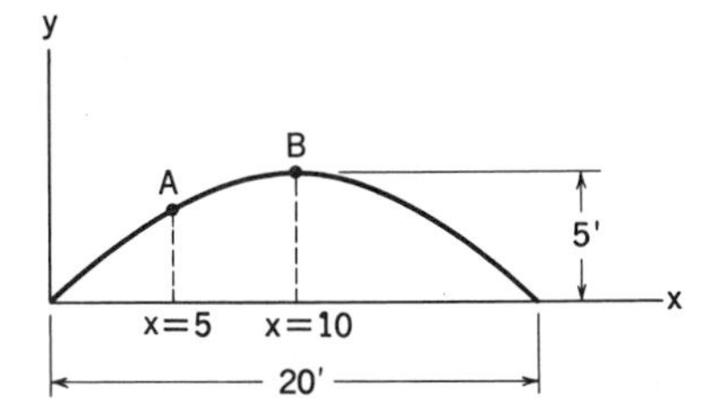

Fig. 11.28

33. [11.6] What is the direction of the normal vector for position A of the path shown in Fig. 11.28?

34. [11.6] What is the direction of the normal vector and the value of the radius of curvature at a position a of the curve shown in Fig. 11.29?

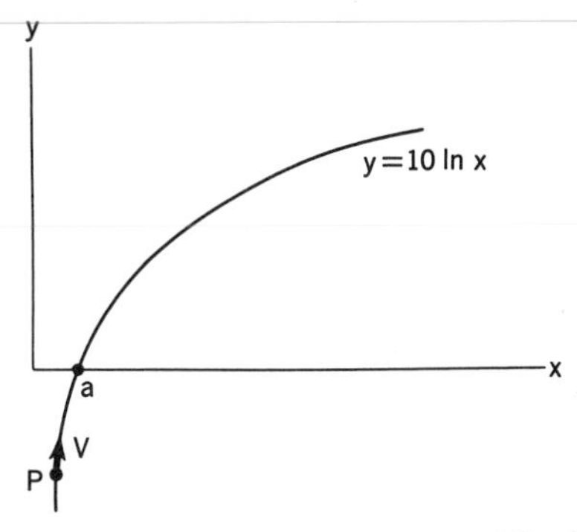

Fig. 11.29

35. [11.6] A particle P moves with constant speed V along the curve $y = 10 \log x$ as shown in Fig. 11.29. At what position x does it have the maximum acceleration? What is the value of this acceleration if $V = 1$ ft/sec?

36. [11.6] A particle moves with constant speed of 5 ft/sec along a path given as $x = y^2 - \ln y$. Give the acceleration vector of the particle in terms of rectangular components when the particle is at position $y = 3$. Do by using path coordinate techniques and then by Cartesian component techniques.

37. [11.6] A particle moves with constant speed of 2 ft/sec along a parabola given as $x = 1 - 2y^2$. Give the position where maximum acceleration takes place. What is the value of this acceleration?

38. [11.6] A particle has a rate of change of speed of 5 ft/sec² and a speed of 10 ft/sec at time t_0 as it moves along a path $y = \ln \sec x$. What is the magnitude of the acceleration vector if the particle is at position $x = 1$ at time t_0?

39. [11.6] At what position along the ellipse shown in Fig. 11.30 does the normal vector have a set of direction cosines (0.707, 0.707, 0)? Recall that the equation for an ellipse in position shown is

$$\frac{x^2}{a^2} + \frac{y^2}{b^2} = 1.$$

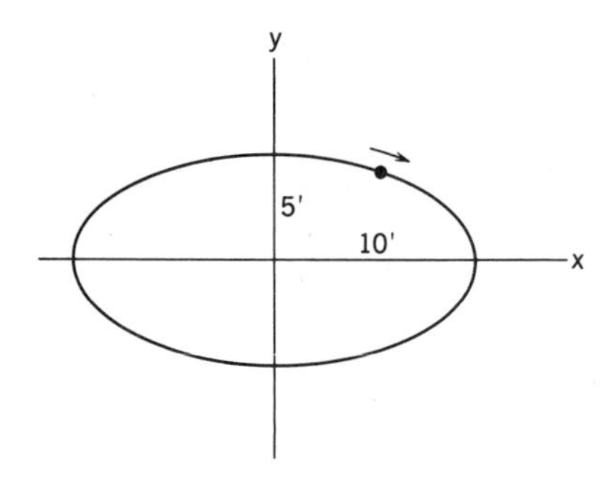

Fig. 11.30

40. [11.6] A particle is moving at constant speed 5 ft/sec along an elliptic path as shown in Fig. 11.30. By inspection at what positions do you have maximum and minimum accelerations? What are the values of these accelerations? Set up equation for determining the position that corresponds to where the acceleration equals the average value value of these accelerations.

41. [11.6] A particle is made to move along a path given in terms of the parameter τ in the following manner:

$$(x)_p = -\sin 2\tau, \quad (y)_p = \cos 2\tau, \quad (z)_p = e^{-\tau}$$

Give a simple sketch of the path. When the particle is at the elevation $z = 1$, the speed along the path is 5 ft/sec and the rate of change of speed along the path is 10 ft/sec². Find the acceleration of the particle at $z = 1$.

42. [11.6] Determine the direction of the osculating plane to the curve of Prob. 41 at position $z = 1$.

43. [11.7] In Fig. 11.31, a particle moves with a constant speed of 5 ft/sec along a straight line having direction cosines $l = 0.5$, $m = 0.3$. What are the cylindrical coordinates when $|\boldsymbol{r}| = 20$ ft? What are the axial, and transverse velocities of the particle at this position?

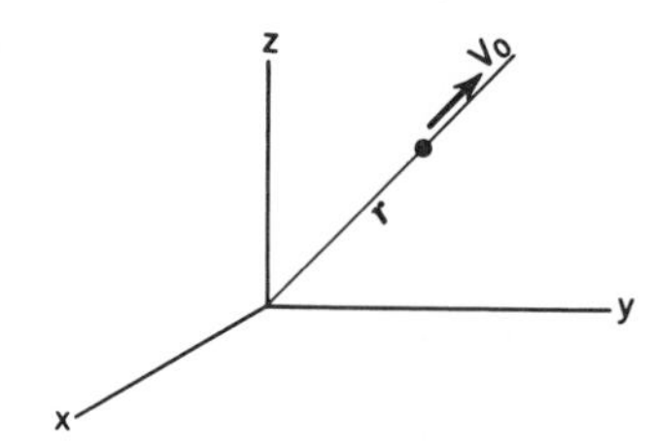

Fig. 11.31

44. [11.7] An airplane is diving at a speed of 900 mi/hr. If the maximum acceleration that the pilot can endure in a direction from toe to head before blacking out is 4 g's, what is the minimum safe radius of curvature for his trajectory as he comes out of the dive?

45. [11.7] A car is moving with a speed of 60 miles per hour and rounds a curve having a radius of curvature of 1000 ft. What is the acceleration of the car?

46. [11.7] A plane is shown in a dive-bombing mission (Fig. 11.32). It has at the instant of interest a speed of 300 mph and is increasing its speed downward at a rate of 50 miles/hour/sec. The propellor is rotating at 150 rpm and has a diameter of 12 ft. What is the velocity of the tip of the propellor shown at A and its acceleration at the instant of interest?

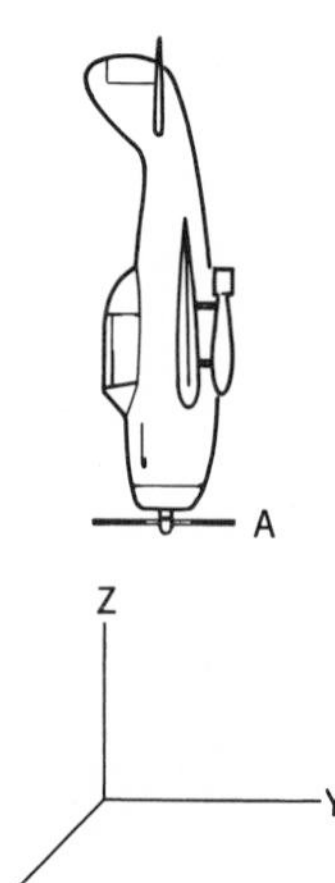

Fig. 11.32

47. [11.7] A wheel of diameter 2 ft is rotated at a speed of 2 rad/sec (see Fig. 11.33). It advances along a screw having a pitch of 0.5 in. What is the acceleration of a particle on the rim in terms of cylindrical components?

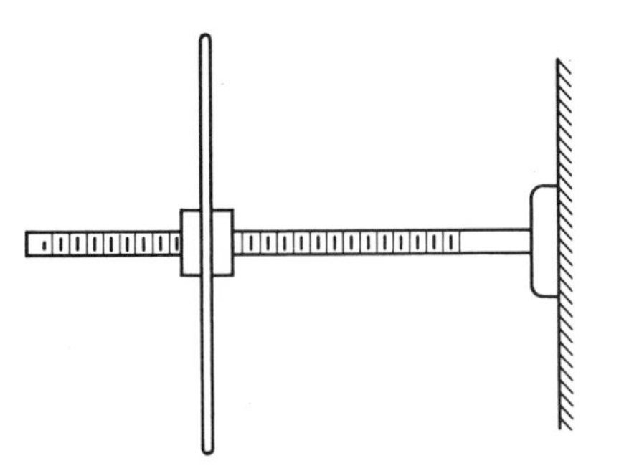

Fig. 11.33

48. [11.7] In Prob. 47, suppose a particle moves along the circumference of the wheel at a constant speed of 10 ft/sec. If the wheel is made to rotate at a speed of 3 rad/sec, what is the acceleration of the particle? The rate of change of angular speed of the wheel is 1 rad/sec^2 at the instant of interest.

49. [11.7] A wheel with a threaded hub is rotating at angular speed of 80 rpm on a right-hand screw having a pitch of 0.5 in. as shown in Fig. 11.34. At the instant of interest, the rate of change of angular speed is 20 rpm/sec. A sleeve A is advancing along a spoke at this instant with a constant speed of 5 ft/sec and is 2 ft from the centerline at O. What are the velocity vector and the acceleration vector of the sleeve?

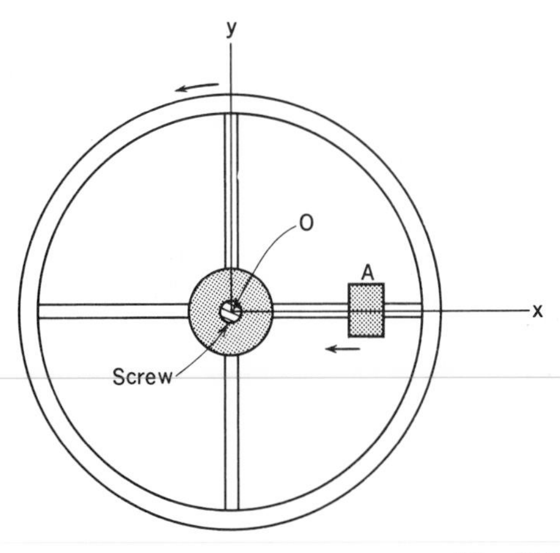

Fig. 11.34

50. [11.7] Repeat the previous problem for the case where the sleeve has at the instant of interest a rate of change of speed in its advance along the spoke of 5 ft/sec^2.

51. [11.7] Suppose in Example 11.3 that the constant $C = 0$. What is the equation of the trajectory for the path in terms of x and y? Compute the acceleration for this problem using cylindrical coordinate techniques and check to see whether Eq. (i) degenerates to your result when you take $C = 0$.

52. [11.7] The rate of change of acceleration $\dot{\boldsymbol{a}}$ (sometimes called the "jerk") has been related to human discomfort in public conveyances. Compute $\dot{\boldsymbol{a}}$ in terms of cylindrical coordinates starting with Eq. 11.41. Now compute the jerk of a particle moving along a rod with a speed of 5 ft/sec relative to the rod (see Fig. 11.35) while the rod rotates in a plane with an angular speed, $\dot{\phi}$, of 5 rad/sec, an angular acceleration, $\ddot{\phi}$, of 10 rad/sec^2, and a $\dddot{\phi}$ of 2 rad/sec^3. The particle is at a position 10 ft from the origin at the instant of interest.

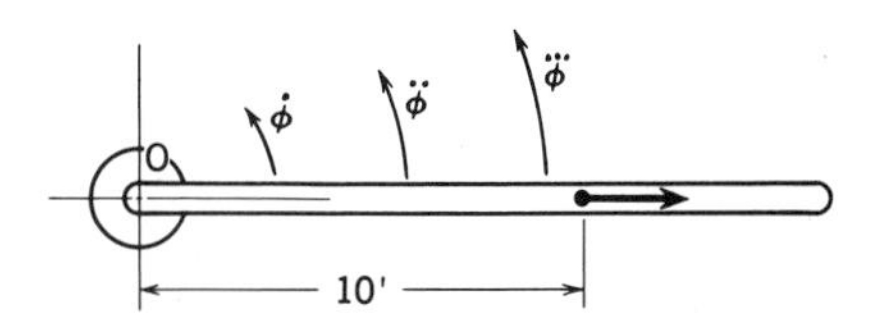

Fig. 11.35

53. [11.7] Show by arguments similar to those used in the text for deriving the relation $d\boldsymbol{\varepsilon}_t/ds = (1/R)\boldsymbol{\varepsilon}_n$ that $d\boldsymbol{\varepsilon}_n/ds = -(1/R)\boldsymbol{\varepsilon}_t$.

54. [11.7] (a) For coplanar paths in the xy plane find the formula for $\dot{\boldsymbol{a}}$—that is, the so-called jerk.

(b) If a particle moves on a plane circular path of radius 5 ft at a speed of 5 ft/sec, and if the rate of change of speed is 2 ft/sec^2, what is $\dot{\boldsymbol{a}}$ for the particle if the second derivative of its speed along the path is 10 ft/sec^3? Hint: Use the result of the preceding problem.

55. [11.7] Do part (b) of the preceding problem using cylindrical coordinates. (Use result of Prob. 52).

56. [11.8] In the study of fluid flow we can often consider that the fluid particles move in a translatory manner—that is, the fluid particles have no rotation relative to some reference. Such flows are termed *irrotational* flows. A simple example is the vortex formed on pulling the stopper in the bath tub. Near the surface of the vortex (see Fig. 11.36) and away from the centerline the velocity of the particles is given approximately as:

$$V_r = 0, \quad V_z = 0, \quad V_\phi = \frac{K}{r}$$

where K is a constant. What are the velocity and acceleration of particle B at $r = 2$ ft relative to particle A at $r = 1$ ft?

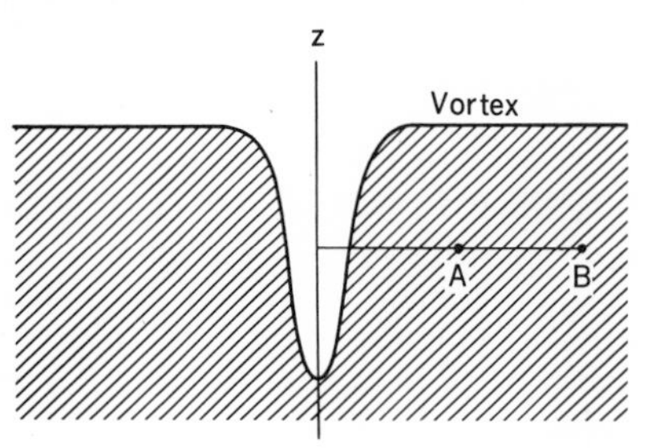

Fig. 11.36

57. [11.8] A rocket is shown in Fig. 11.37 moving at a speed of 2000 ft/sec and accelerating at a rate of 5 g relative to the ground reference XYZ. The products of combustion at A leave the rocket at a speed of 5000 ft/sec relative to the rocket and are accelerating at the rate of 100 ft/sec/sec relative to the rocket. What are the speed and acceleration of an element of the combustion products as seen from the ground? The rocket moves along a straight-line path whose direction cosines for the XYZ reference are $l = 0.6$ and $m = 0.6$.

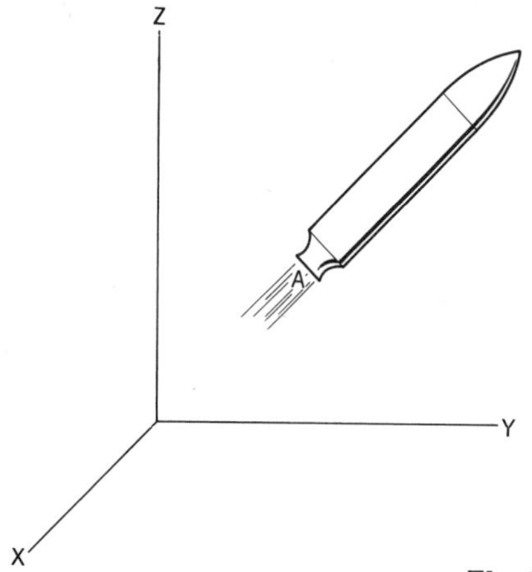

Fig. 11.37

58. [11.8] Shown in Fig. 11.38 is a cockpit C used to carry a worker for service work on road-lighting systems. The cockpit is moved always in a translatory manner. If the angular speed ω of arm AB is 1 rad/min when $\theta = 30°$, what are the velocity and acceleration of any point in the cockpit body relative to the truck? At this instant, what are the velocity and acceleration, relative to the truck, of a particle moving with a horizontal speed V of 0.5 ft/sec and with a rate of change of speed of 0.02 ft/sec^2 both relative to the cockpit?

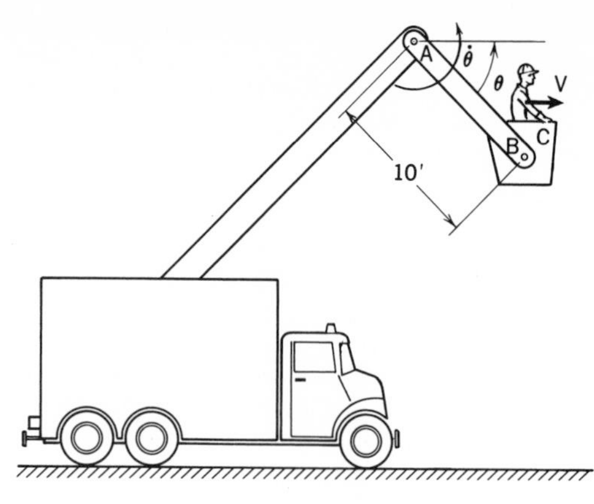

Fig. 11.38

59. [11.8] In the previous problem the truck is moving relative to the ground at a speed of 2 ft/sec with a deceleration of 0.05 ft/sec^2 at the instant of interest. Compute the velocity and acceleration of the cockpit relative to the ground. Also compute the velocity and accelera- of the particle moving in the cockpit relative to the ground.

60. [11.8] Shown in Fig. 11.39 are two wheels rotating about stationary axes each at the same angular velocity, $\dot{\theta} = 5$ rad/sec. A particle A moves along the spoke of the larger wheel at the speed V_1 of 5 ft/sec relative to the wheel and at the instant shown is decelerating at the rate of 3 ft/sec^2. What are the velocity and acceleration of particle A as seen by an observer on the hub of the smaller wheel? What are the velocity and acceleration of particle A to an observer on the hub of the smaller wheel if the larger wheel moves at the instant of interest to the left with a speed of 10 ft/sec while decelerating at the rate of 2 ft/sec^2? Both wheels maintain equal angular speeds.

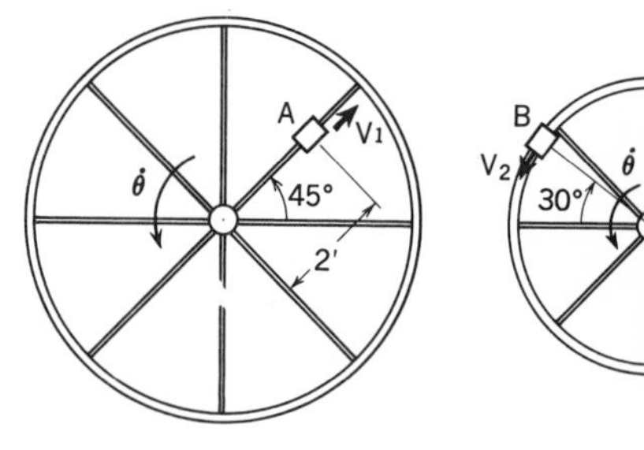

Fig. 11.39

61. [11.8] In Fig. 11.39 the wheels are both rotating at the speed of $\dot{\theta} = 1.0$ rad/sec with an acceleration of 2 rad/sec^2 at the instant of interest. A particle B at this instant is shown moving on the rim of the smaller wheel (radius 3 ft) at the rate, V_2, of 5 ft/sec relative to this wheel and is accelerating at 2 ft/sec^2. What are the velocity and acceleration of particle B as seen from the hub of the larger wheel? What are the velocity and acceleration of particle B as seen from the hub of the larger wheel if, in addition to the aforementioned rotation, the wheels are separating at the rate of 10 ft/sec at the instant of interest and are increasing the rate of separation by 2 ft/sec^2?

62. [11.8] Shown in Fig. 11.40 is a boat about to depart from point A on the shore of a river which has a uniform velocity V_0 of 5 ft/sec. If the boat can move at the rate of 10 ft/sec relative to the water and if we want to move along a straight path from A to B, how long will it take to go from A to B?

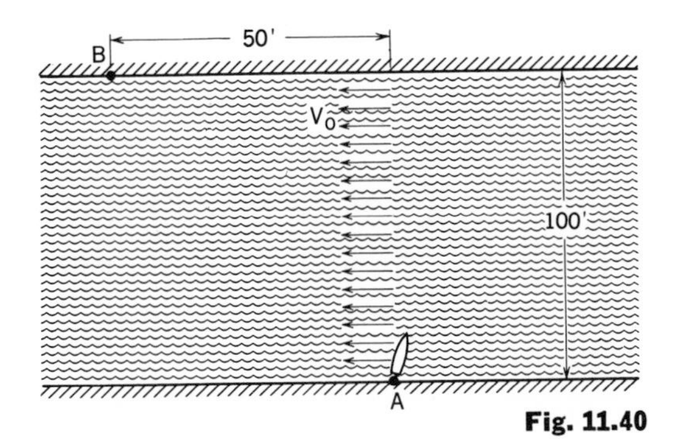

Fig. 11.40

* **63.** [11.8] Work the preceding problem for the case where the river has a velocity which on shore A is zero and on shore B is 8 ft/sec, and which varies linearly in a direction normal to the shores. (Set up the integral formula for t only.)

* **64.** [11.8] Work Prob. 62 for the case where the river has a parabolic velocity profile with a speed of 5 ft/sec at the center and 2 ft/sec at the shores. (Set up the quadrature for t only).

65. [11.8] A uniform cylinder rotates at an angular speed $\dot{\theta}$ of 5 rad/sec (Fig. 11.41). Because it is in a slipping condition at the point of contact, the centerline O moves to the right at the speed V of 2 ft/sec. What are the velocity and acceleration of point A at the position shown, relative to the center of mass of the cylinder? What result do you get if the centerline moves at the speed of 3 ft/sec as a result of slipping?

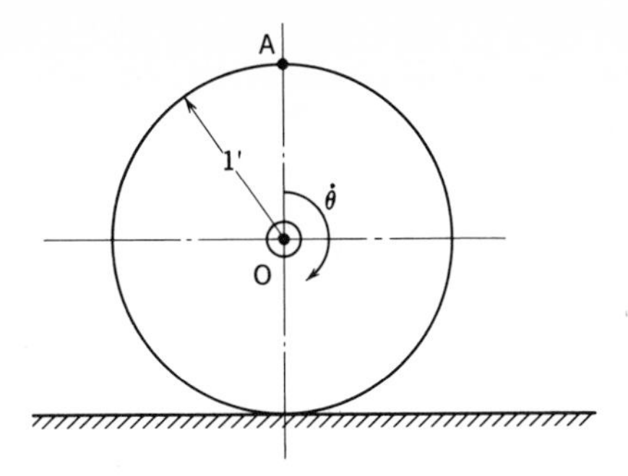

Fig. 11.41

66. [11.8] Shown in Fig. 11.42 are four particles of equal mass undergoing coplanar motion in the xy plane. The following data are given for the velocities:

$$V_1 = 2 \text{ ft/sec}$$
$$V_2 = 3 \text{ ft/sec}$$
$$V_3 = 2 \text{ ft/sec}$$
$$V_4 = 5 \text{ ft/sec}$$

It will be shown in a later chapter that the velocity of the center of mass can be found as follows:

$$(\sum m_i) \boldsymbol{V}_c = \sum m_i \boldsymbol{V}_i$$

where $\boldsymbol{V}_c$ is the velocity of the center of mass. What are the velocities of the particles relative to the center of mass?

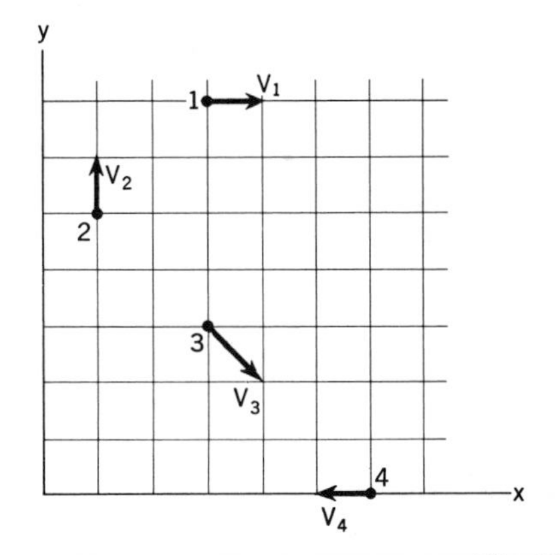

Fig. 11.42

67. [11.9] A device used at amusement parks consists of a circular room (see Fig. 11.43) which is made to revolve about its axis of symmetry. People stand up against the wall, as shown in the diagram. After the whole room has been brought up to speed the floor is lowered. What angular speed is required to insure that a person will not slip down the wall when the floor is lowered? Take $\mu_s = 0.3$.

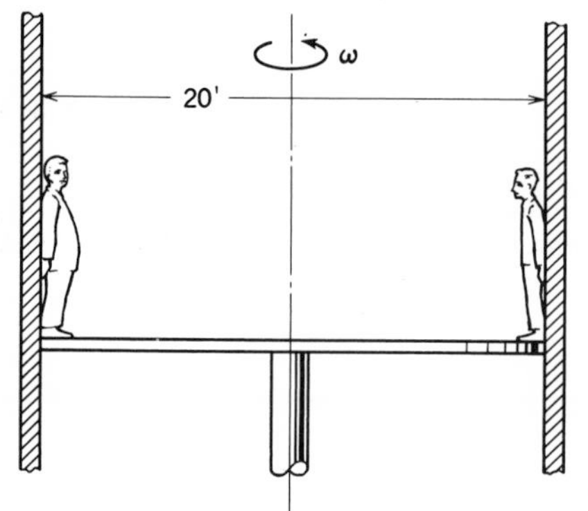

Fig. 11.43

68. [11.9] A simple device for measuring reasonably uniform accelerations is the pendulum (Fig. 11.44). Calibrate θ of the pendulum for accelerations of 5 ft/sec², 10 ft/sec², and 20 ft/sec². The bob weighs 1 lb. The bob is connected to post with a flexible string.

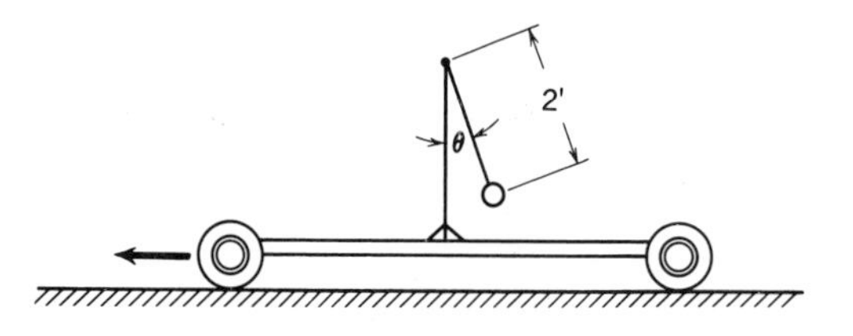

Fig. 11.44

69. [11.9] A particle moves at uniform speed of 10 ft/sec along a plane sinusoidal path given as:

$$y = 5 \sin \pi x$$

What is the position between $x = 0$ and $x = 1$ for the maximum force normal to the curve? What is this force if the mass of the particle is 1 lbm?

70. [11.9] A skier is moving down a hill at a speed of 30 miles per hour when he is at the position shown in Fig. 11.45. If the skier weighs 180 lb, what total force do his skies exert on the snow surface? Assume the coefficient of friction is 0.1. The hill may be taken as a parabolic surface.

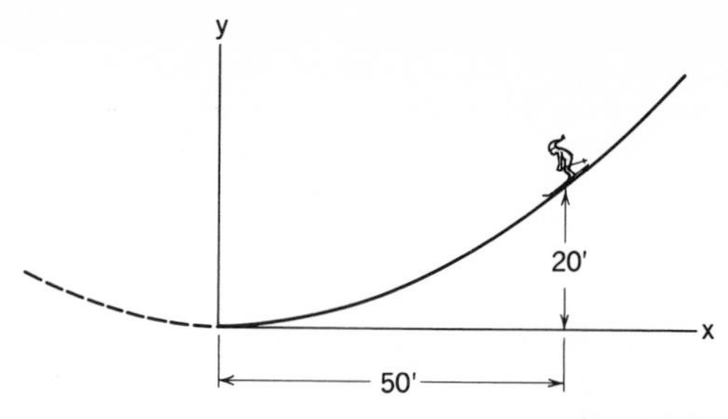

Fig. 11.45

71. [11.9] A wheel is rotating at a speed of 10 rad/sec and has at this instant a rate of change of speed of 5 rad/sec² (see Fig. 11.46). If at this instant, a mass on a spoke has a speed toward the center relative to the spoke of 5 ft/sec and is slowing down at the rate of 2 ft/sec², what is the force that the wheel must exert on this mass at this instant? The body weighs 2 lb and is 1 ft from the center of the wheel at the time of interest.

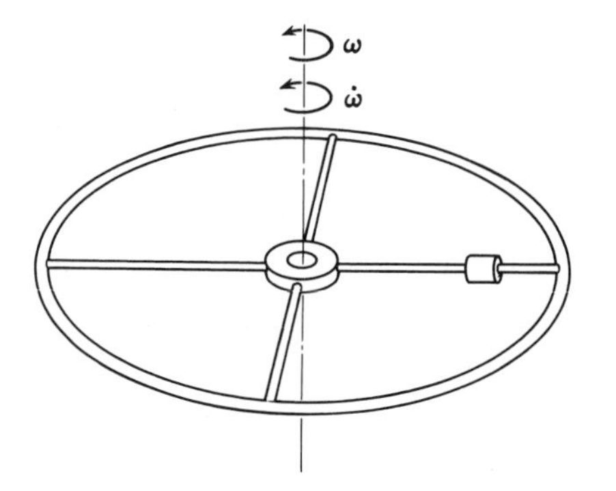

Fig. 11.46

72. [11.9] Shown in Fig. 11.47 is a *catenary* curve whose equation relative to the axes shown can be given as:

$$y = \frac{a}{2}\,(e^{ax} + e^{-ax})$$

A particle is to move at uniform speed of 10 ft/sec along the curve. If the particle has a mass of 1 lbm, what is the force normal to the curve as a function of position x?

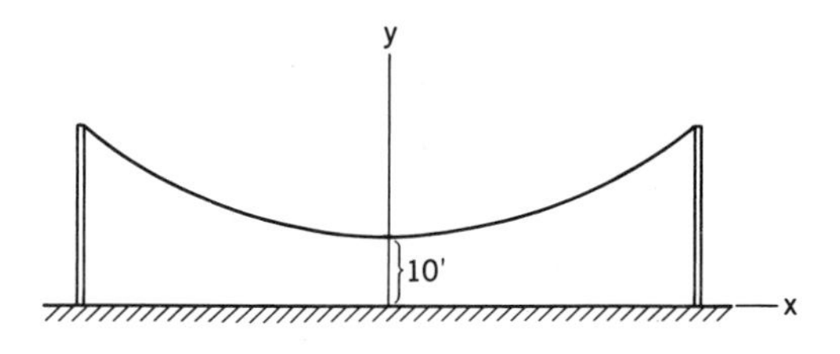

Fig. 11.47

73. [11.9] In Example 11.9, what is the maximum bending moment of the top connecting rods, if the governor has an angular acceleration, $\dot{\omega}$, of 2 cycles/sec^2 at the instant the angular speed, ω, is 300 rpm? The angle θ is fixed. Neglect dynamical effects of the rods and bearing A.

74. [11.9] A particle A of mass 1 lbm is forced to move by the device shown in Fig. 11.48. What total force is exerted on the body at time $t = 6$ sec? What is the maximum total force on the body and when is the first time this force is developed after $t = 0$?

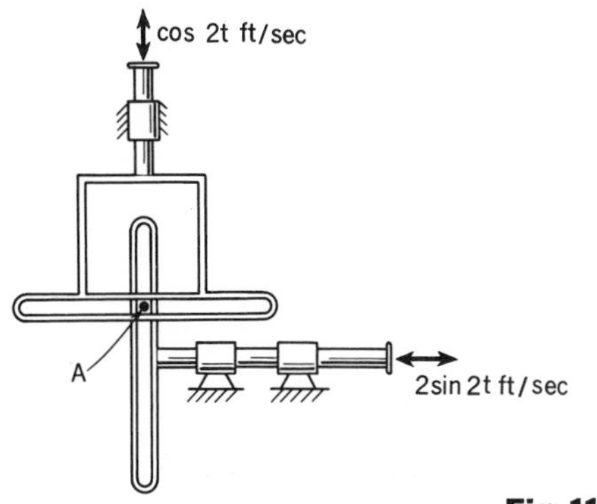

Fig. 11.48

75. [11.9] What is the tension T in Fig. 11.49 to accelerate the end of the cable downward at the rate of 5 ft/sec^2? From body C, weighing 100 lb, is released a body D weighing 25 lb at the rate of 5 ft/sec^2 relative to body C. Neglect the inertia of the pulleys A and B and the cable. Hint: From earlier courses in physics recall that the pulley B is rotating instantaneously about point e, and hence point b has an acceleration half that of point f. We will consider such relations carefully at a later time.

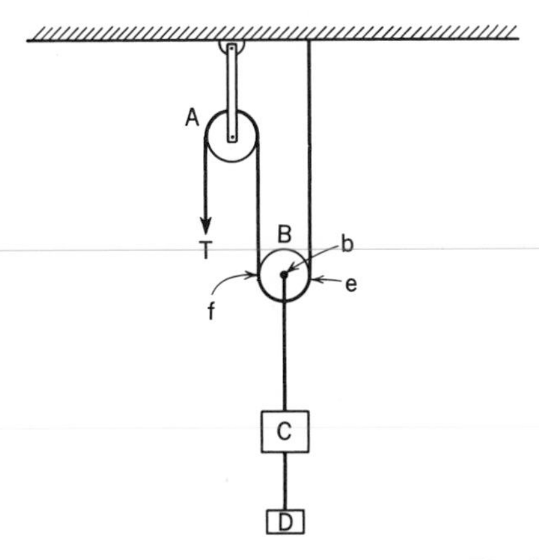

Fig. 11.49

76. [11.9] Shown in Fig. 11.50 is a sled used by researchers to test man's ability to withstand large accelerations over extended periods of time. If the sled is accelerating at 6 g, what force does the man need to exert on a 3-ounce body to give it an acceleration relative to the sled of:

$$30\boldsymbol{i} + 20\boldsymbol{j} \text{ ft/sec}^2$$

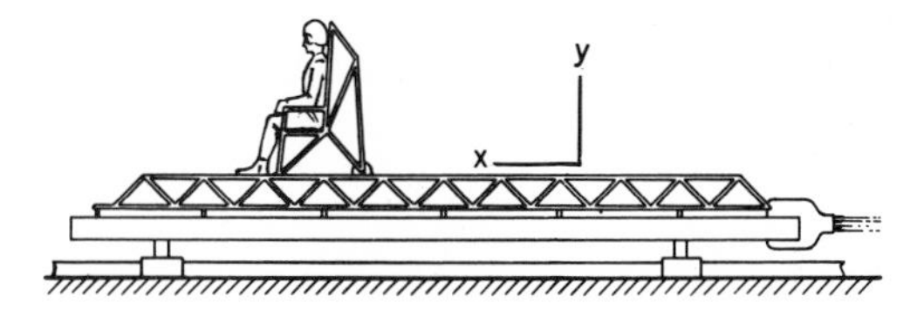

Fig. 11.50

77. [11.9] On the sled of Prob. 76 is a device (see Fig. 11.51) on which mass M rotates about a horizontal axis at an angular speed ω of 5000 rpm. If the inclination θ of the arm BM is maintained at 30° with the vertical plane C–C, what is the total force on the mass M at the instant it is in its uppermost position? The sled is undergoing an acceleration of 5 g. Take M as having a mass of 0.3 lbm.

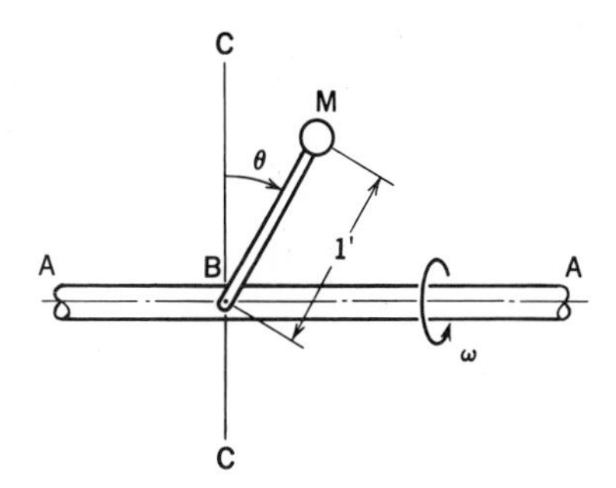

Fig. 11.51

78. [11.9] Shown in Fig. 11.52 is a device wherein a mass M of 1 lbm rotates with an angular speed ω equal to 5 rad/sec relative to a vehicle which translates with a speed V given as $V = 5 \sin 3t$ relative to the ground. When $t = 1$ sec, the rod AM is in the position shown. At this instant what is the total force exerted by the mass M along the axis of rod AM?

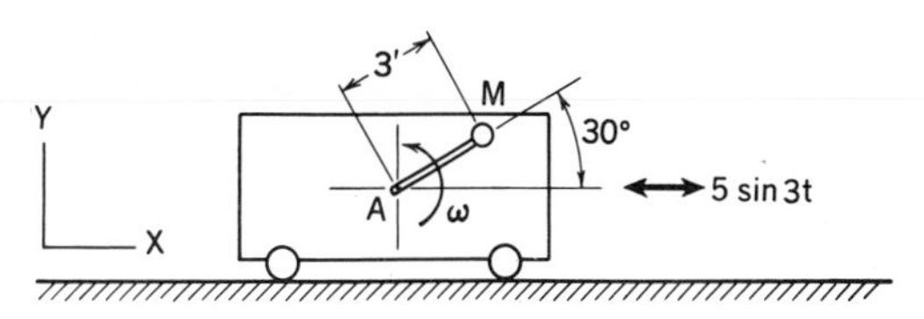

Fig. 11.52

79. [11.9] In the preceding problem what is the frequency of oscillation, Ω, of the vehicle and the value of ω if at the instant shown there is a force on the mass M given as:

$$\boldsymbol{F} = 25\boldsymbol{i} - 35\boldsymbol{j} \text{ lb}$$

80. [11.9] A conical pendulum of length l is shown in Fig. 11.53. It is made to rotate at a constant angular speed of ω about the vertical axis. Compute the tension in the chord if the pendulum bob has weight W. What is the distance of the plane of the trajectory of the bob from the support at O?

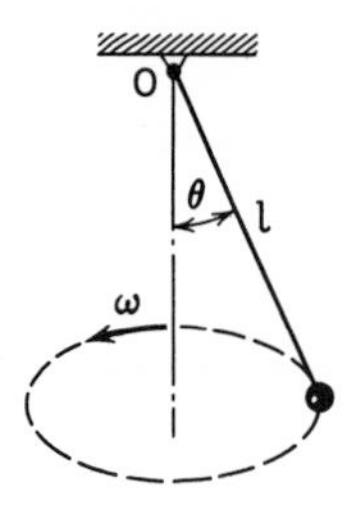

Fig. 11.53

81. [11.9] Find the angular velocity required to maintain the configuration of the flyball governor, as shown in Fig. 11.54. Connection A is fixed in the vertical direction, while weight B may move up or down along the shaft.

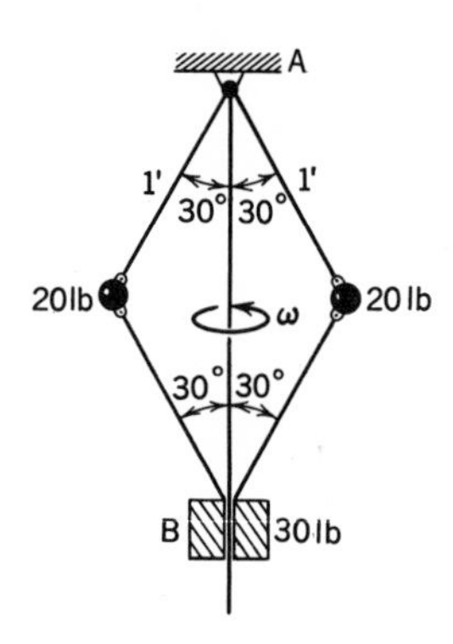

Fig. 11.54

82. [11.9] A shaft AB rotates at an angular velocity of 100 rpm (Fig. 11.55). A body E of weight 20 lb may move without friction along rod CD fixed to AB. If the body E is to remain stationary relative to CD at any position along CD, how must the spring constant K vary?

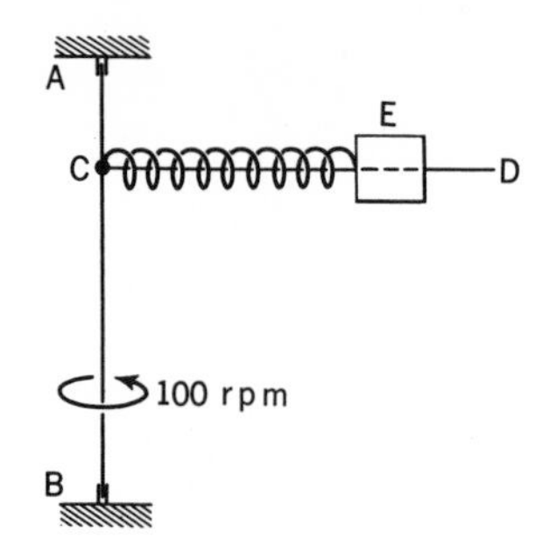

Fig. 11.55

83. [11.9] A platform rotates at 2 rad/sec (Fig. 11.56). A body C weighing 100 lb rests on the platform and is connected by a flexible weightless cord to a mass weighing 50 lb, which is prevented from swinging out by part of the platform. At what extreme value of x will bodies C and B remain stationary relative to the platform? The coefficient of friction for all surfaces is 0.4.

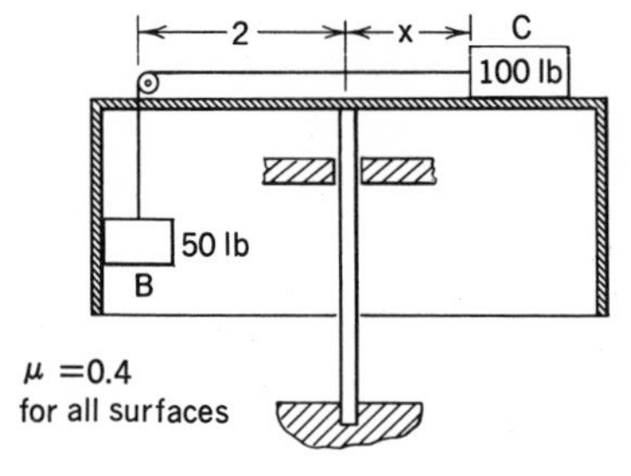

Fig. 11.56

12 Particle Dynamics

PART A. Rectilinear Translation

12.1 Introduction

In Part A we shall consider situations in which the resultant force on a particle has the same direction and line of action at all times. The resulting motion is then entirely confined to a straight line and is sometimes called *rectilinear translation*.

The force may be a constant, a function of time, a function of velocity, a function of position, or any combination of these possibilities. We shall examine these various situations in the succeeding sections of Part A of the chapter as well as in Chapter 20.

12.2 Force is Constant

Shown in Fig. 12.1 is a particle of mass m acted on by a constant force $\boldsymbol{F}$. The plane on which the body moves is frictionless. The force of gravity is equal and opposite to the normal force from the plane so that $\boldsymbol{F}$ is the resultant force acting on the mass. We choose the x axis as collinear with the line of action of the force. We need use only the scalar notation for Newton's law since all vectors involved are collinear. Thus:

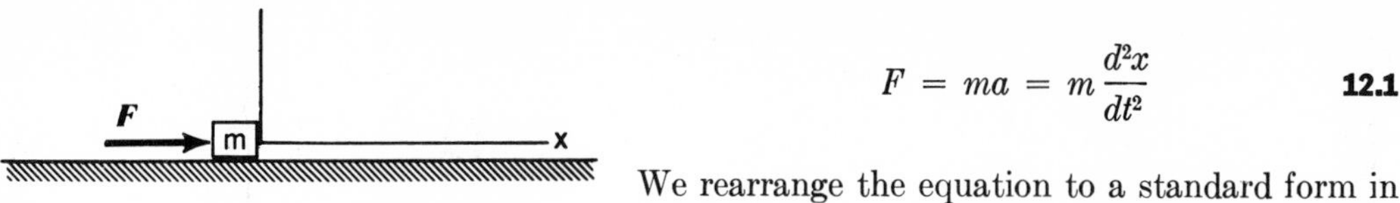

$$F = ma = m\frac{d^2x}{dt^2} \tag{12.1}$$

Fig. 12.1

We rearrange the equation to a standard form in which the highest order derivative appears first with a coefficient of unity:

$$\frac{d^2x}{dt^2} = \frac{F}{m} \tag{12.2}$$

Integration may be carried out by simple quadratures. Thus we get:

$$\frac{dx}{dt} = V = \frac{F}{m}t + C_1 \tag{12.3}$$

where C_1 is a constant of integration. Integration again gives us:

$$x = \frac{F}{m}\frac{t^2}{2} + C_1t + C_2 \tag{12.4}$$

We have thus found the velocity of the particle and the position as functions of time up to two arbitrary constants. These constants may be readily determined by having the solutions yield a certain velocity and position at a time $t = 0$. Usually these conditions are termed *initial conditions*. That is:

$$\text{when } t = 0, \qquad V = V_0, \quad x = x_0 \tag{12.5}$$

This may be accomplished by substituting the initial conditions into Eqs. 12.3 and 12.4 and solving for the constants C_1 and C_2. Thus:

$$V_0 = \frac{F}{m}(0) + C_1$$

$$x_0 = \frac{F}{m}(0) + C_1(0) + C_2$$

Therefore: $\quad C_1 = V_0, \qquad C_2 = x_0$

The equations of motion are then:

$$V = V_0 + \frac{F}{m}t \tag{a}$$

$$x = x_0 + V_0t + \frac{1}{2}\frac{F}{m}t^2 \tag{b} \quad 12.6$$

In the case of a freely falling body, Eq. 12.2 becomes $W/m = g$, where g may be taken as constant for reasonably small drops. If the initial velocity is zero and the initial position is at the origin, we get in this case the formulae:

$$V = gt, \qquad x = \tfrac{1}{2}gt^2 \tag{12.7}$$

which you will no doubt recall from earlier physics courses.

EXAMPLE 12.1

A 100-lb body is initially stationary on a 45° incline as shown in Fig. 12.2(a). The coefficient of dynamic friction μ_d between the block and incline is 0.5. What distance along the incline must the weight slide before it reaches a speed of 40 ft/sec?

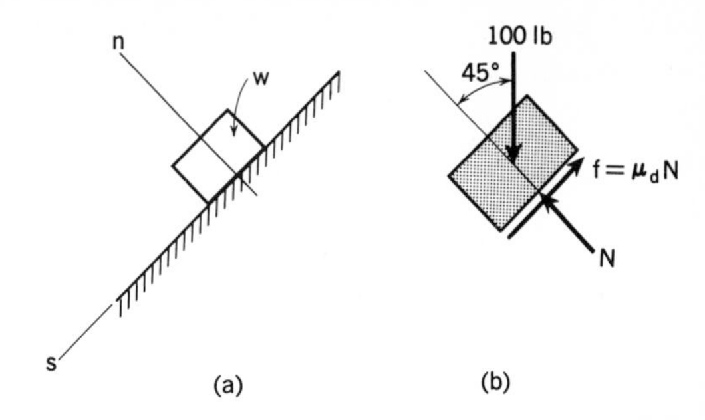

Fig. 12.2

A free-body diagram is shown in Fig. 12.2(b). Since the acceleration is zero in the direction normal to the incline, we have from equilibrium that:

$$100 \cos 45^\circ = N = 70.7 \qquad \textbf{(a)}$$

Now applying Newton's law in a direction along the incline, we have:

$$\left(\frac{100}{g_0}\right)\frac{d^2s}{dt^2} = 100 \sin 45^\circ - \mu_d N$$

$$\therefore \frac{d^2s}{dt^2} = 11.4 \qquad \textbf{(b)}$$

Integrating, we get:

$$\frac{ds}{dt} = 11.4t + C_1 \qquad \textbf{(c)}$$

$$s = 11.4\frac{t^2}{2} + C_1t + C_2 \qquad \textbf{(d)}$$

When $t = 0$, $s = ds/dt = 0$, and so the constants $C_1 = C_2 = 0$. When $ds/dt = 40$ ft/sec we have for t from Eq. (c) the result:

$$40 = 11.4t$$

$$\therefore t = 3.51 \text{ sec}$$

Substituting this value of t in Eq. (d), we can get the distance traveled to reach the speed of 40 ft/sec as follows:

$$s = 11.4\frac{(3.51)^2}{2} = 70.3 \text{ ft} \qquad \textbf{(e)}$$

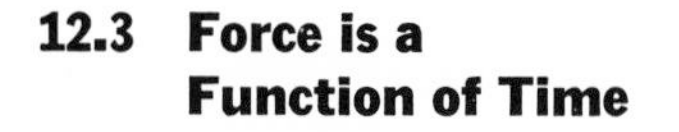

12.3 Force is a Function of Time

Using the diagram in Fig. 12.1, let us now consider the force F as a function of time, $F(t)$. This function need be only piecewise continuous* for the operations to be carried out in the ensuing analysis. Thus, the differential equation can be expressed as:

$$\frac{d^2x}{dt^2} = \frac{F(t)}{m} \qquad \textbf{12.8}$$

Integrating, we have:

$$\frac{dx}{dt} = V = \int \frac{F(t)}{m}\,dt + C_1 \qquad \textbf{12.9}$$

* Having only a finite number of finite discontinuities.

Integrating once again, we get:

$$x = \int \left(\int \frac{F(t)}{m} dt + C_1 \right) dt + C_2 \qquad \textbf{12.10}$$

If the integrals cannot be carried out analytically, we can employ numerical or graphical procedures. As in the previous case, the constants of integration can be ascertained by applying initial conditions.

EXAMPLE 12.2

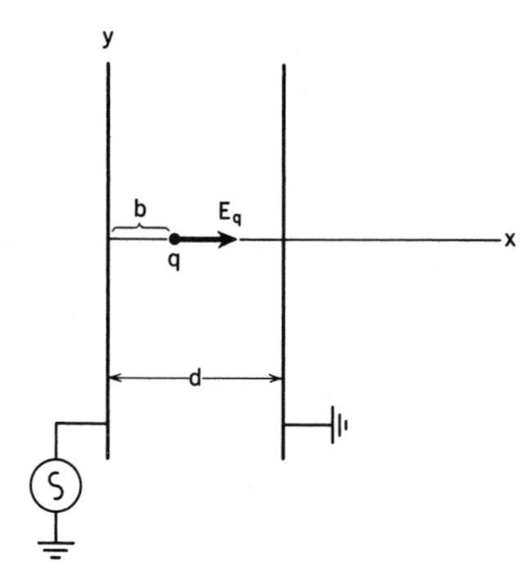

Fig. 12.3

In Fig. 12.3 a charged particle is shown at time $t = 0$ between large parallel condenser plates separated a distance d in a vacuum. A time-varying voltage given as

$$V = 6 \sin \omega t \qquad \textbf{(a)}$$

is applied to the plates. What is the motion of the particle if it has a charge q and if we do not consider gravitational action?

As we learned in physics the field E becomes for this case:

$$E = \frac{V}{d} \qquad \textbf{(b)}$$

The force on the particle is accordingly qE and the resulting motion is that of rectilinear translation. Using Newton's law, we have:

$$\frac{d^2x}{dt^2} = q \frac{6 \sin \omega t}{md} \qquad \textbf{(c)}$$

Integrating, we get:

$$\frac{dx}{dt} = -\frac{6q}{\omega md} \cos \omega t + C_1 \qquad \textbf{(d)}$$

$$x = -\frac{6q}{\omega^2 md} \sin \omega t + C_1 t + C_2 \qquad \textbf{(e)}$$

Applying the initial conditions $x = b$ and $dx/dt = 0$ when $t = 0$, we see that $C_1 = 6q/m\omega d$ and $C_2 = b$. Thus we get:

$$x = -\frac{6q}{\omega^2 dm} \sin \omega t + \frac{6q}{m\omega d} t + b \qquad \textbf{(f)}$$

12.4 Force Is a Function of Speed

We next consider the case where the resultant force on the particle depends only on the value of the speed of the particle. An example of such a force is the aerodynamic drag force on an airplane or missile.

We can express Newton's law in the following form:

$$\frac{dV}{dt} = \frac{F(V)}{m} \qquad \textbf{12.11}$$

where $F(V)$ is a piecewise continuous function representing the force in the positive x direction. If we rearrange the equation in the following manner:

$$\frac{dV}{F(V)} = \frac{1}{m}\,dt$$

we can carry out a quadrature as follows:

$$\int \frac{dV}{F(V)} = \frac{1}{m}t + C_1 \qquad \textbf{12.12}$$

The result will give t as a function of V. It will, however, generally be desirable to solve for V in terms of t. The result will then have the form:

$$V = H(t, C_1)$$

where H is a function of t and the constant of integration C_1. A second integration may now be attempted. Thus:

$$x = \int H(t, C_1)\,dt + C_2 \qquad \textbf{12.13}$$

The constants of integration are now determined from the initial conditions of the problem.

EXAMPLE 12.3

A high-speed land racer is moving at a speed of 300 ft/sec. The resistance to motion of the vehicle is primarily due to aerodynamic drag, which for this speed can be approximated as $0.004V^2$. If the vehicle weighs 4 tons, what distance will it coast before its speed is reduced to 200 ft/sec?

We have, using Newton's law for this case:

$$\frac{dV}{dt} = -\frac{0.004V^2}{\dfrac{(2000)(4)}{32.2}} = -16.1 \times 10^{-6}\,V^2 \qquad \textbf{(a)}$$

Separating the variables, we get:

$$\frac{dV}{V^2} = -16.1 \times 10^{-6}\,dt \qquad \textbf{(b)}$$

Integrating, we have

$$-\frac{1}{V} = -16.1 \times 10^{-6}\,t + C_1 \qquad \textbf{(c)}$$

Taking $t = 0$ when $V = 300$ we get $C_1 = -1/300$. Replacing V by dx/dt, we have next:

$$\frac{1}{V} = \frac{dt}{dx} = 16.1 \times 10^{-6}\,t + \frac{1}{300} \qquad \textbf{(d)}$$

Separating variables once again, we get:

$$\frac{dt}{16.1 \times 10^{-6}\,t + (1/300)} = dx$$

Integrating, we get:

$$\ln\left(16.1 \times 10^{-6}\, t + \tfrac{1}{300}\right) = 16.1 \times 10^{-6}\, x + C_2$$

When $t = 0$ we take $x = 0$ and so $C_2 = \ln(1/300)$. We then have:

$$\ln(0.004830t + 1) = 16.1 \times 10^{-6}\, x \qquad \textbf{(e)}$$

To get the desired numerical result, substitute $V = 200$ in Eq. (d) and solve for x. Thus:

$$\ln[(0.004830)(103.8) + 1] = 16.1 \times 10^{-6}\, x$$

$$\therefore\ x = \frac{0.406}{16.1} \times 10^{6} = 25{,}300 \text{ ft} = 4.80 \text{ miles}$$

12.5 Force Is a Function of Position

As the final case of this series, we now consider the rectilinear motion of a body under the action of a force which is expressible as a general function of position. Perhaps the simplest example of such a case is the frictionless mass-spring system shown in Fig. 12.4. The body is shown at a position where the spring is unrestrained. The horizontal force from the spring at all positions of the body clearly will be a function of position x and will be directed toward the origin.

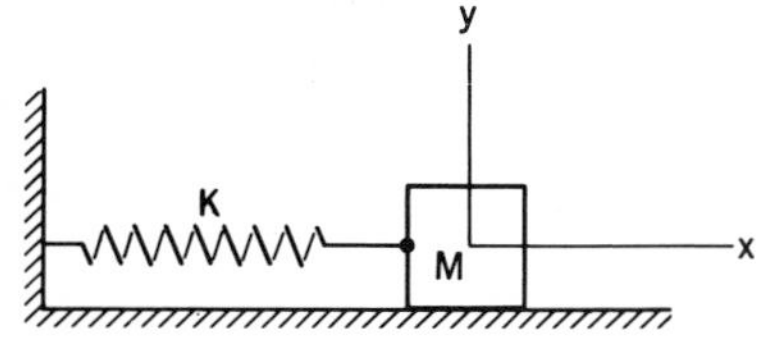

Fig. 12.4

Newton's law for position-dependent forces can be given as

$$m\frac{dV}{dt} = F(x) \qquad \textbf{12.14}$$

We cannot effect a separation of variables for the above form of the equation as in previous cases. However, by using the chain rule of differentiation we can change the left side of the equation to a more desirable form in the following manner:

$$m\frac{dV}{dt} = m\frac{dV}{dx}\frac{dx}{dt} = mV\frac{dV}{dx} \qquad \textbf{12.15}$$

We can now separate the variables in Eq. 12.14 as follows:

$$mV\, dV = F(x)\, dx$$

Integrating, we get:

$$\frac{mV^2}{2} = \int F(x)\, dx + C_1 \qquad \textbf{12.16}$$

Solving for V and using dx/dt in its place, we get:

$$\frac{dx}{dt} = \left[\frac{2}{m}\int F(x)\, dx + C_1\right]^{1/2}$$

Separating variables and integrating again, we get:

$$t = \int \frac{dx}{\left[\frac{2}{m}\int F(x)\,dx + C_1\right]^{1/2}} + C_2 \qquad \textbf{12.17}$$

For a given $F(x)$ Eqs. 12.16 and 12.17 accordingly allow for the evaluation of V and x as functions of time. The constants of integration C_1 and C_2 are determined by the initial conditions.

EXAMPLE 12.4

If the mass in Fig. 12.4 is displaced 3 in. to the right, what is its position after 0.295 seconds? The spring is a linear spring having a spring constant $K = 10$ lb/in. The mass of the body is 15 lbm. The mass of the spring can be neglected.

The force on the mass m at any position x is a *restoring force* given as $-Kx$ lb. Newton's law then becomes for this case:

$$mV\frac{dV}{dx} = -Kx$$

Separating variables and integrating, we get:

$$\frac{mV^2}{2} = \frac{m}{2}\left(\frac{dx}{dt}\right)^2 = \int -Kx\,dx + C_1 = -\frac{Kx^2}{2} + C_1 \qquad \textbf{(a)}$$

Separating variables again and integrating, we have:

$$t = \sqrt{\frac{m}{2}}\int \frac{dx}{[C_1 - (Kx^2/2)]^{1/2}} + C_2 \qquad \textbf{(b)}$$

We may rewrite the integral in the preceding equation in the following manner in order to get into a standard integral form:

$$t = \frac{\sqrt{m}}{\sqrt{K}}\int \frac{dx}{[(2C_1/K) - x^2]^{1/2}} + C_2$$

We can now evaluate the integral.

$$t = \sqrt{\frac{m}{K}}\left[\sin^{-1}\frac{x}{\sqrt{2C_1/K}}\right] + C_2 \qquad \textbf{(c)}$$

Rearranging the equation, we have:

$$\sqrt{\frac{K}{m}}\,(t - C_2) = \sin^{-1}\frac{x}{\sqrt{2C_1/K}}$$

Taking the sine of both sides of the equation, we get:

$$\frac{x}{\sqrt{2C_1/K}} = \sin\sqrt{\frac{K}{m}}\,(t - C_2) \qquad \textbf{(d)}$$

To evaluate the constants of integration we require of Eq. (a) that $x = 3$ in. when $V = 0$. Thus, we have for C_1:

$$C_1 = \frac{Kx^2}{2} = \frac{(10)(9)}{2} = 45$$

Also we require of Eq. (d) that $x = 3$ in. when $t = 0$.

Thus, being careful of units, we have:

$$\frac{3}{\sqrt{\frac{(2)(45)}{10}}} = \sin\left[\sqrt{\frac{(10)(12)}{15/32.2}}(-C_2)\right]$$

$$\therefore\ 1 = -\sin(16.02C_2)$$

Clearly,

$$16.02C_2 = \frac{3\pi}{2}\text{ rad}$$

$$\therefore\ C_2 = 0.295$$

The final statement of Eq. (d) then becomes:

$$x = 3\sin[(16.02)(t - 0.295)] \qquad \textbf{(e)}$$

The position x when $t = 0.295$ sec is back at the origin. The motion is *simple harmonic motion* of the kind that you studied in your physics class.

EXAMPLE 12.5

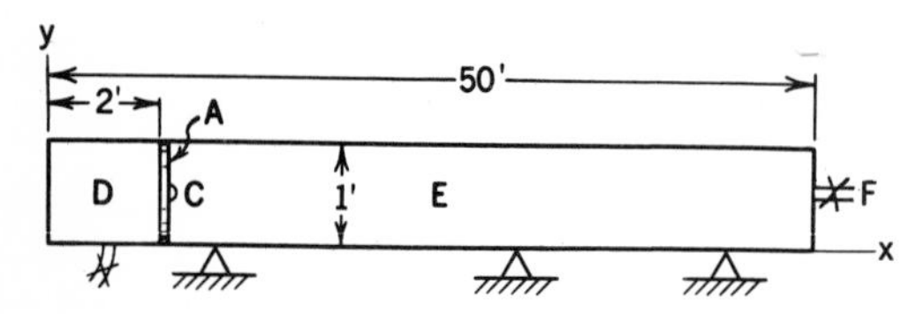

Fig. 12.5

An air gun is used to test the ability of small devices to withstand high accelerations. A floating piston A, on which the device to be tested is mounted, is held at position C while region D is filled with highly compressed air (Fig. 12.5). Region E is initially at atmospheric pressure, but is entirely sealed from the outside. When "fired," a quick-release mechanism releases the piston and it accelerates rapidly toward the other end of the gun where the trapped air in E "cushions" the motion so that the piston will begin eventually to return. However, as it starts back, the high pressure developed in E is released through valve F and the piston only returns a short distance.

Suppose the piston and its test specimen have a mass of 2 lbm and the pressure initially in the chamber D is 1000 psig. Compute the speed of the piston at the halfway point of the air gun if we make the simple assumption that the air in D expands according to pv = const. and the air in E is compressed also according to pv = const.* Take v of this fluid at D to be initially 0.207 ft³/lbm and v in E to be initially 13.10 ft³/lbm. Neglect the inertia of the air.

The force on the piston results from the pressures on each face, and we can show that this force is a function of x. Thus, examining the pressures p_D first, we have from initial conditions:

$$(p_D v_D)_0 = [(1000 + 14.7)(144)](0.207) = 30{,}300 \qquad \textbf{(a)}$$

* You should recall from your earlier work in physics and chemistry that we are using here the *isothermal* form of the equation of state for a perfect gas. Two factors of caution should be pointed out relative to the use of this expression. First, at the high pressures involved in part of the expansion, the perfect gas model is only an approximation for the gas and so the equation of state of a perfect gas which gives us pv = const. is only approximate. Furthermore, the assumption of isothermal expansion gives only an approximation for the actual process. Perhaps a better approximation is to assume an *adiabatic expansion* (i.e., no heat transfer). This is done in Prob. 334.

Furthermore, the mass of fluid D given as M_D is determined from initial data as:

$$M_D = \frac{(V_D)_0}{(v_D)_0} = \frac{(2)(\pi/4)}{0.207} = 7.58 \text{ lb} \qquad \textbf{(b)}$$

where $(V_D)_0$ indicates the volume of the gas D initially. We now have for p_D at any position of the piston:

$$p_D = \frac{30{,}300}{v_D} = \frac{30{,}300}{V_D/M_D} = \frac{30{,}300}{(\pi/4)x/M_D}$$

$$\therefore\ p_D = \frac{293{,}000}{x} \qquad \textbf{(c)}$$

We can similarly get p_E as a function of x. Thus, $(p_E v_E)_0 = (14.7)(144)(13.10) = 27{,}700$

and

$$M_E = \frac{(V_E)_0}{(v_E)_0} = \frac{(48)(\pi/4)}{13.10} = 2.88 \text{ lbm}$$

Hence,

$$p_E = \frac{27{,}700}{v_E} = \frac{27{,}700}{V_E/M_E} = \frac{27{,}700}{(\pi/4)(50 - x)/2.88}$$

$$\therefore\ p_E = \frac{101{,}600}{50 - x}$$

Now we can write Newton's law for this case. We get:

$$MV\frac{dV}{dx} = \left(\frac{\pi}{4}\right)\left[\frac{293{,}000}{x} - \frac{101{,}600}{50 - x}\right] \qquad \textbf{(d)}$$

where M is the mass of piston and load. Separating variables and integrating, we get:

$$\frac{MV^2}{2} = \frac{\pi}{4}\left[293{,}000 \ln x + 101{,}600 \ln (50 - x)\right] + C_1 \qquad \textbf{(e)}$$

To get the constant C_1, set $V = 0$ when $x = 2$ ft. Hence,

$$C_1 = -\frac{\pi}{4}\left[293{,}000 \ln 2 + 101{,}600 \ln 48\right]$$

$$\therefore\ C_1 = -468{,}000$$

Substituting C_1 in Eq. (e), we get:

$$V = \left(\frac{2}{M}\right)^{1/2}\left\{\left(\frac{\pi}{4}\right)\left[293{,}000 \ln x + 101{,}600 \ln (50 - x)\right] - 468{,}000\right\}^{1/2}$$

We may rewrite this as follows:

$$V = 566\left[23 \ln x + 7.98 \ln (50 - x) - 46.8\right]^{1/2}$$

At $x = 25$ ft, we then have for V the result:

$$V = 566\left[23 \ln 25 + 7.98 \ln 25 - 46.8\right]^{1/2}$$
$$= 4120 \text{ ft/sec}$$

It will be useful now to re-examine the spring mass system of Example 12.4 with the view toward solving this problem in a different manner. We express Newton's law for this case as follows:

$$\frac{d^2x}{dt^2} + \frac{K}{m} x = 0 \qquad \textbf{12.18}$$

In this form the equation is called a second-order differential equation. It has constant coefficients. Instead of trying to rearrange the equation to effect a quadrature as we have been doing up to now, we shall take a more general point of view.

To solve this differential equation, we must find a function of time, $x(t)$, which when substituted into the equation satisfies the equation, i.e., reduces it to an identity. We can either guess at $x(t)$ or use a formal procedure. It can be shown in the theory of ordinary differential equations that the most general solution to the above differential equation will consist of the sum of two such functions each multiplied by an arbitrary constant and each nonderivable from the other via simple algebraic means, such as by taking roots or powers. Thus, $C_1 \sin \sqrt{(K/m)}\, t$ and $C_2 \cos \sqrt{(K/m)}\, t$ with C_1 and C_2 as arbitrary constants will each satisfy the differential equation, as you may readily demonstrate by substitution, and are independent of each other in the manner described. Accordingly, the general solution to Eq. 12.18 can be given as:

$$x = C_1 \sin \sqrt{\frac{K}{m}}\, t + C_2 \cos \sqrt{\frac{K}{m}}\, t \qquad \textbf{12.19}$$

Furthermore, we have for V by differentiation the result:

$$V = C_1 \sqrt{\frac{K}{m}} \cos \sqrt{\frac{K}{m}}\, t - C_2 \sqrt{\frac{K}{m}} \sin \sqrt{\frac{K}{m}}\, t \qquad \textbf{12.20}$$

The constants of integration are determined by subjecting Eqs. 12.19 and 12.20 to the initial conditions of the problem.

It will be left as an exercise for you to solve Example 12.4 via this approach rather than the more laborious approach taken earlier. Keep in mind, however, that the initial approach was valid for a force expressible as *any* function of position. The above results are valid only for the case of a restoring force which is expressible as a *linear function of position.* We shall use this approach in the following example.

EXAMPLE 12.6

Shown in Fig. 12.6 is a thin cantilever beam with a mass M at the end. We know from strength of materials that the cantilever will produce a restoring force for displacement of the mass in the x direction. Furthermore, if these displacements are not large, this restoring force is directly proportional to the displacement. Thus the beam acts like the linear spring of Example 12.4 for transverse movements of the mass. The restoring force per unit deflection is called now the *equivalent spring constant* of the system and may be computed from strength of materials. Let us call this constant K_{eq}. We wish to determine the position of the mass at time t after the mass has been released from a position $x = \delta$ at time $t = 0$.

The equation of motion for this problem is:

$$\frac{d^2x}{dt^2} + \frac{K_{eq}}{M} x = 0 \qquad \textbf{(a)}$$

The solution for this differential equation we have shown to be:

$$x = C_1 \sin \sqrt{\frac{K_{eq}}{M}}\, t + C_2 \cos \sqrt{\frac{K_{eq}}{M}}\, t \qquad \textbf{(b)}$$

$$V = C_1 \sqrt{\frac{K_{eq}}{M}} \cos \sqrt{\frac{K_{eq}}{M}}\, t - C_2 \sqrt{\frac{K_{eq}}{M}} \sin \sqrt{\frac{K_{eq}}{M}}\, t \qquad \textbf{(c)}$$

When $t = 0$, we require that $x = \delta$ and $V = 0$. Thus we have from Eqs. (b) and (c) for these initial conditions:

$$C_2 = \delta \qquad \textbf{(d)}$$

$$C_1 = 0 \qquad \textbf{(e)}$$

The equation of motion for this case is then:

$$x = \delta \cos \sqrt{\frac{K_{eq}}{M}}\, t \qquad \textbf{(f)}$$

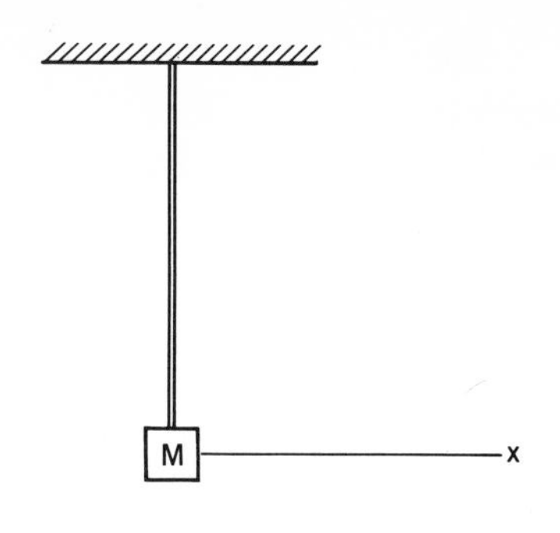

Fig. 12.6

If, in addition to the linear restoring force of the previous discussion, there is applied a constant force P, the equation of motion becomes:

$$\frac{d^2x}{dt^2} + \frac{K}{M} x = \frac{P}{M} \qquad \textbf{12.21}$$

The solution to this differential equation can be effected in a straightforward manner. The theory of differential equations indicates that we can superimpose two solutions here. One of them, the so-called *complementary solution*, denoted as x_c, is found by setting the right side of the above equation equal to zero and then finding the general solution of the resulting equation. From our previous work, this is already available as:

$$x_c = C_1 \sin \sqrt{\frac{K}{M}}\, t + C_2 \cos \sqrt{\frac{K}{M}}\, t \qquad \textbf{12.22}$$

Now find any function or constant which when substituted for x in the full equation (12.21) renders it an identity. Such a solution is called a *particular solution*. It does not have associated with it a constant of integration and is denoted as x_p.

On reinspection of Eq. 12.21, it should be clear that substituting P/K for x will do the trick, and so we have as a particular solution:*

* We are not concerned here with whether there may be other particular solutions. Any one is sufficient for our purposes as is dictated by the theory of differential equations.

$$x_p = \frac{P}{K} \tag{12.23}$$

The general solution to Eq. 12.21 then can be given as:

$$x = x_c + x_p = C_1 \sin \sqrt{\frac{K}{M}}\, t + C_2 \cos \sqrt{\frac{K}{M}}\, t + \frac{P}{K} \tag{12.24}$$

The constants of integration are determined as before from the initial conditions of the problem.

Suppose now that we change the origin of the coordinate x to x' such that:

$$x' = x - \frac{P}{K}$$

Then we get for Eq. 12.24 the following result:

$$x' = C_1 \sin \sqrt{\frac{K}{M}}\, t + C_2 \cos \sqrt{\frac{K}{M}}\, t$$

Note that the force P no longer appears to be the solution and that the solution has identically the same form as Eq. 12.19 derived for a case where only a linear restoring force is involved. Thus by shifting the origin an amount P/K we can then ignore the constant force and formulate the motion as if only a linear restoring force were acting. This shift of the origin means that when $x' = 0$ there is just enough elongation of the spring to counteract the force P, and any change in position x' then brings into play a net restoring force $-Kx'$. Actually, to accomplish this simplified approach, all we need do is to *measure displacements from the position of equilibrium of the body with the force P applied and then treat the problem as a simple mass-spring system.* We shall have ample occasion to do this in the homework problems.

12.6 Note on Other Cases

In the rectilinear motions examined thus far, we could, by manipulations, rearrange Newton's law so as to permit the carrying out of quadratures as learned in elementary calculus. At the end of the previous section, however, we illustrated for the linear restoring force, with and without an additional constant force, how we could employ the theory of differential equations.*

In more complex problems, such as the case where velocity-dependent and time-dependent forces are simultaneously involved, we generally cannot proceed by the simple separation-of-variable technique as we have done up to now. We must in those cases resort to the techniques developed in differential equations. For this reason, we will defer such studies until later in the text.† Since many of the cases we will at that time study will result in motions about some fixed point in inertial space, we will call such motions *vibrations.* Clearly our mass-spring problems comprise simple vibration problems; accordingly, the latter part of Section 12.5 can be considered as a brief introduction to vibrations. It is important to understand, however, that even though we defer vibration studies till later, *such studies are not something apart from the general particle dynamics undertaken in this chapter.*

---

* The linear restoring force plus constant force can also be solved by separation-of-variable techniques. You will be asked to demonstrate this in Prob. 30.

† Most students will be studying differential equations simultaneously with dynamics, and we are "holding off" so as to make the most use of the background developed in the differential equations course.

12.7 Rectilinear Motion of Several Interacting Particles

We now turn to the case where several bodies which interact in some manner are constrained to move in rectilinear motions. Two simple examples are shown in Fig. 12.7. In (a) the masses are connected by an inextensible cable, and in (b) the masses are connected with springs. If we neglect the masses of the connecting devices, then for dynamical considerations we have a system of discrete particles. When a system can be so represented, i.e., as a finite number of particles, we say that it is a *lumped system.* You will recall from statics that the number of

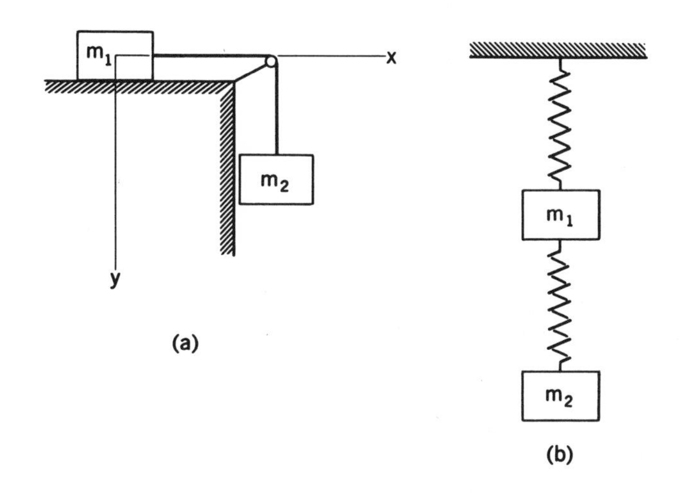

Fig. 12.7

degrees of freedom of a system corresponds to the number of independent coordinates required to locate the system relative to some reference. In Fig. 12.7, the system of masses connected by the inextensible cable has one degree of freedom (we assume that the cable is always in tension for the configurations of interest), whereas the system of masses connected by springs requires the specification of coordinates x_1 and x_2, i.e., a coordinate for each mass* (since no definite relation exists a priori between these coordinates for all motions) and, consequently, this system has two degrees of freedom.

In studying lumped systems, a simple procedure is to take each particle as a free body, write Newton's law for each particle, and carry out integrations making use of any relations between the dependent variables imposed by connections and constraints. We shall follow this procedure in the next section for the cable-connected masses, and we will also set forth another very useful approach for the treatment of such problems. As for the spring-connected masses, we will defer discussions until Chapter 20, where we will consider introductory aspects of the vibration of simple two-degree-of-freedom systems.

12.8 D'Alembert's Principle

We shall investigate briefly the system shown in Fig. 12.7(a). One method of finding the equations of motion in such problems is to isolate each body (Fig. 12.8) and utilize Newton's law. The equations are accordingly (if

* Although constraints are not shown in Fig. 12.7 (b), the bodies are limited to vertical translatory motions only.

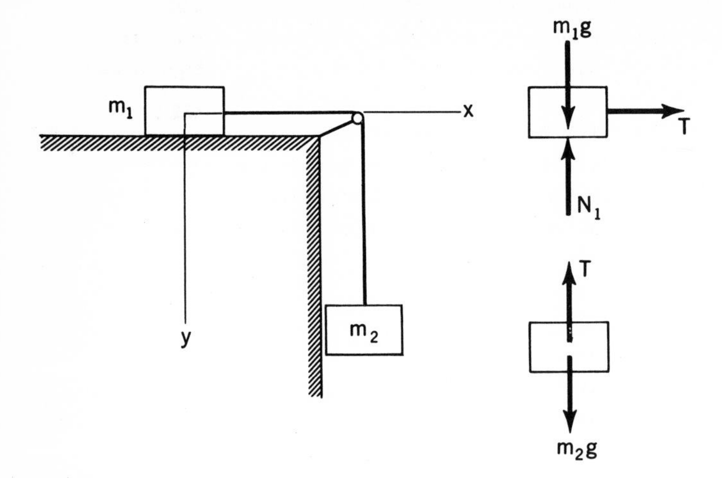

Fig. 12.8

friction is neglected):

$$T = m_1\ddot{x} \qquad \textbf{(a)}$$

$$-T + m_2 g = m_2\ddot{y} \qquad \textbf{(b)} \quad \textbf{12.25}$$

Since the cable is inextensible, $\ddot{x} = \ddot{y}$ and thus if we eliminate $\ddot{x}$ and $\ddot{y}$ from these equations, we get:

$$\frac{T}{m_1} = -\frac{T}{m_2} + g$$

Hence:

$$T = \frac{g}{1/m_1 + 1/m_2} \qquad \textbf{12.26}$$

With T as a known constant force, we can now integrate Eqs. 12.25 to get the motion of either mass by the methods of Section 12.2 for a constant force. Thus we have:

$$T = \frac{g}{1/m_1 + 1/m_2} = m_1\ddot{x} \qquad \textbf{12.27}$$

Hence:

$$\ddot{x} = \ddot{y} = \frac{g}{1 + m_1/m_2} \qquad \textbf{12.28}$$

Integrating, we get:

$$\dot{x} = \frac{g}{1 + m_1/m_2} t + \dot{x}_0 \qquad \textbf{(a)}$$

$$x = \frac{g}{1 + m_1/m_2} t + \dot{x}_0 t + x_0 \qquad \textbf{(b)}$$

and

$$\dot{y} = \frac{g}{1 + m_1/m_2} t + \dot{y}_0 \qquad \textbf{(c)}$$

$$y = \frac{g}{1 + m_1/m_2} t + \dot{y}_0 t + y_0 \qquad \textbf{(d)} \quad \textbf{12.29}$$

There is another extremely effective way of handling such problems. Suppose we write Newton's law for a particle in this manner:

$$\boldsymbol{F} + (-m\boldsymbol{a}) = \boldsymbol{0} \qquad \textbf{12.30}$$

If we consider $-m\boldsymbol{a}$ to be a force, this equation will correspond to an equation of equilibrium for a particle and we can then proceed with the calculations and methods developed in statics. When handled in this manner, the term $-m\boldsymbol{a}$ is called a *D'Alembert force,* and we can, in effect, reduce the methodology of a dynamics problem somewhat to that of a statics problem. In particular, with the problem formulated in this way, we can make use of the method of virtual work studied in Chapter 10. Thus, since only the D'Alembert forces and the gravitational force on m_2 are active forces, for a virtual displacement δx (see Fig. 12.9), we have:

$$-m_1\ddot{x}\delta x + (m_2 g - m_2\ddot{y})\,\delta y = 0 \qquad \textbf{12.31}$$

But since $\delta x = \delta y$ and $\ddot{x} = \ddot{y}$, we get:

$$\ddot{x} = \ddot{y} = \frac{g}{1 + m_1/m_2} \qquad \textbf{12.32}$$

which was developed in the previous procedure. Note that this method did not require the intermediate considerations of T and the free-body considerations; it is thus considerably quicker for problems where a number of bodies are connected so as to have few degrees of freedom. We shall consider a number of such problems in the homework.

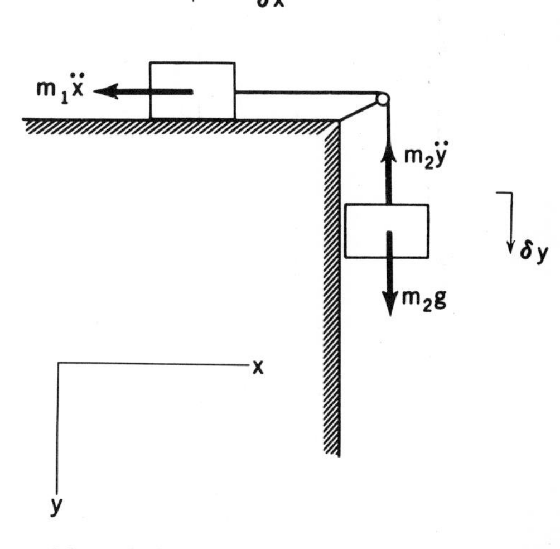

Fig. 12.9

PART B. Central-Force Motion

12.9 Introduction

In Part A we examined particle motion caused by a resultant force which maintains the same direction and line of action. We called such motion rectilinear translation. At this time, we shall consider the motion of a particle on which the resultant force is always directed toward some point fixed in inertial space. Such forces are termed *central forces* and the resulting motion of a particle is called *central-force motion.* A simple example of this is a small body such as a space vehicle moving in space with its own propulsion system off in the vicinity of a large fixed planet. Away from the planet's atmosphere, this vehicle will experience no frictional forces, and, if no other astronautical bodies are reasonably close, the only force acting on the vehicle will be the gravitational attraction of the fixed planet.* This force is directed toward the center of the planet and, from the gravitational law, is given as:

$$\boldsymbol{F} = -G\frac{M_{\text{star}}m_{\text{body}}}{r^2}\,\hat{\boldsymbol{r}} \qquad \textbf{12.33}$$

* We are neglecting such drag as is developed by collisions with solar dust particles.

This situation is illustrated in Fig. 12.10. As explained in statics, we can use the centers of gravity in computing the distance r needed in the preceding equation. In the problem under discussion the position vector $\boldsymbol{r}$, for computing gravitational force, need not be the same as position vector $\boldsymbol{r}'$ for use in Newton's law of motion.* However for problems of the type the vector $(\boldsymbol{r} - \boldsymbol{r}')$ will be very small in magnitude compared to $\boldsymbol{r}$ or $\boldsymbol{r}'$ and so we can replace the body by a particle at the center of gravity *or* the center of mass for computing gravitational force and also for using Newton's law without incurring serious error. Consequently, in ensuing discussions we will not need to differentiate between these points in forming a particle to replace a body.

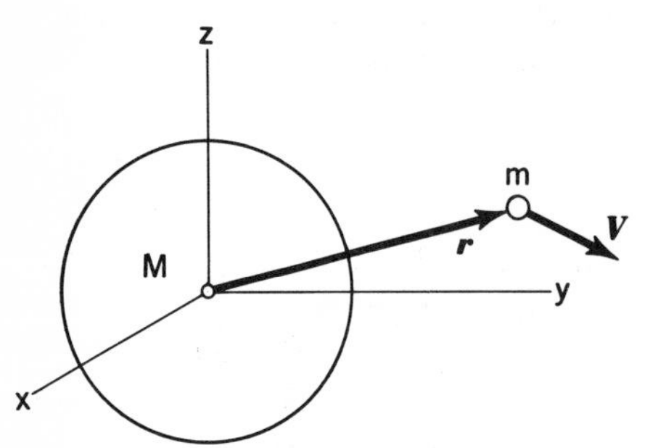

Fig. 12.10

The major portion of Part B of this chapter will be devoted to investigating the possible motions of the aforementioned body whose mass we take as m. An understanding of the results is necessary for even a rudimentary grasp of astronomy and is of singular importance in the increasingly important field of space mechanics.

12.10 General Central-Force Motion

Before considering the case of gravitational central-force motion, let us examine certain characteristics of all central-force motions. If we let $\boldsymbol{F}$ be *any* central force, which we shall express in the form $F\hat{\boldsymbol{r}}$, Newton's law then stipulates that:

$$F\hat{\boldsymbol{r}} = m\frac{d\boldsymbol{V}}{dt} \tag{12.34}$$

Rewriting the right side of the equation, we then have:

$$F\hat{\boldsymbol{r}} = \frac{d}{dt}(m\boldsymbol{V}) \tag{12.35}$$

The term $m\boldsymbol{V}$ is called the *linear momentum vector* and will be studied in more detail later. Take the cross product of $\boldsymbol{r}$ times each side of the above equation:

$$\boldsymbol{r} \times F\hat{\boldsymbol{r}} = \boldsymbol{r} \times \frac{d}{dt}(m\boldsymbol{V}) \tag{12.36}$$

Clearly, the left side of this equation is zero, so we have the result:

$$\boldsymbol{r} \times \frac{d}{dt}(m\boldsymbol{V}) = \boldsymbol{0} \tag{12.37}$$

This relation may be expressed in another way. Carry out the differentiation of $d/dt(\boldsymbol{r} \times m\boldsymbol{V})$ and examine the result:

$$\frac{d}{dt}(\boldsymbol{r} \times m\boldsymbol{V}) = \boldsymbol{r} \times \frac{d}{dt}(m\boldsymbol{V}) + \frac{d\boldsymbol{r}}{dt} \times (m\boldsymbol{V}) \tag{12.38}$$

* As explained in Chapter 4 the center of mass need not coincide with the center of gravity.

Since $d\boldsymbol{r}/dt = \boldsymbol{V}$ and $\boldsymbol{V} \times \boldsymbol{V} = \boldsymbol{0}$, we see that the last expression in the above equation is zero. Thus:

$$\frac{d}{dt}(\boldsymbol{r} \times m\boldsymbol{V}) = \boldsymbol{r} \times \frac{d}{dt}(m\boldsymbol{V}) \qquad \textbf{12.39}$$

Using this result in Eq. 12.37, we can say:

$$\frac{d}{dt}(\boldsymbol{r} \times m\boldsymbol{V}) = \boldsymbol{0} \qquad \textbf{12.40}$$

and consequently:

$$\boldsymbol{r} \times m\boldsymbol{V} = \text{constant vector} = \boldsymbol{H} \qquad \textbf{12.41}$$

This means that the *moment of the momentum vector*, $\boldsymbol{H}$, must always be a constant vector for this motion, and thus the normal to the plane of $\boldsymbol{r}$ and $\boldsymbol{V}$—i.e., the direction of $\boldsymbol{H}$—is fixed. The plane of $\boldsymbol{r}$ and $\boldsymbol{V}$, then, must always have a fixed inclination. Since such motion only takes place if the particle moves in a trajectory that is coplanar, as is shown in Fig. 12.11, we can conclude *that all central-force motions are coplanar.*

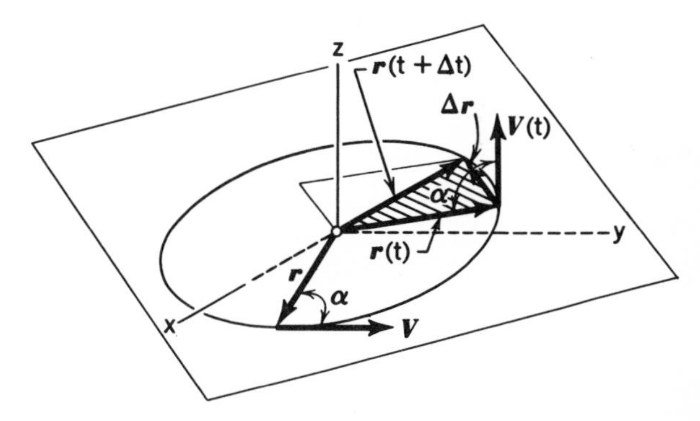

Fig. 12.11

From the fact that $|\boldsymbol{H}|$ is constant in Eq. 12.41, we can draw a second conclusion. Using the basic definition of a cross product, we express Eq. 12.41 in the following way:

$$|\boldsymbol{r}||\boldsymbol{V}|\sin\alpha = \frac{|\boldsymbol{H}|}{m} = \text{const.} \qquad \textbf{12.42}$$

where α is the smaller angle between the position vector $\boldsymbol{r}$ and the velocity $\boldsymbol{V}$. To interpret this relation, consider the particle at positions $\boldsymbol{r}(t + \Delta t)$ and $\boldsymbol{r}(t)$ as shown in Fig. 12.11. Using the chord to the trajectory, $\Delta\boldsymbol{r} = \boldsymbol{r}(t + \Delta t) - \boldsymbol{r}(t)$, we can approximate the velocity of the particle $\boldsymbol{V}$ by $\Delta\boldsymbol{r}/\Delta t$, an approximation that becomes exact as $\Delta t \to 0$. We then have, on substituting for $\boldsymbol{V}$ in this way in the preceding equation:

$$\frac{|\boldsymbol{r}||\Delta\boldsymbol{r}|\sin\alpha}{\Delta t} = \text{const.} \qquad \textbf{12.43}$$

The numerator, $|\boldsymbol{r}||\Delta\boldsymbol{r}|\sin\alpha$, is the area of a parallelogram that has $\boldsymbol{r}$ and $\Delta\boldsymbol{r}$ as sides and α as the included angle. But α is the angle between $\boldsymbol{r}$ and $\boldsymbol{V}$ (and not between $\boldsymbol{r}$ and $\Delta\boldsymbol{r}$ as can readily be seen in Fig. 12.11). However, as $\Delta t \to 0$ the angle between $\boldsymbol{r}$ and $\Delta\boldsymbol{r}$ becomes equal to this angle α, and thus for small Δt we can consider the expression $|\boldsymbol{r}||\Delta\boldsymbol{r}|\sin\alpha$ to be approximately equal to the area of the parallelogram indicated in Fig. 12.11 with sides $\boldsymbol{r}$ and $\Delta\boldsymbol{r}$. Therefore, $\frac{1}{2}|\boldsymbol{r}||\Delta\boldsymbol{r}|\sin\alpha$ is approximately equal to the shaded triangle portion of this parallelogram shown in the diagram. To the same order of accuracy, the area of this triangle represents the area swept out by the position vector $\boldsymbol{r}$ during the time Δt, and so $(\frac{1}{2}|\boldsymbol{r}||\Delta\boldsymbol{r}|\sin\alpha)/\Delta t$ approximates the average rate at which the area is swept out by $\boldsymbol{r}$ during the time interval Δt. In the limit, the above approximations become exact and we can say:

$$\lim_{\Delta t\to 0}\frac{1}{2}\frac{|\boldsymbol{r}||\Delta\boldsymbol{r}|\sin\alpha}{\Delta t} = \begin{pmatrix}\text{exact rate at which } \boldsymbol{r}\\ \text{sweeps out area at time } t\end{pmatrix} = \frac{dA}{dt} \qquad \textbf{12.44}$$

This quantity is called the *areal velocity*. From Eq. 12.43 we can conclude that the *areal velocity must be constant for all central-force motion.* For the case of gravitational central forces, this is Kepler's second law.

For convenience, a coordinate system xy in the plane of the trajectory is set up in Fig. 12.12. The area swept out by the position vector $\boldsymbol{r}$ during a time interval dt is shaded and can be given mathematically as:

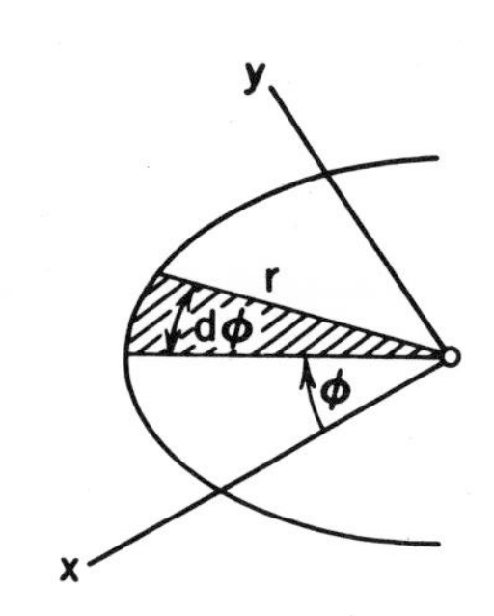

Fig. 12.12

$$dA = \frac{r^2\,d\phi}{2} \qquad \textbf{12.45}$$

Dividing through by dt, we have:

$$\frac{dA}{dt} = \frac{r^2\dot{\phi}}{2} \qquad \textbf{12.46}$$

But since we have shown that dA/dt is constant, we may say:

$$r^2\dot{\phi} = C \qquad \textbf{12.47}$$

where C is a constant for the particular motion under study and can be ascertained from known initial conditions. We will find this relation very useful in subsequent calculations.

12.11 Gravitational Central-Force Motion

Let us consider Newton's law for a body of mass m, moving near a fixed star of mass M, given in the following form:

$$m\frac{dV}{dt} = -G\frac{Mm}{r^2}\hat{\boldsymbol{r}} \qquad \textbf{12.48}$$

Canceling m and using cylindrical coordinates and components, we can express the above equation in the following manner:*

$$(\ddot{r} - r\dot{\phi}^2)\boldsymbol{\varepsilon}_r + (r\ddot{\phi} + 2\dot{r}\dot{\phi})\boldsymbol{\varepsilon}_\phi = -\frac{GM}{r^2}\hat{\boldsymbol{r}} \qquad \textbf{12.49}$$

Since $\boldsymbol{\varepsilon}_r$ and $\hat{\boldsymbol{r}}$ are identical vectors, the scalar equations of the preceding equa-

* Since the motion is in the xy plane, we use the notation r rather than $\bar{r}$, as we explained in Section 11.7.

tion become:

$$\ddot{r} - r\dot{\phi}^2 = -GM/r^2 \qquad \textbf{(a)}$$

$$r\ddot{\phi} + 2\dot{r}\dot{\phi} = 0 \qquad \textbf{(b)} \quad \textbf{12.50}$$

Equation (b) can be expressed in the form $(1/r)(d/dt)(r^2\dot{\phi}) = 0$, as you may readily verify, and we then see as in all central-force motions:

$$r^2\dot{\phi} = \text{const.} = C \qquad \textbf{12.51}$$

In order to determine the general trajectory, we shall replace the independent variable of Eq. 12.50(a). Consider first the time derivatives of r:

$$\dot{r} = \frac{dr}{dt} = \frac{dr}{d\phi}\frac{d\phi}{dt} = \frac{C}{r^2}\frac{dr}{d\phi} \qquad \textbf{12.52}$$

where we have used Eq. 12.51 to replace $d\phi/dt$. Next consider $\ddot{r}$ in a similar manner:

$$\ddot{r} = \frac{d\dot{r}}{dt} = \frac{d}{dt}\left(\frac{C}{r^2}\frac{dr}{d\phi}\right) = \frac{d}{d\phi}\left(\frac{C}{r^2}\frac{dr}{d\phi}\right)\frac{d\phi}{dt} \qquad \textbf{12.53}$$

Again, using Eq. 12.51 to replace $d\phi/dt$, we get:

$$\ddot{r} = \left[\frac{d}{d\phi}\left(\frac{C}{r^2}\frac{dr}{d\phi}\right)\right]\frac{C}{r^2} \qquad \textbf{12.54}$$

For convenience, we now introduce a new dependent variable, $u = 1/r$, into the right side of this equation, which then becomes $-C^2u^2(d^2u/d\phi^2)$, as you may verify. By replacing $\ddot{r}$ in this form into Eq. 12.50(a) and also $\dot{\phi}^2$ in the form C^2u^4 from Eq. 12.51, we get:

$$-C_2u^2\frac{d^2u}{d\phi^2} - C^2u^3 = -GMu^2$$

Cancelling terms, we have:

$$\frac{d^2u}{d\phi^2} + u = \frac{GM}{C^2} \qquad \textbf{12.55}$$

This is the same kind of differential equation examined in Section 12.5. The complementary solution to this differential equation can accordingly be given as:

$$u_c = A\sin\phi + B\cos\phi$$

where A and B are constants of integration. We see by inspection furthermore that a particular solution is $u_p = GM/C^2$. The general solution to the differential equation thus is:

$$u = \frac{1}{r} = \frac{GM}{C^2} + A\sin\phi + B\cos\phi \qquad \textbf{12.56}$$

By simple trigonometric considerations we can put the complementary solution in the equivalent form, $D\cos(\phi - \beta)$, where D and β are then the constants of integration. We then have as an alternative formulation for $1/r$:

$$\frac{1}{r} = \frac{GM}{C^2} + D\cos(\phi - \beta) \qquad \textbf{12.57}$$

You probably recognize this equation as the general conic equation in polar coordinates with the focus at the origin. If you do not, in Appendix I there is a review of conic sections in which we derive the general conic equation with the focus at the origin in the form:

$$\frac{1}{r} = \frac{1}{\epsilon p} + \frac{1}{p}\cos(\phi - \beta) \qquad \textbf{12.58}$$

where ϵ is the eccentricity, p is the distance from the focus to the directrix, and β is the angle between the x axis and the axis of symmetry of the conic section.

Comparing Eqs. 12.58 and 12.57, we see that:

$$p = 1/D \qquad \textbf{(a)}$$

$$\epsilon = DC^2/GM \qquad \textbf{(b)} \quad \textbf{12.59}$$

From our knowledge of conic sections, we can then say that if:

$$\begin{aligned} DC^2/GM &= 1, \text{ the trajectory is a parabola} \\ DC^2/GM &< 1, \text{ the trajectory is an ellipse} \\ DC^2/GM &> 1, \text{ the trajectory is a hyperbola} \\ DC^2/GM &= 0, \text{ the trajectory is a circle} \end{aligned} \qquad \textbf{12.60}$$

It is thus clear that DC^2/GM, the eccentricity, is an extremely important quantity. We shall look into the practical applications of the preceding general theory to problems in space mechanics, after we have generalized the results to the gravitational two-body problem.

12.12 General Two-Body Problem

The above results are applicable, with slight modifications, to the relative motion between *any* two particles moving in space that have only the mutual *gravitational attraction* acting on them. Consider the particles of masses m_1 and m_2 that are moving relative to some inertial reference xyz as shown in Fig. 12.13. Newton's law for each particle is then:

$$m_1 \frac{d^2\boldsymbol{r}_1}{dt^2} = G\frac{m_1 m_2}{|\boldsymbol{r}_2 - \boldsymbol{r}_1|^3}(\boldsymbol{r}_2 - \boldsymbol{r}_1) \qquad \textbf{(a)}$$

$$m_2 \frac{d^2\boldsymbol{r}_2}{dt^2} = G\frac{m_1 m_2}{|\boldsymbol{r}_2 - \boldsymbol{r}_1|^3}(\boldsymbol{r}_1 - \boldsymbol{r}_2) \qquad \textbf{(b)} \quad \textbf{12.61}$$

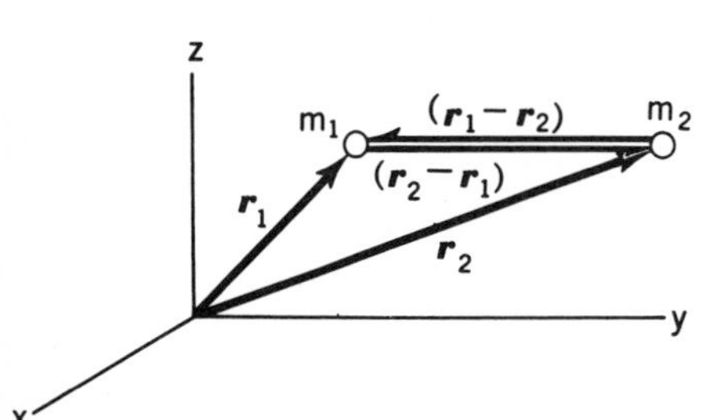

Fig. 12.13

Canceling m_1 in the first equation and m_2 in the second equation, we have on subtracting (b) from (a):

$$\frac{d^2\boldsymbol{r}_1}{dt^2} - \frac{d^2\boldsymbol{r}_2}{dt^2} = \frac{G}{|\boldsymbol{r}_2 - \boldsymbol{r}_1|^3}(\boldsymbol{r}_2 - \boldsymbol{r}_1)(m_2 + m_1) \qquad \textbf{12.62}$$

This can be written as:

$$\frac{d^2}{dt^2}(\boldsymbol{r}_1 - \boldsymbol{r}_2) = -\frac{G(m_2 + m_1)}{|\boldsymbol{r}_2 - \boldsymbol{r}_1|^3}(\boldsymbol{r}_1 - \boldsymbol{r}_2) \qquad \textbf{12.63}$$

This equation describes the motion of particle (1) relative to particle (2).* Its form is the same as if particle (2) were fixed in an inertial reference, except that mass m_2 is replaced by the sum of the masses $(m_1 + m_2)$. We can thus apply the results of the preceding section to the two-body problem by making this substitution for the mass of the particle relative to which the motion is measured.

12.13 Applications to Space Mechanics

We shall now employ the theory developed earlier to study the motion of space vehicles—a problem of great present-day interest. The vehicle is launched from the earth and accelerated to a high speed outside the earth's atmosphere by multistage rockets (see Fig. 12.14). After the final thrust has

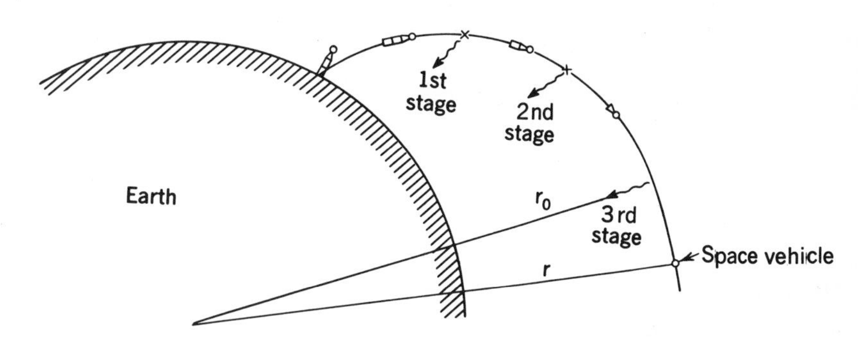

Fig. 12.14

been imparted to the vehicle, it moves under the action of gravity only, and its ensuing motion corresponds to that involved in the two-body problem. Since the mass of the vehicle is very small compared to that of the earth, we can replace $(M_{\text{earth}} + m_{\text{vehicle}})$, which is required by the two-body analysis, by M_{earth}, and consider the center of the earth as effectively fixed in inertial space.

We will assume that at the end of powered flight, the position $\boldsymbol{r}_0$, and velocity $\boldsymbol{V}_0$, of the vehicle are known from rocket calculations. We have shown this diagrammatically in Fig. 12.15. The reference employed at O will be taken an inertial reference and will translate with the earth relative to the "fixed stars." Accordingly the earth will rotate one cycle per day in this reference. We know that the trajectory of the body will form a plane fixed in inertial space and so, for convenience, we take the xy plane of the reference to be the plane of the trajectory. Finally note that we have deliberately chosen the x axis to be the axis of symmetry for the trajectory. If there is a zero radial velocity component at "burnout" (end of powered phase of flight) then the launching clearly occurs at a position along the axis of symmetry of the trajectory, i.e., along the x axis. This case has been indicated in Fig. 12.15

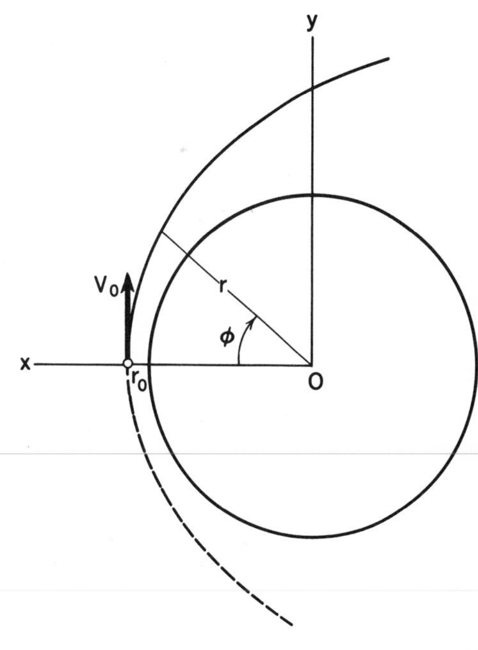

Fig. 12.15

* That is, the motion as seen from a reference translating with m_2 relative to the inertial reference xyz.

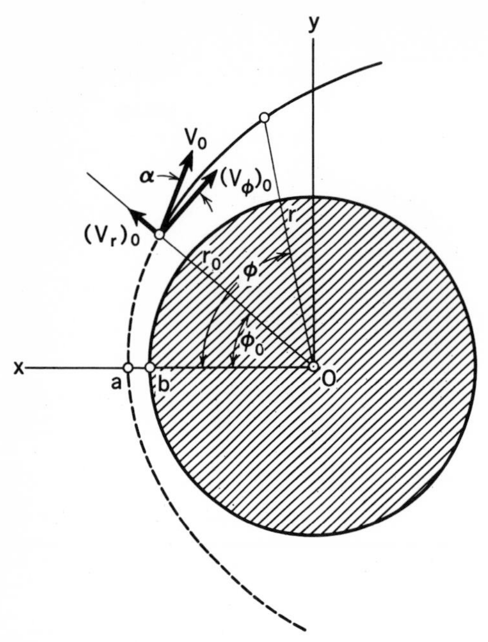

Fig. 12.16

wherein the subscript 0 indicates launch data. If, on the other hand, there is a radial component $(V_r)_0$ at burnout, then the launch condition occurs at some position ϕ_0 from the x axis as is shown in Fig. 12.16. We generally do not know ϕ_0 a priori, since its value depends on the equation of the trajectory. Finally, the angle α shown in the diagram will be called the launching angle in the ensuing discussion.

Since the x axis has been chosen to be the axis of symmetry, the equation of motion of the vehicle after powered flight is given in terms of arbitrary constants C and D by Eq. 12.57 with the angle β set equal to zero.* Thus we have:

$$\frac{1}{r} = \frac{GM}{C^2} + D \cos \phi \qquad \textbf{12.64}$$

The problem devolves around finding the constants C and D from launching data. We shall go into this step in detail in subsequent paragraphs. For now, note that when these constants are evaluated, the value of the eccentricity $\epsilon = DC^2/GM$ is then available so that we can state immediately the general characteristics of the trajectory.

Furthermore, if the vehicle goes into orbit we can readily compute the orbital time τ for one cycle around the earth. We know from the theory that the aerial velocity is constant and given as:

$$\frac{dA}{dt} = \frac{r^2\dot{\phi}}{2} = \text{const.} \qquad \textbf{12.65}$$

But $r^2\dot{\phi}$ equals the constant C in accordance with Eq. 12.47. Hence:

$$dA = \frac{C}{2}\,dt \qquad \textbf{12.66}$$

The area swept out for one cycle is the area of an ellipse given as πab where a and b are the semimajor and semiminor diameters respectively of the ellipse. Hence, we have an integrating Eq. 12.66:

$$A = \pi ab = \int_0^\tau \frac{C}{2}\,dt = \frac{C}{2}\tau$$

$$\therefore \tau = \frac{2\pi ab}{C} \qquad \textbf{12.67}$$

We have shown in Appendix I that:

$$a = \frac{\epsilon p}{1 - \epsilon^2} \qquad \textbf{(a)}$$

$$b = a(1 - \epsilon^2)^{1/2} \qquad \textbf{(b)} \quad \textbf{12.68}$$

* You will note in Appendix II that β is the angle between the x axis and the axis of symmetry of the trajectory.

Replacing p by $1/D$ in accordance with Eq. 12.59(a) we then get:

$$a = \frac{\epsilon}{D(1 - \epsilon^2)} \qquad \textbf{(a)}$$

$$b = a(1 - \epsilon^2)^{1/2} = \frac{\epsilon}{D(1 - \epsilon^2)^{1/2}} \qquad \textbf{(b)} \quad \textbf{12.69}$$

Thus we can get the orbital time τ quite easily once the constants of the trajectory D and C are evaluated.

To illustrate many of the previous general remarks in a most simple manner, we now examine the special case where, as shown in Fig. 12.17, various launchings are made from a given point a such that the launching angle $\alpha = 0$. Clearly $(V_r)_0 = 0$ for these cases and the launching axis corresponds to the axis of symmetry of the various trajectories. Only V_0 will be varied in this discussion.

The constants C and D are readily available for these trajectories. Thus we have from Eq. 12.47:

$$C = r^2\dot{\phi} = rV_\phi = r_0V_0 \qquad \textbf{12.70}$$

And from Eq. 12.64, setting $r = r_0$ when $\phi = \phi_0 = 0$, we get, on solving for D:

$$D = \frac{1}{r_0} - \frac{GM}{C^2} = \frac{1}{r_0} - \frac{GM}{r_0^2V_0^2} \qquad \textbf{12.71}$$

Since C and D depend only on V_0 we conclude that the eccentricity is dependent only on V_0.

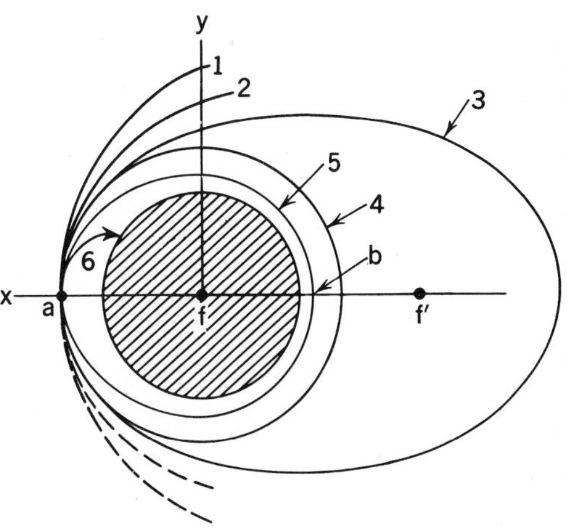

Fig. 12.17

If V_0 is so large that DC^2/GM exceeds unity, the vehicle will have the trajectory of a hyperbola (curve 1) and will eventually leave the influence of the earth. If V_0 is decreased to a value such that the eccentricity is unity, the trajectory becomes a parabola (curve 2). Since a further decrease in the value of V_0 will cause the vehicle to orbit, curve 2 is the limiting trajectory with our launching conditions for outer-space flight. The launching velocity for this case is accordingly called the *escape velocity* and is denoted as $(V_0)_E$. We can solve for $(V_0)_E$ for this launching by substituting for C and D from Eqs. 12.70 and 12.71 into the equation $DC^2/GM = 1$. We get:

$$(V_0)_E = \sqrt{\frac{2GM}{r_0}} \qquad \textbf{12.72}$$

a result which will soon be shown to be correct for more general launching conditions, i.e., for cases where $\alpha \neq 0$. Thus launching a vehicle with a speed equaling or exceeding the above value for a given r_0 will cause the vehicle to leave the earth until such time as the vehicle is influenced by other astronomical bodies or by its own propulsion system. If V_0 is less than the escape velocity, the vehicle will move in the trajectory of an ellipse (curve 3). Such an orbiting vehicle is often called a space or earth satellite. (Kepler, in his famous first law of planetary motion, explained the motion about the sun in this same manner.) One focus for the aforementioned conic curves is at the center of the earth. Another focus f' now moves in from infinity for the satellite trajectories. As the launching speed is decreased, f' moves toward f. When the foci coincide the trajectory is clearly a circle and, as pointed out earlier, the eccentricity is zero. Accordingly the constant D must be zero (the constant C clearly will not be zero) and it is immediately apparent from Eq. 12.71 that the speed for a circular orbit $(V_0)_C$ is:

$$(V_0)_C = \sqrt{\frac{GM}{r_0}} \qquad \textbf{12.73}$$

For launching velocities less than the above value for a given r_0, the focus f' moves to the left of the earth's center, and again the trajectory is that of an ellipse (curve 5). However, the satellite will now come closer to the earth at position (b) than at the launching position, which up to now had been the minimum distance from the earth. If friction is encountered, the satellite will slow up, spiral in toward the atmosphere, and either burn up or crash. If V_0 is small enough, the missile will not go into even a temporary orbit but will plummet to the earth (curve 6). However, for a reasonably accurate description of this trajectory, we must consider friction from the earth's atmosphere. Since this type of force is a function of the velocity of the missile and is not a central force, we cannot use the results here in such situations for other than the very crude calculations.* The closest point on the trajectory to the earth is called *perigee* and the most distant is called *apogee.*† Clearly these points lie along the axis of symmetry, and the launchings considered here must have been from either apogee or perigee.

Before proceeding to the examples, let us consider the computation of GM. We may state for any particle of mass m at the surface of any planet having mass M and radius R that:

$$W = mg = \frac{GMm}{R^2}$$

Solving for GM we have:

$$GM = gR^2 \qquad \textbf{12.74}$$

Thus, knowing the acceleration of gravity at the surface of the planet and its radius, permits the computation of GM needed for orbit calculations around this planet.

EXAMPLE 12.7

The first American satellite, the Vanguard, was launched at a velocity of 18,000 miles per hour at an altitude of 400 miles (see Fig. 12.18). If the "burnout" velocity of the last stage is parallel to the earth's surface, compute the maximum altitude from the earth's surface that the Vanguard satellite will reach.

Consider the earth to be perfectly spherical with a radius of 4000 miles (r_0 is therefore 4400 miles). We must now compute the quantities GM, C, and D from the initial data and other known data.

To determine GM we employ Eq. 12.74. For units of miles and hours we get:

* We shall consider this problem in Part C of this chapter.

† D, of Eq. 12.71, will always be positive if ϕ is measured from perigee.

$$GM = (32.2)\left(\frac{3600^2}{5280}\right)(4000)^2$$

$$= 1.255 \times 10^{12} \frac{\text{miles}^3}{\text{hours}^2} \qquad \textbf{(a)}$$

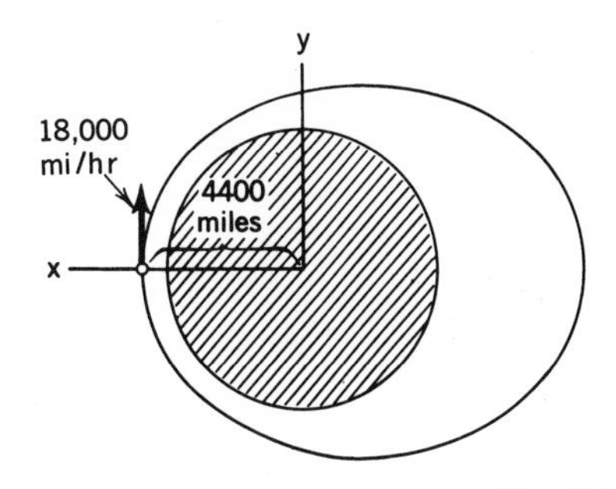

Fig. 12.18

The constant C is readily determined directly from initial data as:

$$C = r_0V_0 = (4400)(18{,}000)$$

$$= 7.92 \times 10^7 \text{ mile}^2/\text{hour} \qquad \textbf{(b)}$$

Finally the constant D is available from Eq. 12.71:

$$D = \frac{1}{r_0} - \frac{GM}{C^2} = \frac{1}{4400} - \frac{1.255 \times 10^{12}}{(7.92 \times 10^7)^2}$$

$$= 0.272 \times 10^{-4} \text{ mile}^{-1} \qquad \textbf{(c)}$$

The eccentricity DC^2/GM can now be computed:

$$\epsilon = \frac{DC^2}{GM} = \frac{(0.272 \times 10^{-4})(7.92 \times 10^7)^2}{(1.255 \times 10^{12})} = 0.136 \qquad \textbf{(d)}$$

The Vanguard will thus definitely not escape into outer space.

The trajectory of this motion is formed from Eq. 12.64:

$$\frac{1}{r} = \frac{1.255 \times 10^{12}}{(7.92 \times 10^7)^2} + 0.272 \times 10^{-4} \cos \phi$$

$$\therefore \frac{1}{r} = 2.00 \times 10^{-4} + 0.272 \times 10^{-4} \cos \phi \qquad \textbf{(e)}$$

We can compute the maximum distance from the earth's surface by setting $\phi = \pi$ in the above equation:

$$1/r_{\text{max}} = (2.00 - 0.272) \times 10^{-4} = 1.728 \times 10^{-4} \text{ mile}^{-1}$$

$$\therefore r_{\text{max}} = 5780 \text{ mi} \qquad \textbf{(f)}$$

By subtracting 4000 miles from this result, we find that the highest point in the trajectory is 1780 miles.

EXAMPLE 12.8

In the previous problem, compute first the escape velocity and then the velocity for a circular orbit.

Using Eq. 12.72, we have for the escape velocity:

$$(V_0)_E = \sqrt{\frac{2GM}{r_0}} = \left[\frac{2(1.255)(10^{12})}{4400}\right]^{1/2}$$

$$= 23{,}900 \text{ mi/hr}$$

For a circular orbit, we have from Eq. 12.73:

$$(V_0)_C = \sqrt{\frac{GM}{r_0}} = 16{,}900 \text{ mi/hr}$$

Thus the Vanguard is almost in a circular orbit.

EXAMPLE 12.9

In Example 12.7 determine the orbital time for the Vanguard satellite.

We employ Eq. 12.69 for the semimajor and semiminor axes of the elliptic orbit. Thus:

$$a = \frac{\epsilon}{D(1-\epsilon^2)} = \frac{0.136}{0.272 \times 10^{-4}(1-0.136^2)}$$

$$= 5090 \text{ miles}$$

$$b = a(1-\epsilon^2)^{1/2} = 5090(1-0.136^2)^{1/2}$$

$$= 5050 \text{ miles}$$

Therefore from Eq. 12.67 we have for the orbital time:

$$\tau = \frac{\pi a b}{C/2} \quad \frac{(\pi)(5090)(5050)}{7.92 \times 10^7/2}$$

$$= 2.03 \text{ hours} = 121.8 \text{ minutes}$$

Now let us consider more general launching conditions where the launching angle α is not zero (see Fig. 12.19). The constant C is still easily evaluated in terms of launching data as $r_0(V_\phi)_0$. To get D we write Eq. 12.64 for launching conditions. Thus:

$$\frac{1}{r_0} = \frac{GM}{C^2} + D\cos\phi_0 \qquad \textbf{12.75}$$

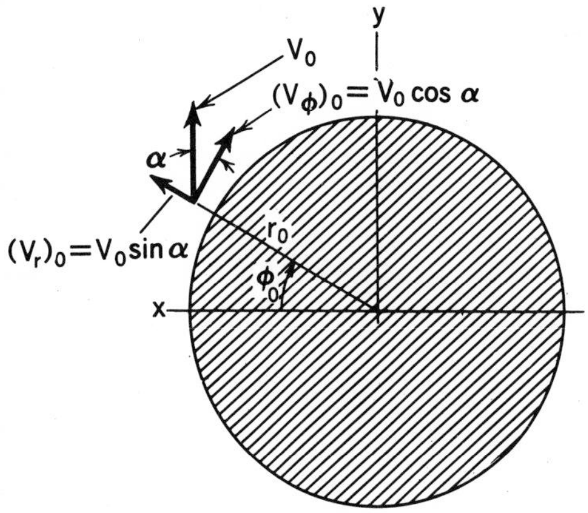

The value of ϕ_0 is not yet known and so we have two unknown quantities in this equation, namely D and ϕ_0. Differentiating Eq. 12.64 with respect to time and solving for $\dot{r}$ we get:

$$\dot{r} = Dr^2\dot{\phi}\sin\phi = DC\sin\phi$$

Noting that $\dot{r}$ is equal to V_r and submitting the preceding equation to launching conditions, we then form a second equation for the evaluation of the unknown constants D and ϕ_0. Thus:

$$(V_r)_0 = DC\sin\phi_0 \qquad \textbf{12.76}$$

Fig. 12.19

Rearranging Eq. 12.75, we have:

$$\frac{1}{r_0} - \frac{GM}{C^2} = D\cos\phi_0 \qquad \textbf{12.77}$$

In Eq. 12.76 divide both sides by C. Now, squaring Eqs. 12.76 and 12.77 and adding terms, we get for the constant D the result:

$$D = \left\{\left(\frac{1}{r_0} - \frac{GM}{C^2}\right)^2 + \left[\frac{(V_r)_0}{C}\right]^2\right\}^{1/2} \qquad \textbf{12.78}$$

We thus have the general evaluation of D and C and we can accordingly write the eccentricity in the following manner:

$$\epsilon = \frac{C^2}{GM}\left\{\left(\frac{1}{r_0} - \frac{GM}{C^2}\right)^2 + \left[\frac{(V_r)_0}{C}\right]^2\right\}^{1/2} \qquad \textbf{12.79}$$

First bringing C^2 into the bracket and then replacing C by $r_0(V_\phi)_0$ in the entire equation, we get the eccentricity conveniently in terms of launching data:

$$\epsilon = \frac{r_0(V_\phi)_0}{GM}\left\{(V_r)_0^2 + \left[(V_\phi)_0 - \frac{GM}{r_0(V_\phi)_0}\right]^2\right\}^{1/2} \qquad \textbf{12.80}$$

With this result, we can immediately show that the angle of launching of the satellite is not significant in determining whether it will escape from the earth. Suppose the launching is at an angle α at position r_0, as shown in Fig. 12.19. Consider the case where the eccentricity is unity, which is the limiting condition for ballistic outer-space flight. Replacing $(V_\phi)_0$ and $(V_r)_0$ by $V_0 \cos \alpha$ and $V_0 \sin \alpha$, respectively, in Eq. 12.80, we have for this condition:

$$1 = \frac{r_0 V_0 \cos \alpha}{GM}\left[(V_0 \sin \alpha)^2 + \left(V_0 \cos \alpha - \frac{GM}{r_0 V_0 \cos \alpha}\right)^2\right]^{1/2} \qquad \textbf{12.81}$$

Squaring both sides and expanding the terms in the bracket, we have, on rearranging terms:

$$(GM)^2 = (r_0 V_0 \cos \alpha)^2\left[V_0^2 \sin^2 \alpha + V_0^2 \cos^2 \alpha - 2\frac{GM}{r_0} + \left(\frac{GM}{r_0 V_0 \cos \alpha}\right)^2\right] \qquad \textbf{12.82}$$

Combining the first two terms in the bracket as V_0^2 and multiplying through by the coefficient of the bracket, we have:

$$(GM)^2 = r_0^2 V_0^4 \cos^2 \alpha - 2 r_0 GM V_0^2 \cos^2 \alpha + (GM)^2 \qquad \textbf{12.83}$$

Canceling the terms $(GM)^2$ and rearranging the equation, we write:

$$r_0 V_0^2 \cos^2 \alpha \, (r_0 V_0^2 - 2GM) = 0 \qquad \textbf{12.84}$$

It is clear from this equation that whenever the bracket is zero the equation is satisfied and we have the limiting condition of outer-space flight. Thus:

$$(V_0)_E = \sqrt{\frac{2GM}{r_0}}$$

which is the escape velocity for *any* inclination α. We have developed this result earlier for the situation where $\alpha = 0$.

It must be remembered that V_E in this formula is measured from a reference xyz at the center of the earth translating in inertial space. The velocity attainable by a rocket system relative to the earth's *surface* does not depend on the position of firing on the earth, but primarily on the rocket system and trajectory of flight. However, the velocity attainable by a rocket system relative to the aforementioned reference xyz *does* depend on the position of firing on the earth's surface, and this position accordingly is important in determining whether an

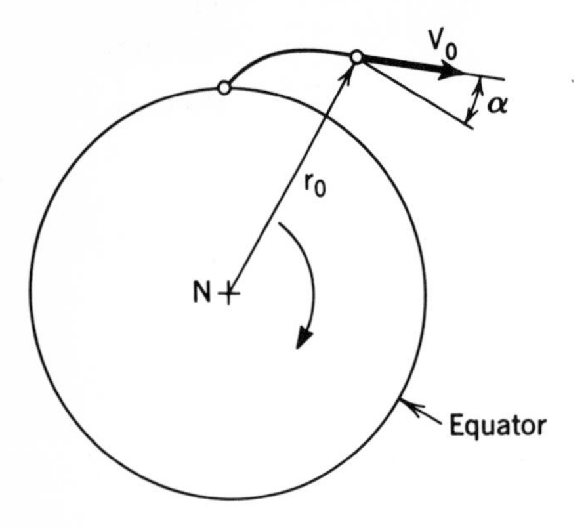

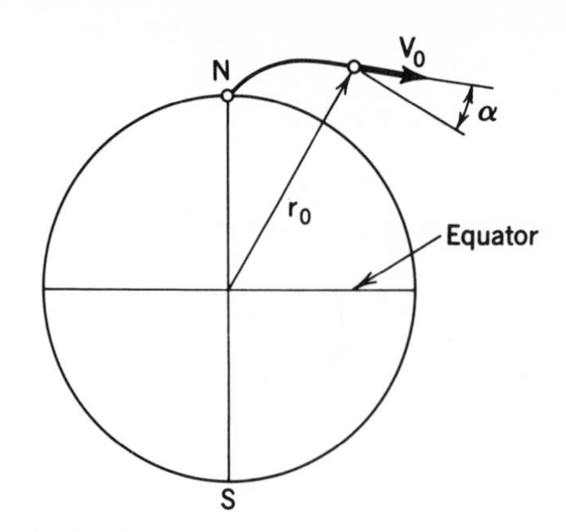

Fig. 12.20

escape velocity can be reached. Figure 12.20 showing the extreme situations of a launching at the equator and at the north pole, should clarify this point. Note that the motion of the earth's surface adds to the final vehicle velocity at the equator, but that no such gain is achieved at the north pole.

EXAMPLE 12.10

Suppose the Vanguard satellite in Example 12.7 is off course by an angle $\alpha = 5°$ at the time of launching but otherwise has the same initial data. Determine whether the satellite goes into orbit. If so, determine the maximum and minimum distances from the earth's surface.

The initial data for the launching are:

$$r_0 = 4400 \text{ mi}, \qquad V_0 = 18{,}000 \text{ mi/hr}$$

Hence:

$$(V_r)_0 = (18{,}000) \sin \alpha = (18{,}000)(0.0872)$$
$$= 1570 \text{ mi/hr}$$
$$(V_\phi)_0 = (18{,}000) \cos \alpha = (18{,}000)(0.996)$$
$$= 17{,}930 \text{ mi/hr}$$

To determine whether we have an orbit, we would have to show first that the eccentricity ϵ is less than unity. This would preclude the possibility of an escape from the earth. Furthermore, we must be sure that the perigee of the orbit is far enough from the earth's surface to insure a reasonably permanent orbit. Actually it is sufficient for both questions only to calculate the perigee, since an infinite value of the perigee will indicate that we have an escape condition and a value not sufficiently large will indicate a crash or a decaying orbit from atmospheric friction.

Using the value of GM as 1.255×10^{12} miles/hour^2 from the previous example and using Eq. 12.78, for the constant D, we can express the trajectory of the satellite (Eq. 12.64) as:

$$\frac{1}{r} = \frac{1.255 \times 10^{12}}{[(4400)(17{,}930)]^2} + \left\{\left[\frac{1}{4400} - \frac{1.255 \times 10^{12}}{[(4400)(17{,}930)]^2}\right]^2 + \left[\frac{1570}{(4400)(17{,}930)}\right]^2\right\}^{1/2} \cos\phi$$

$$\therefore \frac{1}{r} = 2.02 \times 10^{-4} + 3.19 \times 10^{-5} \cos\phi \qquad \text{(a)}$$

For the minimum distance, set $\phi = 0$:

$$1/r_{\text{min}} = 20.2 \times 10^{-5} + 3.19 \times 10^{-5}$$

Hence:

$$r_{\text{min}} = 4275 \text{ mi}$$

Thus after being launched at a position 400 miles above the earth's surface, the satellite comes within 275 miles of the earth as a result of a 5° change in the launching angle. This missile, therefore, must be launched almost parallel to the earth if it is to attain a reasonably permanent orbit.

The maximum distance out from the earth is found by setting $\phi = \pi$ in Eq. (a):

$$1/r_{\text{max}} = 20.2 \times 10^{-5} - 3.19 \times 10^{-5}$$

Hence:

$$r_{\text{max}} = 5880 \text{ mi}$$

EXAMPLE 12.11

Assume a satellite is placed into orbit about a planet that has the same mass and diameter as the earth but that has no atmosphere. At the minimum height of its trajectory, the satellite has an elevation of 400 miles from the planet's surface and a velocity of 18,500 miles per hour. To observe the planet more closely, we send down a smaller satellite from the main body to within 10 miles of this planet. The "sub-satellite" is given a velocity component toward the center of the planet when the main satellite is at its lowest position. What is this radial velocity and what is the eccentricity of the trajectory of the subsatellite?

At the time of launching, the subsatellite has the tangential component $(V_\phi)_0$, which corresponds to the mother ship and an unknown radial component $(V_r)_0$. Thus we have the following data:

$$r_0 = 4400 \text{ mi}$$

$$(V_\phi)_0 = 18{,}500 \text{ mi/hr}$$

$$GM = 1.255 \times 10^{12} \text{ miles}^3/\text{hour}^2$$

Substituting these data into Eq. 12.64 and using Eq. 12.78 for D, we have for the trajectory of the subsatellite:

$$\frac{1}{r} = \frac{1.255 \times 10^{12}}{[(4400)(18{,}500)]^2} + \left\{\left[\frac{1}{4400} - \frac{1.255 \times 10^{12}}{[(4400)(18{,}500)]^2}\right]^2 + \left[\frac{(V_r)_0}{(4400)(18{,}500)}\right]^2\right\}^{1/2} \cos\phi \quad \textbf{(a)}$$

Carrying out the arithmetic operations, we get:

$$\frac{1}{r} = 1.897 \times 10^{-4} + \left[0.141 \times 10^{-8} + \frac{(V_r)_0^2}{66.2 \times 10^{14}}\right]^{1/2} \cos\phi \quad \textbf{(b)}$$

By substituting $\phi = 0$ and $r = 4010$ miles into Eq. (b), we can determine the proper radial launching component, $(V_r)_0$;

$$(V_r)_0 = 3760 \text{ mi/hr}$$

The eccentricity of the trajectory, from Eq. 12.80, is:

$$\epsilon = \frac{(4400)(18{,}500)}{1.255 \times 10^{12}} \times \left\{(3760)^2 + \left[18{,}500 - \frac{1.255 \times 10^{12}}{(4400)(18{,}500)}\right]^2\right\}^{1/2}$$

Hence:

$$\epsilon = 0.317$$

PART C. Special Topics

12.14 Introduction

In Part C we shall consider the motions of shells and charged particles. They cannot generally be considered rectilinear or central-force motions. We will first integrate the scalar components of Newton's laws and then, after the constants of integration have been determined, we will eliminate the parameter time. The relation between the spatial coordinates is called the *trajectory* of the particle. Note we have already used trajectories in our work on central-force motion.

We will begin with a simple study of short-range ballistic missiles with and without friction. This will be followed by a study of the motion of charged particles in electric and magnetic fields.

12.15 Introduction to Ballistics of Shells

Assume (1) that a shell is moving over a short range with a shallow trajectory, (2) that the ground is a plane surface, (3) that the attraction of gravity is in a direction normal to the plane representing the earth's surface, and (4) that the shell is shot with a velocity V_0 at an angle α_0, as is shown in Fig. 12.21. We wish to determine the trajectory of the shell under these extremely simple circumstances. First we shall consider the case when no friction is present.

Case A. No Friction. Newton's law for this case is:

$$m\frac{d^2\mathbf{r}}{dt^2} = -mg\mathbf{j} \qquad \textbf{12.85}$$

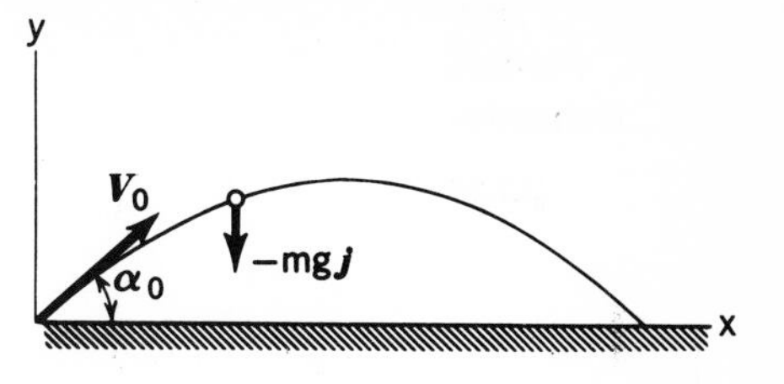

Fig. 12.21

Since there is a unidirectional force on the particle during the motion, it is clear that the trajectory is coplanar, and accordingly we have chosen xy to correspond to this plane. The scalar equations of Eq. 12.85 then become:

$$m\frac{d^2x}{dt^2} = 0 \qquad \textbf{(a)}$$

$$m\frac{d^2y}{dt^2} = -mg \qquad \textbf{(b)} \quad \textbf{12.86}$$

Each equation may readily be integrated—an operation that corresponds to the rectilinear translation problems of Part A. Thus:

$$\frac{dx}{dt} = C_1 \qquad \textbf{(a)}$$

$$x = C_1t + C_2 \qquad \textbf{(b)}$$

$$\frac{dy}{dt} = -gt + C_3 \qquad \textbf{(c)}$$

$$y = -\frac{gt^2}{2} + C_3t + C_4 \qquad \textbf{(d)} \quad \textbf{12.87}$$

The four constants of integration can easily be solved from the initial conditions of the problem, i.e., the firing conditions:

When $t = 0$,

$$\frac{dx}{dt} = V_0 \cos \alpha_0 \qquad \textbf{(a)}$$

$$\frac{dy}{dt} = V_0 \sin \alpha_0 \qquad \textbf{(b)}$$

$$x = 0 \qquad \textbf{(c)}$$

$$y = 0 \qquad \textbf{(d)}$$

It is immediately clear from the above initial conditions (c) and (d) that $C_2 = C_4 = 0$ in Eq. 12.87. Furthermore, initial conditions (a) and (b) give the results $C_1 = V_0 \cos \alpha_0$ and $C_3 = V_0 \sin \alpha_0$ when applied to Eq. 12.87. The equations depicting the motion as a function of time now become:

$$\frac{dx}{dt} = V_0 \cos \alpha_0 \qquad \textbf{(a)}$$

$$x = (V_0 \cos \alpha_0)t \qquad \textbf{(b)}$$

$$\frac{dy}{dt} = -gt + V_0 \sin \alpha_0 \qquad \textbf{(c)}$$

$$y = -\frac{gt^2}{2} + (V_0 \sin \alpha_0)t \qquad \textbf{(d)} \quad \textbf{12.88}$$

To get the trajectory, we simply eliminate the variable t in Eqs. (b) and (d). Solving for t in (b) and substituting into (d), we thus have:

$$y = -\frac{g}{2} \frac{x^2}{(V_0 \cos \alpha_0)^2} + x \tan \alpha_0 \qquad \textbf{12.89}$$

The equation clearly is that of a parabola. There is no longer the possibility of a variety of conic curves, as is the case when the curvature of the earth is accounted for and the force of gravity is directed radially toward the center of the earth.

Employing the above relations, we shall now consider two important features of this motion in the following problems.

EXAMPLE 12.12

Given V_0 and α_0, find the distance covered along the ground, the time elapsed during flight, and the maximum height of the projectile.

To ascertain the distance traveled along the ground we set $y = 0$ in Eq. 12.89 and solve for x. (This assumes that the target position is at the same elevation as the firing position.) Thus:

$$0 = -\frac{g}{2} \frac{x^2}{(V_0 \cos \alpha_0)^2} + x \tan \alpha_0 \qquad \textbf{(a)}$$

There are two roots for x that satisfy the equation. These are:

$$x_1 = 0$$

$$x_2 = \frac{V_0^2 \tan \alpha_0 \cos^2 \alpha_0}{g/2} = \frac{V_0^2 \sin 2\alpha_0}{g} \qquad \textbf{(b)}$$

One root, of course, must be zero, since it must correspond to the firing condition. The desired distance l then is x_2. Thus:

$$l = \frac{V_0^2 \sin 2\alpha_0}{g} \qquad \textbf{(c)}$$

The time duration of the flight may be found by substituting the value x_2 into Eq. 12.88(b) and solving for t:

$$\frac{V_0^2 \sin 2\alpha_0}{g} = (V_0 \cos \alpha_0)t$$

Hence:

$$t = \frac{V_0}{g} \frac{\sin 2\alpha_0}{\cos \alpha_0} = \frac{2V_0 \sin \alpha_0}{g} \qquad \textbf{(d)}$$

The maximum altitude occurs in this problem at $x = l/2$. (This may be seen if we set $dy/dx = 0$ and solve for x.) Substituting $x = l/2 = (V_0^2 \sin 2\alpha_0)/2g$ into Eq. 12.89, cancelling, and collecting terms, we get:

$$y_{\max} = \frac{V_0^2 \sin^2 \alpha_0}{2g} \qquad \textbf{(e)}$$

EXAMPLE 12.13

Consider the inverse problem of Example 12.12. That is, l, the horizontal distance to the target, is given and a muzzle velocity V_0 is stipulated. The information desired is the angle of firing, α_0.

We can use Eq. (c) of the previous example to get the required α_0.

$$\sin 2\alpha_0 = gl/V_0^2 \qquad \textbf{(f)}$$

If the right side exceeds unity in magnitude, it is clear that no α_0 will satisfy the problem, which indicates that there is insufficient muzzle velocity available to reach the target. If gl/V_0^2 is less than unity, there will be two solutions for the angle $2\alpha_0$. With l as a positive measurement, the possible angles $2\alpha_0$ will be in the first and second quadrants, and α_0 itself may be either of two acute angles. This possibility is illustrated in Fig. 12.22.

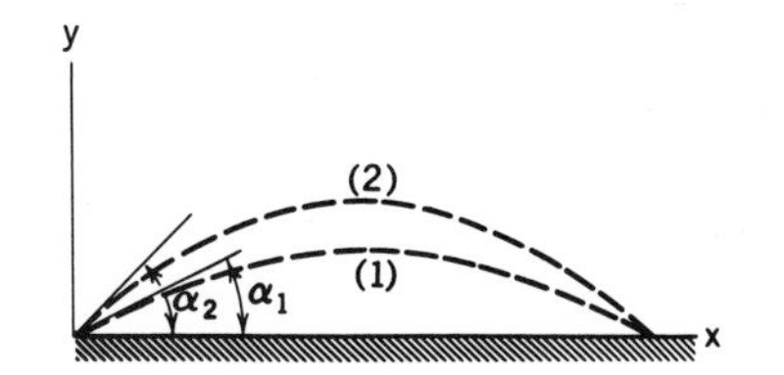

Fig. 12.22

For a given set of initial conditions, Example 12.12 has shown that there is one target, but for a given target and muzzle velocity, we have just demonstrated that there are either two possible initial settings or none.

Case B. Friction Present. Let us now examine the shell problem again, and this time include friction. We will assume that the moving body is either spherical or is so stabilized in its trajectory that it presents the same cross section in the direction of motion. If the object moves through quiescent air which has no strong cross winds and up-drafts, the friction force developed during flight is at all times tangent to the trajectory and always opposing the motion. It has been shown experimentally that the friction force for a given shape of projectile will then be a function of the magnitude of the projectile velocity relative to the air and also a function of such properties of the air as density and viscosity. If the analysis is restricted to trajectories that are fairly shallow, the variation in air properties during flight will be small and the friction force can be expressed in the form:

$$\boldsymbol{f} = -mH(V)\hat{\boldsymbol{V}} \qquad \textbf{12.90}$$

where H, called the *friction function*, is some function of V, and m, the mass of the projectile, is included to simplify subsequent calculations. Figure 12.23 illustrates the various forces that act on a projectile moving in a shallow trajectory. We shall express Newton's law in component form first in the x direction and then in the normal direction n with a sense toward the center of curvature of the trajectory. The equations then are:

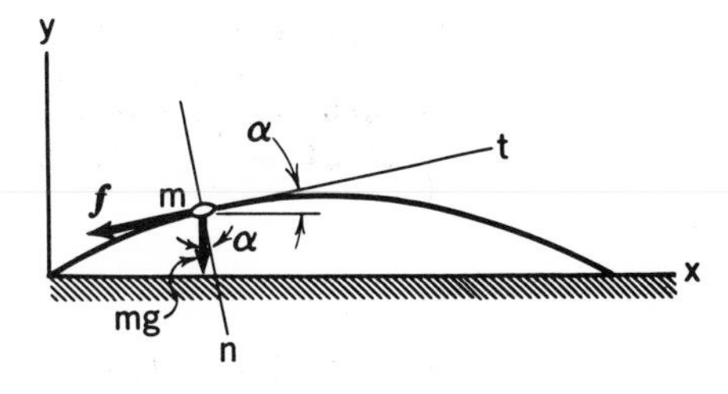

Fig. 12.23

$$m\frac{d^2x}{dt^2} = -mH(V)\cos\alpha \qquad \textbf{(a)}$$

$$ma_n = mg \cos \alpha \qquad \textbf{(b)} \quad \textbf{12.91}$$

Replacing a_n by V^2/R, as was shown in Section 11.6, and cancelling m, we may express Eq. (b) as:

$$\frac{V^2}{R} = g \cos \alpha \qquad \textbf{12.92}$$

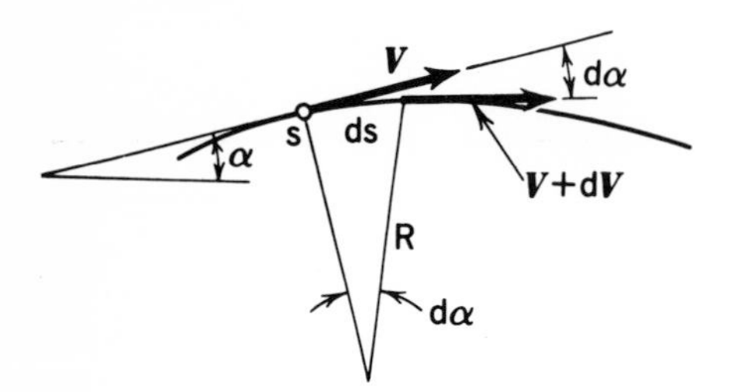

Fig. 12.24

Since the trajectory of our problem always curves toward the ground, it is clear that the tangent to the trajectory has a clockwise angular rotation as we follow the particle in its flight. Hence the differential quantity $d\alpha$ is always negative in our analysis. Since ds is always positive in this discussion, we can see in Fig. 12.24 that R (a positive quantity) can be replaced by $-ds/d\alpha$ in Eq. 12.92. Also replacing V by (ds/dt), we can write:

$$\frac{V^2}{R} = -\frac{(ds/dt)^2}{ds/d\alpha} = -\frac{ds}{dt}\frac{d\alpha}{ds}\frac{ds}{dt} = -\frac{ds}{dt}\frac{d\alpha}{dt} = -V\frac{d\alpha}{dt} \qquad \textbf{12.93}$$

Equation 12.92 now becomes:

$$V\frac{d\alpha}{dt} = -g \cos \alpha \qquad \textbf{12.94}$$

Since $dx/dt = V \cos \alpha$, Eq. 12.91 (a) can be written in the following form after we cancel out m:

$$\frac{d}{dt}(V \cos \alpha) = -H(V) \cos \alpha \qquad \textbf{12.95}$$

From Eq. 12.94 first solve for dt and then substitute into Eq. 12.95. Thus:

$$dt = -\frac{V\, d\alpha}{g \cos \alpha} \qquad \textbf{(a)}$$

$$\therefore \quad \frac{g \cos \alpha}{V}\frac{d(V \cos \alpha)}{d\alpha} = H(V) \cos \alpha \qquad \textbf{(b)} \quad \textbf{12.96}$$

Rearranging the last equation, we get the basic differential equation for the trajectory under the restrictions of this case:

$$\boxed{d(V \cos \alpha) = \frac{VH(V)}{g}\, d\alpha} \qquad \textbf{12.97}$$

This equation is not separable and even with a simple $H(V)$ cannot be integrated in a straightforward manner. But it is in a desirable form for numerical methods of solution starting from known initial data V_0 and α_0, and you can work this problem if you have studied elementary numerical methods. And, with the increasing availability of digital computers, you can readily work this problem by machine methods. We shall here solve this equation analytically for the special case of a very *shallow* trajectory by making certain simplifications (see Example 12.14). Also, we shall present in the homework section several problems (Probs. 90 and 92) to be solved as projects with the aid of a digital computer.

In any case, if V is found as a function of α from Eq. 12.97, we can find $t(\alpha)$, $x(\alpha)$, and $y(\alpha)$ as follows. Integrate Eq. 12.96 (a) from $t = 0$ to t on the left side and from $\alpha = \alpha_0$ to α on the right side. We then have for t the desired result:

$$t = -\int_{\alpha_0}^{\alpha} \frac{V}{g \cos \alpha}\, d\alpha \qquad \textbf{12.98}$$

By multiplying Eq. 12.96 (a) by dx/dt on the left side and by $V \cos \alpha$ (which equals dx/dt) on the right side, we find x by the following quadrature:

$$x = -\int_{\alpha_0}^{\alpha} \frac{V^2 d\alpha}{g} \qquad \textbf{12.99}$$

Finally, multiplying Eq. (12.96) (*a*) by dy/dt on the left side and by $V \sin \alpha$ on the right, we can reach the following quadrature for y:

$$y = -\int_{\alpha_0}^{\alpha} \frac{V^2 \tan \alpha}{g} d\alpha \qquad \textbf{12.100}$$

EXAMPLE 12.14

Consider the case of a *very flat trajectory* where the friction function is known to be κV^2, κ being a constant. Develop an approximate analysis of the trajectory.

We shall first consider the basic differential Eq. 12.97. Expanding the differential on the left side and replacing $H(V)$ by κV^2, we have:

$$\cos \alpha \frac{dV}{d\alpha} - V \sin \alpha = \frac{\kappa V^3}{g} \qquad \textbf{(a)}$$

Since α will be small in this problem, we make the approximation that $\cos \alpha = 1$ and $\sin \alpha = \alpha$. The equation then becomes:

$$\frac{dV}{d\alpha} - V\alpha = \frac{\kappa V^3}{g} \qquad \textbf{(b)}$$

Solving for $dV/d\alpha$, we get:

$$\frac{dV}{d\alpha} = V\left(\alpha + \frac{\kappa V^2}{g}\right) \qquad \textbf{(c)}$$

For a situation where $\alpha_0 \ll \kappa V_0^2/g$ (from known initial conditions) we can reasonably assume that $\alpha \ll \kappa V^2/g$ during the flight, and so we can neglect α in the parentheses of the above equation. The equation then becomes:

$$\frac{dV}{d\alpha} = \frac{\kappa V^3}{g} \qquad \textbf{(d)}$$

Separating variables and integrating, we have:

$$-\frac{V^{-2}}{2}\bigg]_{V_0}^{V} = \frac{\kappa}{g}(\alpha - \alpha_0)$$

$$\therefore V^{-2} - V_0^{-2} = \frac{2\kappa}{g}(\alpha_0 - \alpha)$$

Solving for V^2, we write:

$$V^2 = \frac{1}{(1/V_0)^2 + (2\kappa/g)(\alpha_0 - \alpha)} \qquad \textbf{(e)}$$

We have thus found V as a function of α in an approximate analytic manner. To evaluate the coordinates x and y, substitute (e) into Eqs. 12.99 and 12.100. Thus:

$$x = -\int_{\alpha_0}^{\alpha} \frac{d\alpha}{g[(1/V_0)^2 + (2\kappa/g)(\alpha_0 - \alpha)]} \qquad \textbf{(f)}$$

and, replacing $\tan\alpha$ by α, we have for y:

$$y = -\int_{\alpha_0}^{\alpha} \frac{\alpha\, d\alpha}{g[(1/V_0)^2 + (2\kappa/g)(\alpha_0 - \alpha)]} \qquad \text{(g)}$$

To aid in integration, (f) and (g) can be rewritten as:

$$x = -\frac{1}{2\kappa}\int_{\alpha_0}^{\alpha} \frac{d\alpha}{[g/(2\kappa V_0^2) + \alpha_0] - \alpha}$$

$$y = -\frac{1}{2\kappa}\int_{\alpha_0}^{\alpha} \frac{\alpha\, d\alpha}{[g/(2\kappa V_0^2) + \alpha_0] - \alpha}$$

These can readily be integrated:

$$x = \frac{1}{2\kappa} \ln\left[\left(\frac{g}{2\kappa V_0^2} + \alpha_0\right) - \alpha\right]_{\alpha_0}^{\alpha}$$

$$= \frac{1}{2\kappa}\left\{\ln\left(\frac{g}{2\kappa V_0^2} + \alpha_0 - \alpha\right) - \ln\frac{g}{2\kappa V_0^2}\right\} \qquad \text{(h)}$$

$$y = \frac{1}{2\kappa}\left\{\alpha + \left(\frac{g}{2\kappa V_0^2} + \alpha_0\right)\ln\left(\frac{g}{2\kappa V_0^2} + \alpha_0 - \alpha\right)\right\}_{\alpha_0}^{\alpha}$$

$$= \frac{1}{2\kappa}\left\{(\alpha - \alpha_0) + \left(\frac{g}{2\kappa V_0^2} + \alpha_0\right)\right.$$

$$\left.\times\left[\ln\left(\frac{g}{2\kappa V_0^2} + \alpha_0 - \alpha\right) - \ln\frac{g}{2\kappa V_0^2}\right]\right\} \qquad \text{(i)}$$

We can determine the maximum elevation and its location by substituting $\alpha = 0$ into Eqs. (h) and (i). Thus for the maximum elevation:

$$y_{\max} = \frac{1}{2\kappa}\left\{-\alpha_0 + \left(\frac{g}{2\kappa V_0^2} + \alpha_0\right)\right.$$

$$\left.\times\left[\ln\left(\frac{g}{2\kappa V_0^2} + \alpha_0\right) - \ln\frac{g}{2\kappa V_0^2}\right]\right\} \qquad \text{(j)}$$

To find the distance l along the horizontal where the missile reaches its launching elevation, we set $y = 0$ in Eq. (i) and solve for α:

$$\alpha + \left(\frac{g}{2\kappa V_0^2} + \alpha_0\right)\ln\left(\frac{g}{2\kappa V_0^2} + \alpha_0 - \alpha\right)$$

$$= \alpha_0 + \left(\frac{g}{2\kappa V_0^2} + \alpha_0\right)\ln\frac{g}{2\kappa V_0^2} \qquad \text{(k)}$$

This equation is of the form:

$$\alpha + B\ln(B - \alpha) = C$$

where B and C are known constants. We can solve this transcendental equation by trial and error. It is helpful to rearrange the equation in the following way for such a computation:

$$\alpha = C - B\ln(B - \alpha)$$

Now plot the left side and right side roughly as a function of α, as shown in Fig. 12.25. The point of

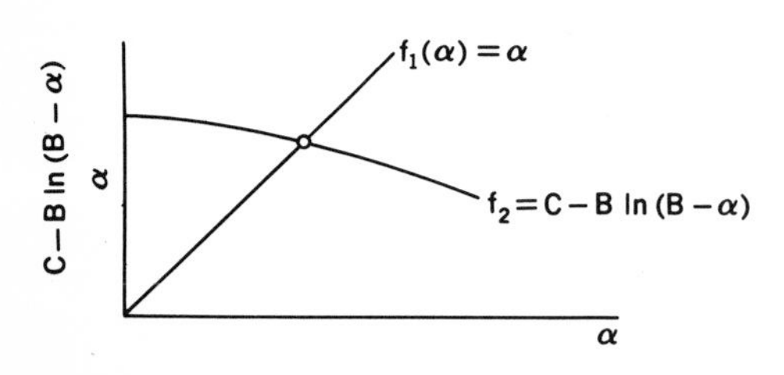

Fig. 12.25

intersection computed to any desired degree of accuracy represents the desired α. Substitute this value of α into Eq. (h) and solve for x, which becomes the desired distance l.

From the complexity of this "simplified" problem, you can begin to appreciate the difficulties involved in trying to account for friction. In Prob. 86 you may be asked to work out this same problem by another method which results in an approximate analytical solution for x and y as functions of time.

*12.16 Remarks Concerning Motion of Charged Particles

In this and the following section we shall present a brief introduction to the ballistics of charged particles in electric and magnetic fields. We shall consider very small bodies such as electrons and ions—that is, bodies at the *microscopic scale.* For such bodies the concept of friction is inapplicable since this concept is purely a *macroscopic phenomenon* resulting from the interaction of countless microscopic bodies associated with the macroscopic body of interest. The closest thing to friction for the microscopic bodies under consideration here would be the possibility of collisions between such bodies—a topic that we shall discuss later. A further result of the small size of the bodies under discussion is that in many problems the forces on the bodies from electric and magnetic fields are considerably larger than gravitational forces. Accordingly we shall neglect gravity in the ensuing discussions.

For certain applications, these particles approach the speed of light, and in these situations classical Newtonian mechanics does not apply. The *special theory of relativity* tells us that we must consider mass m as a variable when the speed of light is approached. This means that Newton's law must be expressed as:

$$\boldsymbol{F} = \frac{d}{dt}(m\boldsymbol{V}) \qquad \textbf{12.101}$$

wherein the mass m is a function of the velocity relative to the inertial reference, expressible as

$$m = \frac{m_0}{\sqrt{1 - V^2/c^2}} \qquad \textbf{12.102}$$

where

m_0 is called the rest mass and corresponds to the mass at zero velocity
c is the velocity of light in a vacuum and thus a universal constant

For m to be appreciably different from m_0, the velocity V obviously must be extremely large,

The behavior of charged particles has always been of paramount importance to electrical engineers, but with the growth of nuclear and thermonuclear technology, all engineers will almost necessarily have to deal with such particles. In fact, the much-publicized field of magneto-hydrodynamics is emerging as an experimental and theoretical field in which the fluid particles are considered to have charges and thus to be subject to electric and magnetic forces in addition to the stresses and body forces usually analyzed in fluid mechanics.

Before applying Newton's laws, let us review the concept of electric and magnetic fields in a vacuum.

1. *Electric Field.* First we will examine Coulomb's law for charged particles whose size is small compared to the separation distance. (Fig. 12.26). Coulomb found that as a result of the charges a central force exists between the particles. This force is analogous to the gravitational force between two particles in that the magnitude of the force is proportional to the product of the charges, (the charges taking the place of the masses), and is inversely proportional to the square of the distance between the particles. The essential difference between gravitational and coulombic forces is that the latter can either be one of the attraction for unlike charges or repulsion for like charges between the particles; gravitational force, on the other hand, is always one of attraction. Coulomb's law is accordingly given as:

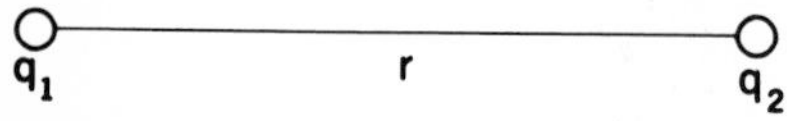

q_1 r q_2

Fig. 12.26

$$\boldsymbol{F} \propto \frac{q_1 q_2}{r^2}\hat{\boldsymbol{r}} \qquad \textbf{12.103}$$

The constant of proportionality depends on the system of units that are employed as well as on the medium between the charges. Using the rationalized MKSC units, for a vacuum (or air) we have the following result:

$$\boldsymbol{F} = \frac{q_1 q_2}{4\pi\epsilon_0 r^2}\hat{\boldsymbol{r}} \qquad \textbf{12.104}$$

where

$\boldsymbol{F}$ is in newtons
q_1, q_2 are the charges in coulombs
r is the separating distance in meters
ϵ_0 is the dielectric constant for a vacuum which equals 8.854×10^{-12} farads/meter

Suppose we have a charge q_1 and a very small positive *test* charge q_2 which we can position anywhere in space. The force on the test charge q_2 is then available from Coulomb's law, Eq. 12.104. If we divide both sides of the equation by q_2, i.e., by the test charge, we have in effect the force per unit positive charge at any point in space resulting from the influence of q_1:

$$\frac{\boldsymbol{F}}{q_2} = \frac{q_1}{4\pi\epsilon_0 r^2}\hat{\boldsymbol{r}} \qquad \textbf{12.105}$$

As pointed out in Chapter 4, a force defined at all points in space is called a *force field.* We have here, then, a force field due to the charge q_1, and we shall call this force field, $\boldsymbol{E}$, the *electric field strength.* Thus:

$$\boldsymbol{E} = \frac{\boldsymbol{F}}{q_2} = \frac{q_1}{4\pi\epsilon_0 r^2}\hat{\boldsymbol{r}} \qquad \textbf{12.106}$$

Any charge q_3 will then have a force on it that is given by the vector $q_3\boldsymbol{E}$, which has a sense toward or away from q_1 depending on whether it has the opposite or the same type of charge as q_1.

We have introduced the concept of $\boldsymbol{E}$ by using a single fixed charge q_1. Actually, fields can be formed by any orientation of discrete charges q_i or by distributions of charges. The force per unit charge on a positively charged particle in space that results from any such configuration is considered to be the electric field $\boldsymbol{E}$ for that arrangement.

2. *Magnetic Field (Steady).** We are all familiar with the fact that when a compass is brought near a magnet or a steady direct current the direction of the needle depends on the position of the compass relative to the magnet or current. We customarily speak of a *magnetic field* in such regions. Experiments indicate that for a vacuum (or air) there is a force on a charged particle moving through a magnetic field. And this force is given by the equation:

$$\boldsymbol{F} = q\boldsymbol{V} \times \boldsymbol{B} \qquad \textbf{12.107}$$

where

$\boldsymbol{F}$ is the force on the particle in newtons
q is the charge on the particle in coulombs
$\boldsymbol{V}$ is the velocity vector of the particle relative to the field in meters/second
$\boldsymbol{B}$ is the magnetic flux density in webers/meter^2

When electric currents are causing the magnetic field, the Biot-Savart law permits us to integrate along the wires and thus to compute the magnetic flux density, $\boldsymbol{B}$, in the following way:

$$\boldsymbol{B} = \int \frac{\mu_0 i}{4\pi r^2}\, ds \times \hat{\boldsymbol{r}} \qquad \textbf{12.108}$$

where

μ_0 is the permeability of free space which equals $4\pi \times 10^{-7}$ henries/meter
i is the current in the wire in amperes
ds is the segment of the wire carrying current i
r is the distance from a point in the field to element ds of the wire in meters
$\hat{r}_1$ is the unit vectory along r

Although we shall not use the Biot-Savart law, Fig. 12.27 illustrates the elements in the equation.

In using vector fields it is helpful to employ, as a graphical aid, a set of curves that are tangent to the vectors at each point. In the case of an electrostatic field about a single charged particle, these would form a set of radial lines as shown in Fig. 12.28. Such lines are called *flux lines* for electrostatic fields, and

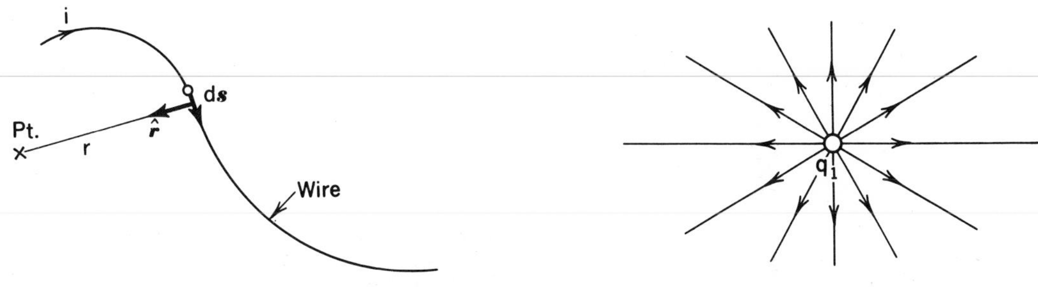

Fig. 12.27

Fig. 12.28

* A *Steady field* is one that is *time-independent.* A *uniform field* at any time *t does not vary with position.* It should be understood that a steady field need not be uniform nor need a uniform field be steady.

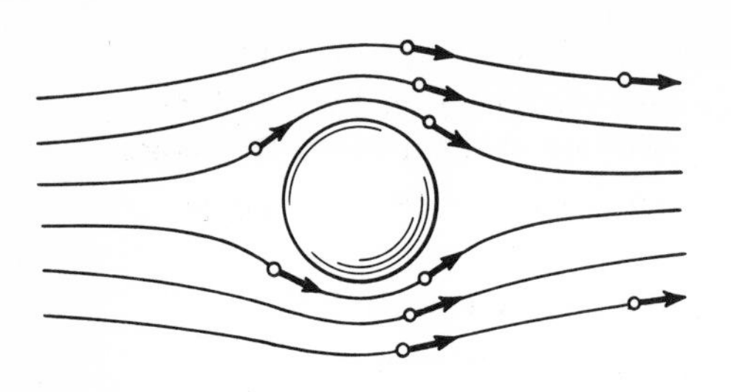

Fig. 12.29

in the case of velocity fields $V(x, y, z, t)$ as used in the flow of fluids, they are called *streamlines*. Figure 12.29 shows a set of streamlines for the velocity field that represents the flow of a fluid around a sphere. Velocity vectors have been shown at several points to illustrate the fact that the streamlines must always be tangent to these vectors at all points along the lines.

Finally, magnetic fields are similarly represented by magnetic field lines. In this section, since we are concerned with uniform magnetic fields, the lines will be straight. For convenience in studying the motion of a particle, we shall consider a uniform field oriented normal to the page of the book. In such a case, the lines appear as dots, if the vectors at each position point out of the page, and as crosses if the vectors point into the page (Fig. 12.30).

Magnetic field pointing out of page

Magnetic field pointing into page

Fig. 12.30

The flux lines of the electric field and the streamlines of fluid flow have a simple meaning. The former represents the direction of the force exerted on a positive charge at any point; the latter represents the direction at each position of the fluid motion. In the case of a magnetic field, the lines actually represent the direction that a tiny compass will take when placed at any position in the magnetic field.

*12.17 Motion of Charged Particles

We can now write the differential equation of motion for a charged particle moving through electric and magnetic fields:

$$\frac{d(m\boldsymbol{V})}{dt} = q\boldsymbol{E} + q\boldsymbol{V} \times \boldsymbol{B} \qquad \textbf{12.109}$$

The equation looks deceivingly simple. Actually, with other than simple uniform magnetic and electric fields it becomes a difficult equation to integrate. This equation is fundamental in the design of cathode ray tubes, particle accelerators, etc. We shall consider only applications involving uniform electric and constant magnetic fields.

Case A. Uniform Electric Field. If a voltage is placed on two parallel plates that have a large cross-sectional area compared to the distance between them, an electric field is formed between the plates which for practical purposes can be considered uniform. Thus, for a constant voltage, a charged particle moving in this region is acted on by a constant force in a direction normal to the plates (Fig. 12.31). Let us assume that the particle is an electron of charge $-e$, moving initially with velocity $\boldsymbol{V}_0$ in the xy plane. We assume that V_0 is small compared

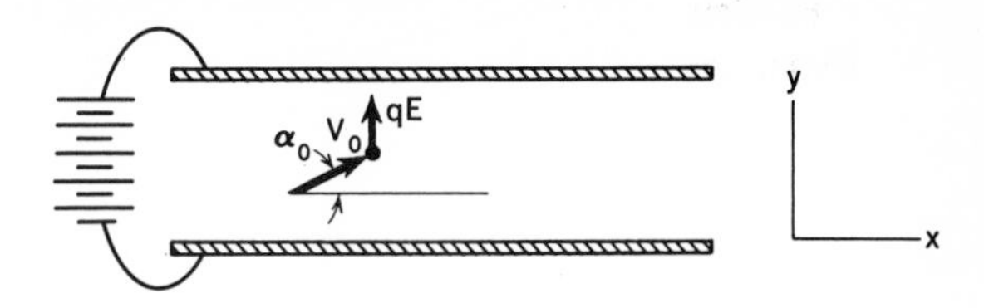

Fig. 12.31

to the speed of light and that the plates are located in a perfect vacuum. The differential equation of motion for the electron can then be given for this problem as:

$$m\frac{d^2\boldsymbol{r}}{dt^2} = eE\boldsymbol{j} \qquad \textbf{12.110}$$

From Eq. 12.85, we see that this problem corresponds to that of the shell moving in a frictionless atmosphere under the influence of a uniform gravitational field. Since, clearly, $-mg$ of the earlier problem corresponds to eE of the present one, we can simply quote from earlier results to express the equations of motion for the charged particle starting from the origin. Thus, examining Eq. 12.88 we get

$$\frac{dx}{dt} = V_0 \cos \alpha_0 \qquad (\textbf{a})$$

$$x = V_0 (\cos \alpha_0) t \qquad (\textbf{b})$$

$$\frac{dy}{dt} = \frac{eE}{m} t + V_0 \sin \alpha_0 \qquad (\textbf{c})$$

$$y = \frac{eEt^2}{2m} + V_0 (\sin \alpha_0) t \qquad (\textbf{d}) \quad \textbf{12.111}$$

The trajectory must be parabolic in nature and is of the form:

$$y = \frac{eE}{2m}\frac{x^2}{(V_0 \cos \alpha_0)^2} + x \tan \alpha_0 \qquad \textbf{12.112}$$

We shall now apply these results to the very interesting problem of the cathode ray tube, which is shown diagrammatically in Fig. 12.32. A heated cathode gives off electrons which are attracted to the positive anode by the electrostatic attraction. Some go through the small hole in the anode and enter the parallel plates with a velocity V_0 and an angle $\alpha_0 = 0$. During the

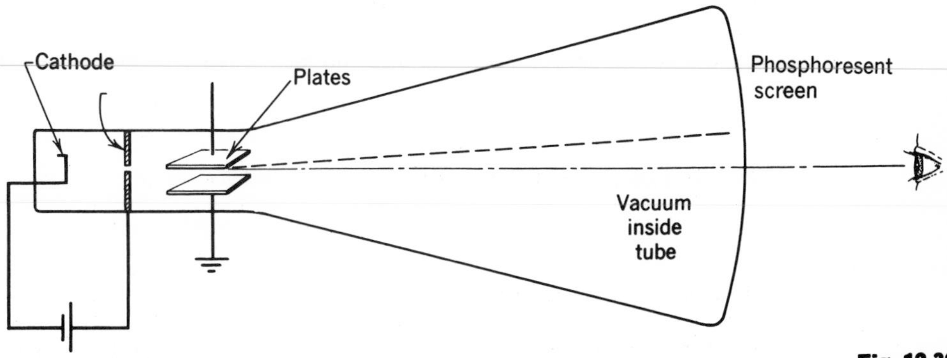

Fig. 12.32

time the electron is between the plates, it undergoes a parabolic trajectory given by Eqs. 12.111 and 12.112, which for $\alpha_0 = 0$ become:

$$\frac{dx}{dt} = V_0 \qquad \text{(a)}$$

$$x = V_0 t \qquad \text{(b)}$$

$$\frac{dy}{dt} = \frac{eEt}{m} \qquad \text{(c)}$$

$$y = \frac{eEt^2}{2m} \qquad \text{(d)}$$

$$y = \frac{eE}{2m}\frac{x^2}{V_0^2} \qquad \text{(e)} \quad \textbf{12.113}$$

After the particle emerges from the plate, it moves along a straight line until it hits the phosphorescent screen. The impact of the electron causes the screen to light up for a short time at the impact point, thus making the impact visible to a viewer on the outside. We shall now develop the relation between the position of the impact on the screen and the voltage on the plates. In Fig. 12.33 appear the necessary geometrical data for this calculation. We assume that the curvature of the screen is so small that we can consider it as a plane.

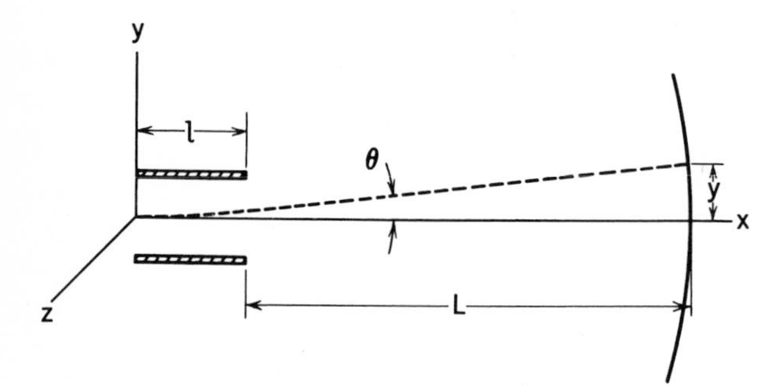

Fig. 12.33

The time that the particle remains between the plates can easily be found from Eq. 12.113 (b). Letting x equal l, we have:

$$\Delta t = \frac{l}{V_0} \qquad \textbf{12.114}$$

Thus the change in elevation, Δy, during this part of the motion is found from Eq. 12.113 (d):

$$\Delta y = \frac{eE}{2m}\left(\frac{l}{V_0}\right)^2 \qquad \textbf{12.115}$$

The exit velocity from the plates in the y direction is also available from Eq. 12.113 (c) as:

$$V_y = \frac{eEl}{mV_0} \qquad \textbf{12.116}$$

On leaving the plates, the electron thus has the direction θ, where:

$$\tan\theta = \frac{V_y}{V_x} = \frac{eEl/mV_0}{V_0} = \frac{eEl}{mV_0^2} \qquad \textbf{12.117}$$

From this point on, the particle moves at this fixed inclination. The position y, where the particle finally strikes the screen at a distance L from the end of the plates, is now determined by superposing two vertical contributions. First there is the vertical contribution that results from the motion outside the plates at the fixed angle θ. Calling this y_1, we can write:

$$\frac{y_1}{L} = \tan\theta = \frac{eEl}{mV_0^2}$$

$$\therefore\ y_1 = \frac{eElL}{mV_0^2} \qquad \textbf{12.118}$$

The change in elevation y_2 during the parabolic motion between the plates is given by Eq. 12.115. The total deflection y is then the sum of the two contributions:

$$y_1 + y_2 = \frac{eElL}{mV_0^2} + \frac{eEl^2}{2mV_0^2} \qquad \textbf{12.119}$$

A steady stream of electrons of velocity V_0 will accordingly produce a luminous spot on the screen at a position y, whose exact location depends on the strength of the field E. But we know from elementary physics that E is proportional to the impressed voltage V, so the position of the spot can be a measure of voltage. If a sinusoidal voltage is placed on the plates, E will vary sinusoidally with time, and the luminous spot will move with harmonic motion in the y direction.

Consider now an additional set of plates at right angles to the preceding set. By the same arguments, we can demonstrate that this new set of plates causes the electrons to move in the z direction, and thus for a sinusoidal voltage on this new set of plates the luminous spot has a harmonic motion in the z direction. In the standard oscilloscope in Fig. 12.34, the plates are arranged so that if we put sinusoidal voltages on both sets of plates simultaneously, we can make the beam of electrons form very interesting patterns on the screen. The patterns depend on the relation of the amplitudes and frequencies of the impressed voltages. It will be left as an exercise to show how a circle and an ellipse can be formed on the screen. Other more complicated figures, sometimes called *Lissajous* figures, are shown in Fig. 12.35. In many applications, one of the plates of the oscilloscope is given a "sawtooth" voltage variation (Fig. 12.36) that causes the electrons to "sweep" across the z axis of the screen at a certain frequency and, in effect, in one direction only. The voltage to be studied, which comes from some pickup such as a piezo-electric crystal or a strain gauge, is then placed on the other set of plates. If the signal voltage is cyclic, we can, by adjusting the frequency of the sweep voltage, form a fixed pattern on the screen that enables us to interpret the incoming signal.

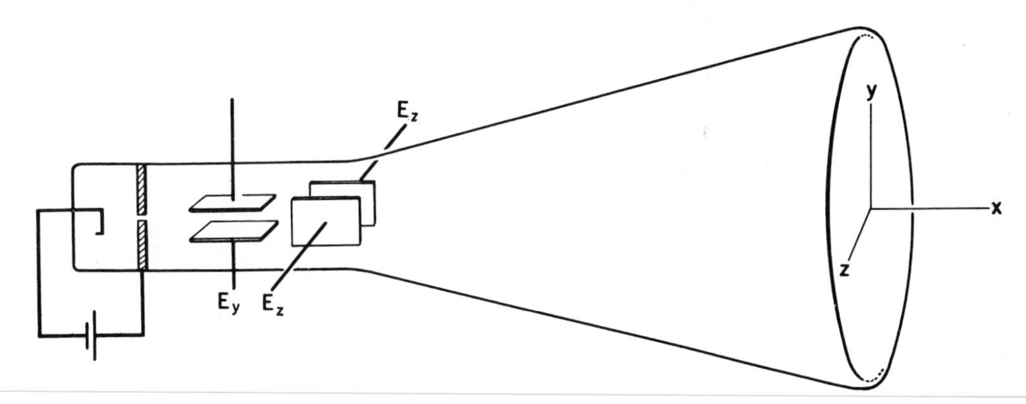

Fig. 12.34

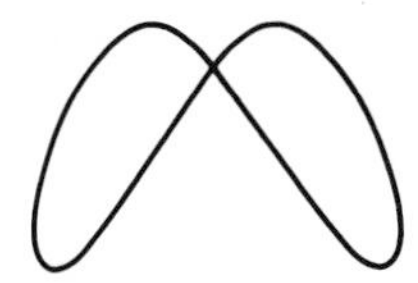
Frequency ratio 2/1

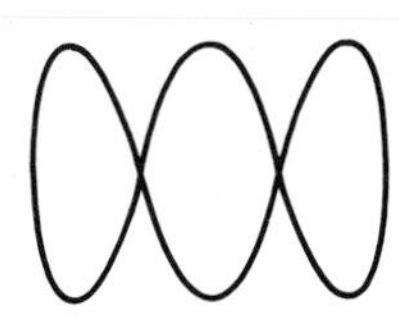
Frequency ratio 3/1

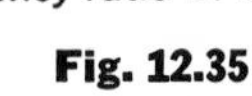

Fig. 12.35

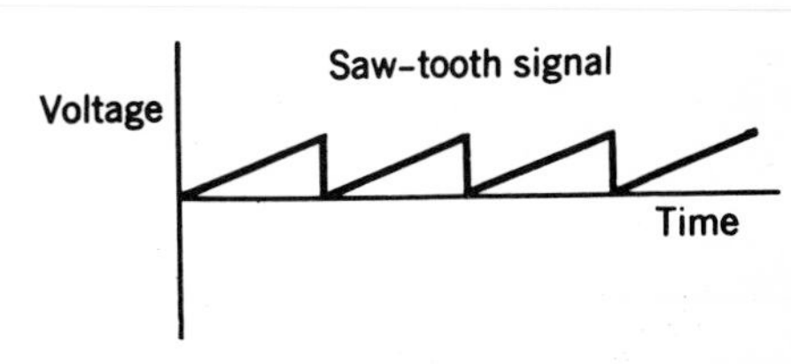

Fig. 12.36

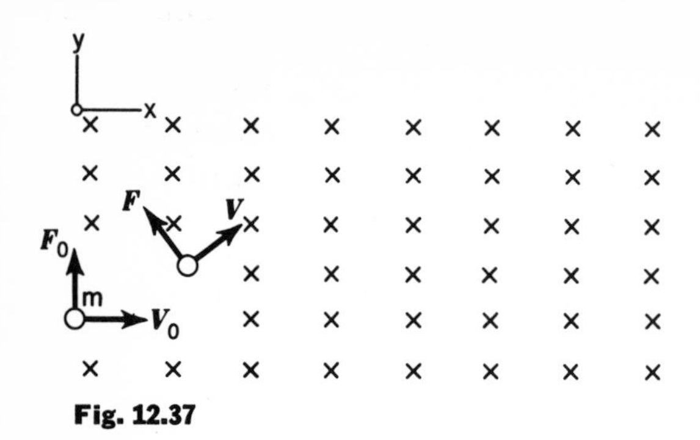

Fig. 12.37

Case B. Steady Uniform Magnetic Field. We now turn to the case of a steady, uniform magnetic field.* This field is directed into the page, as is shown in Fig. 12.37. The field can be given as $-B\boldsymbol{k}$ for the reference chosen. A particle of mass m and charge q is entering the field with a velocity $\boldsymbol{V}_0$ coplanar to the page. The subsequent motion of the particle is given by the following equation, if we neglect gravitational influence:

$$m\boldsymbol{a} = -qB\boldsymbol{V} \times \boldsymbol{k} \qquad \textbf{12.120}$$

To simplify the analysis, let us first make a mental picture of the possible motion. Upon entering the field, the particle is moving in the x direction. The initial force acting on it must be at right angles to the x axis and at right angles to the direction of the field. The previous diagram reveals that initially the force is in the y direction, and thus the motion directly after entering the field will still be in the xy plane but will be inclined to the horizontal. At this later time, as is shown in the diagram, the force $\boldsymbol{F}$ again is in the xy plane and induces a further increase in the velocity at right angles to the trajectory in the xy plane, and so forth. Thus it is clear that the motion must be *coplanar*. Using components in the tangential and normal direction, we can write Eq. 12.120 as:

$$m\left(\frac{d^2s}{dt^2}\boldsymbol{\varepsilon}_t + \frac{V^2}{R}\boldsymbol{\varepsilon}_n\right) = -qBV(\boldsymbol{\varepsilon}_t \times \boldsymbol{k}) \qquad \textbf{12.121}$$

This results in the scalar equation:

$$m\frac{d^2s}{dt^2} = 0 \qquad \textbf{(a)}$$

and noting that $\boldsymbol{\varepsilon}_n = \boldsymbol{\varepsilon}_t \times (-\boldsymbol{k})$ we have in addition:

$$m\frac{V^2}{R} = qBV \qquad \textbf{(b)} \quad \textbf{12.122}$$

From (a) it is apparent that speed ds/dt of the particle is constant and that V is therefore constant. Equation (b) then indicates that the radius of curvature is constant and is given by the equation:

$$R = \frac{mV}{qB} \qquad \textbf{12.123}$$

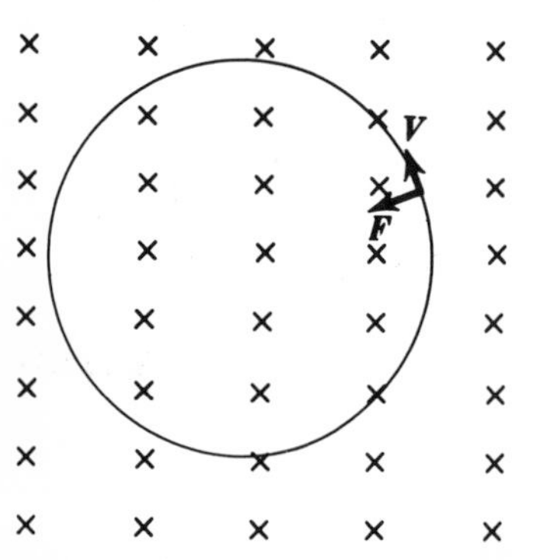

Fig. 12.38

Thus the particle must follow a circular orbit with the above radius, as is shown in Fig. 12.38. If the particle has, on entering the field, a velocity component in the direction of the field, this component, being parallel to $\boldsymbol{B}$, induces a zero force, and the velocity in this direction consequently is unchanged. The result is a trajectory that corresponds to that of a spiral, and the radius of the circular

* See footnote on page 375.

projected motion, called the *Larmor* radius, is determined from the component of the initial velocity normal to the field. Note that the stronger the field, the smaller is the radius of this helical motion.

It must be cautioned that only relatively simple problems of this type submit so easily to a solution. If the influence of gravity is included, the motion has a drift to the right (Fig. 12.39). Can you explain in a qualitative manner why this should happen?

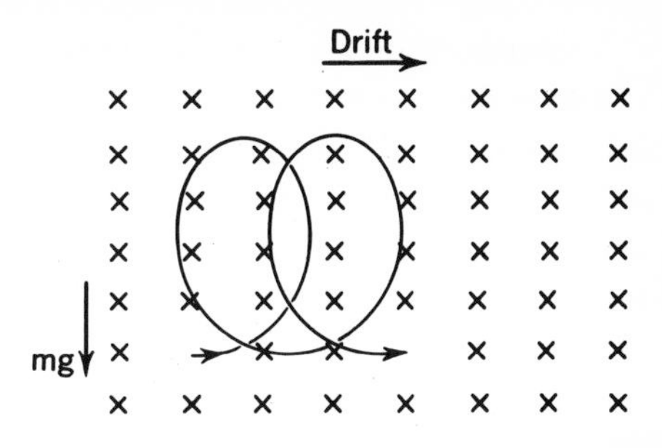

Fig. 12.39

PART D. A System of Particles

12.18 The General Motion of a System of Particles

Let us examine a system of n particles that has interactions between the particles for which Newton's third law of motion (action equals reaction) applies. Newton's second law for any particle (let's say the ith particle) is then:

$$m_i \frac{d^2 \boldsymbol{r}_i}{dt^2} = \boldsymbol{F}_i + \sum_{\substack{j=1 \\ i \neq j}}^{n} \boldsymbol{f}_{ij} \qquad 12.124$$

where $\boldsymbol{f}_{ij}$ is the force on particle i from particle j and is thus considered an *internal* force relative to the system of particles. It is clear that the $j = i$ term of the summation is to be deleted since the ith particle cannot exert force on itself. The force $\boldsymbol{F}_i$ represents the resultant force on the ith particle from the forces *external* to the system of particles (Fig. 12.40).

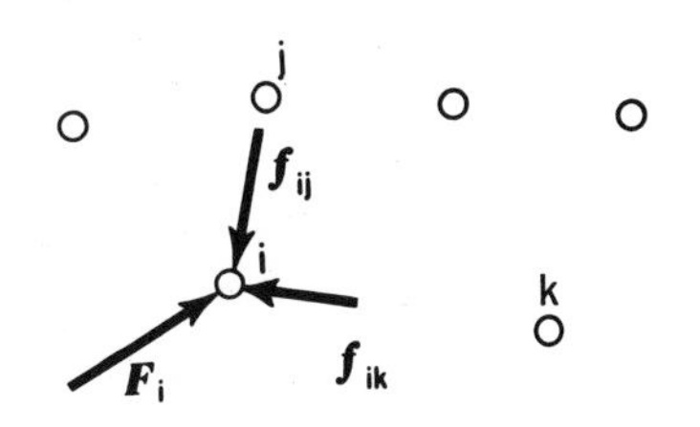

Fig. 12.40

If these equations are added for all n particles, we have:

$$\sum_{i=1}^{n} m_i \frac{d^2 \boldsymbol{r}_i}{dt^2} = \sum_{i=1}^{n} \boldsymbol{F}_i + \sum_{i=1}^{n} \sum_{j=1}^{n} \boldsymbol{f}_{ij} \qquad 12.125$$

Carrying out the double summation and excluding terms with repeated indexes, such as $\boldsymbol{f}_{11}$, $\boldsymbol{f}_{22}$, etc., we find that for each term with any one set of indexes there will be a term with the reverse of these indexes present. For example, there will be for the force $\boldsymbol{f}_{12}$ a force $\boldsymbol{f}_{21}$. A consideration of the meaning of the indices shows that these represent action and reaction forces between a pair of particles, and thus as a result of Newton's third law the double summation in Eq. 12.125 should add up to zero. Newton's second law for a system of particles then becomes:

$$\boldsymbol{F} = \sum_{i=1}^{n} m_i \frac{d^2 \boldsymbol{r}_i}{dt^2} = \frac{d^2}{dt^2} \sum_{i=1}^{n} m_i \boldsymbol{r}_i \qquad 12.126$$

where $\boldsymbol{F}$ now represents the vector sum of *all* the external forces acting on *all* the particles of the system.

To make further useful simplifications, we shall use the first moment of mass of a system of n particles about a point given as:

$$\text{First moment vector} \equiv \sum_{i=1}^{n} m_i \boldsymbol{r}_i$$

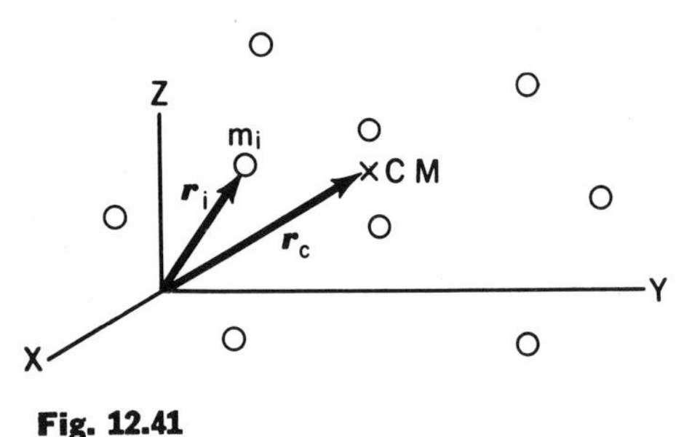

Fig. 12.41

where $\boldsymbol{r}_i$ represents the position from the point to the ith particle. As explained in Chapter 8, we can find a position, called the *center of mass* of the system, with position vector $\boldsymbol{r}_c$, where the entire mass of the system of particles can be concentrated to give the correct first moments (Fig. 12.41). Thus:

$$\boldsymbol{r}_c \sum_{i=1}^{n} m_i = \sum_{i=1}^{n} m_i \boldsymbol{r}_i$$

$$\therefore \ \boldsymbol{r}_c = \frac{\sum m_i \boldsymbol{r}_i}{\sum m_i} = \frac{\sum m_i \boldsymbol{r}_i}{M} \qquad \textbf{12.127}$$

Let us reconsider Newton's law, using the center-of-mass concept. To do this, replace $\sum m_i \boldsymbol{r}_i$ by $M\boldsymbol{r}_c$ in Eq. 12.126. Thus:

$$\boldsymbol{F} = \frac{d^2}{dt^2}(M\boldsymbol{r}_c) = M\frac{d^2\boldsymbol{r}_c}{dt^2} \qquad \textbf{12.128}$$

From this we see that the center of mass *of any aggregate of particle has a motion that can be computed by methods already set forth, since this is a problem involving a single hypothetical particle of mass M*. You will recall that we have alluded to this important relationship several times earlier to justify the use of the particle concept in the analysis of many dynamics problems. It is vital to realize for such an undertaking that $\boldsymbol{F}$ is the total external force acting on all the particles.

EXAMPLE 12.15

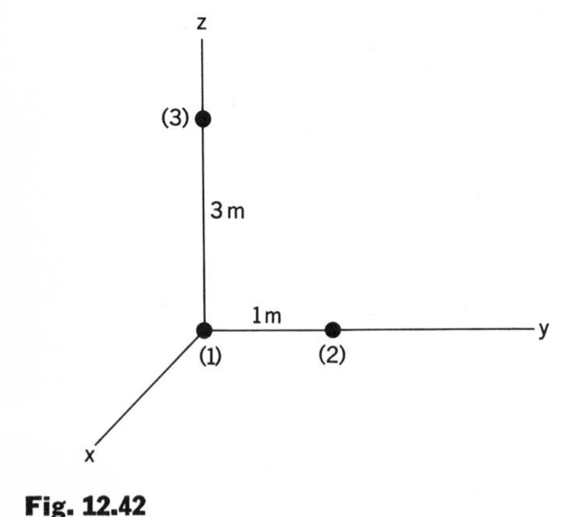

Fig. 12.42

In Fig. 12.42 we have shown three charged particles. Particle (1) has a mass of 10^{-5} kg and a charge of 4×10^{-5} coulomb and is at the instant of interest at the origin. Particles (2) and (3) each have a mass of 2×10^{-5} kg and a charge of 5×10^{-5} coulombs and are respectively located at the instant of interest 1 meter along the y axis and 3 meters along the z axis. An electric field given as:

$$\boldsymbol{E} = 2x\boldsymbol{i} + 3z\boldsymbol{j} + 3(y + z^2)\boldsymbol{k} \text{ newton/coulomb} \qquad \textbf{(a)}$$

is imposed from the outside. Compute the following items: (1) the center of mass for the system, (2) the acceleration of the center of mass, (3) the acceleration of particle (1).

To get the center of mass we merely equate moments of the masses about the origin with that of a particle having a mass equal to the sum of masses of the system. Thus:

$$(1+2+2)\times 10^{-5}\boldsymbol{r}_c = (2\times 10^{-5})\boldsymbol{j} + (2\times 10^{-5})3\boldsymbol{k}$$

$$\therefore\ \boldsymbol{r}_c = 0.4\boldsymbol{j} + 1.2\boldsymbol{k} \text{ meters} \qquad \textbf{(b)}$$

To get the acceleration of the mass center we must find the sum of the forces acting on the particles. We can consider that three forces act on each particle. They are the force of gravity, the electrostatic force from the external field, and finally the mutual electrostatic forces developed from the charges themselves (i.e., the internal electrostatic field). However, since we will be adding these forces, we will have a zero net contribution from the charges themselves due to Newton's third law, and accordingly we need not now consider them. Hence, the total external force for each particle is given as follows:*

$$\boldsymbol{F}_1 = -(9.8)(10^{-5})\boldsymbol{k} + \boldsymbol{0} \text{ newton} \qquad \textbf{(c)}$$

$$\boldsymbol{F}_2 = -(9.8)(2\times 10^{-5})\boldsymbol{k} + (5\times 10^{-5})(3\boldsymbol{k}) \qquad \textbf{(d)}$$

$$\boldsymbol{F}_3 = -(9.8)(2\times 10^{-5})\boldsymbol{k} + (5\times 10^{-5})(9\boldsymbol{j} + 27\boldsymbol{k}) \qquad \textbf{(e)}$$

The sum of these forces $\boldsymbol{F}_T$ is:

$$\boldsymbol{F}_T = 45\times 10^{-5}\boldsymbol{j} + 101\times 10^{-5}\boldsymbol{k} \text{ newton} \qquad \textbf{(f)}$$

Accordingly, we have for $\ddot{\boldsymbol{r}}_c$

$$\ddot{\boldsymbol{r}}_c = \frac{45\times 10^{-5}\boldsymbol{j} + 101\times 10^{-5}\boldsymbol{k}}{5\times 10^{-5}}$$

$$= 9\boldsymbol{j} + 20.2\boldsymbol{k} \text{ meter/sec}^2 \qquad \textbf{(g)}$$

Finally, to get the acceleration of particle (1) we must include the internal coulombic forces from particles (2) and (3). The total internal coulombic force $\boldsymbol{F}_C$ is:

$$\boldsymbol{F}_C = -\frac{(4\times 10^{-5})(5\times 10^{-5})}{(4\pi\epsilon_0)(1^2)}\boldsymbol{j} - \frac{(4\times 10^{-5})(5\times 10^{-5})}{4\pi\epsilon_0(3^2)}\boldsymbol{k}$$

Using the value for ϵ_0 given below Eq. 12.104, we get:

$$\boldsymbol{F}_C = -18\boldsymbol{j} - 2\boldsymbol{k} \text{ newtons} \qquad \textbf{(h)}$$

The total force acting on particle (1) is then:

$$(\boldsymbol{F}_1)_T = \underbrace{-(9.8)(10^{-5})\boldsymbol{k}}_{\text{from weight}} + \underbrace{\boldsymbol{0}}_{\text{from external field}} + \underbrace{(-18\boldsymbol{j} - 2\boldsymbol{k})}_{\text{from internal field}} \text{ newton} \qquad \textbf{(i)}$$

Clearly, the internal field dominates here.

Newton's law then gives us:

$$\ddot{\boldsymbol{r}}_1 = \frac{-18\boldsymbol{j} - 2\boldsymbol{k}}{10^{-5}}$$

$$= -18\times 10^5\boldsymbol{j} - 2\times 10^5\boldsymbol{k} \text{ meter/sec}^2 \qquad \textbf{(j)}$$

---

* Recall that the acceleration of gravity is 9.8 meter/sec.²

We see here from Eqs. (g) and (j) that while the particles tend to "scramble" away from each other due to very strong internal coulombic forces, the center of mass accelerates slowly by comparison.

12.19 Closure

In Parts A and B we integrated Newton's law for rectilinear translation and central-force motion, respectively, and in Part C we integrated Newton's law for certain problems of interest that have a more general motion. Also, with the aid of the mass center, we formulated Newton's law for any aggregate of particles. In the next two chapters, we shall present alternate procedures for treating more efficiently certain classes of dynamics problems for particles. You will note that since the new concepts are all derived from Newton's law, whatever can be solved by these new methods could also be solved by the methods we have already presented. A separate and thorough study of these topics is warranted by the gain in insight into dynamics and the greater facility in solving problems that can be achieved by examining these alternate methods and their accompanying concepts. As in this chapter, we will make certain generalizations applicable to any aggregate of particles. Although the conclusions we will reach will have limited use at present, they will form the basis for the dynamical analysis of rigid bodies in Chapters 17 through 19 and thus their importance should not be underestimated.

PROBLEMS

1. [12.2] A block is permitted to slide down an inclined surface (Fig. 12.43). The coefficient of friction is 0.05. If the velocity of the block is 30 ft/sec on reaching the bottom of the incline, how far up was it released and how many seconds has it traveled?

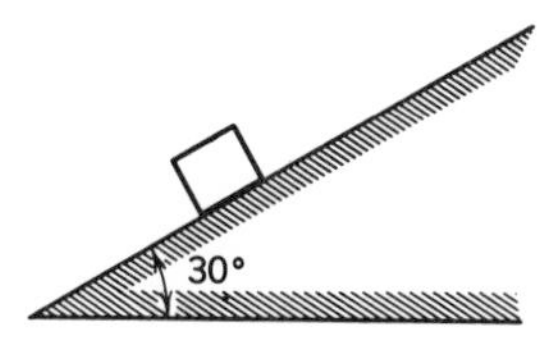

Fig. 12.43

2. [12.2] A body is thrown upward with an initial velocity of 80 ft/sec. How high up does it go and how long does it take to reach the maximum elevation if we neglect friction?

3. [12.2] A drag racer, shown in Fig. 12.44, can develop a torque of 400 ft-lb on the rear wheels. If we assume that this maximum torque is maintained and that there is no wind friction, what is the time for the first quarter mile from a standing start? What is the speed of the vehicle at the quarter-mile mark? The weight of the racer and the driver altogether is 1600 lb. Neglect the rotational effects of the wheels.

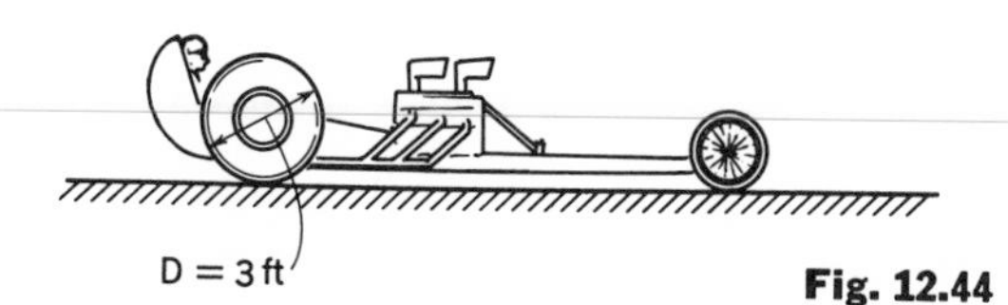

Fig. 12.44

4. [12.2] A mass of 5 lbm (see Fig. 12.45) at $t = 0$ is moving to the left at a speed of 2 ft/sec relative to the ground on a belt which is moving at constant speed to the right at 5 ft/sec. If there is coulomb friction present with $\mu_d = 0.3$, how long does it take before the relative speed between body and belt is 1 ft/sec?

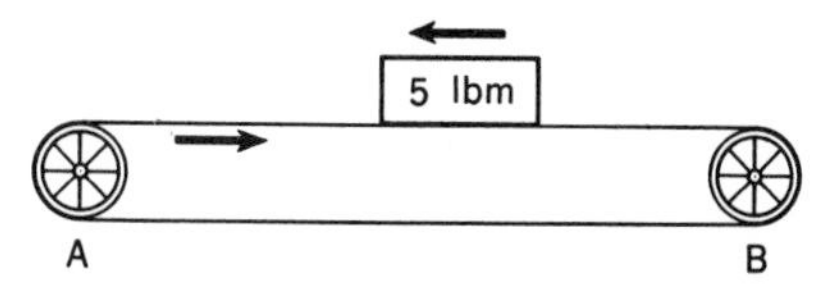

Fig. 12.45

5. [12.2] Do Prob. 4 with the belt system inclined 15° with the horizontal so that end B is above end A.

6. [12.2] A particle of mass 1 slug is moving in a constant force field given as:

$$\boldsymbol{F} = 3\boldsymbol{i} + 10\boldsymbol{j} - 5\boldsymbol{k} \text{ lb}$$

The particle starts from rest at position (3, 5, −4). What is the position and velocity of the particle at time $t = 8$? What is the position when the particle is moving at a speed of 20 ft/sec?

7. [12.2] A particle is moving in a constant force field given as:

$$\boldsymbol{F} = 2m\boldsymbol{i} - 12m\boldsymbol{j}$$

Give the equations for the trajectory of the particle if, at time $t = 0$, it has a velocity $\boldsymbol{V}_0$ given as:

$$\boldsymbol{V}_0 = 6\boldsymbol{i} + 12\boldsymbol{j} + 3\boldsymbol{k} \text{ ft/sec}$$

Also at time $t = 0$ it has a position given as:

$$\boldsymbol{r}_0 = 3\boldsymbol{i} + 2\boldsymbol{j} + 4\boldsymbol{k} \text{ ft}$$

What are coordinates of the body at the instant that the body reaches its maximum height, y_{max}?

8. [12.2] A piston is being moved through a cylinder (see Fig. 12.46). The piston is moved

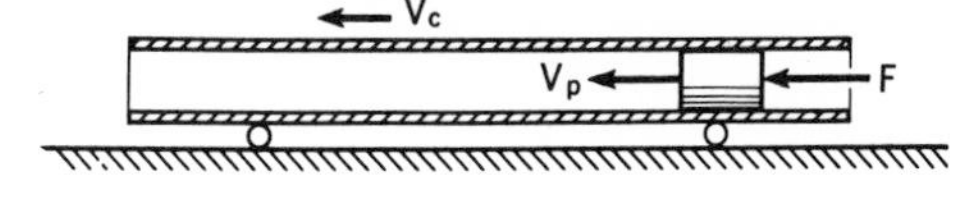

Fig. 12.46

at a constant speed V_p of 2 ft/sec relative to the ground by a force F. The cylinder is free to move along the ground on small wheels. There is a coulomb friction force between the piston and the cylinder such that $\mu_d = 0.3$. What distance must the piston move relative to the ground to advance 0.1 ft along the cylinder if the cylinder is stationary at the outset? The piston weighs 5 lb and the cylinder weighs 10 lb.

9. [12.2] Do the previous problem for the case where the cylinder is initially moving to the left with a speed of 1 ft/sec.

10. [12.3] A force represented as shown in Fig. 12.47 acts on a body having a mass of 1 slug. What is the position and velocity at $t = 30$ sec if the body starts from rest at $t = 0$?

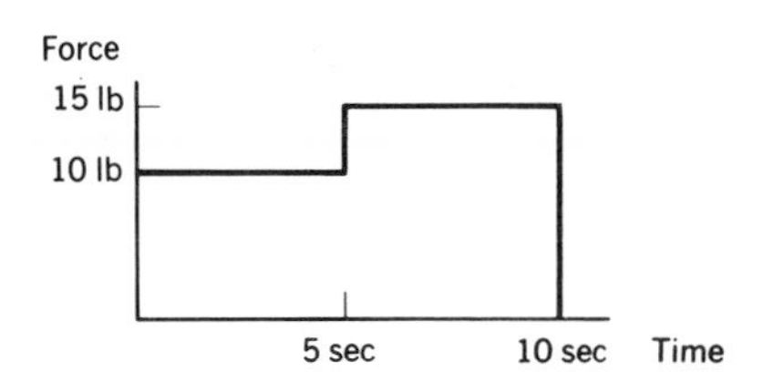

Fig. 12.47

11. [12.3] A body having a mass of 30 lbm is acted on by a force given by the following equation:

$$F = 30t^2 + e^{-t} \text{ lb}$$

If the velocity is 10 ft/sec at $t = 0$, what is its velocity and distance traveled when $t = 2$ sec?

12. [12.3] A body of weight 20 lb is acted on by a force in the x direction, given by the relation $F = 20 \sin 6t$ lb. If the body has a velocity of 10 ft/sec when $t = 0$ and is at position $x = 0$ at that instant, what is the distance reached by the body from the origin at $t = 10$ sec? Sketch the displacement-versus-time curve.

13. [12.3] A body of mass 1 slug is acted on by a force given by the plot in Fig. 12.48. If the velocity of the body is zero at $t = 0$, what is the velocity and distance traversed when $t = 3$ minutes?

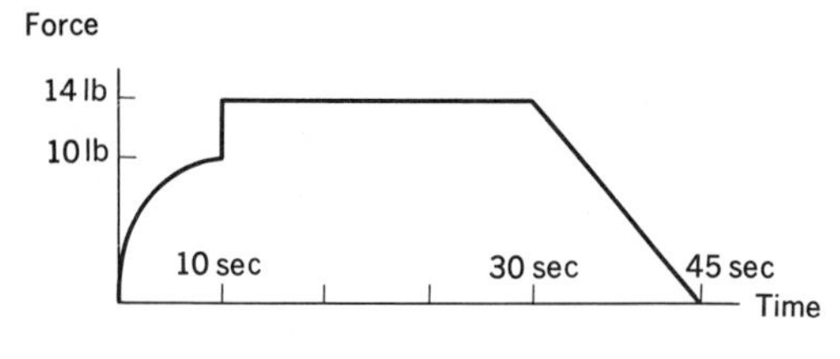

Fig. 12.48

14. [12.3] A force given as $5 \sin 3t$ acts on a mass of 1 slug. What is the position of the mass at $t = 10$ sec? Determine the total distance traveled. Assume the motion started from rest.

15. [12.3] A force given as $10 \sinh 2t + \ln 5t$ lb is applied to a mass of 10 lb. What is the position of the mass at $t = 2$ sec? Take $x = 0$ and $V = 0$ when $t = \frac{1}{5}$ sec.

16. [12.4] The aerodynamic drag on a body is $0.08V^2$ lb. If the initial speed is 100 mph, how far will the body move before its speed is reduced to 20 mph? The mass of the body is 50 lbm.

17. [12.4] A block shown in Fig. 12.49 slides on a film of oil. The resistance to motion of the block is proportional to the speed of the block relative to the incline at the rate of 0.50 lb/ft/sec. If the block is released from rest, what is the *terminal speed*? Show that it takes an infinite amount of time to reach this speed.

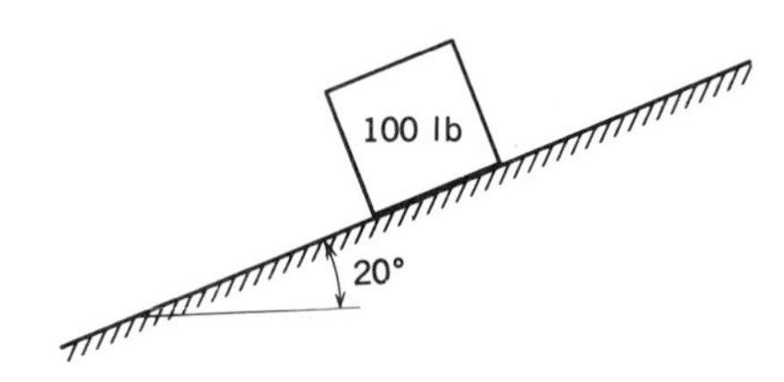

Fig. 12.49

18. [12.4] Using Fig. 12.45, assume that there is a lubricant between the body of mass 5 lbm and the belt such that there is a viscous friction force given as 0.1 lb per unit relative velocity between the body and the belt. The belt moves at a uniform speed of 5 ft/sec to the right and initially the body has a speed to the left of 2 ft/sec relative to ground. At what time later does the body have a zero instantaneous velocity relative to the ground?

19. [12.4] In the previous problem assume that the belt system is inclined 20° from the horizontal with end B above end A. What minimum belt speed is required so that a body of mass M moving downward will come to a permanent halt relative to the ground? Using this belt speed, how long does it take for the body to slow down to half its initial speed relative to the ground?

20. [12.4] Do Prob. 8 for the case where there is viscous friction between piston and cylinder given as 5 lb/ft/sec of relative speed.

21. [12.4] A particle is subject to the following force field:

$$\boldsymbol{F} = m\boldsymbol{i} + 4m\boldsymbol{j} + 16m\boldsymbol{k} \text{ lb}$$

In addition, it undergoes a frictional force $\boldsymbol{f}$ given as:

$$\boldsymbol{f} = -m\dot{x}\boldsymbol{i} - m\dot{y}\boldsymbol{j} + 2m\dot{z}\boldsymbol{k} \text{ lb}$$

The particle is stationary at the origin at time $t = 0$. What is the position and velocity of the particle at time $t = 1$ sec?

22. [12.5] Consider a spring-mass system (see Fig. 12.4). If the spring constant is 10 lb/inch and the mass is 5 lbm, what maximum displacement will the mass reach if given an initial instantaneous speed of 5 ft/sec? Neglect friction and take the initial position of the mass to correspond to the position of the unstretched spring.

23. [12.5] In Fig. 12.4, the spring is nonlinear. That is, K is not a constant, but is a function of the extension of the spring. If $K = (x + 3)$ lb/in., what is the speed of the mass when $x = 0$ after it is released from a state of rest at a position 3 in. from the equilibrium position? The mass of the body is 1 slug.

24. [12.5] A block of wood having a specific weight of $S = 0.5$ floats at the free surface of water as shown in Fig. 12.50. The block is depressed 0.2 ft from its flotation position and then released. If we neglect friction and the dynamic effects of the water, what speed will the block have when it comes back to its original flotation position?

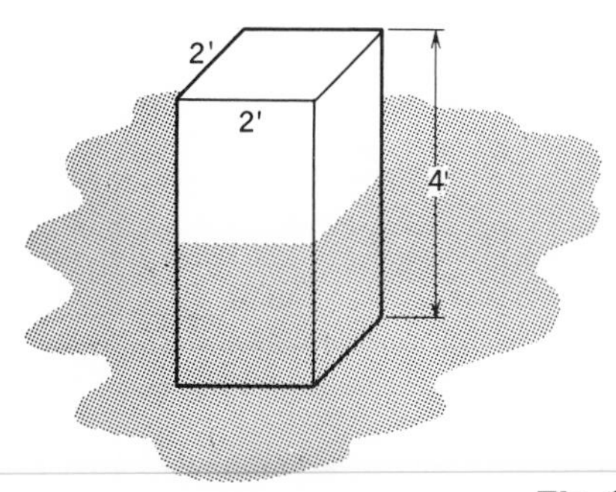

Fig. 12.50

25. [12.5] Do Prob. 24 for the case where the block is metal having a specific weight S of 6 and is in flotation at the interface between mercury and water.

26. [12.5] Shown in Fig. 12.51 is a simply supported beam. You will learn in strength of materials that a vertical force F applied at the center causes a deflection δ at the center given as:

$$\delta = \frac{1}{48}\frac{FL^3}{EI}$$

If a mass of 10 lbm, fastened to the beam at its midpoint, is depressed from the equilibrium position a distance of 0.3 inch and then released, what will its speed be in 1 second? Neglect the mass of the beam. The length of beam L is 20 ft, Young's modulus E is 30×10^6 psi, and the moment of inertia of the cross section I is 20 in.^{4}

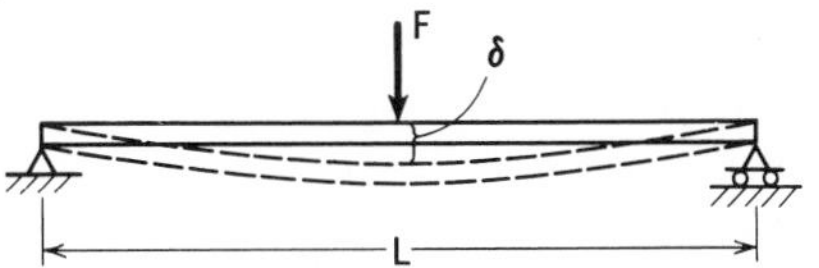

Fig. 12.51

27. [12.5] Shown in Fig. 12.52 is a pendulum of length l with a bob of weight W. If the pendulum swings so that the angle θ is very small, the bob can be considered moving essentially in the x direction. What is the restoring force on the bob per unit angle θ? Neglect the weight of the rod. If the bob is released from a position of 10°, what will be the maximum angular speed $\dot{\theta}$? Take $l = 3$ ft and $W = 2$ lb.

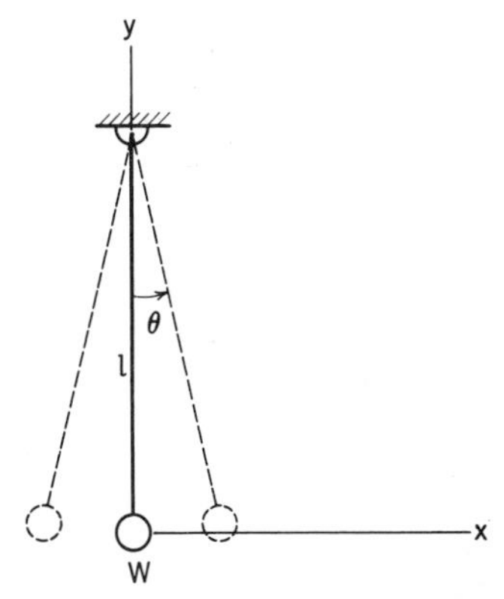

Fig. 12.52

28. [12.5] A mass of 100 lbm is supported by two identical linear springs having a spring constant K of 50 lb/in (Fig. 12.53). What is the total extension of each spring? What is the spring constant of a single equivalent spring to take place of the pair of springs? If the body is

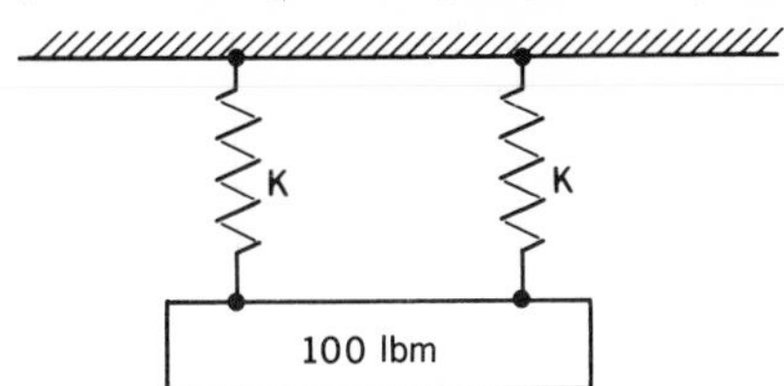

Fig. 12.53

given an instantaneous speed (as a result of an impact) of 5 ft/sec upward at its equilibrium position, what is the maximum height that it rises from the equilibrium position? At what time after the impact does the body reach its maximum height?

29. [12.5] A body having a weight of 100 lb is supported by two dissimilar linear springs having spring constants $K_1 = 5$ lb/in and $K_2 = 10$ lb/in., respectively (Fig. 12.54). What distance does point A move when the 100-lb weight is slowly applied? What is the spring constant of one single equivalent spring to replace the two dissimilar springs? If the 100-lb weight is released 1 in. above its equilibrium position, what is the position of the body after 3 seconds as measured from its equilibrium position?

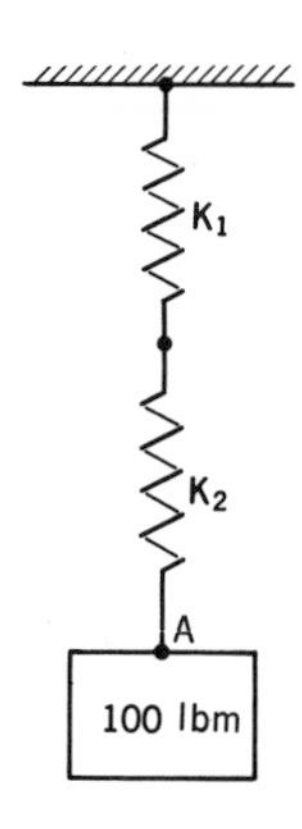

Fig. 12.54

30. [12.5] Show that rectilinear motion involving the combination of a linear restoring force $-Kx$ and a constant force P can be solved by the method of separation of variables.

31. [12.5] For $m = 1$ slug and $K = 10$ lb/in., what is the motion if a force of 5 lb is applied suddenly to the spring-mass system of Fig. 12.4 and then maintained constant? What is the maximum deflection of the spring?

32. [12.5] A 100-lb weight is shown in Fig. 12.55 supported in such a position that the four springs are neither stretched nor compressed. If the body is released slowly, how far will it go down if $K_1 = 10$ lb/in., $K_2 = K_3 = 5$ lb/in., and $K_4 = 20$ lb/in.? What is the spring constant of a single equivalent spring to replace the four springs shown? What is the distance that the weight will drop if it is released suddenly?

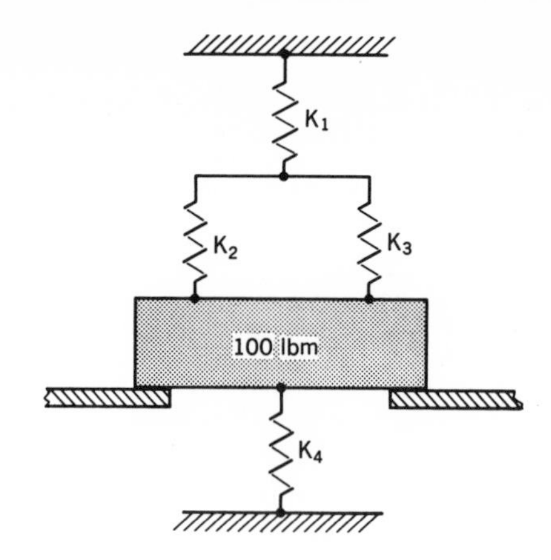

Fig. 12.55

33. [12.5] Shown in Fig. 12.56 is a piston maintaining air at a pressure of 8 psi above that of the atmosphere. If the piston is allowed to accelerate to the left, what is the speed of the piston after it moves 3 inches? The piston assembly has a mass of 3 lbm. Assume that the air expands *adiabatically* (i.e., with no heat transfer). This means that at all times $pV^k =$ const., where V is the volume of the gas and k is a constant which for air equals 1.4. Neglect the inertial effects of gases.

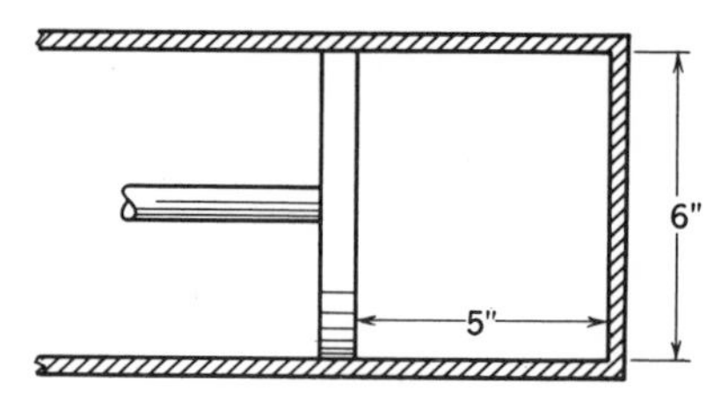

Fig. 12.56

34. [12.5] In Example 12.5 assume that there are adiabatic expansions and compressions of the gases, i.e., that $pv^k =$ const. when $k = 1.4$. Compare the results for speed of the piston. Explain why your result should be higher or lower than for the isothermal case.

35. [12.5] In Example 12.5 find the position at which the maximum speed is reached. What is the value of this speed?

36. [12.5] A particle is subject to the following force field:

$$\boldsymbol{F} = m\boldsymbol{i} - my\boldsymbol{j} + 4mz\boldsymbol{k} \text{ lb}$$

The particle is stationary at the origin at time $t = 0$. When $t = 10$ sec what are the coordinates for the body?

37. [12.8] Body A and body B are connected by an inextensible cord as shown in Fig. 12.57. If both bodies are released simultaneously, what distance do they move in 3 sec? Take $W_A = 50$ lb and $W_B = 10$ lb. Neglect friction. Do two ways.

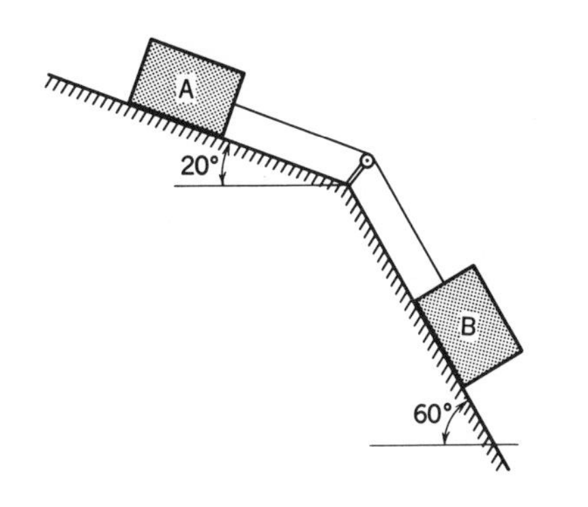

Fig. 12.57

38. [12.8] The system shown in Fig. 12.58 is released from rest. What distance does the body C drop in 2 sec? The cable is inextensible. The coefficient of dynamic friction μ_d is 0.4 for contact surfaces of bodies A and B. Do two ways.

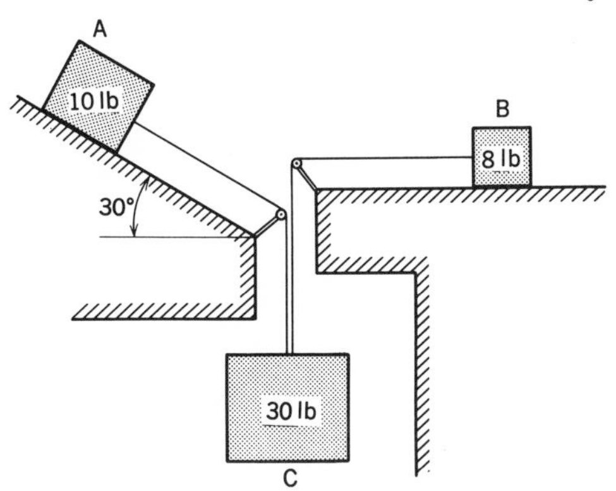

Fig. 12.58

39. [12.8] Do the previous problem for the case where there is viscous damping for the contact surfaces of bodies A and B given as $0.5V$ lb.

40. [12.8] In Fig. 12.59 are shown two bodies A and B having masses of 50 lbm and 30 lbm respectively. The cables are inextensible. Neglecting the inertia of the cable and pulleys at C and D, what is the speed of the block B 1 sec after the system has been released from rest? The coefficient friction for the contact surface of body A is 0.3. Hint: From your earlier work in physics recall that pulley D is instantaneously rotating about point a and hence point c moves at a speed that is twice that of point b.

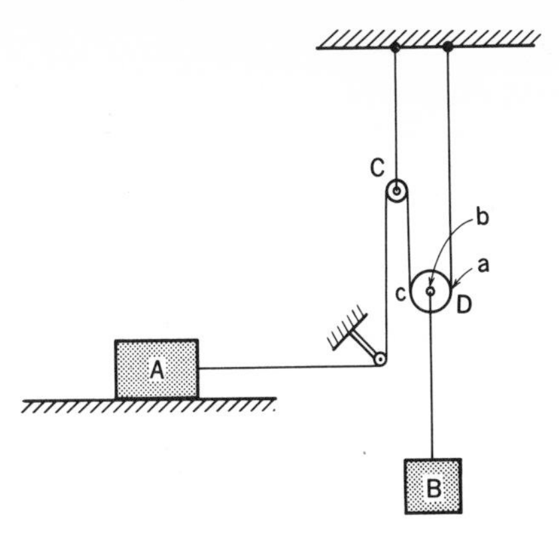

Fig. 12.59

41. [12.8] Do the preceding problem for the case where there is a viscous friction for the contact surface of body A given as $0.4V$ lb.

42. [12.10] A body having a mass of 1000 lbm has, at time t, a position vector $\boldsymbol{r}$ relative to an inertial reference XYZ such that:

$$\boldsymbol{r} = 5000\boldsymbol{i} + 8000\boldsymbol{j} + 2000\boldsymbol{k} \text{ miles}$$

If the body has velocity given as:

$$\boldsymbol{V} = 10{,}000\boldsymbol{i} + 16{,}000\boldsymbol{j} + 2000\boldsymbol{k}$$

miles/hour relative to XYZ

and the total force acting on the body is directed toward the origin O of XYZ, what is the direction of the plane of the trajectory of motion? What is the moment of momentum of this motion?

43. [12.10] A particle moves under gravitational influence about a body M, the center of which may be taken as the origin of an inertial reference (Fig. 12.60). The mass of the particle is 50 slugs. At time t, it is at a position 4500 miles from the center of M with direction cosines $l = 0.5$, $m = -0.5$, $n = 0.707$. The body is moving at a speed of 17,000 miles per hour along the direction $\boldsymbol{\epsilon}_t = 0.8\boldsymbol{i} + 0.2\boldsymbol{j} + 0.566\boldsymbol{k}$. What is the direction of the normal to the plane of the trajectory?

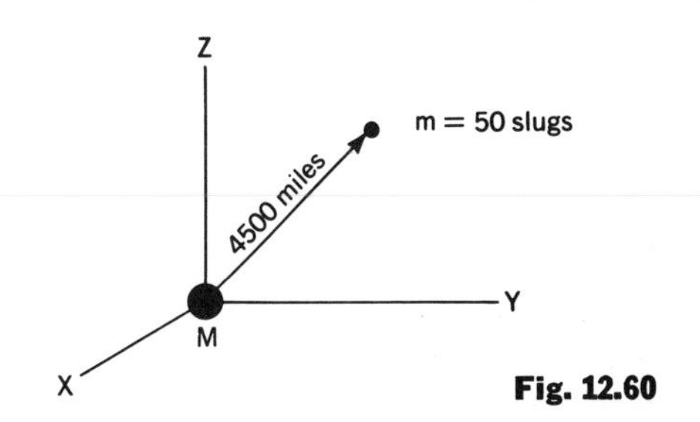

Fig. 12.60

44. [12.10] If the position of the particle in the above problem should reach a distance of 4300 miles from the center of body M when the direction cosines of the position vector are $l = 0.762$, $m = 0.0$, $n = 0.647$, what should the transverse velocity V_ϕ of the particle be?

45. [12.10] A satellite has at one time during its flight around the earth a radial component of velocity of 2000 mi/hr and a transverse component of 16,000 mi/hr. If the satellite is at a distance of 4400 miles from the center of the earth, what is its areal velocity?

46. [12.13] In prob. 45, express the equations of motion of the particle in terms of polar coordinates measured from an xy reference where x corresponds to the direction of r when the particle has the velocity and position as given in the problem.

47. [12.13] According to experiment, the universal constant G is:

$$G = 6.66 \times 10^{-8} \text{ cm}^3 \text{ sec}^{-2} \text{ gm}^{-1}$$

Determine the mass of the earth, using $GM = 14.3 \times 10^{15}$ ft^3/sec. Express the change in the eccentricity occurring when the mass of the space vehicle is included in accordance with the two-body problem. Is there an increase or decrease in the eccentricity as a result in this refinement?

48. [12.13] Using Eqs. 12.59(b) and 12.64, show that if the eccentricity is zero the trajectory must be that of a circle.

49. [12.13] A satellite is launched and attains a velocity of 19,000 miles an hour relative to the center of the earth at a distance of 200 miles from the earth's surface. It has been guided into a path that is parallel to the earth's surface at burnout.

(a) What kind of trajectory will it have?

(b) What is its longest distance from the earth's surface?

(c) If it is in orbit, compute the time it takes to go from the minimum point to the maximum point from the earth's surface.

(d) What would be the minimum escape velocity for this position of launching?

50. [12.13] The acceleration of gravity on the planet Mars is about 0.385 the acceleration of gravity on earth, and the radius of Mars is about 0.532 that of the earth. What is the escape velocity from Mars at a position 100 miles from the surface of the planet?

51. [12.13] Suppose you are in orbit around Mars with an eccentricity of 0.5 for your orbit. At the lowest point in the orbit, you are 200 miles from the surface of Mars.

(a) Compute the maximum velocity of the space vehicle relative to the center of Mars.

(b) Compute the time of one cycle.

(c) Compute the maximum distance from the surface of Mars.

Use data in preceding problem for Mars.

52. [12.13] Compute the escape velocity at a position 5000 miles from the center of the earth (Fig. 12.61). What speed is needed to maintain a circular orbit at that distance from the earth's center? Derive the formula for the speed needed for a circular orbit directly from Newton's law without using information about eccentricities, etc.

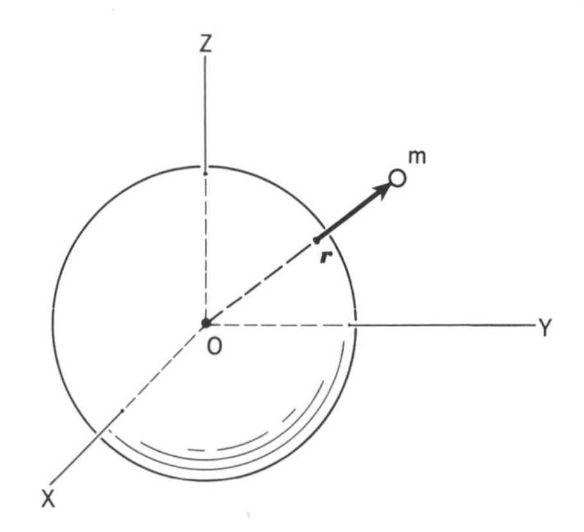

Fig. 12.61

53. [12.13] A man is in orbit around the earth in a space vehicle. At his lowest position, he is moving with a speed of 18,500 miles an hour at an altitude of 200 miles. Since he wants to come back to earth, at his lowest position he fires a retro-rocket straight ahead which slows him up. If he wishes to get within 50 miles from the earth's surface during the first cycle after firing his retro-rocket, what must his decrease in velocity be? How long will it take him to get from the 200-mile altitude to the 50-mile altitude? (Neglect air resistance.)

54. [12.13] A space vehicle is in a circular "parking" orbit around the planet Venus, 200 miles above the surface of this planet. The radius of Venus is 3850 miles and the escape velocity at the surface is given in handbooks as 1.026×10^4 meters per second. A retro-rocket is fired to slow the vehicle so that it will come within 20 miles of the planet. If we consider that the rocket changes the speed of the vehicle over a comparatively short distance of its travel, what is this change of speed? What is the speed of the vehicle at its closest position to the surface of Venus?

55. [12.13] In the previous problem the space vehicle is to change from a circular parking orbit 200 miles above the surface of Venus to one which is 1000 miles above this surface. This will be accomplished by two firings of the rocket system of the vehicle. The first firing causes the vehicle to attain an apogee which is 1000 miles above the surface of Venus. At this apogee a second firing is accomplished so as to achieve the desired circular orbit. What is the change in speed demanded for each firing if the thrust is maintained in each instance over a small portion of the trajectory of the vehicle? Neglect friction.

56. [12.13] A space vehicle approaches the planet Jupiter with a trajectory having an eccentricity of 3. The vehicle comes to within 1000 miles of the surface of Jupiter. What is the speed of the vehicle at this instant? The acceleration of gravity of Jupiter is 90.79 ft/sec^2 at the surface and the radius is 43,400 miles.

57. [12.13] In the preceding problem what change in speed is needed to get the vehicle into a circular parking orbit 1000 miles above the surface of the planet if the retro-rockets are fired when the vehicle is closest to the planet? Next, what change in speed is needed to go from this parking orbit into a trajectory that will just "touch" the planet?

58. [12.13] If the moon has a motion about the earth that has an eccentricity of 0.0549 and a period of 27.3 days, what is the closest distance of the moon to the earth in its trajectory?

59. [12.13] The satellite Hyperion about the planet Saturn has a motion with an eccentricity known to be 0.1043. At its closest distance from Saturn it is 921×10^3 miles from center to center. What is the period of Hyperion about Saturn? The acceleration of gravity of Saturn is 41.8 ft/sec^2 at its surface. The radius of Saturn is 35,700 miles.

60. [12.13] A space vehicle is launched at a speed of 19,000 miles per hour relative to the earth's center at a position 250 miles above the earth's surface. If the vehicle has a radial velocity component of 3000 miles per hour, what is the eccentricity of the trajectory? What is the maximum elevation above the earth's surface reached by the vehicle?

61. [12.13] A rocket system is capable of giving a satellite a velocity of 22,000 miles an hour relative to the earth's surface at an elevation of 200 miles above the earth's surface. What would be its maximum distance from the earth if it were launched (1) from the north pole region or (2) from the equator, utilizing the spin of the earth as an aid? Assume both launchings are from perigee.

62. [12.13] Suppose you are on a planet having no atmosphere (see Fig. 12.62). This planet rotates once every six hours about its axis relative to an inertial reference XYZ at its center. The planet has a radius of 1000 miles and the acceleration of gravity at the surface is 20 ft/sec^2. A bullet is fired by a man at the equator in a direction normal to the surface of the planet as seen by this man. The muzzle velocity of the gun is 5000 ft/sec. What is the eccentricity of the trajectory and the maximum height of the bullet above the surface of the planet?

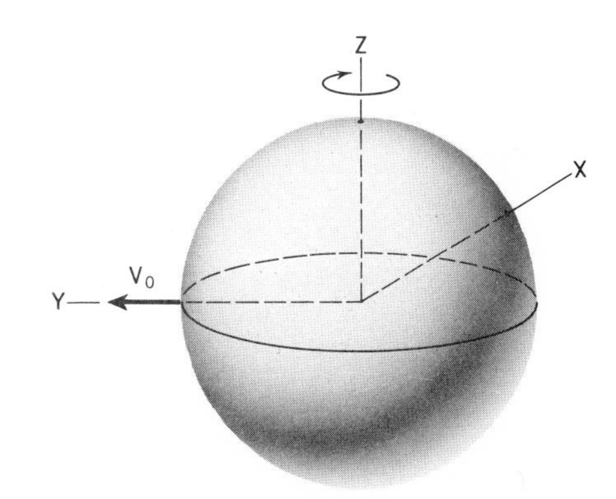

Fig. 12.62

63. [12.13] A meteor is moving at a speed of 20,000 miles an hour relative to the center of the earth when it is 350 miles from the surface of the earth. At that time, it has a radial velocity component of 4000 miles/hr. How close does it come to the earth's surface?

64. [12.13] The moon's radius is about 0.272 that of the earth, and its acceleration of gravity at the surface is 0.165 that of the earth at the earth's surface. A rocket approaches the moon with a velocity component toward the center of the moon of 2000 miles an hour and a transverse component of 5000 miles an hour relative to the center of the moon. The rocket is 2000 miles from the center of the moon when it has these velocity components. Will the rocket go into orbit around the moon if we consider only the gravitational effect of the moon on the rocket? If it goes into orbit, how close will it come to the surface of the moon? If not, does it collide with the moon?

65. [12.13] Shown in Fig. 12.63 are two satellite stations each in a circular orbit around the earth. A small vehicle is shot out of the station at A tangential to the trajectory, to "hit" station B which is shown 50° away at the time of firing. The collision is to occur 15 minutes after firing. What is the velocity of the vehicle relative to station A when it leaves?

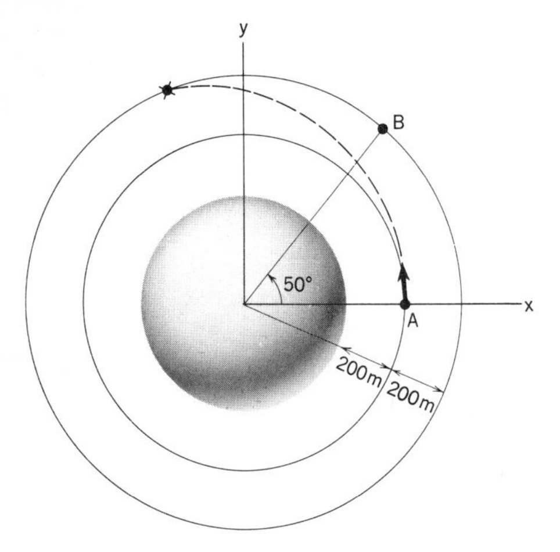

Fig. 12.63

66. [12.13] In the previous problem determine the velocity of the vehicle as it arrives at B as seen by an observer in the satellite from B.

67. [12.13] Shown in Fig. 12.64 is a satellite launching at A. We wish to determine the time required, Δt, to get to position B. Show that for this calculation we can employ the formulation:

$$\Delta t = \frac{1}{C} \int_{\phi_0}^{\phi_B} r^2 \, d\phi$$

For integration purposes show that the above formulation becomes

$$\Delta t = \frac{1}{C} \int_{\phi_0}^{\phi_B} \frac{d\phi}{\left(\frac{GM}{C^2} + D \cos \phi\right)^2}$$

Carry out the integration.

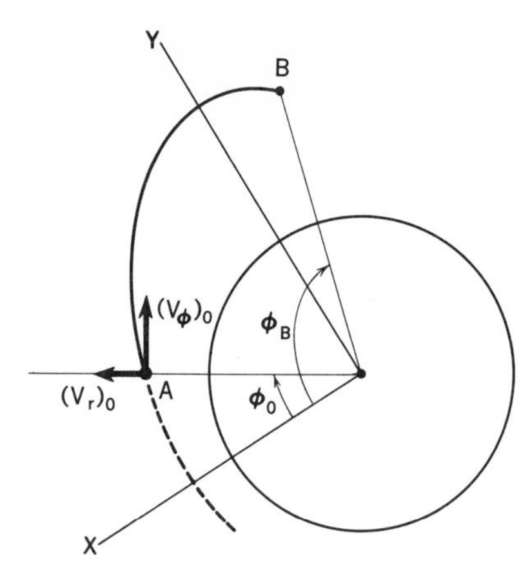

Fig. 12.64

68. [12.13] A satellite is launched at a speed of 20,000 miles per hour relative to the earth's center, at an altitude of 300 miles above the earth's surface. The guidance system has malfunctioned, and the satellite has a direction 20° up from the tangent plane to the earth's surface. Will it go into orbit? Give the time required for one cycle if it goes into orbit or the time it takes before it strikes the earth after firing. Neglect friction in either case. (See Prob. 67 before doing.)

***69.** [12.13] In Prob. 62 compute the distance from the man, standing stationary relative to the planet, to the position of impact of the bullet with the planet. (See Prob. 67 before doing.)

70. [12.15] A bundle of mail falls out of an airplane flying horizontally with speed V_0 at a height h above the ground. How far (measuring in a horizontal direction) from where it was dropped will it hit the earth, and how long will it take?

71. [12.15] A shell is fired from a hill 500 ft above a plain. The angle of firing is 15° above the horizontal, and the muzzle velocity is 3000 ft/sec. At what horizontal distance will it hit the plain? (Neglect friction.)

72. [12.15] A sportsman in a valley is trying to shoot a deer on a hill. He quickly estimates the distance of the deer along his line of sight as 500 yards, and the height of the hill as 100 yards. His gun has a muzzle velocity of 3000 ft/sec. If he has no graduated sight, how many feet above the deer should he aim his rifle in order to hit it? (Neglect friction.)

73. [12.15] A body is moving with constant speed of 20 ft/sec along a horizontal circular path as shown in Fig. 12.65. The radius of the path is 100 ft. If an arrow is shot with a speed of 60 ft/sec. from position A, as shown in the diagram, what angle α_0 is required to strike the body which, at the time of shooting, is at position B? Do not consider friction.

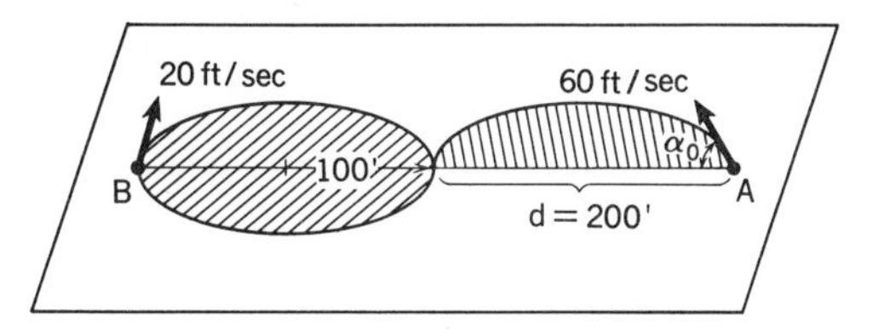

Fig. 12.65

74. [12.15] Do the previous problem for the case where the body has an increase of speed of 2 ft/sec starting from position B.

75. [12.15] A projectile is fired at a speed of 3000 ft/sec at an angle of 40° measured from an inclined surface which is at an angle of 20° from the horizontal. (See Fig. 12.66). If we neglect friction, at what distance along the incline does the projectile hit the incline?

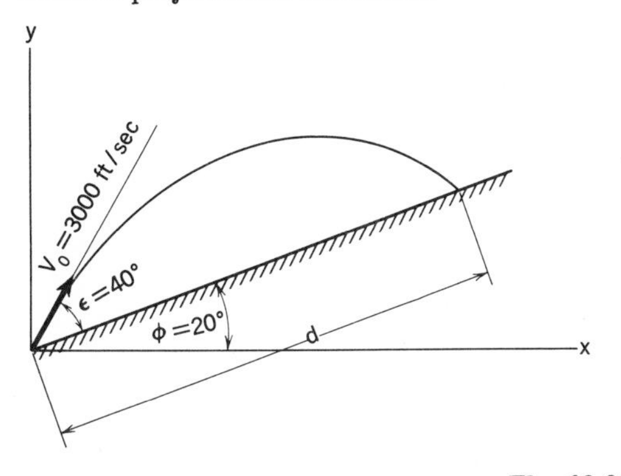

Fig. 12.66

76. [12.15] A projectile is fired at an angle of 60° as shown in Fig. 12.67. At what elevation y does it strike the hill whose equation has been estimated as $y = 10^{-8}x^2$? Neglect friction and take the muzzle velocity as 3000 ft/sec.

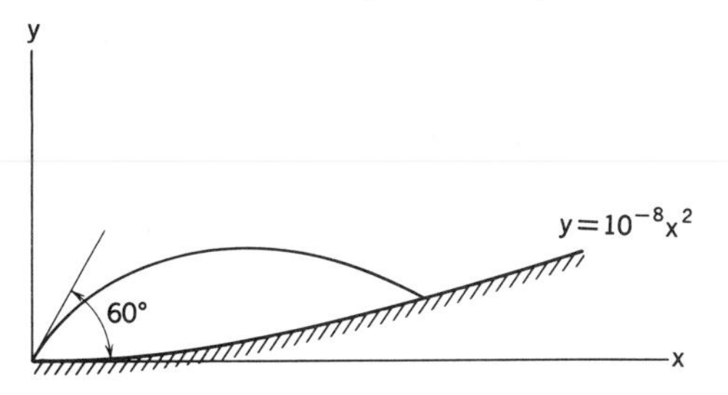

Fig. 12.67

77. [12.15] An archer is chasing a deer in a jeep. If the jeep moves at 30 mi/hr and the deer moves at 15 mi/hr along the same direction, at what inclination must the arrow be shot if the deer is 100 yards ahead of the jeep and the initial speed of the arrow is 200 ft/sec relative to archer? (Neglect friction.)

78. [12.15] Do the above problem if the jeep and deer are moving at right angles to each other. Give, in addition to the inclination of the arrow from the ground, the inclination of the arrow from the line AB in Fig. 12.68.

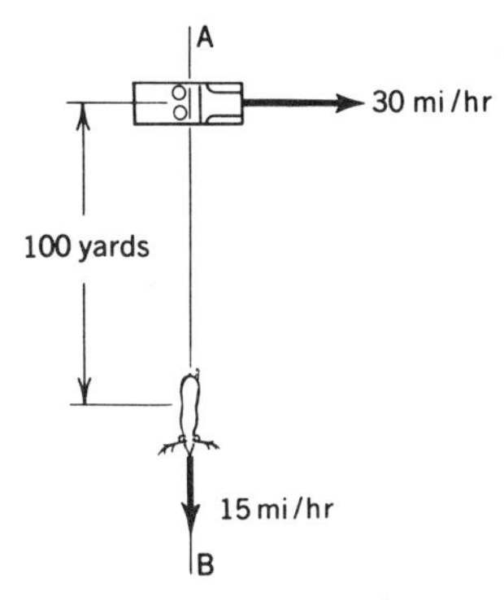

Fig. 12.68

79. [12.15] A projectile is shot at an angle of 45° with a speed of 1000 ft/sec as shown in Fig. 12.69. If the "gravitational force" for this body were given as $-my\boldsymbol{j}$ rather than $-mg\boldsymbol{j}$, what is the equation for the trajectory? What is the value of d for impact?

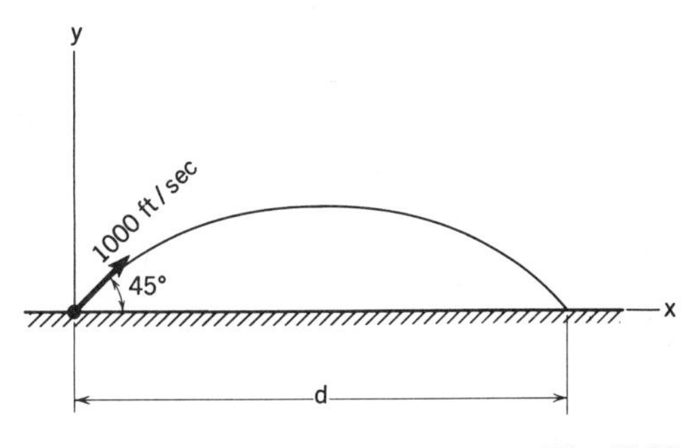

Fig. 12.69

80. [12.15] In Fig. 12.70, a mass is held by four springs. For small motions from the equilibrium position, the motion in the x direction does not affect springs K_1, while the motion in the y direction does not affect springs K_2. Write the differential equations of motion for the mass. Integrate the motion for initial conditions $x = x_0$, $y = y_0$, $\dot{x} = \dot{x}_0$, and $\dot{y} = \dot{y}_0$. If amplitudes in the x and y directions are the same and the spring constants are equal, what is the trajectory of the motion.

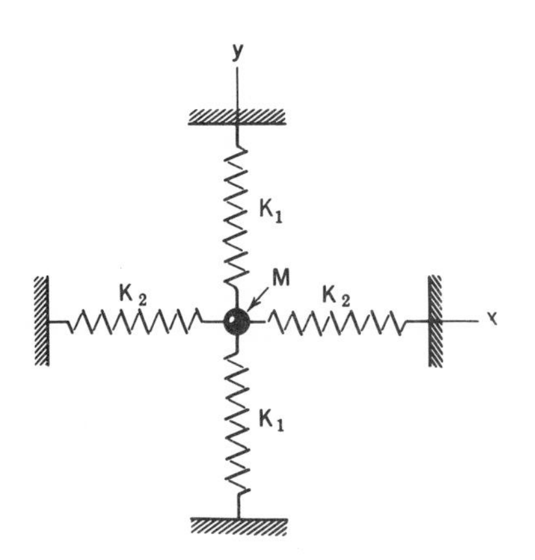

Fig. 12.70

81. [12.15] In the above problem, explain how you would initiate the following trajectories:

(a) A circle of radius r with M moving clockwise.
(b) A circle of radius r with M moving counterclockwise.
(c) A straight line inclined at 45° in the first and third quadrants.
(d) A straight line at 45° in the second and fourth quadrants.

Assume you can choose spring constants at will.

82. [12.15] In Prob. 79 the projectile is fired as described, but is now subject to the following constant force field:

$$\boldsymbol{F} = -5m\boldsymbol{i} - mg\boldsymbol{j} \text{ lb}$$

What is the distance d for this case? At what value of x does the projectile reach its maximum height?

***83.** [12.15] If a rifleman aims and fires at an inclination of 5° from the horizontal, what is the maximum elevation reached by the bullet and at what distance from the rifleman does it hit the ground, which is at the same elevation as the rifle? Take friction into account by assuming that the friction function, $H(V)$, is κV^2 where $\kappa = 10^{-4}$ lb sec²/ft² slug. The muzzle velocity is 2000 ft/sec. Use results from Example 12.14.

***84.** [12.15] We are to fire a projectile at a vertical cliff 5000 yards away (Fig. 12.71). What is the initial inclination of firing, α_0, and the elevation, y, at which the projectile strikes the cliff if we wish the projectile to enter the cliff at right angles to the surface? The muzzle velocity of the gun is 3000 ft/sec, and the friction function is 10^{-4} V^2 lb/slug. Use results from Example 12.14.

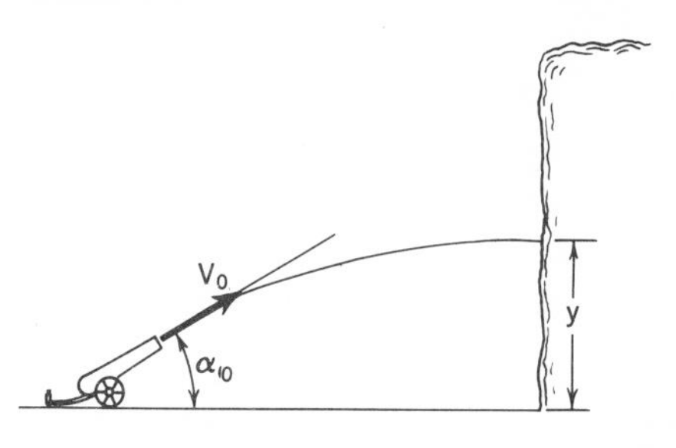

Fig. 12.71

***85.** [12.15] If the friction function is proportional to the velocity, i.e., κV, find an expression for the maximum elevation of a shell in terms of V_0, α_0, and κ for the case of a very shallow trajectory.

***86.** [12.15] We shall develop an analytical expression for the motion of a projectile with a frictional resistance equal to κV^2 tangent to the trajectory for the special case of a shallow trajectory (Fig. 12.72).

(a) Show that the differential equations of motion can be expressed as:

$$m\ddot{x} = -\kappa\dot{x}^2\left[1 + \left(\frac{\dot{y}}{\dot{x}}\right)^2\right]^{1/2} \tag{a}$$

$$m\ddot{y} = -\kappa\dot{x}\dot{y}\left[1 + \left(\frac{\dot{y}}{\dot{x}}\right)^2\right]^{1/2} - mg \tag{b}$$

(b) Assume we have a shallow trajectory so that we can neglect $(\dot{y}/\dot{x})^2$. Show that, with initial conditions $\dot{x} = \dot{x}_0$ when $t = 0$, Eq. (a) can be integrated to give:

$$\dot{x} = \frac{\dot{x}_0}{(\kappa\dot{x}_0/m)t + 1} \tag{c}$$

(c) Employing Eq. (c) in (b), find the complementary solution as:

$$\dot{y}_c = \frac{C}{t + (m/\kappa\dot{x}_0)} \tag{d}$$

where C is a constant of integration. Show that a particular solution is:

$$\dot{y}_p = -\frac{g}{2}\left(t + \frac{m}{\kappa\dot{x}_0}\right) \tag{e}$$

(d) Show that for $\dot{y} = \dot{y}_0$ when $t = 0$, the velocity $\dot{y}$ becomes:

$$\dot{y} = \frac{\dot{y}_0 + (mg/2\kappa\dot{x}_0)}{(\kappa\dot{x}_0/m)t + 1} - \frac{mg}{2\kappa\dot{x}_0}\left(\frac{\kappa\dot{x}_0}{m}t + 1\right) \quad \text{(f)}$$

(e) Determine x and y as functions of time.

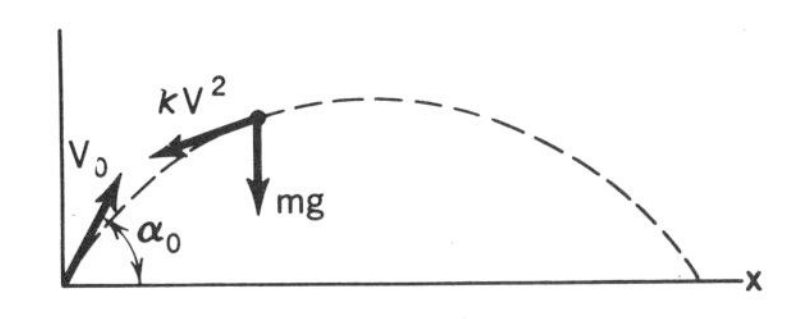

Fig. 12.72

***87.** [12.15] What is the friction function in Prob. 86? Do Prob. 83 using above results.

The following five problems are suggested as possible short projects.

***88.** [12.15] A projectile is shot at an angle of 30° with the horizontal with a muzzle velocity of 2000 ft/sec. If the friction function is $1.2 \times 10^{-5}\, V^2$, what is your estimate, reached by numerical methods, of the horizontal distance from firing to the impact position on a flat terrain?

***89.** [12.15] Do the preceding problem using the results of Example 12.14. Compare the results.

***90.** [12.15] Do Prob. 88 accurately by setting up the problem on a digital computer (such as a 1620 IBM system).

***91.** [12.15] A body is dropped from a supersonic aircraft moving at 1400 miles per hour at an elevation of 50,000 ft. If the friction function for the body is $3 \times 10^{-6}\, V^2$, what is an approximation of the trajectory of this body arrived at by numerical methods?

***92.** [12.15] Do the preceding problem accurately by employing a high-speed digital computer.

93. [12.17] A positive charge of 1 coulomb is present at a position given by the position vector $\boldsymbol{r} = 10\boldsymbol{i} + 6\boldsymbol{j} + 3\boldsymbol{k}$ meters. Also a positive charge of 2 coulombs is present at position $\boldsymbol{r} = 6\boldsymbol{i} + 2\boldsymbol{j}$ meters. What is the force in newtons on a negative charge of $\frac{1}{2}$ coulomb at the position $\boldsymbol{r} = 3\boldsymbol{j}$ meters?

94. [12.17] An electron has a charge of 1.602×10^{-19} coulombs, and a rest mass of 9.106×10^{-31} kilograms. It moves in a magnetic field given as $10x\boldsymbol{i} + 20(y^2 + x^2)^{1/2}\boldsymbol{j} + 6\boldsymbol{k}$ webers/square meter. When the particle is at position $\boldsymbol{r} = 10\boldsymbol{i} + 6\boldsymbol{j} + 3\boldsymbol{k}$ meters, it has a velocity given as $\boldsymbol{V} = 100\boldsymbol{j} + 600\boldsymbol{k}$ meters/sec. What is the force on the particle?

95. [12.17] An electron is moving in a linear accelerator at a speed of 100,000 mi/sec relative to the ground. Using data from Prob. 94, find the mass of the electron relative to the ground. The velocity of light is 186,000 miles/sec.

96. [12.17] We know from elementary physics that the electric field between two parallel large plates, shown in Fig. 12.73, equals V/d where V is the applied voltage in volts and d is the distance between the plates in meters and has a direction from the higher voltage to the lower voltage. An electron enters the plates with a velocity of 10 meters/sec in the vertical direction at the center of the capacitor. If the voltage is 100 volts and the distance d is 10 cm, how far up will the electron move before striking either of the plates?

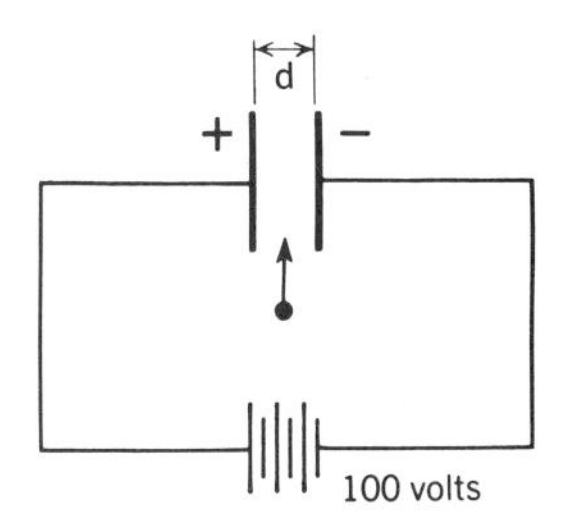

Fig. 12.73

97. [12.17] If there were a uniform magnetic field of 10 webers/cm² into which the electron of the above problem is moving, instead of the electric field, what is the resulting motion if we neglect gravity? (See Fig. 12.74.)

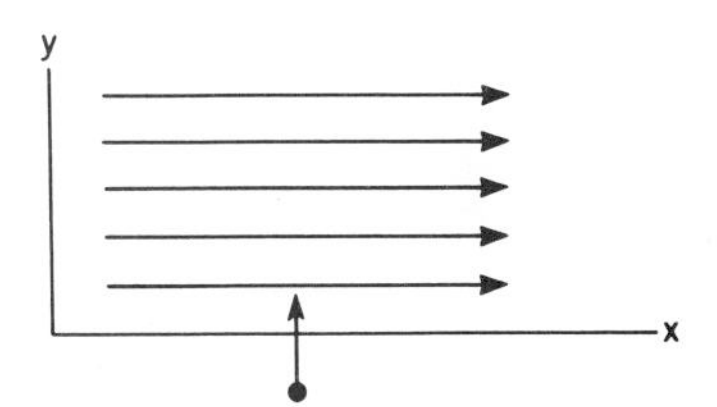

Fig. 12.74

98. [12.17] Shown in Fig. 12.75 is an idealization of the apparatus used by J. J. Thomson to measure the ratio of charge to mass of an electron, i.e., e/m. A heated cathode C gives off thermal electrons which are accelerated toward the anode A, as in the case of the cathode ray tube, and a thin beam of electrons goes through the apertures. A voltage V_0 is placed on the plates D, which tends to deflect the electron. However, the strength of the magnetic field normal to the page as shown is adjusted so that it has a value B_0, which causes the beam of electrons not to deflect. With this value of V_0 and B_0

and the geometry of the tube, compute the velocity of the electron as it approaches the screen. Now take the magnetic field off and measure the deflection δ on the screen. Compute the ratio e/m from these observations.

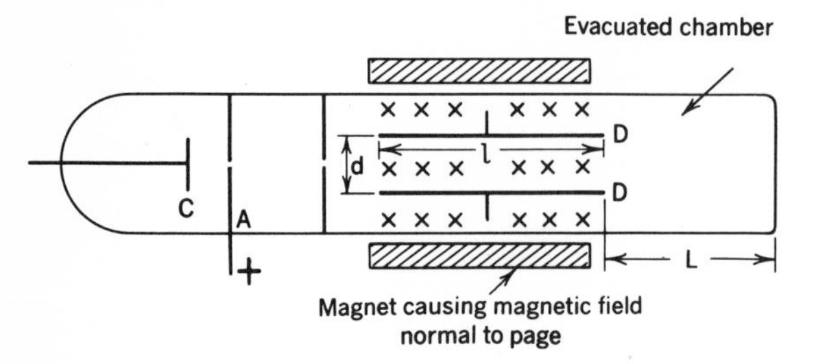

Fig. 12.75

99. [12.17] A hydrogen ion having mass 1.672×10^{-27} kg enters a pair of plates with a kinetic energy of 10^{-17} joules, as shown in Fig. 12.76. The voltage on the upper plate is linearly varied after this instant from 0 to 80 volts in 10^{-7} sec and then drops immediately to zero. Find the velocity of the particle and the distance above or below the x axis when it emerges from the plates.

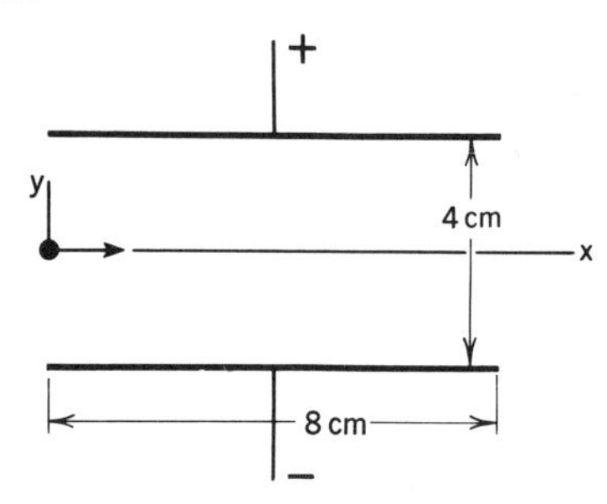

Fig. 12.76

100. [12.17] An electron starts at rest in a uniform electric field E. Find the distance and velocity as functions of time, using relativistic mass.

101. [12.17] In Fig. 12.77, an electron is at the origin at time $t = 0$. A constant electric field $\boldsymbol{E}$ is directed along the y axis and a constant magnetic field $\boldsymbol{B}$ is directed along the x axis. Find the spatial coordinates of the electron in terms of t.

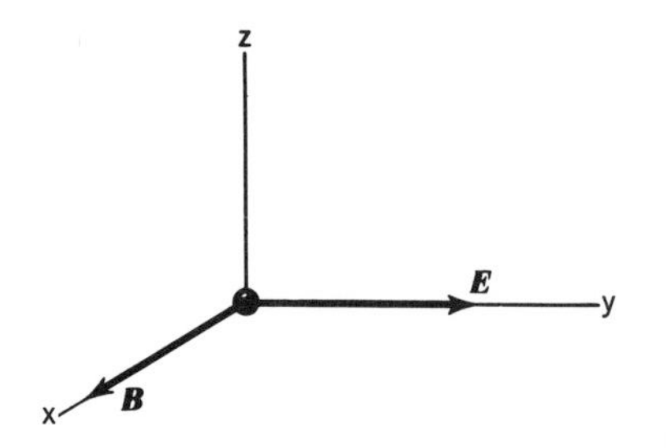

Fig. 12.77

102. [12.17] A sawtooth voltage is placed on the horizontal deflecting plates of a cathode ray oscilloscope giving the instruments a sweep time of $2\pi/\omega$ sec. If a signal voltage given as $E_0 \sin 2\omega t$ is placed on the vertical plates, what view will we get on the screen?

103. [12.17] Certain cathode ray oscilloscopes will perform a single sweep when any slight voltage appears on the vertical deflecting plates. If the sweep time is 2 sec, and the sweep triggers when a voltage of 0.2 volt appears on the vertical deflecting plates, show the picture that would be flashed on screen (this can be photographed) when a signal:

$$V_0 = \tfrac{1}{10}e^t$$

is placed on the vertical deflecting plates. If a 1-cm rise on the screen corresponds to 1 volt of signal, what will be the maximum height of the trajectory as seen on the screen?

104. [12.18] Three bodies are shown in Fig. 12.78 and their weights and positions at time t are given as follows:

$W_1 = 10$ lb, $x_1 = 6$ ft, $y_1 = 10$ ft, $z_1 = 10$ ft

$W_2 = 5$ lb, $x_2 = 5$ ft, $y_2 = 6$ ft, $z_2 = 0$

$W_3 = 8$ lb, $x_3 = 0$, $y_3 = -4$ ft, $z_3 = 0$

Determine the position vector of the center of mass at time t. Determine the velocity of the center of mass if the bodies have the following velocities:

$$\boldsymbol{V}_1 = 6\boldsymbol{i} + 3\boldsymbol{j} \text{ ft/sec}$$

$$\boldsymbol{V}_2 = 10\boldsymbol{i} - 3\boldsymbol{k} \text{ ft/sec}$$

$$\boldsymbol{V}_3 = 6\boldsymbol{k} \text{ ft/sec}$$

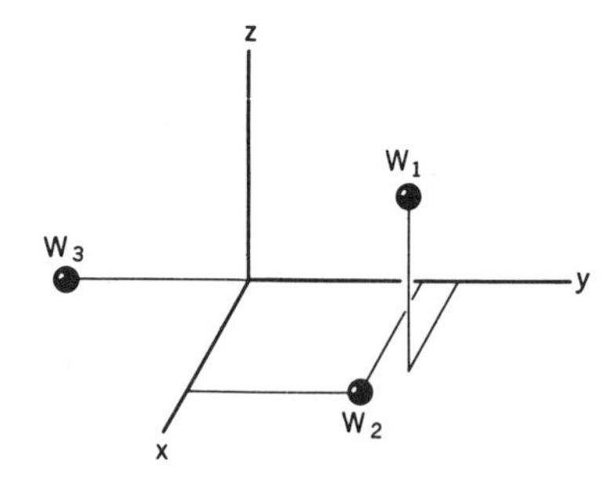

Fig. 12.78

105. [12.18] In the preceding problem the following forces act on the respective particles:

$$\boldsymbol{F}_1 = 6t\boldsymbol{i} + 3\boldsymbol{j} - 10\boldsymbol{k} \quad \text{(particle 1)}$$

$$\boldsymbol{F}_2 = 15\boldsymbol{i} - 3\boldsymbol{j} \quad \text{(particle 2)}$$

$$\boldsymbol{F}_3 = \boldsymbol{0} \quad \text{(particle 3)}$$

What is the acceleration of the center of mass and what is its position after 10 seconds from that given initially?

106. [12.18] Give the following data for a system of particles at time $t = 0$:

$$W_1 = 100 \text{ lb at position } (3, 4, -10)$$

$$W_2 = 50 \text{ lb at position } (-2, 4, -8)$$

$$W_3 = 10 \text{ lb at position } (-8, 16, 3)$$

The particles are acted on by the following respective forces:

$$\boldsymbol{F}_1 = 10\boldsymbol{j} + 2t\boldsymbol{k} \quad \text{(particle 1)}$$

$$\boldsymbol{F}_2 = 10\boldsymbol{k} \quad \text{(particle 2)}$$

$$\boldsymbol{F}_3 = t^2\boldsymbol{i} \quad \text{(particle 3)}$$

What is the velocity of W_1 relative to the mass center after 5 sec, assuming at $t = 0$ the particles are at rest?

107. [12.18] Given the following force field:

$$\boldsymbol{F} = -2x\boldsymbol{i} + 3\boldsymbol{j} - z\boldsymbol{k}$$

which is the force on any particle in the field per unit mass of the particle. If we have two particles initially stationary in the field with position vectors:

$$\boldsymbol{r}_1 = 3\boldsymbol{i} + 2\boldsymbol{j}$$

$$\boldsymbol{r}_2 = 4\boldsymbol{i} - 2\boldsymbol{j} + 4\boldsymbol{k}$$

what is the velocity of each particle relative to the center of mass of the system after 2 seconds have elapsed? Each particle has a weight of 0.1 ounce.

108. [12.18] A stationary uniform block of ice (see Fig. 12.79) is acted on by the forces which at all times maintain constant magnitude and direction. If:

$$F_1 = 50 \text{ lb}$$

$$F_2 = 20 \text{ lb}$$

$$F_3 = 30 \text{ lb}$$

what is the velocity of the center of mass of the block after 10 seconds? Neglect friction.

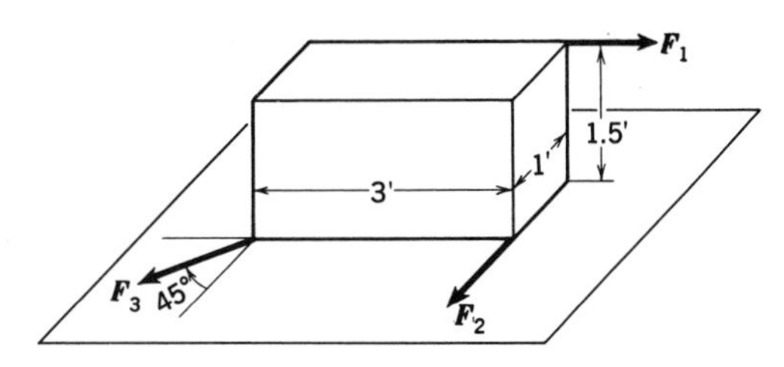

Fig. 12.79

109. [12.18] An object decelerates downward (from C to B) at 1000 mi per hr per sec (Fig. 12.80) while moving in a translatory manner relative to inertial space. Inside is a rod BC rotating in the plane of the paper at a rate of 50 rad/sec relative to the vehicle. Two masses rotate at the rate of 20 rad/sec around BC on rod EF. If the masses are each 1 ft from C, determine the force transmitted (not the couple) at C between BC and EF if the mass of each of the rotating bodies is 10 lbm and the mass of rod EF is 2 lbm. BC is in the vertical position at the time of interest. Neglect gravity.

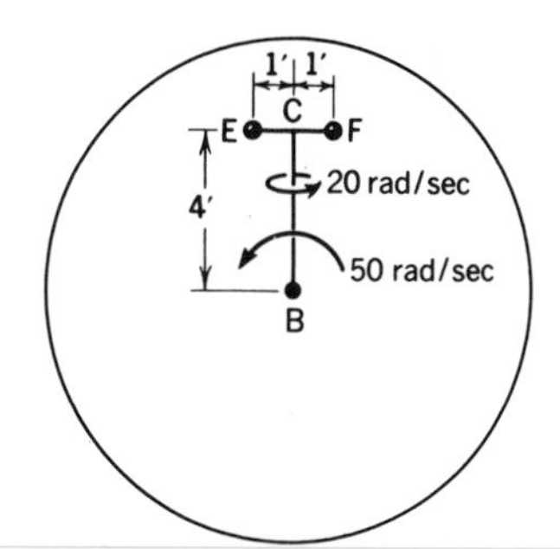

Fig. 12.80

13 Energy Methods

PART A. Analysis for a Single Particle

13.1 Introduction

In the previous chapter, we have integrated the differential equation derived from Newton's law to yield the velocity and position as a function of time for rectilinear translation, for central-force motion, and for certain cases of more general motions. At this time, we will present an alternate procedure, that of the method of energy, and we will see that certain classes of problems can be more easily handled by this method. To set forth the basic equation underlying this approach we start with Newton's law for a particle moving relative to an inertial reference, as shown in Fig. 13.1. Thus:

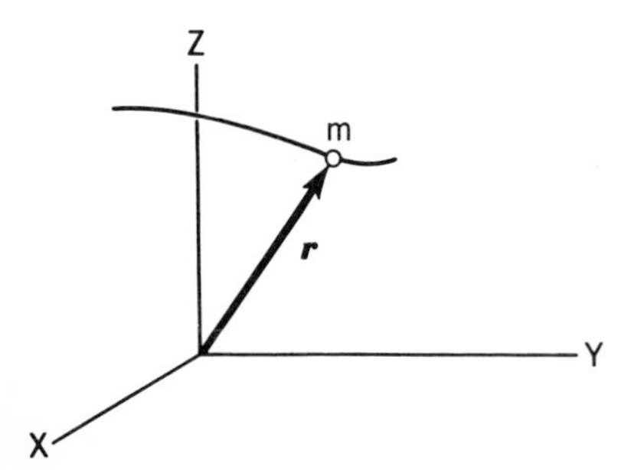

Fig. 13.1

$$\boldsymbol{F} = m\frac{d^2\boldsymbol{r}}{dt^2} = m\frac{d\boldsymbol{V}}{dt} \qquad \textbf{13.1}$$

Multiply each side of this equation by $d\boldsymbol{r}$ as a dot product and integrate from r_1 to r_2 along the path of motion:

$$\int_{r_1}^{r_2} \boldsymbol{F}\cdot d\boldsymbol{r} = m\int_{r_1}^{r_2} \frac{d\boldsymbol{V}}{dt}\cdot d\boldsymbol{r} = m\int_{t_1}^{t_2} \frac{d\boldsymbol{V}}{dt}\cdot\frac{d\boldsymbol{r}}{dt}\,dt$$

In the last integral, we have multiplied and divided by dt, thus changing the variable of integration to t. Since $d\boldsymbol{r}/dt = \boldsymbol{V}$, we then have:

$$\int_{r_1}^{r_2} \boldsymbol{F}\cdot d\boldsymbol{r} = m\int_{t_1}^{t_2} \left(\frac{d\boldsymbol{V}}{dt}\cdot\boldsymbol{V}\right) dt = \frac{1}{2}m\int_{t_1}^{t_2} \frac{d}{dt}(\boldsymbol{V}\cdot\boldsymbol{V})\,dt$$

$$= \frac{1}{2}m\int_{t_1}^{t_2} \frac{d}{dt}V^2\,dt$$

Hence we arrive at the familiar equation:

$$\int_{r_1}^{r_2} \boldsymbol{F}\cdot d\boldsymbol{r} = \tfrac{1}{2}m(V_2^2 - V_1^2) \qquad \textbf{13.2}$$

where the left side is the well-known expression for work (to be denoted at times as W_{1-2}*) and the right side is clearly the change in kinetic energy as the mass moves from position $\boldsymbol{r}_1$ to position $\boldsymbol{r}_2$.†

Suppose we give a scalar component of Newton's law in one direction, say the x direction. Using vector notation, we have:

$$F_x\boldsymbol{i} = m\frac{dV_x}{dt}\boldsymbol{i}$$

Taking the dot product of each side of the above equation with $dx\boldsymbol{i} + dy\boldsymbol{j} + dz\boldsymbol{k}$ ($= d\boldsymbol{r}$), we get, after integrating:

$$\int_{x_1}^{x_2} F_x\,dx = \frac{m}{2}[(V_x)_2^2 - (V_x)_1^2] \qquad \textbf{(a)}$$

Similarly:

$$\int_{y_1}^{y_2} F_y\,dy = \frac{m}{2}[(V_y)_2^2 - (V_y)_1^2] \qquad \textbf{(b)}$$

---

* It is important to note that the work done by a force system depends on that path over which the forces move except in the case of conservative forces to be considered in Section 13.3. Thus W_{1-2} is called a *path function* in thermodynamics. However, kinetic energy depends only on the instantaneous state of motion of the particle and is independent of the path. It is called accordingly a *point function* in thermodynamics.

† We will see in Section 13.7 that for *any system of particles including, of course, rigid bodies, we get a work-energy equation of this form where the velocity is that of the mass center, the force is the resultant external force on the system, and the path of integration is that of the path of the center of mass.* It should then be clear that we can use the particle approach (and consequently Eq. 13.2) for: (1) a rigid body that is translating—since all forces move along identical paths; (2) a body whose size is small compared to its trajectory so that the paths of the points of application of the forces differ little from that of the mass center. Thus, as in our considerations of Newton's law in the preceding chapter, when the motion of the mass center characterizes sufficiently accurately what we want to know about the motion of a body, we can use a particle at the mass center for energy considerations.

$$\int_{z_1}^{z_2} F_z\,dz = \frac{m}{2}[(V_z)_2^2 - (V_z)_1^2] \qquad \text{(c)} \quad 13.3$$

Thus the above equations demonstrate that the work done on a particle in any direction equals the change in kinetic energy associated with the component of velocity in that direction.

We can use the energy equations developed in this section for solving problems, instead of employing Newton's law. This approach is particularly handy when velocities are desired and forces are functions of position. However, it must be understood that any problem solvable by the energy equation can be solved from Newton's law; it is mainly a question of convenience.

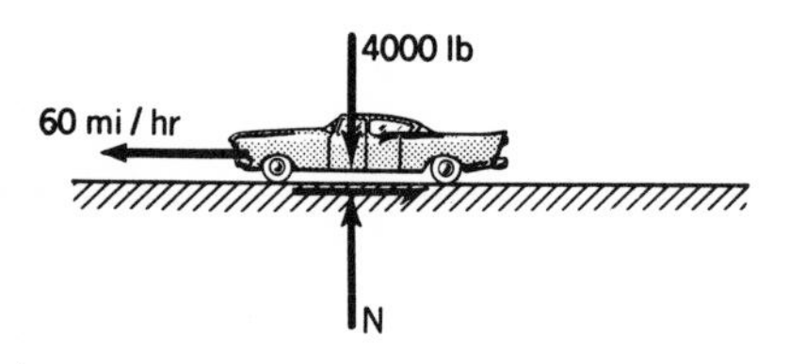

Fig. 13.2

EXAMPLE 13.1

An automobile is moving at 60 mi/hr (see Fig. 13.2) when the driver jams on his brakes and goes into a skid in the direction of motion. The car weighs 4000 lb, and the coefficient of friction between his rubber tires and the concrete road is 0.60. How far, l, will the car move before stopping?

There is a constant friction force acting, which from Coulomb's law is $\mu N = (0.60)(4000) = 2400$ lb. This is the only force performing work and it is clear that it is changing the kinetic energy of the vehicle from that corresponding to the speed of 60 mi/hr (or 88 ft/sec) to zero. (You will learn in thermodynamics that this work facilitates a transfer of kinetic energy of the vehicle to an increase of internal energy of the vehicle, the road, and the air.) The work-energy equation 13.2 then gives us:

$$-2400\,l = \frac{1}{2}\frac{4000}{g}(0 - 88^2)$$

Hence:

$$l = 200 \text{ ft}$$

(Perhaps every driver should do this problem periodically.)

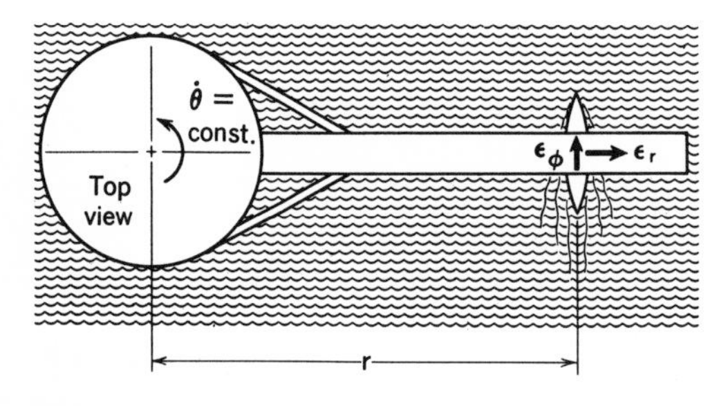

Fig. 13.3

EXAMPLE 13.2

A *towing tank* is a device used for evaluating the drag and stability of ship hulls. Scaled models are moved by a rig along the water at carefully controlled speeds and attitudes, while measurements are being made. Usually the water is contained in a long narrow tank with the rig moving overhead along the length of the tank. However, another useful set-up consists of a rotating radial arm (see Fig. 13.3) which gives the model a transverse motion. A radial motion along the arm is another degree of freedom possible for the model in this system.

Consider the case where a model is being moved out radially so that in one revolution of the main beam it has gone, at constant speed relative to the rig, from a position $r = 10$ ft to $r = 12$ ft. A constant drag in the radial direction of 10 lb is recorded by the machine. A transverse drag of 5 lb is recorded when r is 10 ft, but this drag increases as the square of the angle of rotation θ of the arm until it reaches 6 lb at position $r = 12$ ft, i.e. at the end of one revolution.* Compute the drag work done by the rig for this cycle.

It will be simplest to use cylindrical coordinates here. Accordingly we have:

$$\oint \boldsymbol{F} \cdot \boldsymbol{dr} = \int_0^{2\pi} F_\theta r \, d\theta + \int_{10}^{12} F_r \, dr \qquad \textbf{(a)}$$

We can express r as a function of θ as follows:

$$r = 10 + 2\left(\frac{\theta}{2\pi}\right) = 10 + \frac{\theta}{\pi} \qquad \textbf{(b)}$$

As for F_θ we can say:

$$F_\theta = 5 + \left(\frac{\theta}{2\pi}\right)^2 \qquad \textbf{(c)}$$

Substituting Eqs. (b) and (c) into Eq. (a), we get:

$$\oint \boldsymbol{F} \cdot \boldsymbol{dr} = \int_0^{2\pi} \left(5 + \frac{\theta^2}{4\pi^2}\right)\left(10 + \frac{\theta}{\pi}\right) d\theta + \int_{10}^{12} 10 \, dr \qquad \textbf{(d)}$$

Carrying out the integrations, we get the desired result:

$$\oint \boldsymbol{F} \cdot \boldsymbol{dr} = 117.7\pi + 20 = 390 \text{ ft-lb} \qquad \textbf{(e)}$$

EXAMPLE 13.3

Shown in Fig. 13.4 is a platform B guided by vertical rods. The platform is positioned so that the spring has been compressed 1 inch. In this configuration a body A weighing 40 lb is placed on the platform and released suddenly. If the guide rods give a total resistance force f to downward movement of the platform of 5 lb, what is the largest distance that the weight falls? The spring used here is a *nonlinear* spring requiring $5x^2$ lb of force for a deflection of x inches.

We take as the position of interest for the body the position δ below the initial configuration such that at this position the body reaches zero velocity for the first time after having been released. The change in kinetic energy over the interval of interest is accordingly zero. Thus, zero net work is done by the forces acting on the body A during displacement δ. These forces comprise the force of gravity, the friction force from the guides, and finally the force from the spring. Using as origin for our measurements the *undeformed* end position of the spring, we can accordingly say:

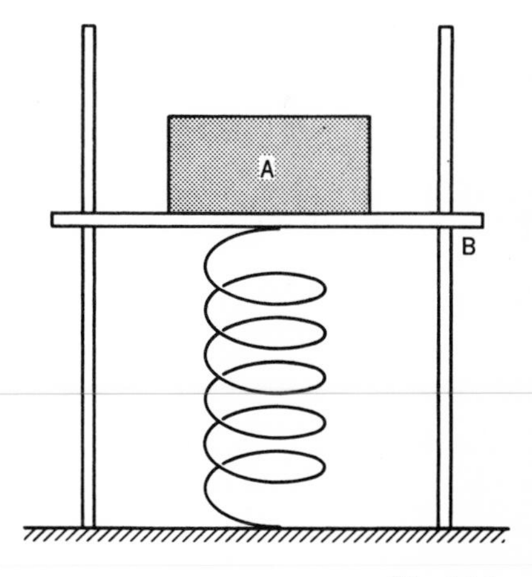

Fig. 13.4

* The increase in drag occurs because for a constant $\dot{\theta}$ of the arm the speed of the model relative to the water increases as it moves out further along the rig.

$$\int_1^{(1+\delta)} \boldsymbol{F}\cdot d\boldsymbol{s} = 0 = \int_1^{1+\delta} (W_A - f - 5x^2)\,dx$$

$$= \int_1^{1+\delta} (40 - 5 - 5x^2)\,dx \qquad \textbf{(a)}$$

Integrating, we get:

$$35\delta - \tfrac{5}{3}[(1+\delta)^3 - 1^3] = 0 \qquad \textbf{(b)}$$

$$\therefore\ \delta^3 - 3\delta^2 - 18\delta = 0 \qquad \textbf{(c)}$$

Factoring out δ (clearly $\delta = 0$ is a possible solution), we then get a quadratic equation in δ which can readily be solved for its two roots. The positive root is the result with physical meaning. Thus:

$$\delta = 3.00 \text{ in.} \qquad \textbf{(d)}$$

---

*13.2 Power Considerations

The rate at which work is performed is very useful for engineering purposes and is called *power*. Using the notation W_k to represent work we have:

$$\text{Power} = \frac{dW_k}{dt}$$

Since dW_k for any given force $\boldsymbol{F}_i$ is $\boldsymbol{F}_i \cdot d\boldsymbol{r}_i$, we can say that the power being developed by a system of n forces at time t is, for a reference xyz,

$$\text{Power} = \frac{\sum_{i=1}^{n} \boldsymbol{F}_i \cdot d\boldsymbol{r}_i}{dt} = \sum_{i=1}^{n} \boldsymbol{F}_i \cdot \boldsymbol{V}_i$$

where $\boldsymbol{V}_i$ is the velocity of the point of application of the ith force at time t as seen from reference xyz.

In the following examples we shall illustrate the use of the power concept. Note however, that we shall find it advantageous to refer to Newton's law for certain phases of the computation.

EXAMPLE 13.4

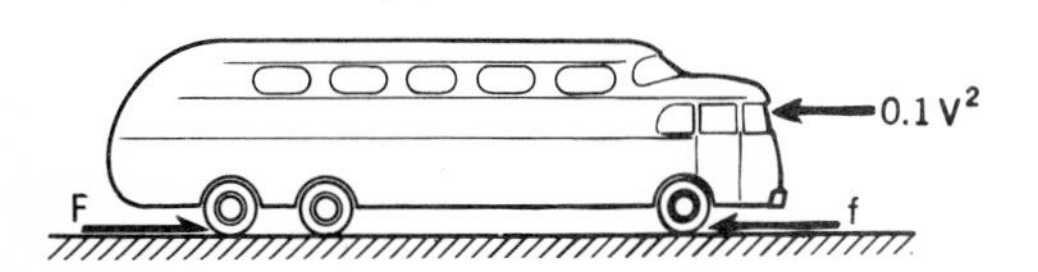

Fig. 13.5

A 15-ton bus (Fig. 13.5) develops on its drive wheels a torque of 800 ft-lb for 60 seconds. At the end of this time interval the throttle is adjusted to maintain uniform speed. If the rolling resistance is 0.005 times the weight of the bus, and the windage resistance is $0.1V^2$ lb, what is the equation for the horsepower developed by the drive system versus time? Neglect the rotational effects of the wheels, whose diameter is 2 ft.

Since one of the forces is a function of V we shall employ Newton's law directly to find V as a function of time. Taking F as the traction force and f as the rolling resistance, we have for Newton's law:

$$F - f - 0.1V^2 = M\frac{dV}{dt} \qquad \textbf{(a)}$$

Evaluating the forces F and f we have:

$$\frac{800}{1} - (0.005)(15)(2000) - 0.1V^2 = \frac{(15)(2000)}{g_0}\frac{dV}{dt}$$

$$\therefore 650 - 0.1V^2 = 932\frac{dV}{dt} \qquad \textbf{(b)}$$

Separating the variables and adjusting the terms, we get:

$$dt = 9320\frac{dV}{6500 - V^2} \qquad \textbf{(c)}$$

Integrating:

$$t = 9320\left(\frac{1}{161.2}\right)\ln\frac{80.6 + V}{80.6 - V} + C \qquad \textbf{(d)}$$

When $t = 0$, $V = 0$ and accordingly the integration constant $C = 0$. Equation (d) then becomes:

$$t = 57.6\ln\frac{80.6 + V}{80.6 - V} \qquad \textbf{(e)}$$

Solving for V, we get:

$$V = \frac{80.6(e^{0.01735\,t} - 1)}{e^{0.01735\,t} + 1} \qquad \textbf{(f)}$$

When $t = 60$ seconds we have for V:

$$V = \frac{80.6(e^{1.040} - 1)}{e^{1.040} + 1} = \frac{80.6(2.83 - 1)}{2.83 + 1}$$

$$= 38.5 \text{ ft/sec} \qquad \textbf{(g)}$$

The horsepower* developed by the drive system is then formulated from Eq. (f) for the first stage of the motion as:

$$\text{Power} = \frac{(F)(V)}{550} = \frac{(800)(80.6)}{550}\frac{(e^{0.01735\,t} - 1)}{(e^{0.01735\,t} + 1)}$$

$$= 117\frac{e^{0.01735\,t} - 1}{e^{0.01735\,t} + 1}$$

At the end of the acceleration phase, i.e., at $t = 60$ sec, the power is:

$$\text{Power} = 56 \text{ hp}$$

While moving at a constant speed of 38.5 ft/sec, we require that the drive system merely overcome rolling resistance of 150 lb and a windage force of $(0.1)(38.5)^2 = 148$ lb. The horsepower needed then is:

$$\text{Power} = \frac{(150 + 148)(38.5)}{550} = 20.8 \text{ hp}$$

This plot of the power requirements versus time is shown in Fig. 13.6.

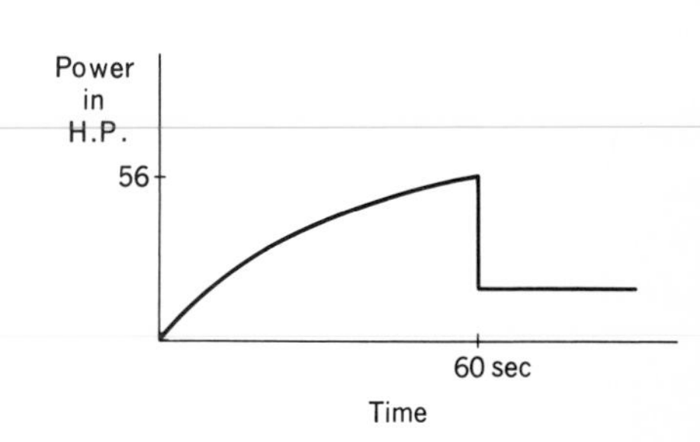

Fig. 13.6

* Recall from physics that 1 hp = 33,000 ft-lb/min = 550 ft-lb/sec.

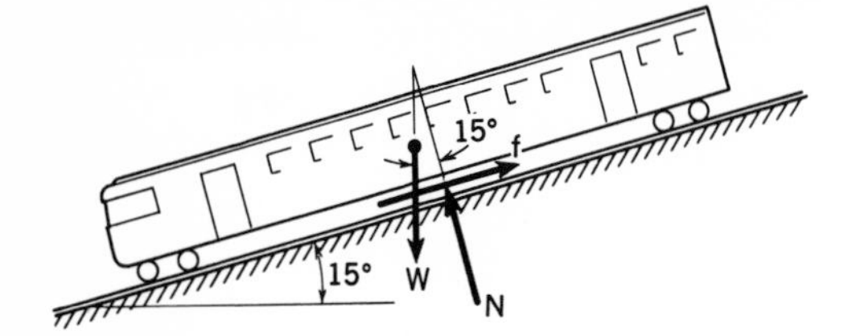

Fig. 13.7

EXAMPLE 13.5

In hilly terrain it is sometimes advantageous to employ the electric motors of an electric train as brakes, particularly on downhill runs. This is accomplished by using the motors as generators. In this way the central power source expends a net amount of energy in the course of one round trip equal to the ohmic heating dissipation and the heat dissipation due to friction of moving parts and windage. Such a train consisting of a single car is shown in Fig. 13.7 moving down a 15° incline at an initial speed of 5 ft/sec. This car weighs 20 tons and has a cog-wheel drive. If the conductor maintains an adjustment of the fields in his generators so as to develop a constant power of 50 kilowatts, how long does it take before the car moves at the rate of 10 ft/sec? Neglect the wind resistance.

We have shown all the forces acting on the car in the diagram. Newton's law along the direction of the incline can be then given as follows:

$$W \sin 15° - f = \frac{W}{g}\frac{dV}{dt} \qquad \textbf{(a)}$$

where f is the traction force developed by the generator action. Multiplying by V we get:

$$W \sin 15° V - fV = \frac{W}{g} V \frac{dV}{dt} \qquad \textbf{(b)}$$

If the *mechanical efficiency* of the generators (i.e., the power output divided by the power input) is 0.90, we can compute fV, which is the power delivered to the generators, in the following manner:

$$(\text{generator output})/(0.90) = fV \qquad \textbf{(c)}$$

Noting that 1 kilowatt is 1.341 horsepower and that 1 horsepower is 550 ft-lb/sec, we have:

$$fV = (500)(1.341)(550)/(0.90) = 41{,}000 \qquad \textbf{(d)}$$

Eq. (b) can now be given as:

$$(20)(2000)(0.259)V - 41{,}000 = \frac{(20)(2000)}{g_0} V \frac{dV}{dt}$$

$$\therefore\ 8.35V - 33.0 = V\frac{dV}{dt} \qquad \textbf{(e)}$$

We can separate the variables for purposes of carrying out a quadrature as follows:

$$dt = \frac{V\,dV}{8.35V - 33.0} \qquad \textbf{(f)}$$

Integrating, we get:

$$t = \frac{1}{83.5^2}$$

$$\times [8.35V - 33.0 + 33.0 \ln (8.35V - 33.0)] + C \qquad \textbf{(g)}$$

To get the constant of integration C note that when

$t = 0$, $V = 5$. Hence:

$$0 = \frac{1}{8.35^2}\{(8.35)(5) - 33.0 + 33.0 \times \ln[(8.35)(5) - 33.0]\} + C$$

$$\therefore C = -1.152$$

We thus have for Eq. (g):

$$t = \frac{1}{8.35^2}[8.35V - 33.0 + 33.0 \times \ln(8.35V - 33.0)] - 1.152 \qquad \textbf{(h)}$$

When $V = 10$ ft/sec we get for t:

$$t = \frac{1}{8.35^2}[83.5 - 33.0 + 33.0 \times \ln(83.5 - 33.0)] - 1.152$$

$$\therefore t = 2.59 \text{ sec} \qquad \textbf{(i)}$$

13.3 Conservative Force Fields

Energy methods are particularly useful with conservative force systems. You will recall from Chapter 10 that a conservative force field is distinguished by the following criteria:

a. It is given as a function of spatial coordinates only. Mathematically this is denoted in the following way:

$$\boldsymbol{F} = \boldsymbol{F}(x, y, z) \qquad \textbf{13.4}$$

b. It is expressible as the gradient of a scalar function called the *force potential.* That is:

$$\boldsymbol{F} = \textbf{grad}\,\phi \qquad \textbf{13.5}$$

It was shown in Chapter 10 that the work done by such a force on a particle moving from position (1) to position (2) *is independent of the path and depends only on the endpoints.* Thus:

$$W_{1-2} = \int_1^2 \boldsymbol{F}\cdot d\boldsymbol{r} = \int_1^2 (\textbf{grad}\,\phi)\cdot d\boldsymbol{r} = \phi_2 - \phi_1 \qquad \textbf{13.6}$$

If the path is such that the particle is brought back to its starting position, it is clear from the above equation that the work done is zero. This may be written in the following manner:

$$\oint \boldsymbol{F}\cdot d\boldsymbol{r} = 0. \qquad \textbf{13.7}$$

The change of potential energy, PE,* of a particle between positions (1)

* You will recall that we used the letter V for potential energy in Chapter 10. This is standard notation in statics. Here, because we are using V for velocity, we prefer to employ the notation PE for the potential energy.

and (2) was defined as a quantity that equals minus the work done by the conservative force field as the particle moves from position (1) to (2). From Eq. 13.6, it is apparent that:

$$PE = -\phi \qquad \mathbf{13.8}$$

Two conservative force fields have been employed in studying the method of virtual work. These force fields and their potential functions and potential energies are:

1. Constant gravitational force

$$\boldsymbol{F} = -mg\boldsymbol{k} \qquad \text{(a)}$$

$$\phi = -mgz \qquad \text{(b)}$$

$$PE = mgz \qquad \text{(c)} \qquad \mathbf{13.9}$$

2. Linear restoring force

$$\boldsymbol{F} = -Kx\boldsymbol{i}\dagger \qquad \text{(a)}$$

$$\phi = -\frac{Kx^2}{2} \qquad \text{(b)}$$

$$PE = \frac{Kx^2}{2} \qquad \text{(c)} \qquad \mathbf{13.10}$$

In previous chapters, several additional force fields were introduced: the gravitational central force field, the electrostatic field, and the magnetic field. Let us see which we can add to our list of conservative force fields. Consider first the central gravitational force field where particle m, shown in Fig. 13.8, experiences a force given by the equation:

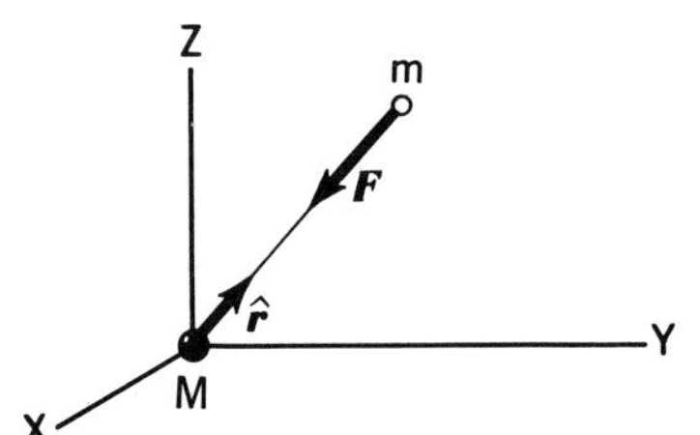

Fig. 13.8

$$\boldsymbol{F} = -G\frac{Mm}{r^2}\hat{\boldsymbol{r}} \qquad \mathbf{13.11}$$

Clearly, this force distribution is a function of spatial coordinates, as demanded by Eq. 13.4, and it can easily be expressed as the gradient of a scalar function in the following manner:

$$\boldsymbol{F} = \textbf{grad}\left(\frac{GMm}{r}\right) \qquad \mathbf{13.12}$$

Accordingly, we have for this force field a potential function ϕ given as:

$$\phi = \frac{GMm}{r}$$

Hence this is a conservative force field. The potential energy is then:

$$PE = -\frac{GMm}{r} \qquad \mathbf{13.13}$$

† Be sure to choose a reference so that when $x = 0$, $F = 0$.

Next, the force on a particle of unit positive charge from a particle of charge q_1 is given by Coulomb's law and appeared in the previous chapter as:

$$\boldsymbol{E} = \frac{q_1}{4\pi\epsilon_0 r^2}\hat{\boldsymbol{r}} \tag{13.14}$$

Since this equation has the same form as Eq. 13.11, we see immediately that the force field from q_1 is conservative. Consequently we have a force potential for this case given as:

$$\phi = -\frac{q_1}{4\pi\epsilon_0 r}$$

The potential energy per unit charge is then:

$$PE = \frac{q_1}{4\pi\epsilon_0 r} \tag{13.15}$$

In this form (i.e., with a zero additive constant), the coulombic potential energy is zero at infinity and, thus, infinity is the datum for this formulation. Equation 13.15 then gives the negative of the work by the Coulomb force when a unit charge is brought from infinity to a position at a distance r from charge q_1. By the same token, it equals the work done by the *external agent* causing the change in position, provided the position change has been performed at conditions approaching equilibrium conditions (i.e., reversibly).

It is, however, the practice in electrostatics to employ the notation $-V$ or $-U$ for ϕ, and to call the term U or V the *electrostatic potential*. This means that the *electric potential energy* (PE) is *equal* to the electrostatic potential, in contrast to corresponding quantities in mechanics where there is a difference of sign.

Since any electrostatic field $\boldsymbol{E}$ can be considered as the superposition of the simple fields described above, $\boldsymbol{E}$ is obviously conservative; thus a scalar function $-U$ exists for any electrostatic field such that:

$$\boldsymbol{E} = \textbf{grad}\ (-U) = -\textbf{grad}\ U$$

The remaining field introduced was the magnetic field. For this field, the force on a charged particle depends on the velocity of the particle. The condition given by Eq. 13.4 is not satisfied, therefore, and the magnetic field does not form a conservative force field.

13.4 Conservation of Mechanical Energy

Let us now consider the motion of a particle acted upon only by a conservative force field. We start with Eq. 13.2:

$$\int_{r_1}^{r_2} \boldsymbol{F}\cdot d\boldsymbol{r} = \tfrac{1}{2}mV_2^2 - \tfrac{1}{2}mV_1^2 \tag{13.16}$$

Using the definition of potential energy, we replace the left side of the equation in the following manner:

$$(PE)_1 - (PE)_2 = \tfrac{1}{2}mV_2^2 - \tfrac{1}{2}mV_1^2 \tag{13.17}$$

Rearranging terms, we reach the following useful relation:

$$\boxed{(PE)_1 + \tfrac{1}{2}mV_1^2 = (PE)_2 + \tfrac{1}{2}mV_2^2} \tag{13.18}$$

Since positions (1) and (2) are arbitrary, it is obvious from the above equation that the *sum of the potential energy and the kinetic energy of a particle remains constant at all times during the motion of the particle.* This statement is sometimes termed the *conservation law of mechanical energy for conservative systems.* The usefulness of this relation can be demonstrated by the following examples.

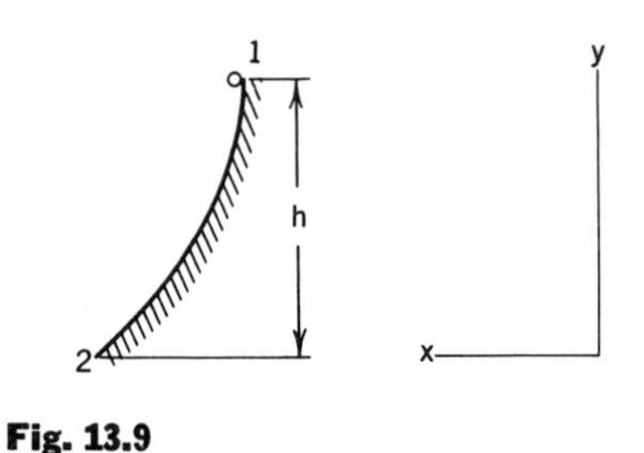

Fig. 13.9

EXAMPLE 13.6

A particle is dropped with zero initial velocity down a frictionless chute (Fig. 13.9). What is the magnitude of its velocity if the vertical drop during the motion is h ft?

For small trajectories, we can assume a uniform force field $-mg\boldsymbol{j}$. Since this is the only force that can perform work on the particle (the normal force from the chute does no work), we can employ the conservation of mechanical energy expression. If we take position (2) as a datum, we then have:

$$mgh + 0 = 0 + m\frac{V_2^2}{2}$$

Solving for V_2, we get:

$$V_2 = \sqrt{2gh}$$

The advantages of the energy considerations for conservative fields become apparent from this problem. That is, not all the forces need be considered in computing velocities, and the path, however complicated, is of no concern. If friction were present, a nonconservative force would perform work, and we would have to go back to the general relation given by Eq. 13.2 for the analysis.

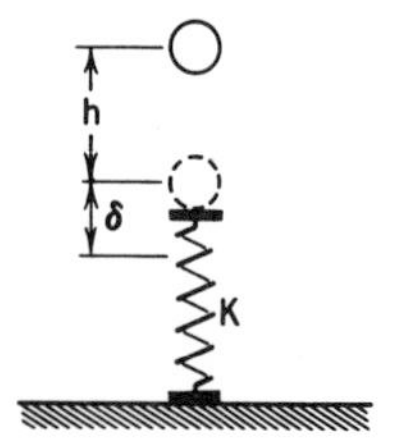

Fig. 13.10

EXAMPLE 13.7

A mass is dropped onto a spring that has a spring constant K and a negligible mass (see Fig. 13.10). What is the maximum deflection δ?

From the previous example, we see that on first contact with the spring the mass has a velocity of $\sqrt{2gh}$. For the motion from this initial condition to the maximum deflection position, only conservative forces are acting—that of gravity and that of the spring—and we can thus use the conservation equation between these two positions. From Eq. 13.10(c) we know that the potential energy of the spring force is $Kx^2/2$, where x is the deflection of the spring from the unextended condition. Using the maximum deflection as a datum for the gravity force, we have:

$$\underset{KE}{mgh} + \underset{\substack{PE\\ \text{due to}\\ \text{gravity}}}{mg\,\delta} + \underset{\substack{PE\\ \text{due to}\\ \text{spring}}}{0} = \underset{KE}{0} + \underset{\substack{PE\\ \text{due to}\\ \text{gravity}}}{0} + \underset{\substack{PE\\ \text{due to}\\ \text{spring}}}{\tfrac{1}{2}K\,\delta^2}$$

Rearranging terms, we have:

$$\delta^2 - \frac{2mg}{K}\,\delta - \frac{2mgh}{K} = 0$$

Solving for the positive value of δ, we get the desired result.

EXAMPLE 13.8

Formulate an expression for the speed of an outer-space meteor relative to a fixed star, using methods of energy. (See Fig. 13.11.)

This problem is identical in nature to the central-force problem studied in Chapter 12. The force field acting on the meteor is the gravitational field from the fixed star. Thus:

$$\boldsymbol{F} = -G\,\frac{mM}{r^2}\,\boldsymbol{\varepsilon}_r$$

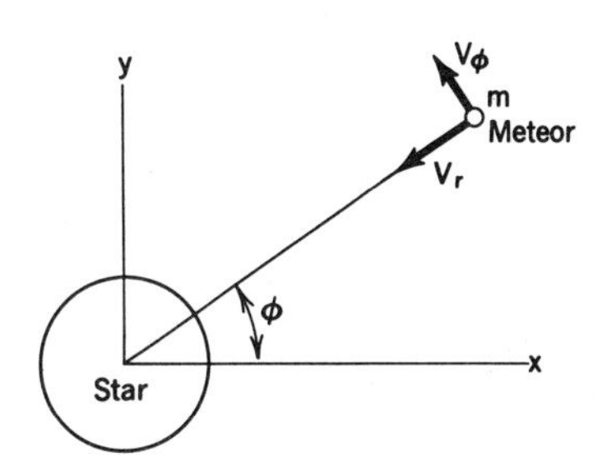

Fig. 13.11

The potential energy is:

$$PE = -G\,\frac{mM}{r} \qquad \textbf{(a)}$$

(Note that $r = \infty$ is the datum for this energy.) The kinetic energy of the motion can be given as:

$$KE = \tfrac{1}{2}mV^2 \qquad \textbf{(b)}$$

Since only a conservative force is present, we can use the conservation law:

$$-\frac{GmM}{r} + \frac{m}{2}\,V^2 = \text{const.} = E \qquad \textbf{(c)}$$

Let us consider the special case where E, the total mechanical energy, is given as zero. This means that the velocity is zero at infinity, and at any other position we see from Eq. (c) that:

$$V = \sqrt{\frac{2GM}{r}} \qquad \textbf{(d)}$$

But this is the escape velocity formulated in Chapter 12 in the discussion of ballistic space vehicles. What is then the connection between our present energy formulations and the results stemming from the direct use of Newton's law?

You will recall that in measuring ϕ from the axis of symmetry of the conic, we formulated for the trajectory the equation:

$$\frac{1}{r} = \frac{GM}{C^2} + D\cos\phi \qquad \textbf{(e)}$$

The criterion for the parabolic path and thus for a minimum escape-velocity trajectory is that $DC^2/GM = 1$. By replacing GM by DC^2 in Eq. (e), we thus have:

$$\frac{1}{r} = D(1 + \cos\phi) \qquad \textbf{(f)}$$

for the minimum escape-velocity condition. As $r \to \infty$, it is clear from this equation that $\phi \to \pi$. Now differentiate the above equation to form the velocity V_r:

$$V_r = Dr^2\dot{\phi} \sin \phi \quad \text{(g)}$$

Replace $r^2\dot{\phi}$ by C.

$$V_r = DC \sin \phi \quad \text{(h)}$$

Since $\phi \to \pi$ when $r \to \infty$, V_r is plainly zero at infinity, and from the constant $C = r^2\dot{\phi}$, it is apparent that since $r \to \infty$, $r\dot{\phi}$, which equals V_ϕ, must go to zero. Thus we have shown that a parabolic trajectory corresponding to a ballistic vehicle just escaping from the earth results in zero velocity at ∞. This is just the condition that the energy considerations generated for the escape condition.

The constant E in Eq. (c) is evaluated for a general trajectory from a known speed at some given position. At any other radial distance, we can then ascertain the proper speed by using Eq. (c). If we obtain an imaginary value in solving for the velocity, this indicates that the value of r substituted into Eq. (c) cannot be reached.

13.5 Alternate form of Work-Energy Equation

With the aid of the material in the previous section, we shall now set forth an alternate energy equation which has much physical appeal and which resembles the first law of thermodynamics that will be employed in other courses. Let us assume that certain of the forces acting on a particle are conservative while others are not. If we remember that for the conservative forces the negative of the change in potential energy between positions (1) and (2) equals the work done by these forces as the particle goes from position (1) to position (2) along any path, we can restate Eq. 13.2 in the following way:

$$\int_1^2 \boldsymbol{F} \cdot d\boldsymbol{r} - \Delta(PE)_{1,2} = \Delta(KE)_{1,2} \quad \textbf{13.19}$$

where the integral represents the work of the nonconservative forces. Calling this integral W_{1-2}, we then have, on rearranging the equation:

$$\Delta(KE + PE) = W_{1-2} \quad \textbf{13.20}$$

In this form we say that the work of nonconservative forces goes into changing the kinetic energy plus the potential energy of the particle. Since potential energies of such common forces as linear restoring forces, coulombic forces, and gravitational forces are so well known, the above formulation is useful in solving problems if it is understood thoroughly and applied properly.

EXAMPLE 13.9

A constant force F is applied to a body of weight W resting on an inclined surface for which the coefficient of friction is μ (Fig. 13.12). The body is acted on by a spring having a spring constant K. If initially the spring is compressed a distance δ, compute the velocity of the body in terms of F and the other parameters that are given, when the body has moved from rest a distance up the incline of $\frac{3}{2}\delta$.

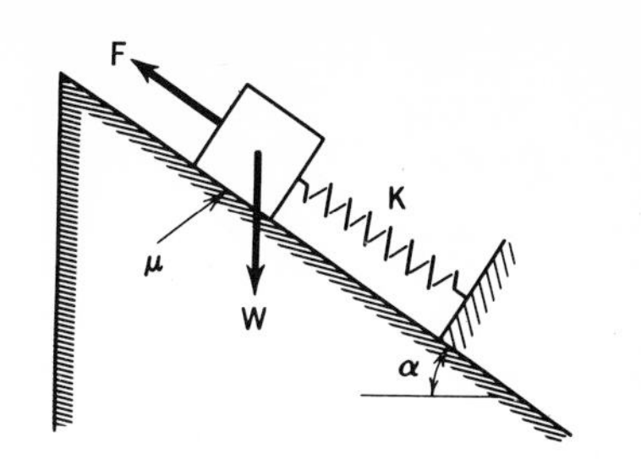

Fig. 13.12

The nonconservative forces are F and a friction force, so the expression W_{1-2} becomes:

$$W_{1-2} = (F)(\tfrac{3}{2}\delta) - (W\mu \cos \alpha)(\tfrac{3}{2}\delta)$$

The change in potential energy of the system is:

$$\Delta PE = W(\tfrac{3}{2}\delta \sin \alpha) + \tfrac{1}{2}K\left(\frac{\delta}{2}\right)^2 - \tfrac{1}{2}K\delta^2$$

$$\therefore\ \Delta PE = \tfrac{3}{2}W\delta \sin \alpha - \tfrac{3}{2}K\left(\frac{\delta}{2}\right)^2$$

Substituting into Eq. 13.20, we then get:

$$\frac{1}{2}\frac{W}{g}V^2 + \tfrac{3}{2}W\delta \sin \alpha - \tfrac{3}{2}K\left(\frac{\delta}{2}\right)^2 = \tfrac{3}{2}F\delta - \tfrac{3}{2}W\delta\mu \cos \alpha$$

We can then solve for the velocity V from this equation:

$$V = \left\{3\delta g\left(\frac{F}{W} - \mu \cos \alpha - \sin \alpha + \frac{K\delta}{4W}\right)\right\}^{1/2}$$

PART B. Systems of Particles

13.6 Work-Energy Equations

We shall now examine a system of particles from an energy viewpoint. Shown in Fig. 13.13 is a general aggregate of n particles. Considering the ith particle, we can say, by employing Eq. 13.2:

$$\int_1^2 \boldsymbol{F}_i \cdot d\boldsymbol{r}_i + \int_1^2 \left(\sum_{\substack{j=1 \\ j\neq i}}^{n} \boldsymbol{f}_{ij}\right) \cdot d\boldsymbol{r}_i = (\tfrac{1}{2}m_i V_i^2)_2 - (\tfrac{1}{2}m_i V_i^2)_1 \qquad \textbf{13.21}$$

where, as in the previous chapter, $\boldsymbol{f}_{ij}$ is the force from the jth particle onto the ith particle, as is illustrated in the diagram, and is thus an internal force, in contrast to $\boldsymbol{F}_i$ which represents the total external force on the ith particle. In words, the above equation says that for a displacement between $\boldsymbol{r}_1$ and $\boldsymbol{r}_2$ along some path, the energy relations for the ith particle are:

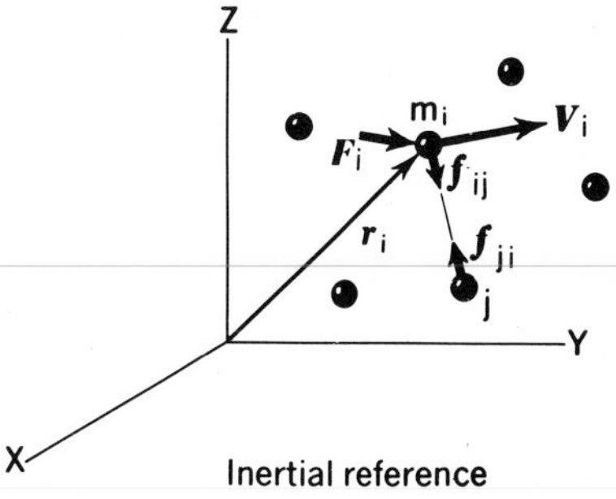

Inertial reference

Fig. 13.13

$$\text{external work} + \text{internal work} = \begin{pmatrix}\text{change in kinetic} \\ \text{energy relative to } XYZ\end{pmatrix} \qquad \textbf{13.22}$$

Furthermore, we can adopt the point of view set forth in Section 13.5 and identify conservative forces, both external and internal, so as to utilize potential energies for these forces in the energy equation. To qualify as conservative, internal forces would have to be functions of only the spatial configuration of the system and expressible as the gradient of a scalar function. Clearly, forces arising (1) from the gravitational attraction between the particles, (2) from the electrostatic forces from electric charges on the particles, and (3) from elastic connectors between the particles with linear characteristics, such as springs, are all conservative internal forces. By summing Eq. 13.21 for all particles and adopting this point of view, we can say for the aggregate:

$$\Delta(KE + PE) = W_{1-2} \qquad \textbf{13.23}$$

where W_{1-2} represents the net work done by internal and external nonconservative forces, and PE represents the total potential energy of the conservative internal and external forces. Since we are taking the *change* in potential energy, the datum chosen for measuring PE is of little significance here.* For instance, any convenient datum for measuring the potential energy due to gravity of the earth yields the same result for the term ΔPE.

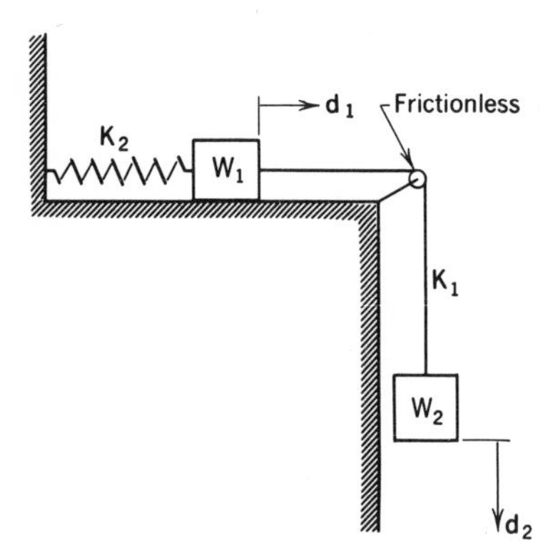

Fig. 13.14

EXAMPLE 13.10

In Fig. 13.14 there are two blocks having weights W_1 and W_2, respectively. They are connected by a flexible, *elastic* cable of negligible mass which has an equivalent spring constant of K_1. Body (1) is connected to the wall by a spring having a spring constant K_2 and slides along a horizontal surface for which the coefficient of friction with the body is μ. Body (2) is supported initially by some external agent so that at the outset of the problem the spring and cable are unstretched. What is the total kinetic energy of the system when, after release, body (2) has moved a distance d_2 and body (1) has moved a smaller distance d_1? Assume that d_1 and d_2 are less than the maximum displacements of the respective bodies.

Use Eq. 13.23. There is only one nonconservative force present in the system and this is the external friction force on body (1). Therefore, the work term of the equation becomes:

$$W_{1-2} = -W_1\mu d_1 \qquad \textbf{(a)}$$

There are three conservative forces present; the spring force and the gravitational force are external and the force from the elastic cable is internal. (We neglect mutual gravitational forces between the bodies.) Using the initial position of W_2 as the datum for gravitational potential energy, we have, for the total change in potential energy:

$$\Delta PE = [\tfrac{1}{2}K_2d_1^2 + \tfrac{1}{2}K_1(d_2 - d_1)^2 - W_2d_2]$$

We can compute the desired change in kinetic energy from Eq. 13.23 as:

---

* There is one precaution in this regard that must again be brought to your attention. You will remember that in the spring-force formula, $-Kx$, the term x represents the elongation or contraction of the spring from the *undeformed* condition. This must not be violated in the potential-energy expression $\frac{1}{2}Kx^2$.

$$\Delta KE = -W_1\mu d_1 - \tfrac{1}{2}K_2 d_1^2 - \tfrac{1}{2}K_1(d_2 - d_1)^2 + W_2 d_2 \quad \textbf{(b)}$$

As an additional exercise, you should arrive at this result by using the basic Eq. 13.21, where you cannot rely on familiar formulae for potential energies.

EXAMPLE 13.11

A chain weighing 5 lb/ft is shown in a slot in Fig. 13.15. If the chain is released from a stationary position at the configuration shown, what will be the speed of the chain after it moves 3 ft? The slot is frictionless.

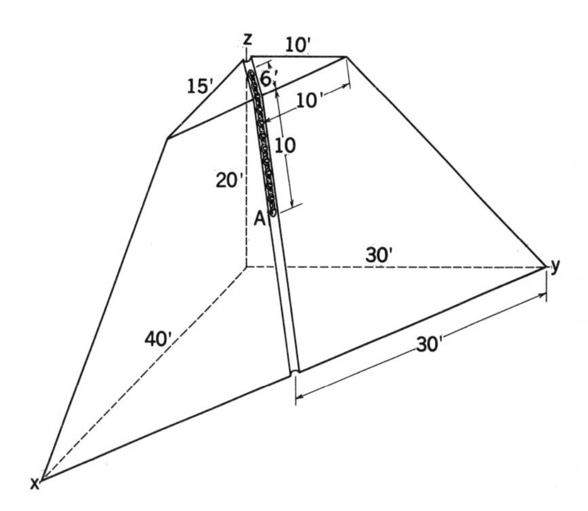

Fig. 13.15

If we employ Eq. 13.23 we have:

$$\Delta(KE + PE) = 0 \quad \textbf{(a)}$$

since only gravity does work here. Using the coordinate s to give the displacement along the slot from the initial configuration, we have for the kinetic energy:

$$KE = \tfrac{1}{2}(16)\left(\frac{5}{32.2}\right)(\dot{s})^2 = 1.240\dot{s}^2 \quad \textbf{(b)}$$

As for the potential-energy change, we shall compute the potential energy of the chain initially using point A as a reference elevation and then the potential energy after the chain has moved a distance s. For this purpose, we have shown both configurations in Fig. 13.16. A unit vector $\hat{\boldsymbol{p}}$ is employed directed along the slot from A upward as indicated in the diagram. We can accordingly say for the initial potential energy, $(PE)_1$:

$$(PE)_1 = \left[6\,\frac{5}{g_0}\right][10\hat{\boldsymbol{p}}\cdot\boldsymbol{k}] + \left[10\,\frac{5}{g_0}\right][5\hat{\boldsymbol{p}}\cdot\boldsymbol{k}] \quad \textbf{(c)}$$

The potential energy $(PE)_2$ after the shift is then:

$$(PE)_2 = \left[(6 - s)\,\frac{5}{g_0}\right][10\hat{\boldsymbol{p}}\cdot\boldsymbol{k}] + \left[10\,\frac{5}{g_0}\right][5\hat{\boldsymbol{p}}\cdot\boldsymbol{k}] - \left[s\,\frac{5}{g_0}\right]\left[\frac{s}{2}\,\hat{\boldsymbol{p}}\cdot\boldsymbol{k}\right] \quad \textbf{(d)}$$

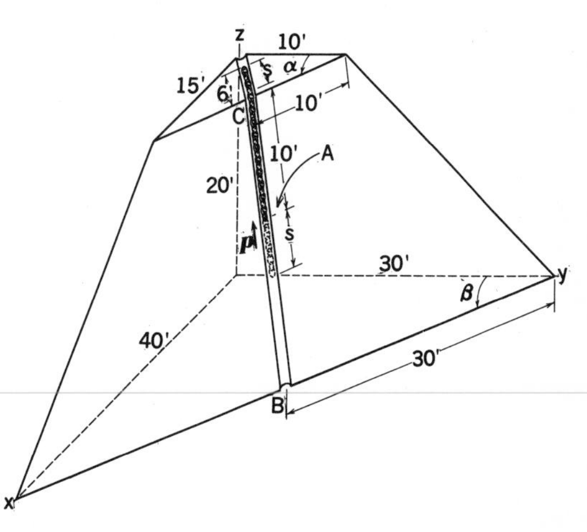

Fig. 13.16

The change in potential energy $\Delta(PE)$ is accordingly:

$$\Delta PE = -\frac{50s}{g_0}\,\hat{\boldsymbol{p}}\cdot\boldsymbol{k} - \frac{2.5}{g_0}\,s^2\hat{\boldsymbol{p}}\cdot\boldsymbol{k} \quad \textbf{(e)}$$

Our task is now to evaluate $\hat{\boldsymbol{p}}$. This can be done by employing position vectors $\boldsymbol{r}_C$ and $\boldsymbol{r}_B$ from the origin respectively to points C and B as denoted in Fig. 13.16. Thus:

$$\hat{\boldsymbol{p}} = \frac{\boldsymbol{r}_C - \boldsymbol{r}_B}{|\boldsymbol{r}_C - \boldsymbol{r}_B|} \quad \textbf{(f)}$$

Observing Fig. 13.16, we have

$$\boldsymbol{r}_C = 10\sin\alpha\boldsymbol{i} + (10 - 10\cos\alpha)\boldsymbol{j} + 20\boldsymbol{k}$$

$$\boldsymbol{r}_B = 30\sin\beta\boldsymbol{i} + (30 - 30\cos\beta)\boldsymbol{j}$$

where

$$\alpha = \tan^{-1}\frac{15}{10} = 56.3°$$

$$\beta = \tan^{-1}\frac{40}{30} = 53.1°$$

Thus we have:

$$r_C = 8.32\boldsymbol{i} + 4.46\boldsymbol{j} + 20\boldsymbol{k}$$

$$r_B = 24\boldsymbol{i} + 12.0\boldsymbol{j}$$

We get $\hat{\boldsymbol{p}}$ by substituting the above results into Eq. (f). Thus:

$$\hat{\boldsymbol{p}} = \frac{-15.68\boldsymbol{i} - 7.54\boldsymbol{j} + 20\boldsymbol{k}}{\sqrt{(15.68)^2 + (7.54)^2 + (20^2)}}$$

$$\therefore\ \hat{\boldsymbol{p}} = -0.592\boldsymbol{i} - 0.285\boldsymbol{j} + 0.755\boldsymbol{k} \qquad \textbf{(g)}$$

Now, employing Eq. (g) in Eq. (e), we get for ΔPE:

$$\Delta PE = -\frac{50}{g_0}(s)(0.755) - \frac{25}{g_0}s^2(0.755)$$

$$\therefore\ \Delta PE = -1.17s - 0.586s^2 \qquad \textbf{(h)}$$

Substituting the results for ΔKE and ΔPE from Eqs. (b) and (h) respectively into Eq. (a), we get:

$$1.240\dot{s}^2 - 1.17s - 0.586s^2 = 0 \qquad \textbf{(i)}$$

When $s = 3$ ft, we get for $\dot{s}$ the following result:

$$\dot{s} = 2.65 \text{ ft/sec} \qquad \textbf{(j)}$$

13.7 Kinetic-Energy Expression Based on Center of Mass

In this and the next section, we shall introduce the center of mass into our discussion in order to develop useful expressions for the kinetic energy of an aggregate and to develop another work-energy equation. These formulations are helpful at present, but they will be of greatest value in later discussions of rigid-body motion.

Consider a system of n particles, shown in Fig. 13.17. The total kinetic energy of a system of particles can be given as:

$$KE = \sum_{i=1}^{n} \tfrac{1}{2}m_iV_i^2 \qquad \textbf{13.24}$$

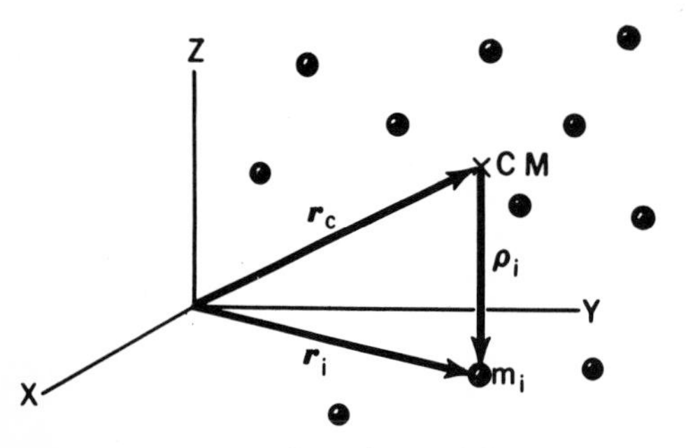

Fig. 13.17

We shall now express Eq. 13.24 in another way by introducing the mass center. Note in the diagram we have employed the vector $\boldsymbol{\rho}_i$ as the displacement vector from the center of mass to the ith particle. We can accordingly say:

$$\boldsymbol{r}_i = \boldsymbol{r}_c + (\boldsymbol{r}_i - \boldsymbol{r}_c) = \boldsymbol{r}_c + \boldsymbol{\rho}_i \qquad \textbf{13.25}$$

Differentiating with respect to time, we get:

$$\dot{\boldsymbol{r}}_i = \dot{\boldsymbol{r}}_c + (\dot{\boldsymbol{r}}_i - \dot{\boldsymbol{r}}_c) = \dot{\boldsymbol{r}}_c + \dot{\boldsymbol{\varrho}}_i$$

$$\therefore\ \boldsymbol{V}_i = \boldsymbol{V}_c + \dot{\boldsymbol{\varrho}}_i \qquad \textbf{13.26}$$

From our earlier discussions on simple relative motion we can say that $\dot{\boldsymbol{\varrho}}$ is the motion of the ith particle *relative to the mass center*. Substituting the above relation into the expression for kinetic energy, Eq. 13.24, we get:

$$KE = \sum_{i=1}^{n} \tfrac{1}{2}m_i(\boldsymbol{V}_c + \dot{\boldsymbol{\varrho}}_i)^2 = \sum_{i=1}^{n} \tfrac{1}{2}m_i(\boldsymbol{V}_c + \dot{\boldsymbol{\varrho}}_i)\cdot(\boldsymbol{V}_c + \dot{\boldsymbol{\varrho}}_i)$$

Carrying out the dot product, we have:

$$KE = \tfrac{1}{2}\sum_{i=1}^{n} m_i V_c^2 + \sum_{i=1}^{n} m_i \boldsymbol{V}_c\cdot\dot{\boldsymbol{\varrho}}_i + \tfrac{1}{2}\sum_{i=1}^{n} m_i\dot{\rho}_i^2 \qquad \textbf{13.27}$$

Since $\boldsymbol{V}_c$ is common for all values of the summation index, we can extract it from the summation operation, and this leaves:

$$KE = \tfrac{1}{2}\left(\sum_{i=1}^{n} m_i\right)V_c^2 + \boldsymbol{V}_c\cdot\left(\sum_{i=1}^{n} m_i\dot{\boldsymbol{\varrho}}_i\right) + \tfrac{1}{2}\sum_{i=1}^{n} m_i\dot{\rho}_i^2 \qquad \textbf{13.28}$$

Replace:

$$\sum_{i=1}^{n} m_i \text{ by } M \quad \text{and} \quad \sum_{i=1}^{n} m_i\dot{\boldsymbol{\varrho}}_i \text{ by } \frac{d}{dt}\sum_{i=1}^{n} m_i\boldsymbol{\varrho}_i$$

We then have:

$$KE = \tfrac{1}{2}MV_c^2 + \boldsymbol{V}_c\cdot\frac{d}{dt}\sum_{i=1}^{n} m_i\boldsymbol{\varrho}_i + \tfrac{1}{2}\sum_{i=1}^{n} m_i\dot{\rho}_i^2 \qquad \textbf{13.29}$$

But the expression

$$\sum_{i=1}^{n} m_i\boldsymbol{\varrho}_i$$

represents the first mass moment of the system of masses about the center of mass for the system. Clearly, this quantity must be zero. The expression for kinetic energy becomes:

$$\boxed{KE = \tfrac{1}{2}MV_c^2 + \tfrac{1}{2}\sum_{i=1}^{n} m_i\dot{\rho}_i^2} \qquad \textbf{13.30}$$

Thus we see that the kinetic energy for some reference can be considered to be composed of *two parts*: *the kinetic energy of the total mass moving relative to the reference with the velocity of the mass center, plus the kinetic energy of the motion of the particles relative to the mass center.*

It should be clear from our discussions in Chapter 11 on simple relative motion that the term $\frac{1}{2}\sum m_i\dot{\rho}_i^2$ will have the same value for any reference translating relative to xyz.

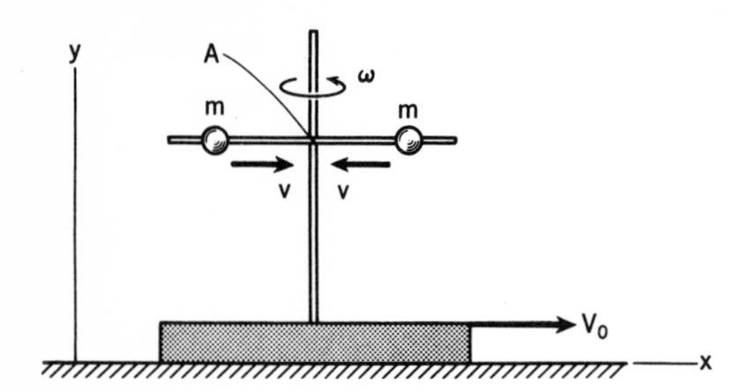

Fig. 13.18

EXAMPLE 13.12

Shown in Fig. 13.18 is a hypothetical vehicle moving at speed V_o. On this vehicle are two bodies each of mass m sliding along a rod at a speed v relative to the rod. This rod is rotating at an angular speed ω rad/sec relative to the vehicle. What is the kinetic energy of the bodies relative to the ground when they are at a distance r from point A?

Clearly the center of mass corresponds to point A and is thus moving at a speed V_o relative to the ground. Hence, we have as part of the kinetic energy the term:

$$\tfrac{1}{2}MV_c^2 = mV_o^2 \tag{a}$$

The velocity of each ball relative to the center of mass is easily formed using cylindrical components. Thus:

$$\dot{\rho}^2 = \dot{r}^2 + (\omega r)^2 = v^2 + (\omega r)^2 \tag{b}$$

The total kinetic energy of the two masses relative to the ground is then:

$$KE = mV_o^2 + m[v^2 + (\omega r)^2] \tag{c}$$

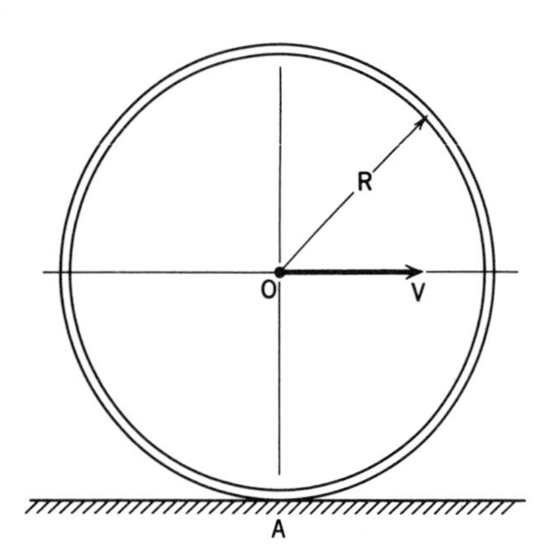

Fig. 13.19

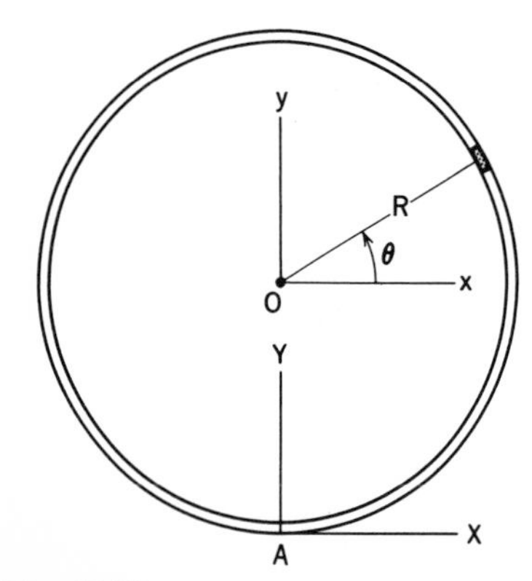

Fig. 13.20

EXAMPLE 13.13

A uniform hoop of radius R is rolling without slipping such that O, the center, moves at a speed V (Fig. 13.19). If the hoop weighs W lb, what is the kinetic energy of the hoop?

The main problem here is to find the kinetic energy of the hoop relative to the mass center O, i.e., relative to a reference xy translating with the mass center as seen from the ground reference XY (see Fig. 13.20). The motion relative to xy is clearly simple rotation; accordingly, we must find the angular velocity of the hoop for this reference. From our earlier studies in physics we know that the no-slipping condition means that the point of contact of the hoop with the ground has instantaneously a zero velocity. Thus, observing from a stationary reference XY, you learned that the body has a pure instantaneous rotational motion about the point of contact. The angular velocity ω for this motion is then easily evaluated by considering point O rotating about the instantaneous center of rotation A. Thus:

$$\omega = \frac{V}{R} \tag{a}$$

Since reference xy translates relative to reference XY, it should be clear that an observer on xy sees the same angular velocity ω for the hoop as the observer on XY. Accordingly, we can now readily evaluate the second term on the right side of Eq. 13.30. Using elements of the hoop $R\,d\theta$ in length, as shown in Fig. 13.20, having a mass per unit length of $W/(2\pi R g_0)$. we have:

$$\frac{1}{2}\sum_{i=1}^{n} m_i\dot{\rho}_i^2 = \frac{1}{2}\int_0^{2\pi}\left[\frac{W}{(g_0)(2\pi R)}(R\,d\theta)\right]\left(\frac{V}{R}R\right)^2$$

$$= \frac{1}{2} \frac{W}{g_0} V^2 \qquad \textbf{(b)}$$

The kinetic energy of the hoop is then in accordance with Eq. 13.30:

$$KE = \frac{1}{2} \frac{W}{g_0} V^2 + \frac{1}{2} \frac{W}{g_0} V^2 = \frac{W}{g_0} V^2 \qquad \textbf{(c)}$$

If the body were some generalized cylinder such as a tire of radius R having O as the center of mass with symmetrical distribution of mass about O, we would express Eq. (b) as follows:

$$\frac{1}{2} \sum_{1}^{n} m_i \dot{\rho}_i = \frac{1}{2} \iiint_M (dm)(r\omega)^2 \qquad \textbf{(d)}$$

You will recall from physics that

$$\iiint r^2 \, dm$$

is the second moment of inertia of the body taken about O. That is:

$$I_{oo} = \iiint r^2 \, dm$$

Thus we have for the kinetic energy of such a body:

$$KE = \frac{1}{2} \frac{W}{g} V^2 + \frac{1}{2} I_{oo} \omega^2 \qquad \textbf{(e)}$$

You may also recall from physics that we could employ the so-called *radius of gyration* k to express I_{oo} as follows:

$$I_{oo} = k^2 M \qquad \textbf{(f)}$$

Hence Eq. (e) can be given as:

$$KE = \frac{1}{2} \frac{W}{g} V^2 + \frac{1}{2} k^2 M \omega^2 \qquad \textbf{(g)}$$

We shall examine the kinetic-energy formulations of rigid bodies carefully in a later chapter. Here we have simply reviewed certain familiar topics pertaining to plane motion of a rolling rigid body. We shall utilize some of these ideas in examples and homework problems.

13.8 Work-Kinetic Energy Expressions Based on Center of Mass

The work-kinetic energy expressions of Section 13.6 were developed for a system of particles without regard to the mass center. We shall now introduce this point into the work-kinetic energy formulations. You will recall that Newton's law for the mass center of any system of particles is:

$$F = M\ddot{r}_c \qquad \textbf{13.31}$$

We can immediately formulate the energy equation for the center of mass alluded to in the footnote on page 399 from the results of Section 13.1. That is:

$$\int_1^2 \boldsymbol{F}\cdot d\boldsymbol{r}_c = (\tfrac{1}{2}MV_c^2)_2 - (\tfrac{1}{2}MV_c^2)_1 \tag{13.32}$$

where the work is that of the *total external force* moving with the mass center. Note from Eq. 13.30 that this expression for work is related to only *part* of the kinetic energy of the system of particles.

The remaining part of the kinetic energy change is shown in the Appendix II to be related to the forces by this rather cumbersome equation:

$$\sum_{i=1}^{n} \int_1^2 \boldsymbol{F}_i\cdot d\boldsymbol{\varrho}_i + \sum_{i=1}^{n}\left(\int_1^2 \sum_{j=1}^{n} \boldsymbol{f}_{ij}\cdot d\boldsymbol{\varrho}_i\right) = \Delta\left(\frac{1}{2}\sum_{i=1}^{n} m_i\dot{\rho}_i^2\right) \tag{13.33}$$

Equation 13.32 relates the motion of the mass center to the external forces, but the above equation relates the motion of the particle *relative* to the mass center with the work done by external and internal forces as they undergo motions relative to the mass center.

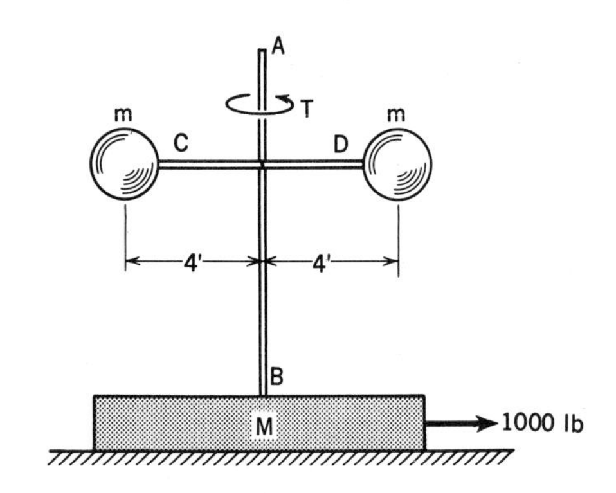

Fig. 13.21

EXAMPLE 13.14

Shown in Fig. 13.21 is a block having a mass M of 500 lbm. It is acted on by a 1000-lb constant force as shown in the diagram. Two bodies each having equal mass m of 50 lbm are mounted on a bar CD which is made to rotate about axis AB by a torque T of 50 lb-ft from a motor mounted on the block. If the 1000-lb load and the 50 lb-ft torque are applied simultaneously, what is the velocity of the block after it has moved 10 ft and what is the angular velocity of rod CD after it has rotated 3 revolutions? The coefficient of friction between block and ground is 0.3.

Clearly the center of mass of the system of three bodies has the same motion as the block itself. In the vertical direction we have zero acceleration of the center of mass. Hence, according to Eq. 15.31 in this direction we have for the normal force N:

$$N = (500) + (2)(50) = 600 \text{ lb} \tag{a}$$

The friction force then is given as $(0.3)(600) = 180$ lb. We may now employ Eq. 13.32 for the horizontal motion. Thus

$$(1000 - 180)(10) = \frac{1}{2}\left[\frac{500 + (2)(50)}{32.2}\right]V^2$$

$$\therefore\ V = 29.7 \text{ ft/sec} \tag{b}$$

To get the angular speed of the rod CD relative to the block we use Eq. 13.33. The only force system that does work when the bodies move relative to the mass center is that of the constant torque T. You will recall from Chapter 10 that the work of a couple rotating about an axis normal to the couple is

$$\int_{\theta_1}^{\theta_2} T\, d\theta$$

and so we have for this case:

$$(50)(2\pi)(3) = \frac{50}{g_0}(4\omega)^2$$

$$\therefore \omega = 6.15 \text{ rad/sec} \qquad \textbf{(c)}$$

EXAMPLE 13.15

In previous problems involving vehicles (such as in Examples 13.4 and 13.5), we have often neglected the rotational effects of the wheels. We shall now include these effects for the case of the farm tractor shown in Fig. 13.22. The tractor plus driver weigh 3000 lb. Wheels A have a weight of 15 lb each, a geometrical diameter of 2 ft, and a radius of gyration (see end of Example 13.13) of 1 ft. Wheels B each weigh 80 lb and have a geometrical diameter of 5 ft and a radius of gyration of 2 ft. If a constant torque of 100 ft-lb is delivered by the drive system to the rear wheels, what is the speed of the tractor when it has moved 10 ft after starting from rest? Neglect rolling resistance and neglect windage resistance. Also neglect the rotational effects of the small front wheels.

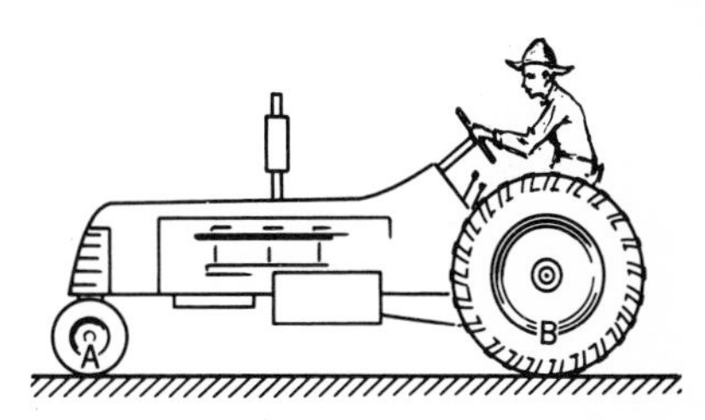

Fig. 13.22

We apply Eq. 13.32 using f to denote the driving force from the torque transmitted to the drive wheels. Since the center of mass is fixed relative to the frame of the tractor, it moves with the tractor body. Accordingly we have:

$$\int_0^{10} f\, dx = \tfrac{1}{2}MV^2 \qquad \textbf{(a)}$$

Inserting known values, we get on integrating and solving for f:

$$f = 4.66V^2 \qquad \textbf{(b)}$$

If we were to neglect rotational effects of the drive wheels, we could immediately determine f as follows:

$$f = \frac{\text{torque}}{\text{radius}} = \frac{100}{2.5} = 40$$

Solving for V in Eq. (b), we get

$$V = \sqrt{8.56} = 2.93 \text{ ft/sec} \qquad \textbf{(c)}$$

The above result essentially stems from a single-particle approach to this problem. By *including* the rotational effects of the drive wheels we must consider f as unknown. Accordingly, for the problem at hand we have a single equation with two unknowns.

For a second independent equation, we consider Eq. 13.33 for this case. The work done by internal and external forces on the mass elements moving relative to the center of mass can be determined by computing the work done by the 100 ft-lb torque delivered from the transmission to the drive wheels plus the work developed by the torque $(f)(2.5)$ on the drive wheels from the ground. For a travel of 10 ft the drive wheels rotate $10/\pi 5 = 0.636$ revolutions $= 4$ radians. Accordingly, we get from Eq. 13.33 for this movement the following relation:

$$[100 - f(2.5)]4 = 2[\tfrac{1}{2}k^2 M\omega^2] \qquad \textbf{(d)}$$

Noting from the no-slipping conditions (see Example 13.13) that $\omega = V/2.5$, we get:

$$400 - 10f = 2\left[\frac{1}{2}(2^2)\left(\frac{80}{32.2}\right)\left(\frac{V}{2.5}\right)^2\right] = 1.590V^2 \qquad \textbf{(e)}$$

Substituting for f from Eq. (b) we have:

$$400 - (10)(4.66V^2) = 1.590V^2$$

$$\therefore\ V = \sqrt{8.31} = 2.88 \text{ ft/sec} \qquad \textbf{(f)}$$

Comparing results from Eqs. (c) and (f) we see that actually little error would have been introduced here had we used the single-particle approach. This may help justify our having made this assumption in so many of the earlier problems.

---

*EXAMPLE 13.16

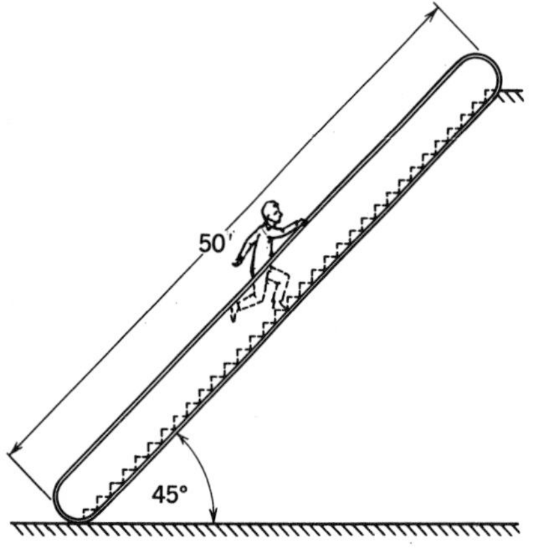

Fig. 13.23

A 180-lb man runs up an escalator while it is not in operation in 10 seconds (see Fig. 13.23). What is the average power developed by the man in units of horsepower? Suppose next that the escalator is running so that the escalator steps move at a speed of 2 ft/sec. What is then the power developed by the man as seen by the ground reference if he moves at the same speed relative to the escalator steps as he did when the escalator is not in operation?

What we mean by "power" here for a given reference is the rate at which work is being done by *reactions* to forces exerted by the man on the surrounding objects in order to change the position and speed of his center of mass in the given reference. Thus, for the reference of interest we can equate the change in kinetic energy plus the change in potential energy of a particle having the mass of the man and moving with his mass center, with the work done by the forces from the surroundings performed along the path of the center of mass. In this problem there is no change in kinetic energy and so we have from Eq. 13.20 for the ground reference:

$$W_{1-2} = (180)(50 \sin 45°) = 6360 \text{ ft-lb} \qquad \textbf{(a)}$$

The work, W_{1-2} is not dependent on the speed of the escalator and accordingly applies to both situations of interest to us here. However, the time in which this work is performed does depend on the speed of the escalator. In the stationary case, the action was accomplished in 10 seconds and so the average power developed by the man is:

$$\text{Power} = \frac{6360}{10} = 636 \text{ ft-lb/sec} = 1.155 \text{ hp} \qquad \textbf{(b)}$$

For the moving escalator the speed of the man relative to the ground is now $2 + (50/10) = 7$ ft/sec. Accordingly, the time involved is $50/7 = 7.14$ sec. The power developed by the man as seen from the ground reference is then, on the average:

$$\text{Power} = \frac{6360}{7.14} = 892 \text{ ft-lb/sec} = 1.630 \text{ hp} \qquad \textbf{(c)}$$

In considering Eqs. (b) and (c) you will probably feel that something is wrong. Shouldn't the man be "exerting himself" more when the escalator is stationary rather than less compared to when the escalator is moving? The answer to this is yes, as we can now show. The fatigue that the man feels for the action will be related to the work he develops as seen from a reference moving with the escalator stairs. Thus, Eq. (a) is related to the fatigue developed by the man for the stationary case. For the moving escalator we note that the man is on the escalator for a time Δt of 7.14 sec as formulated earlier. The increase in elevation Δh for the center of mass of the man as seen from the escalator stairs is easily evaluated by using this time interval and noting that the speed of the man relative to the escalator is the same as the stationary case—namely 5 ft/sec. Thus we have for Δh:

$$\Delta h = (5)(7.14)(0.707) = 25.2 \text{ ft} \qquad \textbf{(d)}$$

Accordingly the work W_{1-2} for the moving reference is then:

$$W_{1-2} = (180)(25.2) = 4540 \text{ ft-lb} \qquad \textbf{(e)}$$

Thus in the escalator reference, where the formulations of mechanics relate to fatigue, the man does indeed do less work and is accordingly less tired. As for the power output we have:

$$\text{Power} = \frac{4540}{7.14} = 636 \text{ ft-lb/sec} \qquad \textbf{(f)}$$

which shows that there is no change for this quantity. Thus the man must have the same strength and agility for both actions (we are not here concerned with getting on and off the escalator), but the escalator reduces the demands on his endurance.

There is increased need to better understand work-physiology relations for man. This problem should indicate somewhat the caution one must employ in relating the laws of mechanics with man's physiological capabilities.*

* Suppose a man is holding a 10-lb weight out in front of him. If he holds it stationary no work at all is developed by the man as seen from the ground reference. Yet this does not prevent him from becoming fatigued. Thus, work as defined in mechanics is not simply related to physiological capabilities of man.

13.9 Closure

In this chapter we have examined certain methods derived from Newton's law, mainly the energy methods. We considered a single particle and systems of particles. In the examples at the end of the chapter and in the homework problems we applied our results to certain simple plane motions of rigid bodies, relying somewhat on simple results relating to the kinematics of rigid bodies as learned in earlier physics courses. In Chapter 18 we shall more carefully consider energy relations for general rigid-body motion.

We now turn to yet another useful set of relations derived from Newton's law, namely the methods of linear momentum and moment of momentum for a particle and systems of particles.

PROBLEMS

1. [13.1] In Fig. 13.24, what constant force P is required to bring the 100-lb body, which starts from rest, to a velocity of 30 ft/sec in 20 ft? Neglect friction.

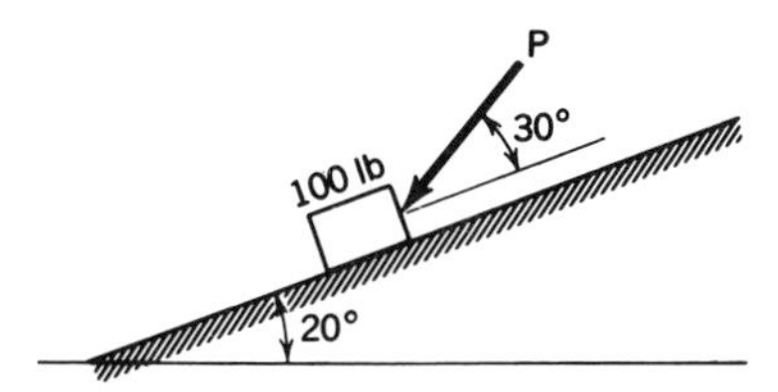

Fig. 13.24

2. [13.1] A light cable passes over a frictionless pulley (Fig. 13.25). Determine the velocity of the 100-lb block after it has moved 30 ft from rest. Neglect the inertia of the pulley.

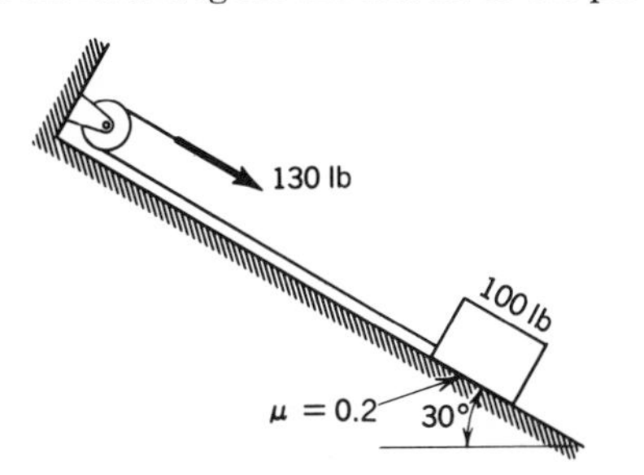

Fig. 13.25

3. [13.1] In Prob. 2, the pulley has a radius of 1 ft and has a resisting torque at the bearing of 10 lb-ft. Neglecting the inertia of the pulley and the mass of the cable, compute the kinetic energy of the 100-lb block after it has moved 30 ft from rest.

4. [13.1] In Fig. 13.26, a light cable is wrapped around two drums fixed between a pair of blocks. The system weighs 100 lb. If a 50-lb tension is exerted on the free end of the cable, what is the velocity change of the system after 10 ft of travel down the incline? The body starts from rest. Take μ for all surfaces as 0.05.

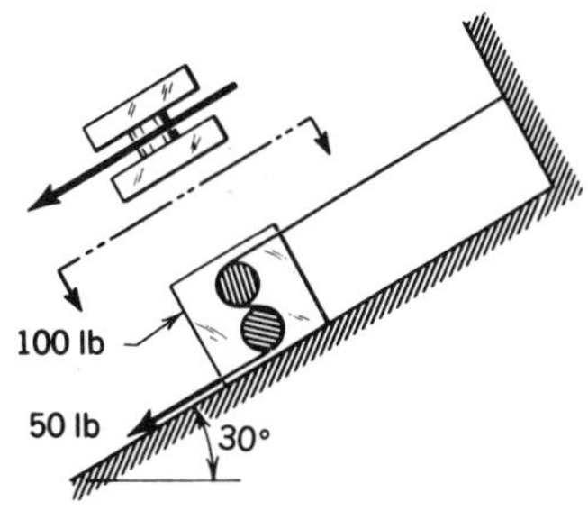

Fig. 13.26

5. [13.1] Explain qualitatively what effects would be present if the mass of the cable were not neglected in Prob. 4.

6. [13.1] In Fig. 13.27, a mass on a spring is moved so that it extends the spring 4 in. from its unextended position. If there is a coefficient of friction of 0.3 between the mass and the supporting surface:

(a) What is the velocity of the mass as it returns to the undeformed configuration of the spring?

(b) How far will the spring be compressed when the mass stops instantaneously before starting to the left?

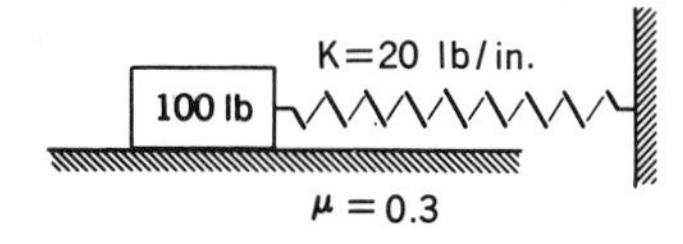

Fig. 13.27

7. [13.1] A truck-trailer is shown in Fig. 13.28 carrying three crushed junk automobile cubes each weighing 2500 lb. An electromagnet is used to pick up the cubes as the truck moves by. Suppose the truck starts at position 1 by applying a constant 300 in.-lb torque on the drive wheels. The magnet picks up only one cube C

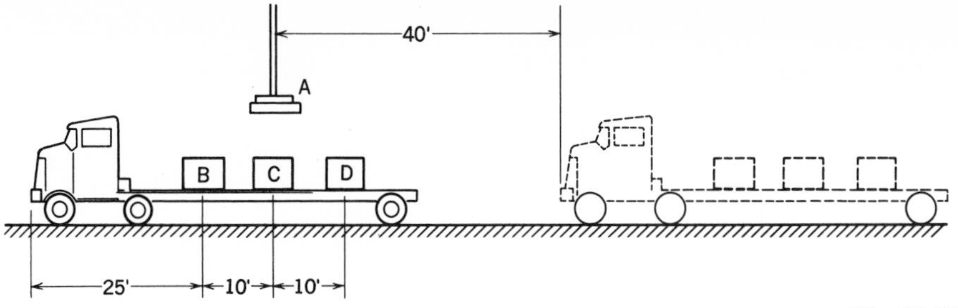

Fig. 13.28

during the process. What will the velocity of the truck be when it has moved a total of 100 ft? The truck unloaded weighs 5000 lb and has a tire diameter of 18 in. Neglect the rotational effects of the tires and all frictional effects.

8. [13.1] Do the previous problem if the first cube B and the last cube D are removed as they go by the magnet.

9. [13.1] A 200-lb block is dropped on the system of springs (Fig. 13.29). If $K_1 = 600$ lb/ft and $K_2 = 200$ lb/ft, what is the maximum force developed on the body?

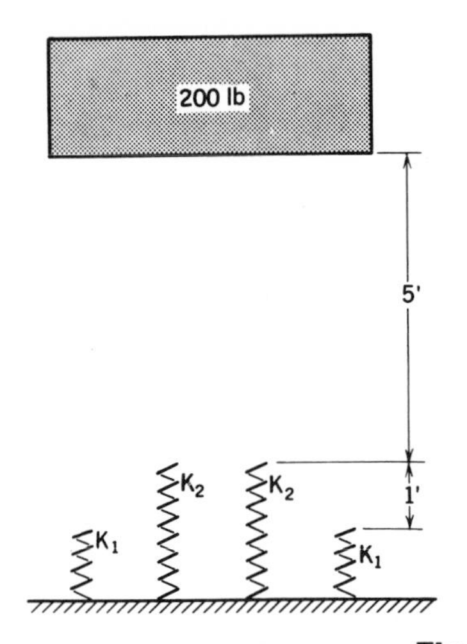

Fig. 13.29

10. [13.1] Shown in Fig. 13.30 is a classroom demonstration unit for illustrating vibrations and interactions of bodies. We have shown a body A having a mass of 1 lbm moving to the left at a speed of 6 ft/sec at the position indicated. The body rides on a cushion of air supplied from the tube B through small openings in the tube. If there is a constant friction force of 0.3 ounce, what speed will A have when it returns to the position shown in the diagram? There are two springs at C each having a spring constant of 1 lb/ft.

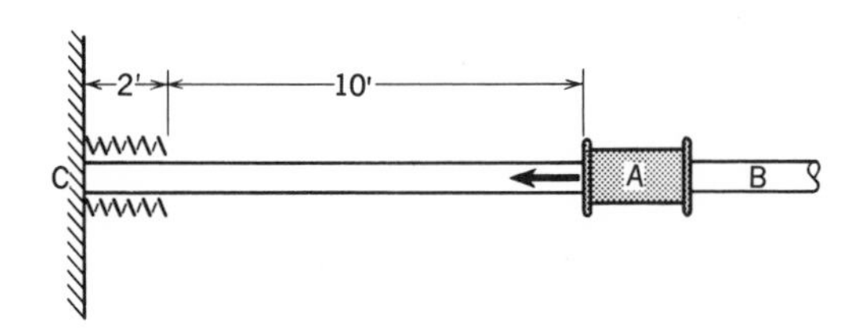

Fig. 13.30

11. [13.1] A block weighing 50 lb is shown in Fig. 13.31 on an inclined surface. It is released at the position shown at a rest condition. What will be the maximum compression of the spring? The spring has a spring constant K of 10 lb/in., and the coefficient of friction between the block and the incline is 0.3.

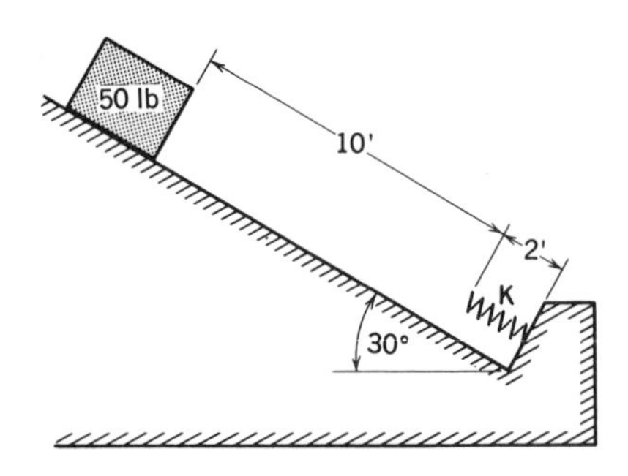

Fig. 13.31

12. [13.1] In Fig. 13.32 a plate AA is held down by screws C and D so that a force of 50 lb is developed in each spring. Weight W of 200 lb is placed on plate AA and released suddenly. What is the maximum distance that plate AA descends if the plate can slide freely down the vertical guide rods? Take $K = 20$ lb/in.

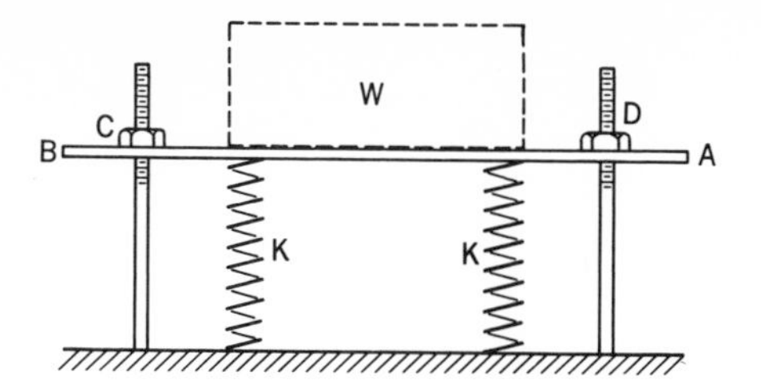

Fig. 13.32

13. [13.1] Do the previous problem for the case when plate AA is moved down an additional 2 inches before the weight is applied.

14. [13.1] A particle of mass 0.3 lbm is acted on by the following force field:

$$\boldsymbol{F} = 5x\boldsymbol{i} + (16 + 2y)\boldsymbol{j} + 20\boldsymbol{k} \text{ lb}$$

When it is at the origin the particle has a velocity $\boldsymbol{V}_0$ given as:

$$\boldsymbol{V}_0 = 5\boldsymbol{i} + 10\boldsymbol{j} + 8\boldsymbol{k} \text{ ft/sec}$$

What is its kinetic energy when it reaches position (20, 5, 10) while moving along a frictionless path? Does the shape of the path between the origin and (20, 5, 10) affect the result?

15. [13.1] A body A (Fig. 13.33) is released from a condition of rest on a frictionless circular surface. It then moves on a horizontal surface CD whose coefficient of friction with the body is 0.2. A spring having a spring constant K = 5 lb/in. is positioned at C as shown in the diagram. How much will the spring be compressed? The body weighs 10 lb.

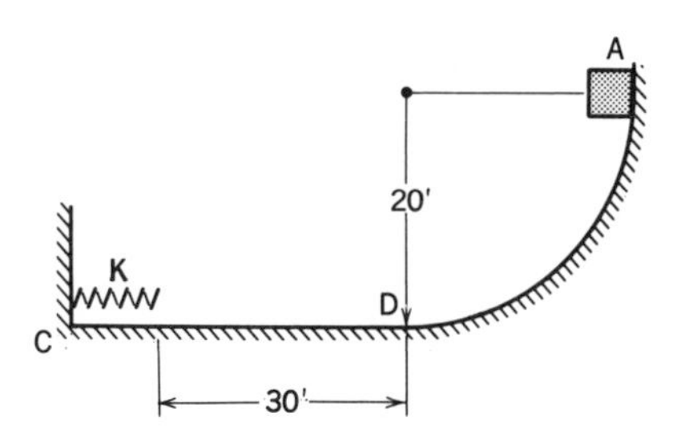

Fig. 13.33

16. [13.1] Do the preceding problem for the case of a nonlinear spring that requires $5x^2$ lb for a compression of x in.

17. [13.1] A car weighing 10 tons is rolling at a speed of 5 ft/sec toward a spring-stop system (Fig. 13.34). If the spring is nonlinear such that it develops $100x^2$ lb force for a deflection of x inches, what is the maximum deceleration that the car A undergoes?

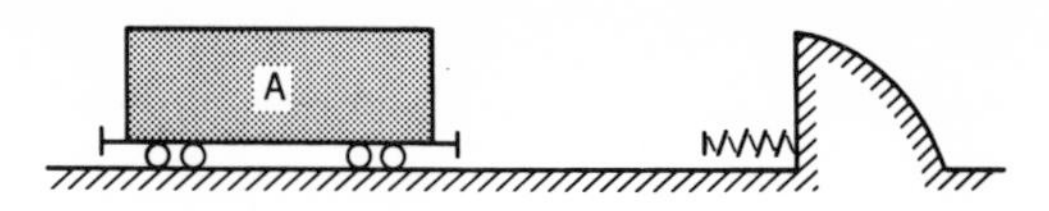

Fig. 13.34

18. [13.1] In Fig. 13.35 is shown a passenger ferry moving onto its dock to unload passengers. As it approaches the dock it has a speed of 3 knots (1 knot = 1.689 ft/sec). If the pilot reverses his engines just as the front of the ferry comes abreast of the first pilings at A, what constant reverse thrust will stop the ferry just as it reaches the ramp B? The ferry weighs 500 tons. Assume that it does not hit the side pilings and undergoes no resistance from them. Neglect the drag of the water.

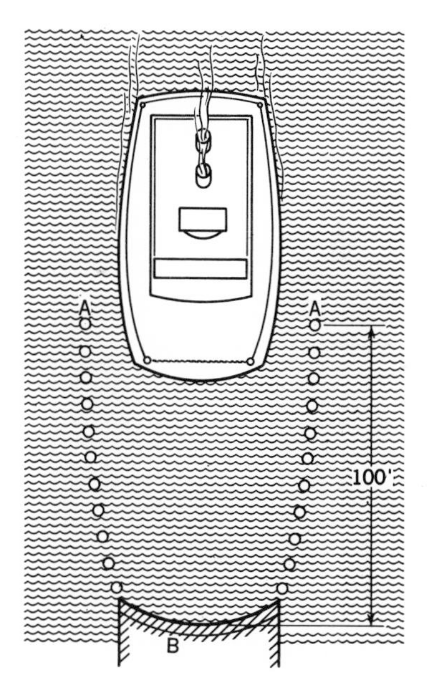

Fig. 13.35

19. [13.1] Do Prob. 18 assuming that the ferry rubs against the pilings as a result of a poor entrance and undergoes a resistance against its forward motion given as:

$$f = 2(x + 50)$$

where x is measured in feet from the first pilings at A to the front of the ferry.

20. [13.1] Shown in Fig. 13.36 is a uniform block A weighing 50 lb. It is hinged at C and supported by a small block B as shown in the diagram. A constant force F of 80 lb is applied to block B. What is the speed of B after it moves 5 ft? The mass of block B is 5 lbm and the coefficient of friction for all contact surfaces is 0.3.

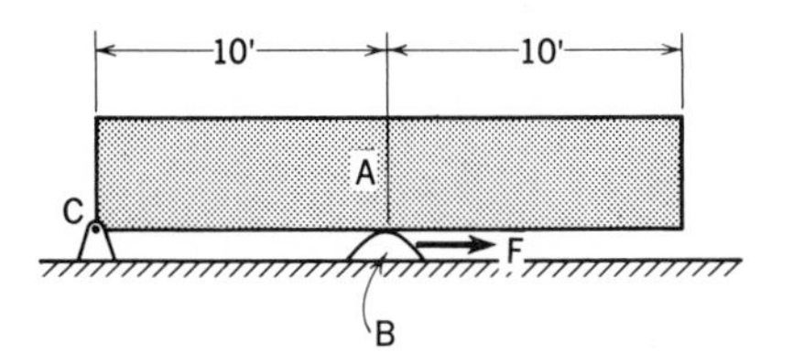

Fig. 13.36

21. [13.1] A triangular block of uniform density and total weight of 100 lb rests on a hinge and on a movable block B (see Fig. 13.37). If a constant force F of 150 lb is exerted on the block B, what will be its speed after it moves 10 ft? The mass of block B is 10 lbm and the coefficient of friction for all contact surfaces is 0.3.

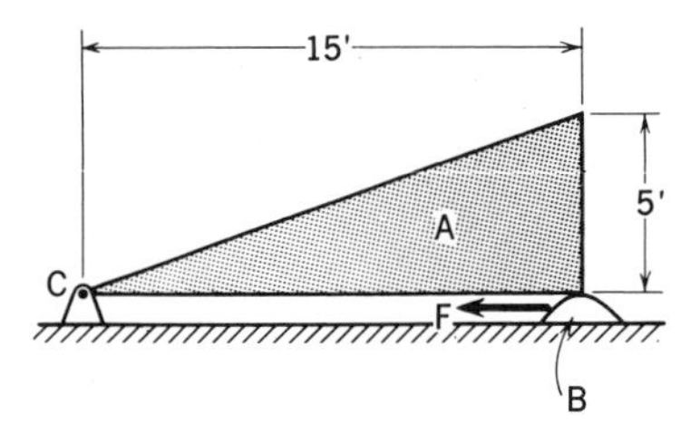

Fig. 13.37

22. [13.1] A block A weighing 20 lb is allowed to slide down an inclined slope. It is stopped at the bottom by two springs (see Fig. 13.38). The longer spring has a spring constant K_2 of 5 lb/in. and the shorter one has a spring constant K_1 of 20 lb/in. How close to the bottom does the block get? The coefficient of friction between block and slide is 0.1.

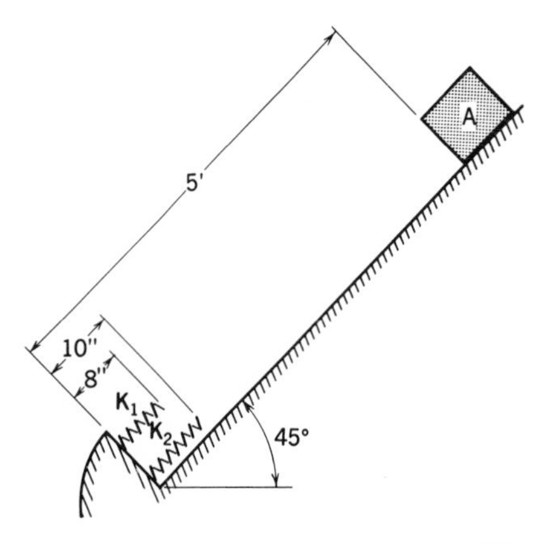

Fig. 13.38

23. [13.1] Do the previous problem for the case where the spring K_1 is nonlinear developing a force of $15x^2$ lb for a deflection of x inches. (Set up equation only.)

24. [13.1] Compute the work done by a compressor piston during a compression stroke. A diagram (called an indicator diagram) of the pressure-versus-piston position is shown in Fig. 13.39. At A, the beginning of the compression stroke, there are 1.7 ft³ of air. The outlet valve is then closed, and we shall consider that an isothermal compression takes place so that $pv =$ const., where v is the specific volume (ft³/lbm). When a 40-psig pressure is reached, the outlet valve opens and the pressure remains constant during the remainder of the stroke while air is pumped into the storage tank. During the compression stroke, the pressure on the rear face of the piston is -1 psig. (The remainder of the cycle consists of the return stroke, shown as a dashed line where the exhaust valve is closed, as the piston goes back and the inlet valve opens at D.)

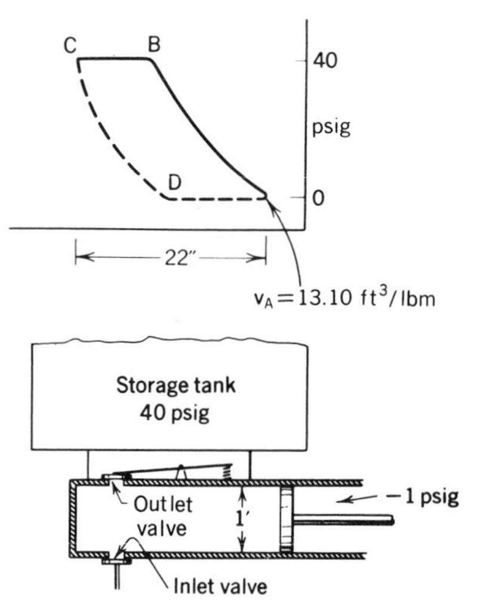

Fig. 13.39

25. [13.1] Referring to Example 12.5, develop an equation for determining how close to the end of the air gun the piston will reach. Solve by trial and error.

26. [13.1] In Fig. 13.40 is a spiral path given parametrically in terms of the parameter τ as follows:

$$x_p = A \sin \eta\tau$$

$$y_p = A \cos \eta\tau$$

$$z_p = C\tau$$

where A, η, and C are known constants. A particle P of mass 1 lbm is released from a position of rest 1 ft above the xy plane. It is constrained by a spring coiled around the path having a spring constant $K = 2$ lb/ft. The spring is unstretched when P is released. Neglecting friction, how far does P drop? Take $\eta = \pi/2$, $A = C = 1$.

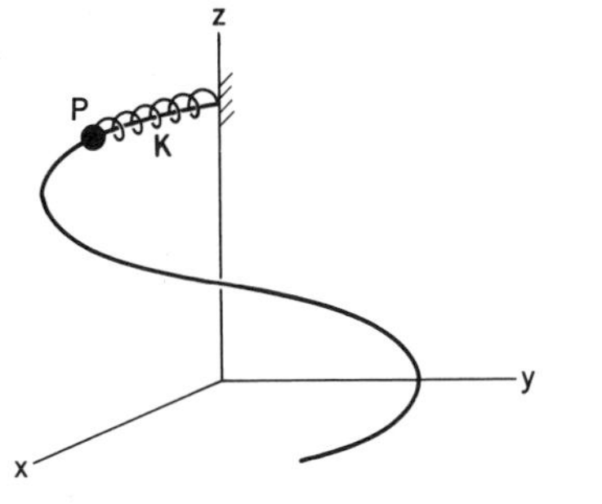

Fig. 13.40

27. [13.1] For the spiral path of the previous problem find the speed of the particle P after it has dropped 1 ft in elevation above the xy plane for the case when there is no restraining spring but instead a constant friction force along the path equal to 3 ounces.

28. [13.1] Shown in Fig. 13.41 is an electron in a circular orbit in a plane at right angles to the direction of a uniform magnetic field B. If the strength of B is slowly changed so that the radius of the orbit is halved, what is the ratio of the final to the initial angular speed of the electron? Explain steps you have taken.

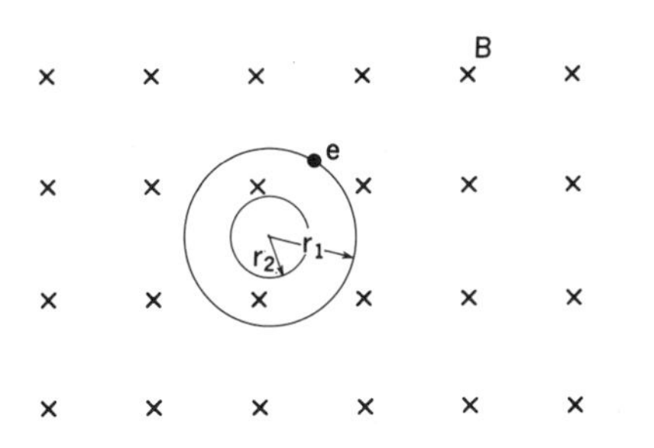

Fig. 13.41

29. [13.1] An electron moves under the action of a uniform electron field $\boldsymbol{E}$ and a uniform magnetic field $\boldsymbol{B}$ as shown in Fig. 13.42. The electric potential at (1) is 1 volt and at (2) is 2 volts. What is the velocity of the electron if it starts from rest? (The electron has a mass of 2.008×10^{-30} lbm and a charge of 1.60×10^{-19} coulomb.) Explain the contribution of the magnetic field to the action. Recall that 1 volt = 1 joule/coul.

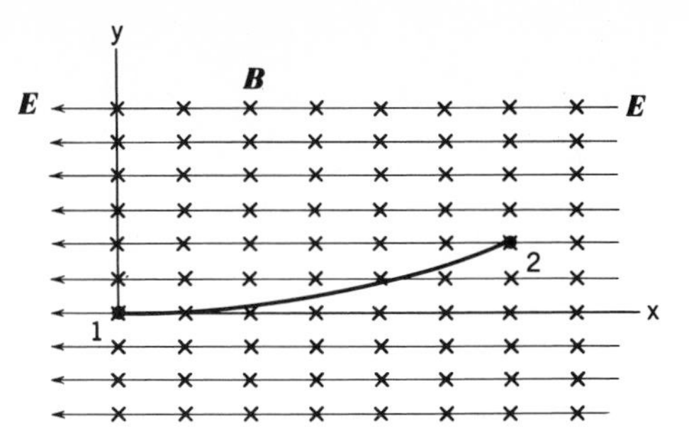

Fig. 13.42

30. [13.2] A jet plane is moving along the runway for a takeoff. If each of its four engines is developing 10,000 lb thrust, what is the horsepower developed when the plane is moving at a speed of 150 mph?

31. [13.2] In Fig. 13.43 is shown a top view of a children's apparatus to be found in many amusement parks. Small boats each weighing 100 lb are rotated in a tank of water. If the system is rotating with a speed $\dot{\theta}$ of 10 rpm, what is the kinetic energy of the system? Assume that each boat has two 60-lb children on board and that the kinetic energy of the supporting structure can be accounted for by "lumping" an additional 30 lbm into each boat. If a wattmeter indicates that 4 kilowatts of power are being absorbed by the motor turning the system, what is the drag for each boat? Take the mechanical efficiency of the motor to be 80 per cent. (1 kilowatt = 1.341 horsepower).

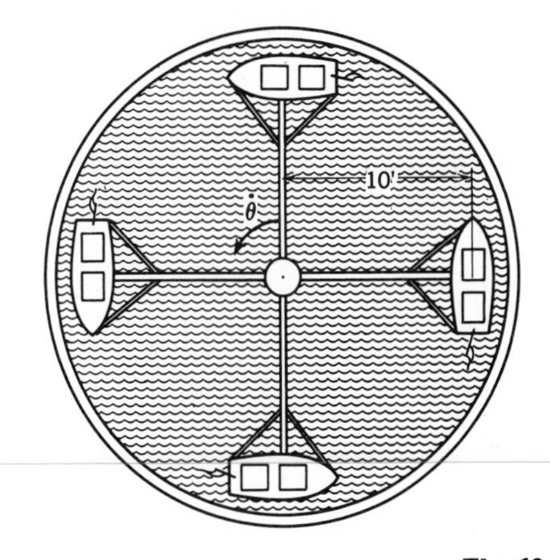

Fig. 13.43

32. [13.2] In the previous problem, using an average drag equal to one-half the drag at the running speed of 10 rmp, how many revolutions will the system rotate before it reaches 1 rpm after the motor has been disengaged?

33. [13.2] Shown in Fig. 13.44 is a device for cutting designs in metal plates. The plate is rotated at constant speed $\dot{\theta}$ while a cutting arm B remains stationary. A cutting tool A in this case is moved sinusoidally in the arm such that it has a motion given as $\delta \sin 10\dot{\theta}t$ about its center position. If the tool A undergoes a constant resisting force given as:

$$\boldsymbol{F} = F_r\boldsymbol{\varepsilon}_r + F_\theta\boldsymbol{\varepsilon}_\theta$$

set up formulation for the work developed on the plate from the cutting tool per revolution of the plate. What is the power put into the plate when tool is at radius R?

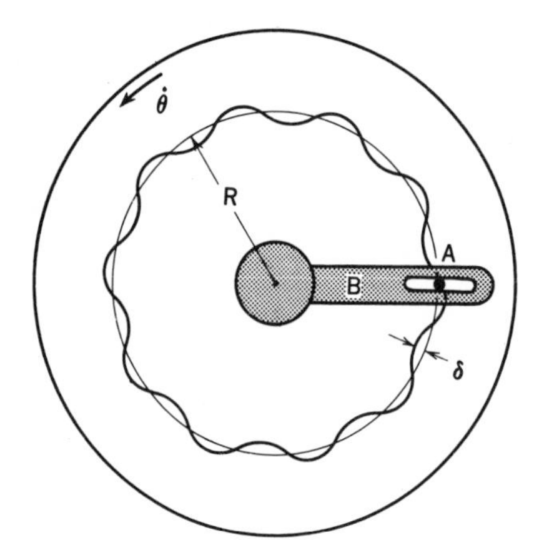

Fig. 13.44

34. [13.2] A rocket is undergoing static thrust tests in a test stand. A thrust of 300,000 lb is developed while 300 gallons of fuel, specific gravity 0.8, are burned per second. The exhaust products of combustion have a speed of 5000 ft/sec relative to the rocket. What power is being developed on the rocket? What is the power developed on the exhaust gases? (1 gallon = 0.1337 ft³.)

35. [13.2] An automobile engine under test is rotating 4400 rpm and develops a torque on a dynamometer (Fig. 13.45) of 350 in.-lb. What is the horsepower developed by the engine? If the dynamometer has a mechanical efficiency of 0.90, what is the kilowatt output of the generator?

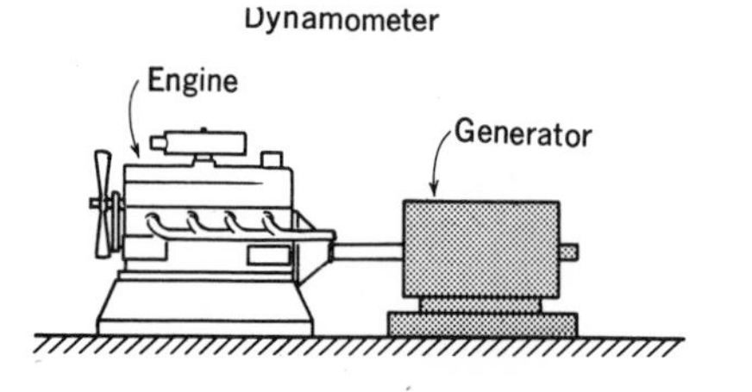

Fig. 13.45

36. [13.2] An aircraft carrier is shown in Fig. 13.46 in the process of launching an airplane via a catapult mechanism. Before leaving the catapult the plane has a speed of 120 mph relative to the ship. If the plane is accelerating at the rate $1g$ and if it weighs 20 tons, what power is being developed by the catapult system on the plane if we neglect drag? The thrust from the jet engines of the plane is 20,000 lb.

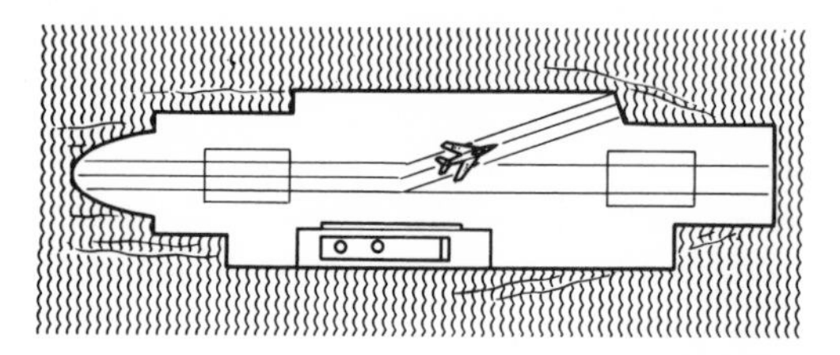
Fig. 13.46

37. [13.2] A 15-ton streetcar (Fig. 13.47) accelerates from rest at a constant rate a_0 until it reaches a speed V_1, at which time there is zero acceleration. The wind resistance is given as κV^2. Formulate expressions for power developed for the aforestated ranges of operation.

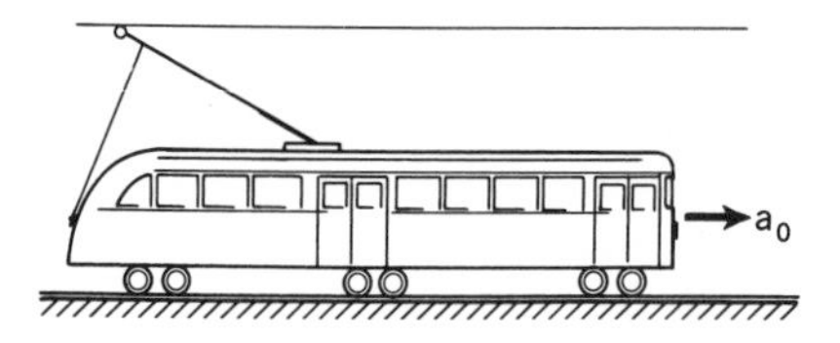

Fig. 13.47

38. [13.2] What is the maximum horsepower that can be developed by a streetcar (Fig. 13.47) weighing 15 tons? The car has a coefficient of static friction of 0.20 between wheels and rail and a drag given as $0.8V^2$ lb, where V is given in terms of ft/sec. All wheels are drive wheels.

39. [13.2] A 15-ton streetcar (Fig. 13.47) is moving at a speed of 10 mph. To cause the car to increase speed the conductor draws 20 kilowatts of power from the line. If this input is maintained constant and if the mechanical efficiency of the motors is 90 per cent, how long does it take to reach a speed of 30 mph? Neglect wind resistance. (1 kilowatt = 1.341 horsepower.)

40. [13.2] Do the preceding problem for the case where there is wind resistance given as $0.9V$ lb.

41. [13.3] A mass of one slug is moving at a speed of 50 ft/sec along a frictionless surface, which later inclines upward at an angle 45° (Fig. 13.48). A spring of constant $K = 5$ lb/in. is present along the incline. How high does the mass move?

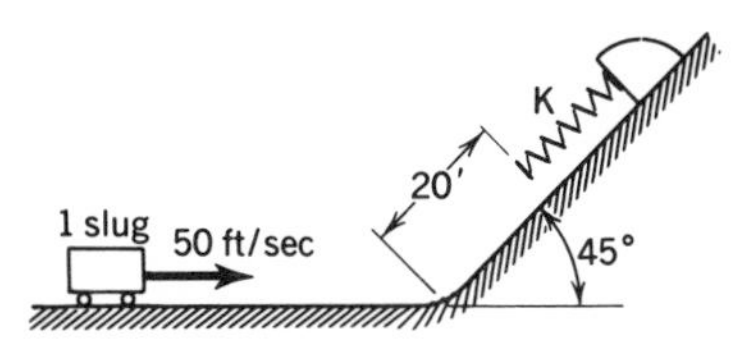

Fig. 13.48

42. [13.3] In Fig. 13.49, a block weighing 10 lb is released from rest, where the springs acting on the body are horizontal and have a tension of 10 lb each. What is the velocity of the block after it has descended 4 in. if each spring has a spring constant $K = 5$ lb/in.?

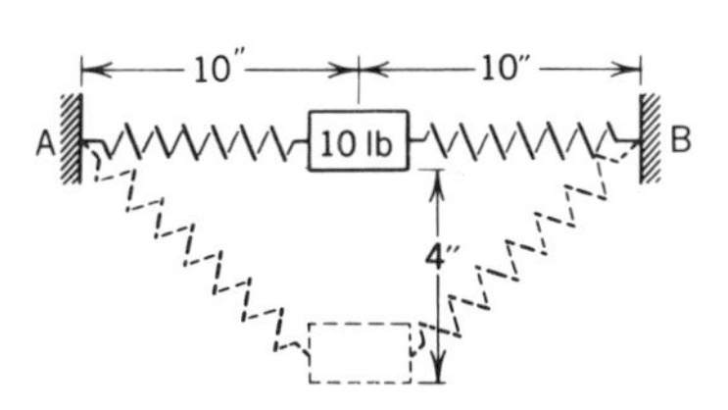

Fig. 13.49

43. [13.3] In Fig. 13.49, the walls at A and B are each moved in 4 in. If the weight is again released from the horizontal position, what will be the velocity after it descends 4 in.? Formulate the equation giving the maximum distance the block descends.

44. [13.3] A railroad car traveling 20 mi/hr runs into a stop at a railroad terminal (Fig. 13.50). A vehicle weighing 2600 lb is held by a linear-restoring system that has an equivalent spring constant of 100 lb/in. If the railroad car is assumed to stop suddenly and if the wheels in the vehicle are free to turn, what is the maximum force developed by the equivalent spring system? Neglect friction and the inertia of the wheels.

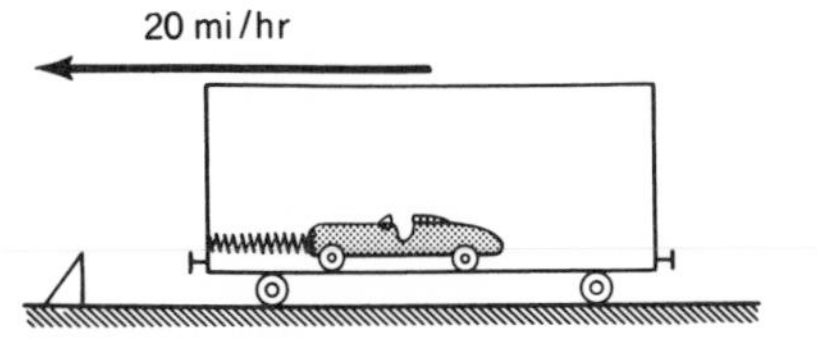

Fig. 13.50

45. [13.3] In Fig. 13.51, a ski jumper moves down the ramp aided only by gravity. If the skier moves 100 ft in the horizontal direction and lands very smoothly, what must be the angle θ for the landing incline? Neglect friction

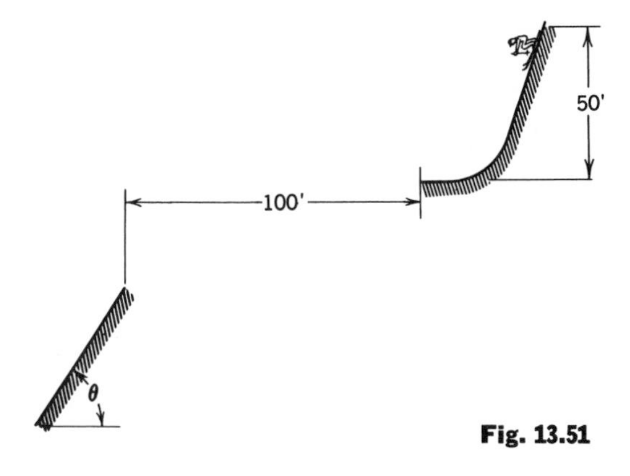

Fig. 13.51

46. [13.3] Given the following conservative force field:

$$\boldsymbol{F} = (10z + y)\boldsymbol{i} + (15yz + x)\boldsymbol{j} + \left(10x + \frac{15y^2}{2}\right)\boldsymbol{k}$$

Find the force potential to within an arbitrary constant. What work is done by the force field on a particle going from $\boldsymbol{r}_1 = 10\boldsymbol{i} + 2\boldsymbol{j} + 3\boldsymbol{k}$ to $\boldsymbol{r}_2 = -2\boldsymbol{i} + 4\boldsymbol{j} - 3\boldsymbol{k}$? [*Hint*: Note that if $\partial\phi/\partial x$ equals some function $(xy^2 + z)$ then we can say on integrating:

$$\phi = \frac{x^2y^2}{2} + zx + g(y, z)$$

where $g(y, z)$ is an arbitrary function of y and z. Note we have held y and z constant during the integration.]

47. [13.3] The following conservative force field is given:

$$\boldsymbol{F} = (5z \sin x + y)\boldsymbol{i} + (4yz + x)\boldsymbol{j} + (2y^2 - 5 \cos x)\boldsymbol{k}$$

Find the force potential up to an arbitrary constant. What is the work done on a particle starting at the origin and moving in a circular path of radius 2 ft to form a semicircle along the x axis? (See hint in last problem.)

48. [13.3] If in the preceding problem the coefficient 5 in the x component of $\boldsymbol{F}$ is changed to 1, is the force field still a conservative force field?

49. [13.4] If a meteor has a velocity of 35,000 miles per hour when it is 5000 miles from the center of the earth, what will its speed be when it is 100 miles from the earth's surface?

50. [13.4] A space station is in a circular parking orbit around the earth at a distance of 5000 miles from the center. A pistol is fired in a direction tangential to the trajectory of the space station with a speed of 5000 mph relative to the space station. What is the maximum distance from the earth reached by the bullet?

51. [13.4] In Fig. 13.52 we have a nonlinear spring which develops a force given as $6x^2$ lb, where x is the amount of compression of the spring in inches. Does such a spring develop a conservative force? If so, what is the potential energy stored in the spring for a deflection of 6 in.?

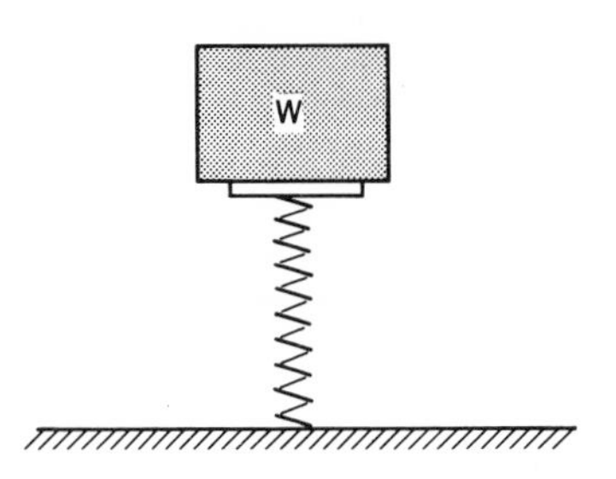

Fig. 13.52

52. [13.4] In the previous problem a weight W of 50 lb is released from rest on the nonlinear spring. What is the maximum deflection of the spring?

53. [13.4] A 30-lb weight falls on the platform as shown in Fig. 13.53. When the legs are at a 60° inclination, the spring is unstretched. What is the maximum elongation of the spring? Neglect friction and the mass of the support.

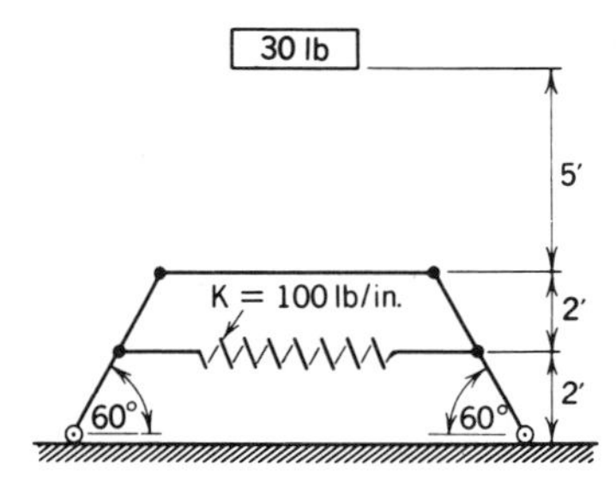

Fig. 13.53

54. [13.4] Weights A and B (both are 150 lb) are constrained to move in frictionless slots (Fig. 13.54). They are connected by a light bar of length 1 ft, and weight B is connected by two springs of equal spring constant K = 5 lb/in. The springs are unstretched when the connecting bar is vertical. What is the velocity of B when A descends a distance of 1 in.?

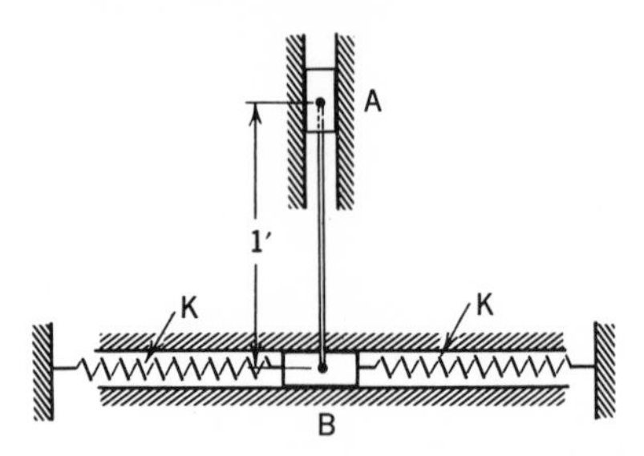

Fig. 13.54

55. [13.4] A body A can slide in a frictionless manner along rod CD (see Fig. 13.55). At the position shown, the spring along CD has been compressed 6 in. and A is at a distance of 4 ft from D. The spring connecting A to E has been elongated 1 in. What is the speed of A after it moves 1 ft? The spring constants are K_1 = 1.0 lb/in. and K_2 = 0.5 lb/in. The mass of A is 30 lbm.

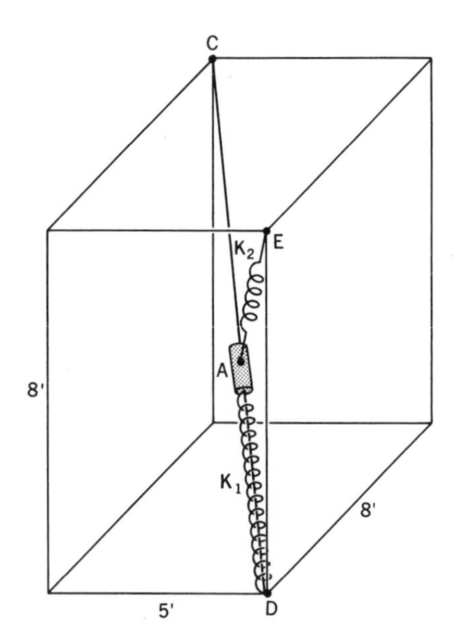

Fig. 13.55

56. [13.4] A body B weighing 120 lb slides in a frictionless slot on an inclined surface as shown in Fig. 13.56. An elastic cord connects B to A. The cord has a "spring constant" of 2 lb/in. If the body B is released from rest from a position where the elastic cord is unstretched, what is its speed after it moves 1 ft?

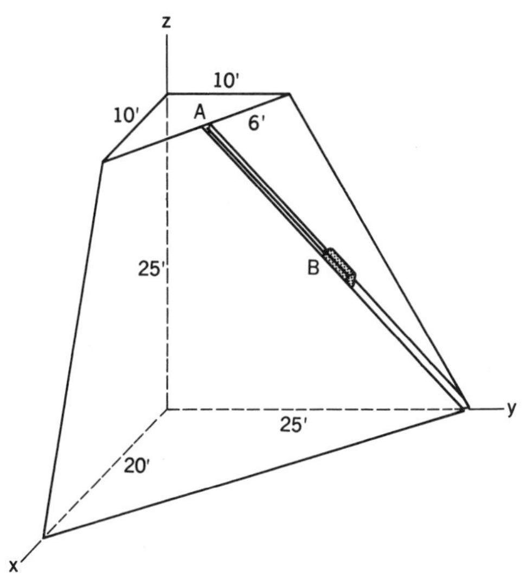

Fig. 13.56

57. [13.4] Do the preceding problem for the case when it requires $0.2x^2$ lb for a stretch of x inches of the cord.

58. [13.5] A constant-torque electric motor A is hoisting a weight W of 30 lb as has been shown in Fig. 13.57. An inextensible cable connects the weight W to the motor over a stationary drum of diameter $D = 1$ ft. The diameter d of the motor drive is 6 in. and the delivered torque is 150 lb-ft. The coefficient of friction for the drum and cable is 0.2. If the system is started from rest, what is the angular speed of the motor after the weight W has been raised 5 ft?

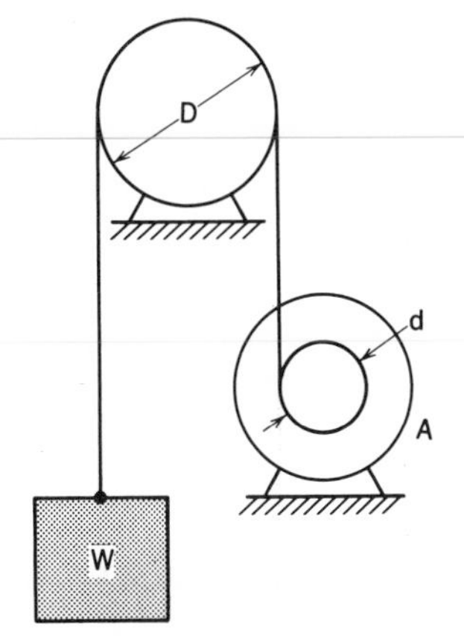

Fig. 13.57

59. [13.5] Shown in Fig. 13.58 is a body A, weighing 10 lb, which can slide along a fixed rod BB. A spring is shown connected between fixed point C and the mass. AC is 2 ft in length when the spring is unextended. If the body is released from rest at the configuration shown, what is its speed when it reaches the y axis? Assume a constant friction force of 6 ounces acts on the body A. The spring constant K is 1 lb/in.

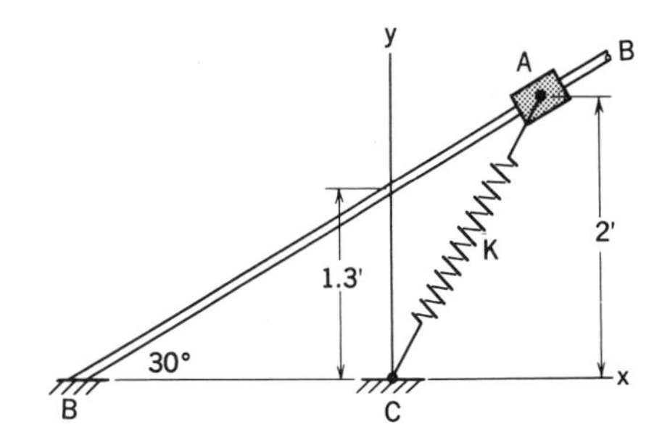

Fig. 13.58

60. [13.5] A body A (see Fig. 13.59) is restrained by an inextensible light wire in a circular path. The body A has a speed of 5 ft/sec and there is no friction. If the body A is now drawn in by a constant radial force of 2 lb, what is the speed of A when it is a distance 1 ft from the center? The mass of A is 1 lbm. Now use the conservation of moment of momentum principle (see Section 12.10) to compute the radial and transverse velocities when $r = 1$ ft.

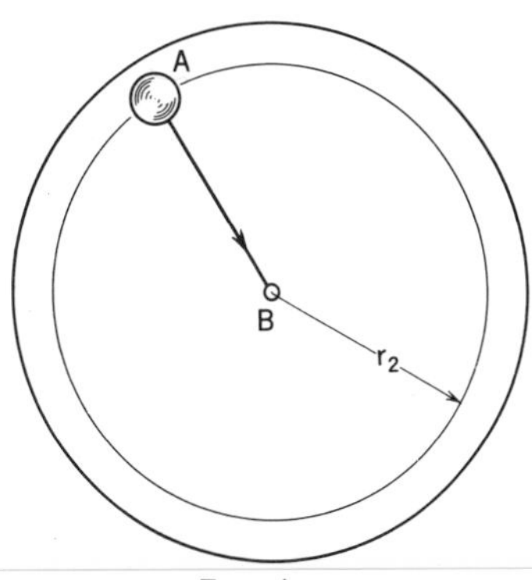

Fig. 13.59

61. [13.5] Shown in Fig. 13.60 is a diesel-powered electric train moving up a 7° grade. If a torque of 500 ft-lb is developed at each of 6 drive wheels, what is the increase in speed of the train after it moves 100 yards? The train has initially a speed of 10 miles/hour and weighs 10 tons. The drive wheels have a diameter of 2 ft. Neglect rotational effects of wheels.

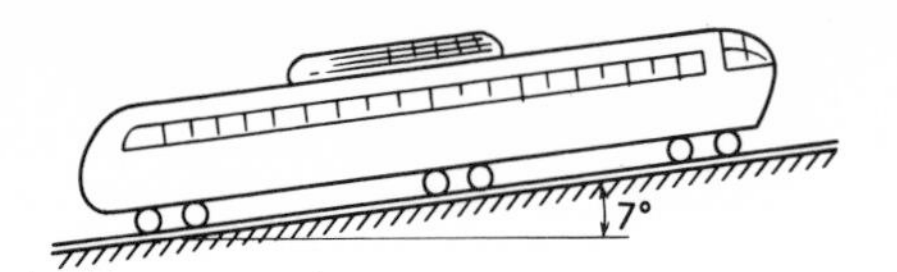

Fig. 13.60

62. [13.5] In ordnance work a very vital test for equipment is the shock test, which determines whether a piece of equipment can withstand a certain level of acceleration of short duration. A common technique for this test is the drop test (see Fig. 13.61). The specimen is mounted on a rigid carriage, which upon release is dropped along guide rods onto a set of lead pads resting on a heavy rigid anvil. The pads deform and absorb the energy of the carriage

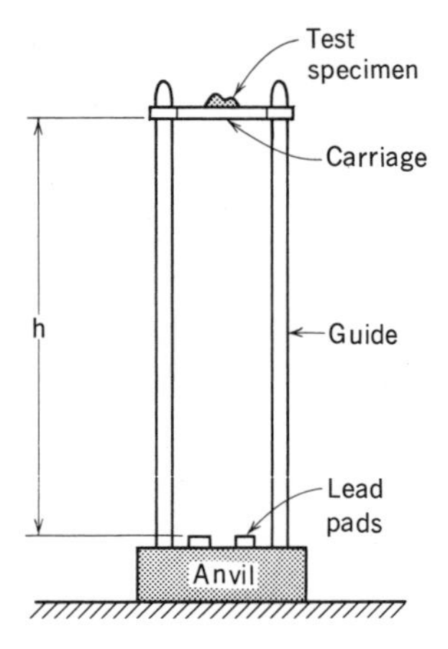

Fig. 13.61

and specimen. It is estimated through other tests that the energy E absorbed by a pad versus compression distance δ is given as shown in Fig. 13.62, where the curve can be taken as a parabola. For four such pads and a height h of 10 ft, what is the compression of the pads? The carriage and specimen together weigh 100 lb. Neglect the friction of the guides.

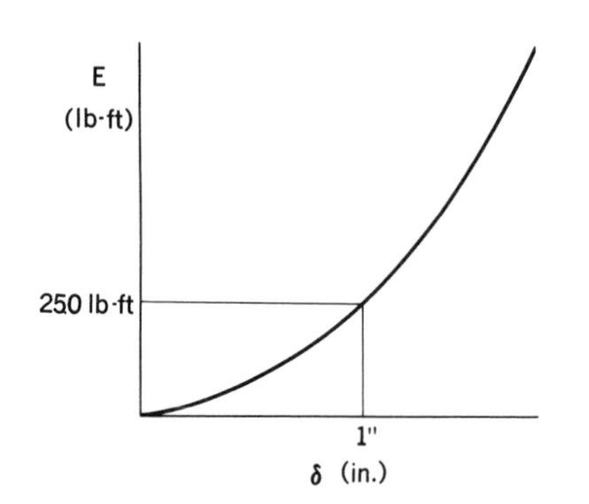

Fig. 13.62

63. [13.5] In the preceding problem if the force to compress a pad varies directly as α times the time rate of energy absorption by the pads, what is the equation of V vs. δ during deformation process?

64. [13.5] A body A is released from rest on a vertical circular path as shown in Fig. 13.63. If there is a constant resistance force of 0.2 lb along the path, what is the speed of the body when it reaches B? The mass of the body is 1 lbm and the radius r of the path is 5 ft.

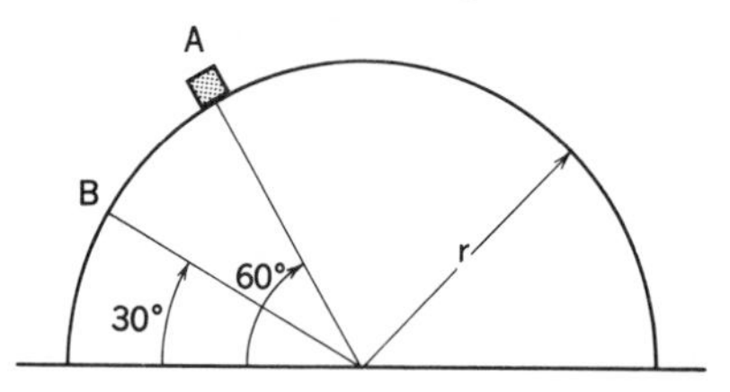

Fig. 13.63

65. [13.5] In the previous problem assume coulomb friction is present with a coefficient of dynamic friction $\mu_d = 0.3$. Set up formulations for finding the speed of the body at B. Do not attempt to solve, however.

The following three problems are suggested as short projects.

***66.** [13.5] A body A of mass 1 lb is moving at time $t = 0$ with a speed V of 1 ft/sec on a cylinder as shown in Fig. 13.64. Coulomb friction acts on the body with a damping constant $\mu = 0.2$. Using a numerical scheme, estimate the speed of the body when it arrives at B. Take $r = 2$ ft.

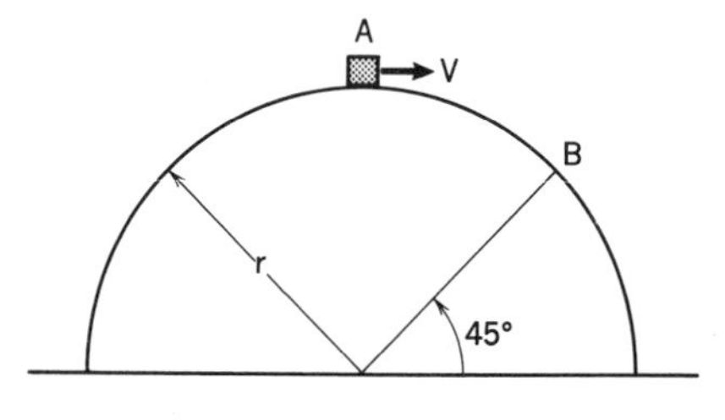

Fig. 13.64

***67.** [13.5] Set up the previous problem on a digital computer.

***68.** [13.5] Using a digital computer, estimate when body A of Prob. 67 leaves the circular surface.

69. [13.5] A 100-lb boy climbs up a rope in gym (see Fig. 13.65) in 10 seconds and slides down at uniform speed in 4 seconds. What is the horsepower developed by the boy going up? What is the average horsepower dissipated on the rope by the boy going down?

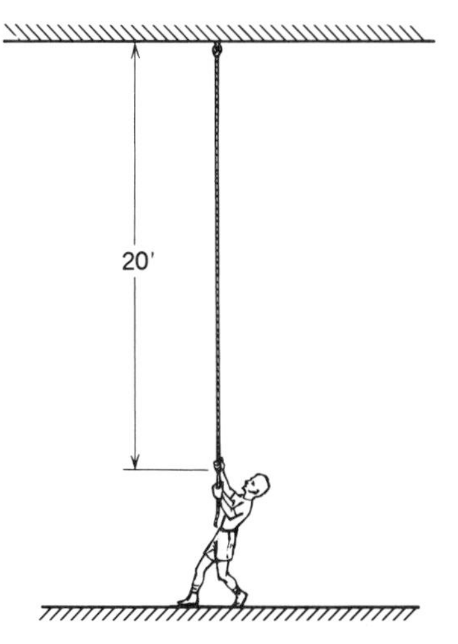

Fig. 13.65

70. [13.6] In Fig. 13.66, two bodies are connected by an inextensible cord over a frictionless pulley. If released from rest, what velocity will they reach when the 500-lb body has dropped 5 ft?

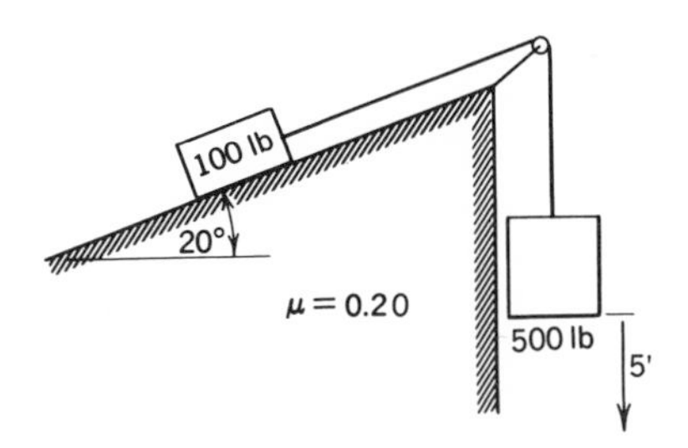

Fig. 13.66

71. [13.6] Shown in Fig. 13.67 are three blocks connected by an inextensible flexible cable. The blocks are released from a rest configuration with the cable taut. If A can only fall a distance h equal to 2 ft, what is the velocity of bodies C and B after each has moved a distance of 3 ft? Each body weighs 100 lb. The coefficient of friction for body C is 0.3 and for body B is 0.2.

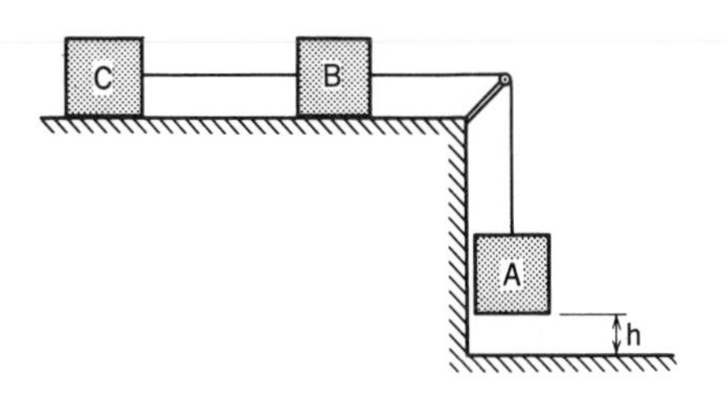

Fig. 13.67

72. [13.6] Suppose in the previous problem that the coefficient of friction for body B is 0.4 and for body C is 0.1. What is the speed of each body after it has moved 3 ft? If the cable between bodies C and B is 5 ft in length, how far does each body move before there is a collision? (Use Newton's law directly if necessary.)

73. [13.6] A flyball governor is shown in Fig. 13.68. When $\omega = 0$ we can assume that $\theta \approx 0$ and that the spring restraining collar A is unstretched. The moving parts are the masses M, the four arms, and the collars B on top and A below. If a constant torque of 50 in.-lb is applied to the collar B, set up equations for number of revolutions required before θ equals 45°? The following data apply:

$$M = 2 \text{ lbm}$$

$$K = 10 \text{ lb/in.}$$

$$l = 1 \text{ ft}$$

Neglect all mass except that of the bodies M.

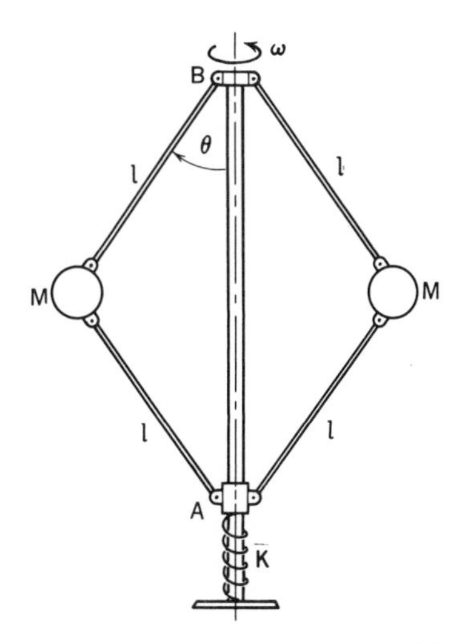

Fig. 13.68

74. [13.6] Three coupled streetcars (Fig. 13.69) are moving at the speed of 20 mph down a 7° incline. Each car weighs 22 tons. The cars must stop within 150 ft beyond the position where the brakes are fully applied so as to cause the wheels to lock. What is the maximum number of brake failures that can be tolerated and still satisfy this specification? Assume that the weight is loaded equally among the wheels and that we have 24 brake systems—one for each wheel. Take $\mu_d = 0.45$.

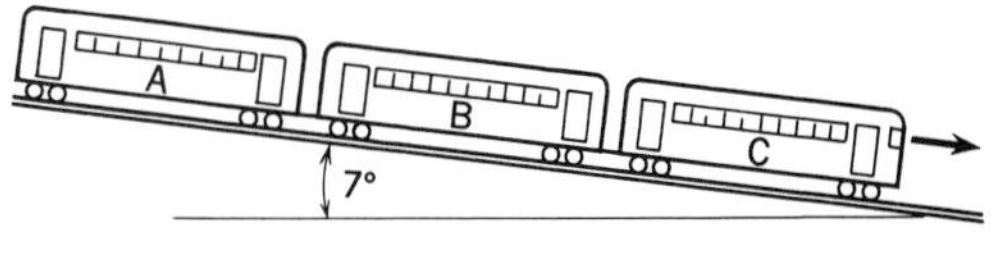

Fig. 13.69

75. [13.6] Suppose in the preceding problem only the brakes on train A operate. What is the distance before stopping? Also determine the force in each coupling of the system.

76. [13.6] We have shown in Fig. 13.70 a chain of length 50 ft and weight 100 lb. A force P of 80 lb has been applied at the configuration shown. What is the speed of the chain after force P has moved 10 ft? The coefficient of friction between the chain and the supporting surface is 0.3. Give approximate analysis.

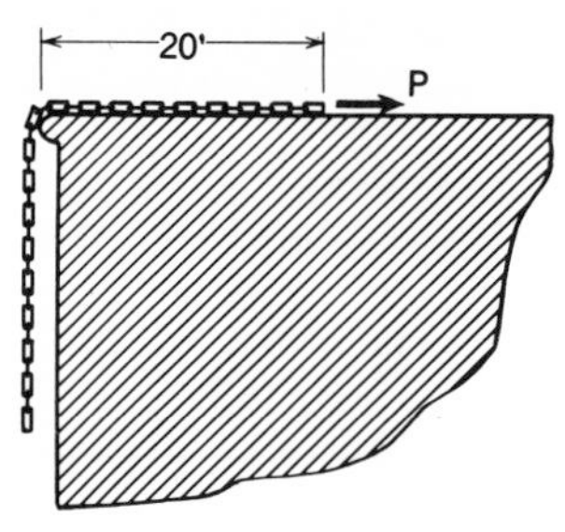

Fig. 13.70

77. [13.6] A chain of total length L is released from rest on a smooth support as shown in Fig. 13.71. Determine the velocity of the chain when the last link moves off the horizontal surface.

In this problem neglect friction. Also do not attempt to account for centrifugal effects stemming from the chain links rounding the corner.

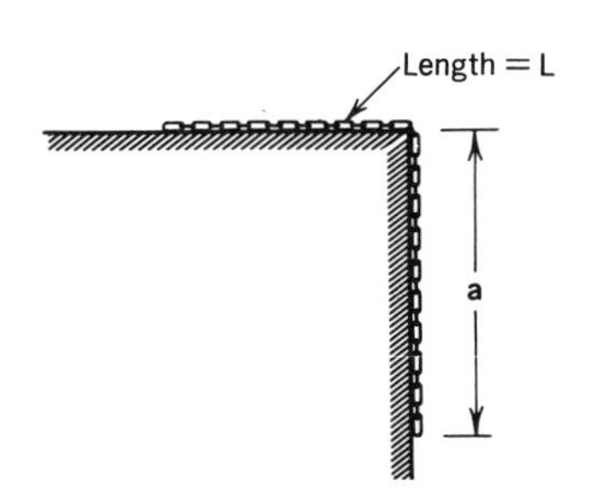

Fig. 13.71

78. [13.6] A bullet of weight W_1 is fired into a block of wood weighing W_2 lb (Fig. 13.72). The bullet lodges in the wood and both bodies then move to the dashed position indicated in the diagram before falling back. Compute the amount of internal work done during the action. Discuss the effects of this work. The bullet has a speed V_0 before hitting the block. Neglect the mass of the supporting rod and friction at A.

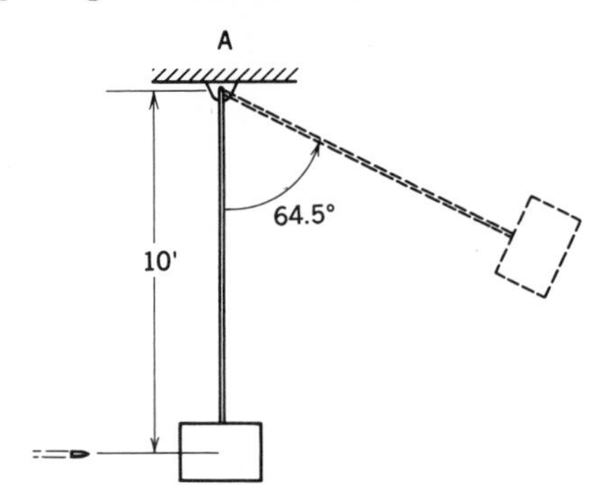

Fig. 13.72

79. [13.6] Shown in Fig. 13.73 are three weights A, B, and C which slide frictionlessly along the system of connected rods. The bodies are connected by a light, flexible, inextensible wire that is directed by frictionless small pulleys at E and F. If the system is released from rest, what is its speed after it has moved 1 ft? Employ the following data for the body weight:

Body A: 10 lb

Body B: 8 lb

Body C: 15 lb

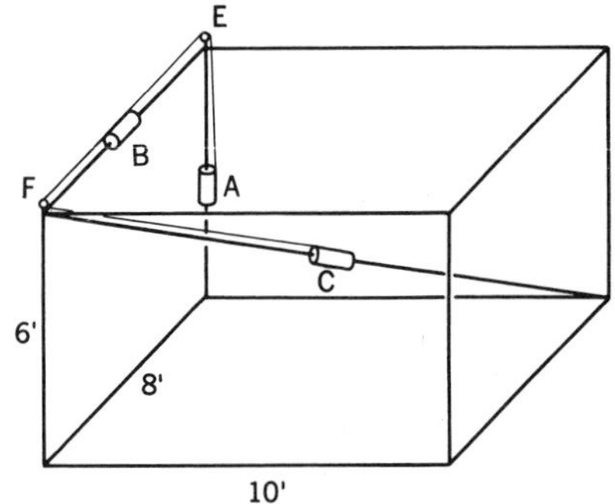

Fig. 13.73

80. [13.6] Bodies E and F slide in frictionless grooves (see Fig. 13.74). They are interconnected by a light, flexible, inextensible cable (not shown). What is the speed of the system after it has moved 2 ft? The weights of bodies E and F are 10 lb and 20 lb, respectively. B is equidistant from A and C.

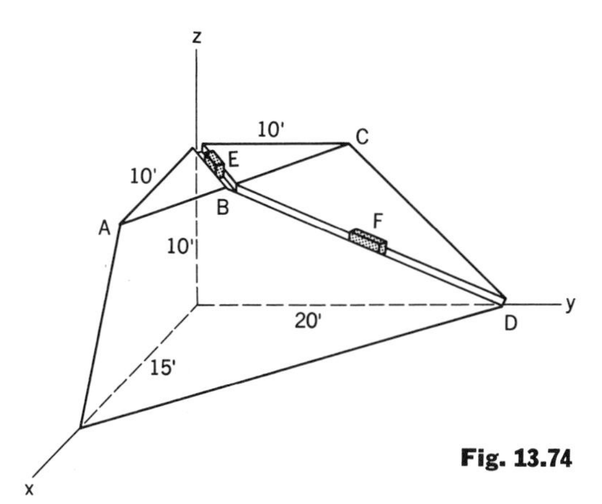

Fig. 13.74

81. [13.6] Bodies A, B, and C move in frictionless grooves (see Fig. 13.75). Body B is connected to body A by a light flexible cable. Body C is also similarly connected to body A. If the system is released from rest, how far does A move along the slot before it has a speed of 2 ft/sec? The following data apply:

$$W_A = 20 \text{ lb}$$
$$W_C = 5 \text{ lb}$$
$$W_B = 8 \text{ lb}$$

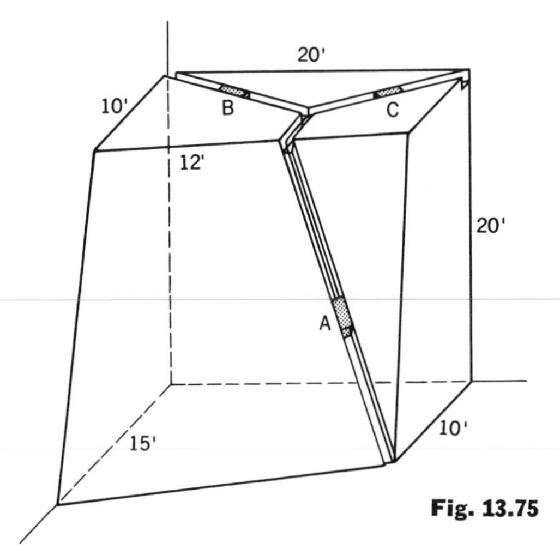

Fig. 13.75

82. [13.7] Shown in Fig. 13.76 is a hoop, with four spokes, rolling without slipping such that the center C moves at a speed V of 5 ft/sec. The diameter of the hoop is 10 ft and the weight per unit length of the rim is 1 lb per ft. The spokes are uniform rods also having a weight of 1 lb per ft. Assuming that rim and spokes are thin, what is the kinetic energy of the body?

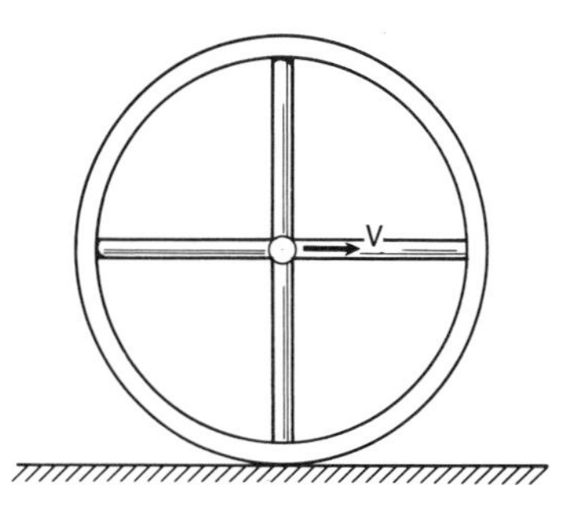

Fig. 13.76

83. [13.7] A uniform circular plate (Fig. 13.77) rolls without slipping such that the center moves at a speed V. What is the formula for kinetic energy of the body for a diameter D, a density ρ, and a thickness t?

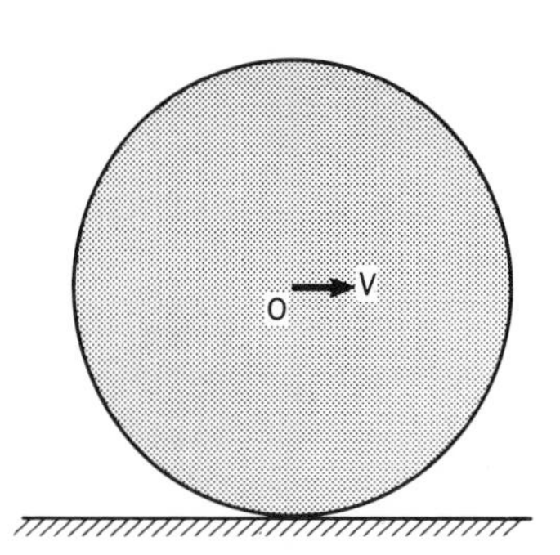

Fig. 13.77

84. [13.7] A uniform cylinder having a diameter of 2 ft and a weight of 100 lb rolls down a 30° incline without slipping, as shown in Fig. 13.78. What is the speed of the center after it has moved 20 ft? Compare this result with that for the case when there is no friction present.

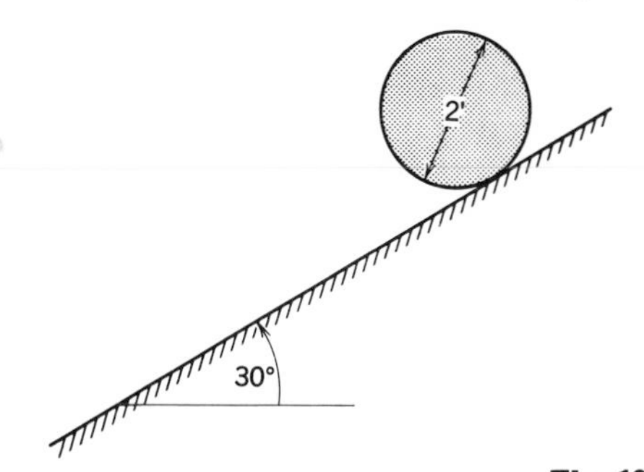

Fig. 13.78

85. [13.7] A uniform hollow cylinder is shown in Fig. 13.79 rolling without slipping such that the geometric center moves at a speed V. Derive the expression for the kinetic energy of the body in terms of the inner diameter d_1, outer diameter d_2, and mass M.

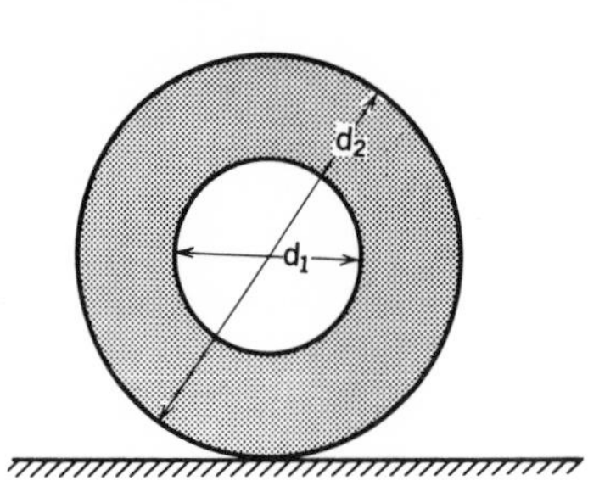

Fig. 13.79

86. [13.7] A pendulum is shown in Fig. 13.80. The bob is a comparatively large uniform disc of diameter 2 ft and mass M of 3 lbm. At the instant shown, the system has an angular speed $\dot{\theta}$ of 0.3 rad per second. If we neglect the mass of the rod, what is the kinetic energy of the pendulum at this instant? What error is incurred if one considers the bob to be a particle as we have done earlier for smaller bobs?

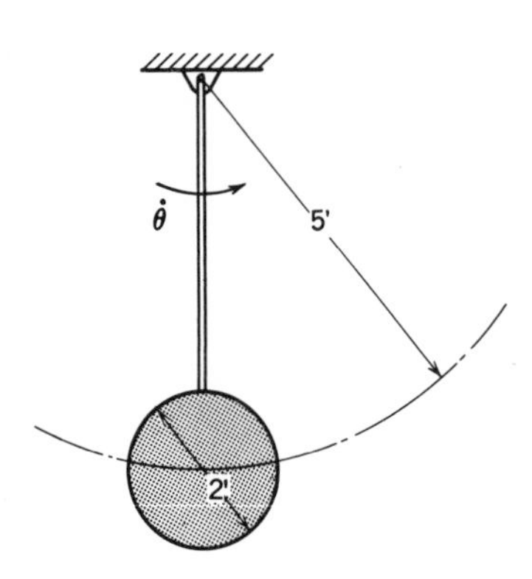

Fig. 13.80

87. [13.7] In the previous problem compute the maximum angle that the pendulum rises.

88. [13.7] What is the kinetic energy of a uniform sphere of radius R (Fig. 13.81) rolling without slipping? Take the speed of the center of the sphere to be V and the density to be ρ. [*Hint*: Consider the sphere to be composed of plates of infinitesimal thickness parallel to the xy plane and utilize the results of Prob. 83.]

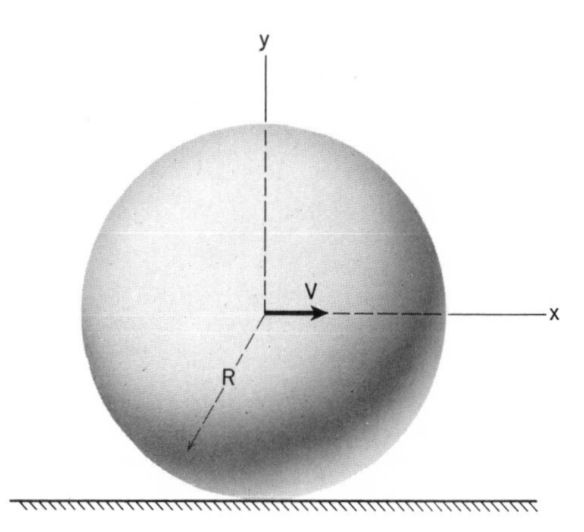

Fig. 13.81

89. [13.7] A tank is moving at the speed V of 10 miles per hour (Fig. 13.82). What is the kinetic energy of the treads for this tank if they each have a weight of 40 lb/ft?

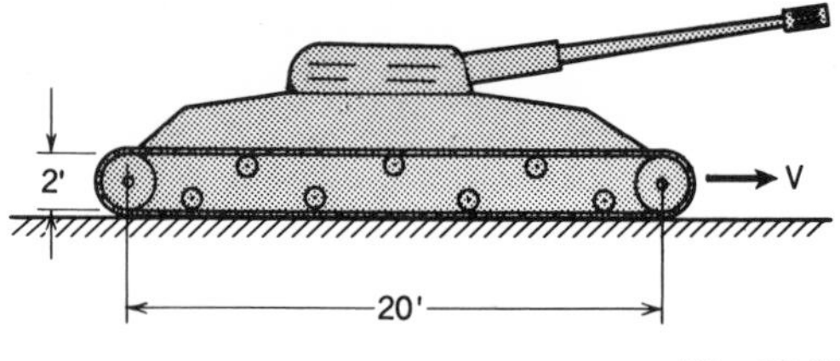

Fig. 13.82

90. [13.7] Cylinders B and C each weigh 100 lb and have a diameter of 2 ft (see Fig. 13.83). Body A, weighing 300 lb, rides on these cylinders. If there is no slipping anywhere, what is the kinetic energy of the system when the body A is moving at a speed V of 10 ft/sec? (Suggestion: Do this by considering each rigid body separately.)

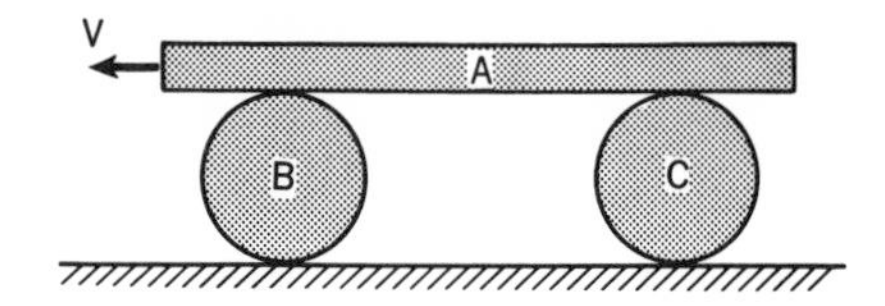

Fig. 13.83

91. [13.7] Cylinders A and B in Fig. 13.84 each have a weight of 50 lb and a diameter of 1 ft. Block C, riding on A and B, has a weight of 200 lb. If the system is released from rest at the configuration shown, what is the speed of C after the cylinders have made half a revolution?

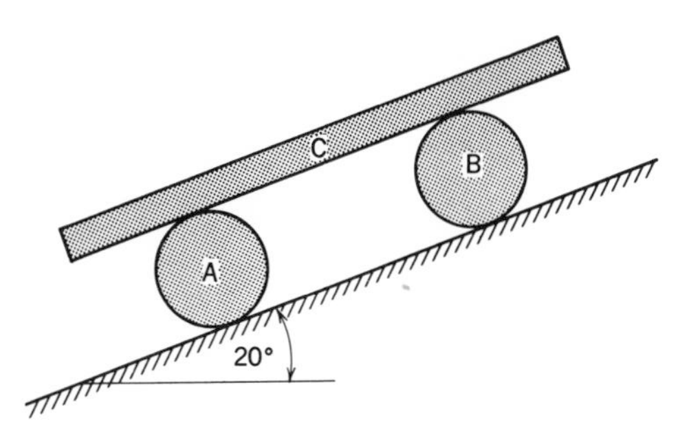

Fig. 13.84

92. [13.7] In Fig. 13.85, a device is mounted on a platform that is rotating with an angular speed of 10 rad/sec. It consists of two masses (each is 0.1 slug) rotating on a spindle, with an angular speed of 5 rad/sec relative to the platform. The masses are moving radially outward with a speed of 10 ft/sec, and the entire platform is being raised at a speed of 5 ft/sec. Compute the kinetic energy of the system of particles when they are 1 ft from the spindle.

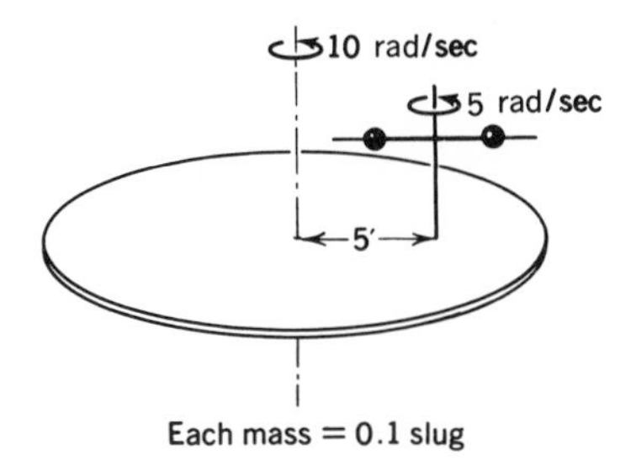

Fig. 13.85

93. [13.8] Shown in Fig. 13.86 are two identical blocks A and B. A force F of 50 lb is applied to a light structural member C resting on the blocks. Show from work-kinetic energy considerations involving the center of mass that the speeds of A and B must be mutually equal despite the nature of F or the kind of friction encountered by the structural device C.

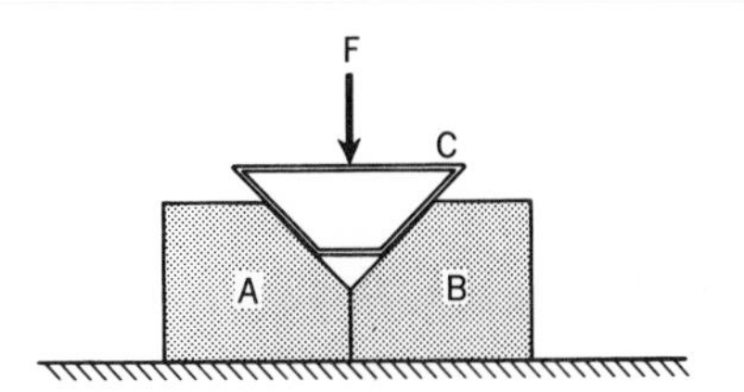

Fig. 13.86

94. [13.8] A constant force F of 10 lb is applied to the axis of a cylinder, as shown in Fig. 13.87, causing the axis to increase its speed from 1 ft/sec to 3 ft/sec in 10 ft. What is the friction force acting on the cylinder? The cylinder weighs 100 lb.

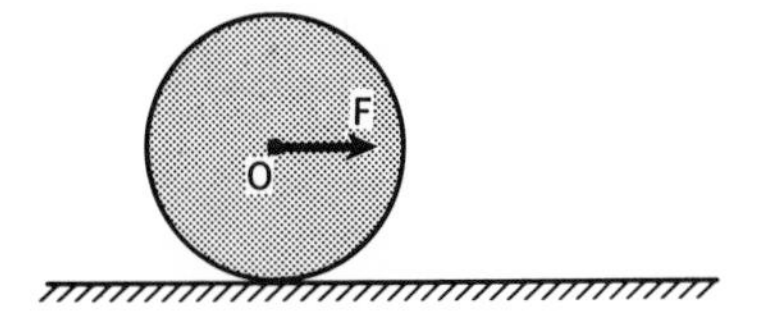

Fig. 13.87

95. [13.8] A cylinder weighing 50 lb is released from rest on an incline, as shown in Fig. 13.88. The diameter of the cylinder is 1 ft. If the cylinder rolls without slipping, compute the speed of the centerline 0 after it has moved 5 ft along the incline. Using energy methods, ascertain the friction force acting on the cylinder.

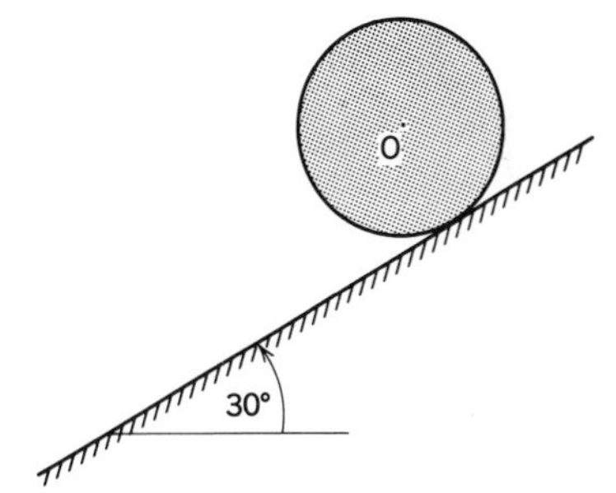

Fig. 13.88

96. [13.8] In Fig. 13.89, a 30-lb vehicle has two bodies (each weighing 2 lb) mounted on it, and these bodies rotate at an angular speed of 50 rad/sec relative to the vehicle. If a 100-lb force acts on the vehicle for a distance of 50 ft, what is the kinetic energy of the system, assuming that the vehicle starts from rest and the bodies in the vehicle have constant rotational speed? Neglect friction and the inertia of the wheels.

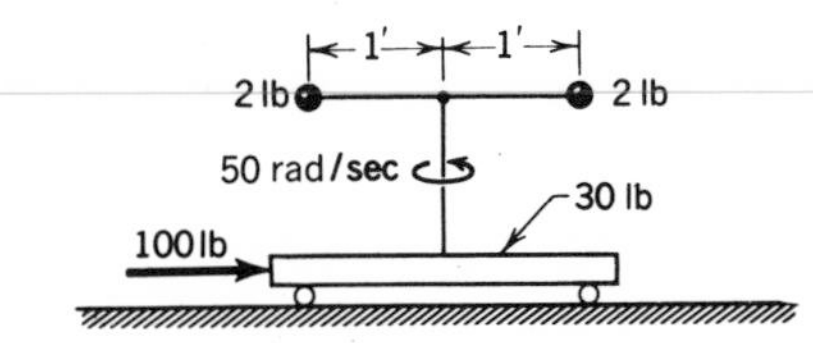

Fig. 13.89

97. [13.8] Shown in Fig. 13.90 are two identical blocks A and B, each weighing 50 lb. A force F of 100 lb is applied to the lower block, causing it to move to the right. Block A, however, is restrained by the wall C. If block B

reaches a speed of 10 ft/sec in 2 ft starting from rest at the position shown in the diagram, what is the restraining force from the wall? The coefficient of friction between B and the ground surface is 0.3. Do this first by using Eq. 13.32. Then check the result by using separate free-body diagram and so on.

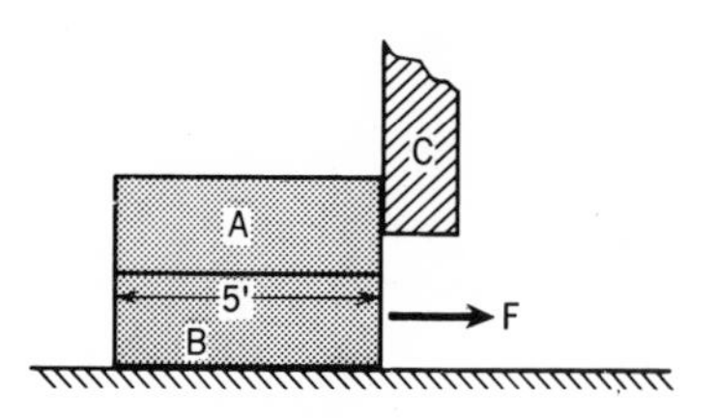

Fig. 13.90

98. [13.8] Do example 13.15 for the case where there is a rolling resistance of 0.04 N for each wheel. N represents the normal force transmitted to the ground through the wheel. Center of mass is $\frac{1}{4}\overline{AB}$ from the right end.

99. [13.8] Show that the work-energy equation for a particle may be expressed in the following way:

$$\int_0^x F\,dx = \int_0^V V\,d(mV)$$

Integrating the right side by parts, and using relativistic mass, show that a relativistic form of this equation can be given as:

$$\int_0^x F\,dx = \frac{m_0c^2}{\sqrt{1 - v^2/c^2}} - m_0c^2 = mc^2 - m_0c^2$$

so that the relativistic kinetic energy is:

$$KE = mc^2 - m_0c^2$$

100. [13.8] By combining the kinetic energy and m_0c^2 to form E, the total energy, we get the famous formula of Einstein:

$$E = mc^2$$

which equates energy with mass. How much energy is equivalent to an ounce of matter? How high could a weight of 100 lb be lifted with such energy?

14 Methods of Momentum

PART A. Linear Momentum

14.1 Impulse and Momentum Relations for a Particle

In Section 12.3 we integrated differential equations of motion for particles that are acted upon by forces which are functions of time. In this chapter we shall again consider such problems and shall present alternative formulations, called *methods of momentum*, for the handling of certain of these problems in a convenient and straightforward manner. We start by considering Newton's law for a particle:

$$\boldsymbol{F} = m\frac{d\boldsymbol{V}}{dt} \qquad 14.1$$

Multiply both sides by dt and integrate from some initial time t_i to some final time t_f:

$$\int_{t_i}^{t_f} \boldsymbol{F}\,dt = \int_{t_i}^{t_f} m\frac{d\boldsymbol{V}}{dt}\,dt = m\boldsymbol{V}_f - m\boldsymbol{V}_i \qquad 14.2$$

Note first that this is a vector equation, in contrast to the work-kinetic energy Eq. 13.2 of the last chapter. The integral

$$\int_{t_i}^{t_f} \boldsymbol{F}\,dt$$

which we shall denote as $\boldsymbol{I}$, is called the *impulse* of the force $\boldsymbol{F}$ during the time interval $t_f - t_i$, while $m\boldsymbol{V}$ is the *linear momentum vector* of the particle. *The equation* 14.2, *then, states that the impulse* $\boldsymbol{I}$ *over a time interval equals the change in momentum of a particle during that time interval.* As we will demonstrate later, the impulse of a force may be known even though the force itself is not known.

Finally, you must remember that to produce an impulse a force need only exist for a time interval. Sometimes we use the work integral so much that we tend to think—erroneously—that a stationary force does not produce an impulse.

EXAMPLE 14.1

A particle initially at rest is acted on by a force whose variation with time is shown graphically in Fig. 14.1. If the mass of the particle is one slug and it is constrained to move rectilinearly in the direction of the force, what is the speed after fifteen seconds?

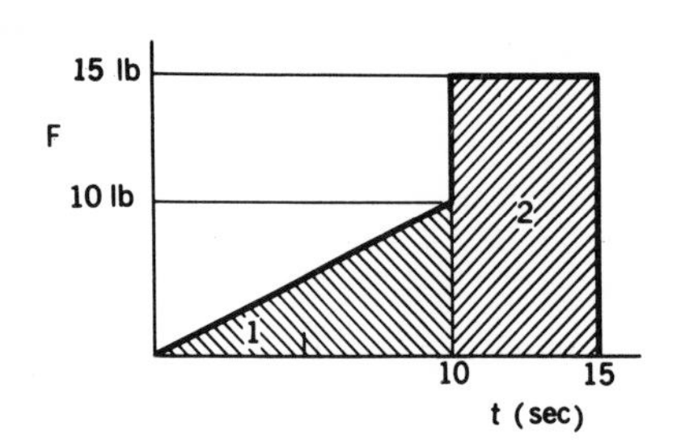

Fig. 14.1

It is clear from the definition of the impulse that the area under the force-time curve will, in the one-dimensional example, equal the impulse magnitude, so that we need simply to compute this area between the times $t = 0$ and $t = 15$ seconds:

$$\text{impulse} = \underbrace{\tfrac{1}{2}(10)(10)}_{\text{area 1}} + \underbrace{(5)(15)}_{\text{area 2}} = 125 \text{ lb-sec}$$

The final velocity, then, is given as:

$$125 = (1)(V_f) - 0, \qquad \therefore\ V_f = 125 \text{ ft/sec}$$

Note that the impulse-momentum equation is useful when the force variation during a time interval is not a curve that can be conveniently expressed mathematically. The impulse can then be found with the help of a *planimeter*, thus permitting a quick solution of the velocity change during the time interval.

EXAMPLE 14.2

A particle A with a mass of one slug has an initial velocity $\boldsymbol{V}_0 = 10\boldsymbol{i} + 6\boldsymbol{j}$. After the particle strikes a particle B, the velocity becomes $\boldsymbol{V} = 16\boldsymbol{i} - 3\boldsymbol{j} + 4\boldsymbol{k}$. If the time of encounter is 10 milliseconds, what average force was exerted on the particle A? What is the change of momentum of the particle B?

The impulse $\boldsymbol{I}$ acting on A is immediately determined by computing the change in momentum during the encounter:

$$\begin{aligned}\boldsymbol{I}_A &= (1)(16\boldsymbol{i} - 3\boldsymbol{j} + 4\boldsymbol{k}) - (1)(10\boldsymbol{i} + 6\boldsymbol{j})\\ &= 6\boldsymbol{i} - 9\boldsymbol{j} + 4\boldsymbol{k} \text{ lb-sec}\end{aligned}$$

Since

$$\int_{t_i}^{t_f} \boldsymbol{F}_A \, dt = (\boldsymbol{F}_{av})_A \, \Delta t,$$

the average force $(\boldsymbol{F}_{av})_A$ becomes:

$$(\boldsymbol{F}_{av})_A(0.010) = 6\boldsymbol{i} - 9\boldsymbol{j} + 4\boldsymbol{k}$$

$$\therefore \; (\boldsymbol{F}_{av})_A = 600\boldsymbol{i} - 900\boldsymbol{j} + 400\boldsymbol{k} \text{ lb}$$

Owing to the principle that action equals reaction, an equal but opposite average force must act on the object B during the 10-millisecond time interval. Thus the impulse on particle B is $-\boldsymbol{I}_A$. Equating this impulse to the change in linear momentum, we get:

$$\Delta(m\boldsymbol{V})_B = -\boldsymbol{I}_A = -6\boldsymbol{i} + 9\boldsymbol{j} - 4\boldsymbol{k} \text{ lb-sec}$$

It is during impacts where the exact force variation is unknown that the impulse-momentum principle is very useful. We shall examine this in more detail in a later section.

EXAMPLE 14.3

Two bodies, 1 and 2, are connected by an inextensible and weightless cord (Fig. 14.2). Initially, the bodies are at rest. If the coefficient of friction is μ for body 1 on the surface inclined at angle α, compute the velocity of the bodies at a time t that is small enough so that body 1 has not reached the end of the incline.

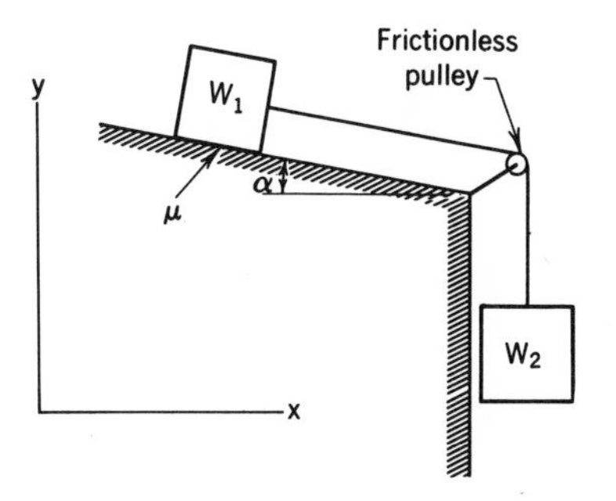

Fig. 14.2

Since we have here only constant forces and since a time interval has been specified, we can use momentum considerations advantageously. The free-body diagrams of bodies 1 and 2 are accordingly shown in Fig. 14.3. Equilibrium considerations dictate that $N_1 = W_1 \cos \alpha$, so the friction force f_1 is:

$$f_1 = \mu N_1 = \mu W_1 \cos \alpha$$

Also for body 1 take the component of the impulse-momentum equation along the incline:

$$\int_0^t (-\mu W_1 \cos \alpha + W_1 \sin \alpha + T) \, dt = \frac{W_1}{g} V - 0$$

Integrating, we have:

$$(-\mu W_1 \cos \alpha + W_1 \sin \alpha + T)t = \frac{W_1}{g} V \qquad \textbf{(a)}$$

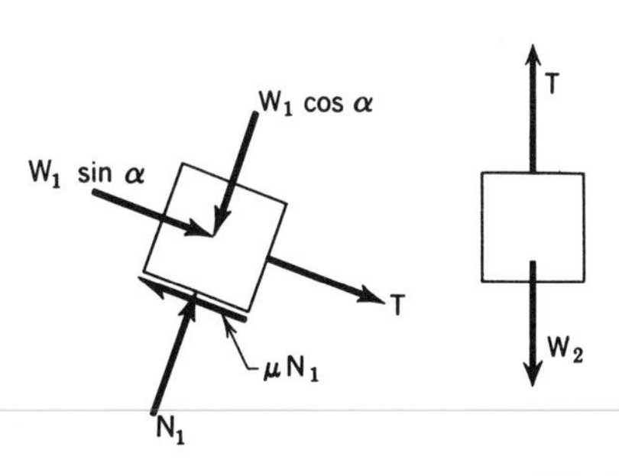

Fig. 14.3

For body 2 we have for the momentum equation in the vertical direction:

$$\int_0^t (W_2 - T) \, dt = \frac{W_2}{g} V - 0$$

where, because of the inextensible property of the cable and the frictionless condition of the pulley, the magnitudes of the velocity V and the force T are the same for bodies 1 and 2. Integrating in the above equation, we write:

$$(W_2 - T)t = \frac{W_2}{g} V \tag{b}$$

By adding Eqs. (a) and (b) we can eliminate T and solve for the desired unknown V. Thus:

$$(-\mu W_1 \cos \alpha + W_1 \sin \alpha + W_2)t = \frac{V}{g}(W_1 + W_2)$$

$$\therefore V = \frac{gt}{W_1 + W_2}(W_2 + W_1 \sin \alpha - \mu W_1 \cos \alpha) \tag{c}$$

Note that we have used considerations of linear momentum for a *single* particle in solving this problem. In the following section we shall approach this problem as a two-particle system.

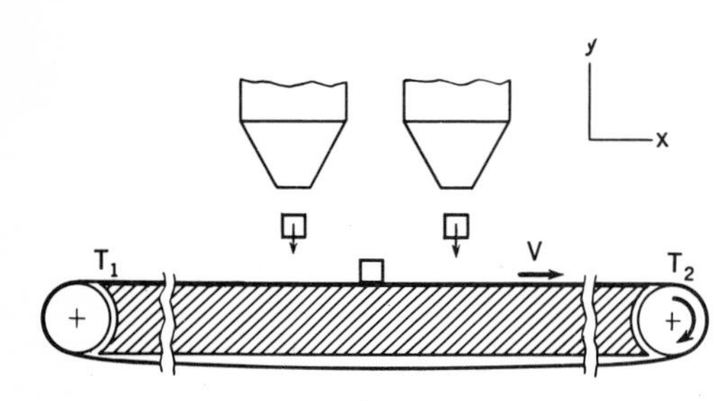

Fig. 14.4

EXAMPLE 14.4

Shown in Fig. 14.4 is a portion of a conveyor belt moving from left to right at a speed V of 1 ft/sec. Hoppers drop objects onto the belt at the rate n of 4 per second. The objects each have a weight W of 2 lb and fall a height h of 1 ft before landing on the conveyor belt. Further along the belt (not shown) the objects are removed by personnel so that, for steady-state operation, the number N of objects on the belt at any time is ten. If the coefficient of friction between belt and conveyor bed is 0.2, estimate the average difference in tension $T_2 - T_1$ of the belt to maintain this operation. Do not consider weight of the belt.

We shall superpose the following effects to get the desired result.

1. There is a friction force from the bed onto the belt as a result of the static weight of the N objects riding on the belt.
2. There is also a friction force from the bed onto the belt as a result of the force in the y direction needed to change the vertical linear momentum, of the falling n objects per second, from a value corresponding to the free-fall velocity just before impact to a value of zero after impact.
3. Finally the belt must supply a force in the x direction to change the horizontal linear momentum of the n falling objects per second from a value of zero to a value corresponding to the speed of the belt.

Thus, we have for the first contribution, which we denote as ΔT_1, the following result:

$$\Delta T_1 = (N)(W)(\mu) = (10)(2)(0.2) = 4 \text{ lb} \tag{a}$$

As for the second contribution, we can only compute an average value $(\Delta T_2)_{av}$ by noting that each impacting object is given a vertical impulse equal to:

$$\text{vertical impulse per object} = \frac{W}{g}(\sqrt{2gh})$$

$$= \frac{2}{g}\sqrt{(2g)(1)}$$

$$= 0.498 \text{ lb-sec}$$

where we have assumed a free fall starting with zero velocity at the hopper. For four impacts per second we have as the total vertical impulse per second the value 1.992 lb. The average force during the one-second interval to maintain the impulse is clearly 1.992 lb. Since this result is correct for every second, we then have the average normal force that the bed of the conveyor must transmit to the belt for arresting the vertical motion of the falling objects. The desired $(\Delta T_2)_{av}$ for the belt is accordingly given as:

$$(\Delta T_2)_{av} = (\mu)(1.922) = 0.398 \text{ lb} \qquad \textbf{(b)}$$

Finally for the last contribution $(\Delta T_3)_{av}$, we note that the belt must give in the horizontal direction for each impacting object an impulse having the value:

$$\text{horizontal impulse per object} = \left(\frac{W}{g}\right)(1)$$

$$= 0.0622 \text{ lb-sec}$$

For four impacts per second we have as the total horizontal impulse per second developed by the belt the value 0.249 lb. The average force needed for this impulse is clearly 0.249 lb. Thus we have:

$$(\Delta T_3)_{av} = 0.249 \text{ lb} \qquad \textbf{(c)}$$

The total average difference in tension is then:

$$(\Delta T)_{av} = 4 + 0.398 + 0.249 = 4.65 \text{ lb} \qquad \textbf{(d)}$$

14.2 Linear Momentum Considerations for a System of Particles

In the previous section we considered impulse-momentum relations for a single particle. Although Examples 14.3 and 14.4 involved several particles, the analyses nevertheless employed impulse-momentum considerations of a single particle only. (This was accomplished, you will recall, by summing single-particle results over a convenient time interval to obtain a suitable average.) We now wish to set forth impulse-momentum relations for a *system* of particles.

Let us accordingly consider a system of n particles. We may start with Newton's law that was developed previously for a system of particles:

$$\boldsymbol{F} = \sum_{j=1}^{n} m_j \frac{d\boldsymbol{V}_j}{dt} \qquad \textbf{14.3}$$

Since we know that the internal forces cancel, $\boldsymbol{F}$ must be the total external force on the system of n particles. Multiplying by dt as before and integrating between t_i and t_f, we write:

$$\int_{t_i}^{t_f} \boldsymbol{F}\,dt = \boldsymbol{I}_{\text{ext}} = \left(\sum_{j=1}^{n} m_j \boldsymbol{V}_j\right)_f - \left(\sum_{j=1}^{n} m_j \boldsymbol{V}_j\right)_i \qquad 14.4$$

Thus we see that *the impulse of the total external force on the system of particles during a time interval equals the sum of the changes of the linear momentum vectors of the particles during the time interval.*

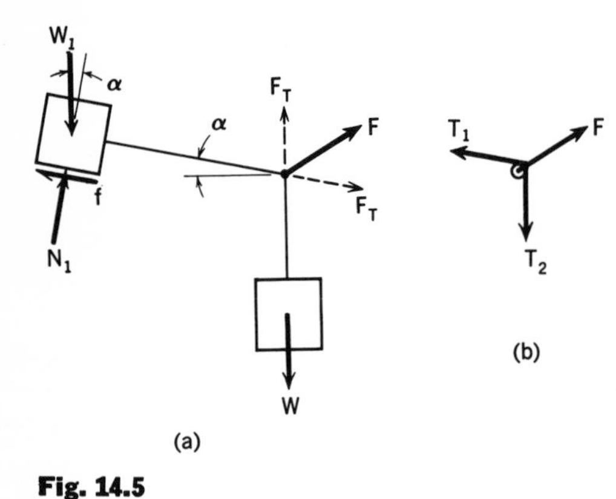

Fig. 14.5

EXAMPLE 14.5

We shall now return to Example 14.3 and treat it as a two-particle system in the impulse-momentum considerations.

Accordingly we have shown a free-body diagram of the system of particles in Fig. 14.5(a). Equilibrium considerations in the direction normal to the incline for body 1 and the slipping condition yield the following results:

$$N_1 = W_1 \cos\alpha, \qquad f_1 = \mu W_1 \cos\alpha \qquad \textbf{(a)}$$

In Fig. 14.5(b) we have shown the free-body diagram of the pulley. Considering moments about the center of the pulley, we can conclude that $T_1 = T_2$. This means that the components of force F along the direction of the inextensible cord are equal; they will be denoted as F_T as shown in Fig. 14.5(a).

Now employ Eq. 14.4 in a direction along the incline. Integrating from 0 to t we get:

$$[W_1 \sin\alpha - \mu W_1 \cos\alpha + W_2 \sin\alpha + F_T(1 - \sin\alpha)]t = \left(\frac{W_1}{g} + \frac{W_2}{g}\sin\alpha\right)V \qquad \textbf{(b)}$$

Next employ Eq. 14.4 in a downward vertical direction. Integrating again from 0 to t we get:

$$[W_1 - \mu W_1 \cos\alpha \sin\alpha - W_1 \cos^2\alpha - F_T(1 - \sin\alpha) + W_2]t = \left(\frac{W_2}{g} + \frac{W_1}{g}\sin\alpha\right)V \qquad \textbf{(c)}$$

To eliminate F_T we add Eqs. (b) and (c) to get:

$$[(W_1 + W_2)(1 + \sin\alpha) - \mu W_1 \cos\alpha(1 + \sin\alpha) - W_1 \cos^2\alpha]t = \frac{1}{g}(W_1 + W_2)(1 + \sin\alpha)V$$

Solving for V we get:

$$V = gt\left[1 - \frac{\mu W_1}{W_1 + W_2}\cos\alpha - \frac{W_1}{W_1 + W_2}\,\frac{\cos^2\alpha}{1 + \sin\alpha}\right] \qquad \textbf{(d)}$$

It will be left for you to show that Eq. (d) can be put into the identical form as Eq. (c) of Example 14.3.

It is apparent from the previous example that no great gain is realized by approaching such problems as a system as compared to the earlier single-particle technique. However, we shall be able to make good use of the system approach in the following problem, where the external forces acting on the system are easily evaluated. There is then a saving of work in that the internal forces need not be considered.

EXAMPLE 14.6

Shown in Fig. 14.6 are two vehicles designed for moving up icy inclines. Vehicle B weighs 1000 lb, rides on skis, and pulls itself up the incline using its own winch b. It tows a second vehicle A, weighing 800 lb. Vehicle A is also equipped with its own winch a. During an interval of ten seconds, the winch b is kept at constant torque so that the cable bc is at a constant tension of 1100 lb. At the outset of the interval the winch a is operated so that A is gaining on B at the rate of 2 ft/sec and at the end of the interval it is only gaining on B at the rate of 1 ft/sec. What is the change of speed of vehicle B during this interval? The coefficient of friction for both vehicles with snow is 0.1. Neglect wind resistance.

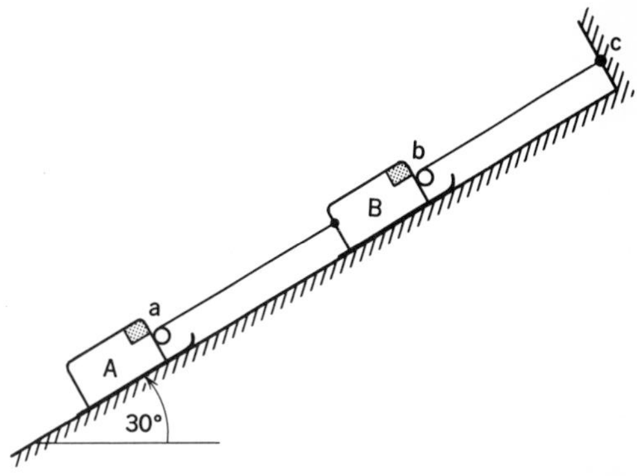

Fig. 14.6

We have here a system of two particles, on which all external forces have been shown in Fig. 14.7. Equilibrium considerations in the direction normal to the inclined plane give the following results for the normal forces N_A and N_B:

$$N_A = 800 \cos 30° = 693 \text{ lb} \qquad \textbf{(a)}$$

$$N_B = 1000 \cos 30° = 866 \text{ lb} \qquad \textbf{(b)}$$

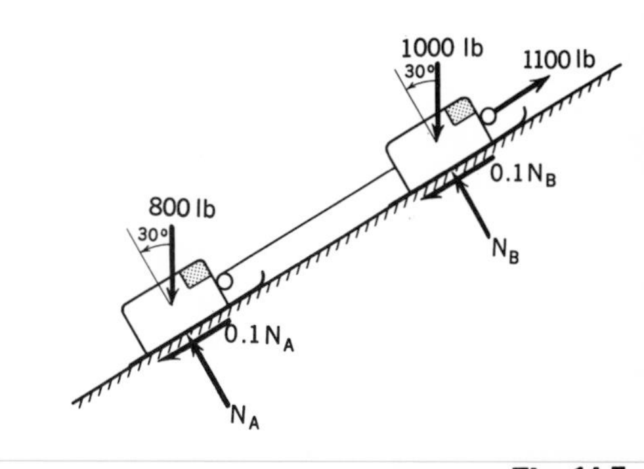

Fig. 14.7

To get the desired result it is now easiest to employ Eq. 14.4 in the direction along the incline. The impulse $\boldsymbol{I}_{\text{ext}}$ is given as:

$$\int_0^{10} F\,dt = \int_0^{10} (1100 - 1000 \sin 30° - 800 \sin 30° - 69.3 - 86.6)\,dt = 440 \text{ lb-sec} \qquad \textbf{(c)}$$

The momentum of the system at time $t = 0$ is:

$$\left(\sum_{j=1}^{n} m_j V_j\right)_{t=0} = \frac{1000}{g_0}(V_B)_1 + \frac{800}{g_0}[(V_B)_1 + 2] = 55.9(V_B)_1 + 49.6 \qquad \textbf{(d)}$$

The momentum of the system at time $t = 10$ is:

$$\left(\sum_{j=1}^{n} m_j V_j\right)_{t=10} = \frac{1000}{g_0}(V_B)_2 + \frac{800}{g_0}[(V_B)_2 + 1] = 55.9(V_B)_2 + 24.8 \qquad \textbf{(e)}$$

We then have for the momentum equation of the system of particles:

$$440 = 55.9[(V_B)_2 - (V_{1B})] + 24.8 - 49.6 \quad \textbf{(f)}$$

Solving for $(V_B)_2 - (V_B)_1$ we get:

$$(V_B)_2 - (V_B)_1 = 8.32 \text{ ft/sec} \quad \textbf{(g)}$$

It is an easy matter to introduce mass center quantities into Eq. 14.4. You will remember that:

$$M\boldsymbol{r}_c = \sum_{j=1}^{n} m_j \boldsymbol{r}_j \quad \textbf{14.5}$$

Differentiating with respect to time, we get the result:

$$M\boldsymbol{V}_c = \sum_{j=1}^{n} m_j \boldsymbol{V}_j \quad \textbf{14.6}$$

Thus we see from this equation that *the total momentum of a system of particles equals the momentum of a particle that has the total mass of the system and that moves with the velocity of the mass center.* Using Eq. 14.6 to replace the right side of Eq. 14.4, we can say:

$$\int_{t_i}^{t_f} \boldsymbol{F}\, dt = \boldsymbol{I}_{\text{ext}} = M(\boldsymbol{V}_c)_f - M(\boldsymbol{V}_c)_i \quad \textbf{14.7}$$

Thus, we can relate the *total external impulse on a system of particles with the change in momentum of a hypothetical particle having the mass of the entire aggregate and moving with the mass center.*

When the separate motions of the individual particles are reasonably simple, as a result of constraints, and the motion of the mass center is not easily available, then Eq. 14.4 may be employed for linear momentum considerations. This was the case for the previous two examples. On the other hand, when the motions of the particles individually are very complex and the motion of the mass center of the system is reasonably simple, then clearly Eq. 14.7 can be of great value for linear momentum considerations. We illustrate such a case in the following example.

EXAMPLE 14.7

A unicyclist (see Fig. 14.8) wishes to go from 2 ft/sec to 12 ft/sec as quickly as possible while riding on a wet slick pavement. If $\mu = 0.2$ for the contact surface of wheel and road, what is the shortest time in which he can do this? The cyclist weighs 150 lb and his unicycle weighs 20 lb. Neglect windage resistance.

The external forces acting on cyclist and unicycle have been shown in Fig. 14.8. If we assume the center of mass of the system remains at the same vertical elevation during this motion, we can say from Newton's law for the center of mass in the vertical direction that

Fig. 14.8

the normal force N is 170 lb. Consequently, using Eq. 14.7 for the center of mass and assuming that the cyclist manages to maintain the condition of impending slippage at the contact surface, we have:

$$\int_0^t \mu N\,dt = \frac{W}{g_0}(12 - 2)$$

$$\therefore\ 34t = \frac{170}{g_0}(10) \qquad \textbf{(a)}$$

The time is then:

$$t = 1.56 \text{ seconds} \qquad \textbf{(b)}$$

If the cyclist were on a bicycle (see Fig. 14.9) he would perhaps be able to ride more easily, but we would find doing this problem much more difficult. The reason for the increase in difficulty is that the normal force N_1 will depend on the acceleration of the bike, which will in turn depend on μN_1. Thus, in contrast to the unicycle, N_1 is not easily available. Clearly we need another independent equation here. We shall be able to examine this kind of problem at a later stage in our study.

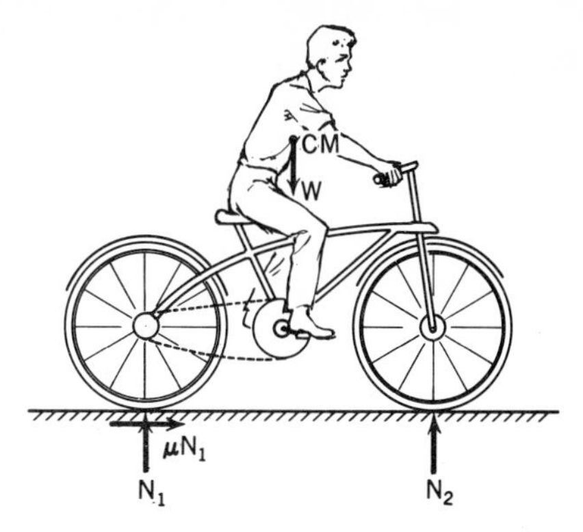

Fig. 14.9

14.3 Conservation of Linear Momentum—Impact of Particles

If the total external force on a system of particles is zero, it is clear from the previous section that there can be no change in the linear momentum of the system. This is the principle of *conservation of momentum*. It means, furthermore, that *with a zero total impulse on an aggregate of particles, there can be no change in the velocity of the mass center.*

Let us now examine the action involved in the explosion of a bomb that is initially suspended from a wire, as shown in Fig. 14.10. First consider the situation directly after the explosion has been set off. Since very large forces are present from expanding gases, a fragment of the bomb receives an appreciable impulse during this short time interval. Also, directly after the explosion, the gravitational forces are no longer counteracted by the supporting wire, so there is an additional impulse acting on the fragments. But since the gravitational force is small compared to forces from the explosion, the gravitational impulse can be considered negligibly small for the period of time under discussion. Most important here is the fact that since the explosive action is internal to the bomb, it causes impulses that for any direction have equal and opposite counterparts, and *thus the total impulse on the bomb due to the explosion is zero.* We can thus conclude that *directly after* the explosion the center of mass of the bomb has not moved appreciably despite the high velocity of the fragments in all directions, as is illustrated in Fig. 14.10. As time progresses beyond the short time interval described above, the gravitational impulse increases and has significant effect. Were there no friction, the center of mass would descend from the position of support as a freely falling body under this action of gravity.

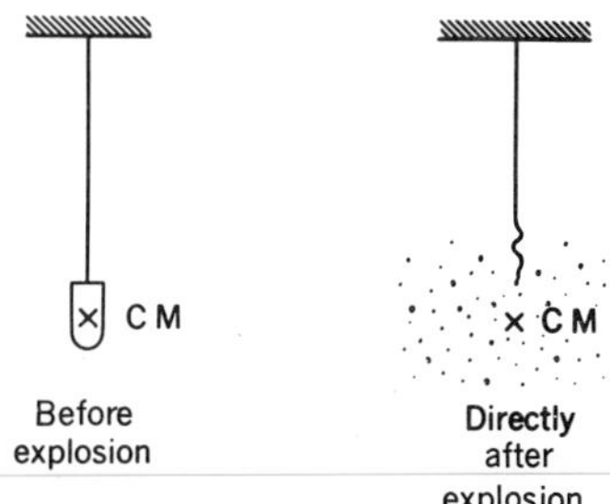

Fig. 14.10

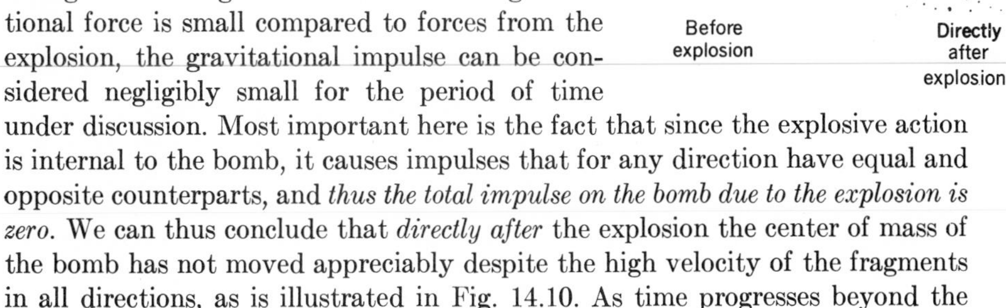

There will be other situations in which the time interval of interest is so small that only extremely large forces acting during the interval will have impulses which are not negligibly small. For instance, two particles usually collide during a very short time interval, and comparatively large forces are developed on each of the particles. This action is called an *impact*. The time interval for such actions is usually small enough so that for each particle the force of gravity causes a negligible impulse during the action. The impact forces on the bodies are always equal and opposite to each other, so the net impulse on the *pair* of bodies is zero. This means that the total momentum directly after impact equals the total momentum directly before impact.

We shall consider at this time two types of impact, for which certain definitions are needed. We will call the normal to the *plane of contact* during the collision of two bodies *the line of impact*. If the centers of mass of the two colliding bodies lie along the line of impact, the action is called *central impact*, and is shown for the case of two spheres in Fig. 14.11. If, in addition, the velocity vectors of the particles approaching the collision are collinear with the line of impact, the action is called *direct central impact*. This is illustrated by V_1 and V_2 in the diagram. Should one (or both) of the velocities have a line of action not collinear with the line of impact—say, for example, V_1' and/or V_2'—the action is termed *oblique central impact*.

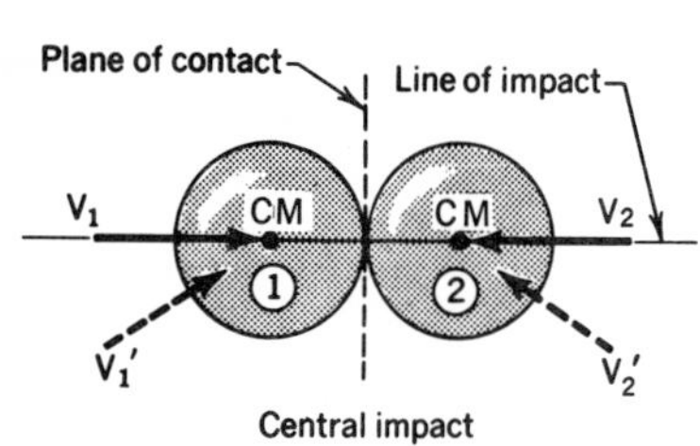

Fig. 14.11

In either case, there is conservation of momentum during the short time interval, from directly before the collision (indicated with the subscript i) to directly after the collision (indicated with subscript f). That is:

$$(m_1V_1)_i + (m_2V_2)_i = (m_1V_1)_f + (m_2V_2)_f \qquad \textbf{14.8}$$

In the direct central impact case for smooth bodies, this equation becomes a single scalar equation, since $(V_1)_f$ and $(V_2)_f$ will be collinear with the line of impact. Usually the initial velocities are known and the final values are desired, which means that we have for this case one scalar equation involving two unknowns. Clearly, we must know more about the manner of interaction of the bodies, since Eq. 14.8 as it stands is valid for materials of any consistency (for example, putty or hardened steel) and takes no account of such important considerations.*

For the oblique case, we can write components of the equation along the line of impact and along two other directions at right angles to the line of impact. If we know the initial velocities, we have six unknown final velocity components and only three equations, so we need even more information to establish fully the final velocities after this more general type of impact. We now consider each case in more detail in order to establish these additional relations.

Case 1. *Direct Central Impact.* Let us first examine the direct central impact case. We will consider the period of collision to be made up of two subintervals of time. The *period of deformation* refers to the duration of the collision, starting from the first initial contact of the bodies and ending with the time of maximum

* This means that we cannot consider the bodies undergoing impact only as particles as has been the case thus far, but must, in addition, consider them as deformable bodies of finite size in order to generate enough information to solve the problem at hand.

deformation. During this period, we shall consider that impulse $\int D\,dt$ acts oppositely on each of the bodies. The second period, covering the time from the maximum deformation condition to the condition in which the bodies just separate, we shall term the *period of restitution*. The impulse acting oppositely on each body during this period we shall indicate as $\int R\,dt$. If the bodies are *perfectly elastic*, they will re-establish their initial shapes during the period of restitution (if we neglect the internal vibrations of the bodies), as is shown in Fig. 14.12(a). When the bodies do not re-establish their initial shapes (Fig. 14.12(b)), we say that *plastic deformation* has taken place.

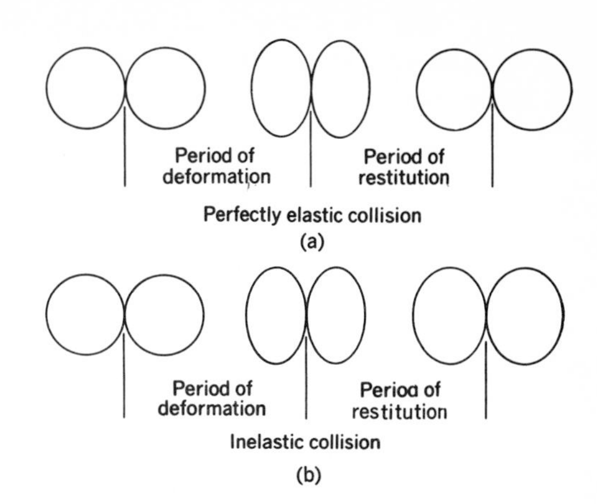

Fig. 14.12

The ratio of the impulse during the restitution period $\int R\,dt$ to the impulse during the deformation period $\int D\,dt$ is a number ϵ, which depends mainly on the physical properties of the bodies in collision. We call this number the *coefficient of restitution*. Thus

$$\epsilon = \frac{\text{impulse during restitution}}{\text{impulse during deformation}} = \left(\int R\,dt \Big/ \int D\,dt\right) \qquad \textbf{14.9}$$

We must strongly point out that the coefficient of restitution depends also on the size, shape, and velocities of the bodies before impact. These factors result from the fact that plastic deformation depends on the magnitude and nature of the stress distributions and also on the rate of loading. However, values of ϵ have been established for different materials and can be used for approximate results in the computations to follow. We will now formulate the relation between the coefficient of restitution and the initial and final velocities of the bodies undergoing impact.

Let us consider one of the bodies during the two phases of the collision. If we call the velocity at the maximum deformation condition $(V)_D$, we can say for mass (1):

$$\int D\,dt = -[(m_1V_1)_i - (m_1V_1)_D] \qquad \textbf{14.10}$$

During the period of restitution, the statement becomes:

$$\int R\,dt = -[(m_1V_1)_D - (m_1V_1)_f] \qquad \textbf{14.11}$$

Dividing Eq. 14.11 by Eq. 14.10, cancelling out m_1, and noting the definition, Eq. 14.9, we can say:

$$\epsilon = \frac{(V_1)_D - (V_1)_f}{(V_1)_i - (V_1)_D} \qquad \textbf{14.12}$$

A similar analysis for the other mass (2) gives this result:

$$\epsilon = \frac{(V_2)_D - (V_2)_f}{(V_2)_i - (V_2)_D} = \frac{(V_2)_f - (V_2)_D}{(V_2)_D - (V_2)_i} \qquad \textbf{14.13}$$

In the last expression, we have changed the sign of numerator and denominator. At the intermediate position between deformation and restitution, the masses have essentially the same velocity. Thus, $(V_1)_D = (V_2)_D$. Since the quotients in Eqs. 14.12 and 14.13 are equal to each other, we can add numerators and denominators to form another equal quotient. Noting the above-mentioned equality of the V_D terms, we have the desired result:

$$\epsilon = -\frac{(V_2)_f - (V_1)_f}{(V_2)_i - (V_1)_i} = -\frac{\text{velocity of separation}}{\text{velocity of approach}} \tag{14.14}$$

This equation involves the coefficient ϵ, which is presumably known or estimated, and the initial and final velocities of the bodies undergoing impact. Thus it is this equation that enables us to solve the final velocities of the bodies after collision when it is used with the momentum Eq. 14.8 for the case of direct central impact.

During a *perfectly elastic* collision, the impulse for the period of restitution equals the impulse for the period of deformation,* so the coefficient of restitution is *unity* for this case. For non-elastic collisions, the coefficient of restitution is less than unity, since the impulse is diminished on restitution as a result of the failure of the bodies to resume their original geometries. For a *perfectly plastic* impact, $\epsilon = 0$, i.e., $(V_2)_f = (V_1)_f$, and the bodies remain in contact.

Case 2. Oblique Central Impact. Let us now consider the case of oblique central impact. The velocity components along the line of impact may be related by the scalar component of the momentum Eq. 14.8 in this direction and also by Eq. 14.14 where velocity components along the line of impact are used and where the coefficient of restitution may be considered (for smooth bodies) to be the same as for the direct central impact case. If we know the initial conditions, we can accordingly solve for those velocity components after impact in the direction of the line of impact. As for the other components of velocity, we can say that for smooth bodies these velocity components are unaffected by the collision, since no impulses act in these directions on either body. That is, the velocity components normal to the line of impact for each body are the same immediately after impact as before. Thus the final velocity components of both bodies can be established and the motions of the bodies can be determined within the limits of the discussion. The following examples illustrate the use of the preceding formulations.

EXAMPLE 14.8

To check the muzzle velocity of a rifle, we shoot a bullet into a block of wood suspended from a light flexible wire (Fig. 14.13). The bullet lodges in the wood and causes it to swing to some maximum angle θ,

* The impulses are equal because during the period of restitution the body can be considered to undergo identically the reverse of the process corresponding to the deformation period. Thus from a thermodynamics point of view we are considering the elastic impact to be a reversible process.

which we then measure. Knowing the distance l from the center of the wood to the support, show that we can ascertain the velocity of the bullet just before it hits the wood. This may be taken as the muzzle velocity if the gun is reasonably close to the block.

Since the action of the bullet in imbedding itself in the block is an impact that has only a period of

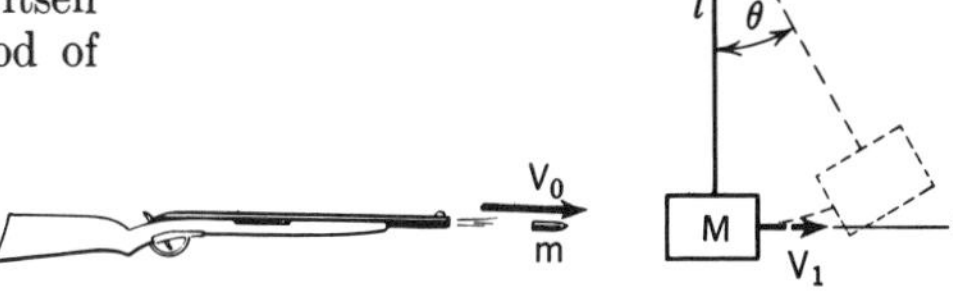

Fig. 14.13

deformation, the velocities of both bodies are the same after impact. We can assume that the action takes place so rapidly that the block M does not move appreciably during the deformation period but nevertheless acquires a velocity V_1, in accordance with the momentum considerations discussed earlier. Conservation of momentum of the two particles accordingly requires that

$$mV_0 + M(0) = (m + M)V_1 \qquad \textbf{(a)}$$

This is an equation with the two unknowns V_0 and V_1.

To get further information, examine the motion after impact. The bullet and the wood block may be considered a single particle that is constrained to move in a circular path. Note that after impact only the force of gravity $-mg\boldsymbol{j}$, a conservative force, performs work on the particle and therefore we may use the conservation-of-energy equation as presented in the previous chapter. Using the lowest position of the masses as the reference, we thus have:

$$(m + M)\frac{V_1^2}{2} = (m + M)g(l - l\cos\theta) \qquad \textbf{(b)}$$

We can now determine V_1 from this equation, since θ is known. Finally, if we return to Eq. (a) we can evaluate V_0.

EXAMPLE 14.9

Two billiard balls (of same size and mass) collide with the velocities of approach shown in Fig. 14.14. For a coefficient of restitution of 0.90, what are the final velocities of the balls directly after they part? What is the loss in kinetic energy?

A reference is established so that the x axis is along line of centers and the y axis is in the plane of contact. The reference plane is parallel to the billiard table. The approach velocities have been decomposed into components along these references. The velocity components $(V_1)_y$ and $(V_2)_y$ are unchanged during the action. Along the line of impact, momentum considerations give:

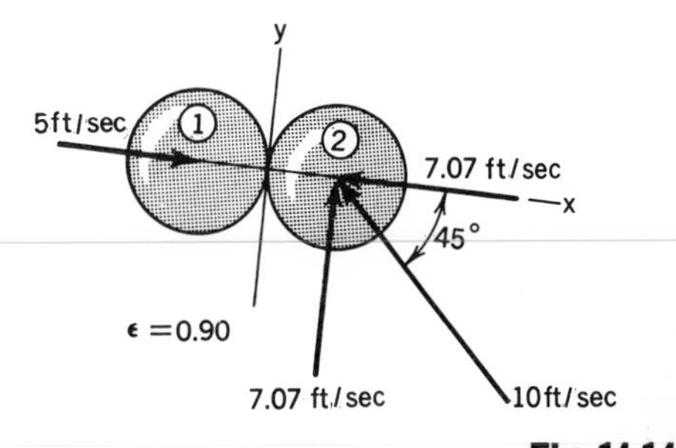

Fig. 14.14

$$5m - 7.07m = m[(V_1)_x]_f + m[(V_2)_x]_f \qquad \textbf{(a)}$$

Using the coefficient of restitution relation in Eq. 14.14, we have:

$$\epsilon = 0.90 = -\frac{[(V_2)_x]_f - [(V_1)_x]_f}{-7.07 - 5} \qquad \textbf{(b)}$$

We thus have two equations, (a) and (b), for the unknown components in the x direction. Simplifying these equations, we have:

$$[(V_1)_x]_f + [(V_2)_x]_f = -2.07 \qquad \textbf{(c)}$$

$$[(V_1)_x]_f - [(V_2)_x]_f = -10.86 \qquad \textbf{(d)}$$

Adding, we get:

$$[(V_1)_x]_f = -6.46 \text{ ft/sec}$$

Solving for $[(V_2)_x]$ in Eq. (c), we write:

$$[(V_2)_x]_f - 6.46 = -2.07$$

$$\therefore [(V_2)_x]_f = 4.39 \text{ ft/sec}$$

The final velocities after collision are then:

$$(\boldsymbol{V}_1)_f = -6.46\boldsymbol{i}$$

$$(\boldsymbol{V}_2)_f = 4.39\boldsymbol{i} + 7.07\boldsymbol{j}$$

The loss in kinetic energy is given as:

$$(KE)_i - (KE)_f = (\tfrac{1}{2}m5^2 + \tfrac{1}{2}m10^2) - [\tfrac{1}{2}m6.46^2 + \tfrac{1}{2}m(7.07^2 + 4.39^2)]$$

$$\Delta KE = \tfrac{1}{2}m[25 + 100 - (41.7 + 50.0 + 19.3)] = 7.0m \text{ ft-lb}$$

If ϵ is unity, i.e., a perfectly elastic impact, the loss of energy is zero, as you can readily verify.

---

*14.4 Collision of a Particle with a Massive Rigid Body

In the previous section we employed conservation-of-momentum considerations and the concept of the coefficient of restitution to examine the impact of two smooth bodies of comparable size. Now we will extend this approach to include the impact of a spherical body with a much larger and more massive *rigid* body. This has been shown in Fig. 14.15.

The procedure we shall follow is to consider the massive body to be a spherical body of *infinite* mass with a radius equal to the local radius of curvature of the surface of the massive body at the point of contact A. This has been shown in Fig. 14.15. The line of impact then becomes identical with the normal n to the surface of the massive body at the point of impact. Note that the case we have shown in the diagram corresponds to oblique central impact. With no friction, clearly only the components along the line of impact n can change as a result of impact. But

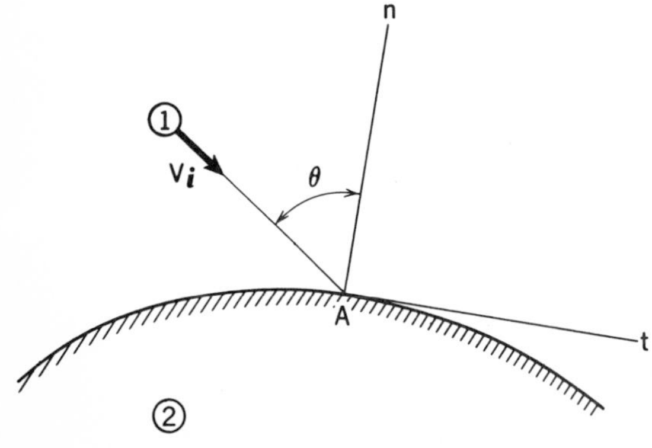

Fig. 14.15

in this case, the velocity of the sphere representing the massive body must undergo no change in value after impact because of its infinite mass.* We cannot make good use here of the conservation-of-momentum equation in the direction n because the infinite mass of the hypothetical body (2) will render the equation indeterminate. However, we can use Eq. 14.14, assuming we have a coefficient of restitution ϵ for the action. Noting that the velocity of the massive body does not change, we accordingly get:

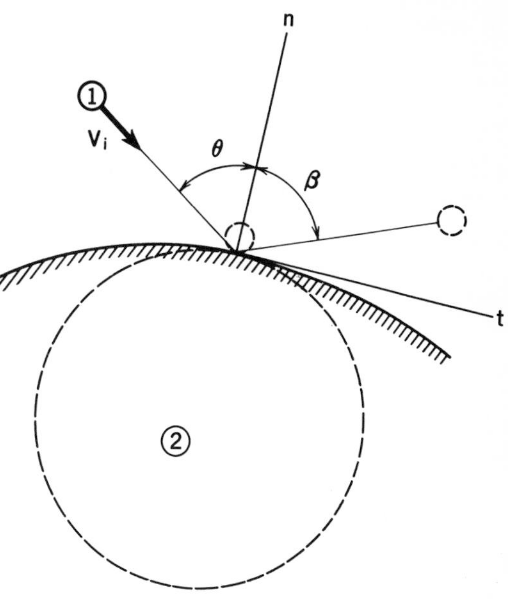

Fig. 14.16

$$\epsilon = -\frac{[(V_1)_n]_f - [(V_2)_n]}{[(V_1)_n]_i - [(V_2)_n]}$$

Thus, knowing the velocities of the bodies before impact, as well as the quantity ϵ, we are able to compute the velocity of the particle after impact. If the collision is perfectly elastic, $\epsilon = 1$ and we see from Eq. 14.14 that for a stationary massive body

$$[(V_1)_n]_i = -[(V_1)_n]_f$$

This means that the angle of incidence θ (see Fig. 14.16) equals the angle of deflection β. For $\epsilon < 1$, i.e., for inelastic collision, the angle of deflection β will clearly exceed θ.

We now illustrate the use of these formulations.

EXAMPLE 14.10

A ball is dropped onto a concrete floor from height h (Fig. 14.17). If there is a coefficient of restitution of 0.90 for the action, to what height will the ball rise on the rebound?

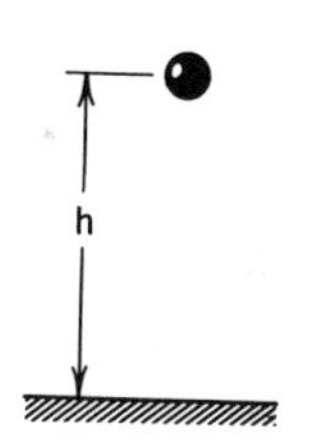

Fig. 14.17

Here the massive body has an infinite radius at the surface. Furthermore, we have a direct central impact. Accordingly, from Eq. 14.14 we have:

$$\epsilon = -\frac{(V)_f - 0}{(V)_i - 0} = -\frac{\sqrt{2gh'}}{\sqrt{2gh}}$$

Solving for h', the height of rebound, we get:

$$h' = \epsilon^2 h = 0.81h$$

EXAMPLE 14.11

A satellite in the form of a sphere with radius R [Fig. 14.18(a)] is moving in a region above the earth's surface where there is highly rarefied atmosphere. We wish to estimate the drag on the satellite. Neglect the contribution from the antennae.

* Otherwise there would be an infinite change in momentum for this sphere.

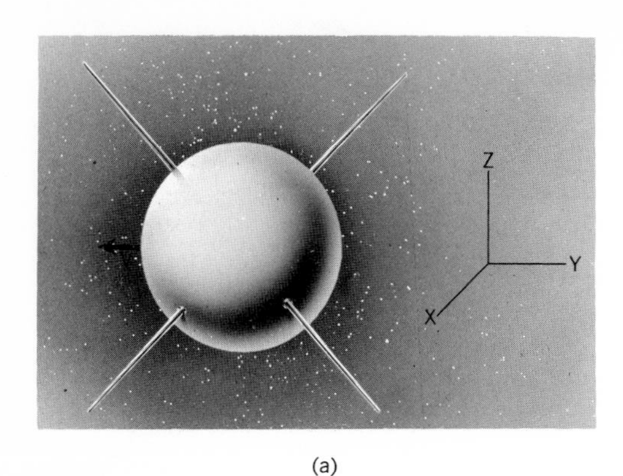

(a)

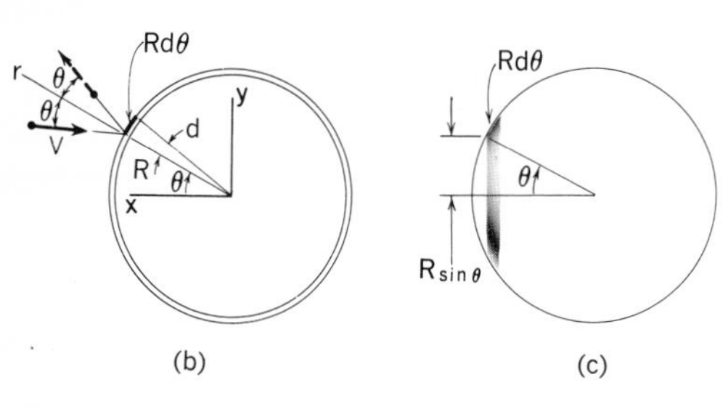

(b) (c)

Fig. 14.18

We cannot use the continuum approach of fluid dynamics here, but must consider collisions of the individual molecules with the satellite*. The mass per molecule is m slugs and the number density of the molecules is n molecules/unit volume. Since the satellite is moving with a speed V much greater than the speed of the molecules (the molecules move at about the speed of sound) we can assume that the molecules are stationary relative to inertial space reference XYZ and that only the satellite is moving. Furthermore we assume that when the satellite hits a molecule there is an elastic frictionless collision.

To study this problem we have shown a section of the satellite in Fig. 14.18(b). A reference xyz is fixed to the satellite at its center. We will consider this reference also to be an inertial reference—a step which for small drag will introduce little error for the ensuing calculations. Relative to this reference the molecules approach the satellite with a velocity V, as shown for one molecule in the diagram, collide with the surface with an angle of incidence measured by the polar coordinate θ, and deflect with an equal angle of deflection of θ. The component of the impulse given to the molecule in the x direction $(I_{\text{mol}})_x$ is:

$$(I_{\text{mol}})_x = (mV \cos 2\theta) + mV$$
$$= mV(1 + \cos 2\theta) \qquad \textbf{(a)}$$

This is the impulse component that would be given to any molecule hitting a strip which is $R\,d\theta$ in width and which is revolved around the x axis as shown in Fig. 14.18(c). The number of such collisions per second for this strip can readily be calculated as follows:

Collisions for strip per sec.

$$= \begin{bmatrix}\text{projected area}\\ \text{of the strip}\\ \text{in } x \text{ direction}\end{bmatrix}\begin{bmatrix}\text{distance the}\\ \text{strip moves}\\ \text{in 1 sec}\end{bmatrix}\begin{bmatrix}\text{no. of}\\ \text{molecules per}\\ \text{unit volume}\end{bmatrix}$$

$$= [(R\,d\theta \cos\theta)(2\pi R \sin\theta)][V][n]$$

$$= 2\pi R^2 nV \sin\theta \cos\theta\, d\theta \qquad \textbf{(b)}$$

The impulse component dI_x for the strip in 1 second is then:

$$dI_x = 2\pi mnR^2V^2 (\sin\theta\cos\theta)(1 + \cos 2\theta)\, d\theta \qquad \textbf{(c)}$$

Noting that $2 \sin\theta \cos\theta = \sin 2\theta$, we have:

$$dI_x = \pi mnR^2V^2 (\sin 2\theta + \sin 2\theta \cos 2\theta)\, d\theta$$
$$= \pi mnR^2V^2 \left(\sin 2\theta + \frac{\sin 4\theta}{2}\right) d\theta$$

Integrating from $\theta = 0$ to $\theta = \pi/2$, we get the total impulse for 1 second. Thus:

* The mean free path between collisions is assumed to be of the same order of size as the satellite dimensions, and so we must discard the continuum approach here.

$$I_x = \pi mnR^2V^2\left[\int_0^{\pi/2} \sin 2\theta\, d\theta + \frac{1}{2}\int_0^{\pi/2} \sin 4\theta\, d\theta\right]$$

$$= \pi mnR^2V^2\left[-\frac{1}{2}\cos 2\theta\Big|_0^{\pi/2} - \frac{1}{8}\cos 4\theta\Big|_0^{\pi/2}\right]$$

$$= \pi mnR^2V^2(1+0) = \pi mnR^2V^2 \qquad \textbf{(d)}$$

The average force needed to give this impulse to the particle is clearly πmnR^2V^2 and so the reaction to this force is the desired drag.

EXAMPLE 14.12

Shown in Fig. 14.19 is a "beebee" gun firing at a point A on a hard, smooth spherical surface. Point A is at the intersection of the mid-longitudinal and mid-latitudinal planes for the single quadrant section of the surface shown. If the velocity of the beebee is 500 ft/sec, what is the velocity of the ricochet for a coefficient of restitution $\epsilon = 0.8$?

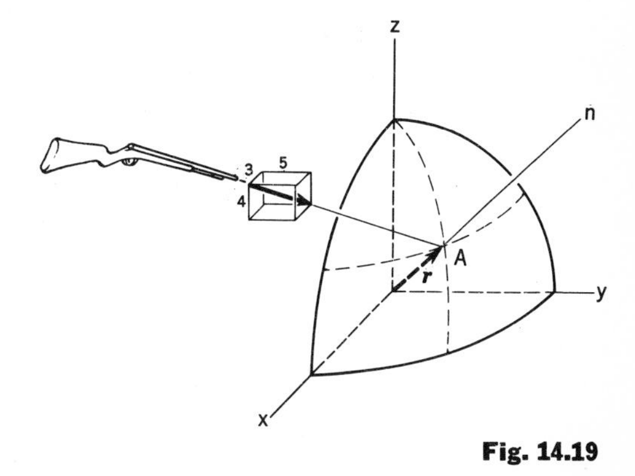

Fig. 14.19

As a first step, we shall evaluate the position vector to point A. Thus, from simple geometric considerations, we get:

$$\boldsymbol{r}_A = r_A\,(\cos 45°)^2\boldsymbol{i} + r_A\,(\cos 45°)^2\boldsymbol{j} + r_A\,(\cos 45°)\boldsymbol{k}$$

$$\therefore\ \boldsymbol{r}_A = r_A(0.5\boldsymbol{i} + 0.5\boldsymbol{j} + 0.707\boldsymbol{k}) \qquad \textbf{(a)}$$

The unit normal vector $\boldsymbol{n}$ to the surface at A is accordingly:

$$\boldsymbol{n} = 0.5\boldsymbol{i} + 0.5\boldsymbol{j} + 0.707\boldsymbol{k} \qquad \textbf{(b)}$$

Consulting the diagram, we next express the velocity of the beebee in rectangular coordinates as follows:

$$(\boldsymbol{V})_i = (500)\left[-\frac{3}{\sqrt{50}}\boldsymbol{i} + \frac{5}{\sqrt{50}}\boldsymbol{j} - \frac{4}{\sqrt{50}}\boldsymbol{k}\right]$$

$$= -212\boldsymbol{i} + 354\boldsymbol{j} - 283\boldsymbol{k}\ \text{ft/sec} \qquad \textbf{(c)}$$

The velocity component normal to the surface is determined as follows:

$$(V_n)_i = (\boldsymbol{V})_i \cdot (\boldsymbol{n}) = -129\ \text{ft/sec} \qquad \textbf{(d)}$$

The velocity vector $(\boldsymbol{V}_n)_i$ is then:

$$(\boldsymbol{V}_n)_i = (-129)(\boldsymbol{n})$$

$$= -64.5\boldsymbol{i} - 64.5\boldsymbol{j} - 91.2\boldsymbol{k} \qquad \textbf{(e)}$$

The velocity vector $(\boldsymbol{V}_t)_i$ can now be evaluated as follows:

$$(\boldsymbol{V}_t)_i = (\boldsymbol{V})_i - (\boldsymbol{V}_n)_i$$

$$= -147.5\boldsymbol{i} + 418.5\boldsymbol{j} - 191.8\boldsymbol{k} \qquad \textbf{(f)}$$

We can now say for the velocity components after impact:

$$(\boldsymbol{V}_t)_f = (\boldsymbol{V}_t)_i = -147.5\boldsymbol{i} + 418.5\boldsymbol{j} - 191.8\boldsymbol{k}$$

$$(V_n)_f = -\epsilon(V_n)_i = 51.5\boldsymbol{i} + 51.5\boldsymbol{j} + 73.0\boldsymbol{k} \qquad \text{(g)}$$

The final velocity $(V)_f$ is then:

$$(V_f) = (V_n)_f + (V_t)_f$$
$$= -96\boldsymbol{i} + 469\boldsymbol{j} - 118.8\boldsymbol{k} \text{ ft/sec}$$

---

*14.5 A Note on Energy Loss

In Example 14.9 our computations indicated that there is a loss of kinetic energy in an inelastic collision despite the fact that the momentum of the system is conserved. This may seem strange and should be examined further. We will first prove that kinetic energy must be conserved for a perfectly elastic collision. For simplicity, we consider a direct central impact. With $\epsilon = 1$, Eq. 14.14 becomes:

$$(V_2)_i - (V_1)_i = (V_1)_f - (V_2)_f$$

Rearranging terms, we have:

$$(V_1)_i + (V_1)_f = (V_2)_f + (V_2)_i \qquad \textbf{14.15}$$

Next we write the momentum equation.

$$m_1(V_1)_i + m_2(V_2)_i = m_1(V_1)_f + m_2(V_2)_f \qquad \textbf{14.16}$$

Rearranging this equation, we have:

$$m_1[(V_1)_i - (V_1)_f] = m_2[(V_2)_f - (V_2)_i] \qquad \textbf{14.17}$$

Now multiply the corresponding sides of Eqs. 14.17 and 14.15:

$$m_1[(V_1)_i - (V_1)_f][(V_1)_i + (V_1)_f] = m_2[(V_2)_f - (V_2)_i][(V_2)_f + (V_2)_i]$$

$$\therefore m_1[(V_1)_i^2 - (V_1)_f^2] = m_2[(V_2)_f^2 - (V_2)_i^2] \qquad \textbf{14.18}$$

Dividing through by 2 and rearranging, we have:

$$\left(\frac{m_1V_1^2}{2}\right)_i + \left(\frac{m_2V_2^2}{2}\right)_i = \left(\frac{m_1V_1^2}{2}\right)_f + \left(\frac{m_2V_2^2}{2}\right)_f \qquad \textbf{14.19}$$

This clearly shows that there is no loss in kinetic energy during an elastic impact.

During an inelastic impact, the momentum is conserved but there is a loss however of mechanical energy, as was demonstrated in the example. The momentum conservation results from the fact that on each mass there is a contact force at all times equal and opposite to the corresponding contact force on the other mass. By integrating these forces with time and adding the results, we get impulses that must cancel.

For energy considerations during an inelastic impact, we shall consider the colliding bodies each to be a system of subparticles* [see Fig. 14.20(a)].

---

* In the engineering sciences and physics one often attempts to explain certain effects occurring at one order of size by going to models at a smaller order of size. Thus to explain the equation of state or the viscosity of a gas occurring at the continuum or so-called macroscopic level of analysis we must go to the molecular or so-called microscopic level (i.e., we go to the kinetic theory of gases.)

The energy of this system of subparticles is, according to Eq. 13.30:

$$KE = \tfrac{1}{2}MV_c^2 + \tfrac{1}{2}\sum_{i=1}^{n} m_i\dot{\rho}_i^2 \qquad \textbf{14.20}$$

Also Eq. 12.128 is applicable in the form:

$$F = M\frac{dV_c}{dt} \qquad \textbf{14.21}$$

Since the resultant external force is zero during the collision of the two bodies, Eq. 14.21 clearly indicates that there is no change in the velocity of the mass center and thus the term $\frac{1}{2}MV_c^2$ in Eq. 14.20 remains constant during the collision. The remaining term on the right side of Eq. 14.20 is equal to the work done by the interval forces of the system as the subparticles move relative to the mass center (see Eq. 13.33). During the deformation period, the subparticles of the bodies have a general decelerating motion toward the center of mass. Hence, there is a net amount of negative work done by the internal forces as they resist this motion. This decreases the term $\frac{1}{2}\sum m_i\dot{\rho}_i^2$ and thus, according to Eq. 14.20, reduces the kinetic energy of the bodies. If the bodies are perfectly elastic, the forces perform an equal amount of positive work during the period of restitution [Fig. 14.20(b)], with the result that that there is no net change in kinetic energy after impact. However, in the extreme case of a *perfectly plastic* impact [Fig. 14.20(c)], there will be no period of restitution and consequently only the negative work performed during the period of deformation is present. It is then possible for the impact to cause a considerable decrease in kinetic energy. Between the extreme ranges of a perfectly plastic and a perfectly elastic impact is the range of partially plastic impact in which the loss of kinetic energy is dependent on the degree of permanent deformation developed.

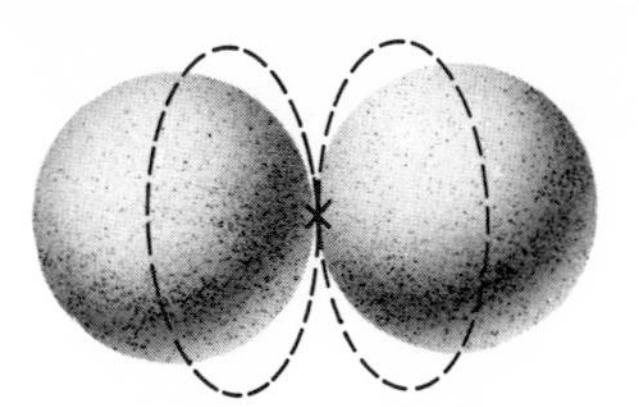

Period of deformation
Negative work
(a)

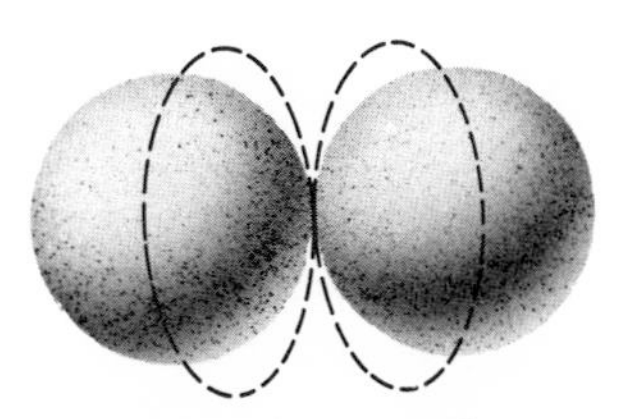

Period of restitution
for elastic body
Equal positive work
(b)

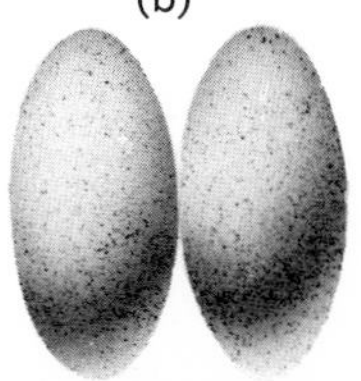

Perfect plastic deformation
No period of restitution
Zero work
(c)

Fig. 14.20

PART B. Moment of Momentum

14.6 Moment of Momentum Equation for a Single Particle

At this time we shall introduce another auxiliary statement that follows from Newton's law and that will have great value when extended to the case of a rigid body. We start with Newton's law in the following form:

$$F = \frac{d}{dt}(mV) = \dot{P} \qquad \textbf{14.22}$$

where it is apparent that the symbol $\boldsymbol{P}$ represents the linear momentum of the particle. We next take the moment of each side of the equation about a point a in space:

$$\boldsymbol{\varrho}_a \times \boldsymbol{F} = \boldsymbol{\varrho}_a \times \dot{\boldsymbol{P}} \qquad 14.23$$

If the aforementioned point a is positioned at a fixed point in the same inertial reference relative to which $\dot{\boldsymbol{P}}$ is measured, we will be able to simplify the right side of the above equation. Accordingly, examine the expression $(d/dt)\ (\boldsymbol{\varrho}_a \times \boldsymbol{P})$. Thus:

$$\frac{d}{dt}(\boldsymbol{\varrho}_a \times \boldsymbol{P}) = \boldsymbol{\varrho}_a \times \dot{\boldsymbol{P}} + \dot{\boldsymbol{\varrho}}_a \times \boldsymbol{P} \qquad 14.24$$

But the expression $\dot{\boldsymbol{\varrho}}_a \times \boldsymbol{P}$ can be written as $\dot{\boldsymbol{\varrho}}_a \times m\dot{\boldsymbol{r}}$. The vectors $\boldsymbol{\varrho}_a$ and $\boldsymbol{r}$ are measured in the same reference from a fixed point a to the particle, and from the origin to the particle, respectively. They are thus different at all times to the extent of a constant vector. Therefore, $\dot{\boldsymbol{\varrho}}_a = \dot{\boldsymbol{r}}$ and the expression $\dot{\boldsymbol{\varrho}}_a \times m\dot{\boldsymbol{r}}$ is zero. Thus Eq. 14.24 becomes:*

$$\frac{d}{dt}(\boldsymbol{\varrho}_a \times \boldsymbol{P}) = \boldsymbol{\varrho}_a \times \dot{\boldsymbol{P}} \qquad 14.25$$

and Eq. 14.23 can be written in the form:

$$\boldsymbol{\varrho}_a \times \boldsymbol{F} = \boldsymbol{M}_a = \frac{d}{dt}(\boldsymbol{\varrho}_a \times \boldsymbol{P}) = \dot{\boldsymbol{H}}_a \qquad 14.26$$

where $\boldsymbol{H}_a$ is the *moment about point* a *of the linear momentum vector*. Sometimes $\boldsymbol{H}$ is termed the *angular momentum vector*. The above equation, then, states that *the moment of the resultant force on a particle about a point* a, *fixed in an inertial reference, equals the time rate of change of moment about point* a *of the momentum relative to the inertial reference*. This is the desired alternate form of Newton's law.

You will recall that the moment of momentum concept was used (although not formally) in connection with the central-force problem in Chapter 12.

EXAMPLE 14.13

Shown in Fig. 14.21 is a rod rotating freely in a horizontal plane about centerline O with angular speed $\dot{\theta}$ equal to 0.3 rad/sec. A heavy mass having a mass M of 1 slug rides on the rod at a distance of 2 ft from the center O. If a radial force from O draws the mass M toward O at the rate of 1 ft/sec, what is $\dot{\theta}$ and $\ddot{\theta}$ of the rod when the mass is 1 ft from O? Neglect the mass of the rod.

The net force acting on the mass M is the radial force from O which we denote as F. Taking the mass M as a particle and applying Eq. 14.26 about point O, we get:

$$\boldsymbol{r} \times (-F\boldsymbol{\varepsilon}_r) = \dot{\boldsymbol{H}} \qquad \textbf{(a)}$$

---

* Equation 14.25 is also valid at a time t when the point a has a zero velocity at time t. We suggest you show this.

But $\boldsymbol{r} \times \boldsymbol{\varepsilon}_r = \boldsymbol{0}$ and accordingly, like all central-force motions about a point fixed in inertial space $\boldsymbol{H}$, the moment of momentum is constant. Initially, we have for $\boldsymbol{H}$:

$$\boldsymbol{H}_1 = \boldsymbol{r}_1 \times m\boldsymbol{V}_1 = (2)(m)[(2)(0.3)]\boldsymbol{k} = 1.2m\boldsymbol{k} \qquad \textbf{(b)}$$

When $r = 1$ ft we have:

$$\boldsymbol{H}_2 = (1)(m)[(1)\dot{\theta}_2]\boldsymbol{k} = m\dot{\theta}_2\boldsymbol{k} \qquad \textbf{(c)}$$

Equating $\boldsymbol{H}_1$ and $\boldsymbol{H}_2$, we get:

$$\dot{\theta}_2 = 1.2 \text{ rad/sec} \qquad \textbf{(d)}$$

To get $\ddot{\theta}$ we proceed as follows:

$$\frac{d}{dt}\boldsymbol{H} = \frac{d}{dt}(\boldsymbol{r} \times m\boldsymbol{V}) = \frac{d}{dt}(r^2 m\dot{\theta})\boldsymbol{k} = \boldsymbol{0}$$

$$\therefore\ 2r\dot{r}m\dot{\theta} + r^2 m\ddot{\theta} = 0 \qquad \textbf{(e)}$$

Solving for $\ddot{\theta}$, we get:

$$\ddot{\theta} = \frac{2\dot{r}\dot{\theta}}{r} \qquad \textbf{(f)}$$

At the position of interest we have for $\ddot{\theta}$:

$$\ddot{\theta}_2 = \frac{(2)(1)(1.2)}{(1)} = 2.4 \text{ rad/sec}^2 \qquad \textbf{(g)}$$

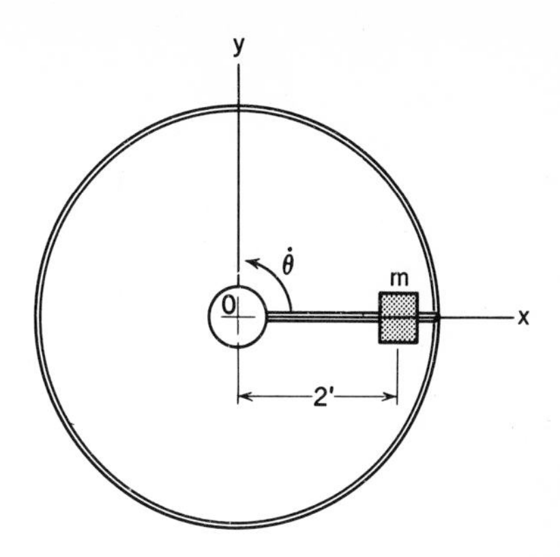

Fig. 14.21

14.7 Moment of Momentum Equation for a System of Particles

Shown in Fig. 14.22 is an aggregate of n particles and an inertial reference. The moment of momentum equation for the ith particle is now written about the origin of this reference:

$$\boldsymbol{r}_i \times \boldsymbol{F}_i + \boldsymbol{r}_i \times \left(\sum_{\substack{j=1 \\ i \neq j}}^{n} \boldsymbol{f}_{ij} \right) = \frac{d}{dt}(\boldsymbol{r}_i \times \boldsymbol{P}_i) \qquad \textbf{14.27}$$

where, as usual, $\boldsymbol{f}_{ij}$ is the internal force from the jth particle on the ith particle. We now sum this equation for all n particles:

$$\sum_{i=1}^{n} \boldsymbol{r}_i \times \boldsymbol{F}_i + \sum_{i=1}^{n}\sum_{j=1}^{n} (\boldsymbol{r}_i \times \boldsymbol{f}_{ij}) = \frac{d}{dt}\left[\sum_{i=1}^{n} (\boldsymbol{r}_i \times \boldsymbol{P}_i) \right] = \dot{\boldsymbol{H}}_{\text{total}} \qquad \textbf{14.28}$$

where the summation operation has been put before the differentiation on the right side, a step that is permissible because of the distributive property of differentiation with respect to addition. For any pair of particles, the internal forces will be equal and opposite, and if they are collinear* (see Fig. 14.23), the forces will have a zero moment about the origin. This is most easily

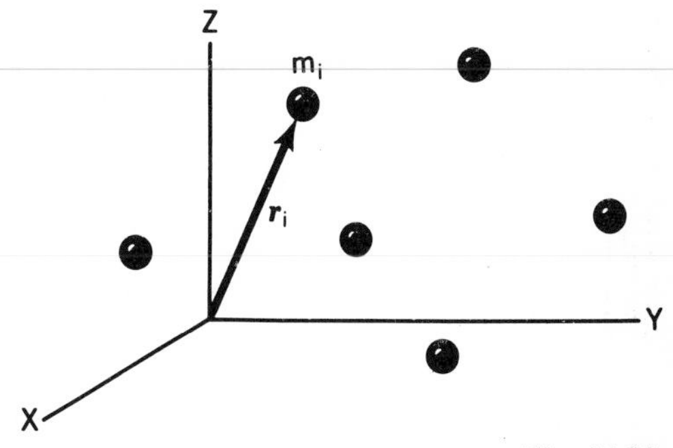

Fig. 14.22

* You will recall that magnetic forces between particles are not necessarily collinear. We shall not consider such forces here.

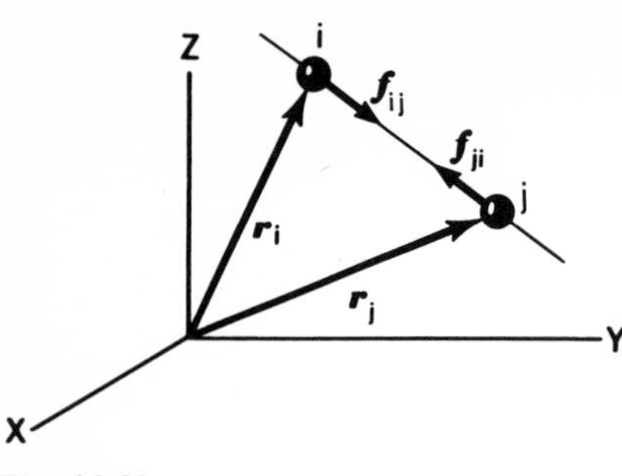

Fig. 14.23

understood by remembering that, for purposes of taking moments about a point, forces are transmissible. We can then conclude that the term

$$\sum_{i=1}^{n} \sum_{j=1}^{n} (\boldsymbol{r}_i \times \boldsymbol{f}_{ij})$$

in the above equation is zero, and we have as a result:

$$\boxed{\boldsymbol{M} = \dot{\boldsymbol{H}}} \qquad \textbf{14.29}$$

This statement indicates that *the total moment of external forces acting on an aggregate of particles about a point fixed in an inertial reference* (the point in the development was picked as the origin merely for convenience) *equals the time rate of change of the total moment of the momentum relative to the inertial reference, where this moment is taken about the aforementioned point.*

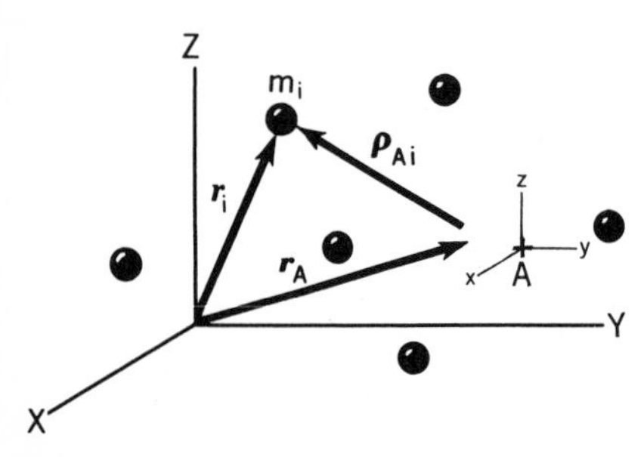

Fig. 14.24

We will now show that an equation having the same form as Eq. 14.29 can be written with respect to other points that are *not fixed* in the inertial reference. Let us, then, consider any point A moving relative to the inertial reference X, Y, Z (Fig. 14.24) and see what restrictions must be placed on this point if we are properly to apply Eq. 14.29 to this point. The position vector to the ith particle can then be given as:

$$\boldsymbol{r}_i = \boldsymbol{r}_A + \boldsymbol{\rho}_{Ai} \qquad \textbf{14.30}$$

We substitute for $\boldsymbol{r}_i$ in Eq. 14.28, using the above relation. Dropping the second expression in Eq. 14.28, which we have shown to be zero, we get:

$$\sum_{i=1}^{n} (\boldsymbol{r}_A + \boldsymbol{\rho}_{Ai}) \times \boldsymbol{F}_i = \sum_{i=1}^{n} \frac{d}{dt}[(\boldsymbol{r}_A + \boldsymbol{\rho}_{Ai}) \times \boldsymbol{P}_i] \qquad \textbf{14.31}$$

But, from the previous section we know that:

$$\frac{d}{dt}[(\boldsymbol{r}_A + \boldsymbol{\rho}_{Ai}) \times \boldsymbol{P}_i] = (\boldsymbol{r}_A + \boldsymbol{\rho}_{Ai}) \times \dot{\boldsymbol{P}}_i$$

and so Eq. 14.31 becomes, after we carry out the cross products and extract $\boldsymbol{r}_A$ from summations:

$$\boldsymbol{r}_A \times \sum_{i=1}^{n} \boldsymbol{F}_i + \sum_{i=1}^{n} \boldsymbol{\rho}_{Ai} \times \boldsymbol{F}_i = \boldsymbol{r}_A \times \sum_{i=1}^{n} \dot{\boldsymbol{P}}_i + \sum_{i=1}^{n} \boldsymbol{\rho}_{Ai} \times \dot{\boldsymbol{P}}_i \qquad \textbf{14.32}$$

We know from Newton's law for a system of particles, however, that:

$$\sum_{i=1}^{n} \boldsymbol{F}_i = \frac{d}{dt}\left(\sum_{i=1}^{n} m_i \boldsymbol{V}_i\right) = \sum_{i=1}^{n} \dot{\boldsymbol{P}}_i$$

so the first expressions on each side of the equation clearly cancel out, leaving this equation:

$$\sum_{i=1}^{n} \boldsymbol{\varrho}_{Ai} \times \boldsymbol{F}_i = \sum_{i=1}^{n} \boldsymbol{\varrho}_{Ai} \times \dot{\boldsymbol{P}}_i \qquad \textbf{14.33}$$

The left side is the total moment $\boldsymbol{M}_A$ of the forces about point A. To evaluate the right side, rewrite $\dot{\boldsymbol{P}}_i$ in the following manner.

$$\dot{\boldsymbol{P}}_i = m_i \ddot{\boldsymbol{r}}_i = m_i(\ddot{\boldsymbol{r}}_A + \ddot{\boldsymbol{\varrho}}_{Ai}) \qquad \textbf{14.34}$$

Substituting into Eq. 14.33 and extracting $\ddot{\boldsymbol{r}}_A$ from the summation sign, we can then write, using $\boldsymbol{M}_A$ for the left side:

$$\boldsymbol{M}_A = \left[\sum_{i=1}^{n} m_i \boldsymbol{\varrho}_{Ai} \right] \times \ddot{\boldsymbol{r}}_A + \sum_{i=1}^{n} \boldsymbol{\varrho}_{Ai} \times m_i \ddot{\boldsymbol{\varrho}}_{Ai} \qquad \textbf{14.35}$$

Recall from Chapter 11 that $\dot{\boldsymbol{\varrho}}_{Ai}$ and $\ddot{\boldsymbol{\varrho}}_{Ai}$ are the velocity and acceleration vectors respectively of the ith particle relative to point A. Accordingly we can denote these quantities as $(\boldsymbol{V}_i)_{xyz}$ and $(\dot{\boldsymbol{V}}_i)_{xyz}$ respectively where xyz is a reference at A translating relative to XYZ (see Fig. 14.24). Now carry out the following differentiation operation:

$$\frac{d}{dt} \sum_{i=1}^{n} \boldsymbol{\varrho}_{Ai} \times m_1 (\boldsymbol{V}_i)_{xyz} = \sum_{i=1}^{n} \dot{\boldsymbol{\varrho}}_{Ai} \times m_i (\boldsymbol{V}_i)_{xyz} + \sum_{i=1}^{n} \boldsymbol{\varrho}_{Ai} \times m_i (\dot{\boldsymbol{V}}_i)_{xyz}$$

$$= \sum_{i=1}^{n} (\boldsymbol{V}_i)_{xyz} \times m_i (\boldsymbol{V}_i)_{xyz} + \sum_{i=1}^{n} \boldsymbol{\varrho}_{Ai} \times m_i (\dot{\boldsymbol{V}}_i)_{xyz}$$

Clearly the first expression on the right side is zero, and, noting that the last term is identical with the last expression of Eq. 14.35, we can then rewrite Eq. 14.35 using the left side of the above equation in the following manner:

$$\boldsymbol{M}_A = [\sum_{i=1}^{n} m_i \boldsymbol{\varrho}_{Ai}] \times \ddot{\boldsymbol{r}}_A + \frac{d}{dt} \sum_{i=1}^{n} \boldsymbol{\varrho}_{Ai} \times m_i (\boldsymbol{V}_i)_{xyz}$$

The last expression in the above equation can be interpreted as the time rate of change of the total moment about point A of the momentum relative to A. We call this quantity $\dot{\boldsymbol{H}}_A$. The above equation becomes:

$$\boldsymbol{M}_A = \left(\sum_{i=1}^{n} m_i \boldsymbol{\varrho}_{Ai} \right) \times \ddot{\boldsymbol{r}}_A + \dot{\boldsymbol{H}}_A \qquad \textbf{14.36}$$

If the first term on the right side is zero, the resulting equation is of the form of Eq. 14.29. There are two situations where this is possible.

Case 1. If point A is the center of mass of the system, then:

$$\sum_{i=1}^{n} m_i \boldsymbol{\varrho}_{Ai}$$

which is the first mass moment about A, must be zero. The resulting equation is then given as:

$$\boxed{\boldsymbol{M}_C = \dot{\boldsymbol{H}}_C} \qquad \textbf{14.37}$$

Case 2. Let us rewrite the expression:

$$\sum_{i=1}^{n} m_i \boldsymbol{\varrho}_{Ai}$$

in the following manner, using the definition of the center of mass:

$$\sum_{i=1}^{n} m_i \boldsymbol{\varrho}_{Ai} = M\boldsymbol{D} \qquad \textbf{14.38}$$

where $\boldsymbol{D}$ is the position vector from the point A to the center of mass of the system, as is shown in Fig. 14.25. We now have for Eq. 14.36:

$$\boldsymbol{M}_A = M(\boldsymbol{D} \times \ddot{\boldsymbol{r}}_A) + \dot{\boldsymbol{H}}_A \qquad \textbf{14.39}$$

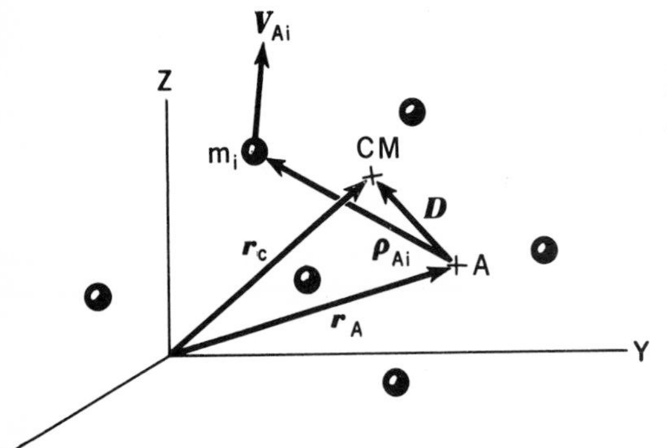

Fig. 14.25

If the acceleration of point A, i.e., $\ddot{\boldsymbol{r}}_A$, is in the same direction as $\boldsymbol{D}$, we again reduce to the simple form. This means *that point A is accelerating toward or away from the mass center*. We then have:

$$\boxed{\boldsymbol{M}_A = \dot{\boldsymbol{H}}_A} \qquad \textbf{14.40}$$

Thus besides the points fixed in the inertial reference, there are two other kinds of "noninertial" points for which Eq. 14.29 is valid. They are: the mass center and any point accelerating toward the mass center. By far the most useful of the two is the mass center, and we shall restrict our attention primarily to this point.

EXAMPLE 14.14

A clockwise couple acts on the particles A and B fixed to the rim of a wheel of diameter D which rotates in the plane of the paper (Fig. 14.26). The forces F of the couple always remain equal in magnitude and have a direction always tangent to the rim of the wheel. Thus the couple-moment is a constant vector having a magnitude of FD. On spokes of the wheel two particles G and H, initially at distance d from the center, are acted on by constant forces P radially inward. Take each of the four bodies to have a mass m and neglect the mass of the wheel. Set up the differential equation of motion of the particles G and H along the spoke.

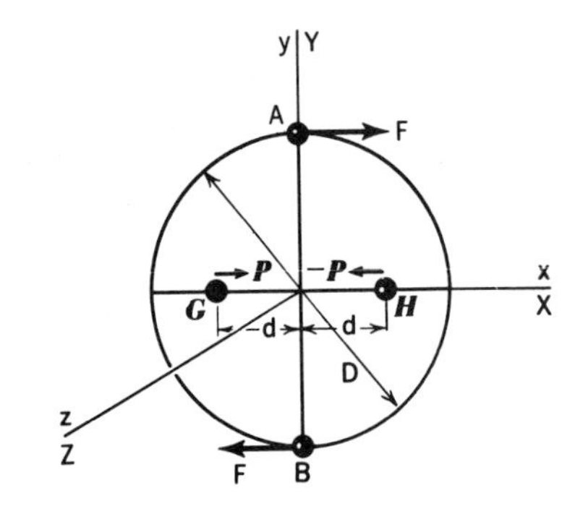

Fig. 14.26

Let us first consider the question of rotation of the wheel. If we take moments of external forces about the center of mass, we have:

$$\begin{aligned} -FD\boldsymbol{k} = \frac{d}{dt}\bigg[&\frac{D}{2}\,\boldsymbol{j} \times \left(m\omega\,\frac{D}{2}\,\boldsymbol{i}\right) \\ &+ \left(-\frac{D}{2}\right)\boldsymbol{j} \times \left(-m\omega\,\frac{D}{2}\,\boldsymbol{i}\right) \\ &+ r\boldsymbol{i} \times (-\dot{r}\boldsymbol{i} - m\omega r\boldsymbol{j}) \\ &+ (-r)\boldsymbol{i} \times (\dot{r}\boldsymbol{i} + m\omega r\boldsymbol{j})\bigg] \end{aligned} \qquad \textbf{(a)}$$

where r is used to position the masses along the spoke. Carrying out the cross products and collecting terms, we have:

$$-FD\boldsymbol{k} = \frac{d}{dt}\left(-\frac{D^2}{2}m\omega - 2r^2m\omega\right)\boldsymbol{k} \qquad \textbf{(b)}$$

The scalar equation then becomes:

$$FD = m\frac{D^2}{2}\dot{\omega} + 2r^2m\dot{\omega} + 4r\dot{r}m\omega \qquad \textbf{(c)}$$

We have two unknowns, r and ω, in this equation. Next let us consider the particle H sliding along the bar. The total force on the particle includes the radial force P and, neglecting friction, a force normal to the spoke, which we shall call force N. We shall now employ Newton's law, using cylindrical coordinates and components as we learned in Section 11.7. Thus:

$$-N\boldsymbol{\varepsilon}_\phi - P\boldsymbol{\varepsilon}_r = m(\ddot{r} - r\omega^2)\boldsymbol{\varepsilon}_r + (r\dot{\omega} + 2\dot{r}\omega)\boldsymbol{\varepsilon}_\phi \qquad \textbf{(d)}$$

Consequently:

$$-P = m(\ddot{r} - r\omega^2) \qquad \textbf{(e)}$$

Solving for ω, we have:

$$\omega = \left(\frac{P}{rm} + \frac{\ddot{r}}{r}\right)^{1/2}$$

And:

$$\dot{\omega} = \frac{1}{2}\left(\frac{P}{rm} + \frac{\ddot{r}}{r}\right)^{-1/2}\left(-\frac{P\dot{r}}{r^2m} - \frac{\dot{r}\ddot{r}}{r^2} + \frac{\dddot{r}}{r}\right) \qquad \textbf{(f)}$$

Substituting $\dot{\omega}$ into Eq. (c), we get:

$$FD = \frac{1}{2}\left(\frac{mD^2}{2} + 2r^2m\right)\left(\frac{P}{rm} + \frac{\ddot{r}}{r}\right)^{-1/2}$$

$$\times\left(-\frac{P\dot{r}}{r^2m} - \frac{\dot{r}\ddot{r}}{r^2} + \frac{\dddot{r}}{r}\right) + 4r\dot{r}m\left(\frac{P}{rm} + \frac{\ddot{r}}{r}\right)^{1/2} \qquad \textbf{(g)}$$

This is the desired differential equation for r. It is clearly an extremely complex nonlinear differential equation and would have to be solved by numerical or machine methods. Our main purpose here was to set up the equation. The given distances d (Fig. 14.26) enter as initial conditions.

Much time will be spent later in the text in applying Eq. 14.29 or Eq. 14.37 to a rigid body. This is done by considering the rigid body to be made up of an infinite number of contiguous elements. Summations then give way to integration, and so on. The final equations of this section accordingly are among the most important in mechanics. At this time we will apply Eq. 14.29 to a body constrained to rotate on a shaft held by bearings. This is the kind of problem you worked hard on in your earlier physics course.

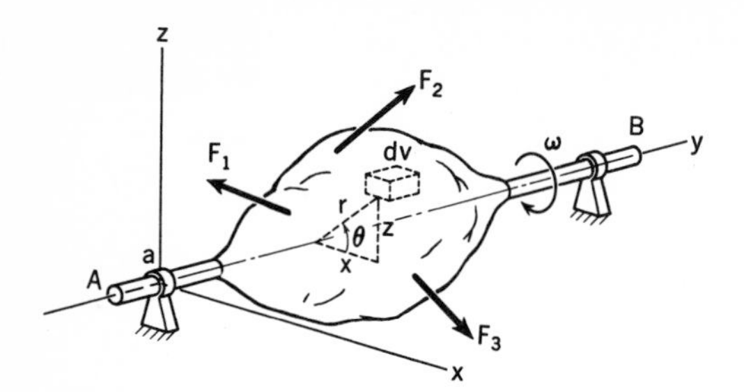

Fig. 14.27

EXAMPLE 14.15

Shown in Fig. 14.27 is an arbitrary rigid body mounted on a freely rotating shaft AB and acted on by a system of forces. Neglecting the mass of the shaft, we wish to get a formula for the angular acceleration $\dot{\omega}$ of the rigid body taken about the axis of rotation.

To do this we shall employ Eq. 14.37 about a convenient fixed point in inertial space denoted in the diagram as a. Furthermore we shall take the component of the equation along the centerline of the shaft, i.e., along the axis of the rotation. To facilitate computations we embed a coordinate system xyz in the body with the origin at a. Clearly the y axis corresponds to the axis of rotation while the x and z axes rotate in inertial space. The y component of the moment of forces about point a is clearly the familiar torque T about the axis of rotation. To get H_y, we examine a volume element dv of the rigid body. We have for dH_y for this element (see Fig. 14.27):

$$dH_y = (\mathbf{r} \times \rho\, dv\, \mathbf{V})_y = (zV_x - xV_z)\rho\, dv \qquad \textbf{(a)}$$

But for kinematical considerations:

$$V_x = \omega r \sin\theta = \omega z \qquad \textbf{(b)}$$

$$V_z = -\omega r \cos\theta = -\omega x \qquad \textbf{(c)}$$

Accordingly, on substitution of the above quantities into Eq. (a) we get:

$$dH_y = (z^2 + x^2)\omega\rho\, dv \qquad \textbf{(d)}$$

To get H_y we integrate over the volume V of the body. Thus:

$$H_y = \omega \iiint\limits_V (z^2 + x^2)\rho\, dx\, dy\, dz \qquad \textbf{(e)}$$

We shall later see that the integral

$$\iiint\limits_V (z^2 + x^2)\rho\, dx\, dy\, dz$$

called the mass moment of inertia and denoted as I_{yy} is one of nine such integrals that arise in the dynamical consideration of rigid bodies. These nine terms are components of the so-called *inertia tensor*.* We shall consider these integrals carefully in Chapter 16 preparatory to the study of rigid-body dynamics. Clearly I_{yy} for reference xyz fixed to the body is a constant for the problem and so we have:

$$\dot{H}_y = I_{yy}\dot{\omega} \qquad \textbf{(f)}$$

Now going to the moment of momentum equation we have:

* The second moments of inertia of an area are simply related to the inertia tensor as indicated earlier in Chapter 8, and it is for this reason that we will use the same notation here as was used in Chapter 8.

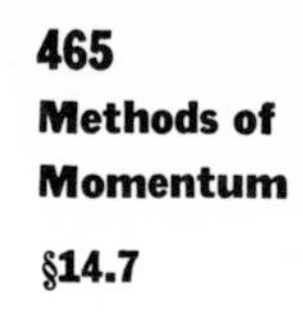

$$M = \frac{dH}{dt} = \frac{d}{dt}(H_x i + H_y j + H_z k)$$

Noting that d/dt is a derivative taken relative to inertial space we have:

$$M = \dot{H}_x i + H_x \dot{i} + \dot{H}_y j + \dot{H}_z k + H_z \dot{k} \qquad \textbf{(g)}$$

where i and k rotate in inertial space with angular velocity ω and are consquently time-dependent. Since these vectors rotate with angular speed ω about the y axis their derivatives are given simply as:

$$\dot{i} = -\omega k \qquad \dot{k} = \omega i \qquad \textbf{(h)}$$

as you should yourself justify. Thus the scalar component of Eq. (g) in the y direction becomes a familiar equation from earlier work in physics:

$$M_y = T = \dot{H}_y = I_{yy}\dot{\omega} \qquad \textbf{(i)}$$

We can now solve for $\dot{\omega}$. Later we will show that the above equation is a special simple form of the so-called *Euler* equations. These equations will permit us to solve for more complicated angular motion of rigid bodies.

EXAMPLE 14.16

A uniform cylinder A is acted on by a 100-lb force as shown by Fig. 14.28. If the cylinder rolls without slipping, what is the angular acceleration of the cylinder? Take the weight of the cylinder as 64.4 lb.

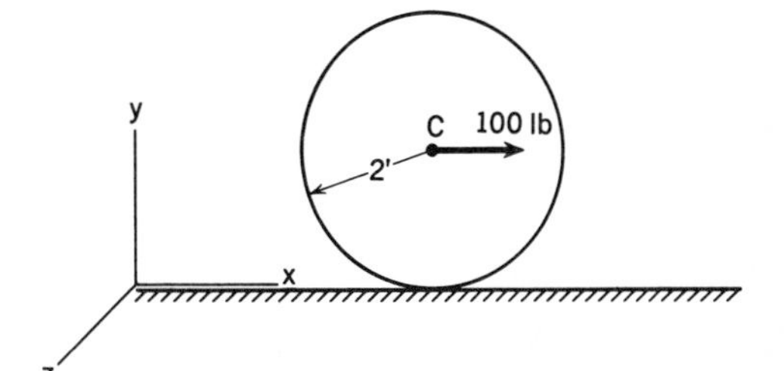

Fig. 14.28

A free-body diagram of the cylinder is shown in Fig. 14.29. The friction force f is as yet unknown.

The motion of the body relative to the mass center is that of pure rotation, as indeed it must be for any rigid-body motion. Accordingly the computation of H_c is identically the same as the computation of H about a stationary axis of rotation as set forth in the previous example. Thus:

$$H_c = I_{cc}\,\omega k \qquad \textbf{(a)}$$

where I_{cc} is the mass moment of inertia about the centerline of the cylinder. It will be left as an exercise for you to show that for a uniform cylinder $I_{cc} = \frac{1}{2}Mr^2$. Hence we have:

$$H_c = \tfrac{1}{2}Mr^2\omega k = \frac{1}{2}\frac{64.4}{g_0}4\omega k = 4\omega k \qquad \textbf{(b)}$$

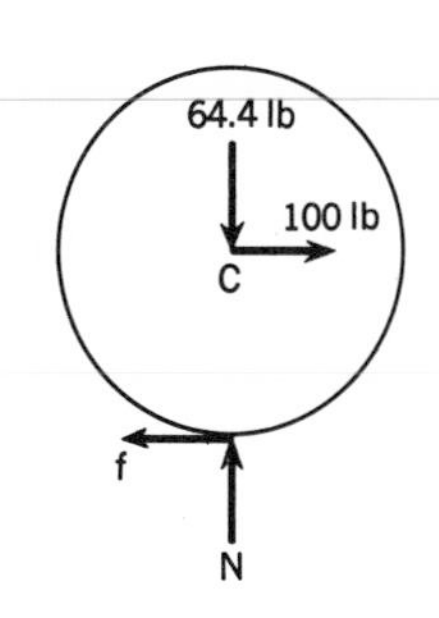

Fig. 14.29

Now, employing the component of the basic moment of momentum equation about the mass center in the z direction, we get as in the previous example:

$$M_c = -2f = \dot{H}_c = -4\dot{\omega}$$

$$\therefore \dot{\omega} = \tfrac{1}{2}f \qquad \textbf{(c)}$$

To get f we consider Newton's law for the mass center (Fig. 14.29). Thus in the x direction we have:

$$100 - f = \frac{64.4}{g_0}\ddot{x}_c = 2\ddot{x}_c \qquad \textbf{(d)}$$

Using kinematics for the case of plane motion of a cylinder rolling without slipping (as learned in earlier physics courses), we can say on realizing that we have pure rotation as seen from the ground reference about the point of contact:

$$\ddot{x} = \dot{\omega}r = 2\dot{\omega} \qquad \textbf{(e)}$$

Hence Eq. (d) can be written as:

$$f = -4\dot{\omega} + 100 \qquad \textbf{(f)}$$

Substituting Eq. (f) into Eq. (c), we get:

$$\dot{\omega} = -2\dot{\omega} + 50$$

$$\therefore\ \dot{\omega} = 16.67 \text{ rad/sec}^2$$

14.8 Angular Impulse: Conservation of Moment of Momentum

Just as we formulated the concept of the impulse of a force, we also find occasionally useful the concept of the *angular impulse* of a force defined as:

$$\boldsymbol{I}_{\text{Ang}} = \int_{t_1}^{t_2} \boldsymbol{M}\, dt \qquad \textbf{14.41}$$

where $\boldsymbol{M}$ is taken about any one of the three classes of points described in the previous section. Integrating Eq. 14.29 from t_1 to t_2 and employing Eq. 14.41 we then may state:

$$\boldsymbol{I}_{\text{Ang}} = \boldsymbol{H}_2 - \boldsymbol{H}_1 \qquad \textbf{14.42}$$

where the right side represents the change in moment of momentum of the system of particles during the chosen time interval. If the net impulse on a system of particles is zero, we have the situation where there is conservation of angular momentum.

The above formulations are clearly illustrated in many familiar activities such as athletics and the ballet. For example, consider a high diver in action. As the diver leaves the springboard he gives himself, through the reactive force of the springboard, a torsional impulse having a strength dependant on the type of dive he is to execute. Once free of the springboard, he is torque-free and according to Eq. 14.42 the angular momentum of the diver must remain constant until the water is reached. Now by adjusting the configuration of his body through internal forces, he changes the moment of inertia I about the rotation axis going through his center of mass. As a consequence the angular velocity changes. One of the goals in diving is to so time these bodily configuration changes that the diver enters the water in a vertical orientation with the body fully stretched to minimize the angular velocity. As another illustration, watch a good figure skater go into a spin or take a jump. Here, by proper use of the edges of the skates, an angular impulse is developed about a vertical axis through the center of mass. In the spin or jump configuration effectively there is zero angular impulse, and it is the orientation of the body that controls thereafter the angular motion of the skater until the blades are again employed to develop angular impulse.

If you ski you should be able to explain why your instructor wants you to adopt stances at times that may feel contrary to your instincts of safety so as to weight or unweight a ski properly to accomplish a certain maneuver.

Although mechanics may not make you a better athlete (as your author can sadly attest) you may better understand mechanics by reconsidering athletics from this point of view.

14.9 Closure

One of the topics studied in this chapter was the impact of bodies under certain restricted conditions. For such problems, we can consider the bodies as particles before and after impact, but during impact the bodies act as deformable media for which a particle model is not meaningful. By making an elementary picture of the action, we introduced the coefficient of restitution to yield additional information we needed to determine velocities after impact. This is an empirical approach, and it limits our analysis to simple problems. To handle more complex problems or to do the simple ones more precisely, we would have to make a more rational investigation of the deformation actions taking place during impact—that is, a continuum approach to part of the problem would be required. However we cannot make a careful study of the deformation aspects in this text since the subject of high-speed deformation of solids is a difficult one that is still under careful study by engineers and physicists.

In our study of moment of momentum for a system of particles, we set forth one of the key equations of mechanics, $\boldsymbol{M} = \dot{\boldsymbol{H}}$ and we introduced in the examples several considerations whose more careful and complete study will occupy a good portion of the remainder of the text. Thus in Example 14.16 we had "in miniature," as it were, the major elements involved in the study of much rigid-body dynamics. Recall that we employed Newton's law for the mass center and the moment of momentum equation about the mass center to reach the desired results. In so doing, however, we had to make use of certain elementary kinematical ideas from our earlier work in physics. Accordingly, in order to prepare ourselves for general rigid-body dynamics in Chapter 17 we shall devote ourselves in the next chapter to a rather careful examination of the general kinematics of a rigid body. In addition, recall that the moment of inertia entered prominently in the use of the moment of momentum equation for rigid bodies. To enable ourselves to effectively handle general dynamical considerations of a rigid body, we shall embark in Chapter 16 on a study of the inertia tensor.

Although we will be much concerned in the following chapter with the kinematics of rigid bodies, we will not cease to consider particles. You will see that an understanding of rigid-body kinematics will permit us to formulate very powerful relations for the general relative motions of a particle involving references which move in any arbitrary manner with respect to each other.

PROBLEMS

1. [14.1] A body weighing 100 lb reaches an incline of 30° while it is moving at 50 ft/sec (Fig. 14.30). If the coefficient of friction is 0.3, how long is it before the body stops?

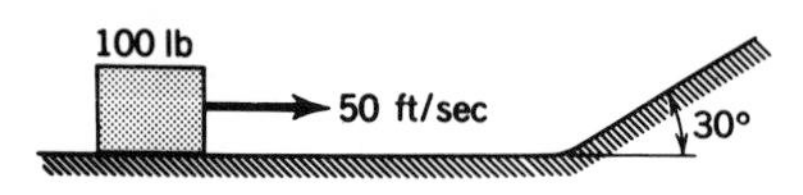

Fig. 14.30

2. [14.1] A particle of mass one slug is initially stationary at the origin of a reference. A force having a known variation with time acts on the particle. That is:

$$F(t) = t^2\boldsymbol{i} + (6t + 10)\boldsymbol{j} + 1.6t^3\boldsymbol{k}$$

After 10 sec what is the velocity of the body?

3. [14.1] A unidirectional force acting on a particle of mass one slug is plotted in Fig. 14.31. What is the velocity of the particle at 40 sec? Initially the particle is at rest.

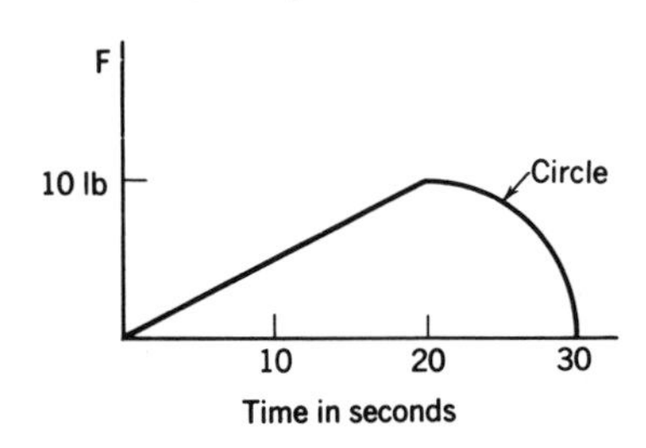

Fig. 14.31

4. [14.1] A body is dropped from rest. (a) Determine the time required for it to acquire a velocity of 50 ft/sec. (b) Determine the time needed to increase its velocity from 50 to 70 ft/sec.

5. [14.1] A body having a mass of 5 lbm is acted on by the following force:

$$\boldsymbol{F} = 8t\boldsymbol{i} + (6 + 3\sqrt{t})\boldsymbol{j} - (16 + 3t^2)\boldsymbol{k}$$

What is the velocity of the body after 5 seconds, if the initial velocity is:

$$\boldsymbol{V}_1 = 6\boldsymbol{i} + 3\boldsymbol{j} - 10\boldsymbol{k} \text{ ft/sec?}$$

6. [14.1] A body with a mass of one slug is required to change its velocity from $\boldsymbol{V}_1 = 2\boldsymbol{i} + 4\boldsymbol{j} - 10\boldsymbol{k}$ ft/sec to a velocity $\boldsymbol{V}_2 = 10\boldsymbol{i} - 5\boldsymbol{j} + 20\boldsymbol{k}$ ft/sec in 10 seconds. What average force $\boldsymbol{F}$ over this time interval will do the job?

7. [14.1] In the preceding problem determine the force for the case where it varies linearly with time starting with a zero value.

8. [14.1] In Prob. 6 determine the force for the case where it varies as the square of the time and has initially a value:

$$\boldsymbol{F}_1 = \boldsymbol{i} - 3\boldsymbol{j} + 2\boldsymbol{k} \text{ lb}$$

9. [14.1] A hockey puck moves at 30 ft/sec from goal A to B in Fig. 14.32. It is intercepted by a player who whisks it at 80 ft/sec toward goal A, as shown. The puck is also rising from the ice at a rate of 10 ft/sec. What is the impulse on the puck, whose weight is 5 oz?

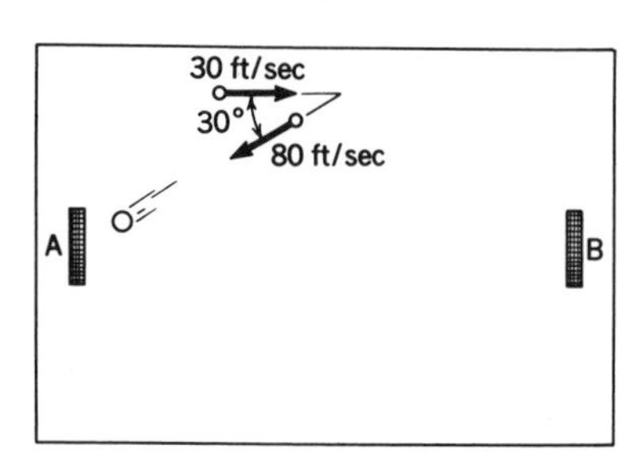

Fig. 14.32

10. [14.1] Do Prob. 4 in Chapter 12 by methods of momentum.

11. [14.1] Do Prob. 5 in Chapter 12 by methods of momentum.

12. [14.1] Show that Eq. 12.11 is the linear momentum equation in differential form with the force given as a function of velocity. If a mass of one slug has a speed of 20 ft/sec and a drag force equal to $(0.008)V^2$ acts on the body, how much time is required for the speed to be halved? What is the impulse on the body during this period? (You will have to separate variables and integrate to get the time desired.)

13. [14.1] A plunger is allowed to slide down a pipe from a position of rest (Fig. 14.33). The annular region between the plunger and pipe is lubricated by a fluid having a viscosity $\mu = 0.020$ lb sec/ft². The diameter $D = 6$ in., $\epsilon = 0.02$., and the plunger weighs 100 lb.

(a) Determine the terminal velocity and the time required to reach one-half the terminal velocity.

(b) What is the impulse on the pipe during this time?

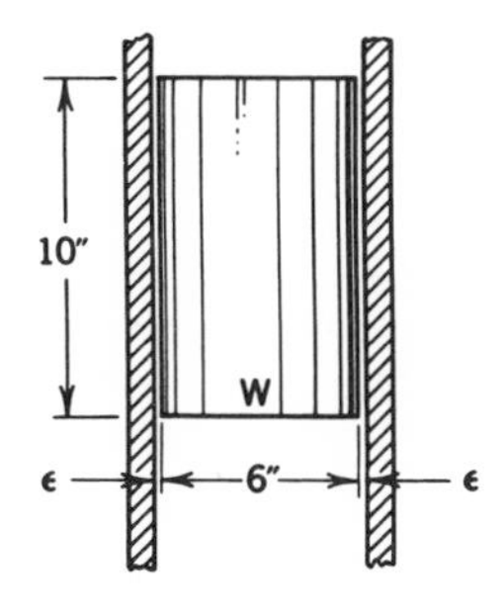

Fig. 14.33

14. [14.1] In making buckshot, molten drops of metal, each of mass m, are allowed to drip through holes of a container (see Fig. 14.34). The droplets of radius R harden as they fall through the air and into a container of water where the cooling process is completed. If the resistance to motion offered by the water is κV^2, determine the time after entering the water for a pellet to reach one half the terminal velocity V_c. Use the differential form of the momentum equation for this. Compute the impulse given the pellet as a function of time directly after it enters the water. Get results in terms of h, m, and κ. Include buoyant force.

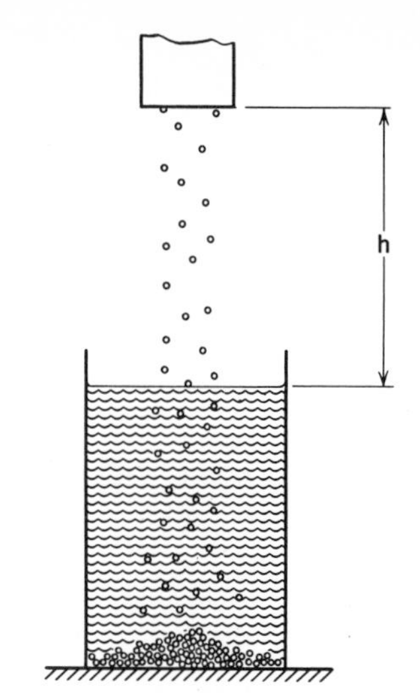

Fig. 14.34

15. [14.1] In Fig. 14.35, compute the velocity of the bodies after 10 sec if they start from rest. The cable is inextensible and the pulleys are frictionless.

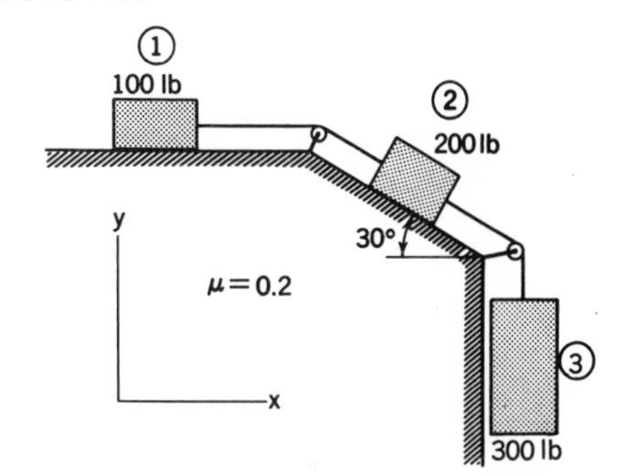

Fig. 14.35

16. [14.1] Neglecting friction and the inertia of the pulleys, determine the velocity of body A and body B after 3 sec if the system in Fig. 14.36 is released from rest.

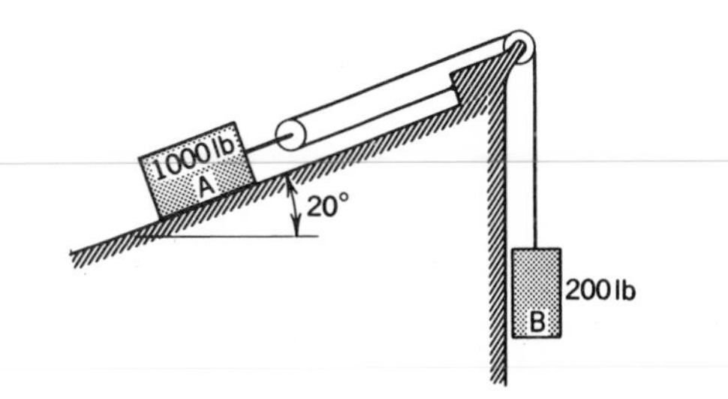

Fig. 14.36

17. [14.1] Shown in Fig. 14.37 are three bodies towed by a force

$$F = 100 + 50e^{-t} \text{ lb}$$

If $W_1 = 30$ lb, $W_2 = 60$ lb, and $W_3 = 50$ lb, what is the change in speed over a period of 5 seconds after the application of the given force? The coefficient of friction is 0.3 for all surfaces.

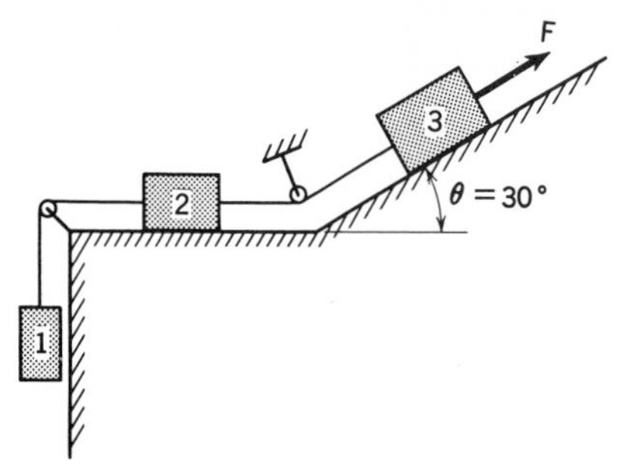

Fig. 14.37

18. [14.1] A torpedo boat weighing 100,000 lb moves at 40 knots (1 knot = 6080 ft/hr) away from an engagement. To go even faster, all four 50-caliber machine guns are ordered to fire simultaneously toward the rear. Each weapon fires at a muzzle velocity of 3000 ft/sec and fires 3000 rounds per minute. Each slug weighs 2 oz. How much is the average force on the boat increased by this action? Neglect the rate of change of the total mass of boat.

19. [14.1] Shown in Fig. 14.38 is a vertical conveyor. Sprocket A is the driver and sprocket B turns freely. The bodies to be lifted are pushed onto the conveyor by a plunger C and are taken off from the conveyor at D as shown in the diagram. If the belt runs at 2 ft/sec and the bodies being transported each weigh 8 ounces, what average torque is required by the driving sprocket A? Neglect friction everywhere. There are on the average 20 bodies on the conveyor at any time.

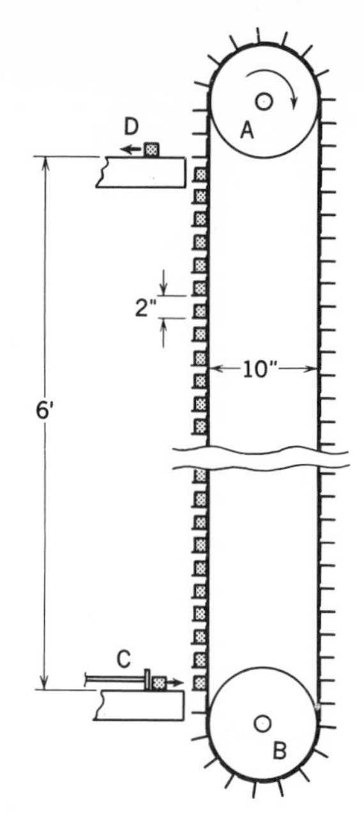

Fig. 14.38

20. [14.1] Shown in Fig. 14.39 is a conveyor A feeding boxes onto a conveyor B. Each box weighs 2 lb and lands on conveyor B with a downward speed component of 0.3 ft/sec and a speed component in the direction of conveyor A of 0.2 ft/sec. If conveyor B runs at a speed of 2 ft/sec and if 5 boxes land per second on the average, what net average force T_2 must be exerted on the conveyor belt B to slide it over its bed? At any time there are 50 boxes on belt B. Take $\mu = 0.2$ for all surfaces.

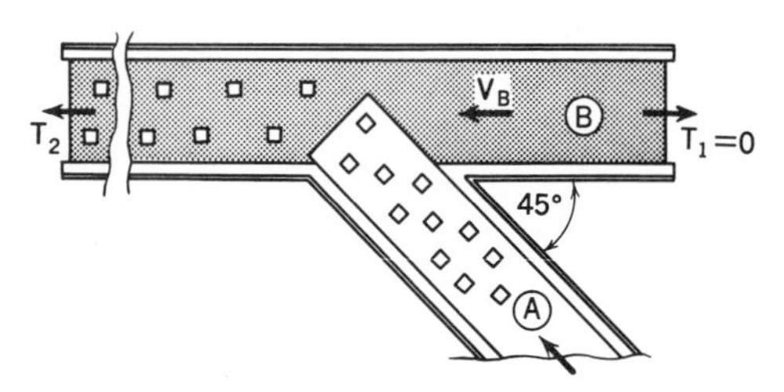

Fig. 14.39

21. [14.1] A disc is rotated in the horizontal plane (Fig. 14.40) with a constant angular speed ω. A body A having a mass of 0.4 lbm is moved in a frictionless slot at a uniform speed of 1 ft/sec relative to the platform by a force F as shown. What is the linear momentum of the body relative to the ground reference XY when $r = 2$ ft and $\theta = 45°$? What is the impulse developed on the body as it goes from $r = 2$ ft to $r = 1$ ft?

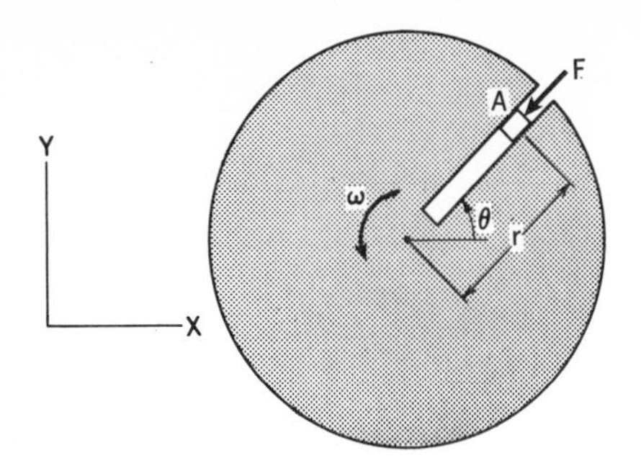

Fig. 14.40

22. [14.1] An idealized one-dimensional pressure wave (i.e. pressure is a function of one coordinate and time) generated by an explosion travels at a speed V of 1200 ft/sec as is shown at time $t = 0$ in Fig. 14.41. The peak pressure of this wave is 5 psia. What impulse per square foot is delivered to a surface oriented at right angles to the x axis? The wave is reflected from the wall, and the pressure at the wall is double the incoming pressure at all times. (Do for four time intervals.)

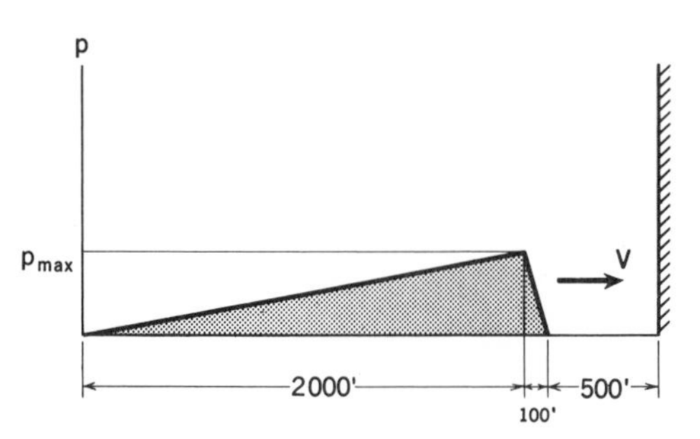

Fig. 14.41

23. [14.1] A commuter train made up of 2 cars is moving at a speed of 50 mi/hr. The first car weighs 20 tons and the second 15 tons.

(a) If the brakes are applied simultaneously to both cars, determine the minimum time the cars travel before stopping. Take the coefficient of friction to be 0.3 between wheels and rail.

(b) If the brakes on the first car only are applied, determine the time the cars travel before stopping and the force transmitted between the cars.

24. [14.2] Do Prob. 15 by considering a system of particles.

25. [14.2] Do Prob. 16 by considering a system of particles.

26. [14.2] Two vehicles connected by an inextensible cable are rolling along a road (Fig. 14.42). Vehicle B, using a winch, draws A toward it so that the relative speed is 5 ft/sec at $t = 0$ and 10 ft/sec at $t = 20$ sec. Vehicle A weighs 2000 lb and vehicle B weighs 3000 lb. Each has a rolling resistance which is .01 times the weight of the vehicle. What is the speed of A relative to the ground at $t = 20$ sec if A is initially moving to the right at a speed of 10 ft/sec?

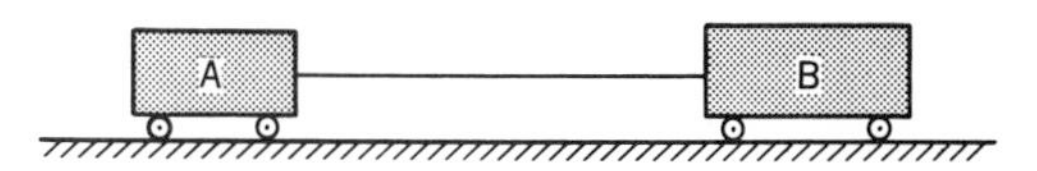

Fig. 14.42

27. [14.2] In Fig. 14.43 are shown two trucks moving up at 10° incline. Truck A weighs 3 tons and is developing a 3000-lb driving force on the road. Truck B weighs 2 tons. It is connected by an inextensible cable to truck A. By operating a winch b it approaches truck A with a constant acceleration of 1 ft/sec². If at time $t = 0$ both trucks have a speed of 30 ft/sec, what are their speeds at time $t = 15$ sec?

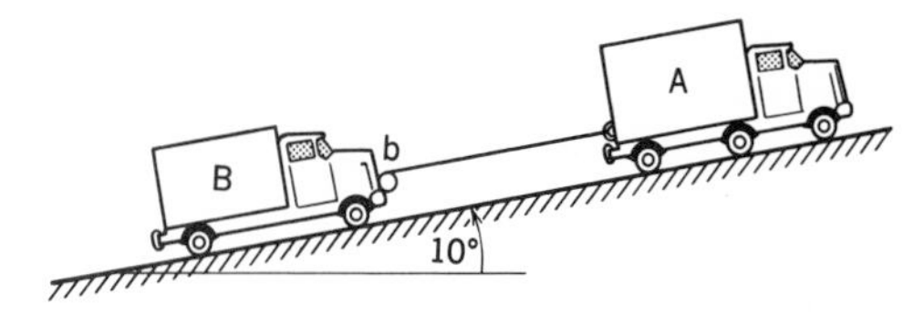

Fig. 14.43

28. [14.2] Do the preceding problem for the case where there is a rolling resistance of $0.1W$ for truck A and $0.15W$ for truck B where W is the weight of the vehicle.

29. [14.2] Shown in Fig. 14.44 are three bodies A, B, and C weighing respectively 20 lb, 40 lb, and 100 lb. Body B pulls body A towards it with a rate of acceleration given as 2 ft/sec² and decreases the separation from itself to body C at a rate of acceleration given as 3 ft/sec². If the coefficient of friction for all bodies and the ground is 0.3, what is the speed of body B five seconds after the action is begun from a stationary configuration? What friction force is developed by body C?

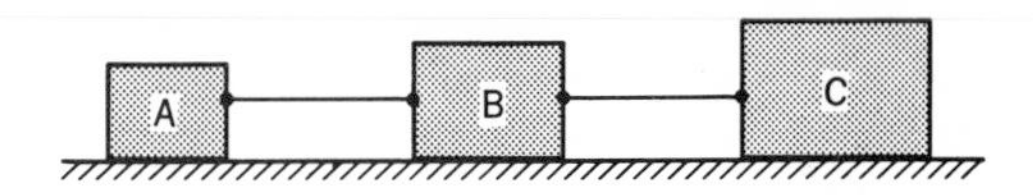

Fig. 14.44

30. [14.2] A truck weighing when loaded 4 tons is moving at a speed of 60 mph (Fig. 14.45). The driver suddenly applies his brakes so as to lock the wheels. The load A weighing 1 ton breaks from some of its ropes and is sliding relative to the truck at the rate of 3 ft/sec after 4 seconds. What is the change in speed of the truck in that time? Take μ for tires and pavement to be 0.4.

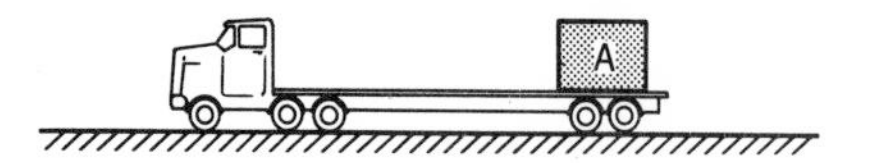

Fig. 14.45

31. [14.2] In the previous problem, assume the load moves uniformly relative to the truck at the rate of 5 ft/sec from the time $t = 0$ that the brakes are applied. What is the speed of the truck after 2 seconds?

32. [14.2] Blocks A and B move on frictionless surfaces in Fig. 14.46. They are interconnected by a light bar. Body A weighs 30 lb; the weight of body B is not known. A constant force F of 100 lb is applied at the configuration shown. If a speed of 25 ft/sec is reached by A after 1 sec, what impulse is developed on the vertical wall? Take $W_B = 20$ lb. Assume A has moved 4 ft.

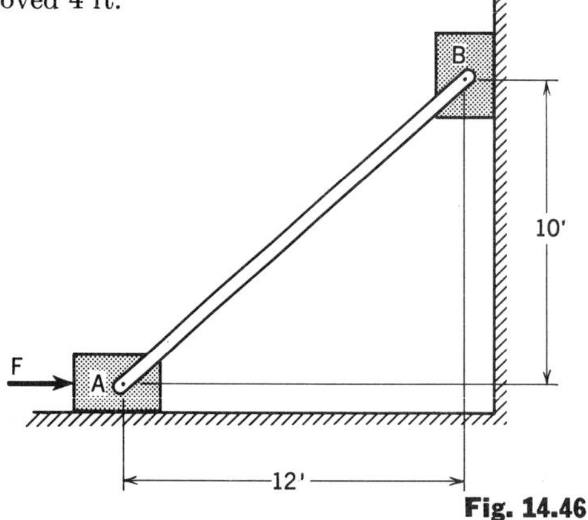

Fig. 14.46

33. [14.2] In the previous problem compute the impulse of the horizontal surface. A moves 4 ft and $W_B = 20$ lb.

34. [14.2] Shown in Fig. 14.47 is a 2600-lb jeep carrying three 200-lb passengers. It is in four-wheel drive and is under test to see what maximum speed is possible in 5 seconds for a start on an icy road surface for which $\mu = 0.1$. Are the normal forces at each wheel constant before and during the test? Explain, using the D'Alembert principle. Compute V_{max} at $t = 5$ sec.

Fig. 14.47

35. [14.2] Shown in Fig. 14.48 is a three-seater racing scull poised for a start. The scull weighs 300 lb and each occupant weighs about 150 lb. We want to know the speed of the scull after 2 seconds. At the sound of the starting gun each man exerts a 30-lb constant push on the water from each oar in the direction of the axis of the boat. At the 2-second mark each man is moving relative to the hull with a speed of 1 ft/sec. Neglect the inertia of the oars and neglect water and air friction.

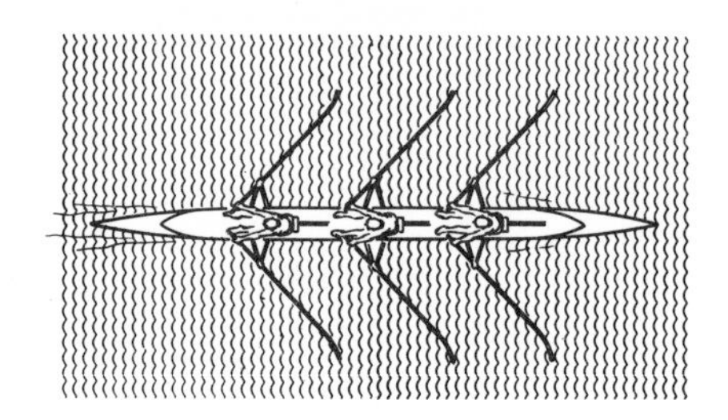

Fig. 14.48

36. [14.2] In Fig. 14.49 is a truck having two rectangular compartments of identical size that are built to contain water. Each container has dimensions of $20' \times 10' \times 8'$. Initially tank A is full and tank B is empty. A pump in tank A begins to deliver water from A to B at the rate of 10 cfs, and 10 seconds later is delivering water at the rate of 30 cfs. If the level of the water remains horizontal in both tanks, what is the average force needed to restrain the truck from moving during the interval? Hint: Find the horizontal component of the velocity of the center of mass of the water.

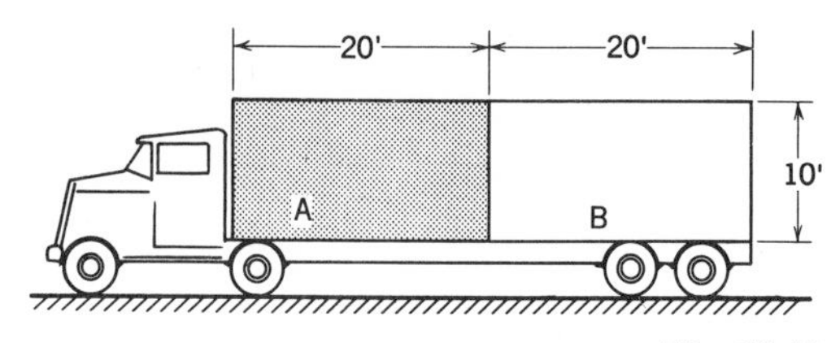

Fig. 14.49

37. [14.3] A body A weighing 2 tons is allowed to slide down an incline on a barge as shown in Fig. 14.50. It moves a distance of 25 ft along the incline before it is stopped at B. If we neglect water resistance, how far does the barge shift in the horizontal direction? If the maximum speed of the body A relative to the incline of the barge is 2 ft/sec, what is the maximum speed of the barge relative to the water? The weight of the barge is 20 tons.

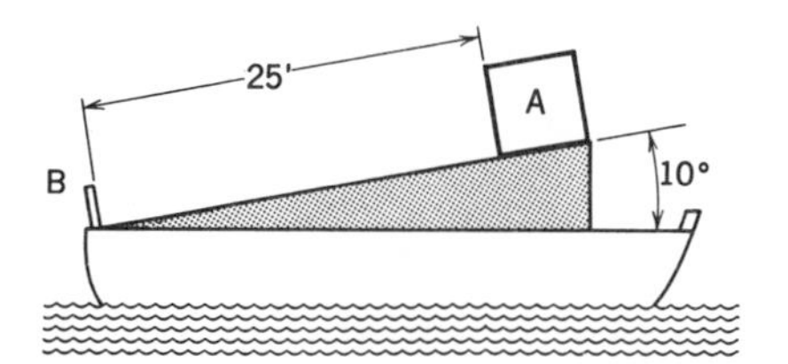

Fig. 14.50

38. [14.3] If the contact surface is frictionless in the preceding problem, what will be the shift of the barge when the body A is stopped at B? Explain what happens to the potential energy that was given up by body A in going to the position at B.

39. [14.3] Two men climb aboard a barge at A to shift a load (Fig. 14.51) with the aid of a fork lift. The barge weighs 20 tons and is 30 ft long. The load consists of four containers each weighing 1.3 tons and each having a length of 3 ft. The men shift the containers to the opposite end of the barge, put the fork lift where they found it, and prepare to step off the barge at A where they came on. If the barge has not been constrained and if we neglect water friction, currents, wind, and so on, how far has the barge shifted its position? The fork lift weighs 1 ton.

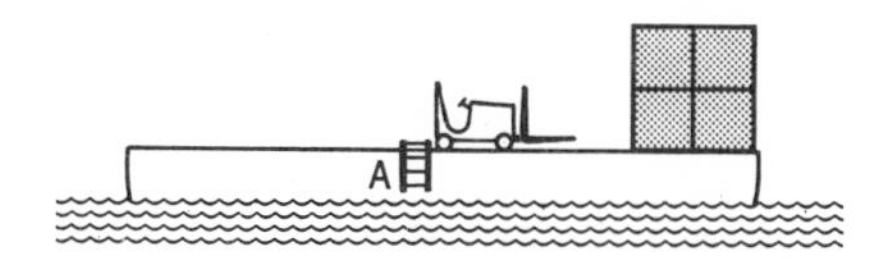

Fig. 14.51

40. [14.3] A toboggan has just entered the horizontal part of its run (see Fig. 14.52). It carries three people weighing respectively 120 lb, 180 lb, and 150 lb. Suddenly a pedestrian weighing 200 lb strays onto the course and is turned end for end by the toboggan, landing safely among the riders. Since the toboggan path is icy, we can neglect friction with the toboggan path for all actions described here. If the toboggan is traveling at a speed of 35 mph just before collision occurs, what is the speed after the collision when the pedestrian has become a rider? The toboggan weighs 30 lb.

Fig. 14.52

41. [14.3] A young man is standing in a canoe awaiting a young lady (Fig. 14.53). The man weighs 200 lb and is at the far end of the canoe, which also weighs 200 lb. When the young lady appears, he scrambles forward to greet her, but when he has moved the 20 ft to the forward end of the canoe, to his surprise he finds that he cannot reach her. How far is the tip of the canoe from the dock when our "gallant" has made the 20-ft dash? The canoe is in no way tied to the pier, and there are no currents in the water.

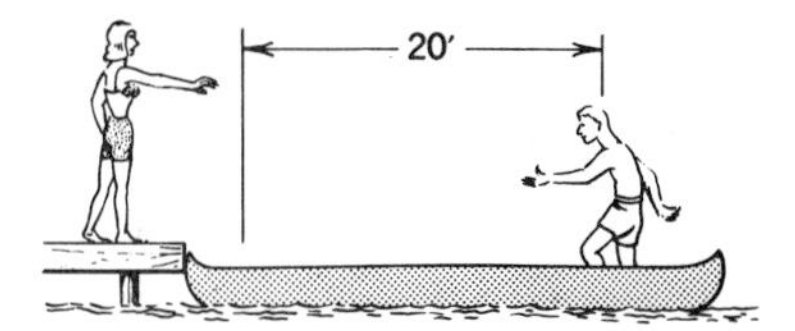

Fig. 14.53

42. [14.3] A 2000-lb cannon with recoil spring $K = 200$ lb/ft fires a 10-lb projectile with a muzzle velocity of 2000 ft/sec at an angle of 50° (Fig. 14.54). Assuming the recoil velocity of the cannon is instantaneously achieved, determine the maximum compression of the spring.

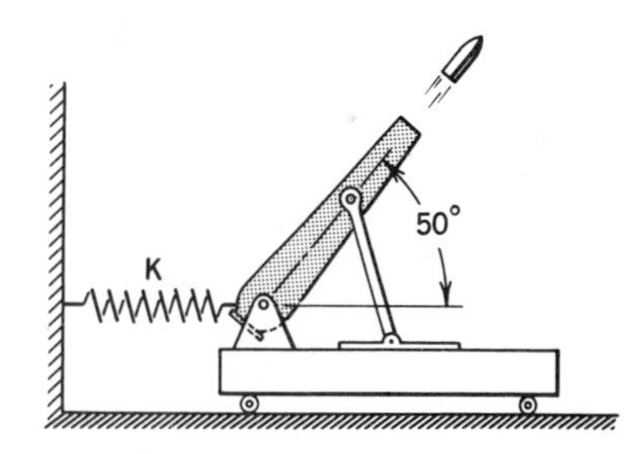

Fig. 14.54

43. [14.3] In Fig. 14.55, if the coefficient of restitution is 0.8, what are the maximum angles from the vertical that bodies will reach after the first impact? Neglect the mass of the cable.

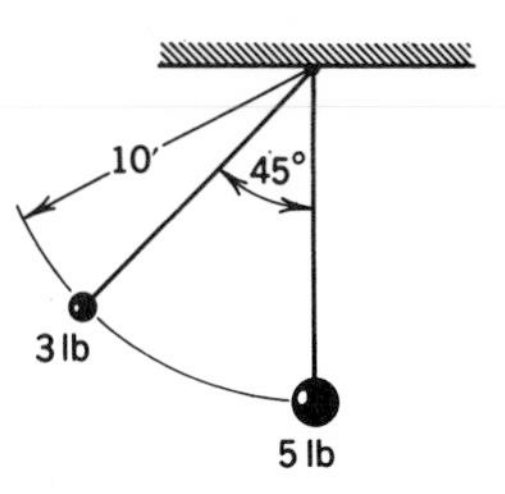

Fig. 14.55

44. [14.3] Assuming that the spheres in the above problem always move in the plane of the paper, determine the maximum elevations of the bodies after the second impact.

45. [14.3] An antitank airplane fires two 20-lb projectiles at a tank. The muzzle velocity of the guns is 3000 ft/sec relative to the plane. If the plane weighs 15,000 lb and is moving with a velocity of 200 mi/hr, compute the change in its speed when it fires the two projectiles.

46. [14.3] Shown in Fig. 14.56 are two cylinders moving along a rod in a frictionless manner. Cylinder A weighs 20 lb and moves to the right at a speed of 10 ft/sec while cylinder B weighs 10 lb and moves to the left at a speed of 8 ft/sec. What is the speed of cylinder B after impact for a coefficient of restitution ϵ of 0.8? What is the loss in kinetic energy?

Fig. 14.56

47. [14.3] Two smooth cylinders of identical radius (see Fig. 14.57) roll toward each other such that their centerlines are perfectly parallel. Cylinder A weighs 20 lb and cylinder B weighs 15 lb. What is the speed at which cylinder A moves directly after collision for a coefficient of restitution $\epsilon = 0.75$?

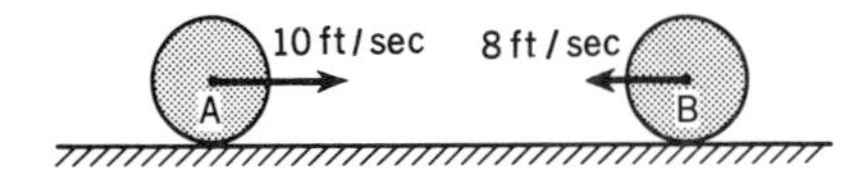

Fig. 14.57

48. [14.3] Cylinder A, weighing 20 lb, is moving at a speed of 20 ft/sec when it is at a distance 10 ft from cylinder B which is stationary (Fig. 14.58). Cylinder B weighs 15 lb and has a coefficient of friction with the rod on which it rides of 0.3. Cylinder A has a coefficient of friction of 0.1 with the rod. What is the coefficient of restitution if cylinder B comes to rest after collision at a distance 12 ft to the right of the initial position?

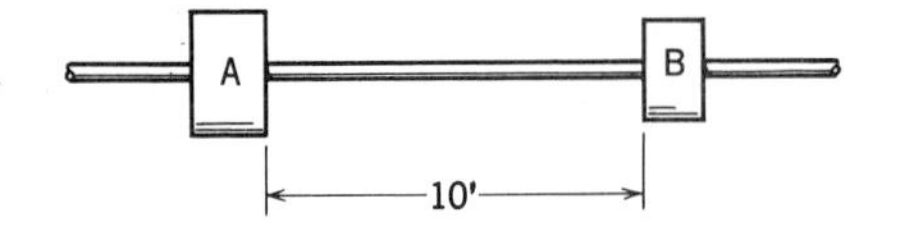

Fig. 14.58

49. [14.3] Cylinder A (Fig. 14.59), weighing 10 lb, moves toward cylinder B, weighing 40 lb, at the speed of 20 ft/sec. Mass B is attached to a spring having a spring constant K equal to 10 lb/in. If the collision has a coefficient of restitution $\epsilon = 0.9$, what is the maximum deflection of the spring? Assume there is no friction along the rod and that the spring has negligible mass.

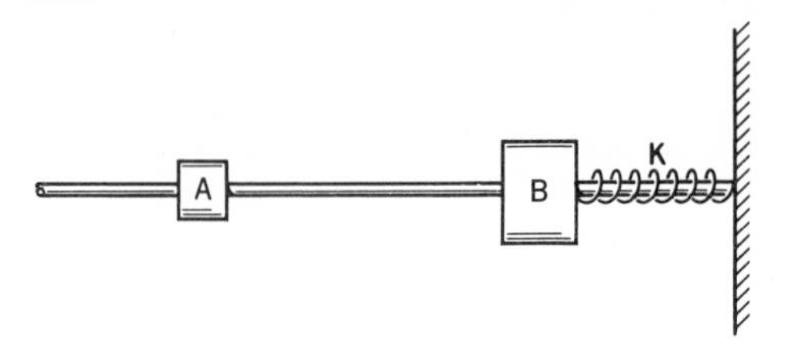

Fig. 14.59

50. [14.3] Do the previous problem for the case where there is a perfectly plastic impact and the spring is nonlinear, requiring $50(\delta^{3/2})$ lb for a deflection of δ inches.

51. [14.3] In Fig. 14.60, assume a perfectly plastic impact as the 10-lb body falls from a height of 8 ft onto a plate of weight 5 lb. This plate is mounted on a spring having a spring constant of 10 lb/in. Neglecting the mass of the spring and friction, compute the maximum deflection of the spring after impact.

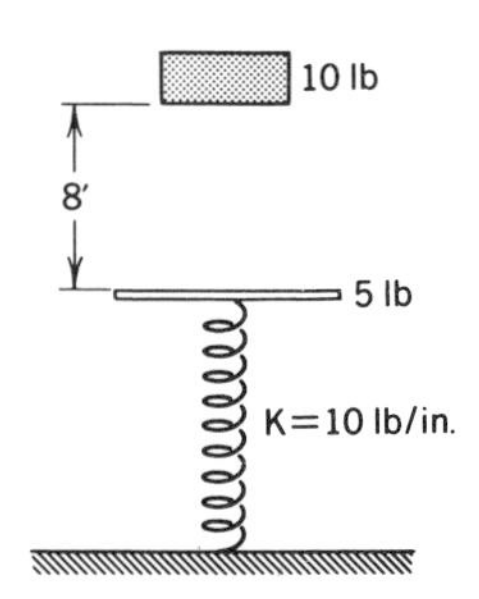

Fig. 14.60

52. [14.3] Several identical spheres B, C, and D lie along a straight line on a frictionless surface. Body A, which is identical to the others, moves at a speed of V_A in a direction collinear with the centers of the spheres.

(a) For perfectly elastic collisions, what are the final velocities of the bodies?

(b) What is the final velocity of sphere D if $\epsilon = 0.80$ for all spheres and $V_A = 50$ ft/sec?

(c) Set up a formula for the velocity of additional identical billiard balls placed after D for $\epsilon = 0.80$ and $V_A = 50$ ft/sec.

53. [14.3] Thin discs A and B slide along a frictionless surface (see Fig. 14.61). Each disc has a radius of 1 in. Disc A weighs 3 ounces while disc B weighs 8 ounces. What are the speeds of the discs after collision for $\epsilon = 0.7$? Assume the lateral surfaces of the discs are smooth.

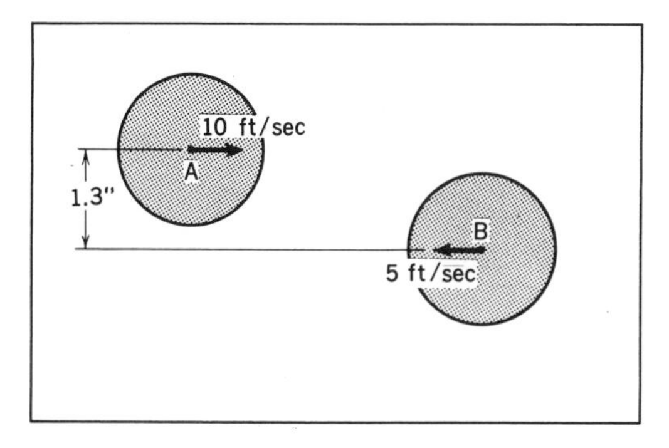

Fig. 14.61

54. [14.3] A thin disc A weighing 5 lb translates along a frictionless surface (Fig. 14.62) at a speed of 20 ft/sec. It strikes a square stationary plate B weighing 10 lb at the center of a side, as indicated in the diagram. What are the velocity and direction of the plate and the disc after collision? Assume the surfaces of the plate and disc are smooth. Take $\epsilon = 0.7$.

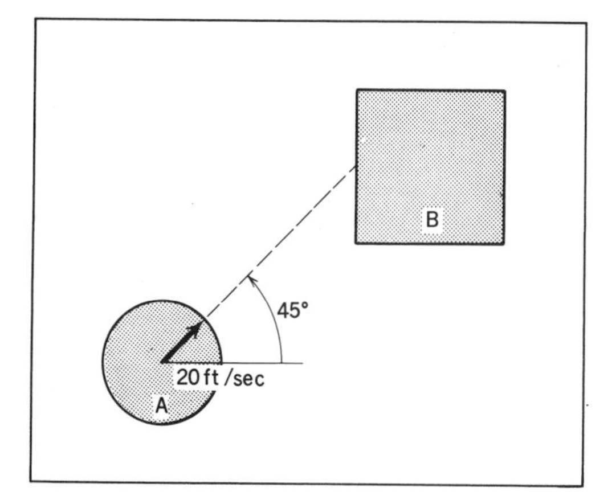

Fig. 14.62

55. [14.3] In the previous problem, at the instant of contact between the bodies a clamping device firmly connects the bodies together so as to form one rigid unit. Find the velocity of the center of mass of the system after impact.

56. [14.3] A chain of wrought iron, with a length of 20 ft and a weight of 200 lb, is held so that it just touches the support AB (Fig. 14.63). If the chain is released, determine the total impulse during 2 seconds in the vertical direction experienced by the support if the impact is plastic and if we move the support so that the links land on the platform and not on each other.

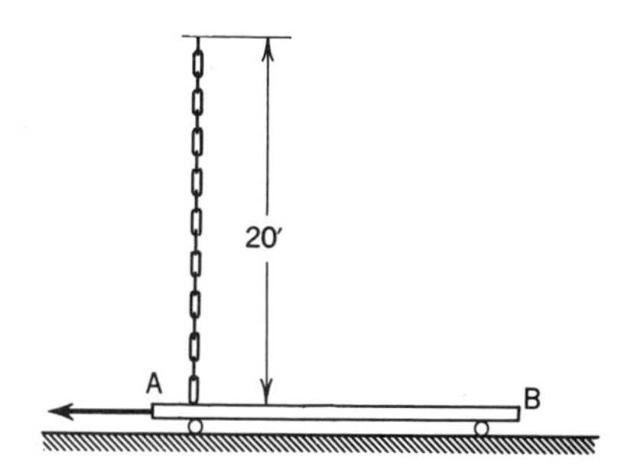

Fig. 14.63

57. [14.3] In Prob. 51, if $\epsilon = 0.8$ for the 10-lb weight and plate, determine the speed of both bodies 0.05 seconds after impact.

***58.** [14.3] Two bodies A and B (Fig. 14.64) move at constant speed V of 5 ft/sec toward a spring whose spring constant is 25 lb/ft. Body A weighs 50 lb and body B weighs 20 lb. If the impact is plastic as a result of a "quick-connect" device between the bodies, what is the maximum deflection of the spring?

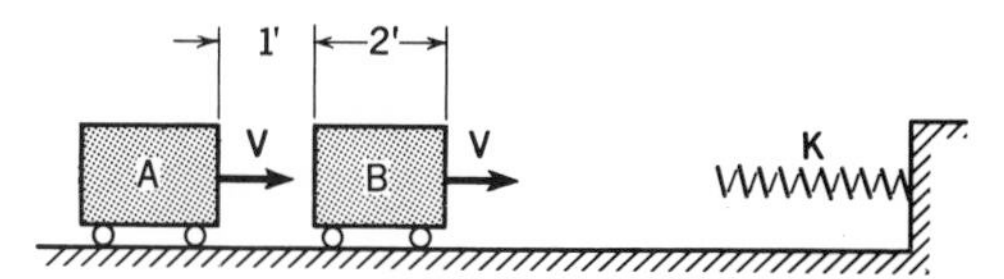

Fig. 14.64

***59.** [14.3] If the coefficient of restitution in the previous problem is 0.9, what is the maximum deflection of the spring? Assume only 1 impact is allowed.

60. [14.4] A ball is thrown against a wall at an angle of 60° with a speed at impact of 50 ft/sec (Fig. 14.65). What is the angle of rebound, α, if $\epsilon = 0.7$?

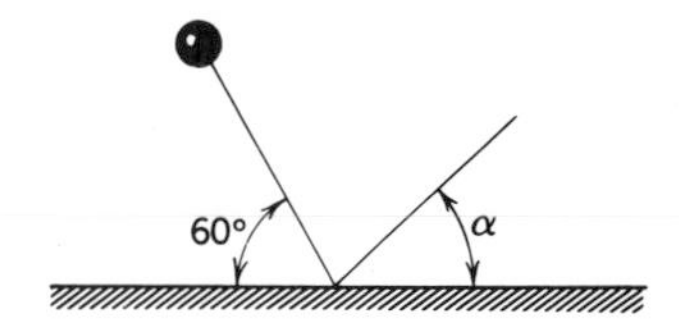

Fig. 14.65

61. [14.4] A body strikes the xy plane in Fig. 14.66 at a corner of smooth surfaces at $\boldsymbol{r} = 3\boldsymbol{i} + 7\boldsymbol{j}$ ft. It has a velocity $\boldsymbol{V} = -10\boldsymbol{i} - 10\boldsymbol{j} - 15\boldsymbol{k}$ ft/sec. The coefficient of restitution is 0.8. Determine the final velocity $\boldsymbol{V}_2$ after it bounds off the xy, yz, and xz planes once. Neglect gravity.

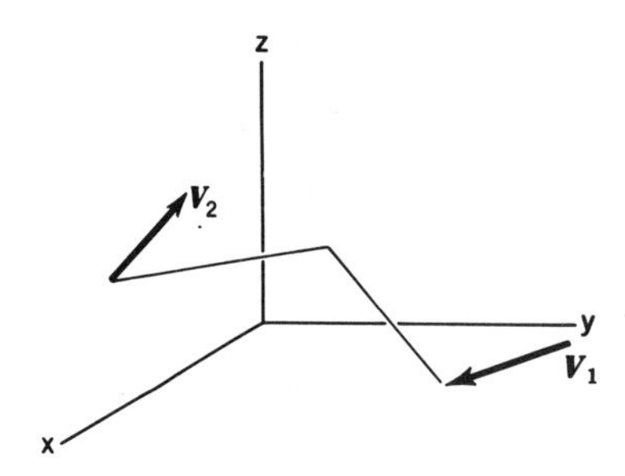

Fig. 14.66

62. [14.4] In the above problem, determine where the body strikes the yz and xz planes.

63. [14.4] A space vehicle in the shape of a cone-cylinder (see Fig. 14.67) is moving at a speed V many times the speed of sound through highly rarefied atmosphere. If each molecule of the gas has a mass m and if there are, on the average, n molecules per unit volume, compute the drag on the cone-cylinder. The cone half-angle is 30°. Take the collision to be perfectly elastic.

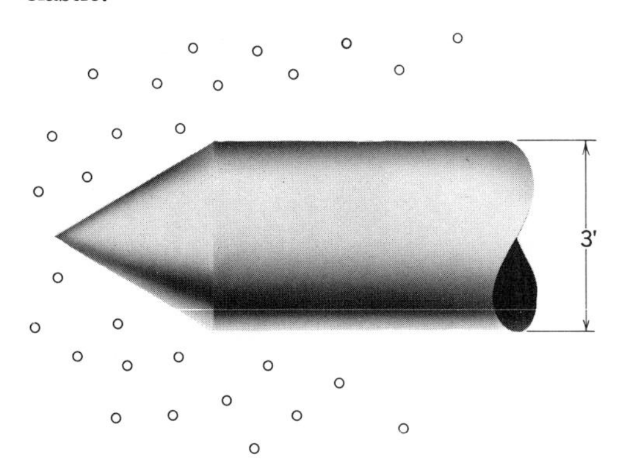

Fig. 14.67

64. [14.4] Do the previous problem for a case where it is assumed that inelastic collisions take place. Assume the coefficient of restitution to be 0.8.

65. [14.4] A double-wedge airfoil section for a space glider is shown in Fig. 14.68. If the glider moves in highly rarefied atmosphere at a speed V many times greater than the speed of sound, what is the drag per unit length of this airfoil? Assume the collision to be perfectly elastic.

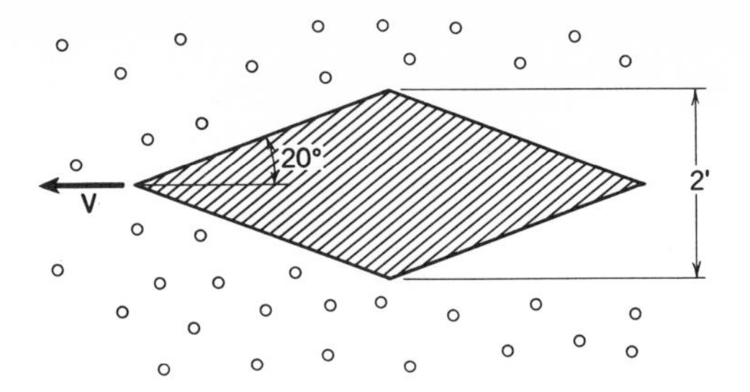

Fig. 14.68

66. [14.4] If a parallel beam of light, having an energy flux of S watts/cm², shines normal to a flat surface, and if this energy is completely absorbed by this surface, you learned in physics that an impulse dI is developed by the surface during time dt given by the formula:

$$dI = \frac{S}{c}\,dt\,dA$$

where c is the speed of light in vacuo. If the surface reflects the light then we have an impulse dI developed by the surface given as:

$$dI = 2\,\frac{S}{c}\,dt\,dA$$

Compute the force stemming from the reflection of light shining normal to a perfectly reflecting mirror having an area of 10 cm². The light has an energy flux of 20 watts/cm². Take the speed $c = 3 \times 10^8$ meters/sec. What is the radiation pressure "p_{rad}" on the mirror?

67. [14.4] A parallel beam of light shines on a flat surface at an inclination θ with the normal n (Fig. 14.69). Using the results of Prob. 66, show that the radiation pressure on the surface for complete absorption is:

$$p_{rad} = \frac{S}{c}\cos^2\theta$$

and for complete reflection is:

$$p_{rad} = 2\,\frac{S}{c}\cos^2\theta$$

Now compute the force on a flat black surface from a uniform beam of light having an energy flux of 20 watts/cm² and oriented at an angle of 30° toward the normal to the surface. Take the area of the surface as 20 cm². ($c = 3 \times 10^8$ meters/sec.)

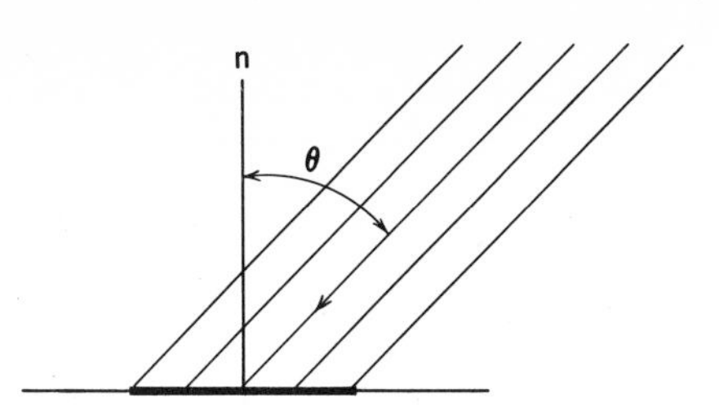

Fig. 14.69

68. [14.4] The Echo satellite is a device which when put into orbit is inflated into a 135-ft diameter sphere having a skin made up of a laminate of 0.0002-in. aluminum over 0.003-in. mylar over 0.0002-in. aluminum. This skin is highly reflectant of light and for this reason many readers may have seen this satellite in orbit. Because of the small mass of this satellite, it may be affected by small forces such as that stemming from the reflection of light. If a parallel beam of light having an energy density of 500 watts/cm^2 impinges on the Echo satellite, what total force is developed on the satellite from this source? (See Probs. 66 and 67 before doing.)

69. [14.4] A "beebee" is shot at the hard rigid surface shown in Fig. 14.70. The speed of the pellet is 300 ft/sec as it strikes the surface. If the direction of the velocity for the pellet is given by the following unit vector:

$$\hat{\boldsymbol{\varepsilon}} = -0.6\boldsymbol{i} - 0.8\boldsymbol{k}$$

what is the final velocity vector of the pellet for a collision having $\epsilon = 0.7$?

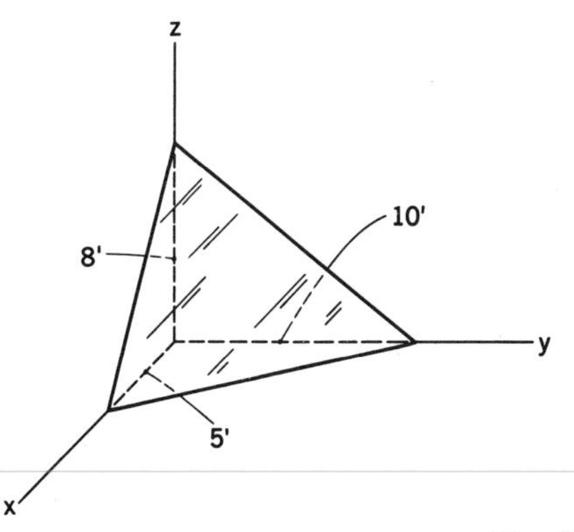

Fig. 14.70

70. [14.4] A small elastic ball is dropped from a height of 15 ft onto a rigid cylindrical body (Fig. 14.71) having a radius of 5 ft. At what position on the x axis does the ball land?

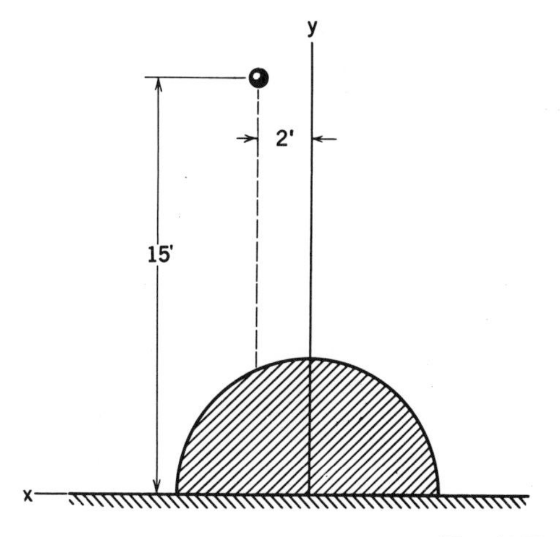

Fig. 14.71

71. [14.4] Do the preceding problem for an inelastic impact with $\epsilon = 0.6$.

72. [14.4] A small elastic sphere is dropped from position (2, 3, 30) onto a hard spherical body (Fig. 14.72) having a radius of 5 ft positioned so that the z axis of the reference shown is along a diameter. For a perfectly elastic collision give the maximum height the sphere reaches on its rebound.

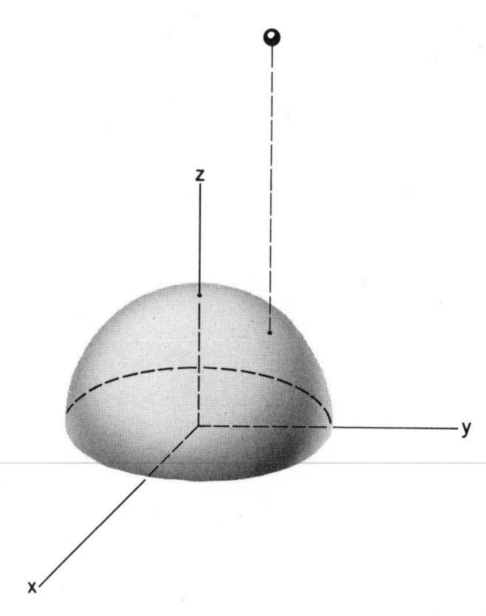

Fig. 14.72

73. [14.4] Do the preceding problem for an inelastic impact with $\epsilon = 0.6$.

74. [14.4] A bullet hits a smooth, hard, massive two-dimensional body whose boundary has been shown (see Fig. 14.73) as a parabola. If the bullet strikes 5 ft above the x axis and if the collision is perfectly elastic, what is the maximum height reached by the bullet as it ricochets? Neglect air resistance and take the the velocity of the bullet on impact as 2000 ft/sec with a direction that is parallel to the x axis.

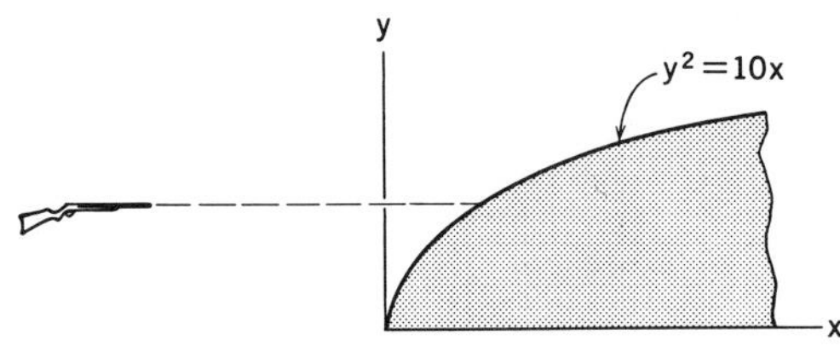

Fig. 14.73

75. [14.4] In the preceding problem assume an inelastic impact with $\epsilon = 0.8$. At what distance along the x direction does the bullet strike the parabolic surface after the impact? Set up only.

76. [14.6] In Fig. 14.74, a particle rotates at 30 rad/sec along a frictionless surface, at a distance 2 ft from the center. A flexible cord restrains the particle. If this cord is pulled so that the particle moves inward at a velocity of 5 ft/sec, what is the magnitude of the total velocity when the particle is 1 ft from the center?

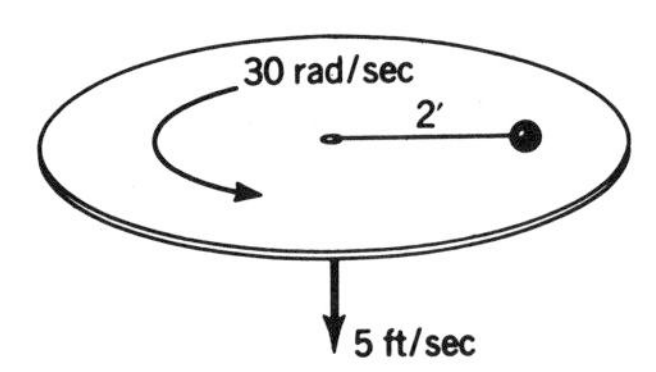

Fig. 14.74

77. [14.6] A satellite has an apogee of 4400 miles. It is moving at a speed of 19,000 miles per hour. What is the transverse velocity of the satellite when $r = 4300$ miles? What interpretation can you now give to mC where C is the constant employed in Chapter 12 on central-force motion?

78. [14.6] Do Prob. 54 in Chapter 12 by conservation of energy and moment of momentum considerations.

79. [14.6] Solve the first part of Prob. 53 in Chapter 12 using the principle of conservation of energy and moment of momentum.

80. [14.6] Do Prob. 63 in Chapter 12 using the principle of conservation of energy and angular momentum.

81. [14.6] Identical masses A and B (see Fig. 14.75) slide on a horizontal rod which is attached to a freely turning vertical shaft. When the masses are in the position shown in the diagram, the system rotates at a speed ω of 5 rad/sec. The masses are released suddenly from this position and move out toward the identical springs, which have a spring constant $K = 1$ lb/in. Set up the equation for the compression δ of the spring once all motions of the bodies relative to the rod have damped out? The mass of each body is 10 lbm. Neglect the mass of the rods and coulomb friction.

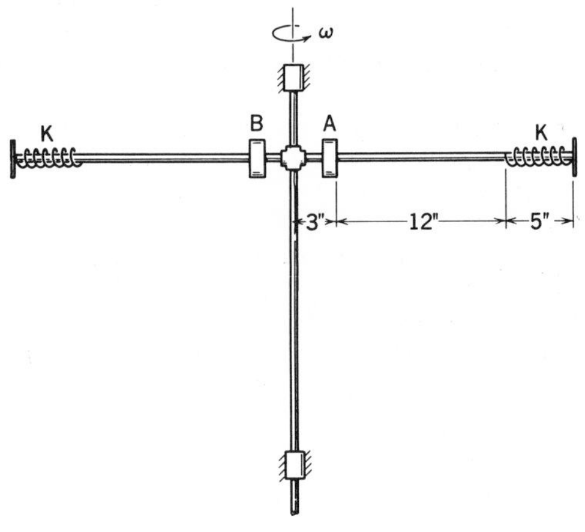

Fig. 14.75

82. [14.6] Do the preceding problem for the case where the mass of A is 5 lbm and the mass of B is 8 lbm. Also consider the spring constant of the spring associated with A to be 2 lb/in. and that of the other spring to be 1 lb/in.

83. [14.6] A system is shown in Fig. 14.76 rotating freely with an angular speed ω of 2 rad/sec. A mass A of 3 lbm is held at a against a spring such that the spring is compressed 4 in. If the device a holding the mass in position is suddenly removed, determine how far toward the vertical axis of the system the mass will move. The spring constant K is 3 lb/in. Neglect all friction and inertia of the bars.

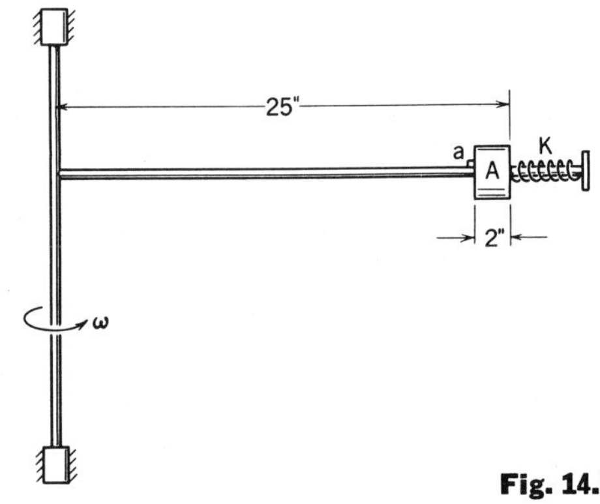

Fig. 14.76

84. [14.6] Do the preceding problem for the case where there is coulomb friction between the mass A and the horizontal rod with a constant μ_d equal to 0.1.

85. [14.6] In Prob. 83 what is the angular acceleration of the system when body A is moving relative to the rod at the speed of V_r ft/sec? The spring is compressed δ in. and the angular speed is ω.

86. [14.6] In Prob. 81 formulate the differential equation of radial motion for mass A when it is not in contact with the spring and when it is in contact with the spring.

87. [14.6] A man is moving in a boat (see Fig. 14.77). He throws out a light rope so as to lasso a piling on the dock at A. He starts drawing in on the rope so that, when he is in the position shown in the diagram, the rope is taut and has a length of 25 ft. His speed V_1 at this instant is 5 ft/sec as shown. If he now draws in steadily with a force of 50 lb, what is the component of his velocity toward A after he has pulled in 3 ft of rope? Neglect friction and consider that boat and man together weigh 350 lb.

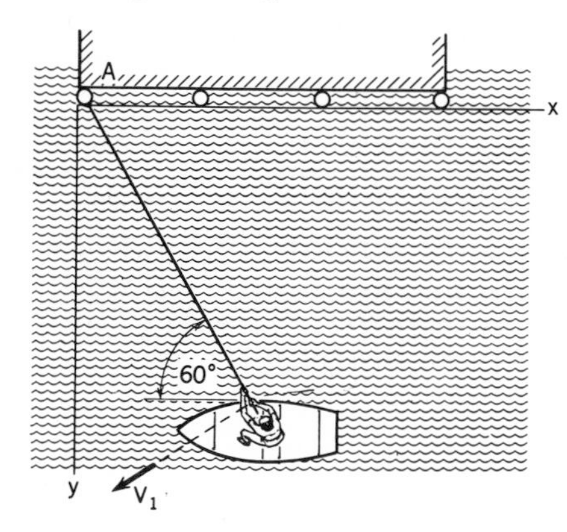

Fig. 14.77

88. [14.6] A body A weighing 10 lb is moving at a speed of V_1 of 20 ft/sec on a frictionless surface (Fig. 14.78). An elastic cord AO, which has a length l of 20 ft, becomes taut at the position shown in the diagram. What is the radial speed toward O of the body when the cord is stretched 2 ft? The cord has an equivalent spring constant of 0.3 lb/in.

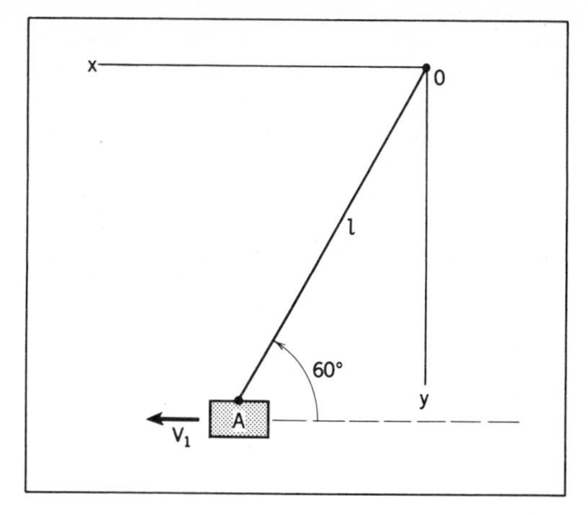

Fig. 14.78

89. [14.7] Shown in Fig. 14.79 is a system composed of three identical bodies A, B, and C each of mass 3 lbm moving along frictionless bars 120° apart on a wheel. Each of these bodies is connected by an inextensible cord to the freely hanging weight D. The connection of the cords to D is such that no torque can be transmitted to D. Initially the three masses A, B, and C are held at a distance of 2 ft from the centerline while the wheel rotates at 3 rad/sec. What is the angular speed of the wheel and the velocity of descent of D if, after release of the radial bodies, bodies, body D moves 1 ft? Assume that body D in initially stationary—i.e., is not rotating. Body D weighs 100 lb.

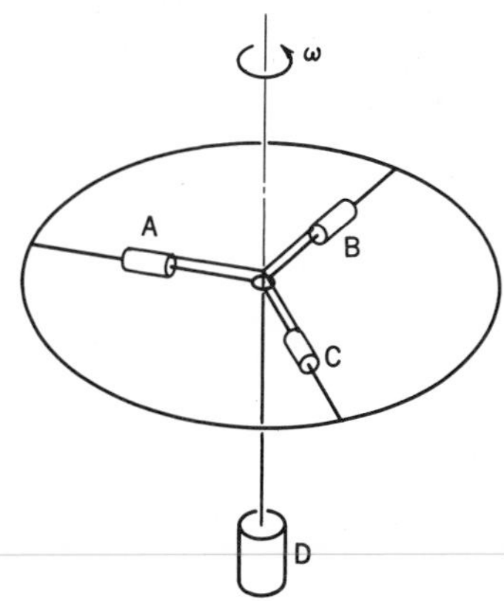

Fig. 14.79

90. [14.7] Do the first part of the preceding problem for the case where there is a constant friction force on each mass of 4 ounces and where the body D develops an angular speed of 1 rad/sec during the action. Body D has a radius of 2 in.

91. [14.7] In Fig. 14.80 a heavy chain of length l is shown lying on a plate A which is freely rotating at a speed of 1 rad/sec. A channel C on the plate A acts as a guide for the chain on the plate, and a stationary pipe B acts as a guide for the chain below the plate. The chain weighs 10 lb/ft and is 20 ft long. What is the speed of the chain and the angular speed of the platform after the chain moves 5 ft? Neglect friction completely and neglect the momentum of the plate and the momentum of the vertical section of chain about its own axis.

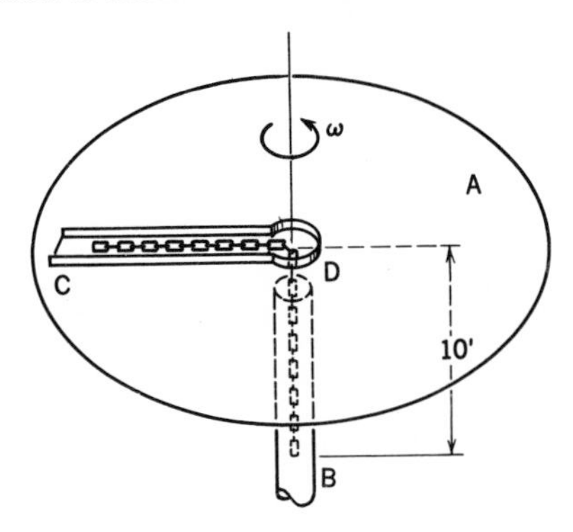

Fig. 14.80

92. [14.7] In Fig. 14.81 is shown a system of particles at time t moving in the xy plane. The following data apply:

$m_1 = 1$ lbm $\quad V_1 = 5\boldsymbol{i} + 5\boldsymbol{j}$ ft/sec

$m_2 = 0.7$ lbm $\quad V_2 = -4\boldsymbol{i} + 3\boldsymbol{j}$

$m_3 = 2$ lbm $\quad V_3 = -4\boldsymbol{j}$

$m_4 = 1.5$ lbm $\quad V_4 = 3\boldsymbol{i} - 4\boldsymbol{j}$

(a) What is the total linear momentum of the system?

(b) What is the linear momentum of the center of mass?

(c) What is the total moment of momentum of the system about the origin and about point (2, 6)?

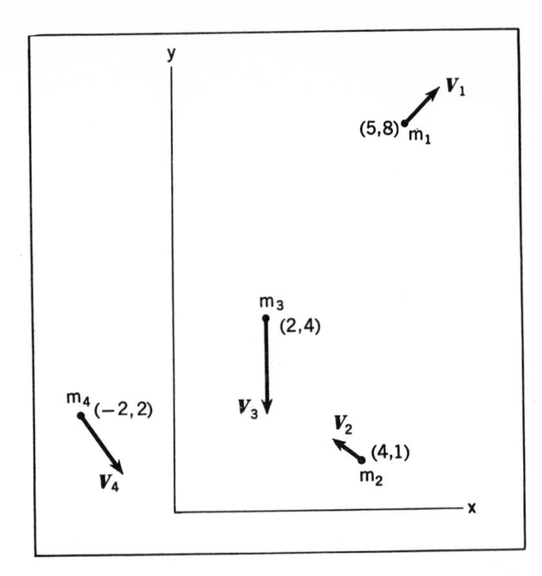

Fig. 14.81

93. [14.7] Shown in Fig. 14.82 is a system of particles at time t. The following data apply at this instant:

$V_1 = 20$ ft/sec $\quad m_1 = 1$ lbm

$V_2 = 18$ ft/sec $\quad m_2 = 3$ lbm

$V_3 = 15$ ft/sec $\quad m_3 = 2$ lbm

$V_4 = 5$ ft/sec $\quad m_4 = 1$ lbm

Determine (a) the total linear momentum of the system, (b) the angular momentum of the system about the origin, (c) the angular momentum of the system about point a.

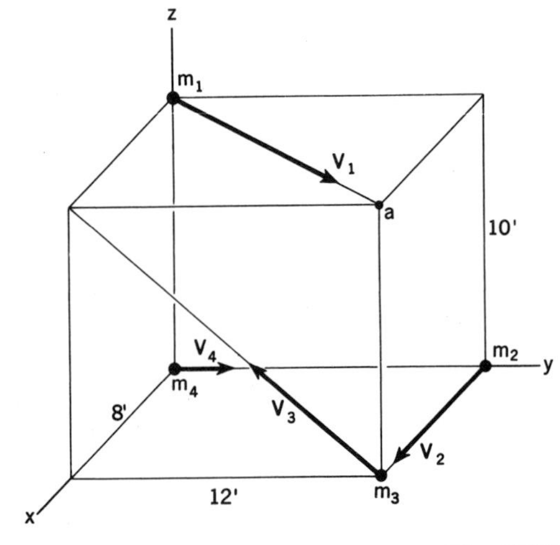

Fig. 14.82

94. [14.7] Two masses slide along bar AB at a constant speed of 5 ft/sec (Fig. 14.83). Bar AB rotates freely about axis CD. Considering only the mass of the sliding bodies, determine the angular acceleration of AB when the bodies are 5 ft from CD if the angular velocity at that instant is 10 rad/sec.

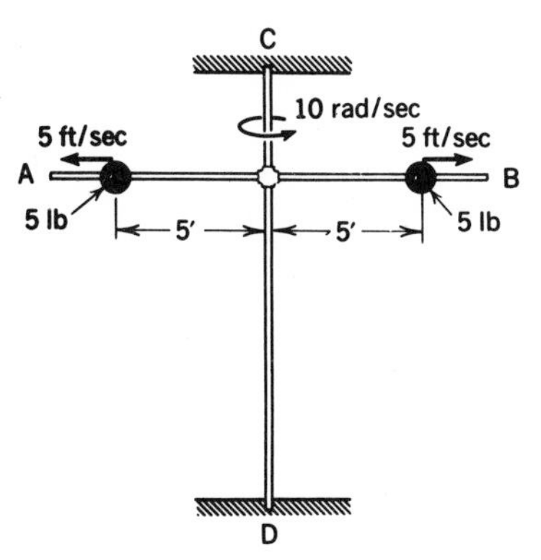

Fig. 14.83

95. [14.7] In Fig. 14.84, a set of particles, each having a mass of one-half slug, rotates about axis AA. The masses are moving out radially at a constant speed of 5 ft/sec at the same time that they are rotating about the AA axis. When they are 1 ft from AA, the angular velocity is 5 rad/sec and at that instant a torque is applied in the direction of motion which varies with time as:

$$\text{torque} = (6t^2 + 10t) \text{ lb-ft}$$

What is the angular velocity when the masses have moved out radially to 2 ft?

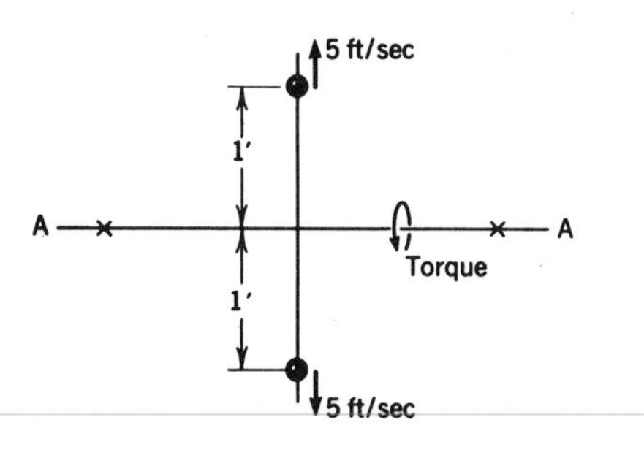

Fig. 14.84

96. [14.7] In Fig. 14.85, two sets of particles a, b and c, d (each particle of mass m) are moving along two shafts AB and CD, which are in turn rigidly attached to a crossbar EF. All particles are moving at a constant speed V_1 away from EF, and their positions at the moment of interest are as shown. The system is rotating about G, and a constant torque of magnitude T is acting in the plane of the system. Assuming that all masses other than the concentrated masses are negligible, and that the angular velocity of the system at the instant of discussion is ω, determine the instantaneous angular acceleration in terms of m, T, ω, s_1, and s_2.

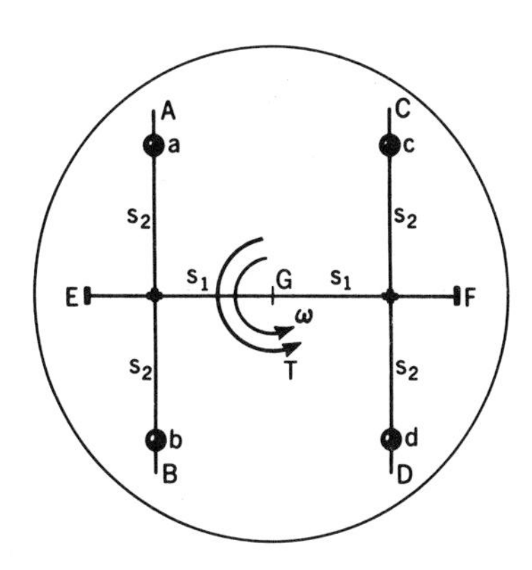

Fig. 14.85

97. [14.7] Compute the angular momentum of a uniform rod of length $L = 10$ ft and weight of 5 lb/ft (see Fig. 14.86) about O at the instant when it is vertical and has an angular speed ω of 3 rad/sec.

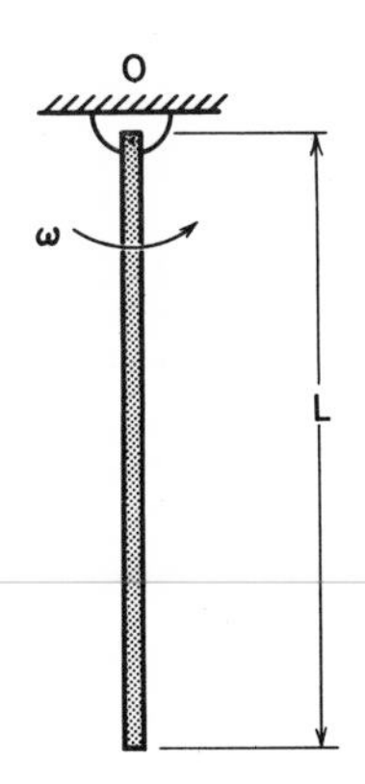

Fig. 14.86

98. [14.7] A wheel consisting of a thin rim and four thin spokes is shown rotating about its axis in Fig. 14.87 at a speed ω of 2 rad/sec. The radius of the wheel R is 2 ft and the weight per unit length of rim and spoke is 2 lb/ft. What is the moment of momentum of the wheel about O? What is the total linear momentum?

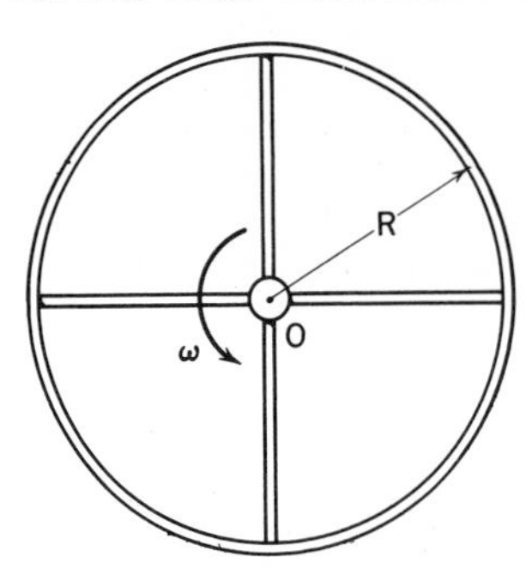

Fig. 14.87

99. [14.7] In Fig. 14.88 are shown two uniform connected cylinders A and B. The density of the cylinders is 300 lbm/ft^3 and the system is rotating at a speed ω of 10 rad/sec about its geometric axis. What is the angular momentum of the body?

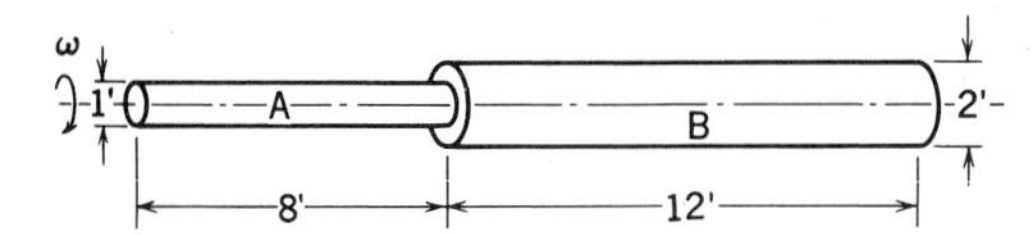

Fig. 14.88

100. [14.7] A closed container of water is shown in Fig. 14.89. By rotating the container for some time and then suddenly holding the container stationary we develop a rotational motion of the water which, you will learn in fluid mechanics, resembles a vortex. If the velocity of the fluid elements is zero in the radial direction and is given as $10/r$ ft/sec in the transverse direction, what is the moment of momentum of the water?

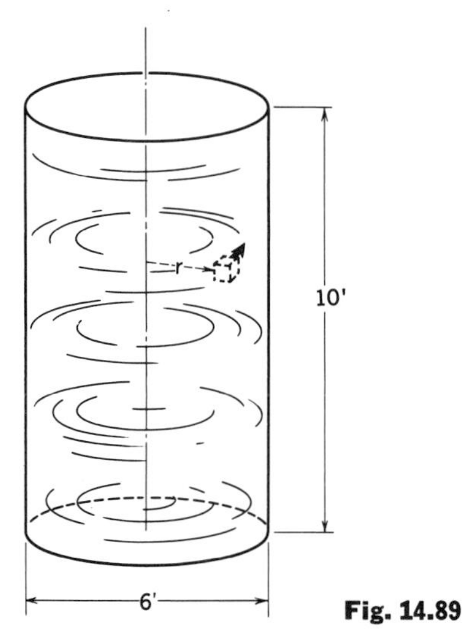

Fig. 14.89

101. [14.7] A canal with a rectangular cross section is shown in Fig. 14.90 having a width of 30 ft and a depth of 5 ft. The velocity of the water is assumed zero at the banks and varies parabolically over the section as shown in the diagram. Using δ as the radial distance from the centerline of the channel, the transverse velocity V_ϕ is given as:

$$V_\phi = \tfrac{1}{20}(225 - \delta^2) \text{ ft/sec}$$

The radial component V_r is everywhere zero. What is the moment of momentum $\boldsymbol{H}$ at any time t of the water in the circular portion of the canal—i.e., between the x and y axes?

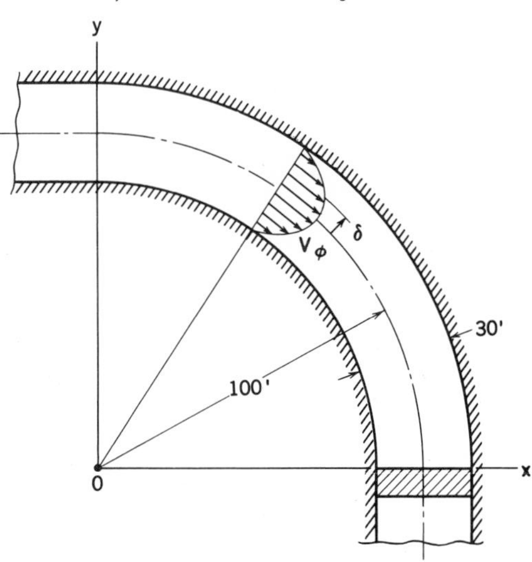

Fig. 14.90

102. [14.7] A hoop weighing 5 lb/ft rests on a frictionless surface (see Fig. 14.91). A 100-lb force is suddenly applied. What is the angular acceleration of the hoop? What is the acceleration of the mass center?

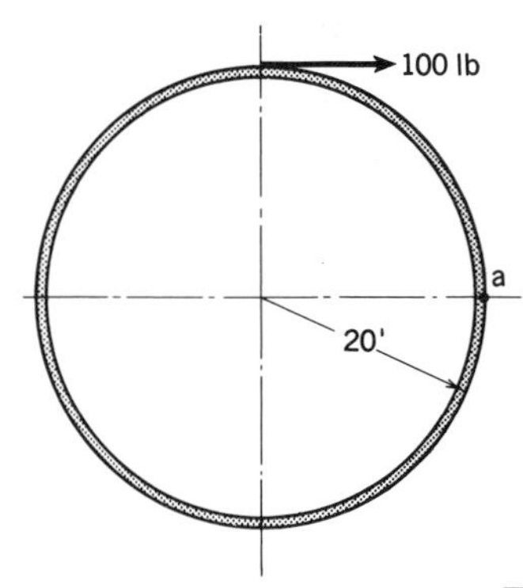

Fig. 14.91

103. [14.7] Do the previous problem for the case where a force given as:

$$\boldsymbol{F} = 10\boldsymbol{i} + 15\boldsymbol{j}$$

is applied at point a instead of the 100-lb force.

104. [14.7] A cylinder weighing 50 lb rests on a frictionless surface as shown in Fig. 14.92. Two forces are applied simultaneously as shown in the diagram. What is the angular acceleration of the cylinder? What is the acceleration of the mass center?

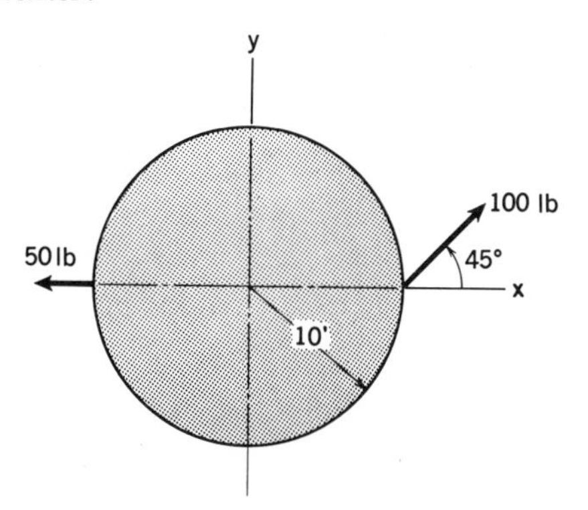

Fig. 14.92

105. [14.7] A uniform rod weighing 5 lb/ft rests on a frictionless surface (see Fig. 14.93). A force of 50 lb acts on the rod as shown in the diagram. What is the angular acceleration of the rod? What is the acceleration of the mass center?

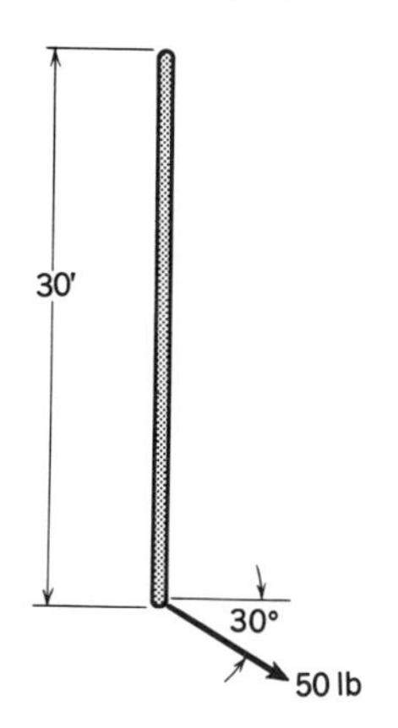

Fig. 14.93

106. [14.7] A uniform hoop rolls without slipping down a 30° incline as shown in Fig. 14.94. The hoop material weighs 5 lb/ft and has a radius R of 4 ft. What is the angular acceleration of the hoop?

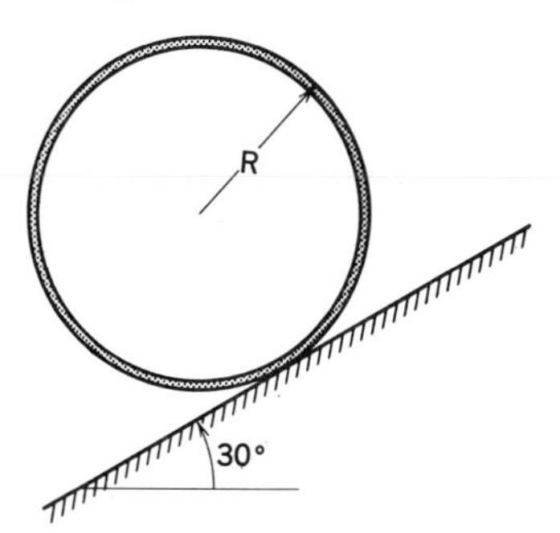

Fig. 14.94

107. [14.7] A uniform cylinder of radius 3 ft rolls without slipping down a 30° incline as shown in Fig. 14.95. What is the angular acceleration of the cylinder if it has a weight of 100 lb?

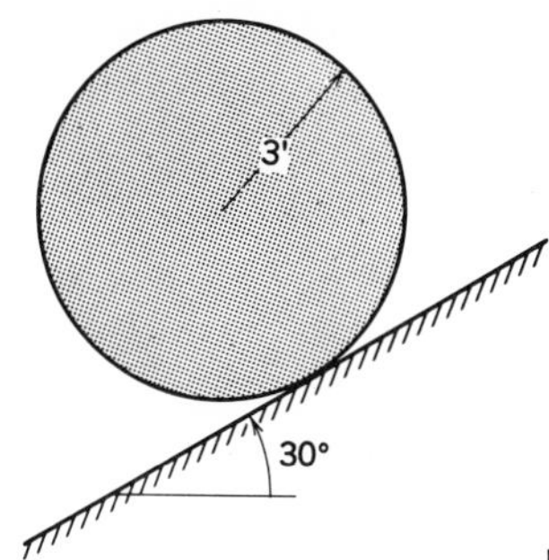

Fig. 14.95

108. [14.8] In Fig. 14.96(a) is shown a system of particles at time t_1 having masses:

$$m_1 = 2 \text{ lbm}, \quad m_2 = 1 \text{ lbm}, \quad m_3 = 3 \text{ lbm}$$

The same system of masses is shown in Fig. 14.96(b) at time t_2. What is the total linear impulse on the system during this time interval? What is the total angular impulse during this time interval about the origin?

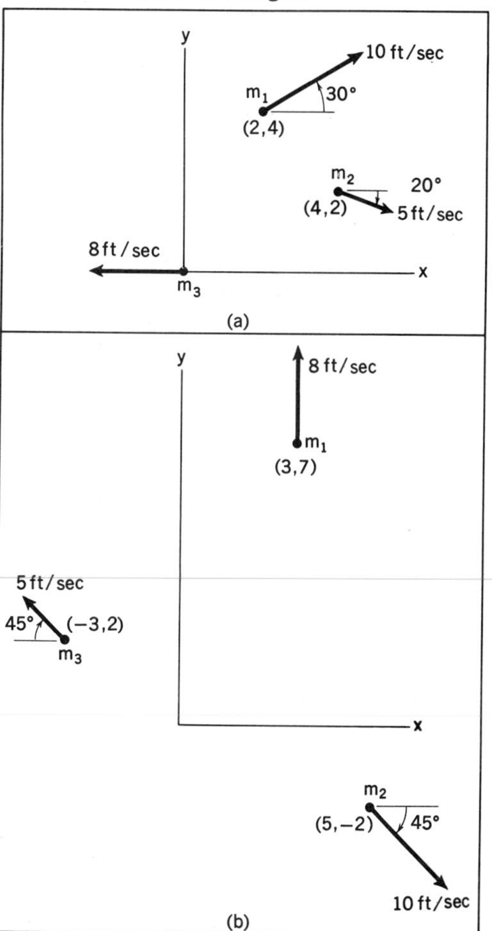

Fig. 14.96

109. [14.8] A cylinder of length 10 ft and weight 100 lb (see Fig. 14.97) is acted on by a torque about its geometric axis given as:

$$T = 8t + 15t^2 \text{ ft-lb}$$

What is the angular speed after 20 seconds? The cylinder is at rest when its torque is applied.

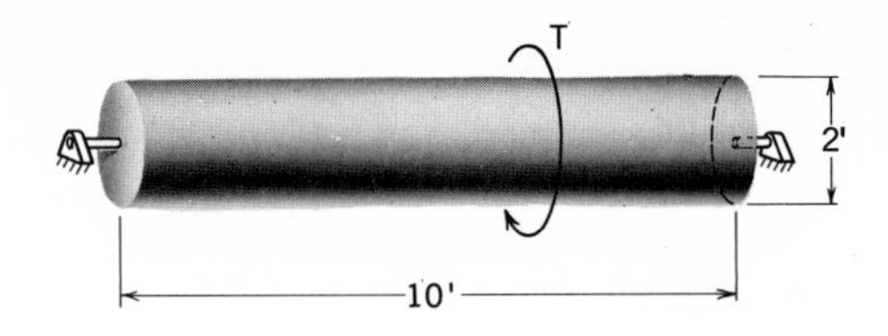

Fig. 14.97

15

Kinematics of Rigid Bodies: Relative Motion

15.1 Introduction

In Chapter 11 we made a study of the kinematics of a particle. During virtually all of this study only a single reference was used. However, at the end of that chapter we briefly introduced the use of several references—namely the case of *simple relative motion* involving two references *translating* relative to each other.

One of the things we will do in this chapter is to generalize the formulations for multireference analysis. There are two reasons for doing this. First, we will be able to analyze complicated motions in a more simple systematic way by using several references. Second, it is often the case that motion of a particle is known relative to a moving body (such as an airplane), to which we can fix a reference xyz, while the motion of this body is known relative to an inertial reference XYZ (such as the ground). Since Newton's law is valid for an inertial reference, we must then express the motion of the particle relative to the inertial reference directly, and so for practical reasons we must accordingly become involved in multireference systems.

A reference is a rigid body, and before we can set forth multireference considerations we must first study the kinematics of a rigid body. In so doing we will also set the stage for our main effort in the remaining portion of the text involving the dynamics of rigid bodies.

15.2 Translation and Rotation of Rigid Bodies

For purposes of dynamics, a rigid body is considered to be composed of a continuous distribution of particles having mutual distances that are inextensible. We may profitably define once again two simple types of motion of a rigid body.

1. *Translation.* As pointed out in Chapter 11, if a body moves so that all the particles have at at time t the same velocity relative to some reference, the body is said to be in *translation* relative to this reference at this time. The velocity of a translating body, it should be understood, may vary with time and so may be represented as $\boldsymbol{V}(t)$. Accordingly, translational motion does not necessarily mean motion along a straight line. For example, the body shown in Fig. 15.1 is in translation over the interval indicated because at each instant, each particle in the body has a common velocity. A characteristic of translational motion is that any straight line in the body always retains an orientation parallel to its *original* direction during such a motion.

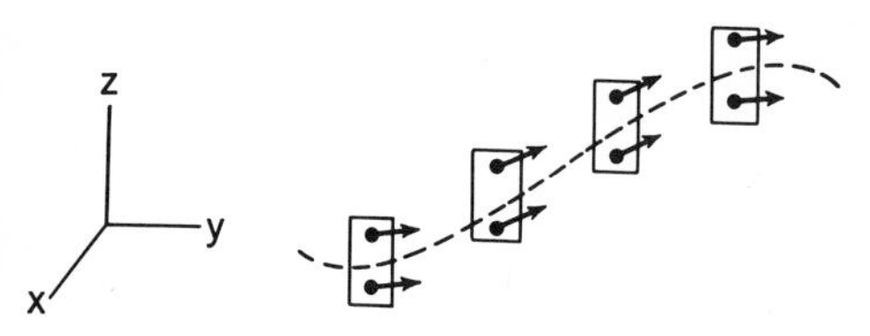

Fig. 15.1

2. *Rotation.* If a body moves so that along some straight line all the particles of a body, or a hypothetical extension of the body, have a zero velocity relative to some reference, the body is said to be in *rotation* relative to this reference. The line of stationary particles is called the *axis of rotation.*

We shall now consider carefully how we measure the rotation of a body. A single revolution is defined as the amount of rotation in either a clockwise or a counterclockwise direction about the axis of rotation that brings the body back to its original position. Partial revolutions can conveniently be measured by observing *any* line segment such as AB in the body (Fig. 15.2) from a viewpoint directed along the axis of rotation. In Fig. 15.3 we have shown this line segment at the beginning and at the end of a partial rotation projected onto a plane perpendicular to the axis of rotation and extended to form an angle β' in this plane. Since the radial distance from the axis of rotation cannot change, the points A and B of the line segment must traverse circular paths during the rotation about O, as is shown. Every radial line such as OA sweeps through an angle β during the motion. It may be easily shown that the angle β' between AB and $A'B'$ equals this angle β. Note first that areas AFB and $A'F'B'$, formed by the radial lines from O, the circular arcs about O, and the line segments AB and $A'B'$, are congruent. This must clearly be the case since these areas can be considered

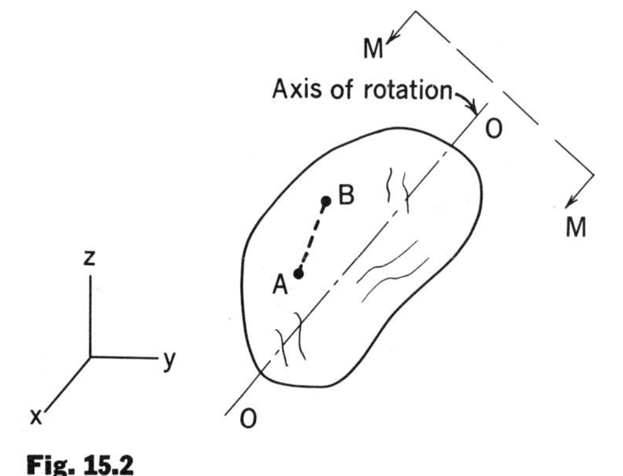

Fig. 15.2

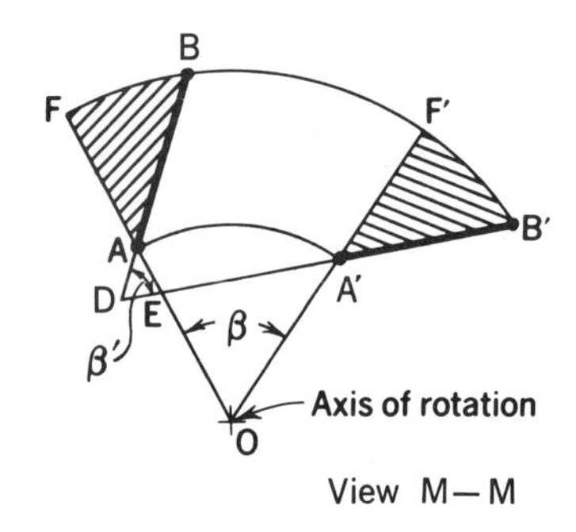

Fig. 15.3

as the same undeformable internal surface of the rigid body (or hypothetical extension thereof) viewed at two locations and since the orientation of this surface relative to the axis of rotation (which also can be considered as part of the rigid body or hypothetical extension thereof) must remain unchanged, the areas must be congruent. Thus, in considering triangles DAE and $OA'E$, we see that angles $\sphericalangle DAE$ and $\sphericalangle EA'O$ must be equal. Furthermore, since angles $\sphericalangle AED$ and $\sphericalangle A'EO$ are also equal, the triangles DAE and $OA'E$ are similar, and we can conclude that $\beta = \beta'$. Thus the projections of line segments onto a plane perpendicular to the axis of rotation rotate through the *same* angle β. This angle then serves as the measure of rotation.

In Chapter 1 of statics, we pointed out that finite rotations, although they have a magnitude and a direction along the axis of rotation, are not vectors, since the superposition of rotations is not commutative and therefore does not add according to the parallelogram law, which, you will recall, is a requirement of all vector quantities. However, it may be shown (see Appendix III) that as rotations become infinitesimal, they satisfy in the limit the commutative law of addition, so that infinitesimal rotations $d\beta$ are vector quantities. Therefore, the angular velocity is a vector quantity having a magnitude $d\beta/dt$ and a direction parallel to the axis of rotation with a sense in accordance with the right-hand screw rule. We shall employ $\boldsymbol{\omega}$ to represent the angular velocity vector. Note that this definition does not prescribe the line of action of this vector, for the line of action may be considered at positions other than the axis of rotation. It depends on the situation (as will be discussed in later sections).

15.3 Chasle's Theorem

We have just considered two simple motions of a body, namely, translation and rotation. We will now demonstrate that at each instant, the motion of any rigid body can be thought of as the superposition of both a translational and a rotational motion.

Consider for simplicity a body moving in a plane. Positions of the body have been shown at times t and $(t + \Delta t)$ in Fig. 15.4. Let us select any point B of the body. Imagine that the body is displaced without rotation from its position at time t to the position at time $(t + \Delta t)$ so that point B reaches its correct final position B'. The displacement vector for this translation is shown as $\Delta \boldsymbol{R}_B$. To reach the correct orientation for $(t + \Delta t)$, we must now rotate the body an angle $\Delta\phi$ about an axis of rotation normal to the plane and going through point B'.

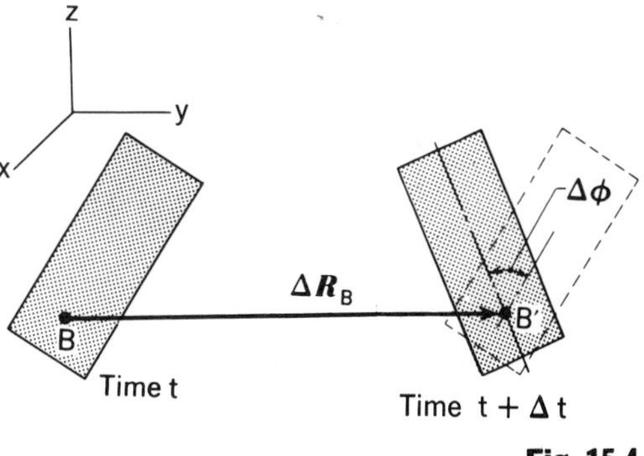

Fig. 15.4

What changes would occur had we chosen some other point C for such a procedure? Consider Fig. 15.5, where we have added an alternative procedure by translating the body so that point C reaches the correct final position C'. Next we must rotate about an axis of rotation normal to the plane and going through C' to get to the final orientation. Thus we have indicated two routes. It is apparent from the diagram that the displacement $\Delta \boldsymbol{R}_C$ differs from $\Delta \boldsymbol{R}_B$ but there is no differ-

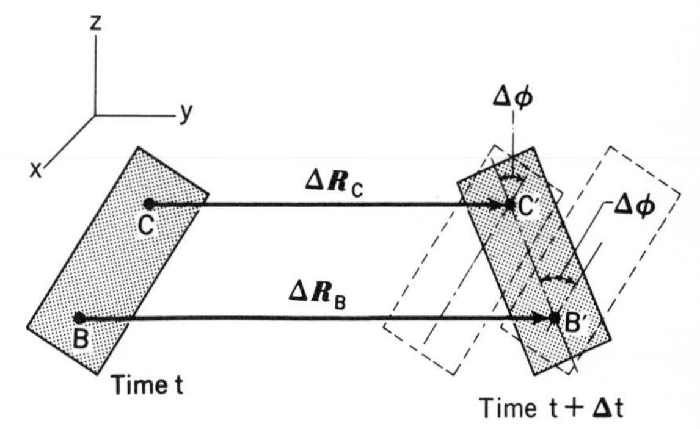

Fig. 15.5

ence in the amount of rotation $\Delta\phi$, and so in general $\Delta \boldsymbol{R}$ *will depend on the point chosen, while the amount of rotation* $\Delta\phi$ *will be the same for all such points.*

Consider now the ratios $\Delta \boldsymbol{R}/\Delta t$ and $\Delta\phi/\Delta t$. These may be taken as an average translational velocity and average rotational speed, respectively, of the body, which we could superpose to get from the initial position to the final position in the time Δt. *If we go to the limit by letting* $\Delta t \to 0$, *we have instantaneous translational and rotational velocities which, when superposed, give the instantaneous motion of the body.* Since the chosen point B in the previous discussion undergoes no motion during the time Δt other than the translation, we can conclude that, in the limit, the translational velocity used for the body corresponds to the *actual instantaneous* velocity of the chosen point at time t. The angular velocity to be used is the same for all points and is accordingly the angular velocity of the body at time t. In the Appendix IV the preceding argument is carried out for the general motion of a rigid body in space. We can then make the following statements for the description of the general motion of a rigid body relative to some reference at time t. These statements comprise *Chasle's theorem.*

1. Select any point B in the body. Assume that all particles of the body have at the time t a velocity equal to $\boldsymbol{V}_B$, the actual velocity of the point B.
2. Superpose a pure rotational velocity $\boldsymbol{\omega}$ about an axis of rotation going through point B. With the proper $\boldsymbol{\omega}$, the actual instantaneous motion of the body is determined, and $\boldsymbol{\omega}$ will be the same for all points B which might be chosen. Thus, only the translational velocity and the axis of rotation change when different points B are chosen. It should be clearly understood, however, that the *actual instantaneous axis of rotation* at time t is the one going through those points of the body having zero velocity at time t.

15.4 Derivative of a Vector Fixed in a Moving Reference

In Fig. 15.6 we have shown two references XYZ and xyz moving arbitrarily relative to each other. Assume we are observing xyz from XYZ. Since a reference is a rigid system we can apply Chasle's theorem to reference xyz. Thus, choosing the origin O, we can superpose a translation velocity $\dot{\boldsymbol{R}}$ equal to the velocity of the origin of xyz plus a rotational velocity $\boldsymbol{\omega}$ with an axis of rotation through O to fully describe the motion of xyz relative to XYZ.

Now suppose there is a vector $\boldsymbol{A}$ of fixed length and of fixed orientation as seen from reference xyz. We say that such a vector is "fixed" in reference xyz. It is clear that the time rate of change of $\boldsymbol{A}$ as seen from reference xyz must be zero. We can express this mathematically as follows:

$$\left(\frac{d\boldsymbol{A}}{dt}\right)_{xyz} = \boldsymbol{0}$$

However, as seen from XYZ the time rate of change $\boldsymbol{A}$ will not necessarily be zero. To evaluate $(d\boldsymbol{A}/dt)_{XYZ}$ we employ Chasle's theorem in the following manner:

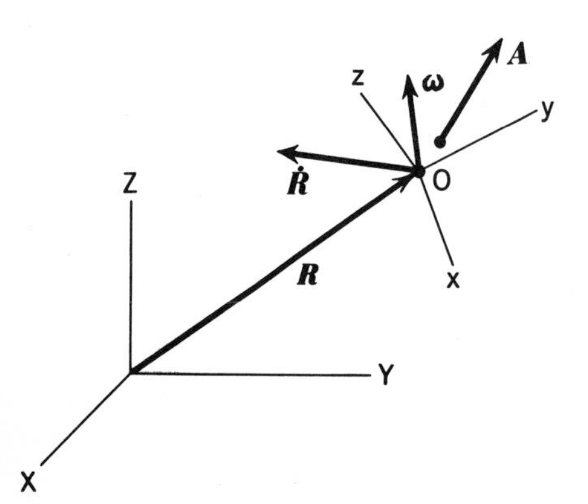

Fig. 15.6

1. The translation motion $\dot{\boldsymbol{R}}$ for the whole system does not alter the direction of $\boldsymbol{A}$ and, since the magnitude is fixed, there can be no change of the vector $\boldsymbol{A}$ as a result of this motion.

2. We can next consider a pure rotation contribution about an axis of rotation through O. This is shown in Fig. 15.7, where the ends of vector $\boldsymbol{A}$ form circular arcs about the axis of rotation. It is simplest to decompose $\boldsymbol{A}$ into cylindrical components with the axis of rotation forming the axial direction z', as shown in the diagram. Thus:

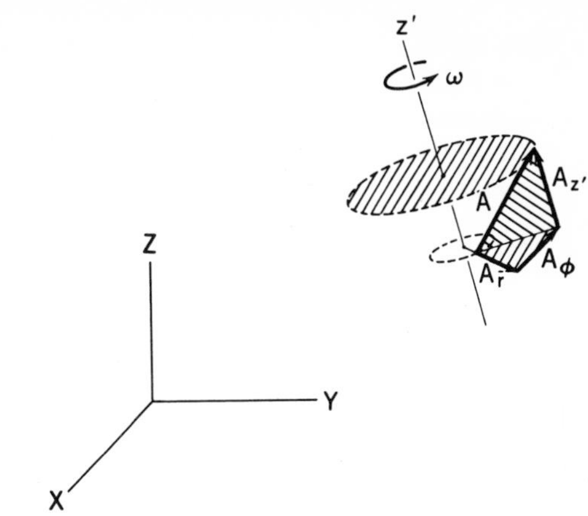

Fig. 15.7

$$\boldsymbol{A} = A_{z'}\boldsymbol{\varepsilon}_{z'} + A_\phi\boldsymbol{\varepsilon}_\phi + A_{\bar{r}}\boldsymbol{\varepsilon}_{\bar{r}}$$

Clearly as $\boldsymbol{A}$ rotates about z' there is no change in the values of the components $A_{\bar{r}}$, $A_{z'}$, and A_ϕ. Accordingly $\dot{A}_{\bar{r}} = \dot{A}_\phi = \dot{A}_{z'} = 0$. Also noting that $\dot{\boldsymbol{\varepsilon}}_{z'} = \boldsymbol{0}$ we have for $(d\boldsymbol{A}/dt)_{XYZ}$:

$$\left(\frac{d\boldsymbol{A}}{dt}\right)_{XYZ} = A_\phi\left(\frac{d\boldsymbol{\varepsilon}_\phi}{dt}\right)_{XYZ} + A_{\bar{r}}\left(\frac{d\boldsymbol{\varepsilon}_{\bar{r}}}{dt}\right)_{XYZ}$$

We have already evaluated the derivatives of the unit vectors in the above equation in Section 11.6. Using Eqs. 11.36 and 11.40 we have:

$$\left(\frac{d\boldsymbol{A}}{dt}\right)_{XYZ} = -A_\phi\omega\boldsymbol{\varepsilon}_{\bar{r}} + A_{\bar{r}}\omega\boldsymbol{\varepsilon}_\phi$$

But the right side is simply the cross product of $\boldsymbol{\omega}$ and $\boldsymbol{A}$, as you can see by carrying out the cross product with cylindrical components. Thus:

$$\begin{aligned}\boldsymbol{\omega} \times \boldsymbol{A} &= \omega\boldsymbol{\varepsilon}_{z'} \times (A_{z'}\boldsymbol{\varepsilon}_{z'} + A_\phi\boldsymbol{\varepsilon}_\phi + A_{\bar{r}}\boldsymbol{\varepsilon}_{\bar{r}}) \\ &= -\omega A_\phi\boldsymbol{\varepsilon}_{\bar{r}} + \omega A_{\bar{r}}\boldsymbol{\varepsilon}_\phi\end{aligned}$$

We can then conclude from these considerations that

$$\left(\frac{d\boldsymbol{A}}{dt}\right)_{XYZ} = \boldsymbol{\omega} \times \boldsymbol{A} \qquad \textbf{15.1}$$

for a vector $\boldsymbol{A}$ fixed in a reference xyz moving arbitrarily relative to reference XYZ. From this result, we see that $(d\boldsymbol{A}/dt)_{XYZ}$ depends only on the vectors $\boldsymbol{A}$ and $\boldsymbol{\omega}$ and not their lines of action. Thus we can conclude that the time rate of change of $\boldsymbol{A}$ fixed in xyz is not altered when:

(a). The vector $\boldsymbol{A}$ is fixed at some new position in xyz provided the vector itself is not changed,

(b). The *actual* axis of rotation of the xyz system is shifted to a new parallel position.

We may differentiate the terms in Eq. 15.1 a second time. We thus get:

$$\left(\frac{d^2A}{dt^2}\right)_{XYZ} = \omega \times \left(\frac{dA}{dt}\right)_{XYZ} + \left(\frac{d\omega}{dt}\right)_{XYZ} \times A \qquad 15.2$$

Using Eq. 15.1 to replace $(dA/dt)_{XYZ}$ and using $\dot{\omega}$ to replace $(d\omega/dt)_{XYZ}$, since it is clear what reference is being used for this derivative,* we get:

$$\left(\frac{d^2A}{dt^2}\right)_{XYZ} = \omega \times (\omega \times A) + \dot{\omega} \times A \qquad 15.3$$

You can compute higher-order derivatives by continuing the process. It is suggested that only Eq. 15.1 be remembered and that all subsequent higher-order derivatives be evaluated.

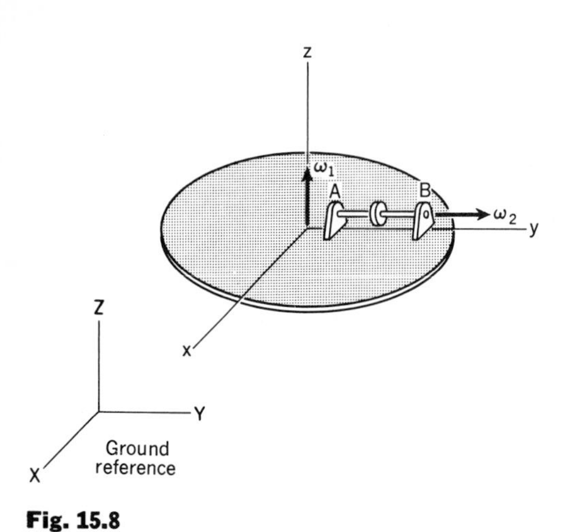

Fig. 15.8

EXAMPLE 15.1

In Fig. 15.8 is a shaft AB spinning with constant angular speed ω_2 within its bearings. This system is mounted on a platform which rotates with an angular vector ω_1 relative to the ground reference XYZ. What are the first and second time derivatives of the vector ω_2 as seen from the ground reference?

We will attach a reference xyz to the platform as shown in the diagram. Clearly the vector ω_2 is "fixed" in this reference and we may use the results of this section. Thus we have:

$$\left(\frac{d\omega_2}{dt}\right)_{XYZ} = \omega_1 \times \omega_2$$

$$\left(\frac{d^2\omega_2}{dt^2}\right)_{XYZ} = \omega_1 \times \dot{\omega}_2 + \dot{\omega}_1 \times \omega_2$$

$$= \omega_1 \times (\omega_1 \times \omega_2) + \dot{\omega}_1 \times \omega_2$$

Although we shall formally examine the case of the time derivative of vector A as seen from XYZ when A is not fixed in reference xyz, we can handle such cases less formally with what we already know. The procedure generally is to decompose A into rectangular components along axes of a convenient reference xyz whose motion is known, using i, j, and k as unit vectors along these axes. Now employ the rule for differentiation of a product and note that unit vectors i, j, and k are fixed in reference xyz, permitting us to use Eq. 15.1 for $\dot{i}$, $\dot{j}$, and $\dot{k}$. We illustrate these steps in the following example.

* We will use the dot when it is perfectly clear from the context of a discussion what reference is being used.

EXAMPLE 15.2

In the system shown in Fig. 15.8, $\omega_2 = 6$ rad/sec and $\dot{\omega}_2 = 2$ rad/sec^2 relative to the platform while $\omega_1 = 2$ rad/sec and $\dot{\omega}_1 = -3$ rad/sec^2 relative to the ground. What is the angular acceleration vector for the rotating disc at the instant of interest?

The total angular velocity of the disc relative to the ground at the instant of interest is given as:

$$\boldsymbol{\omega}_{AB} = \boldsymbol{\omega}_1 + \boldsymbol{\omega}_2 = 2\boldsymbol{k} + 6\boldsymbol{j} \text{ rad/sec} \qquad \textbf{(a)}$$

To get $\dot{\boldsymbol{\omega}}_{AB}$ we fix a reference xyz onto the platform as in the previous problem and express $\boldsymbol{\omega}_{AB}$ as follows:

$$\boldsymbol{\omega}_{AB} = \omega_2\boldsymbol{j} + \omega_1\boldsymbol{k} \qquad \textbf{(b)}$$

where $\boldsymbol{j}$ and $\boldsymbol{k}$ are unit vectors of reference xyz. Now take the time derivative of $\boldsymbol{\omega}_{AB}$ as seen from XYZ. Thus, using the product rule differentiation, we get:

$$\left(\frac{d\boldsymbol{\omega}_{AB}}{dt}\right)_{XYZ} = \dot{\omega}_2\boldsymbol{j} + \omega_2\dot{\boldsymbol{j}} + \dot{\omega}_1\boldsymbol{k} + \omega_1\dot{\boldsymbol{k}} \qquad \textbf{(c)}$$

The vectors $\boldsymbol{j}$ and $\boldsymbol{k}$ are "fixed" in the reference xyz and so we have for the time derivative of these vectors:

$$\dot{\boldsymbol{j}} = \boldsymbol{\omega}_1 \times \boldsymbol{j} = \omega_1\boldsymbol{k} \times \boldsymbol{j} = -\omega_1\boldsymbol{i} = -2\boldsymbol{i}$$
$$\dot{\boldsymbol{k}} = \boldsymbol{\omega}_1 \times \boldsymbol{k} = \omega_1\boldsymbol{k} \times \boldsymbol{k} = \boldsymbol{0} \qquad \textbf{(d)}$$

Returning to Eq. (c), we get:

$$\left(\frac{d\boldsymbol{\omega}_{AB}}{dt}\right)_{XYZ} = 2\boldsymbol{j} + (6)(-2)\boldsymbol{i} - 3\boldsymbol{k}$$
$$= -12\boldsymbol{i} + 2\boldsymbol{j} - 3\boldsymbol{k} \text{ rad/sec}^2 \qquad \textbf{(e)}$$

While it is often possible to work with components of a vector $\boldsymbol{A}$ along axes of a reference xyz whose motion is known (with the result that only one $\boldsymbol{\omega}$ suffices for the computation of $\dot{\boldsymbol{i}}$, $\dot{\boldsymbol{j}}$, and $\dot{\boldsymbol{k}}$), there are times when the desirable components to work with are *not* orthogonal at all times. In that case, we must often use different angular velocity vectors in the computation of the time derivatives of the unit vectors along the respective direction of the chosen components of the vector $\boldsymbol{A}$. The following example illustrates this case.

***EXAMPLE 15.3**

In Fig. 15.9 is shown a body AB which is constrained to move in such a way that a point B is always fixed.* Thus the axis of rotation for this body relative to the ground always goes through ball-joint connection B. We can set forth three convenient angular velocity vectors for this problem. They are:

* We shall examine carefully the dynamics of a rigid body about a fixed point in Chapter 19.

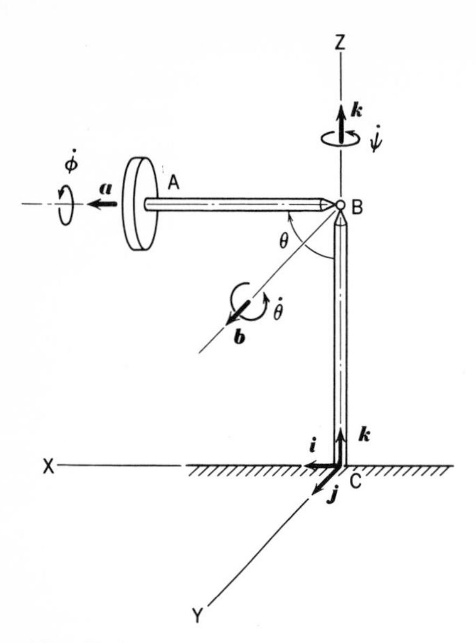

Fig. 15.9

1. An angular motion $\dot{\psi}$ of the centerline of A about the vertical axis BC. (This is called the *precession* velocity for such problems.)
2. An angular motion of the centerline of A in the plane ABC given by $\dot{\theta}$. (This is actually an angular velocity of the centerline about an axis normal to AB and BC and is called the *nutation velocity*.)
3. An angular motion of the body about its centerline given by $\dot{\phi}$. (This velocity has a direction collinear with the centerline and is called the *spin velocity*.)

We are to determine the total angular velocity of A relative to the ground as well as its total angular acceleration relative to the ground at the instant of interest corresponding to the configuration shown. It is assumed that $\ddot{\psi}$, $\ddot{\theta}$, and $\ddot{\phi}$ are not zero.

At the instant of interest, the aforementioned velocity vectors are at right angles to each other and can accordingly be given as follows:

$$\boldsymbol{\omega} = \dot{\phi}\boldsymbol{i} + \dot{\theta}\boldsymbol{j} + \dot{\psi}\boldsymbol{k} \text{ rad/sec} \qquad \textbf{(a)}$$

We cannot, however, differentiate the above expression because it is correct only *instantaneously* since the directions of the angular velocity vectors are at right angles only at the instant of interest. At all other times they are not entirely mutually perpendicular. *Clearly we cannot form a second convenient reference xyz as we have done earlier to give us the proper direction for the above angular velocities to be valid at all times.* We must proceed somewhat differently here in order to get $\dot{\boldsymbol{\omega}}$.

We shall use here a unit vector $\boldsymbol{a}$ fixed along the centerline of AB and a unit vector $\boldsymbol{b}$ at right angles always to unit vectors $\boldsymbol{a}$ and $\boldsymbol{k}$. (Unit vector $\boldsymbol{b}$ is thus always at right angles to the plane ABC.) Thus, vector $\boldsymbol{a}$ is always collinear with the angular velocity corresponding to $\dot{\phi}$, and $\boldsymbol{b}$ is always collinear with the angular velocity vector corresponding to $\dot{\theta}$. Associating $\boldsymbol{i}$ and $\boldsymbol{j}$ with reference XYZ (see Fig. 15.9), note that at the instant of interest $\boldsymbol{a} = \boldsymbol{i}$ and $\boldsymbol{b} = \boldsymbol{j}$ but that at all other times these equalities do not hold. We can now express $\boldsymbol{\omega}$ at *all times* in this form:

$$\boldsymbol{\omega} = \dot{\phi}\boldsymbol{a} + \dot{\theta}\boldsymbol{b} + \dot{\psi}\boldsymbol{k}$$

And because this expression is valid at all times we can differentiate with respect to time to get:

$$\dot{\boldsymbol{\omega}} = \ddot{\phi}\boldsymbol{a} + \dot{\phi}\dot{\boldsymbol{a}} + \ddot{\theta}\boldsymbol{b} + \dot{\theta}\dot{\boldsymbol{b}} + \ddot{\psi}\boldsymbol{k} + \dot{\psi}\dot{\boldsymbol{k}} \qquad \textbf{(b)}$$

We know the angular velocity of the centerline of AB and accordingly that of unit vector $\boldsymbol{a}$. Thus, imagining that $\boldsymbol{a}$ is fixed in a rigid body having angular speeds $\dot{\psi}$ and $\dot{\theta}$, we have

$$\dot{\boldsymbol{a}} = (\dot{\psi}\boldsymbol{k} + \dot{\theta}\boldsymbol{b}) \times \boldsymbol{a} \qquad \textbf{(c)}$$

We can now replace $\boldsymbol{a}$ by $\boldsymbol{i}$ and $\boldsymbol{b}$ by $\boldsymbol{j}$. Accordingly we get for $\dot{\boldsymbol{a}}$ at the instant of interest:

$$\dot{a} = \dot{\psi} j - \dot{\theta} k \qquad \text{(d)}$$

As for $\dot{b}$ we can imagine that b is fixed in a rigid body having an angular speed $\dot{\psi}$.* We thus have:

$$\dot{b} = \dot{\psi} k \times b \qquad \text{(e)}$$

At the instant of interest $b = j$ and we get

$$\dot{b} = -\dot{\psi} i \qquad \text{(f)}$$

Since $\dot{k} = 0$, we get the following result on substituting for $\dot{a}$ and $\dot{b}$ in Eq. (b) and replacing a by i and b by j:

$$\dot{\omega} = \ddot{\phi} i + \dot{\theta}\dot{\psi} j - \dot{\phi}\dot{\theta} k + \ddot{\theta} j - \dot{\theta}\dot{\psi} i + \ddot{\psi} k$$

$$\therefore \dot{\omega} = (\ddot{\phi} - \dot{\theta}\dot{\psi}) i + (\ddot{\theta} + \dot{\theta}\dot{\psi}) j + (\ddot{\psi} - \dot{\phi}\dot{\theta}) k \text{ rad/sec}^2 \qquad \text{(g)}$$

15.5 Application of the Fixed Vector Concept

In the previous section we computed the time variations of a vector A fixed in a reference xyz as seen from some other reference XYZ relative to which xyz has an arbitrary motion. Now consider a rigid body (Fig. 15.10) having an arbitrary motion which is expressed as some translational velocity $\dot{R}$ plus a rotational velocity ω relative to reference XYZ in accordance with Chasle's theorem. A displacement vector ρ_{ab} connecting two points a and b in the body has been shown. If a reference xyz were attached to move with the rigid body, we could say that ρ_{ab} is a vector fixed in reference xyz. However, there is no need to bring such a reference into the discussion here except to clearly establish the identity of ρ_{ab} as a special case of the vector A of the previous section. Also, since only one reference will be in use here we can freely use dots alone to indicate time derivatives with no danger of ambiguity. Thus we have:

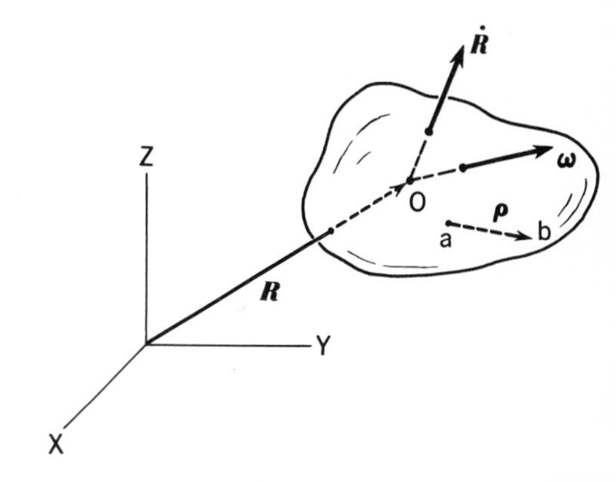

Fig. 15.10

$$\dot{\rho}_{ab} = \omega \times \rho_{ab} \qquad \text{(a)}$$

$$\ddot{\rho}_{ab} = \omega \times (\omega \times \rho_{ab}) + \dot{\omega} \times \rho_{ab} \qquad \text{(b)} \qquad \mathbf{15.4}$$

We will now reiterate certain conclusions reached earlier in Section 11.8 in order to better understand the physical interpretation of the vector $\dot{\rho}_{ab}$. Thus, consider two points O and P moving in space as shown in Fig. 15.11. A displacement vector ρ connects these points. We have shown two references—reference XYZ as well as a reference $\xi\eta\zeta$ attached to point O and translating with respect to reference XYZ. In

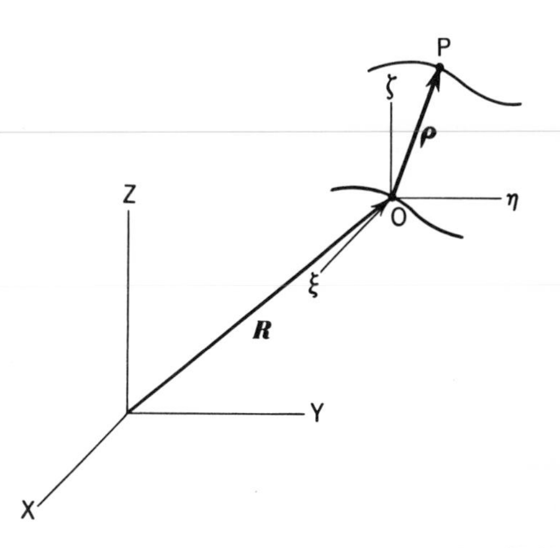

Fig. 15.11

* Note that b must always remain at right angles to the Z axis.

Section 11.8 we have shown that $d\boldsymbol{\rho}/dt$ has the same value as seen from either reference $\xi\eta\zeta$ or XYZ (as for that matter for *any* reference translating with respect to XYZ). By observing from $\xi\eta\zeta$ we can most easily visualize the fact that $\dot{\boldsymbol{\rho}}$ is the velocity of point P relative to reference $\xi\eta\zeta$ and hence relative to point O. In a broader sense we can say that $\dot{\boldsymbol{\rho}}$ *is the velocity of point P relative to point O as seen from reference XYZ* (or any other reference translating with respect to XYZ). Returning to the rigid body and $\boldsymbol{\rho}_{ab}$ we conclude that $\dot{\boldsymbol{\rho}}_{ab}$ is the relative velocity between points b and a of a rigid body. Furthermore, in accordance with Eq. 15.4 $\dot{\boldsymbol{\rho}}_{ab}$ does not depend on the line of action of $\boldsymbol{\omega}$. That is, *the relative velocity between two points of a rigid body does not depend on the line of action of the axis of rotation.*

It was strongly emphasized in Section 11.8 furthermore that the relative velocity between two particles as seen from a reference is actually the *difference* between the respective velocities of these points as seen from this reference. Thus, we can say:

$$\dot{\boldsymbol{\rho}}_{ab} = \boldsymbol{V}_b - \boldsymbol{V}_a \qquad \textbf{15.5}$$

Hence employing Eq. 15.4(a) we can form the following useful formula:

$$\boxed{\boldsymbol{V}_b = \boldsymbol{V}_a + \boldsymbol{\omega} \times \boldsymbol{\rho}_{ab}} \qquad \textbf{15.6}$$

This states that the velocity of particle b of a rigid body as seen from XYZ equals the velocity of any other particle a of this body as seen from XYZ plus the velocity of particle b relative to particle a.

Differentiating Eq. 15.6 again, we can get a relation involving the acceleration vectors of two points on a rigid body:

$$\boxed{\boldsymbol{a}_b = \boldsymbol{a}_a + \boldsymbol{\omega} \times (\boldsymbol{\omega} \times \boldsymbol{\rho}_{ab}) + \dot{\boldsymbol{\omega}} \times \boldsymbol{\rho}_{ab}} \qquad \textbf{15.7}$$

We have thus formulated relations between *the motions of two points of a rigid body as seen from a single reference.* Such relations can be very useful in the study of machine elements; we shall illustrate this in the following examples as well as in the homework problems.

EXAMPLE 15.4

Shown in Fig. 15.12 is a rigid body moving at time t such that the velocity of point a is zero. Displaced from point a is point b such that:

$$\boldsymbol{\rho}_{ab} = 5\boldsymbol{i} - 2\boldsymbol{j} + 10\boldsymbol{k} \text{ ft} \qquad \textbf{(a)}$$

The velocity of point b is known at this instant to be:

$$\boldsymbol{V}_b = -2\boldsymbol{i} - 5\boldsymbol{j} \text{ ft/sec} \qquad \textbf{(b)}$$

(Note that $\boldsymbol{V}_b \cdot \boldsymbol{\rho}_{ab} = 0$. Why must this be so?) What is the angular velocity of the body and what is the *actual* instantaneous axis of rotation?

We may apply Eq. 15.6 directly. Thus:

$$-2\boldsymbol{i} - 5\boldsymbol{j} + 8\boldsymbol{k} = \boldsymbol{0} + \boldsymbol{\omega} \times (5\boldsymbol{i} - 2\boldsymbol{j} + 10\boldsymbol{k}) \quad \textbf{(c)}$$

The resulting scalar equations are:

$$\begin{aligned} -2 &= 10\omega_y + 2\omega_z \\ -5 &= 5\omega_z - 10\omega_x \\ 0 &= -2\omega_x - 5\omega_y \end{aligned} \quad \textbf{(d)}$$

If we attempt to solve for the angular velocity components we get indeterminate results. Thus if we use Cramer's rule, we get for each unknown the indeterminate form 0/0, as you should yourself demonstrate. Clearly the equations are not all independent of each other. Physically what this means is that we have not supplied enough information to reach a definite answer. Specifically, it is easily seen that the component of $\boldsymbol{\omega}$ along the direction of $\boldsymbol{\rho}_{ab}$ will have no effect on the quantity $\boldsymbol{V}_b - \boldsymbol{V}_a$. That is, an infinite number of $\boldsymbol{\omega}$'s will give the proper difference in velocity of particles a and b specified in the problem. These $\boldsymbol{\omega}$'s will all have the *same* vector component *normal* to $\hat{\boldsymbol{\rho}}_{ab}$ but they may have any component whatever collinear with $\hat{\boldsymbol{\rho}}_{ab}$. Additional information must be specified as to the value of $\boldsymbol{\omega}$ along $\hat{\boldsymbol{\rho}}_{ab}$ before we can reach a determinate result. Let us say here that $\boldsymbol{\omega}_{ab} = \boldsymbol{0}$. That is:

$$\boldsymbol{\omega} \cdot \boldsymbol{\rho}_{ab} = 0 \quad \textbf{(e)}$$

Substituting from Eq. (a), we thus have an additional equation for the unknown components:

$$5\omega_x - 2\omega_y + 10\omega_z = 0 \quad \textbf{(f)}$$

Now, solving Eq. (f) simultaneously with any two of Eqs. (d), we get the desired result:

$$\boldsymbol{\omega} = 0.388\boldsymbol{i} - 0.1550\boldsymbol{j} - 0.225\boldsymbol{k} \quad \textbf{(g)}$$

The actual instantaneous axis of rotation must have a direction which is the same as the angular velocity vector $\boldsymbol{\omega}$ and, because point a is stationary at time t, the line of action of this axis must go through point a.

(If you were asked in a problem only to determine the component of $\boldsymbol{\omega}$ normal to $\boldsymbol{\rho}_{ab}$, how would you proceed?)

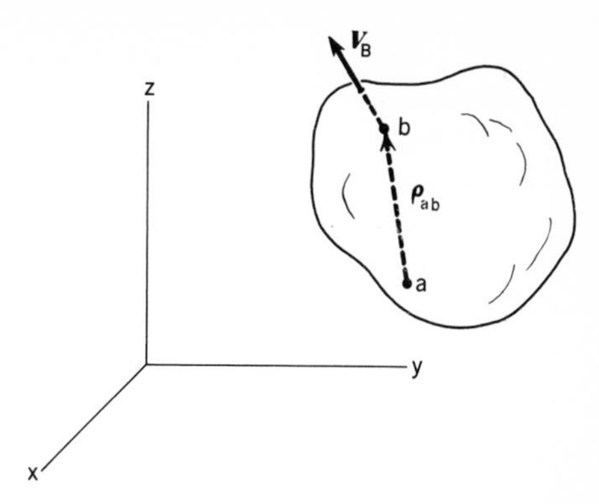

Fig. 15.12

EXAMPLE 15.5

A wheel of diameter 2 ft rolls without slipping so that the hub moves with a velocity of 50 ft/sec (Fig. 15.13). Compute the angular velocity of the wheel.

We have already examined a similar problem at the end of the previous chapter, making use at that time of our earlier work in physics. We shall now reexamine this problem to illustrate the use of Eq. 15.6 for a simple plane motion problem.

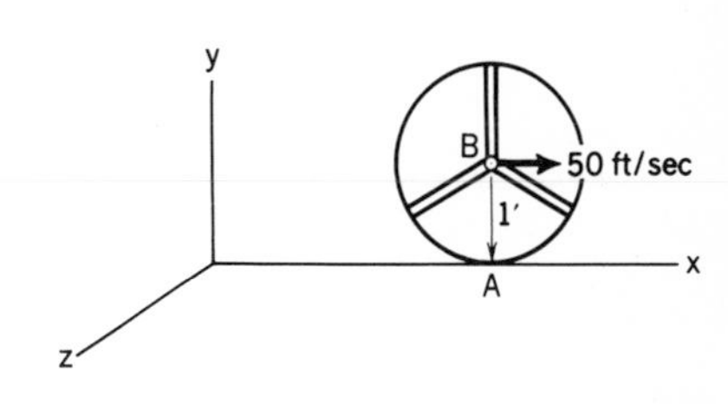

Fig. 15.13

First, note that we know the velocity of two points of the body. Thus we have:

$$\boldsymbol{V}_A = \boldsymbol{0} \qquad \textbf{(a)}$$

$$\boldsymbol{V}_B = 50\boldsymbol{i} \qquad \textbf{(b)}$$

Result (a) clearly stems from the no-slipping condition. Furthermore, because we have plane motion, we know that the direction of $\boldsymbol{\omega}$ for the body must be normal to the plane. Consequently, we can get all that we need from Eq. 15.6:

$$\boldsymbol{V}_B = \boldsymbol{V}_A + \boldsymbol{\omega} \times \boldsymbol{\rho}_{AB} \qquad \textbf{(c)}$$

Substituting, we get:

$$50\boldsymbol{i} = \boldsymbol{0} + (\dot{\phi}\boldsymbol{k}) \times \boldsymbol{j} = -\dot{\phi}\boldsymbol{i} \qquad \textbf{(d)}$$

Clearly the angular speed must be 50 rad/sec in the clockwise direction.

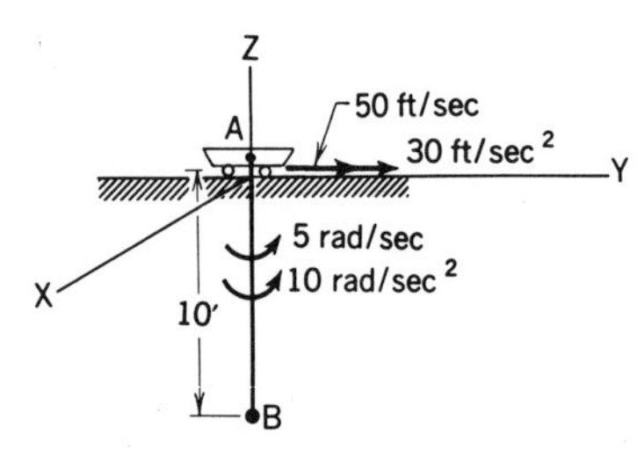

Fig. 15.14

EXAMPLE 15.6

A support moves along a straight line at a speed of 50 ft/sec and is accelerating at 30 ft/sec² along this line (Fig. 15.14). A rod AB extends from the support and is undergoing an angular rotation of 5 rad/sec relative to the ground and an acceleration of 10 rad/sec² relative to the ground, both in the plane of the page. At the instant of interest, the rod is vertical. Determine the velocity and acceleration of the particle at B relative to the ground reference XYZ shown in the diagram.

Here we have a rigid body AB moving so that the velocity and acceleration of one point, A, of the body are known, as are the angular velocity and angular acceleration of the body. Thus we can say:

$$\boldsymbol{V}_B = \boldsymbol{V}_A + \boldsymbol{\omega} \times \boldsymbol{\rho}_{AB} = 50\boldsymbol{j} + 5\boldsymbol{i} \times (-10\boldsymbol{k})$$
$$= 50\boldsymbol{j} + 50\boldsymbol{j} = 100\boldsymbol{j} \text{ ft/sec}$$

Also:

$$\boldsymbol{a}_B = \dot{\boldsymbol{V}}_A + \dot{\boldsymbol{\omega}} \times \boldsymbol{\rho}_{AB} + \boldsymbol{\omega} \times (\boldsymbol{\omega} \times \boldsymbol{\rho}_{AB})$$
$$= 30\boldsymbol{j} + 10\boldsymbol{i} \times (-10\boldsymbol{k}) + 5\boldsymbol{i} \times [5\boldsymbol{i} \times (-10\boldsymbol{k})]$$
$$= 30\boldsymbol{j} + 100\boldsymbol{j} + 250\boldsymbol{k} = 130\boldsymbol{j} + 250\boldsymbol{k} \text{ ft/sec}^2$$

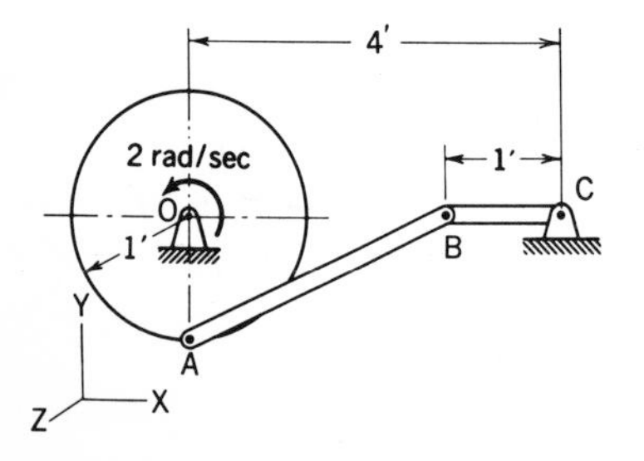

Fig. 15.15

EXAMPLE 15.7

In the device in Fig. 15.15, find the velocity of point B and the angular velocities and angular accelerations of both bars.

We shall first solve for the velocity at pin B. It is clear that the direction of this velocity from pure rotation about C must be in the positive Y direction at this instant. Thus:

$$\boldsymbol{V}_B = V_B\boldsymbol{j} \qquad \textbf{(a)}$$

It is also clear on inspection that:

$$V_A = 2i \quad \textbf{(b)}$$

(More formally we could arrive at this by noting that $V_A = V_O + 2k \times (-j) = 0 + 2i$.)

As for the angular velocity of the bar AB, it is immediately apparent that, because we have plane motion in the XY plane, the angular velocity vector ω_{AB} must be oriented in the Z direction. Employing Eqs. (a) and (b), we can next determine both V_B and ω_{AB} as follows:

$$V_B = V_A + \omega_{AB} \times \rho_{AB}$$

$$\therefore\ V_B j = 2i + (\omega_{AB} k) \times (3i + j) \quad \textbf{(c)}$$

The scalar equations are:

$$V_B = 3\omega_{AB}$$

$$0 = 2 - \omega_{AB}$$

We therefore have:

$$\omega_{AB} = 2 \text{ rad/sec}, \qquad V_B = 6 \text{ ft/sec} \quad \textbf{(d)}$$

It is now a simple matter to find ω_{BC}. Thus:

$$\omega_{BC} = -\frac{V_B}{\rho_{BC}} = -6 \text{ rad/sec} \quad \textbf{(e)}$$

Let us turn next to the angular acceleration of the bars. Using kinematics of circular motion, we can compute the acceleration of point A immediately. Thus:

$$a_A = (r\omega^2) j = 4j \quad \textbf{(f)}$$

As for point B, we can say similarly:

$$a_B = \rho_{BC}\omega_{BC}^2 i - \rho_{BC}\dot{\omega}_{BC} j$$

$$\therefore\ a_B = 36i - \dot{\omega}_{BC} j \quad \textbf{(g)}$$

Considering bar AB, we can state:

$$a_B = a_A + \omega_{AB} \times (\omega_{AB} \times \rho_{AB}) + \dot{\omega}_{AB} \times \rho_{ab} \quad \textbf{(h)}$$

Substituting previously computed values for the terms in the equation, we get:

$$36i - \dot{\omega}_{BC} j = 4j + 2k \times [(2k) \times (3i + j)] + (\dot{\omega}_{AB} k) \times (3i + j)$$

Evaluating the terms, we get:

$$36i - \dot{\omega}_{BC} j = 4j - 12i - 4j + 3\dot{\omega}_{AB} j - \dot{\omega}_{AB} i \quad \textbf{(i)}$$

The scalar equations are:

$$\dot{\omega}_{AB} = -48$$

$$-\dot{\omega}_{BC} - 3\dot{\omega}_{AB} = 0$$

We thus have the results:

$$\dot{\omega}_{AB} = -48 \text{ rad/sec}^2$$

$$\dot{\omega}_{BC} = 144 \text{ rad/sec}^2 \quad \textbf{(j)}$$

EXAMPLE 15.8

In the preceding example find the instantaneous axis of rotation for the rod AB.

The intersection of the instantaneous axis of rotation with the xy plane will be a point E in a hypothetical rigid-body extension of bar AB having zero velocity at the instant of interest. We can accordingly say:

$$\boldsymbol{V}_E = \boldsymbol{V}_A + \boldsymbol{\omega}_{AB} \times \boldsymbol{\varrho}_{AE}$$

$$\therefore \mathbf{0} = 2\boldsymbol{i} + (2\boldsymbol{k}) \times (\Delta x \boldsymbol{i} + \Delta y \boldsymbol{j}) \qquad \textbf{(a)}$$

where Δx and Δy are the components of the displacement from point A to the center of rotation. The scalar equations are:

$$0 = 2 - 2\,\Delta y$$

$$0 = 2\,\Delta x$$

Clearly $\Delta y = 1$ and $\Delta x = 0$. Thus the center of rotation is point O.

We could have easily deduced this by inspection in this case. The velocity of each point of bar AB must be at right angles to a line from the center of rotation to the point. The velocity of point A is in the horizontal direction and the velocity of point B is in the vertical direction. Clearly point O is the only point from which lines to points A and B are normal to the velocities at these points.

***EXAMPLE 15.9**

Shown in Fig. 15.16 is a wheel E rotating at a constant angular speed of 5 rad/sec. A bar CD is held by the wheel at D by a ball-joint connection and is guided along AB by a slider at C having a second ball-joint connection as is shown in the diagram. Compute the velocity of C and the component of the angular velocity of the bar CD normal to the centerline of CD.

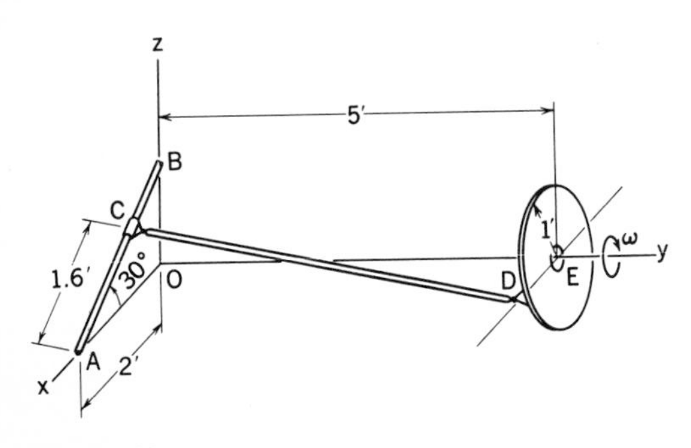

Fig. 15.16

We shall need the displacement vector $\boldsymbol{\varrho}_{DC}$. Thus:

$$\boldsymbol{\varrho}_{DC} = \boldsymbol{r}_C - \boldsymbol{r}_D$$

$$= \{[2 - 1.6\,(\cos 30°)]\boldsymbol{i} + 1.6\,(\sin 30°)\boldsymbol{k}\}$$

$$- \{5\boldsymbol{j} + \boldsymbol{i}\}$$

$$\boldsymbol{\varrho}_{DC} = -0.385\boldsymbol{i} - 5.00\boldsymbol{j} + 0.800\boldsymbol{k} \text{ ft} \qquad \textbf{(a)}$$

Furthermore, we see by inspection that the velocity of point D is:

$$\boldsymbol{V}_D = 5\boldsymbol{k} \text{ ft/sec} \qquad \textbf{(b)}$$

We now employ Eq. 15.6 for the rod CD as follows:

$$\boldsymbol{V}_C = 5\boldsymbol{k} + \boldsymbol{\omega}_{DC} \times (-0.385\boldsymbol{i} - 5.00\boldsymbol{j} + 0.800\boldsymbol{k}) \qquad \textbf{(c)}$$

Noting that:

$$V_C = V_C(-0.866\boldsymbol{i} + 0.500\boldsymbol{k}) \qquad \textbf{(d)}$$

and putting $\boldsymbol{\omega}_{DC}$ in terms of rectangular components we get, on dropping the DC subscript for simplicity:

$$\begin{aligned} -0.866V_C\boldsymbol{i} + 0.500V_C\boldsymbol{k} = 5\boldsymbol{k} &+ (5\omega_z + 0.800\omega_y)\boldsymbol{i} \\ &+ (-0.800\omega_x - 0.385\omega_z)\boldsymbol{j} \\ &+ (0.385\omega_y - 5.00\omega_x)\boldsymbol{k} \qquad \textbf{(e)} \end{aligned}$$

The scalar equations are:

$$-0.866V_C = 5\omega_z + 0.800\omega_y \qquad \textbf{(f)}$$

$$0.800\omega_x = -0.385\omega_z \qquad \textbf{(g)}$$

$$0.500V_C = 5 + 0.385\omega_y - 5.00\omega_x \qquad \textbf{(h)}$$

We have here four unknowns involved in only three equations. It should be clear that the component of $\boldsymbol{\omega}_{DC}$ along the line CD does not affect the velocities of points C and D, as was pointed out in Example 15.4. And, accordingly, because $\boldsymbol{\omega}_{DC}$ is involved in Eq. (c) only as a cross product with $\boldsymbol{\rho}_{DC}$, this component is left undetermined. To insure that ω_x, ω_y, and ω_z in Eqs. (f), (g), and (h) represent only the components of $\boldsymbol{\omega}_{DC}$ *perpendicular* to the centerline DC, we need only impose the condition (as we did in Example 15.4) that the component of $\boldsymbol{\omega}_{DC}$ along $\boldsymbol{\rho}_{DC}$ be zero. That is:

$$\boldsymbol{\omega}_{DC} \cdot \hat{\boldsymbol{\rho}}_{DC} = 0$$

This becomes:

$$-0.385\omega_x - 5\omega_y + 0.800\omega_z = 0 \qquad \textbf{(i)}$$

Equation (i) gives the fourth equation to be solved simultaneously with Eqs. (f), (g), and (h). The results for this example can then be given as:

$$V_C = -4.68\boldsymbol{i} + 2.67\boldsymbol{k} \qquad \textbf{(j)}$$

$$(\boldsymbol{\omega}_{CD})_\perp = 0.441\boldsymbol{i} - 0.178\boldsymbol{j} - 0.905\boldsymbol{k} \qquad \textbf{(k)}$$

---

*EXAMPLE 15.10

Do the previous example for the case where at C there is a pin connection (see Fig. 15.17) rather than a ball-joint connection.

In the previous example the angular motion of the connecting rod CD was indeterminate, and we deliberately set the component of $\boldsymbol{\omega}_{CD}$ along CD equal to zero to get the angular motion of the centerline itself. In this example the pin connection puts a constraint on the motion of rod, the mathematical expression of which permits the complete determination of the angular velocity of the rod CD. To facilitate this, we have established a system of orthogonal vectors in the diagram. Unit vector $\boldsymbol{s}$ is collinear with bar AB. Clearly CD can have an angular velocity component along direction $\boldsymbol{s}$ by virtue of the slider at C and the ball joint at D. A second unit vector $\boldsymbol{n}_2$ is established normal to the plane ADC (shown crosshatched). Again

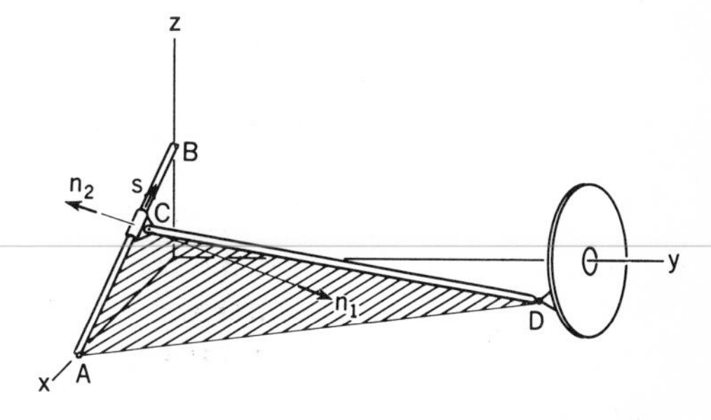

Fig. 15.17

CD can have an angular velocity component in this direction by virtue of the pin connection at C and the ball joint at D. Finally we have the third unit vector $\boldsymbol{n}_1$, which must be in plane ADC and be normal to AB. Along this direction the connection at C precludes the possibility of an angular velocity component. Accordingly, we have as the constraint requirement:

$$\boldsymbol{\omega}_{DC} \cdot \boldsymbol{n}_1 = 0 \tag{a}$$

We must next establish the unit vector $\boldsymbol{n}_1$. To do this we shall first establish vectors $\boldsymbol{s}$ and $\boldsymbol{n}_2$. We can then form $\boldsymbol{n}_1$ as follows:

$$\boldsymbol{n}_1 = \boldsymbol{s} \times \boldsymbol{n}_2 \tag{b}$$

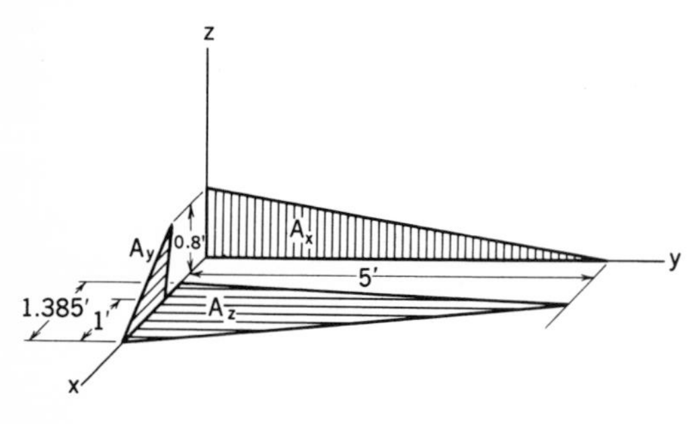

Fig. 15.18

The vector $\boldsymbol{n}_2$ is normal to area ACD. For this reason we have shown the projection of this area onto the coordinate planes in Fig. 15.18. We can then say for $\boldsymbol{n}_2$:

$$\boldsymbol{n}_2 = \frac{A_x}{ADC}\boldsymbol{i} + \frac{A_y}{ADC}\boldsymbol{j} + \frac{A_z}{ADC}\boldsymbol{k} \tag{c}$$

Noting that:

$$A_x = \tfrac{1}{2}(5)(0.8) = 2.0 \text{ ft}^2$$
$$A_y = \tfrac{1}{2}(1)(0.8) = 0.4 \text{ ft}^2$$
$$A_z = \tfrac{1}{2}(1.385)(5) = 3.46 \text{ ft}^2$$
$$ABC = \sqrt{2^2 + 0.4^2 + 3.46^2} = 4.01 \text{ ft}^2$$

we get for $\boldsymbol{n}_2$:

$$\boldsymbol{n}_2 = 0.498\boldsymbol{i} + 0.0996\boldsymbol{j} + 0.862\boldsymbol{k} \tag{d}$$

Now, returning to Eq. (b), it is an easy matter to establish $\boldsymbol{n}_1$. Equation (a) is easily set forth in terms of the three unknowns ω_x, ω_y, and ω_z. It should be clear that Eqs. (f), (g), and (h) of the previous example still apply, and so we have four equations for the four unknowns V_C, ω_x, ω_y, and ω_z. We leave the details of carrying out these computations to the student.

15.6 General Relationship Between Derivatives of a Vector for Different References

In Section 15.4 we considered the time derivatives of a vector $\boldsymbol{A}$ "fixed" in a reference xyz moving arbitrarily relative to XYZ. Our conclusions were:

$$\left(\frac{d\boldsymbol{A}}{dt}\right)_{xyz} = \boldsymbol{0}$$

$$\left(\frac{d\boldsymbol{A}}{dt}\right)_{XYZ} = \boldsymbol{\omega} \times \boldsymbol{A}$$

We now wish to extend these considerations to include time derivatives of a vector $\boldsymbol{A}$ which is not necessarily fixed in reference xyz. Primarily, it will be our intention in this section to relate time derivatives of such vectors $\boldsymbol{A}$ as seen both from reference xyz and from reference XYZ, two references moving arbitrarily relative to each other.

For this purpose consider Fig. 15.19, where a particle P is shown moving along a trajectory C. Such a situation might be simulated by a body that is represented by the particle P moving in a known manner relative to the interior of an airplane, represented by the moving reference xyz, while the airplane (i.e., xyz) has a known motion relative to the ground, XYZ, given in terms of the vectors $\dot{\boldsymbol{R}}$ and $\boldsymbol{\omega}$. We shall now formulate a relation between the derivatives $d\boldsymbol{\rho}/dt$ as observed from both references and we can then consider the results applicable to any vector $\boldsymbol{A}$. To reach the desired results effectively, it will be helpful to express the vector $\boldsymbol{\rho}$ in terms of components parallel to the xyz reference. Thus:

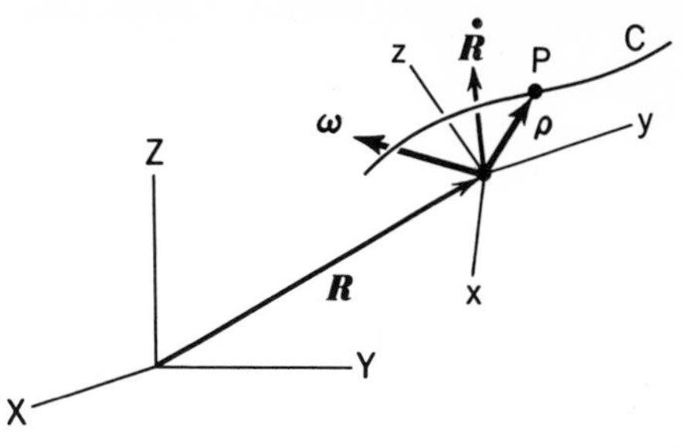

Fig. 15.19

$$\boldsymbol{\rho} = x\boldsymbol{i} + y\boldsymbol{j} + z\boldsymbol{k} \tag{15.8}$$

where $\boldsymbol{i}$, $\boldsymbol{j}$, and $\boldsymbol{k}$ are unit vectors for reference xyz. Differentiating the above form with respect to time for the xyz reference, we have:

$$\left(\frac{d\boldsymbol{\rho}}{dt}\right)_{xyz} = \dot{x}\boldsymbol{i} + \dot{y}\boldsymbol{j} + \dot{z}\boldsymbol{k} \tag{15.9}$$

If we next take the derivative of $\boldsymbol{\rho}$ with respect to time for the XYZ reference, we must remember that $\boldsymbol{i}$, $\boldsymbol{j}$, and $\boldsymbol{k}$ of Eq. 15.8 generally will each be a function of time, since these vectors will generally have some rotational motion relative to the XYZ reference. Thus, using dots for the time derivatives:*

$$\left(\frac{d\boldsymbol{\rho}}{dt}\right)_{XYZ} = (\dot{x}\boldsymbol{i} + \dot{y}\boldsymbol{j} + \dot{z}\boldsymbol{k}) + (x\dot{\boldsymbol{i}} + y\dot{\boldsymbol{j}} + z\dot{\boldsymbol{k}}) \tag{15.10}$$

The unit vector $\boldsymbol{i}$ is a vector fixed in reference xyz and accordingly $\dot{\boldsymbol{i}}$ equals $\boldsymbol{\omega} \times \boldsymbol{i}$. The same conclusions apply to $\boldsymbol{j}$ and $\boldsymbol{k}$. The last expression in parentheses can then be stated as:

$$\begin{aligned} x\dot{\boldsymbol{i}} + y\dot{\boldsymbol{j}} + z\dot{\boldsymbol{k}} &= x(\boldsymbol{\omega} \times \boldsymbol{i}) + y(\boldsymbol{\omega} \times \boldsymbol{j}) + z(\boldsymbol{\omega} \times \boldsymbol{k}) \\ &= \boldsymbol{\omega} \times (x\boldsymbol{i}) + \boldsymbol{\omega} \times (y\boldsymbol{j}) + \boldsymbol{\omega} \times (z\boldsymbol{k}) \\ &= \boldsymbol{\omega} \times (x\boldsymbol{i} + y\boldsymbol{j} + z\boldsymbol{k}) = \boldsymbol{\omega} \times \boldsymbol{\rho} \end{aligned} \tag{15.11}$$

In Eq. 15.10, we can replace $(\dot{x}\boldsymbol{i} + \dot{y}\boldsymbol{j} + \dot{z}\boldsymbol{k})$ by $(d\boldsymbol{\rho}/dt)_{xyz}$, according to Eq. 15.9, and $(x\dot{\boldsymbol{i}} + y\dot{\boldsymbol{j}} + z\dot{\boldsymbol{k}})$ by $\boldsymbol{\omega} \times \boldsymbol{\rho}$, according to Eq. 15.11. Hence:

$$\left(\frac{d\boldsymbol{\rho}}{dt}\right)_{XYZ} = \left(\frac{d\boldsymbol{\rho}}{dt}\right)_{xyz} + \boldsymbol{\omega} \times \boldsymbol{\rho} \tag{15.12}$$

We can generalize the preceding result for any vector $\boldsymbol{A}$:

* The quantities x, y, and z in Eq. 15.8 are scalar quantities and, despite the fact that they are associated with coordinate axes, their time derivatives are not dependent on references of observation. Think of the time rate of change of the scalar quantity temperature measured at some position in space. Most certainly this time derivative does not relate specifically to spatial references of observation. The temperature and its time rate of change are the same to any and all viewers (assuming no relativistic effects).

$$\left(\frac{dA}{dt}\right)_{XYZ} = \left(\frac{dA}{dt}\right)_{xyz} + \boldsymbol{\omega} \times \boldsymbol{A} \qquad 15.13$$

where, you must remember, $\boldsymbol{\omega}$ is the angular velocity of the xyz reference relative to the XYZ reference. Note that Eq. 15.1 is a special case of the above equation since for $\boldsymbol{A}$ fixed in xyz, $(d\boldsymbol{A}/dt)_{xyz} = \mathbf{0}$. We shall have much use for this relationship in the succeeding sections.

15.7 The Relationship Between Velocities of A Particle for Different References

We will now define the velocity of a particle again in the presence of several references:

> *The velocity of a particle relative to a reference is the derivative as seen from the reference of the position vector of the particle in the reference.*

In Fig. 15.20, the velocities of the particle P relative to the XYZ and the xyz references are, respectively:*

$$\boldsymbol{V}_{XYZ} = \left(\frac{d\boldsymbol{r}}{dt}\right)_{XYZ}, \quad \boldsymbol{V}_{xyz} = \left(\frac{d\boldsymbol{\rho}}{dt}\right)_{xyz} \qquad 15.14$$

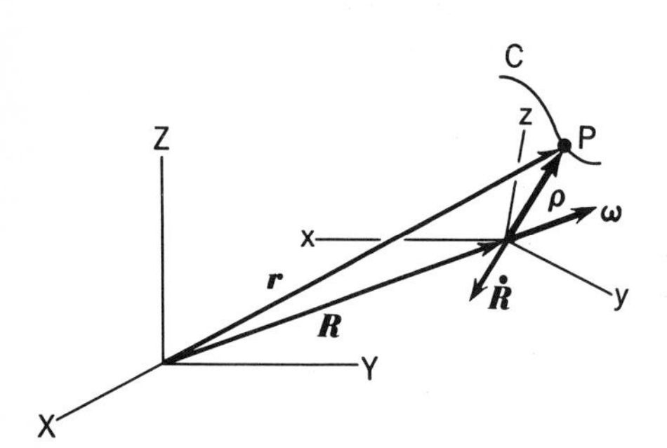

Fig. 15.20

It is to be pointed out that $(\boldsymbol{V})_{XYZ}$ may be expressed in components parallel to the xyz reference at any time t, while $(\boldsymbol{V})_{xyz}$ may be expressed in components parallel to the XYZ reference.

Now it will be of interest to relate these velocities, which we may readily do by first noting that:

$$\boldsymbol{r} = \boldsymbol{R} + \boldsymbol{\rho} \qquad 15.15$$

Differentiating with respect to time for the XYZ reference, we have:

$$\left(\frac{d\boldsymbol{r}}{dt}\right)_{XYZ} = \boldsymbol{V}_{XYZ} = \left(\frac{d\boldsymbol{R}}{dt}\right)_{XYZ} + \left(\frac{d\boldsymbol{\rho}}{dt}\right)_{XYZ} \qquad 15.16$$

The term $(d\boldsymbol{R}/dt)_{XYZ}$ is clearly the velocity of the origin of the xyz reference relative to the XYZ reference, according to our definitions, and we denote this as $\dot{\boldsymbol{R}}$. The term $(d\boldsymbol{\rho}/dt)_{XYZ}$ can be replaced, by using Eq. 15.12, in which $(d\boldsymbol{\rho}/dt)_{xyz}$ is the velocity of the particle for the xyz reference. Denoting $(d\boldsymbol{\rho}/dt)_{xyz}$ simply as $\boldsymbol{V}_{xyz}$, the above expression then becomes the desired relation:

$$\boldsymbol{V}_{XYZ} = \boldsymbol{V}_{xyz} + \dot{\boldsymbol{R}} + \boldsymbol{\omega} \times \boldsymbol{\rho} \qquad 15.17$$

We shall now show that Eq. 15.6, wherein we relate the velocities of two points a and b of a rigid body, is actually a special form of the above relation.

* Generally we have employed $\boldsymbol{r}$ as a position vector and $\boldsymbol{\rho}$ as a displacement vector. With two references involved, we will often use $\boldsymbol{\rho}$ to denote a position vector for one of the references.

To do this, imagine the references xyz embedded in the rigid body with the origin at point a as shown in Fig. 15.21. Clearly any point b of the body would have a velocity $\boldsymbol{V}_{xyz}$ equal to zero. And since the origin of xyz corresponds to point a, we can say $\dot{\boldsymbol{R}} = \boldsymbol{V}_a$. Accordingly, Eq. 15.17 becomes for this case:

$$\boldsymbol{V}_b = \boldsymbol{V}_a + \boldsymbol{\omega} \times \boldsymbol{\varrho}_{ab}$$

which is our previous result.

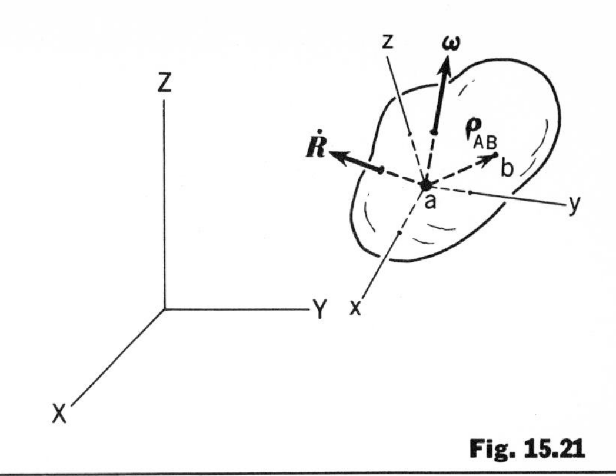

Fig. 15.21

EXAMPLE 15.11

In Fig. 15.22 a rod CB rotates in a clockwise direction at the rate $\dot{\theta}_1$ of 2 rad/sec. At A a slider rides on this rod but is also connected by a pin to a second slider moving in a circular slot having a radius of 3 ft. When $\theta_1 = 60°$, determine the velocity $\boldsymbol{V}$ of A relative to the ground. The angle θ_2 at the instant of interest is given as 30°.

We shall need the distance AB and so we have drawn a simplified diagram of the system as shown in Fig. 15.23. It is a simple matter from this diagram to deduce that $AB = 1.73$ ft. Next we attach a reference xyz to rod BC (see Fig. 15.23) so that at the instant of interest the origin of xyz coincides with the slider A. We can now employ Eq. 15.17. Observing Figs. 15.22 and 15.23, we have for the various vectors in terms of components parallel to the ground reference XYZ:

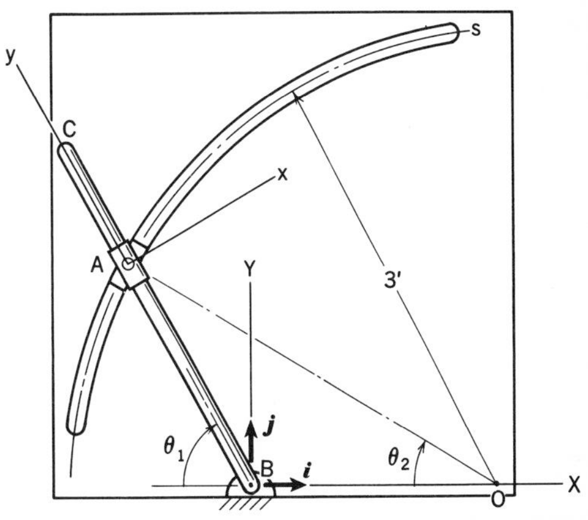

Fig. 15.22

$$\boldsymbol{V}_{XYZ} = V_{XYZ}(0.5\boldsymbol{i} + 0.866\boldsymbol{j})$$

$$\boldsymbol{V}_{xyz} = V_{xyz}(-0.5\boldsymbol{i} + 0.866\boldsymbol{j})$$

$$\boldsymbol{\varrho} = \boldsymbol{0}$$

$$\boldsymbol{\omega} = -\dot{\theta}_1\boldsymbol{k} = -2\boldsymbol{k}$$

$$\dot{\boldsymbol{R}} = (1.730\dot{\theta}_1)(0.866\boldsymbol{i} + 0.5\boldsymbol{j})$$

$$= 1.50\dot{\theta}_1\boldsymbol{i} + 0.865\dot{\theta}_1\boldsymbol{j}$$

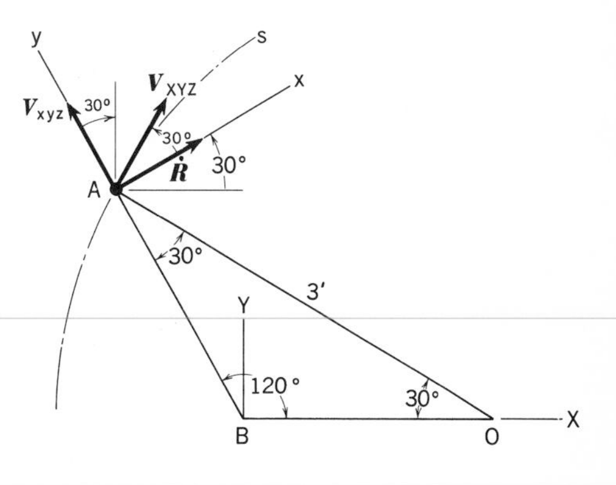

Fig. 15.23

Accordingly, we get:

$$V_{XYZ}(0.5\boldsymbol{i} + 0.866\boldsymbol{j}) = V_{xyz}(-0.5\boldsymbol{i} + 0.866\boldsymbol{j}) + (3.0\boldsymbol{i} + 1.730\boldsymbol{j}) + \boldsymbol{0} \qquad \textbf{(a)}$$

The scalar equations are:

$$0.5(V_{XYZ} + V_{xyz}) = 3 \qquad \textbf{(b)}$$

$$0.866(V_{XYZ} - V_{xyz}) = 1.730 \qquad \textbf{(c)}$$

Solving simultaneously, we get:

$$V_{XYZ} = 4 \text{ ft/sec}$$

$$V_{xyz} = 2 \text{ ft/sec} \qquad \textbf{(d)}$$

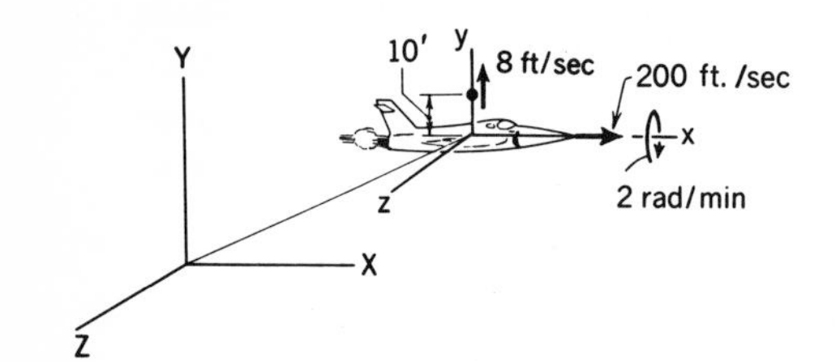

Fig. 15.24

EXAMPLE 15.12

An airplane moving at 200 ft/sec is undergoing a roll of two radians per minute (Fig. 15.24). When the plane is horizontal, an antenna is moving out at a speed of 8 ft/sec relative to the plane and is at a position of 10 ft from the centerline of the plane. Assuming that the axis of roll corresponds to the centerline, what is the velocity of the antenna end relative to the ground when the plane is horizontal?

A stationary reference on the ground has been set up as shown, while the airplane is selected as the moving reference. By choosing the x axis to coincide with the axis of rotation we can immediately establish that $\dot{\boldsymbol{R}}$ has the value $200\boldsymbol{i}$ ft/sec. For convenience we choose the y axis to coincide with the centerline of the antenna.

Let us first establish the *motion of the antenna end relative to the moving reference.* The items are:

$$\boldsymbol{\rho} = 10\boldsymbol{j} \text{ ft}$$

$$\boldsymbol{V}_{xyz} = \left(\frac{d\boldsymbol{\rho}}{dt}\right)_{xyz} = 8\boldsymbol{j} \text{ ft/sec}$$

The *motion of the moving reference relative to the ground* is:*

$$\dot{\boldsymbol{R}} = 200\boldsymbol{i} \text{ ft/sec}$$

$$\boldsymbol{\omega} = -\tfrac{1}{30}\boldsymbol{i} \text{ rad/sec}$$

By employing Eq. 15.17 we thus get the desired result:

$$\boldsymbol{V}_{XYZ} = 200\boldsymbol{i} + 8\boldsymbol{j} - \tfrac{1}{3}\boldsymbol{k} \text{ ft/sec}$$

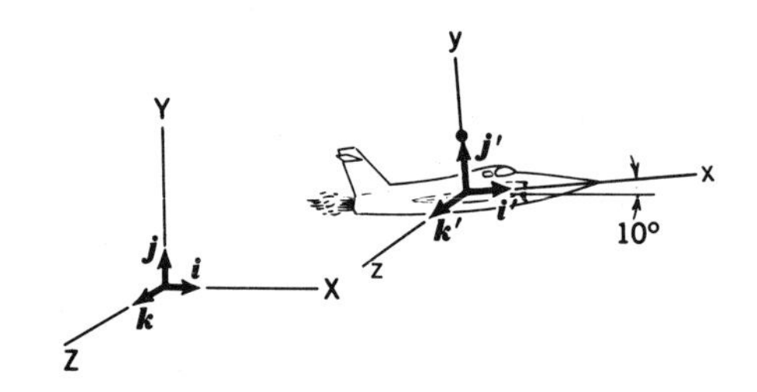

Fig. 15.25

EXAMPLE 15.13

In the preceding problem, assume the plane is climbing at a 10° angle at the instant that the other data are presented, as is illustrated in Fig. 15.25. The vectors used for the *motion of the particle relative to the xyz reference* will be expressed in components parallel to the XYZ reference in the following manner:

$$\boldsymbol{\rho} = 10\boldsymbol{j}' = -10 \sin 10°\boldsymbol{i} + 10 \cos 10°\boldsymbol{j}$$

$$\boldsymbol{V}_{xyz} = 8\boldsymbol{j}' = +8 \sin 10°\boldsymbol{i} + 8 \cos 10°\boldsymbol{j}$$

The *translation and rotation vectors of the new reference* are:

$$\dot{\boldsymbol{R}} = 200 \cos 10°\boldsymbol{i} + 200 \sin 10°\boldsymbol{j}$$

$$\boldsymbol{\omega} = -\tfrac{1}{30} \cos 10°\boldsymbol{i} - \tfrac{1}{30} \sin 10°\boldsymbol{j}$$

The result can then be found directly from Eq. 15.17. Thus:

* Note that since the corresponding axes of the references are parallel to each other at the instant of interest, the unit vectors $\boldsymbol{i}, \boldsymbol{j}$, and $\boldsymbol{k}$ apply to either reference at the instant of interest.

$$V_{XYZ} = -8 \sin 10°\boldsymbol{i} + 8 \cos 10°\boldsymbol{j} + 200 \cos 10°\boldsymbol{i} + 200 \sin 10°\boldsymbol{j} - (\tfrac{1}{30} \cos 10°\boldsymbol{i} + \tfrac{1}{30} \sin 10°\boldsymbol{j}) \times (-10 \sin 10°\boldsymbol{i} + 10 \cos 10°\boldsymbol{j})$$

$$V_{XYZ} = (200 \cos 10° - 8 \sin 10°)\boldsymbol{i} + (200 \sin 10° + 8 \cos 10°)\boldsymbol{j} - \tfrac{1}{3}\boldsymbol{k}$$

We can also carry out the problem, using components for the vectors parallel to the xyz reference. *The motion of the particle relative to xyz is given in terms of*:

$$\boldsymbol{\varrho} = 10\boldsymbol{j}', \qquad V_{xyz} = 8\boldsymbol{i}'$$

The motion of xyz relative to XYZ becomes:

$$\dot{\boldsymbol{R}} = 200\boldsymbol{i}', \qquad \boldsymbol{\omega} = -\tfrac{1}{30}\boldsymbol{i}'$$

The result is:

$$V_{XYZ} = 200\boldsymbol{i}' + 8\boldsymbol{j}' - \tfrac{1}{3}\boldsymbol{k}'$$

It will be left for you to show that this is the same vector that we developed earlier, which indicates that it makes no difference what components we want to work with as far as the final result is concerned.

EXAMPLE 15.14

In an *impulse turbine*, high-speed gas is directed toward blades extending radially out from a turbine wheel as shown in Fig. 15.26, which is a highly idealized diagram viewing the turbine from a direction normal to the axis of rotation of the turbine wheel. A few blades are shown on edge and a blade entrance angle θ is indicated. The gas expanding to supersonic speeds in the nozzle impinges on the blades and causes a force to be developed which maintains the rotation of the turbine wheel. For the efficient operation of an impulse turbine the blade entrance angle θ must be made equal to the direction of the fluid velocity relative to the blades. The blades have a speed relative to the ground of 300 feet per second, while the speed of the fluid is 2000 feet per second relative to the ground at a direction of 20° as shown. What must θ be?

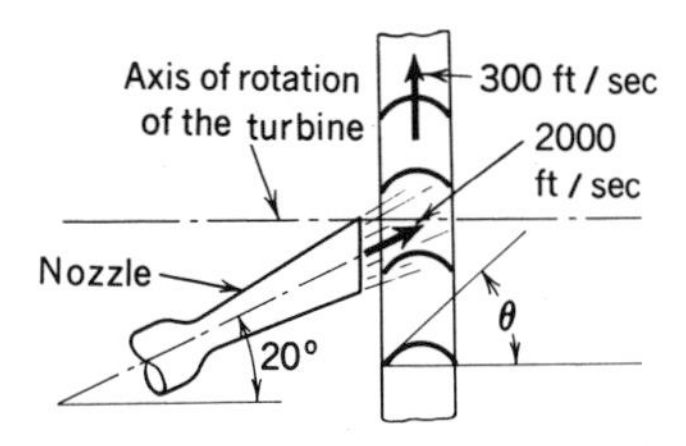

Fig. 15.26

Here we may establish two references. One we will fix to the nozzle, since we know the velocity of the fluid relative to this reference. The second reference will be established so as to translate with the blades in the plane of the page (Fig. 15.27). Note that the blades are actually rotating about the axis of the turbine shaft. However, the motion of the fluid can be considered not to be affected by this aspect of the blade motion, and so for simplicity the second reference is not completely attached to the blades. Since $\boldsymbol{\omega} = \boldsymbol{0}$ for the xyz reference relative to the XYZ reference, the velocities of fluid particles relative to the references are related as:

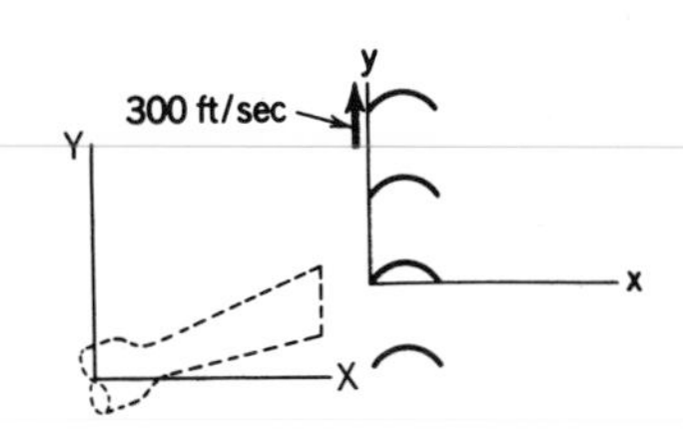

Fig. 15.27

$$V_{XYZ} = V_{xyz} + \dot{\boldsymbol{R}} \qquad \textbf{(a)}$$

Now $\dot{\boldsymbol{R}}$ is $300\boldsymbol{j}$ and the velocity of the fluid relative to the XYZ is available as:

$$V_{XYZ} = 2000 \sin 20^\circ \boldsymbol{j} + 2000 \cos 20^\circ \boldsymbol{i}$$
$$= 1880\boldsymbol{i} + 684\boldsymbol{j} \qquad \textbf{(b)}$$

The velocity relative to the xyz reference, i.e., to the moving reference, is unknown. This quantity, particularly its direction, will then give the correct angle for the blade entrance. Substituting Eq. (b) into Eq. (a), we get:

$$1880\boldsymbol{i} + 684\boldsymbol{j} = \boldsymbol{V}_{xyz} + 300\boldsymbol{j}$$
$$\boldsymbol{V}_{xyz} = 1880\boldsymbol{i} + 384\boldsymbol{j}$$

Getting θ is now a simple matter:

$$\tan \theta = \tfrac{384}{1880} = 0.205$$
$$\theta = 11.6^\circ$$

Thus for the fluid to enter smoothly into the blade system for the operating conditions specified, the entrance angle of the blading must be 11.6°.

15.8 The Acceleration of a Particle for Different References

The acceleration of a particle relative to a coordinate system is simply the time derivative as seen from the coordinate system of the velocity relative to the coordinate system. Thus, observing Fig. 15.20:

$$\boldsymbol{a}_{XYZ} = \left(\frac{d}{dt}\boldsymbol{V}_{XYZ}\right)_{XYZ} = \left(\frac{d^2\boldsymbol{r}}{dt^2}\right)_{XYZ}$$

$$\boldsymbol{a}_{xyz} = \left(\frac{d}{dt}\boldsymbol{V}_{xyz}\right)_{xyz} = \left(\frac{d^2\boldsymbol{\rho}}{dt^2}\right)_{xyz} \qquad \textbf{15.18}$$

This notation may seem cumbersome to you, but once you are familiar with it most of the subscripts can be dropped.

Let us now relate the acceleration vectors for two references moving arbitrarily relative to each other. We can accomplish this by differentiating with respect to time the terms in Eq. 15.17 for the XYZ reference. Thus:

$$\boldsymbol{a}_{XYZ} = \left(\frac{d\boldsymbol{V}_{XYZ}}{dt}\right)_{XYZ} = \left(\frac{d\boldsymbol{V}_{xyz}}{dt}\right)_{XYZ} + \ddot{\boldsymbol{R}} + \left[\frac{d}{dt}(\boldsymbol{\omega} \times \boldsymbol{\rho})\right]_{XYZ} \qquad \textbf{15.19}$$

It will be convenient to carry out the derivative of the cross product using the product rule. Thus the above equation becomes:

$$\boldsymbol{a}_{XYZ} = \left(\frac{d\boldsymbol{V}_{xyz}}{dt}\right)_{XYZ} + \ddot{\boldsymbol{R}} + \boldsymbol{\omega} \times \left(\frac{d\boldsymbol{\rho}}{dt}\right)_{XYZ} + \left(\frac{d\boldsymbol{\omega}}{dt}\right)_{XYZ} \times \boldsymbol{\rho} \qquad \textbf{15.20}$$

To introduce more meaningful terms, we can replace:

$$\left(\frac{d\boldsymbol{V}_{xyz}}{dt}\right)_{XYZ} \quad \text{and} \quad \left(\frac{d\boldsymbol{\rho}}{dt}\right)_{XYZ}$$

using Eq. 15.13 in the following way:

$$\left(\frac{d\boldsymbol{V}_{xyz}}{dt}\right)_{XYZ} = \left(\frac{d\boldsymbol{V}_{xyz}}{dt}\right)_{xyz} + \boldsymbol{\omega} \times \boldsymbol{V}_{xyz}$$

$$\left(\frac{d\boldsymbol{\varrho}}{dt}\right)_{XYZ} = \left(\frac{d\boldsymbol{\varrho}}{dt}\right)_{xyz} + \boldsymbol{\omega} \times \boldsymbol{\varrho}$$

Substituting into Eq. 15.20, we get:

$$\boldsymbol{a}_{XYZ} = \left(\frac{d\boldsymbol{V}_{xyz}}{dt}\right)_{xyz} + \ddot{\boldsymbol{R}} + \boldsymbol{\omega} \times \boldsymbol{V}_{xyz} + \boldsymbol{\omega} \times \left(\frac{d\boldsymbol{\varrho}}{dt}\right)_{xyz} + \boldsymbol{\omega} \times (\boldsymbol{\omega} \times \boldsymbol{\varrho}) + \left(\frac{d\boldsymbol{\omega}}{dt}\right)_{XYZ} \times \boldsymbol{\varrho}$$

You will note that $(d\boldsymbol{V}_{xyz}/dt)_{xyz}$ is $\boldsymbol{a}_{xyz}$; that $(d\boldsymbol{\varrho}/dt)_{xyz}$ is $\boldsymbol{V}_{xyz}$; and that $(d\boldsymbol{\omega}/dt)_{XYZ}$ is $\dot{\boldsymbol{\omega}}$. Hence, rearranging terms, we have:

$$\boldsymbol{a}_{XYZ} = \boldsymbol{a}_{xyz} + \ddot{\boldsymbol{R}} + 2\boldsymbol{\omega} \times \boldsymbol{V}_{xyz} + \dot{\boldsymbol{\omega}} \times \boldsymbol{\varrho} + \boldsymbol{\omega} \times (\boldsymbol{\omega} \times \boldsymbol{\varrho}) \qquad \textbf{15.21}$$

where $\boldsymbol{\omega}$ and $\dot{\boldsymbol{\omega}}$ are the angular velocity and acceleration, respectively, of the xyz reference relative to the XYZ reference. The vector $2(\boldsymbol{\omega} \times \boldsymbol{V}_{xyz})$ is called the *Coriolis acceleration vector*; we will examine its interesting effects in Section 15.10.

As with the case of velocity, Eq. 15.7 used for the acceleration computation of points in a rigid body is simply related to the above equation, and indeed may be considered a special case of this equation. To see this, examine Fig. 15.21 again where two points a and b of a rigid body are shown—the rigid body having an arbitrary motion relative to reference XYZ. We know from Eq. 15.7 that:

$$\boldsymbol{a}_b = \boldsymbol{a}_a + \boldsymbol{\omega} \times (\boldsymbol{\omega} \times \boldsymbol{\varrho}_{ab}) + \dot{\boldsymbol{\omega}} \times \boldsymbol{\varrho}_{ab} \qquad \textbf{15.22}$$

Now embed a reference xyz in a body with the origin at a as has been shown in the diagram. In using Eq. 15.21 for the acceleration of point b we have, as result of the rigid-body requirement, the following immediate simplifications:

$$\boldsymbol{a}_{xyz} = \boldsymbol{0} \qquad \textbf{(a)}$$

$$\boldsymbol{V}_{xyz} = \boldsymbol{0} \qquad \textbf{(b)} \quad \textbf{15.23}$$

Noting next that the acceleration of the origin of the reference as given by $\ddot{\boldsymbol{R}}$ corresponds to the acceleration of point a as given by $\boldsymbol{a}_a$, we then get Eq. 15.22 directly from the more general formulation.

Although Eq. 15.21 may seem somewhat terrifying at first, you will find that by using it, problems that would otherwise be tremendously difficult can readily be carried out in a systematic manner. *You should keep in mind in solving problems that any of the methods developed in Chapter 11 can be used for determining the motion of the particle relative to the xyz reference or for determining the motion of the origin of xyz relative to the XYZ reference.* We shall now examine several problems, in which we shall use the notation, $\boldsymbol{\omega}_1$, $\boldsymbol{\omega}_2$, etc., to denote the various angular velocities involved. The notation, $\boldsymbol{\omega}$ (i.e., without subscripts), however, will be reserved to represent the angular velocity of the xyz reference relative to the XYZ reference.

EXAMPLE 15.15

Find the acceleration of slider A of Example 15.11 for the case where $\ddot{\theta}_1 = 3$ rad/sec² at the instant of interest.

We have the following results from earlier considerations, where we employed reference xyz *fixed* to the rotating rod with the origin coinciding with the center of A at the instant of interest:

$$\begin{aligned} \boldsymbol{\rho} &= \mathbf{0} \\ \boldsymbol{\omega} &= -2\boldsymbol{k} \\ \boldsymbol{R} &= -0.865\boldsymbol{i} + 1.5\boldsymbol{j} \\ \dot{\boldsymbol{R}} &= 1.500\dot{\theta}_1\boldsymbol{i} + 0.865\dot{\theta}_1\boldsymbol{j} \\ \boldsymbol{V}_{xyz} &= 2(-0.5\boldsymbol{i} + 0.866\boldsymbol{j}) = -\boldsymbol{i} + 1.732\boldsymbol{j} \end{aligned}$$

Now consider the terms in Eq. 15.21:

$$\boldsymbol{a}_{XYZ} = \boldsymbol{a}_{xyz} + \ddot{\boldsymbol{R}} + 2\boldsymbol{\omega} \times \boldsymbol{V}_{xyz} + \dot{\boldsymbol{\omega}} \times \boldsymbol{\rho} + \boldsymbol{\omega} \times (\boldsymbol{\omega} \times \boldsymbol{\rho}) \quad \textbf{(a)}$$

Because A must move along rod AB we have

$$\boldsymbol{a}_{xyz} = a_{xyz}(0.866\boldsymbol{j} - 0.5\boldsymbol{i}) \quad \textbf{(b)}$$

A must also move along the circular path with origin at 0 and so we have using path coordinates

$$\begin{aligned} \boldsymbol{a}_{XYZ} &= \ddot{s}\boldsymbol{\varepsilon}_t + \frac{(\dot{s})^2}{\overline{AO}}\boldsymbol{\varepsilon}_n = \dot{V}_{XYZ}\,\boldsymbol{\varepsilon}_t + \frac{V_{XYZ}^2}{\overline{AO}}\boldsymbol{\varepsilon}_n \\ &= \dot{V}_{XYZ}(0.866\boldsymbol{j} + 0.5\boldsymbol{i}) \\ &\quad + \left(\frac{V_{XYZ}}{3}\right)^2(-0.5\boldsymbol{j} + 0.866\boldsymbol{i}) \\ &= (0.866\dot{V}_{XYZ} - 2.66)\boldsymbol{j} + (0.5\dot{V}_{XYZ} + 4.61)\boldsymbol{i} \end{aligned} \quad \textbf{(c)}$$

Also, since the origin of xyz executes plane circular motion in the XY plane about B we have:

$$\begin{aligned} \ddot{\boldsymbol{R}} &= (\overline{AB}\dot{\theta}_1^2)(-0.866\boldsymbol{j} + 0.5\boldsymbol{i}) \\ &\quad + (\overline{AB}\ddot{\theta}_1)(0.5\boldsymbol{j} + 0.866\boldsymbol{i}) \\ &= (1.730)(4)(-0.866\boldsymbol{j} + 0.5\boldsymbol{i}) \\ &\quad + (1.730)(3)(0.5\boldsymbol{j} + 0.866\boldsymbol{i}) \\ &= 7.9\boldsymbol{i} - 3.40\boldsymbol{j} \end{aligned} \quad \textbf{(d)}$$

Thus, noting that the last two terms in Eq. (a) will disappear because $\boldsymbol{\rho} = \mathbf{0}$, we see that only two unknowns, a_{xyz} and $\dot{V}_{XYZ}$, are present when we substitute Eqs. (b), (c), and (d) into Eq. (a). Using known data, we get:

$$\begin{aligned} &(0.866\dot{V}_{XYZ} - 2.66)\boldsymbol{j} + (0.5\dot{V}_{XYZ} + 4.61)\boldsymbol{i} \\ &= a_{xyz}(0.866\boldsymbol{j} - 0.5\boldsymbol{i}) + 7.95\boldsymbol{i} - 3.40\boldsymbol{j} + 2(-2\boldsymbol{k}) \\ &\qquad \times (-\boldsymbol{i} + 1.732\boldsymbol{j}) \end{aligned} \quad \textbf{(e)}$$

The scalar equations are:

$$\dot{V}_{XYZ} + a_{xyz} = 20.5$$
$$\dot{V}_{XYZ} - a_{xyz} = 3.76 \qquad \textbf{(f)}$$

Solving simultaneously, we get:

$$\dot{V}_{XYZ} = 12.13 \text{ ft/sec}$$
$$a_{xyz} = 8.37 \text{ ft/sec} \qquad \textbf{(g)}$$

Accordingly, we may compute $\boldsymbol{a}_{XYZ}$ using Eq. (c). Thus:

$$\boldsymbol{a}_{XYZ} = [(0.5)(12.13) + 4.61]\boldsymbol{i} + [(0.866)(12.13) - 2.66]\boldsymbol{j}$$
$$= 10.68\boldsymbol{i} + 7.84\boldsymbol{j} \text{ ft/sec}^2 \qquad \textbf{(h)}$$

Examples 15.11 and 15.15 illustrate plane motion problems. The following examples are three-dimensional problems. A more formal approach is taken in the analysis of these more complex problems, and we urge you to follow this approach in your homework problems.

EXAMPLE 15.16

Shown in Fig. 15.28 is a wheel rotating with a constant angular speed ω_1 equal to 10 rad/sec relative to a platform which in turn is rotating with a constant angular speed ω_2 equal to 5 rad/sec relative to the ground. We are to find the velocity and acceleration of a particle at b at the instant when it is directly vertically above point a.

We choose the reference xyz as fixed to the platform, while XYZ is fixed to the ground. At the instant of interest, the references coincide.

We shall proceed next in a methodical way which we urge you to follow.

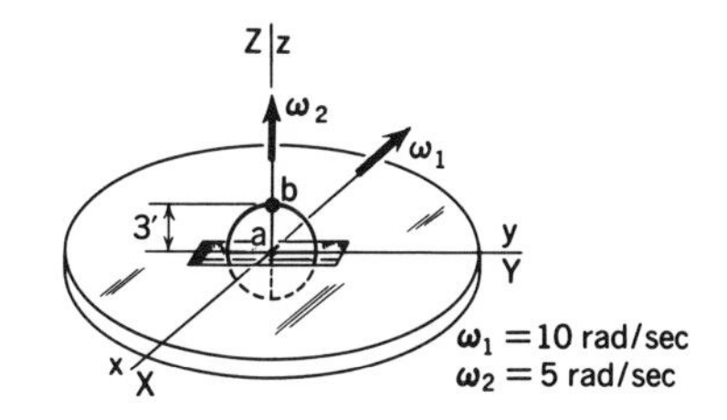

Fig. 15.28

A. *Motion of particle relative to xyz.*

$$\boldsymbol{\rho} = 3\boldsymbol{k}$$

Noting that $\boldsymbol{\rho}$ is fixed in the wheel, we have:

$$\boldsymbol{V}_{xyz} = \left(\frac{d\boldsymbol{\rho}}{dt}\right)_{xyz} = \boldsymbol{\omega}_1 \times \boldsymbol{\rho} = (-10\boldsymbol{i}) \times (3\boldsymbol{k}) = 30\boldsymbol{j}$$

Differentiating again, we get

$$\boldsymbol{a}_{xyz} = \left(\frac{d\boldsymbol{V}_{xyz}}{dt}\right)_{xyz} = \boldsymbol{\omega}_1 \times \dot{\boldsymbol{\rho}} + \dot{\boldsymbol{\omega}}_1 \times \boldsymbol{\rho}$$
$$= \boldsymbol{\omega}_1 \times \boldsymbol{V}_{xyz} + \boldsymbol{0}$$
$$= (-10\boldsymbol{i}) \times (30\boldsymbol{j}) = -300\boldsymbol{k}$$

B. *Motion of xyz relative to XYZ.*

$$\boldsymbol{R} = \boldsymbol{0}, \qquad \dot{\boldsymbol{R}} = \boldsymbol{0}, \qquad \ddot{\boldsymbol{R}} = \boldsymbol{0}$$

$$\boldsymbol{\omega} = \boldsymbol{\omega}_2 = 5\boldsymbol{k}, \qquad \dot{\boldsymbol{\omega}} = \boldsymbol{0}$$

Substitute from A and B into the velocity equation:

$$\begin{aligned} \boldsymbol{V}_{XYZ} &= \boldsymbol{V}_{xyz} + \dot{\boldsymbol{R}} + \boldsymbol{\omega} \times \boldsymbol{\rho} \\ &= 30\boldsymbol{j} + \boldsymbol{0} + 5\boldsymbol{k} \times 3\boldsymbol{k} = 30\boldsymbol{j} \text{ ft/sec} \end{aligned}$$

And for the acceleration:

$$\begin{aligned} \boldsymbol{a}_{XYZ} &= \boldsymbol{a}_{xyz} + \ddot{\boldsymbol{R}} + 2\boldsymbol{\omega} \times \boldsymbol{V}_{xyz} \\ &\qquad + \dot{\boldsymbol{\omega}} \times \boldsymbol{\rho} + \boldsymbol{\omega} \times (\boldsymbol{\omega} \times \boldsymbol{\rho}) \\ &= -300\boldsymbol{k} + \boldsymbol{0} + 2(5\boldsymbol{k}) \\ &\qquad \times (30\boldsymbol{j}) + \boldsymbol{0} + 5\boldsymbol{k} \times (5\boldsymbol{k} \times 3\boldsymbol{k}) \\ &= -300\boldsymbol{k} - 300\boldsymbol{i} \text{ ft/sec}^2 \end{aligned}$$

Notice that the essential aspects of the analysis come in the consideration of parts A and B of the problem, while the remaining portion involves direct substitution and vector algebraic operations.

EXAMPLE 15.17

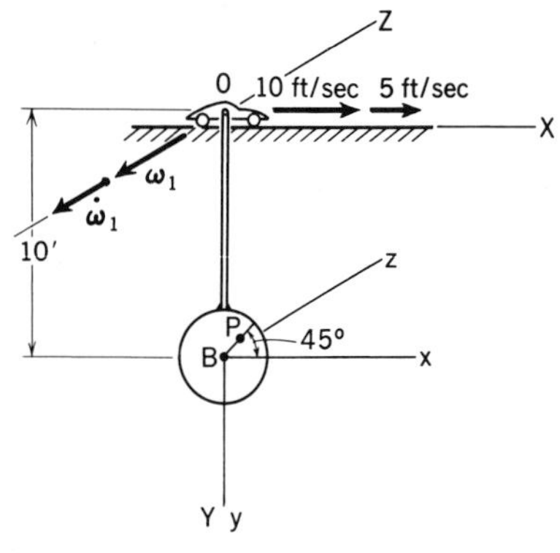

Fig. 15.29

Shown in Fig. 15.29 is a vehicle O which moves along a straight track at a speed of 10 ft/sec and which accelerates at a rate of 5 ft/sec². A pendulum is suspended from the vehicle; when it is vertical it has an angular motion in the XY plane of 2 rad/sec and also an acceleration in the XY plane of 5 rad/sec². At the instant of interest a bead P is moving on the pendulum bob at a speed of 5 ft/sec relative to the bob and in a direction of 45° to the horizontal away from point B. The bead also has a deceleration of 10 ft/sec². Using the geometry afforded by Fig. 15.29, ascertain the acceleration of the bead relative to the ground, i.e., the indicated XYZ reference.

In this problem as we have presented it, we know what the motion of the bead is relative to the bob, and the motion of the bob is given relative to the ground. Since we want to know the motion of the bead relative to the ground, we shall establish a second reference that is fixed to the bob and, at the instant under consideration, is parallel to the ground reference XYZ (see Fig. 15.29). The pertinent data will be established for each reference.

A. *Motion of bead relative to the xyz reference.*

$$\begin{aligned} \boldsymbol{\rho} &= 0.707\boldsymbol{i} - 0.707\boldsymbol{j} \\ \boldsymbol{V}_{xyz} &= (5)(0.707)\boldsymbol{i} - (5)(0.707)\boldsymbol{j} \\ \boldsymbol{a}_{xyz} &= -(10)(0.707)\boldsymbol{i} + (10)(0.707)\boldsymbol{j} \end{aligned}$$

B. *Motion of xyz relative to XYZ.*

$\boldsymbol{R} = 10\boldsymbol{j}, \quad \boldsymbol{L} = 10\boldsymbol{j} \quad$ ($\boldsymbol{L}$ goes from O to B)

$\dot{\boldsymbol{R}}$ Note that the origin of xyz is fixed in the pendulum, whose angular motion and an-

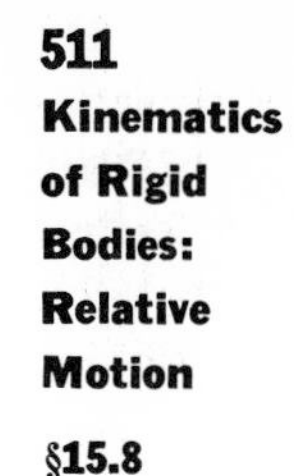

gular acceleration are known relative to the ground. Furthermore, the point O of the pendulum has a known motion relative to the ground. We can then say using Eq. 15.6:

$$\dot{\boldsymbol{R}} = \boldsymbol{V}_0 + \boldsymbol{\omega}_1 \times \boldsymbol{L} = 10\boldsymbol{i} + (-2\boldsymbol{k}) \times 10\boldsymbol{j}$$

$$= 10\boldsymbol{i} + 20\boldsymbol{i} = 30\boldsymbol{i}$$

$\ddot{\boldsymbol{R}}$ Differentiating the above relation and noting that $\boldsymbol{L}$ is fixed in a rigid body which has an angular velocity $\boldsymbol{\omega}_1$, we write:

$$\ddot{\boldsymbol{R}} = \dot{\boldsymbol{V}}_0 + \boldsymbol{\omega}_1 \times (\boldsymbol{\omega}_1 \times \boldsymbol{L}) + \dot{\boldsymbol{\omega}}_1 \times \boldsymbol{L}$$

$$= 5\boldsymbol{i} + (-2\boldsymbol{k}) \times (20\boldsymbol{i}) + (-5\boldsymbol{k}) \times 10\boldsymbol{j}$$

$$= 55\boldsymbol{i} - 40\boldsymbol{j}$$

$$\boldsymbol{\omega} = \boldsymbol{\omega}_1 = -2\boldsymbol{k}$$

$$\dot{\boldsymbol{\omega}} = \dot{\boldsymbol{\omega}}_1 = -5\boldsymbol{k}$$

The acceleration, then, is:

$$\boldsymbol{a}_{XYZ} = \boldsymbol{a}_{xyz} + \ddot{\boldsymbol{R}} + 2\boldsymbol{\omega} \times \boldsymbol{V}_{xyz} + \dot{\boldsymbol{\omega}} \times \boldsymbol{\rho} + \boldsymbol{\omega} \times (\boldsymbol{\omega} \times \boldsymbol{\rho})$$

$$= -7.07\boldsymbol{i} + 7.07\boldsymbol{j} + 55\boldsymbol{i} - 40\boldsymbol{j} + 2(-2\boldsymbol{k}) \times (3.54\boldsymbol{i} - 3.54\boldsymbol{j}) + (-5\boldsymbol{k}) \times (0.707\boldsymbol{i} - 0.707\boldsymbol{j}) + (-2\boldsymbol{k}) \times [(-2\boldsymbol{k}) \times (0.707\boldsymbol{i} - 0.707\boldsymbol{j})]$$

$$= 27.4\boldsymbol{i} - 47.8\boldsymbol{j} \text{ ft/sec}^2$$

EXAMPLE 15.18

As shown in Fig. 15.30(a), a wheel rotates in the plane of a platform with a speed ω_1 of 4 rad/sec and accelerates at a rate of 6 rad/sec²—all relative to the platform. The platform, meanwhile, rotates with an angular speed ω_2 of 2 rad/sec relative to the ground and decelerates at a rate of 3 rad/sec². A bead slides along a spoke of the wheel, as shown in Fig. 15.30(a) and more carefully in Fig. 15.30(b) where a portion of the wheel is shown enlarged. It has a speed of 5 ft/sec along the spoke toward O of the wheel and is accelerating at a rate of 10 ft/sec². At the instant of interest, the bead is 1 ft from the center of the wheel. Find the velocity and acceleration of the bead relative to the ground.

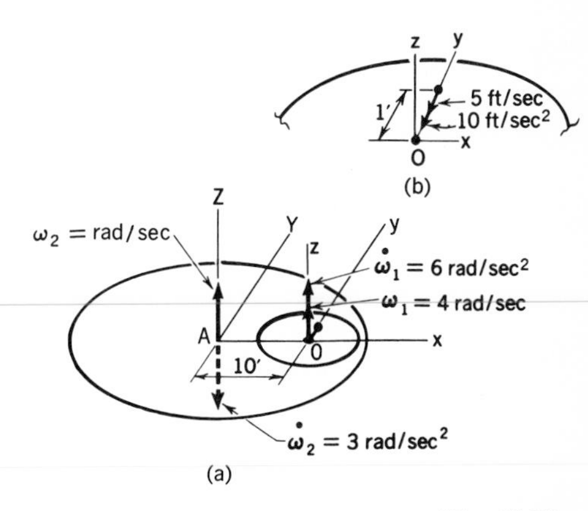

Fig. 15.30

We choose the ground reference so that Y is parallel to the spoke carrying the bead at the instant of interest, as shown in the diagram. We shall solve this problem by two different analyses.

Analysis 1. Fix xyz onto the wheel.

A. *Motion of particle relative to xyz.*

$$\boldsymbol{\varrho} = \boldsymbol{j}, \qquad \boldsymbol{V}_{xyz} = -5\boldsymbol{j}, \qquad \boldsymbol{a}_{xyz} = -10\boldsymbol{j}$$

B. *Motion of xyz relative to XYZ.*

$$\boldsymbol{R} = 10\boldsymbol{i}$$

$$\dot{\boldsymbol{R}} = \boldsymbol{\omega}_2 \times \boldsymbol{R} = 2\boldsymbol{k} \times 10\boldsymbol{i} = 20\boldsymbol{j}$$

$$\ddot{\boldsymbol{R}} = \dot{\boldsymbol{\omega}}_2 \times \boldsymbol{R} + \boldsymbol{\omega}_2 \times \dot{\boldsymbol{R}} = -3\boldsymbol{k} \times 10\boldsymbol{i} + 2\boldsymbol{k} \times 20\boldsymbol{j}$$
$$= -30\boldsymbol{j} - 40\boldsymbol{i}$$

$$\boldsymbol{\omega} = \boldsymbol{\omega}_1 + \boldsymbol{\omega}_2 = 4\boldsymbol{k} + 2\boldsymbol{k} = 6\boldsymbol{k}$$

$$\dot{\boldsymbol{\omega}} = \dot{\boldsymbol{\omega}}_1 + \dot{\boldsymbol{\omega}}_2 = 6\boldsymbol{k} - 3\boldsymbol{k} = 3\boldsymbol{k}$$ (The angular velocity vectors $\boldsymbol{\omega}_1$ and $\boldsymbol{\omega}_2$ do not change direction.)

Hence:

$$\boldsymbol{V}_{XYZ} = \boldsymbol{V}_{xyz} + \dot{\boldsymbol{R}} + \boldsymbol{\omega} \times \boldsymbol{\varrho}$$
$$= -5\boldsymbol{j} + 20\boldsymbol{j} + 6\boldsymbol{k} \times \boldsymbol{j} = 15\boldsymbol{j} - 6\boldsymbol{i} \text{ ft/sec}$$

$$\boldsymbol{a}_{XYZ} = \boldsymbol{a}_{xyz} + \ddot{\boldsymbol{R}} + 2\boldsymbol{\omega} \times \boldsymbol{V}_{xyz} + \dot{\boldsymbol{\omega}} \times \boldsymbol{\varrho} + \boldsymbol{\omega} \times (\boldsymbol{\omega} \times \boldsymbol{\varrho})$$
$$= -10\boldsymbol{j} - 30\boldsymbol{j} - 40\boldsymbol{i} + 2(6\boldsymbol{k}) \times (-5\boldsymbol{j}) + 3\boldsymbol{k} \times \boldsymbol{j} + 6\boldsymbol{k} \times (6\boldsymbol{k} \times \boldsymbol{j})$$
$$= 17\boldsymbol{i} - 76\boldsymbol{j} \text{ ft/sec}^2$$

Analysis 2. Fix *xyz* onto the platform so that the wheel spins relative to *xyz*. Note that the bead now has a complex motion in the *xyz* reference, with the position vector changing in value while it is rotating. This is not an advisable reference to use for this reason.

A. *Motion of particle relative to xyz.* We may use cylindrical coordinates here with the z direction taken as the axial direction. Thus, using the results from Section 11.7, we have:

$$\boldsymbol{\varrho} = (1)\boldsymbol{\varepsilon}_{\bar{r}} = \boldsymbol{j}$$

$$\boldsymbol{V}_{xyz} = \dot{\bar{r}}\boldsymbol{\varepsilon}_{\bar{r}} + \bar{r}\dot{\phi}\boldsymbol{\varepsilon}_{\phi} + \dot{z}\boldsymbol{\varepsilon}_z$$
$$= -5\boldsymbol{\varepsilon}_{\bar{r}} + (1)(4)\boldsymbol{\varepsilon}_{\phi} + \boldsymbol{0}$$
$$= -5\boldsymbol{j} - 4\boldsymbol{i}$$

$$\boldsymbol{a}_{xyz} = (\ddot{\bar{r}} - \bar{r}\dot{\phi}^2)\boldsymbol{\varepsilon}_{\bar{r}} + (\bar{r}\ddot{\phi} + 2\dot{\bar{r}}\dot{\phi})\boldsymbol{\varepsilon}_{\phi} + \ddot{z}\boldsymbol{\varepsilon}_z$$
$$= [-10 - (1)(16)]\boldsymbol{\varepsilon}_{\bar{r}} + [(1)(6) - (2)(5)(4)]\boldsymbol{\varepsilon}_{\phi} + \boldsymbol{0}$$
$$= -26\boldsymbol{j} + 34\boldsymbol{i}$$

As a matter of interest we shall also reach the above results without the use of formulas by carrying out direct differentiations in the following manner:

$$\boldsymbol{\varrho} = |\boldsymbol{\varrho}|\,\hat{\boldsymbol{\varrho}} = \boldsymbol{j}$$

$$V_{xyz} = \left(\frac{d\boldsymbol{\varrho}}{dt}\right)_{xyz} = |\,\boldsymbol{\varrho}\,|\dot{\hat{\boldsymbol{\varrho}}} + \frac{d\,|\,\boldsymbol{\varrho}\,|}{dt}\hat{\boldsymbol{\varrho}}$$

$$= |\,\boldsymbol{\varrho}\,|\,\boldsymbol{\omega}_1 \times \hat{\boldsymbol{\varrho}} + \frac{d\,|\,\boldsymbol{\varrho}\,|}{dt}\hat{\boldsymbol{\varrho}}$$

$$= 4\boldsymbol{k} \times \boldsymbol{j} - 5\boldsymbol{j} = -4\boldsymbol{i} - 5\boldsymbol{j} \qquad \text{(a)}$$

Differentiating Eq. (a) with respect to time again we get, on collecting terms:

$$\boldsymbol{a}_{xyz} = 2\frac{d\,|\,\boldsymbol{\varrho}\,|}{dt}\boldsymbol{\omega}_1 \times \hat{\boldsymbol{\varrho}} + |\,\boldsymbol{\varrho}\,|\,\dot{\boldsymbol{\omega}}_1 \times \hat{\boldsymbol{\varrho}}$$

$$+ |\,\boldsymbol{\varrho}\,|\,\boldsymbol{\omega}_1 \times (\boldsymbol{\omega}_1 \times \hat{\boldsymbol{\varrho}}) + \frac{d^2\,|\,\boldsymbol{\varrho}\,|}{dt^2}\hat{\boldsymbol{\varrho}}$$

$$= -10(4\boldsymbol{k} \times \boldsymbol{j}) + 6\boldsymbol{k} \times \boldsymbol{j}$$

$$+ 4\boldsymbol{k} \times (4\boldsymbol{k} \times \boldsymbol{j}) - 10\boldsymbol{j}$$

$$= 40\boldsymbol{i} - 6\boldsymbol{i} - 16\boldsymbol{j} - 10\boldsymbol{j} = -26\boldsymbol{i} + 34\boldsymbol{j}$$

B. *Motion of xyz relative to XYZ.*

$$\left.\begin{aligned} \boldsymbol{R} &= 10\boldsymbol{i} \\ \dot{\boldsymbol{R}} &= 20\boldsymbol{j} \\ \ddot{\boldsymbol{R}} &= -30\boldsymbol{j} - 40\boldsymbol{i} \end{aligned}\right\}\ \text{Same as in Analysis 1}$$

$$\boldsymbol{\omega} = \boldsymbol{\omega}_2 = 2\boldsymbol{k}$$

$$\dot{\boldsymbol{\omega}} = \dot{\boldsymbol{\omega}}_2 = -3\boldsymbol{k}$$

Hence:

$$V_{XYZ} = V_{xyz} + \dot{\boldsymbol{R}} + \boldsymbol{\omega} \times \boldsymbol{\varrho}$$

$$= -4\boldsymbol{i} - 5\boldsymbol{j} + 20\boldsymbol{j} + 2\boldsymbol{k} \times \boldsymbol{j}$$

$$= 15\boldsymbol{j} - 6\boldsymbol{i}\ \text{ft/sec}$$

$$\boldsymbol{a}_{XYZ} = \boldsymbol{a}_{xyz} + \ddot{\boldsymbol{R}} + 2\boldsymbol{\omega} \times V_{xyz} + \dot{\boldsymbol{\omega}} \times \boldsymbol{\varrho}$$

$$+ \boldsymbol{\omega} \times (\boldsymbol{\omega} \times \boldsymbol{\varrho})$$

$$= 34\boldsymbol{i} - 26\boldsymbol{j} - 30\boldsymbol{j} - 40\boldsymbol{i} + 2(2\boldsymbol{k})$$

$$\times (-4\boldsymbol{i} - 5\boldsymbol{j})$$

$$+(-3\boldsymbol{k}) \times \boldsymbol{j} + 2\boldsymbol{k} \times (2\boldsymbol{k} \times \boldsymbol{j})$$

$$= 17\boldsymbol{i} - 76\boldsymbol{j}\ \text{ft/sec}^2$$

It is clear that the second approach makes for undue hardships.

***EXAMPLE 15.19**

A cart is moving with a speed of 50 ft/sec along a circular path of radius 100 ft (Fig. 15.31). It is decelerating at a rate of 20 ft/sec². A pair of governor weights is shown on spindle *CD*. The bars supporting the weights are rotating with a speed of 10 rad/sec

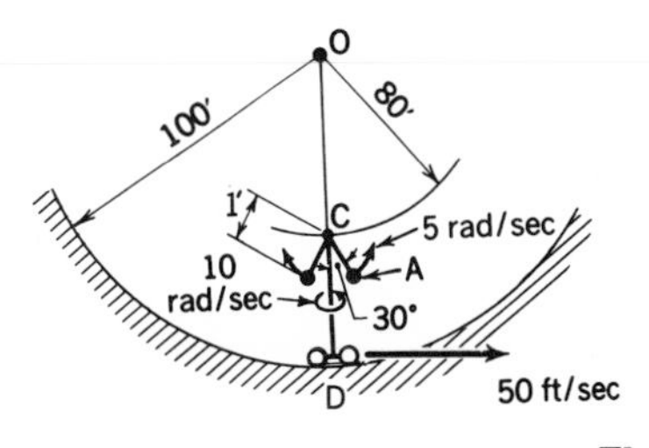

Fig. 15.31

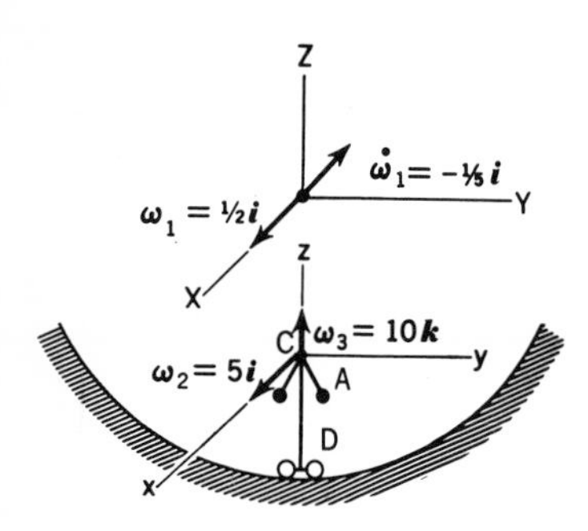

Fig. 15.32

about spindle CD relative to the cart and are being raised at a rate of 5 rad/sec relative to the spindle. The bars are at the instant of interest in the plane of the paper at an angle 30°. Find the acceleration and velocity of weight A relative to the ground.

Let us first formulate the various angular velocities present. The cart moves with a speed of 50 ft/sec along a circular path so that the angular speed of OC, and therefore of the cart itself, is easily determined from our work on plane circular motion to be $\frac{50}{100} = \frac{1}{2}$ rad/sec. And, because of the deceleration of 20 ft/sec², the cart must also have a rate of change of angular speed of $\frac{20}{100} = \frac{1}{5}$ rad/sec². These angular motions are clearly given relative to the ground. In Fig. 15.32, the vectorial representations of these quantities are shown as ω_1 and $\dot{\omega}_1$ along the axes of stationary reference XYZ. There are two angular motions of the weights—a rotation of the spindle CD, shown in the diagram as ω_3, and a rotation of the weights about the spindle, shown in the diagram as ω_2, having at the instant of interest a direction normal to the page. It should be clear, from the constraints of the construction, that the direction of $\boldsymbol{\omega}_2$ will change continually as a result of the angular motion $\boldsymbol{\omega}_3$, and the direction of $\boldsymbol{\omega}_3$ will change as a result of $\boldsymbol{\omega}_1$. We shall solve this problem by using two different types of moving references.

Analysis 1. Fix xyz directly to the moving cart so that it has only the motion of the cart.

A. *Motion of particle relative to xyz.*

$$\boldsymbol{\varrho} = -0.866\boldsymbol{k} + 0.5\boldsymbol{j}$$

Since CA can be considered fixed in a rigid body having an angular velocity equal to $(\boldsymbol{\omega}_2 + \boldsymbol{\omega}_3)$, we have:

$$\boldsymbol{V}_{xyz} = \left(\frac{d\boldsymbol{\varrho}}{dt}\right)_{xyz} = (\boldsymbol{\omega}_2 + \boldsymbol{\omega}_3) \times \boldsymbol{\varrho}$$

$$= (5\boldsymbol{i} + 10\boldsymbol{k}) \times (-0.866\boldsymbol{k} + 0.5\boldsymbol{j})$$

$$= -5\boldsymbol{i} + 4.33\boldsymbol{j} + 2.5\boldsymbol{k}$$

Differentiating again, we get:

$$\boldsymbol{a}_{xyz} = \left(\frac{d\boldsymbol{V}_{xyz}}{dt}\right)_{xyz} = (\boldsymbol{\omega}_2 + \boldsymbol{\omega}_3) \times \dot{\boldsymbol{\varrho}} + (\dot{\boldsymbol{\omega}}_2 + \dot{\boldsymbol{\omega}}_3) \times \boldsymbol{\varrho}$$

$$= (\boldsymbol{\omega}_2 + \boldsymbol{\omega}_3) \times (-5\boldsymbol{i} + 4.33\boldsymbol{j} + 2.5\boldsymbol{k})$$

$$+ (\dot{\boldsymbol{\omega}}_2 + \dot{\boldsymbol{\omega}}_3) \times (-0.866\boldsymbol{k} + 0.5\boldsymbol{j})$$

It is clear that $\dot{\boldsymbol{\omega}}_3 = \boldsymbol{0}$ as seen from the xyz reference since it changes neither in magnitude nor in direction relative to this reference. However, the vector $\boldsymbol{\omega}_2$ rotates with an angular velocity $\boldsymbol{\omega}_3$ relative to the xyz reference. Because, furthermore, $\boldsymbol{\omega}_2$ has a constant magnitude, we can think of it as "fixed" in a body having an angular velocity $\boldsymbol{\omega}_3$ relative to xyz. Accordingly, we can say:

$$\dot{\boldsymbol{\omega}}_2 = \boldsymbol{\omega}_3 \times \boldsymbol{\omega}_2$$

Thus:

$$\begin{aligned} \boldsymbol{a}_{xyz} &= (5\boldsymbol{i} + 10\boldsymbol{k}) \times (-5\boldsymbol{i} + 4.33\boldsymbol{j} + 2.5\boldsymbol{k}) \\ &\quad + (10\boldsymbol{k} \times 5\boldsymbol{i}) \times (-0.866\boldsymbol{k} + 0.5\boldsymbol{j}) \\ &= -86.6\boldsymbol{i} - 62.5\boldsymbol{j} + 21.7\boldsymbol{k} \end{aligned}$$

B. *Motion of xyz relative to XYZ.*

$$\boldsymbol{R} = \overrightarrow{OC} = -80\boldsymbol{k}$$

Considering Fig. 15.31, it is clear that we can consider $\boldsymbol{R}$ to be fixed in reference xyz. Accordingly:

$$\begin{aligned} \dot{\boldsymbol{R}} &= \boldsymbol{\omega}_1 \times \boldsymbol{R} = \tfrac{1}{2}\boldsymbol{i} \times (-80\boldsymbol{k}) = 40\boldsymbol{j} \\ \ddot{\boldsymbol{R}} &= \dot{\boldsymbol{\omega}}_1 \times \boldsymbol{R} + \boldsymbol{\omega}_1 \times \dot{\boldsymbol{R}} \\ &= -\tfrac{1}{5}\boldsymbol{i} \times (-80\boldsymbol{k}) + \tfrac{1}{2}\boldsymbol{i} \times 40\boldsymbol{j} \\ &= -16\boldsymbol{j} + 20\boldsymbol{k} \\ \boldsymbol{\omega} &= \boldsymbol{\omega}_1 = \tfrac{1}{2}\boldsymbol{i} \\ \dot{\boldsymbol{\omega}} &= \dot{\boldsymbol{\omega}}_1 = -\tfrac{1}{5}\boldsymbol{i} \end{aligned}$$

We may now ascertain the acceleration $\boldsymbol{a}_{XYZ}$. Thus:

$$\begin{aligned} \boldsymbol{a}_{XYZ} &= \boldsymbol{a}_{xyz} + \ddot{\boldsymbol{R}} + 2\boldsymbol{\omega} \times \boldsymbol{V}_{xyz} \\ &\qquad + \dot{\boldsymbol{\omega}} \times \boldsymbol{\rho} + \boldsymbol{\omega} \times (\boldsymbol{\omega} \times \boldsymbol{\rho}) \\ &= -86.6\boldsymbol{i} - 62.5\boldsymbol{j} + 21.7\boldsymbol{k} - 16\boldsymbol{j} + 20\boldsymbol{k} \\ &\quad + 2(\tfrac{1}{2}\boldsymbol{i}) \times (-5\boldsymbol{i} + 4.33\boldsymbol{j} + 2.5\boldsymbol{k}) \\ &\quad - \tfrac{1}{5}\boldsymbol{i} \times (-0.866\boldsymbol{k} + 0.5\boldsymbol{j}) \\ &\quad + \tfrac{1}{2}\boldsymbol{i} \times [\tfrac{1}{2}\boldsymbol{i} \times (-0.866\boldsymbol{k} + 0.5\boldsymbol{j})] \\ &= -86.6\boldsymbol{i} - 81.3\boldsymbol{j} + 46.1\boldsymbol{k} \text{ ft/sec}^2 \end{aligned}$$

Analysis 2. Fix xyz directly onto the spindle. This gives the particle a simple plane circular motion in the xyz reference. We can use Fig. 15.31 again.

A. *Motion of particle relative to xyz.*

$$\boldsymbol{\rho} = -0.866\boldsymbol{k} + 0.5\boldsymbol{j}$$

$$\begin{aligned} \boldsymbol{V}_{xyz} &= \left(\frac{d\boldsymbol{\rho}}{dt}\right)_{xyz} = \boldsymbol{\omega}_2 \times \boldsymbol{\rho} = 5\boldsymbol{i} \times (-0.866\boldsymbol{k} + 0.5\boldsymbol{j}) \\ &= 4.33\boldsymbol{j} + 2.5\boldsymbol{k} \end{aligned}$$

Using results for plane circular motion we next get:

$$\begin{aligned} \boldsymbol{a}_{xyz} &= \rho\omega_2^2\boldsymbol{\varepsilon}_n + \rho\dot{\omega}_2\boldsymbol{\varepsilon}_t \\ &= (1)(25)(0.866\boldsymbol{k} - 0.5\boldsymbol{j}) + \boldsymbol{0} \\ &= 21.7\boldsymbol{k} - 12.5\boldsymbol{j} \end{aligned}$$

B. *Motion of xyz relative to XYZ.*

$$\left.\begin{aligned} \boldsymbol{R} &= -80\boldsymbol{k} \\ \dot{\boldsymbol{R}} &= 40\boldsymbol{j} \\ \ddot{\boldsymbol{R}} &= -16\boldsymbol{j} + 20\boldsymbol{k} \end{aligned}\right\}$$

These are the same as for Analysis 1, since the origin of xyz for either case is identical.

$$\omega = \omega_1 + \omega_3 = \tfrac{1}{2}\boldsymbol{i} + 10\boldsymbol{k}$$

$\dot{\omega}$ Note that the magnitude of ω_1 is changing. Furthermore, the direction of ω_3 is changing due to the constraints of the problem such that the vector ω_3 can be considered fixed in a body rotating with angular velocity ω_1 relative to XYZ. Thus:

$$\begin{aligned}\dot{\omega} &= \dot{\omega}_1\boldsymbol{i} + \omega_1 \times \omega_3 = -\tfrac{1}{5}\boldsymbol{i} + (\tfrac{1}{2}\boldsymbol{i} \times 10\boldsymbol{k}) \\ &= -\tfrac{1}{5}\boldsymbol{i} - 5\boldsymbol{j}\end{aligned}$$

We can now find the acceleration as:

$$\begin{aligned}\boldsymbol{a}_{XYZ} &= \boldsymbol{a}_{xyz} + \ddot{\boldsymbol{R}} + 2\omega \times \boldsymbol{V}_{xyz} + \dot{\omega} \times \boldsymbol{\varrho} \\ &\qquad + \omega \times (\omega \times \boldsymbol{\varrho})\end{aligned}$$

$$\begin{aligned}\boldsymbol{a}_{XYZ} &= 21.7\boldsymbol{k} - 12.5\boldsymbol{j} - 16\boldsymbol{j} + 20\boldsymbol{k} + 2(\tfrac{1}{2}\boldsymbol{i} + 10\boldsymbol{k}) \\ &\quad \times (4.33\boldsymbol{j} + 2.5\boldsymbol{k}) - (\tfrac{1}{5}\boldsymbol{i} + 5\boldsymbol{j}) \\ &\quad \times (-0.866\boldsymbol{k} + 0.5\boldsymbol{j}) + (\tfrac{1}{2}\boldsymbol{i} + 10\boldsymbol{k}) \\ &\quad \times [(\tfrac{1}{2}\boldsymbol{i} + 10\boldsymbol{k}) \times (-0.866\boldsymbol{k} + 0.5\boldsymbol{j})] \\ &= -86.6\boldsymbol{i} - 81.3\boldsymbol{j} + 46.1\boldsymbol{k} \text{ ft/sec}^2\end{aligned}$$

15.9 Forces on a Particle Having a Known Motion

In Chapter 11 we discussed the solution of forces whose motion is known relative to an inertial reference. Although this is properly the province of dynamics, we examined this problem in a chapter on kinematics because the essence of the analysis was kinematical in nature. We propose to extend that discussion to cover the situation where the forces are desired for a particle having a known motion relative to a reference xyz which in turn has a known motion relative to an inertial reference XYZ. Such a situation would arise when we must determine the forces to accomplish a certain motion of machine components in an airplane or space vehicle wherein this motion is known (and makes sense only) relative to the vehicle. Meanwhile the vehicle may be undergoing some severe maneuver relative to inertial space, and this motion must also be taken into account in evaluating the forces.

To properly employ Newton's law for a particle of mass m we have:

$$\boldsymbol{F} = m\boldsymbol{a}_{XYZ} \tag{15.24}$$

where XYZ must be an inertial reference. For circumstances described in the previous paragraph we can say, using Eq. 15.21:

$$\boldsymbol{F} = m[\boldsymbol{a}_{xyz} + \ddot{\boldsymbol{R}} + 2\omega \times \boldsymbol{V}_{xyz} + \dot{\omega} \times \boldsymbol{\varrho} + \omega \times (\omega \times \boldsymbol{\varrho})] \tag{15.25}$$

where xyz is a noninertial reference whose motion (as given by $\ddot{\boldsymbol{R}}$, ω, and $\dot{\omega}$) is known relative to an inertial reference XYZ. It is common practice to put the above equation in the following form:

$$\boldsymbol{F} - m[\ddot{\boldsymbol{R}} + 2\omega \times \boldsymbol{V}_{xyz} + \dot{\omega} \times \boldsymbol{\varrho} + \omega \times (\omega \times \boldsymbol{\varrho})] = m\boldsymbol{a}_{xyz} \tag{15.26}$$

where we have the familiar mass times acceleration on the right side of the equation. The new terms appearing on the left side are now considered as *inertial forces* arising from the use of a noninertial reference *xyz*. In particular, we call $m(2\boldsymbol{\omega} \times \boldsymbol{V}_{xyz})$ the *Coriolis force*. The point of view to be adopted is that in using Newton's law for a noninertial reference we must include as forces not only the external resultant force but, in addition, the inertial forces given in Eq. 15.26.

The additional terms on the left side of Eq. 15.26 result in baffling actions that are sometimes contrary to our intuition. Most of us during most of our lives have been involved in actions where the reference used (knowingly or not) has been an inertial reference—usually the earth's surface. We have accordingly become conditioned to associating an acceleration proportional to, and in the same direction as, the applied force. Occasions do arise when man finds himself relating his motions to a reference which is highly noninertial. Thus in the First World War aviators were required to carry out actions in a cockpit of a plane while the plane was undergoing severe maneuvers and accordingly were using the cockpit interior as a reference. Unexpected results would frequently occur for the flyer. Thus to move his hand from one position to another relative to the cockpit sometimes required an exertion which was not the one anticipated, causing considerable confusion. The next example will illustrate this, and the sections that follow will explore further some of these interesting effects.*

EXAMPLE 15.20

In Fig. 15.33 is the plan view of a rotating platform. A man is seated at the position labeled A and is facing point O of the platform. He is carrying a mass of 1/50 slug at the rate of 10 ft/sec in a direction straight ahead of him—i.e., to the center of the platform. If this platform has an angular speed of 10 rad/sec and an angular acceleration of 5 rad/sec² relative to the ground at this instant, what force must he exert to cause the mass to accelerate 5 ft/sec² toward the center?

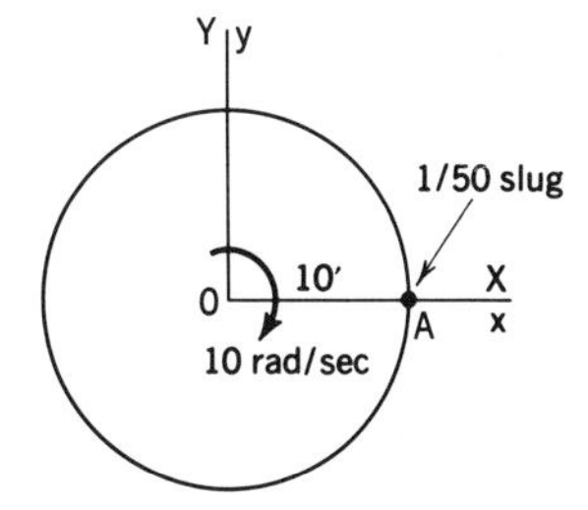

Fig. 15.33

Reference xyz is fixed to the rotating member, while XYZ is stationary relative to the ground. The former is not an inertial reference, so we shall have to ascertain the acceleration of the mass relative to the ground. This may be done in the following manner.

A. *Motion of mass relative to xyz reference.*

$$\boldsymbol{\rho} = 10\boldsymbol{i}, \qquad \boldsymbol{V}_{xyz} = -10\boldsymbol{i}, \qquad \boldsymbol{a}_{xyz} = -5\boldsymbol{i}$$

B. *Motion of moving reference relative to inertial reference.*

---

* At this juncture it might be well to remind ourselves that "physical feel" or "intuition" is really a direct consequence of past experiences. For this reason many of the things you will later formally learn will at first be at variance with your physical feel and intuition. Thus certain phenomena occurring in supersonic fluid flow will seem very strange since your direct experience with fluid flow (faucets, swimming, and so on) has been entirely subsonic. Because you have not moved with speeds approaching the speed of light and because you have not been prowling around the nucleus of an atom you will find the tenets of relativity theory and quantum mechanics absolutely bizarre. Should you have little feel for the Coriolis force at this time this should not cause undue concern (unless you have spent a lot of time moving about high-speed merry-go-rounds). We must in such instances rely on the theory. Working with the theory, we can often build up a strong "physical feel" in the new areas.

$$\dot{R} = 0, \quad \ddot{R} = 0, \quad \omega = -10\boldsymbol{k}, \quad \dot{\omega} = -5\boldsymbol{k}$$

Hence:

$$\boldsymbol{a}_{XYZ} = -5\boldsymbol{i} + 2(-10\boldsymbol{k}) \times (-10\boldsymbol{i})$$
$$-5\boldsymbol{k} \times 10\boldsymbol{i} + (-10\boldsymbol{k}) \times (-10\boldsymbol{k} \times 10\boldsymbol{i})$$
$$\therefore \boldsymbol{a}_{XYZ} = -5\boldsymbol{i} + 200\boldsymbol{j} - 50\boldsymbol{j} - 1000\boldsymbol{i}$$
$$= 150\boldsymbol{j} - 1005\boldsymbol{i} \text{ ft/sec}^2$$

Employing Newton's law for the mass, we get:

$$\boldsymbol{F} = \tfrac{1}{50}(150\boldsymbol{j} - 1005\boldsymbol{i})$$
$$\therefore \boldsymbol{F} = 3\boldsymbol{j} - 20.1\boldsymbol{i} \text{ lb}$$

This is the total force coming onto the mass. Since the man must exert this force and also withstand the pull of gravity in the $-\boldsymbol{k}$ direction, the force exerted by the man on the mass is:

$$\boldsymbol{F}_{\text{mass}} = 3\boldsymbol{j} - 20.1\boldsymbol{i} + \frac{g}{50}\boldsymbol{k} \text{ lb} \qquad \textbf{(a)}$$

If the platform were *not* rotating at all, it could serve as an inertial reference. Then we would have:

$$\boldsymbol{F}_{\text{mass}} = \tfrac{1}{50}(-5\boldsymbol{i}) = -\tfrac{1}{10}\boldsymbol{i} \text{ lb}$$

Including gravity, we get:

$$\boldsymbol{F}_{\text{mass}} = -\frac{1}{10}\boldsymbol{i} + \frac{g}{50}\boldsymbol{k} \text{ lb} \qquad \textbf{(b)}$$

This force is considerably different from that given in Eq. (a).

As a matter of interest it might be noted that aviators of the First World War were required to carry out such maneuvers on a rapidly rotating and accelerating platform so as to introduce them safely to these "peculiar" effects.

15.10 The Coriolis Force

Of great interest is the Coriolis force, defined in the previous section, particularly as it relates to certain terrestrial actions. It has been pointed out that for many of our problems the earth's surface serves with sufficient accuracy as an inertial reference. However, where the time interval of interest is large (such as in the flight of rockets, or the flow of rivers, or the movement of winds and ocean currents), we must consider such a reference as noninertial in certain instances and accordingly, when using Newton's law, we must include some or all of the inertial forces given in Eq. 15.26. For such problems (as you will recall from Chapter 12) we often use an inertial reference that has an origin at the center of the earth (see Fig. 15.34) with the Z axis collinear with the N–S axis of the earth and moving such that the earth rotates 1 revolution per 24 hours relative to the reference. Thus, the reference approaches a translatory motion about the sun. To a high degree of accuracy, it is an inertial reference.

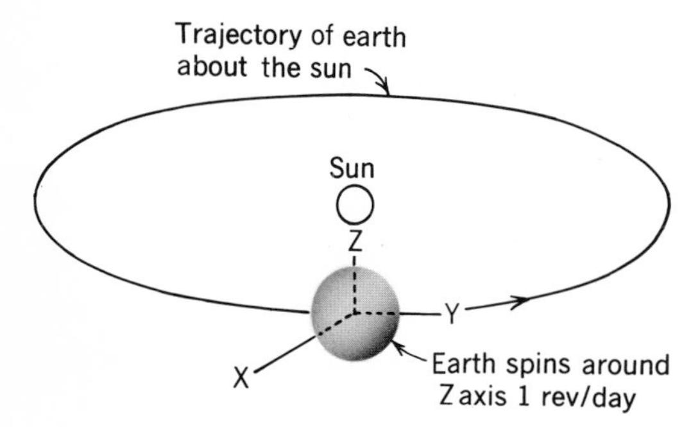

Fig. 15.34

We start by considering particles that are stationary relative to the earth. We choose a reference xyz fixed to the earth at the equator as shown in Fig. 15.35. The angular velocity of xyz fixed anywhere on the earth's surface can readily be evaluated as follows:

$$\boldsymbol{\omega} = \frac{2\pi}{(24)(3600)} \boldsymbol{k} = 7.29 \times 10^{-5} \boldsymbol{k} \text{ rad/sec} \qquad \textbf{15.27}$$

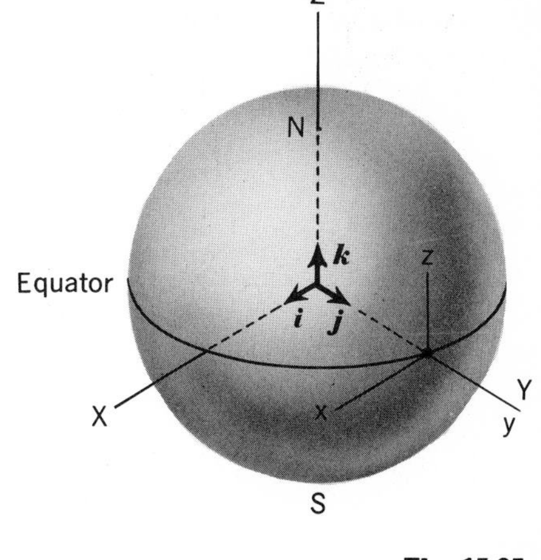

Fig. 15.35

Newton's law, in the form of Eq. 15.26, for a "stationary" particle positioned at the origin of xyz simplifies to:

$$\boldsymbol{F} - m\ddot{\boldsymbol{R}} = \boldsymbol{0} \qquad \textbf{15.28}$$

since $\boldsymbol{\rho}$ and $\boldsymbol{V}_{xyz}$ are zero vectors. Let us next evaluate the inertial force, $-m\ddot{\boldsymbol{R}}$, for the particle, using $R = 4000$ miles:

$$-m\ddot{\boldsymbol{R}} = -m(-|\boldsymbol{R}|\,\omega^2\boldsymbol{j}) = m(4000)(5280) \times (7.29 \times 10^{-5})^2\boldsymbol{j}$$

$$= m(0.1122)\boldsymbol{j}$$

Clearly, this is a "centrifugal force," as we learned in physics. Note that the direction of this force is collinear with the gravitational force on a particle, but with opposite sense. Note further that it has a magnitude that is $(0.1122/32.2) \times 100 = 0.35$ per cent of the gravitational force at the indicated location. It is clear why, in the usual engineering problems, such effects are neglected.

Assume that the particle is restrained by a flexible cord. According to Eq. 15.28, the external force $\boldsymbol{F}$ (which includes gravitational attraction and the force from the cord) and the centrifugal force add up to zero, and hence these forces are in equilibrium. They are shown in Fig. 15.36, in which T represents the contribution of the cord. Clearly, a force T radially out from the center of the earth will restrain the particle, and so the direction of the flexible cord will point toward the center of the earth. On the other hand, at a non-equatorial location this will not be true. The gravity force points toward the center of the earth, but the centrifugal force—now having the value $m[R(\sin\theta)\omega^2]$—points radially out from the Z axis, and thus T, the restraining force, must be inclined somewhat from a direction toward the center of the earth (see Fig. 15.37). Therefore, except at the equator or at the poles (where the centrifugal force is zero), a plumb bob does not point directly toward the center of the earth. However, this deviation is very small and is negligible for most engineering work.

Consider next a *free falling body* at the equator near the earth's surface. In addition to the centrifugal force, the Coriolis force will now also act on the particle. Assuming again that at the particle is at the origin of the xyz reference at the equator, we can write the equation of motion in this way:

$$-mg\boldsymbol{j} - m\ddot{\boldsymbol{R}} - 2m(\boldsymbol{\omega} \times \boldsymbol{V}_{xy}) = m\boldsymbol{a}_{xyz} \qquad \textbf{15.29}$$

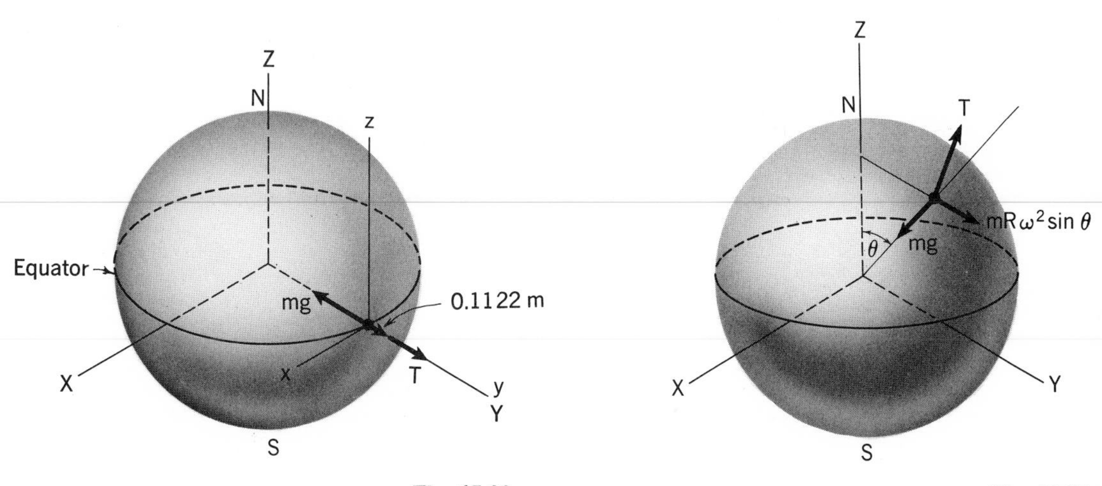

Fig. 15.36

Fig. 15.37

Thus a body moving radially inward toward the center of the earth, as shown in Fig. 15.38, has a Coriolis force acting in the negative x direction, which causes an acceleration relative to the observer in xyz in the negative x direction (Fig. 15.39). If we dropped a mass from a position in xyz above a target, therefore, the mass would curve slightly away from the target even if there were no friction or wind, etc., to complicate matters. (What happens if the mass has at the time of release a motion in, say, the x direction relative to the earth's surface, as in the case of a bomber?) Furthermore, the induced motion in the x direction itself induces Coriolis force components of a smaller order in yet another direction, and so forth. You will surely begin to appreciate how difficult a "free fall" can really become when great precision is attempted.

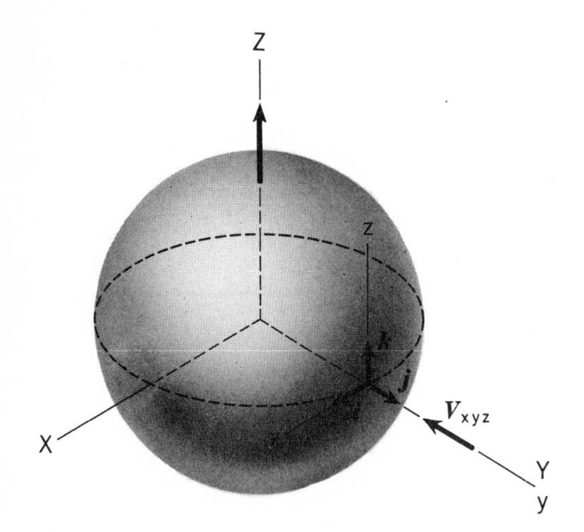

Fig. 15.38

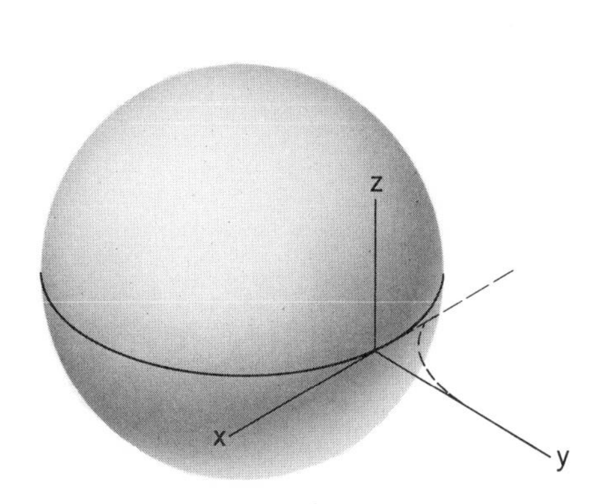

Fig. 15.39

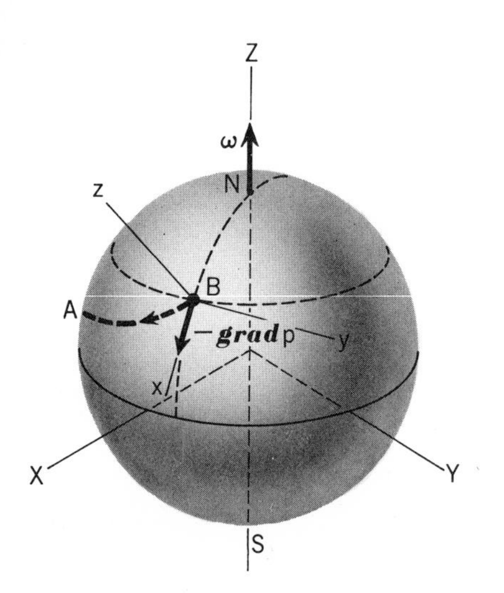

Fig. 15.40

Finally, consider a current of air or a current of water moving in the Northern Hemisphere. In the absence of a Coriolis force, the fluid would move in the direction opposite to the pressure gradient vector. In Fig. 15.40 the vector, −**grad** p, has been shown for simplicity along a meridian line pointing toward the equator. For fluid motion in this direction, a Coriolis force will be present in the minus y direction and so the fluid will follow the dotted path BA. The induced motion is to the right of the direction of flow developed by the pressure gradient alone. By a similar argument, you can demonstrate that in the Southern Hemisphere the Coriolis force induces a motion to the left of the flow that would be present under the action of the pressure gradient alone. Such effects are of significance in meteorology and oceanography.*

The conclusions in the preceding paragraph explain why cyclones and whirlpools rotate in a counterclockwise direction in the Northern Hemisphere and a clockwise direction in the Southern Hemisphere. In order to start, a whirlpool or cyclone needs a low-pressure region with pressure increasing radially outward. The negative gradient vectors are shown as full lines in Fig. 15.41. For such a

* It is important to keep in mind that the Coriolis force in these situations is small but, because it persists during long time intervals and because the resultants of other forces are often also small, this force often must carefully be taken into account in studies of meteorology and oceanography.

pressure distribution, the air will begin to move radially inward along the negative gradient directions. As this happens, the Coriolis force causes the fluid in the Northern Hemisphere to swerve to the right of its motion as indicated by the dotted lines. This result is the beginning of a counterclockwise motion. You can readily demonstrate that in the Southern Hemisphere a clockwise rotation will be induced.

As the space age descends on us, we will, as engineers, have to be increasingly more cognizant of such fascinating problems as we have presented here, which in former times we were able to disregard.

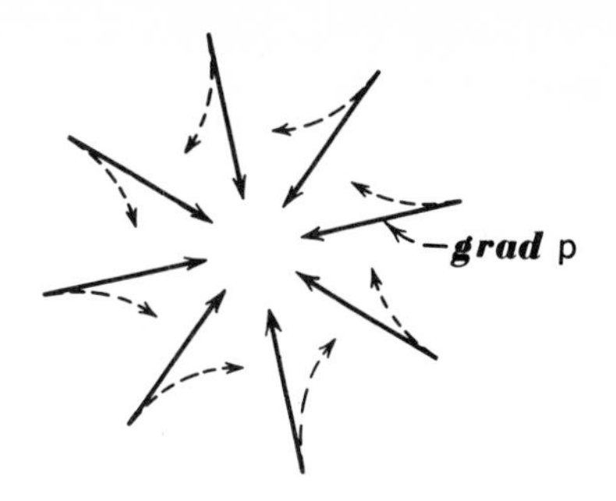

Fig. 15.41

15.11 Closure

In this chapter we first presented Chasle's theorem for describing the motion of a rigid body. Making use of Chasle's theorem for describing the motion of a reference xyz moving relative to a second reference XYZ, we presented next a simple differentiation formula for vectors $\boldsymbol{A}$ fixed in the reference xyz. Thus:

$$\left(\frac{d\boldsymbol{A}}{dt}\right)_{XYZ} = \boldsymbol{\omega} \times \boldsymbol{A} \qquad \textbf{15.30}$$

where $\boldsymbol{\omega}$ is the angular velocity of xyz relative to XYZ. We next recalled from Chapter 11 that for any two points a and b moving arbitrarily we could say:

$$\left(\frac{d\boldsymbol{\rho}_{ab}}{dt}\right)_{XYZ} = \boldsymbol{V}_b - \boldsymbol{V}_a \qquad \textbf{15.31}$$

If the points a and b are points in a rigid body, we could then employ Eq. 15.30 with $\boldsymbol{\rho}_{ab}$ in place of $\boldsymbol{A}$ to get the following formula:

$$\boldsymbol{V}_b = \boldsymbol{V}_a + \boldsymbol{\omega} \times \boldsymbol{\rho}_{ab} \qquad \textbf{15.32}$$

where $\boldsymbol{\omega}$ is the angular velocity of the rigid body relative to XYZ. Differentiating again, we get:

$$\boldsymbol{a}_a = \boldsymbol{a}_b + \boldsymbol{\omega} \times (\boldsymbol{\omega} \times \boldsymbol{\rho}_{ab}) + \dot{\boldsymbol{\omega}} \times \boldsymbol{\rho}_{ab} \qquad \textbf{15.33}$$

These formulations are helpful in the kinematical studies of machines, where two points on a rigid body are often of interest.

We next permitted the vector $\boldsymbol{A}$ to vary arbitrarily as seen from xyz and we found the relation:

$$\left(\frac{d\boldsymbol{A}}{dt}\right)_{XYZ} = \left(\frac{d\boldsymbol{A}}{dt}\right)_{xyz} + \boldsymbol{\omega} \times \boldsymbol{A} \qquad \textbf{15.34}$$

as a generalization of Eq. 15.30. By making use of this formulation we developed the relation between the velocities and acceleration of a moving particle as seen from both references. Thus:

$$\boldsymbol{V}_{XYZ} = \dot{\boldsymbol{R}} + \boldsymbol{V}_{xyz} + \boldsymbol{\omega} \times \boldsymbol{\rho} \qquad \textbf{(a)}$$

$$\boldsymbol{a}_{XYZ} = \boldsymbol{a}_{xyz} + \ddot{\boldsymbol{R}} + 2\boldsymbol{\omega} \times \boldsymbol{V}_{xyz} + \dot{\boldsymbol{\omega}} \times \boldsymbol{\rho} + \boldsymbol{\omega} \times (\boldsymbol{\omega} \times \boldsymbol{\rho}) \qquad \textbf{(b)} \quad \textbf{15.35}$$

You will recall that Eqs. 15.32 and 15.33 for rigid bodies can be considered as special cases of the above equations reached by having xyz fixed in the rigid body with the origin at point a.

In computing $\boldsymbol{V}_{xyz}$, $\boldsymbol{a}_{xyz}$, $\dot{\boldsymbol{R}}$, and $\ddot{\boldsymbol{R}}$ we use the various techniques presented in Chapter 11 for computing the velocity and acceleration of a particle relative to a given reference. Thus use may be made of cartesian components, path components, and cylindrical components as presented in that chapter.

Using Eq. 15.35(b), we then explored some interesting and often unexpected effects that occur when we use a noninertial reference.

You will have occasion to use these important formulations in your basic studies of solid and fluid mechanics as well as in your courses in kinematics of machines and machine design.

Now that we can express the motion of a rigid body in terms of a velocity vector $\dot{\boldsymbol{R}}$ and an angular velocity vector $\boldsymbol{\omega}$, our next job will be to relate these quantities with the forces acting on the body. We have already had a simple introduction to this study in Chapter 14, where we considered a body rotating about an axis in inertial space and in this way formulated the simple $T = I\ddot{\theta}$ formula familiar to all from earlier studies of physics. The term I, which you will recall as the mass moment of inertia, is an important quantity which enters into all dynamical considerations of a rigid-body motion. We shall, as a next step, examine this quantity carefully in the following chapter.

PROBLEMS

1. [15.2] Is the motion of the cabin of a ferris wheel rotational or translational if the wheel moves at uniform speed and the occupants cause no disturbances? Why?

2. [15.2] A cylinder rolls without slipping down an inclined surface. What is the axis of rotation at any instant? Why? How is this axis moving?

3. [15.4] A reference xyz is moving (see Fig. 15.42) such that the origin O has at time t a velocity relative to reference XYZ given as:

$$\boldsymbol{V}_O = 6\boldsymbol{i} + 12\boldsymbol{j} + 13\boldsymbol{k} \text{ ft/sec}$$

The xyz reference has an angular velocity $\boldsymbol{\omega}$ relative to XYZ at time t given as:

$$\boldsymbol{\omega} = 10\boldsymbol{i} + 12\boldsymbol{j} + 2\boldsymbol{k} \text{ rad/sec}$$

What is the time rate of change of a directed line segment $\boldsymbol{\varrho}$ going from position (3, 2, −5) to (−2, 4, 6) in xyz? What is the time rate of change of position vectors $\boldsymbol{i}'$ and $\boldsymbol{k}'$?

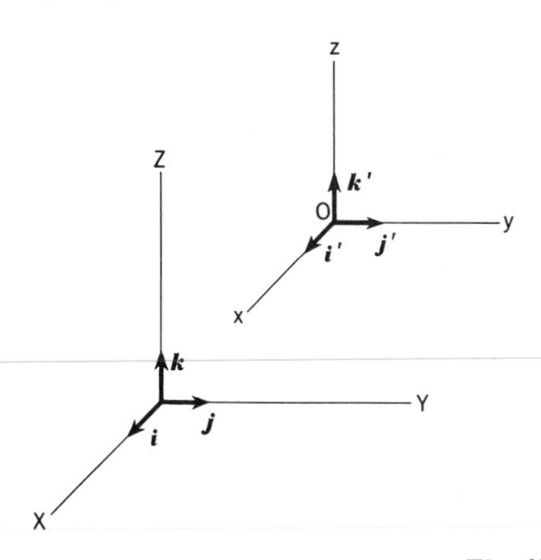

Fig. 15.42

4. [15.4] In Fig. 15.43 is shown a reference xyz moving relative to XYZ with a velocity of the origin given at time t as:

$$\boldsymbol{V}_O = 6\boldsymbol{i} + 4\boldsymbol{j} + 6\boldsymbol{k} \text{ ft/sec}$$

The angular velocity of reference xyz relative to XYZ is:

$$\boldsymbol{\omega} = 3\boldsymbol{i} + 14\boldsymbol{j} + 2\boldsymbol{k} \text{ rad/sec}$$

What is the time rate of change as seen from XYZ of a displacement vector in xyz going from position (1) to position (2) where the position vectors for these points are respectively:

$$\boldsymbol{\varrho}_1 = 2\boldsymbol{i}' + 3\boldsymbol{j}'$$

$$\boldsymbol{\varrho}_2 = 3\boldsymbol{i}' - 4\boldsymbol{j}' + 2\boldsymbol{k}'$$

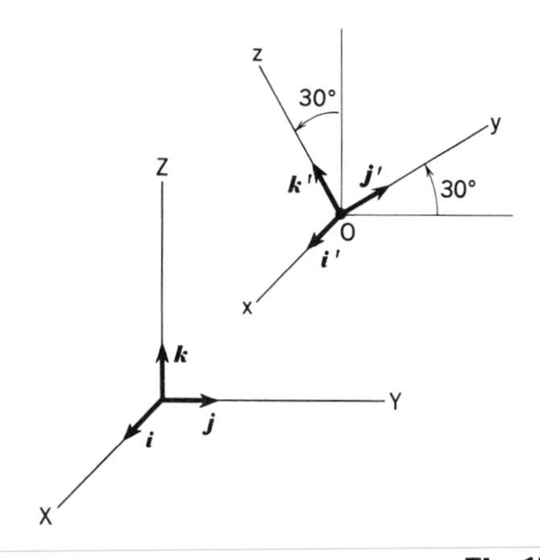

Fig. 15.43

5. [15.4] Find the second derivatives as seen from XYZ of the displacement vector $\boldsymbol{\varrho}$ and the unit vectors $\boldsymbol{i}'$, $\boldsymbol{j}'$, and $\boldsymbol{k}'$ specified in Prob. 3. The angular acceleration of xyz relative to XYZ at the instant of interest is:

$$\dot{\boldsymbol{\omega}} = 5\boldsymbol{i} + 2\boldsymbol{j} + 3\boldsymbol{k} \text{ rad/sec}^2$$

6. [15.4] Find the second derivative as seen from XYZ of the displacement vector $\boldsymbol{\varrho}$ specified in Prob. 4. Take the angular acceleration of xyz relative to XYZ at the instant of interest as:

$$\dot{\boldsymbol{\omega}} = 15\boldsymbol{i} - 2\boldsymbol{k} \text{ rad/sec}^2$$

7. [15.4] A reference xyz has an angular velocity vector and an angular acceleration vector relative to XYZ (see Fig. 15.44) given respectively as:

$$\boldsymbol{\omega} = 3\boldsymbol{i} + 3\boldsymbol{j} + 2\boldsymbol{k} \text{ rad/sec}$$

$$\dot{\boldsymbol{\omega}} = 2\boldsymbol{i} + 5\boldsymbol{k} \text{ rad/sec}^2$$

What is the time rate of change of the position vector $\boldsymbol{r}$ in XYZ as seen from xyz at time t? Compute the second time derivative of $\boldsymbol{r}$ as seen from xyz.

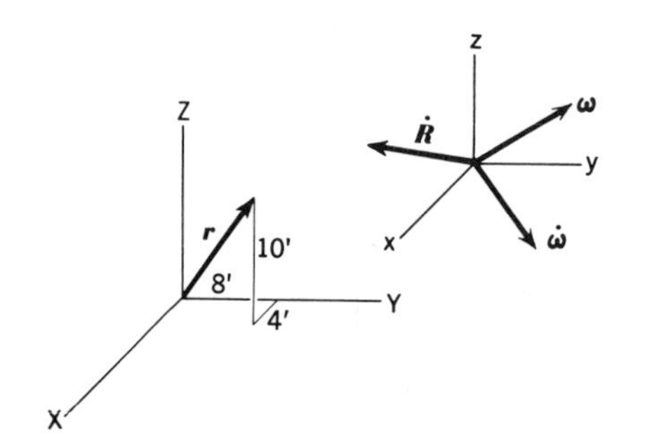

Fig. 15.44

8. [15.4] In Fig. 15.45 we have shown an electric motor M mounted on a plate A which is welded to a shaft D. The motor has a constant angular speed relative to plate A of 1750 rpm. The plate A at the instant of interest is in a vertical position as shown and is rotating with an angular speed ω_1 equal to 100 rpm and a rate of change of angular speed $\dot{\omega}_1$ equal to 30 rpm/sec—all relative to the ground. The normal projection of the centerline of the motor shaft onto the plate A is at an angle of 45° with the edge of the plate FE. Compute the first and second derivatives of $\boldsymbol{\omega}_2$ as seen from the ground.

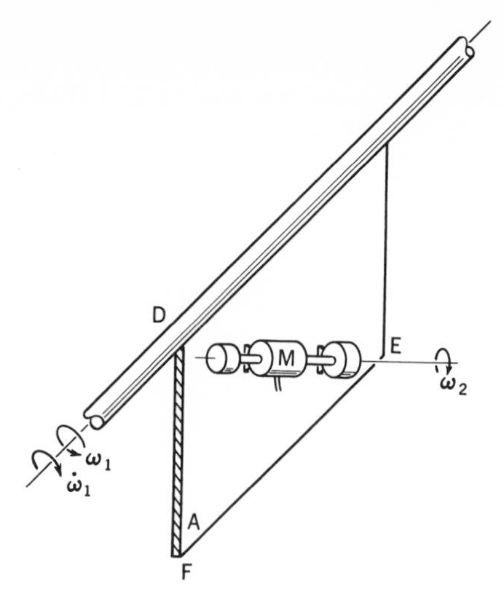

Fig. 15.45

9. [15.4] Shown in Fig. 15.46 is a platform rotating with a constant speed ω_1 of 10 rad/sec relative to the ground. A shaft is mounted on the platform and rotates relative to the platform at a speed ω_2 of 5 rad/sec. What is the angular velocity of the shaft relative to the ground? What are the first and second time derivatives of the angular velocity of the shaft relative to the ground.

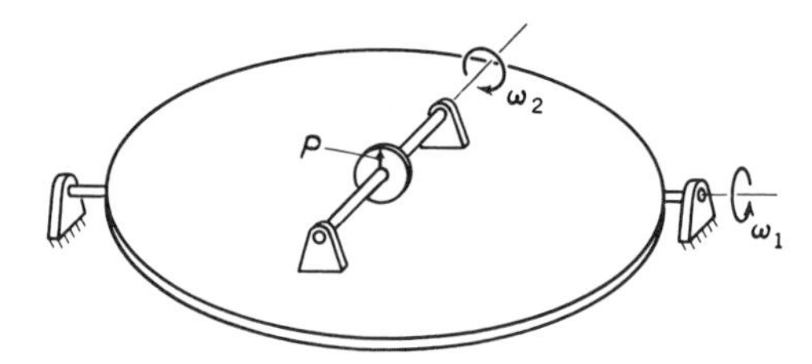

Fig. 15.46

10. [15.4] In the preceding problem, what are the first and second time derivatives of a displacement vector $\boldsymbol{\varrho}$ in the disc at the instant that the system has the geometry shown in Fig. 15.46? The displacement vector is of length 1 ft?

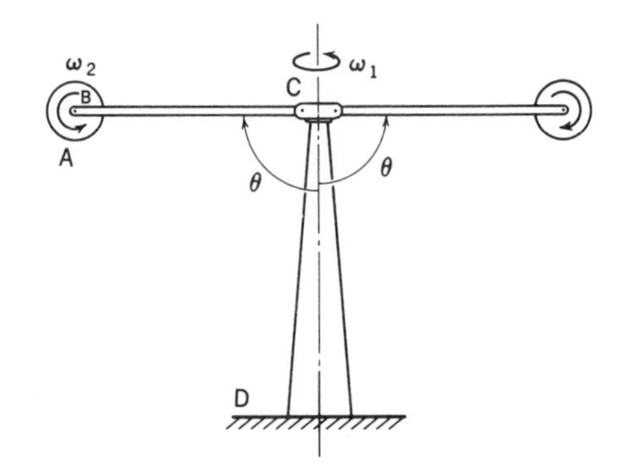

Fig. 15.47

11. [15.4] In Fig. 15.47 is shown a setup to be found at some amusement parks. A cockpit A holds a passenger. It rotates at angular speed ω_2 relative to arm BC which rotates at angular speed ω_1 relative to the tower. If θ is fixed at 90°, what are the total angular velocity and angular acceleration of the cockpit relative to the ground? Use $\omega_1 = 0.2$ rad/sec and $\omega_2 = 0.6$ rad/sec.

12. [15.4] Do Prob. 11 for the case where θ is equal to 45°.

13. [15.4] Do Prob. 11 for the case where $\dot{\omega}_1 = 0.2$ rad/sec² and $\dot{\omega}_2 = 0.3$ rad/sec².

14. [15.4] Shown in Fig. 15.48 is a tank maneuvering its gun into position. At the instant of interest, the turret A is rotating at an angular speed $\dot{\theta}$ of 2 rad/sec relative to the tank and is in position $\theta = 20°$. Also, at this instant, the gun is rotating at an angular speed $\dot{\phi}$ of 1 rad/sec relative to the turret and forms an angle $\phi = 30°$ with the horizontal plane. What are the angular velocity and acceleration of the gun relative to the ground?

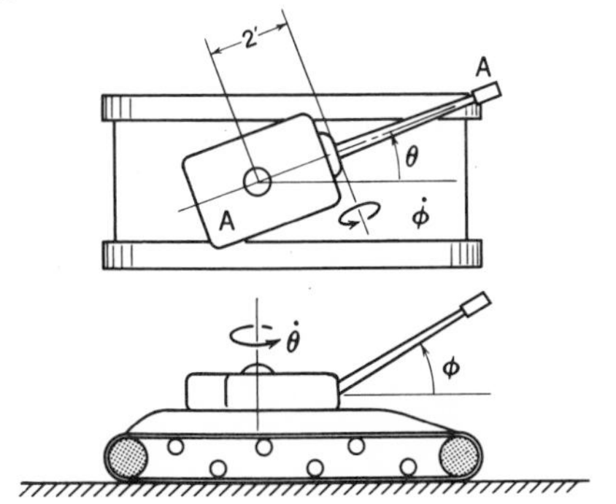

Fig. 15.48

15. [15.4] Do the preceding problem assuming that the tank is also rotating about the axis shown at a rate of 0.2 rad/sec relative to the ground in a clockwise direction as viewed from above.

16. [15.4] A particle is made to move at constant speed V equal to 10 ft/sec along a straight groove on a plate B (see Fig. 15.49). The plate rotates at a constant angular speed ω_2 equal to 3 rad/sec relative to a platform C while the platform rotates with a constant angular speed ω_1 of 5 rad/sec relative to the ground reference XYZ. Choose a reference in which the vector $\boldsymbol{V}$ is "fixed." Now find the first and second derivatives of $\boldsymbol{V}$ as seen from the ground reference.

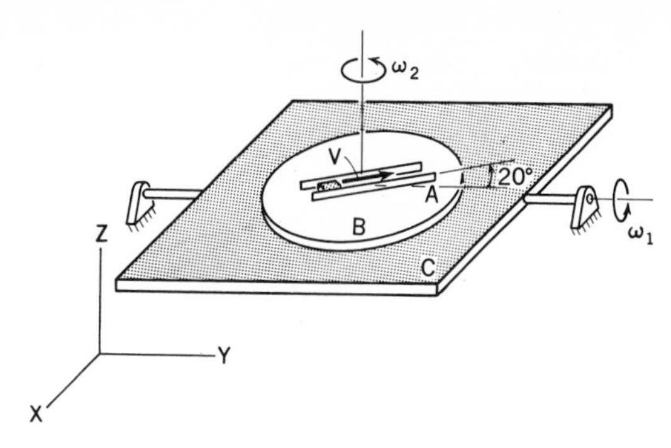

Fig. 15.49

17. [15.4] A cone is shown in Fig. 15.50 rolling without slipping such that its centerline rotates at the rate ω_1 of 5 revolutions per second about the Z axis. What is the angular velocity of the body relative to the ground? What is the angular acceleration vector for the body? Hint: What is the direction of the total angular velocity of the cone?

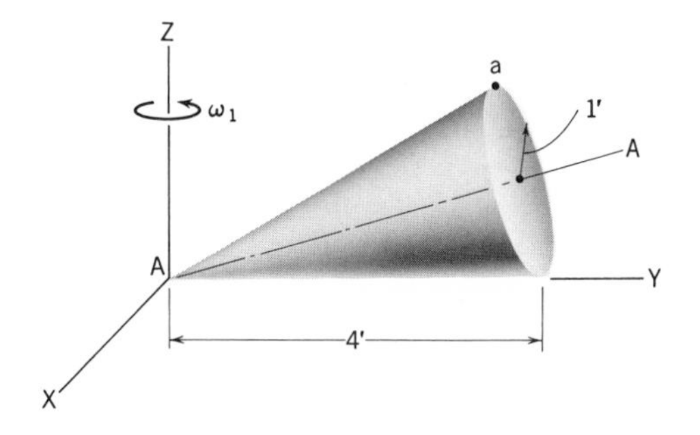

Fig. 15.50

18. [15.4] In Fig. 15.50 the centerline AA of the cone moves about the Z axis at the rate of 2 rad/sec and has, at this instant, an angular rate of increase of 3 rad/sec² about the Z axis. What is the angular acceleration vector for the cone if it rolls without slipping?

19. [15.4] Shown in Fig. 15.51 is a small cone A rolling without slipping inside a large conical cavity B. What is the angular velocity of cone A relative to the large cone cavity B if the centerline of A undergoes an angular speed ω_1 of 5 rotations per second about the axis of the large cone?

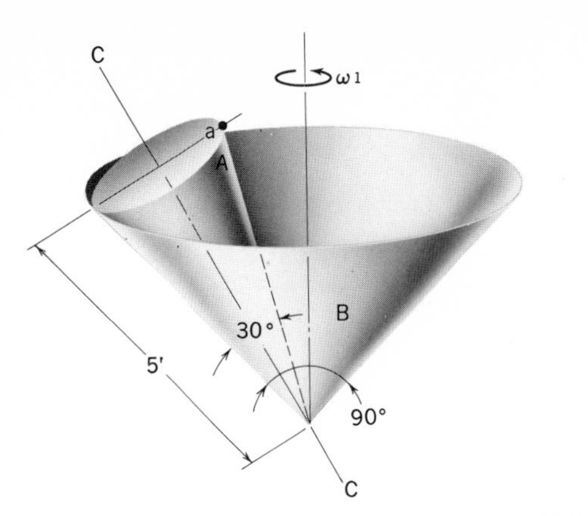

Fig. 15.51

20. [15.4] In the previous problem compute the angular acceleration of the centerline CC if $\dot{\omega}_1 = 2$ rad/sec^2.

***21.** [15.4] In Fig. 15.52 a cone A rotates without slipping in a conical cavity B such that the centerline of A undergoes an angular velocity ω_1 of 2 rotations per second relative to B. Meanwhile B rotates without slipping on cone C such that the centerline of B undergoes an angular velocity ω_2 of 0.3 rotations/sec relative to C. What are the angular velocity and angular acceleration of cone A relative to cavity B and relative to cone C at the instant shown?

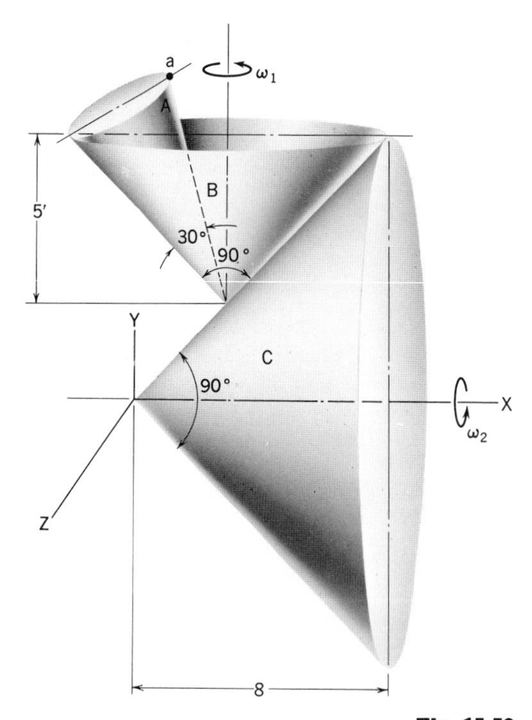

Fig. 15.52

***22.** [15.4] In Fig. 15.52 cone A rotates without slipping in a conical cavity B such that at the configuration shown the centerline has an angular speed ω_1 of 3 rad/sec relative to B and a rate of change of angular speed $\dot{\omega}_1$ of 2 rad/sec^2. Meanwhile, B rotates without slipping on cone C such that the centerline of B undergoes an angular speed ω_2 of 0.2 rad/sec and an angular acceleration $\dot{\omega}_2$ of 1 rad/sec^2 relative to C. What are the angular velocity and angular acceleration of cone A relative to cone B and relative to cone C at the instant shown?

23. [15.4] Shown in Fig. 15.53 is a body AB spinning about its own axis at a speed $\omega_1 =$ 2 rad/sec. The centerline meanwhile has indicated angular speeds ω_2 and ω_3 given as 3 rad/sec and 1 rad/sec, respectively. If $\theta = 90°$ at the instant of interest, and also if $\dot{\omega}_1 = 2$ rad/sec^2, $\dot{\omega}_2 = 0.1$, and $\dot{\omega}_3 = 5$ rad/sec^2, determine the angular velocity and acceleration of AB relative to the ground reference XYZ.

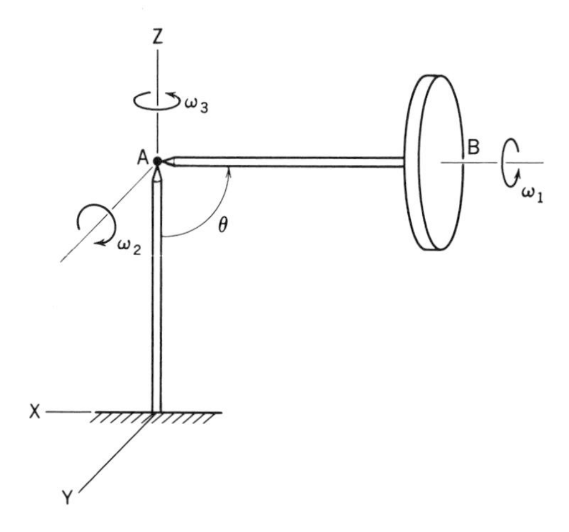

Fig. 15.53

24. [15.4] Do the preceding problem for the case where $\theta = 45°$ with the other data as given.

25. [15.4] In Fig. 15.47 is shown a device found in amusement parks. (The explanation of the terms is to be found in Prob. 11.) Find the total angular velocity and the total angular acceleration of cockpit A relative to the ground if, at the instant shown, $\theta = 90°$ and $\dot{\theta} = 2$ rad/sec. Take $\omega_1 = 4$ rad/sec, $\dot{\omega}_1 = 0.2$ rad/sec^2, $\omega_2 =$ 0.3 rad/sec, and $\dot{\omega}_2 = 0$.

26. [15.4] Do the preceding problem for $\theta = 45°$.

27. [15.5] A body is spinning about an axis having direction cosines $l = 0.5$, $m = 0.5$, $n = 0.707$, as shown in Fig. 15.54. The angular speed is 50 rad/sec. What is the velocity of a point in the body having a position vector $\boldsymbol{r} = 6\boldsymbol{i} + 4\boldsymbol{j}$ ft?

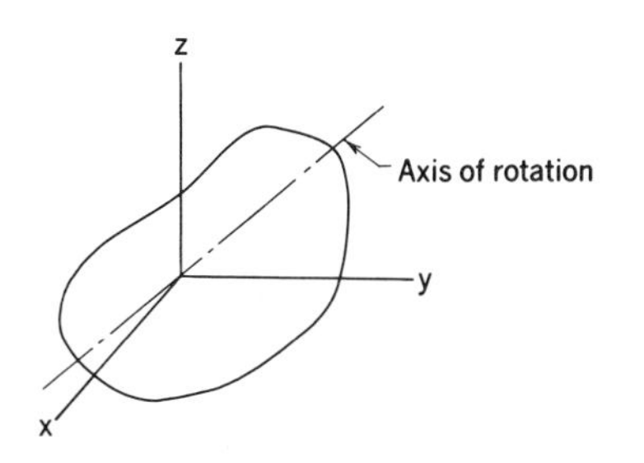

Fig. 15.54

28. [15.5] In the above problem, what is the relative velocity between a point in the body at position $x = 10$, $y = 6$, $z = 3$, and a point in the body at position $x = 2$, $y = -3$, $z = 0$? Coordinates are in units of ft.

29. [15.5] If the body in Prob. 27 is given an additional angular velocity $\boldsymbol{\omega} = 6\boldsymbol{j} + 10\boldsymbol{k}$ rad/sec, what is the direction of the axis of rotation? Compute the velocity at $\boldsymbol{r} = 10\boldsymbol{j} + 3\boldsymbol{k}$ ft if the axis of rotation goes through the origin.

30. [15.5] A cylinder rotates about its centerline with an angular speed of $(100/\pi)$ revolutions/second (Fig. 15.55). What is the velocity of point b? If the cylinder is now made to rotate instead about BB with $(100/\pi)$ revolutions/second, what is the velocity of b? Determine the relative velocity between points b and a for both axes.

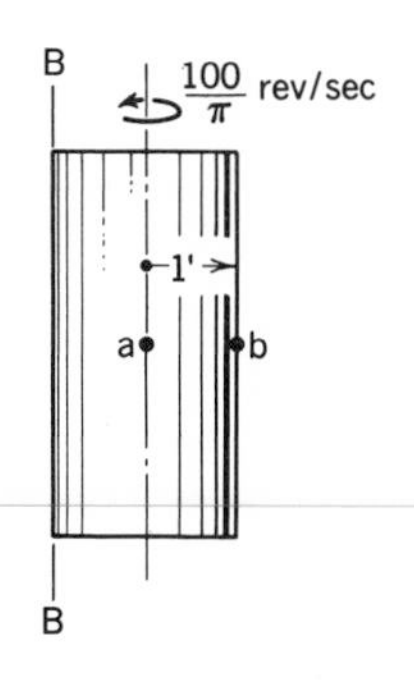

Fig. 15.55

31. [15.5] A rigid body is shown moving relative to xyz in Fig. 15.56. Two points a and b of the rigid body have position vectors at the time of interest which are given as:

$$\boldsymbol{r}_a = 10\boldsymbol{i} + 15\boldsymbol{j} + 20\boldsymbol{k} \text{ ft}$$

$$\boldsymbol{r}_b = 15\boldsymbol{i} + 20\boldsymbol{j} + 5\boldsymbol{k} \text{ ft}$$

The velocities of the points at the instant of interest are:

$$\boldsymbol{V}_a = 5\boldsymbol{i} + 20\boldsymbol{j} + 10\boldsymbol{k} \text{ ft/sec}$$

$$\boldsymbol{V}_b = 10\boldsymbol{i} + 18\boldsymbol{j} + (V_b)_z\boldsymbol{k} \text{ ft/sec}$$

Determine $(V_b)_z$. What is the angular velocity vector if ω_{ab}, the component of $\boldsymbol{\omega}$ along ab, has a value of 1 rad/sec?

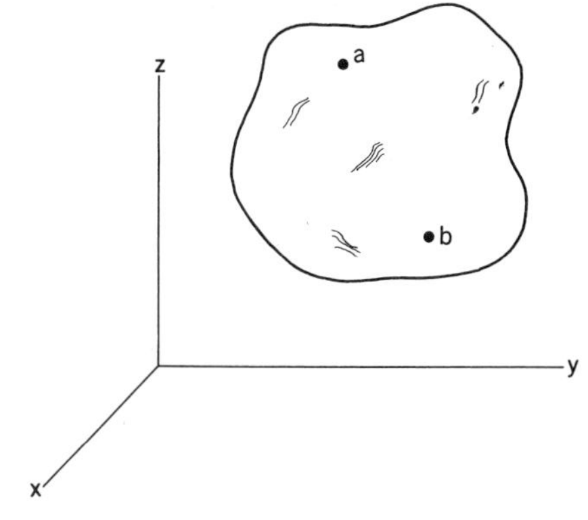

Fig. 15.56

32. [15.5] Using the results of the preceding problem, compute the angular acceleration of the body if, at the instant of interest, we know that:

$$\boldsymbol{a}_a = 5\boldsymbol{i} + 10\boldsymbol{j}$$

$$\boldsymbol{a}_b = 10\boldsymbol{i} + 12\boldsymbol{k}$$

Assume here that $\dot{\omega}_{ab} = 2$ rad/sec^2.

33. [15.5] Two points move in space with the following velocities at a certain time t.

$$\boldsymbol{V}_1 = 6\boldsymbol{i} + 10\boldsymbol{j}, \qquad \boldsymbol{V}_2 = 3\boldsymbol{k}$$

(a) What is the relative velocity between the particles?

(b) What is the angular velocity of a line going through the particles if they have positions $\boldsymbol{r}_1 = -3\boldsymbol{i}$ and $\boldsymbol{r}_2 = 10\boldsymbol{i}$ at the instant t?

34. [15.5] A wheel is rolling along at 50 ft/sec without slipping (Fig. 15.57). What is the angular speed? What is the velocity of point B on the rim of the wheel?

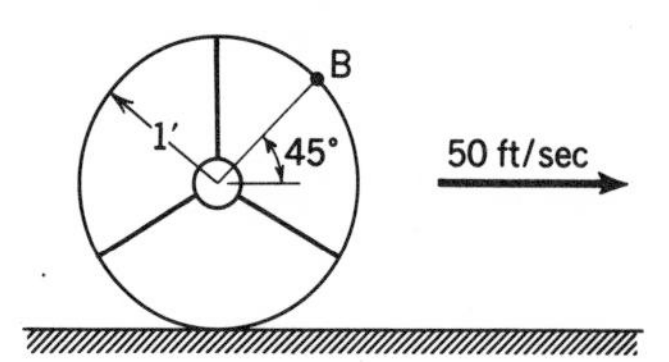

Fig. 15.57

35. [15.5] A flexible cord is wrapped around a spool and is pulled at a velocity of 10 ft/sec relative to the ground (Fig. 15.58). If there is no slipping, what is the velocity of points O and D?

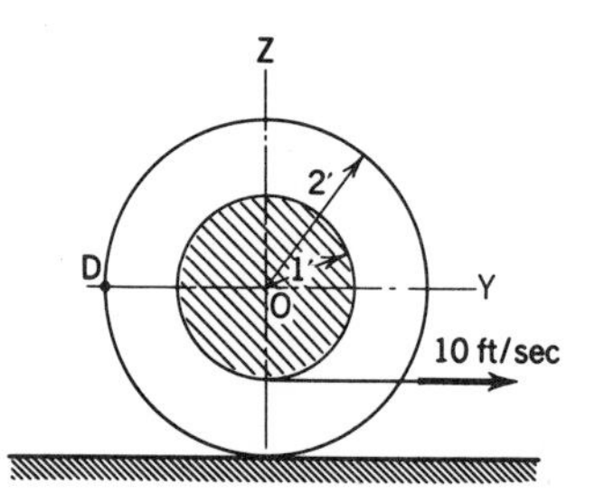

Fig. 15.58

36. [15.5] A rod moves in the plane of the paper in such a way that end A has a speed of 10 ft/sec (Fig. 15.59). What is the velocity of point B of the rod when the rod is inclined at 45° to the horizontal? B is at the upper supporting edge.

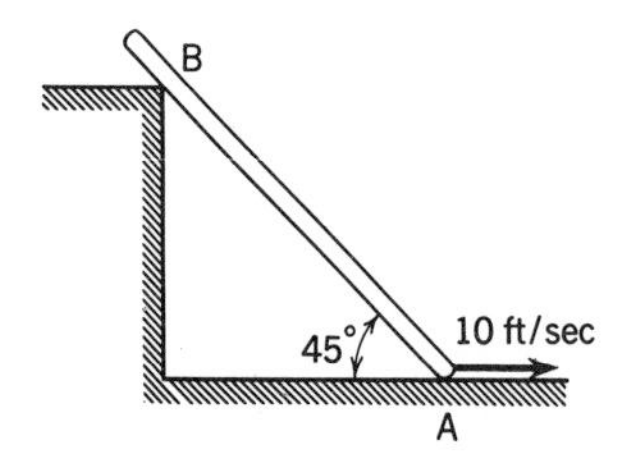

Fig. 15.59

37. [15.5] In Fig. 15.60 member AB is rotating at a constant speed of 4 rad/sec in a counterclockwise direction. What is the angular velocity of bar BC for the position shown in the diagram? What is the velocity of point D at the center of bar BC? Bar BC is 3 ft in length.

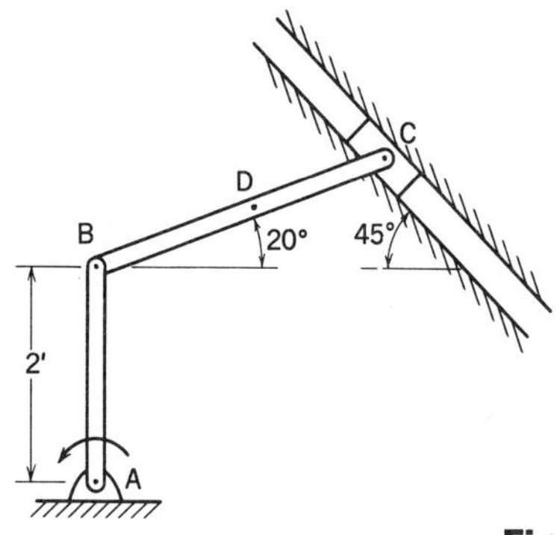

Fig. 15.60

38. [15.5] In Fig. 15.60 suppose bar AB has an angular velocity of 3 rad/sec counterclockwise and an angular acceleration of 5 rad/sec². What is the angular acceleration of bar BC, which is 3 ft in length?

39. [15.5] Shown in Fig. 15.61 is a slider A having at the instant of interest a speed V_A of 10 ft/sec with a deceleration of 5 ft/sec². Compute the angular velocity and angular acceleration of bar AB at the instant of interest. What is position of the instantaneous axis of rotation of bar AB?

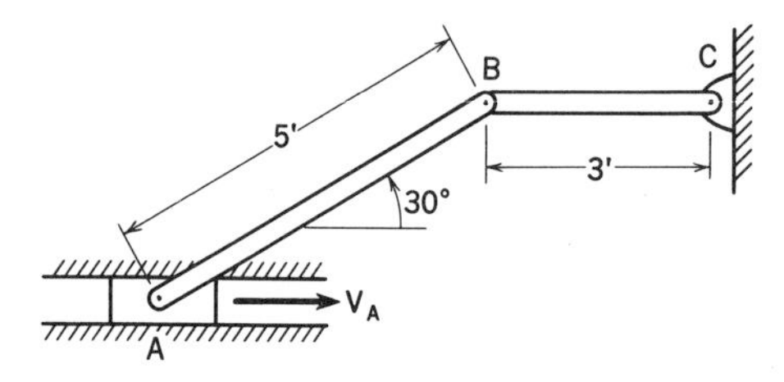

Fig. 15.61

40. [15.5] In Fig. 15.62 is shown a piston P moving downward at the constant speed of 1 ft/sec. What is the speed of slider A at the instant of interest?

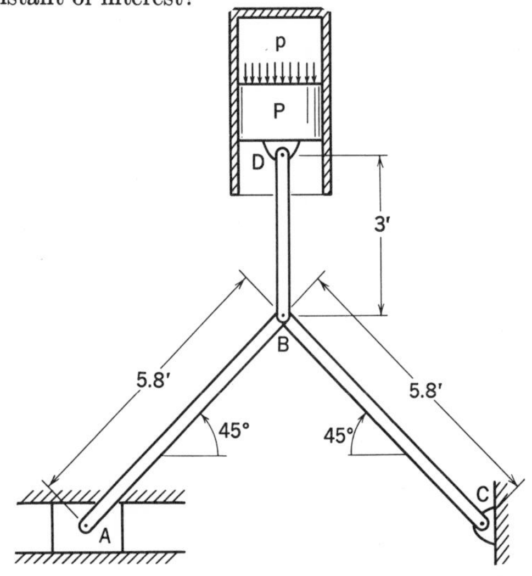

Fig. 15.62

41. [15.5] In Fig. 15.62 assume the piston is moving at the speed of 2 ft/sec but is decelerating at the rate of 3 ft/sec². Compute the angular acceleration of bar *DB*.

42. [15.5] In Fig. 15.63 is shown a mechanism with two sliders. Slider *A* at the instant of interest has a speed of 10 ft/sec and is accelerating at the rate of 5 ft/sec². If member *AB* is 8 ft in length, what are the angular velocity and angular acceleration for this member?

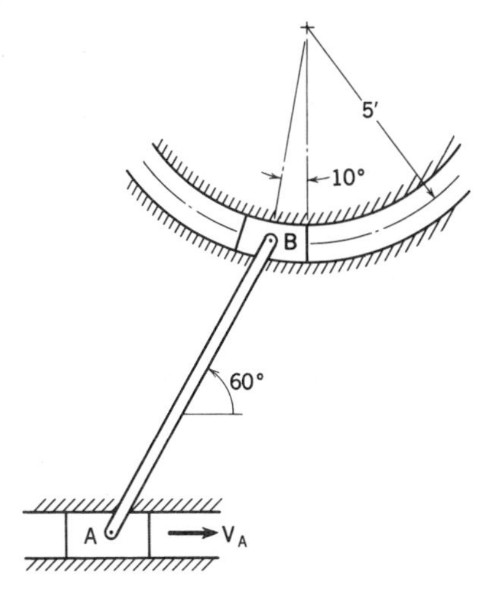

Fig. 15.63

43. [15.5] In Prob. 42 find the instantaneous center of rotation of bar *AB* if V_A is 8 ft/sec and is decelerating at the rate of 5 ft/sec².

44. [15.5] In Fig. 15.64 is a device wherein bar *AB* is rotating at a constant speed of 5 rad/sec clockwise. What is the angular velocity of bar *BD* and body *EFC*? Determine the velocity of point *D*. Hint: What is the direction of the velocity of point *G*?

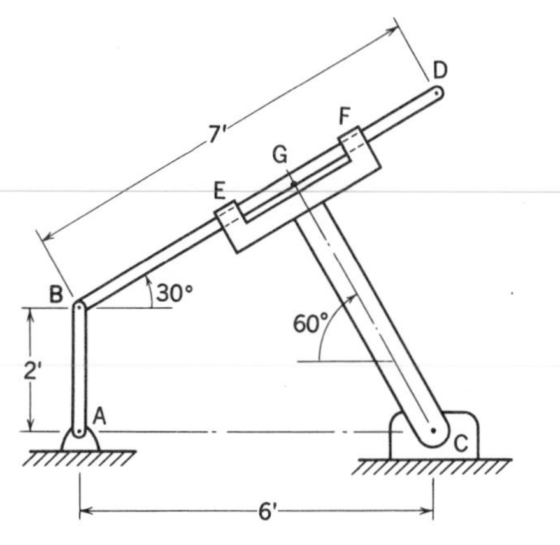

Fig. 15.64

45. [15.5] In Fig. 15.64 bar *AB* is rotating at a speed of 10 rad/sec clockwise and is decelerating at a rate of 3 rad/sec². What is the angular acceleration of body *EFC*?

46. [15.5] A bar moves in the plane of the paper so that end *A* has a velocity of 20 ft/sec and decelerates at a rate of 10 ft/sec² (Fig. 15.65). What are the velocity and acceleration of point *C* when *BA* is at 30° to the horizontal?

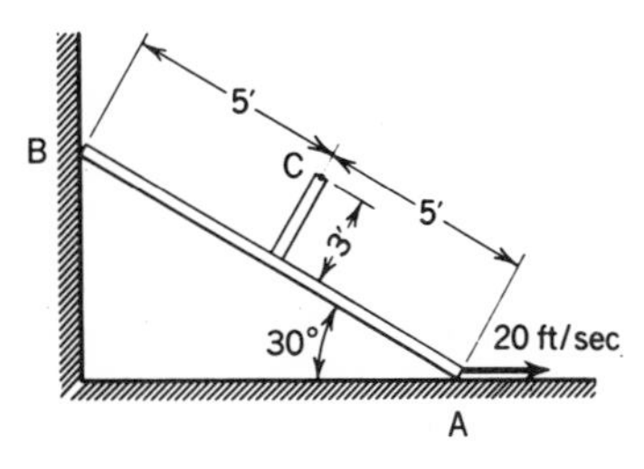

Fig. 15.65

47. [15.5] A wheel rotates with an angular speed of 20 rad/sec (Fig. 15.66). A connecting rod connects point *A* on the wheel with a slider at *B*. Compute the angular velocity of the connecting rod and the velocity of the slider when the apparatus is in the position shown in the diagram.

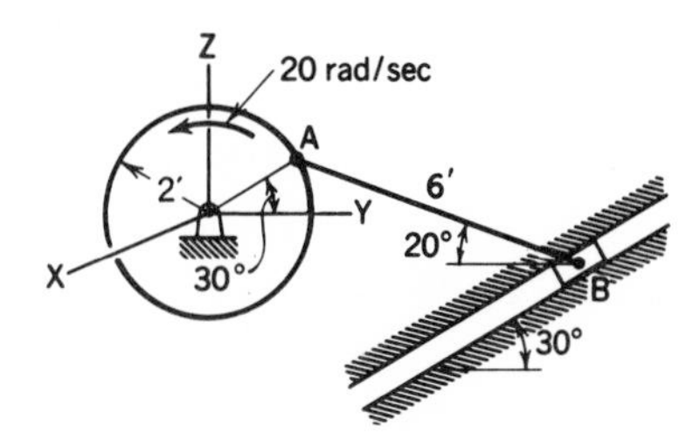

Fig. 15.66

48. [15.5] Shown in Fig. 15.67 are a piston, connecting rod, and crankshaft of an engine. The engine is rotating at 3000 rpm. At the piston shown, what is the velocity of pin *A* relative to the engine block and what is the angular velocity of the connecting rod?

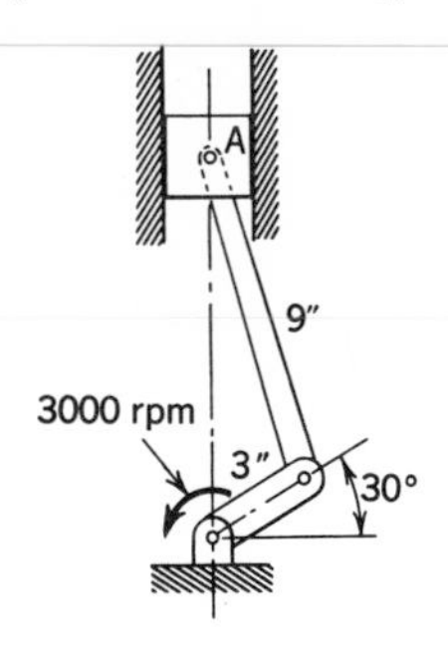

Fig. 15.67

49. [15.5] In Fig. 15.68, find the velocity of point B relative to the ground. The wheel rolls without slipping. Also find the angular velocity of the slotted bar in which the point B of the wheel slides when θ of the bar is 30°.

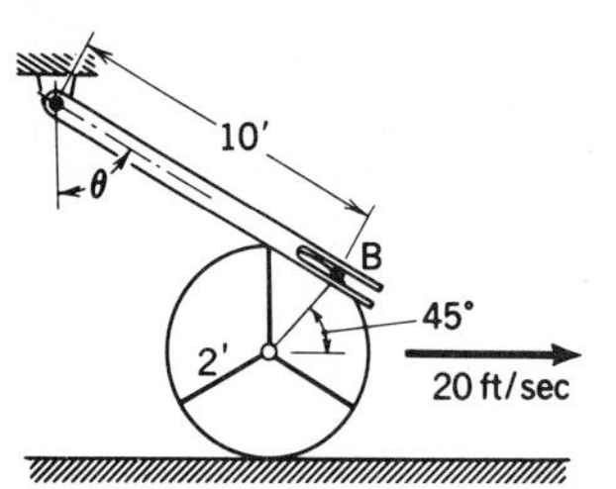

Fig. 15.68

50. [15.5] Find the acceleration of point B relative to the ground in Prob. 49.

51. [15.5] In Prob. 49, slippage at the contact surface makes the velocity of the wheel at the contact point 5 ft/sec to the right. What are the velocity of point B and the angular velocity of the bar?

52. [15.5] What is the angular acceleration of the disc—i.e., $\dot{\omega}$—shown rotating in Fig. 15.69 with an angular speed of 10 rad/sec in a fork which itself rotates with a speed of 50 rad/sec?

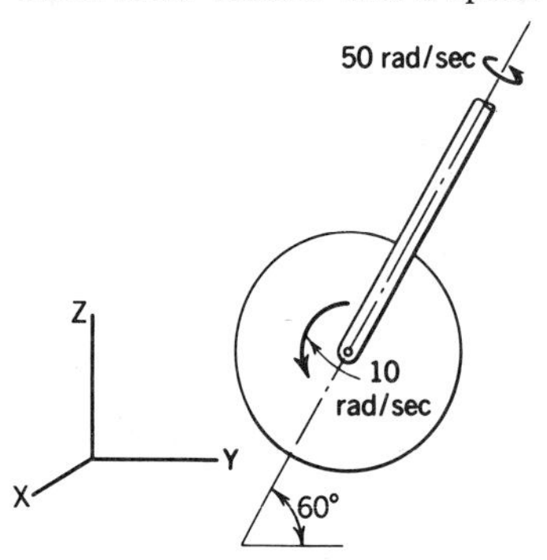

Fig. 15.69

53. [15.5] A disc mounted on shaft AB rotates with an angular speed of $(20/\pi)$ rev/min on a platform which rotates on bearings CD with a speed of $(40/\pi)$ rev/min (Fig. 15.70). What is the angular acceleration of the disc?

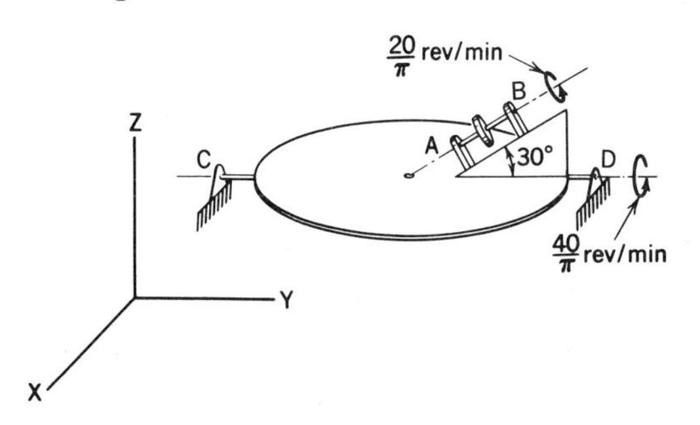

Fig. 15.70

54. [15.5] A vehicle moves down the incline at a speed of 50 ft/sec (Fig. 15.71). A shaft and platform move with the vehicle but have a spin of 5 rad/sec about the centerline AB, which remains vertical. What is the velocity of point D on the platform at the instant it is in the YZ plane, as shown in the diagram?

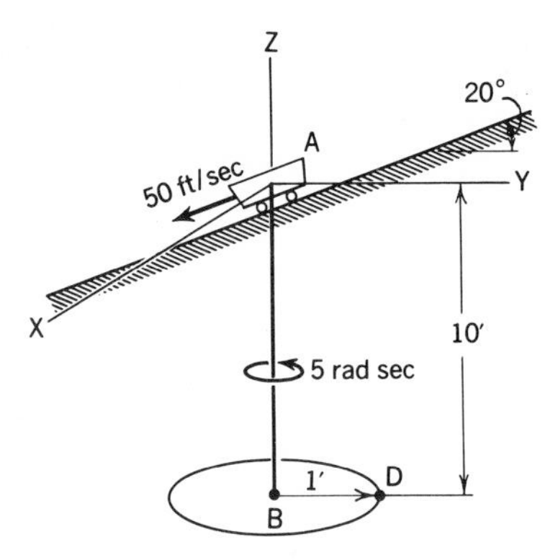

Fig. 15.71

55. [15.5] In Prob. 54 shaft AB is given the additional motion of swinging in the YZ plane with an angular speed of 10 rad/sec (Fig. 15.72). Compute the velocity of point D on the edge of the platform at the instant shaft AB is vertical. The point D is in such a position at this instant that the radial line DB is parallel to the X axis. What is the angular acceleration of the platform?

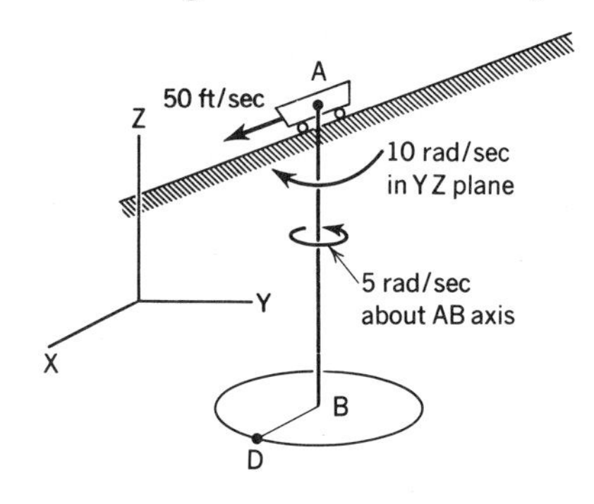

Fig. 15.72

56. [15.5] In Prob. 54 compute the acceleration of point D if the vehicle A is known to have a deceleration of 5 ft/sec² at the instant BD is parallel to the Y axis.

57. [15.5] In Prob. 55 compute the acceleration of point D. The vehicle at A has a uniform velocity at the instant that D is in the position shown.

58. [15.5] If $\omega_1 = 5$ rad/sec for bar CD in Fig. 15.73, compute the angular velocity of the gear D relative to CD and relative to the ground. Next compute the velocity of point A relative to the ground.

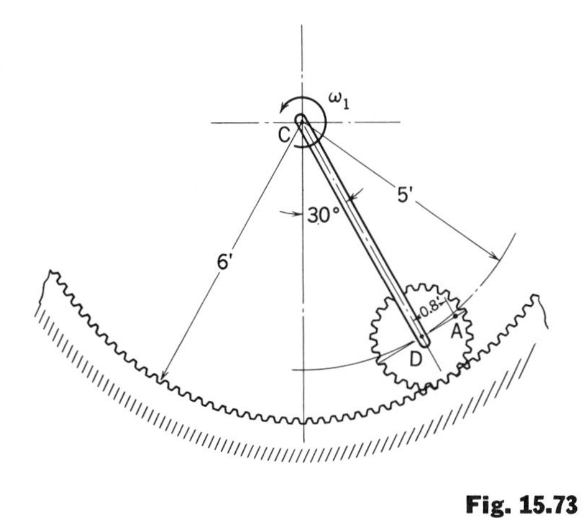

Fig. 15.73

59. [15.5] In Fig. 15.74 wheel D rotates at an angular speed ω_1 of 2 rad/sec. Find the velocity of point A relative to the ground. Next find angular velocity $\boldsymbol{\omega}_A$ of the gear relative to the ground.

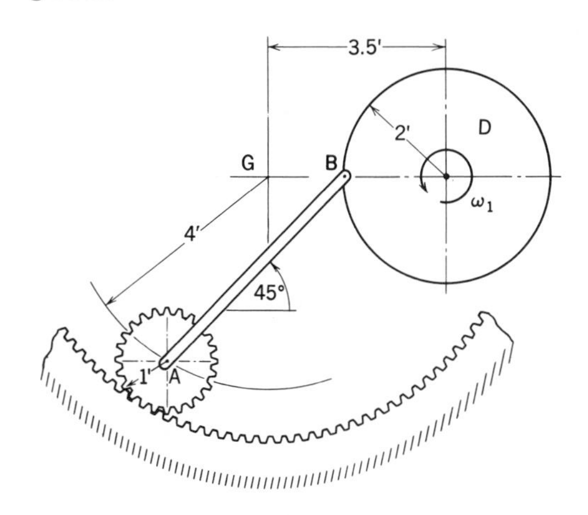

Fig. 15.74

60. [15.5] In Fig. 15.75 a cylinder C rolls without slipping on a half-cylinder D. Rod BA is 20 ft long and is connected at A to a slider which at the instant of interest is moving in a groove at the speed V of 10 ft/sec. What is the angular speed of cylinder C relative to the ground? What is the angular speed of C relative to the rod BA?

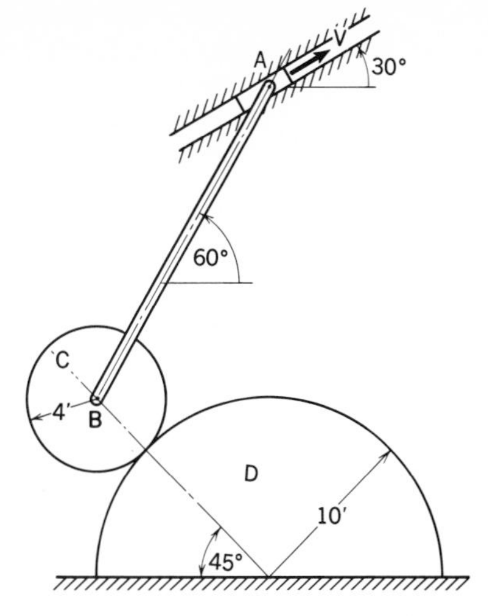

Fig. 15.75

61. [15.5] In Fig. 15.76 are shown two stationary half-cylinders F and I on which roll cylinders G and H. If the motion is such that line BA has an angular speed of 2 rad/sec clockwise, what is the angular speed of cylinder H relative to the ground? The cylinders roll without slipping.

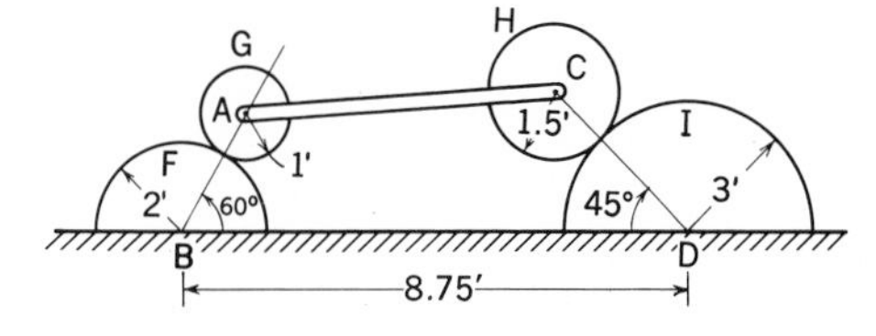

Fig. 15.76

62. [15.5] In the previous problem assume that cylinder G is rotating at a speed of 5 rad/sec clockwise as seen from the ground. What is the speed of point C relative to the ground? What is the angular speed of H relative to the ground?

***63.** [15.5] In Fig. 15.77 is shown a device whereby rod AC is connected to a gear D and is guided by a bearing B. Bearing B is stationary but can rotate in the plane of the gears. If the angular speed of AC is 5 rad/sec clockwise, what is the angular speed of gear D relative to rod AC and relative to the ground? The diameter of gear C is 2 ft.

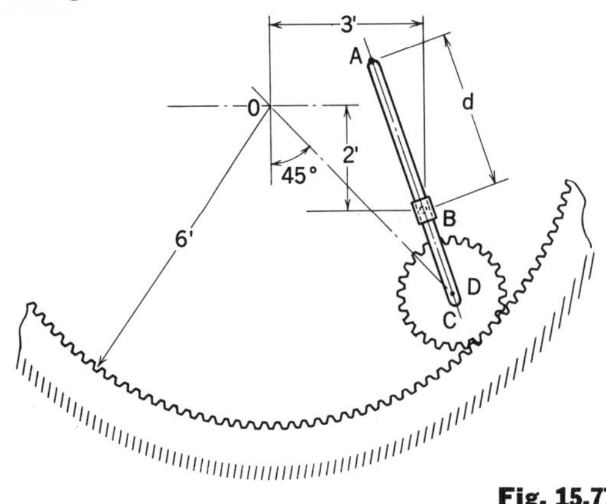

Fig. 15.77

***64.** [15.5] In the preceding problem compute the velocity of point A at the instant of interest. The distance d at this instant is 3 ft.

In Probs. 65 to 76 set up the equations that are to be solved simultaneously, if time is short. If not, you might use a computer.

65. [15.5] A bar AB can slide along members CD and FG of a rigid structure shown in Fig. 15.78. If A is moving at a speed of 1 ft/sec along CD toward D and is at this instant a distance of 1 ft from C, what are the speed of B along FG and the angular velocity vector component of bar AB normal to the centerline of the bar? At A and B there are ball-joint connections.

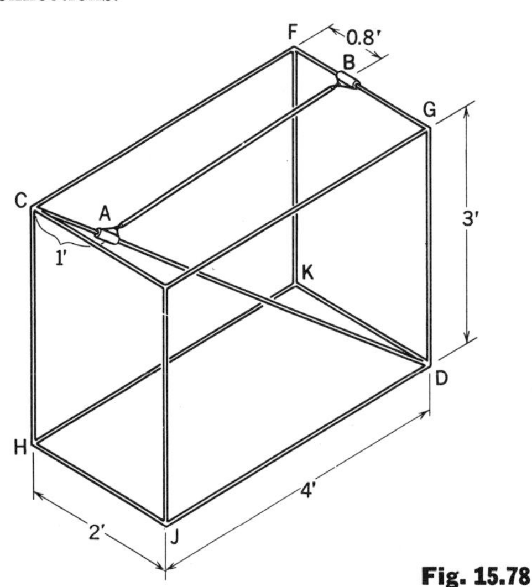

Fig. 15.78

66. [15.5] In Fig. 15.78 take the speed of point B to be 3 ft/sec toward F. Point A is 1 ft from C at this instant. What is the angular velocity component of bar AB normal to the centerline (or in other words what is the angular velocity of the centerline of AB)?

67. [15.5] Shown in Fig. 15.79 is a bar FG moving such that end G has a constant speed $V = 5$ ft/sec along a bar parallel to the y axis and in the zy plane, while end F moves in a slot DB cut in the surface ABC of a solid. If $CD = 7$ ft and $DF = 6$ ft at the instant of interest, what are the velocity of point F and the angular velocity component of the bar FG normal to the centerline of the bar?

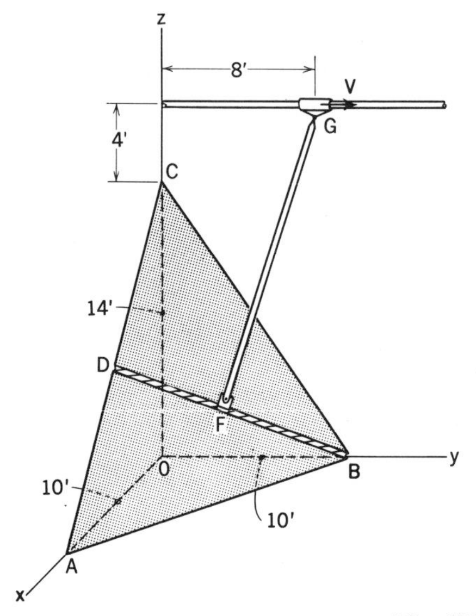

Fig. 15.79

68. [15.5] In the previous problem compute the angular acceleration component of the bar normal to the centerline of the bar.

69. [15.5] In Example 15.9 find the acceleration of point C for the case where $\dot{\omega}$ is given as 5 rad/sec² in a clockwise direction as you look in from the y direction towards the origin O.

70. [15.5] A wheel D of radius $R_1 = 6$ in. rotates at a speed $\omega_1 = 5$ rad/sec as shown in Fig. 15.80. A second wheel C is connected to wheel D by connecting rod AB. What is the angular speed of wheel C at the instant shown? The radius $R_2 = 12$ in. The wheels are separated by a distance $d = 2$ ft.

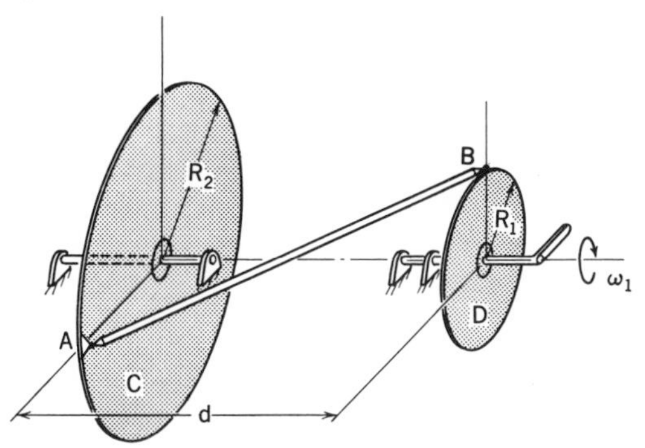

Fig. 15.80

71. [15.5] In the previous problem compute the acceleration of point A if $\dot{\omega}_1 = -5$ rad/sec^2. Find the angular acceleration component along AB of the bar AB.

72. [15.5] A pin A moves in a circular slot in plate M shown in Fig. 15.81. A rod connects this pin with a slider at B. Find the velocity and acceleration of slider B if the angular velocity of OA is 5 rad/sec and its angular acceleration is 3 rad/sec^2. The radius OA is 2 ft.

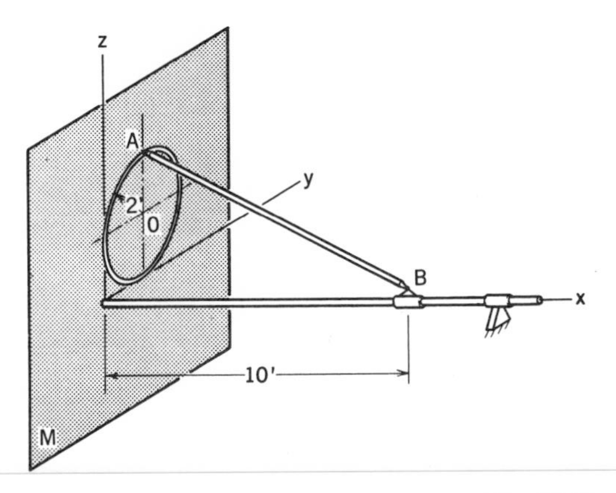

Fig. 15.81

73. [15.5] In Prob. 65 compute the speed of B along FG for the case where there is a pin connection at A with the pin oriented normal to the centerline of CD.

74. [15.5] In Prob. 67 compute the velocity of point F for the case where there is a pin joint at G with the pin oriented normal to the centerline of the guide shaft.

***75.** [15.5] In Fig. 15.82 is shown a device whereby two plates A and B are connected by a system of identical rigid rods. Plate A is fixed to the shaft while plate B can rotate and slide along the shaft. If plate B is dropping at the rate of 2 ft/sec, what must be its angular velocity? What is the magnitude of the angular velocity component of each rod normal to the centerline of the rod?

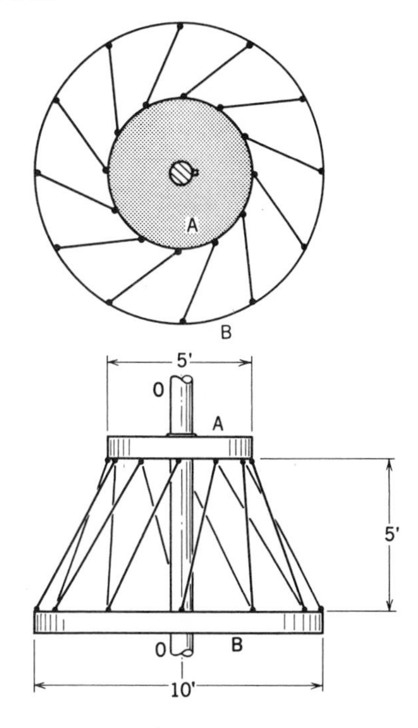

Fig. 15.82

***76.** [15.5] For the device of Fig. 15.82, if the lower plate is given an angular acceleration 1 rad/sec^2 in a clockwise direction as viewed from below, what is the vertical acceleration of the plate? Assume that the angular velocity of plate B is zero when this is done.

77. [15.7] In Fig. 15.83 is a device where a rod BO rotates at a constant angular speed $\dot{\theta}$ of 5 rad/sec clockwise. A slider A on the rod is pinned to a second slider C which moves in the groove shown in the diagram. When $\theta = 60°$, compute the velocity of the slider A relative to the ground. What is the speed of the slider A relative to the rod?

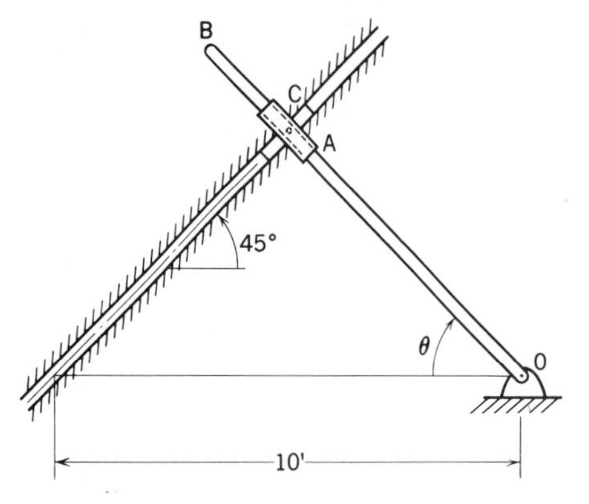

Fig. 15.83

78. [15.7] Do the previous problem assuming that pin O is on rollers moving to the right at a speed of 3 ft/sec relative to the ground. In addition OB rotates at a constant angular speed $\dot{\theta}$ of 5 rad/sec clockwise.

79. [15.7] In Fig. 15.84 is shown a device whereby rod AD rotates at a constant speed $\dot{\theta}_1$ of 2 rad/sec. Slider C on the rod DA is constrained to move in the circular groove shown in the diagram. When the rod is at the position shown, compute the velocity of slider C relative to the ground. What is the velocity of slider C relative to the rod AD? Point A is stationary.

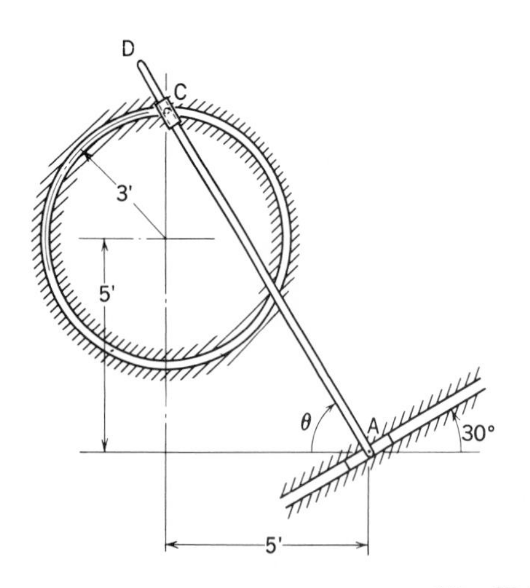

Fig. 15.84

80. [15.7] In the previous problem assume, in addition to the rotation of bar AD, that pin A is moving at a speed of 5 ft/sec up the grooved incline.

81. [15.8] What is the acceleration of slider C in Fig. 15.84 relative to the ground for the following data at the configuration shown:

$$\dot{\theta} = 5 \text{ rad/sec}$$
$$\ddot{\theta} = -2 \text{ rad/sec}^2$$
$$V_A = 0$$
$$\dot{V}_A = 0$$

What is the acceleration of the slider C relative to rod AD?

82. [15.8] What is the acceleration of the slider C in Fig. 15.84 relative to the ground for the following data at the configuration shown:

$$\theta = 2 \text{ rad/sec}$$
$$\ddot{\theta} = 3 \text{ rad/sec}^2$$
$$V_A = 2 \text{ ft/sec}$$
$$\dot{V}_A = 3 \text{ ft/sec}^2$$

Also determine the acceleration of the slider relative to the rod AD.

83. [15.7] A particle rotates at a constant angular speed of 10 rad/sec on a platform, while the platform rotates with a constant angular speed of 50 rad/sec about axis AA (Fig. 15.85). What is the velocity of the particle P at the instant the platform is in the XY plane and the radius vector to the particle forms an angle of 30° with the Y axis as shown?

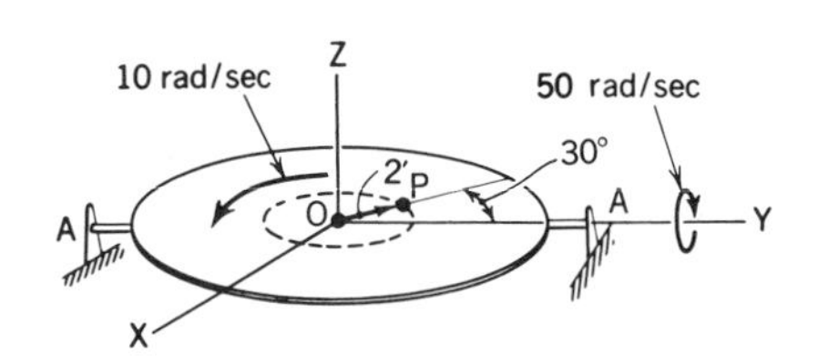

Fig. 15.85

84. [15.7] A propeller-driven airplane is undergoing a yaw rotation of $\frac{1}{4}$ rad/sec and is simultaneously undergoing a loop rotation of $\frac{1}{4}$ rad/sec (Fig. 15.86). The propeller is rotating at the rate of 100 rpm with a sense in the positive Y direction. What is the relative velocity between the tip of the propeller a and the hub B at the instant that the plane is horizontal as shown? The propeller is 10 ft in total length and at the instant of interest the blade is in a vertical position.

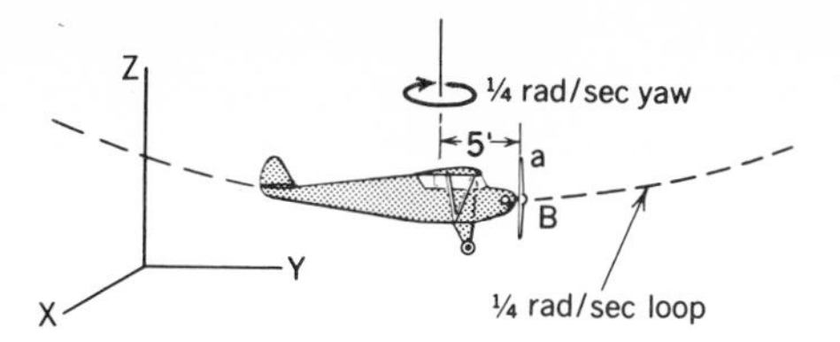

Fig. 15.86

85. [15.7] Bodies a and b (Fig. 15.87) slide away from each other with a constant velocity of 5 ft/sec along the axis CC mounted on a platform which rotates relative to the ground reference XYZ at an angular velocity of 10 rad/sec about axis EE and has an angular acceleration of 5 rad/sec² relative to the ground reference XYZ at the time when the bodies are at a distance $r = 3$ ft from EE. Determine the velocity of particle b relative to the ground reference.

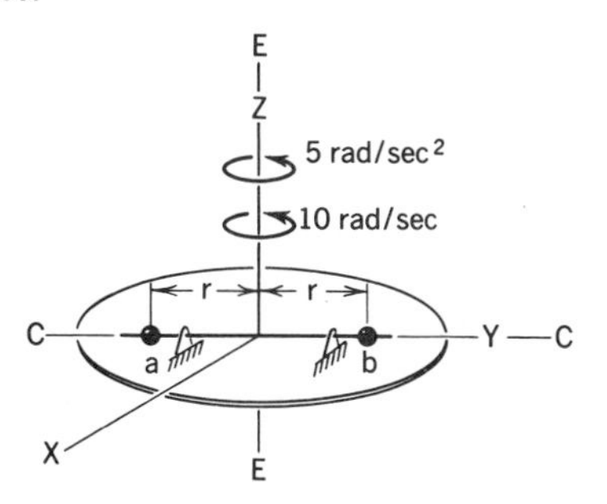

Fig. 15.87

86. [15.7] Shown in Fig. 15.88 is a device at an amusement park. The cockpit containing two occupants can rotate at an angular speed ω_1 relative to the main arm. The arm can rotate with angular speed ω_2 relative to the ground. For the position shown in the diagram and for $\omega_1 = 2$ rad/sec and $\omega_2 = 0.2$ rad/sec, find the velocity of point A (corresponding to the position of an ear of an occupant) relative to the ground.

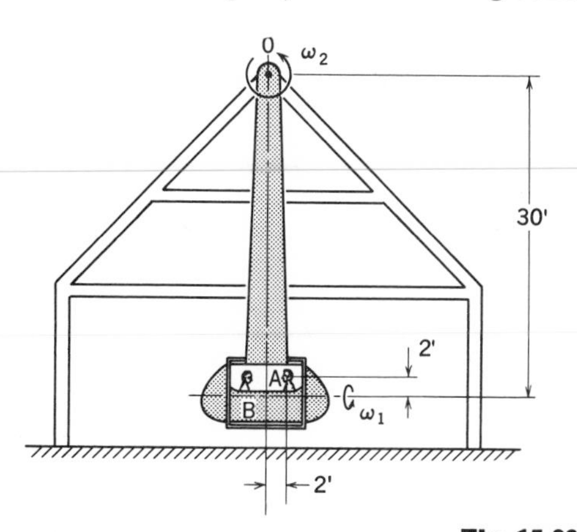

Fig. 15.88

87. [15.7] Shown in Fig. 15.89 is a tank moving up an incline with a speed of 10 miles/hour and an acceleration of 5 miles/hour/second. The turret is rotating at a speed ω_1 of 2 rad/sec relative to the tank, and the gun barrel is rotating at a speed ω_2 of 0.3 rad/sec relative to the turret. What is the velocity of point A of the gun barrel relative to the tank and relative to the ground? The gun barrel is 10 ft in length.

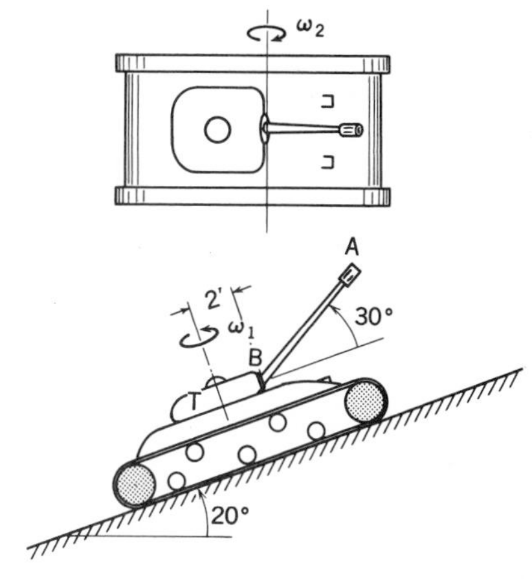

Fig. 15.89

88. [15.7] Find the velocity of the particle D relative to XYZ (fixed to the ground), using a moving reference, for Prob. 54.

89. [15.7] Find the velocity of the particle D relative to XYZ, using a moving reference, for Prob. 55.

90. [15.7] A vehicle moves along the track with a velocity of 50 ft/sec (Fig. 15.90). A pendulum extends from the vehicle and swings in the XZ plane with an angular speed of 2 rad/sec. Along the circular path in the pendulum bob, a particle performs 5 revolutions per second relative to the bob. Find the velocity of this particle relative to the track when the pendulum is in a vertical position. Let the particle be at the bottom of the circle at this instant, as shown.

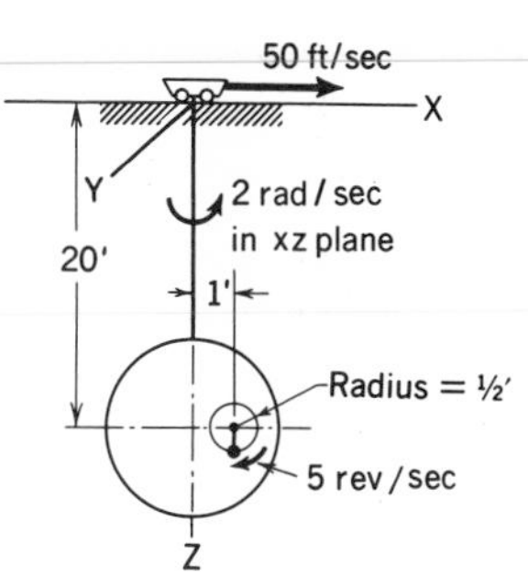

Fig. 15.90

91. [15.7] In Prob. 90, if the pendulum is also spinning about its own axis with an angular velocity of 10 rad/sec in the positive Z direction, what is the velocity of the particle relative to the track?

92. [15.7] In Fig. 15.50 the cone is rolling without slipping about the Z axis such that its centerline rotates at the rate ω_1 of 5 rad/sec. Using a multireference approach, determine the total angular speed of the body. What is the velocity of point a relative to the ground?

93. [15.7] In Prob. 19 find the angular velocity of cone A relative to the ground by employing a multireference approach. What is the velocity of point a relative to the ground?

94. [15.7] Shown in Fig. 15.91 are portions of a merry-go-round. The main platform rotates at the rate ω_1 of 10 revolutions per minute. A set of 45° bevel gears causes B to rotate at an angular speed $\dot{\theta}$ relative to the platform. The horse is mounted on AB which slides in a slot at C and is moved at A by shaft B, as indicated in the diagram. If $AB = 1$ ft and AC is 15 ft, compute the velocity of the points A and C relative to the platform. Then compute the velocity of the points relative to the ground. Take $\theta = 45°$ at the instant of interest. What is the angular velocity of the horse relative to the platform and relative to the ground at the instant of interest?

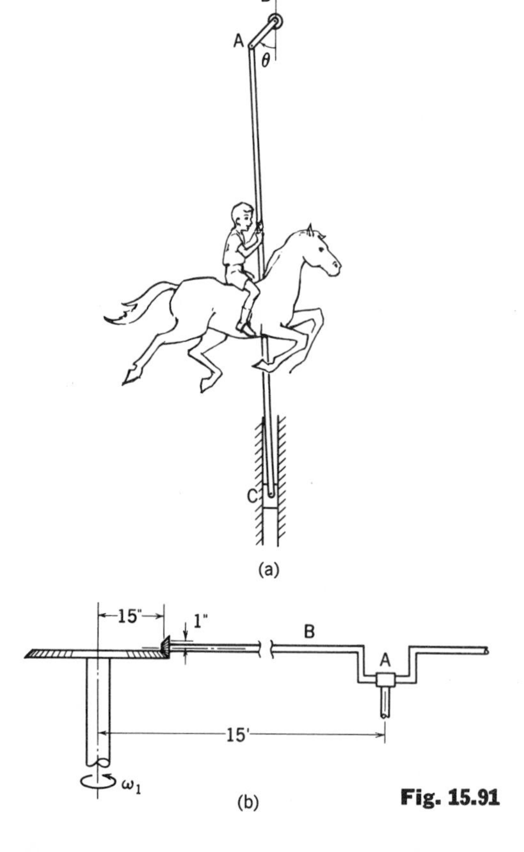

Fig. 15.91

95. [15.7] In Prob. 21, using multireference analysis, compute the angular velocity of cylinder A relative to the ground. Compute the velocity of point a relative to the ground.

In the following problems you may use the simple kinematic relation for rolling of a cylinder without slipping; $V_c = r\dot{\theta}$, where V_c is the speed of the center.

96. [15.8] A truck has a speed V of 20 mph (see Fig. 15.92) and an acceleration $\dot{V}$ of 3 mph/sec at time t. A cylinder of radius equal to 2 ft is rolling without slipping at time t such that it has an angular speed and angular acceleration respectively of 2 rad/sec and 1 rad/sec^2. Using a multi-reference approach, what are the velocity and acceleration of the center of the cylinder relative to the truck? Using a multireference approach again determine the velocity and acceleration of the center relative to the ground?

Fig. 15.92

97. [15.8] A truck is moving at a constant speed $V = 5$ ft/sec at time t (see Fig. 15.93). The truck loading compartment has at this instant a constant angular speed $\dot{\theta}$ of 0.1 rad/sec at an angle $\theta = 45°$. A cylinder of diameter of 2 ft rolls relative to the compartment at a speed of 1 rad/sec, accelerating at a speed of 0.5 rad/sec^2 at time t. What are the velocity and acceleration of the center of the cylinder relative to the compartment at time t? What are the velocity and acceleration of the center of the cylinder relative to the ground at time t? The distance d at time t is 15 ft.

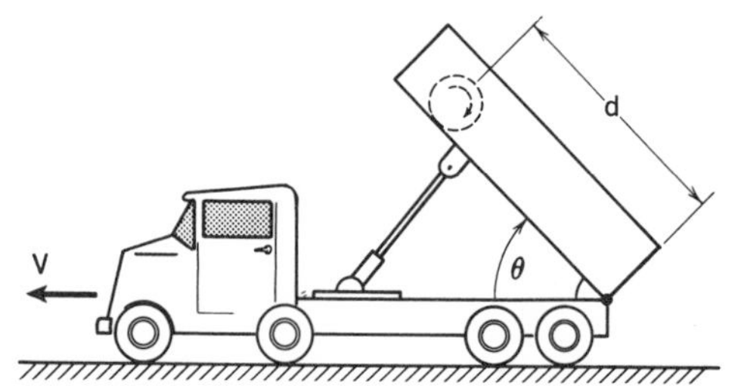

Fig. 15.93

98. [15.8] In the previous problem take at time t the following additional data:

$$\dot{V} = 2 \text{ ft/sec}^2$$

$$\ddot{\theta} = 0.2 \text{ rad/sec}^2$$

What are the speed and acceleration of the center of the cylinder relative to the truck? What are the speed and acceleration of the center of the cylinder relative to the ground?

99. [15.8] In Fig. 15.83 determine the velocity and acceleration of slider A relative to the ground and relative to rod BO. The following information applies:

$$\theta = 60°$$

$$\dot{\theta} = 2 \text{ rad/sec} \quad \text{(clockwise)}$$

$$\ddot{\theta} = -1 \text{ rad/sec}^2$$

100. [15.8] If in Fig. 15.73 $\omega_1 = 3$ rad/sec and $\dot{\omega}_1 = 5$ rad/sec², find the velocity and acceleration of point A relative to the ground. What is the acceleration of point A relative to rod CD?

101. [15.8] In Prob. 83 find the acceleration of the particle P relative to the ground reference.

102. [15.8] In Prob. 83 the line OP to particle P has an angular acceleration of 8 rad/sec² relative to the platform while the platform is decelerating at the rate of 5 rad/sec². Compute the velocity and acceleration of the particle.

103. [15.8] In Prob. 85 find the acceleration of particle b if, at the instant of interest, particle b has a speed of 10 ft/sec and an acceleration relative to the rod of 1 ft/sec² away from the center.

104. [15.8] A wheel rotates with an angular speed of 5 rad/sec on a platform which rotates with a speed of 10 rad/sec as shown in Fig. 15.94. A bead moves down the spoke of the wheel, and when the spoke is vertical the bead has a speed of 20 ft/sec, an acceleration of 10 ft/sec² along the spoke, and is positioned 1 ft from the shaft centerline of the wheel. Compute the velocity and acceleration of the bead relative to the ground at this instant.

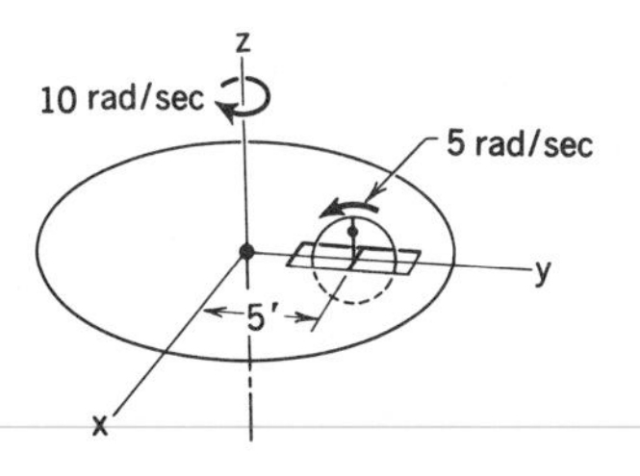

Fig. 15.94

105. [15.8] In the previous problem, the wheel accelerates at the instant under discussion with 5 rad/sec², and the platform accelerates with 10 rad/sec². Find the velocity and acceleration of the bead.

106. [15.8] In Fig. 15.88 find the acceleration of point A for the configuration shown. Take $\omega_1 = 2$ rad/sec, $\dot{\omega}_1 = 3$ rad/sec², $\omega_2 = 0.1$ rad/sec, and $\dot{\omega}_2 = 2$ rad/sec². How many g's of acceleration is this position subject to?

107. [15.8] The tank shown in Fig. 15.89 is moving up an incline at a speed of 10 mph but is decelerating at the instant of interest at the rate of 3 mph/sec. The turret T is rotating with a speed $\omega_1 = 3$ rad/sec and is accelerating at the rate of 2 rad/sec² relative to the tank. The gun barrel is rotating at the speed ω_2 of 3 rad/sec and is changing angular speed at the rate of 4 rad/sec² relative to the turret. What is the acceleration of point A of the gun barrel relative to the ground? The gun barrel is 10 ft in length.

108. [15.8] In Fig. 15.95 is shown a barge with a derrick arrangement. The main beam AB is 40 ft in length. The whole system at the instant of interest is rotating with a speed ω_1 of 1 rad/sec and an acceleration $\dot{\omega}_1$ of 2 rad/sec² relative to the barge. Also at this instant $\theta = 45°$, $\dot{\theta} = 2$ rad/sec, and $\ddot{\theta} = 1$ rad/sec². What are the velocity and acceleration of point B relative to the barge?

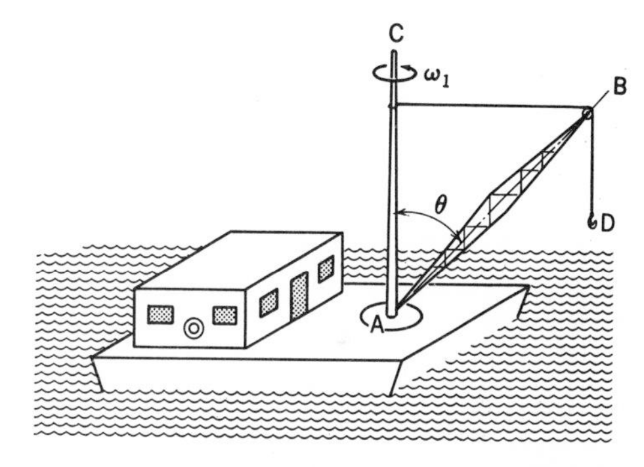

Fig. 15.95

109. [15.8] In the preceding problem compute the velocity and acceleration of B relative to the shore for the case where at the instant of interest the barge is moving ahead at a uniform speed of 2 ft/sec and is rotating about CA clockwise looking from C to A at a constant speed of 0.1 rad/sec, all relative to the shore.

110. [15.8] In Fig. 15.96 is shown a truck carrying a cockpit for a worker who repairs overhead road fixtures. At the instant shown in the diagram the base D is rotating with constant speed ω_2 of 1 rad/sec relative to the truck. Arm AB is rotating at constant angular speed ω_1 of 2 rad/sec relative to DA. Cockpit C is rotating relative to AB so as always to keep the man upright. What are the velocity and acceleration of the man relative to the ground if $\alpha = 45°$ and $\beta = 30°$ at the instant of interest? The truck is stationary. Take $DA = 40$ ft.

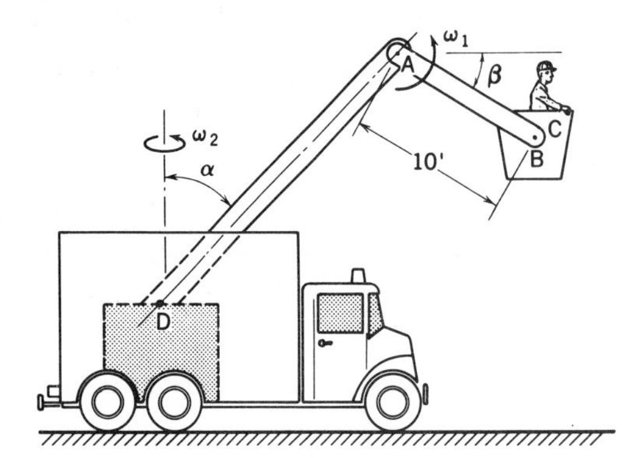

Fig. 15.96

111. [15.8] Do the previous problem for the case where these additional data apply:

$$\dot{\omega}_2 - 0.1 \text{ rad/sec}^2$$

$$\dot{\omega}_1 = 0.3 \text{ rad/sec}^2$$

Also, the truck has a speed of 5 ft/sec and is accelerating at the speed of 2 ft/sec² at the instant of interest.

112. [15.8] Shown in Fig. 15.97 is a platform A rotating with constant angular speed ω_1 of 1 rad/sec. A second platform B rides on A and contains a row of test tubes as shown in the diagram. It has a constant angular speed ω_2 of 0.2 rad/sec relative to the platform A. A third platform C is in no way connected with platform A and B. It is positioned above A and B as shown in the diagram and carries dispensers of chemicals which are electrically operated at proper times to dispense drops into the test tubes held by B below. What should the angular speed ω_3 be for platform C if it is to dispense a drop of chemical having a zero tangential velocity relative to the test tube below? What is the angular acceleration of platform C if it is to dispense a drop having the same tangential acceleration relative to the test tube below?

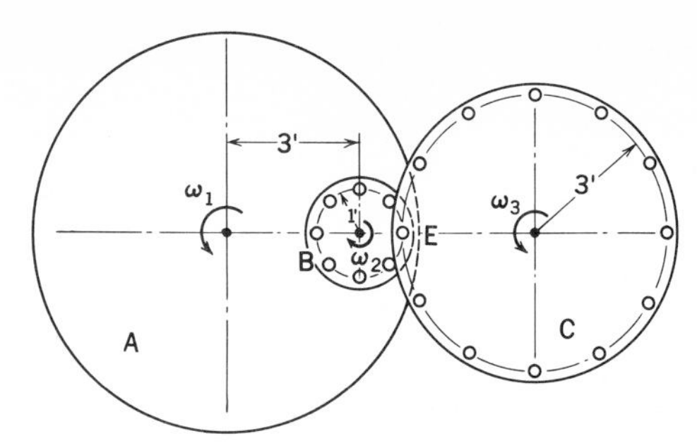

Fig. 15.97

113. [15.8] Do the previous problem for the case where at the instant of interest $\dot{\omega}_1 = 1$ rad/sec² and $\dot{\omega}_2 = 0.2$ rad/sec².

114. [15.8] In Prob. 14 find the velocity and acceleration of the tip of the gun A if the gun barrel has a length of 10 ft.

115. [15.8] In Prob. 15 find the velocity and acceleration of the tip A of the gun if the gun barrel is 12 ft in length.

116. [15.8] In Prob. 90 find the acceleration of the particle relative to the track.

117. [15.8] In Prob. 91 find the acceleration of the particle relative to the track.

***118.** [15.8] To simulate the flight conditions of a space vehicle, engineers have developed the *centrifuge*, shown diagrammatically in Fig. 15.98. A main arm, 40 ft long, rotates about the AA axis. The pilot sits in the cockpit, which may rotate about axis CC. The seat for the pilot may rotate inside the cockpit about an axis shown at the point B. These rotations are controlled by a computer that is set to simulate certain maneuvers corresponding to the entry and exit from the earth's atmosphere, malfunctions of the control system, and so on. When a pilot sits in the enclosure, his head, particularly his ears, has the position shown in Fig. 15.99. If the main arm is rotating at 10 rpm and accelerating at 5 rpm² and the capsule is rotating at a constant speed about CC at 10 rpm and the seat rotates at a speed of 5 rpm inside the capsule, how many g's is the pilot's head subjected to?

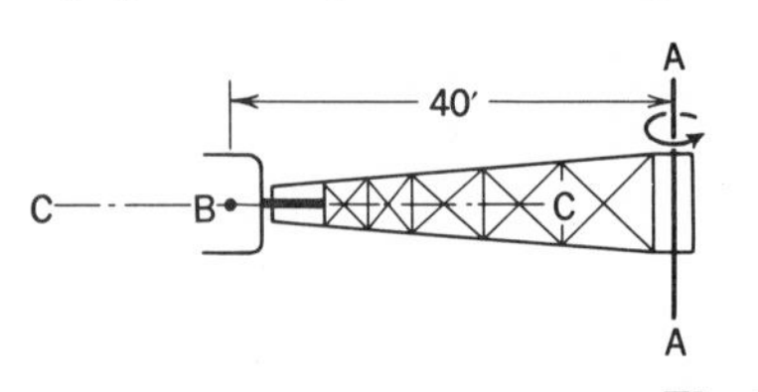

Fig. 15.98

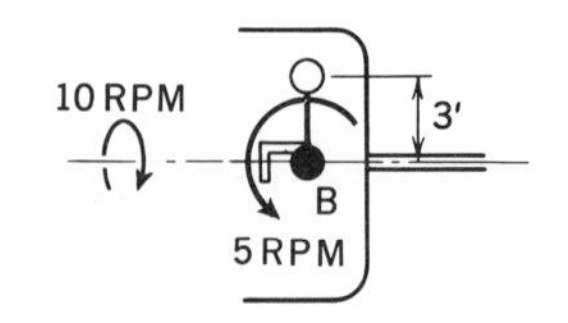

Fig. 15.99

***119.** [15.8] Do the above problem by using two viewpoints that are different from the ones you utilized in your last analysis.

***120.** [15.8] A pilot has different tolerances for acceleration components. They are roughly:

> In a vertical direction, i.e., toe to head—5 g's. (Here the pilot experiences blackout or may pass out completely.)
>
> Front to rear—15 g's. (Here vision becomes greatly distorted.)

Arrange a test program on the centrifuge so that each acceleration is reached separately while the other accelerations are kept below one-half their tolerance levels.

121. [15.9] In Fig. 15.60 what is the force on the slider at C at the instant shown? Bar AB has an angular speed ω of 3 rad/sec and is accelerating at a rate of 2 rad/sec^2. Bar BC is 3 ft in length. The slider has a mass of 2 lbm.

122. [15.9] What is the total force on the slider at A for the device shown in Fig. 15.61? The rod BC is rotating clockwise at the rate of 2 rad/sec and is decelerating at the rate of 1 rad/sec^2. The slider has a weight of 1 lb.

123. [15.9] In Fig. 15.63 find the total force on each slider at the instant shown. Slider A has a speed of 10 ft/sec to the right and is decelerating at the rate of 2 ft/sec^2. Member AB is 8 ft in length. The mass of each slider is 0.1 slug. What is the total force acting on the bar AB if it weighs 10 lb?

124. [15.9] In Prob. 96 what is the sum of the forces acting on the cylinder for the case when:

$$V = 5 \text{ ft/sec}$$
$$\dot{V} = -2 \text{ ft/sec}^2$$
$$\omega = 2 \text{ rad/sec}$$
$$\dot{\omega} = 1 \text{ rad/sec}^2$$

The mass of the cylinder is 100 lbm.

125. [15.9] In Prob. 97 what is the sum of the forces on the cylinder for the following data:

$$V = 15 \text{ ft/sec}$$
$$\dot{V} = -3 \text{ ft/sec}^2$$
$$\theta = 60°$$
$$\dot{\theta} = 0.2 \text{ rad/sec}$$
$$\ddot{\theta} = 0.1 \text{ rad/sec}^2$$

The cylinder weighs 50 lb and has an angular speed and an angular acceleration relative to the compartment of 2 rad/sec and 3 rad/sec^2 respectively.

126. [15.9] In Prob. 84 what is the total force on the propeller? The propeller weighs 60 lb and is 5 ft from the center of rotation of the plane.

***127.** [15.9] In Fig. 15.79 determine the force on the slider G at the instant shown. The slider has a speed V of 3 ft/sec. The length DC is 7 ft and the distance DF is 6 ft at the instant of interest but is increasing at the rate of 0.5 ft/sec.^{2} Slider G has a mass of 1 lbm.

***128.** [15.9] In Fig. 15.81 compute the force on slider B having a mass of 1 lbm. The angular velocity of OA is 3 rad/sec and is decelerating at the rate of 2 rad/sec^2 at the configuration shown. What is the total force on the slider A if it has a mass of 1 lbm? If rod AB weighs 5 lb, what is the total force on it?

129. [15.9] A truck is moving at constant speed V of 10 mph (Fig. 15.100). A crane AB is at time t at $\theta = 45°$ with $\dot{\theta} = 1$ rad/sec and $\ddot{\theta} = 0.2$ rad/sec^2. Also at time t, $\omega = 1$ rad/sec relative to the truck. If AB is 30 ft in length, what are the axial force and bending moments at A as a result of mass M of 100 lbm at B?

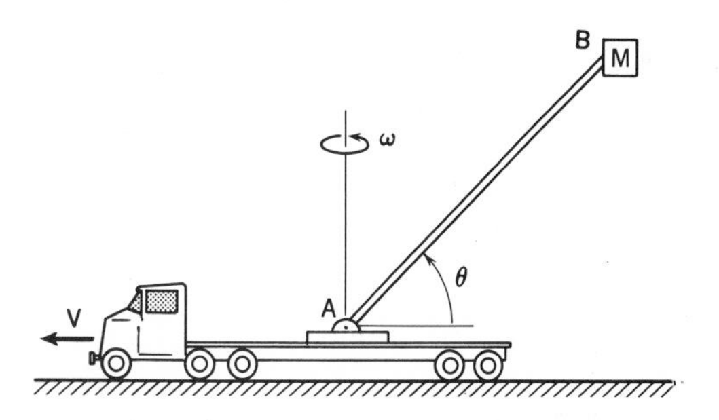

Fig. 15.100

130. [15.9] Do the previous problem for the case where the following data apply:

$$\dot{V} = 1.0 \text{ ft/sec}^2$$
$$\dot{\omega} = 0.3 \text{ rad/sec}^2$$

131. [15.9] In Prob. 110 find the bending moments and axial force for the beam AB at A resulting from cockpit C which weighs with occupant 300 lb. Also compute the same at D. The following data apply:

$$\beta = 20°$$
$$\alpha = 60°$$
$$\omega_1 = 0.2 \text{ rad/sec}$$
$$\omega_2 = 0.1 \text{ rad/sec}$$

132. [15.9] A mass A weighing four ounces is made to rotate at a constant angular speed of $\omega_2 = 15$ rad/sec relative to a platform (Fig. 15.101). This motion is in the plane of the platform, which, at the instant of interest itself, is rotating at an angular speed of $\omega_1 = 10$ rad/sec and decelerating at a rate of 5 rad/sec² relative to the ground. If we neglect the mass of the rod supporting the mass A, what are the axial force, bending moment, and shear force at the base of the rod (i.e., at O)? The rod at the instant of interest is shown in the diagram.

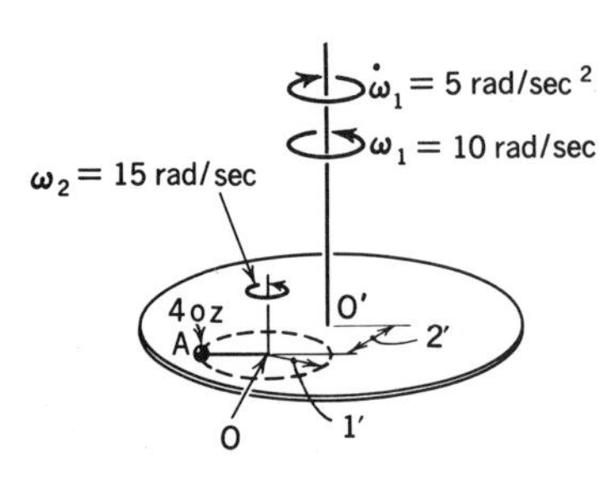

Fig. 15.101

133. [15.9] In the above problem, mass A may slide along the rod. What radial force is required to accelerate the mass at 5 ft/sec² along the rod toward O for the conditions given in the problem? The initial velocity of the mass A relative to the rod is zero.

134. [15.9] An exploratory probe shot from the earth is returning to the earth. On entering the earth's atmosphere, it has an angular velocity component of 10 rad/sec about an axis normal to the page and a component of 50 rad/sec about the vertical axis. The velocity of the object at the time of interest is 4000 ft/sec vertically with a deceleration of 500 ft/sec². A small sphere is rotating at 5 rad/sec inside the probe, as shown in Fig. 15.102. At the time of interest, the probe is oriented so that the trajectory of the sphere in the probe is in the plane of the page and the arm is vertical. What are the axial force in the arm and the bending moment at its base (neglect the mass of the arm) at this instant of time, if the sphere has a mass of 0.02 slugs?

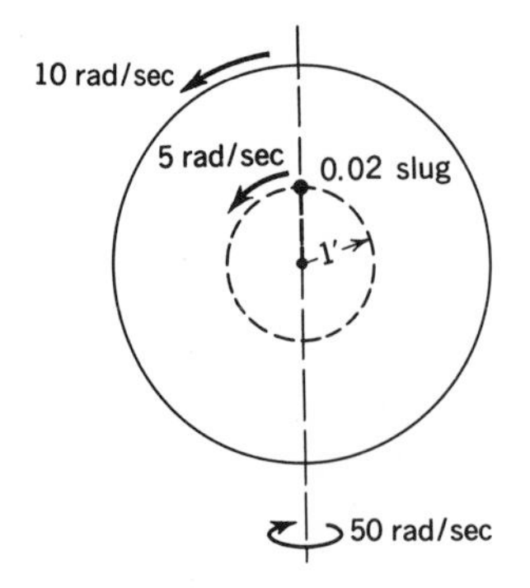

Fig. 15.102

135. [15.10] A man throws a ball from one side of a rotating platform to a man diametrically opposite, as shown in Fig. 15.103. What is the Coriolis acceleration of the ball?

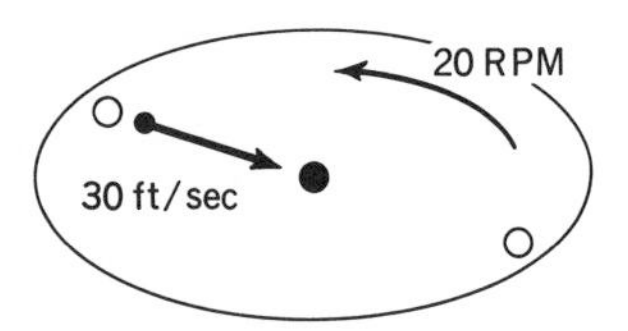

Fig. 15.103

136. [15.10] A river flows at 2 ft/sec average velocity in the Northern Hemisphere at a latitude of 40° in the north-south direction (Fig. 15.104). What is the Coriolis acceleration of the water relative to the center of the earth?

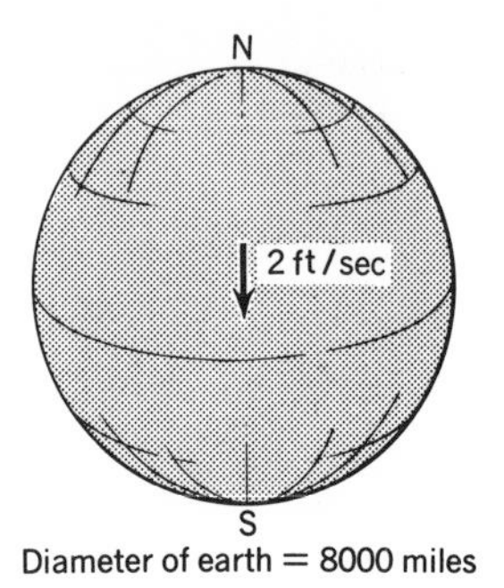

Fig. 15.104

16

The Inertia Tensor

16.1 Introduction

You will recall from Section 14.7 that the mass moment of inertia about an axis, as learned in physics, entered into consideration of the dynamics of a body undergoing simple rotation about an axis fixed in inertial space. For more complex motions of a rigid body, other mass moments of inertia enter and become an important part of the calculations. We shall now define and study these mass moments of inertia, and we shall find that these terms are related to the stress terms in a certain vital way.

We will best understand this relation between the stress terms and the moment-of-inertia terms by recalling from Chapter 9 that the two-dimensional stress components transform at a point in the same way as do the second moments and the products of inertia of a plane area. In other words, the inherent similarity of the two-dimensional stress components and the moments and products of inertia of plane areas lies in the manner in which their components change as the reference, relative to which the components are measured, is rotated about a point. And, just as the two-dimensional plane stress components constitute a special case of the stress tensor at a point, so the area moments and products of inertia (which describe in a certain way the disposition of area relative to a reference in the plane of the area) are special cases of the mass inertia tensor (which describes in a certain way the distribution of mass relative to a three-dimensional reference).

In this chapter we shall set forth the transformation formulations that distinguish tensor quantities. Accordingly, any conclusions that we reach in this chapter pertaining to these transformation formulations will apply to the stress tensor as well.

16.2 Formal Definition of Inertia Quantities

We shall now formally define a set of quantities that give information about the distribution of mass of a rigid body relative to a cartesian reference. For this purpose a rigid body of mass M and a reference xyz are presented in Fig. 16.1. This reference and the body may have any motion whatever relative to each other. The ensuing discussion then holds for the instantaneous orientation shown at time t. We will consider that the body is composed of a continuum of particles each of which was a mass given by $\rho\, dv$, where ρ is the mass density and dv is a volume element. We define the mass inertia components of the body M for the reference xyz at time t in the following manner:*

$$I_{xx} = \iiint_V (y^2 + z^2)\rho\, dv \quad \text{(a)} \qquad I_{xy} = \iiint_V xy\rho\, dv \quad \text{(d)}$$

$$I_{yy} = \iiint_V (x^2 + z^2)\rho\, dv \quad \text{(b)} \qquad I_{xz} = \iiint_V xz\rho\, dv \quad \text{(e)} \qquad \mathbf{16.1}$$

$$I_{zz} = \iiint_V (x^2 + y^2)\rho\, dv \quad \text{(c)} \qquad I_{yz} = \iiint_V yz\rho\, dv \quad \text{(f)}$$

The terms I_{xx}, I_{yy}, and I_{zz} in the above set are called the *mass moments of inertia* of the body about the x, y, and z axes, respectively. Note that in each such case we are in effect integrating the mass elements, $\rho\, dv$, times the *perpendicular distance squared* from the corresponding axis. Each of the terms with mixed indices is called the *mass product of inertia* about the pair of axes given by the indices. It is clear from the definition of the product of inertia that we could reverse indices and thereby form a total of nine such quantities for a reference; the additional three quantities formed in this way, however, are equal to the corresponding terms of the original set. That is:

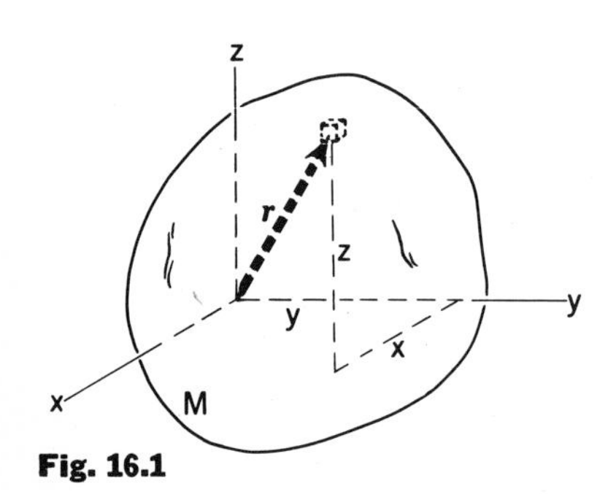

Fig. 16.1

$$I_{xy} = I_{yx}, \qquad I_{xz} = I_{zx}, \qquad I_{yz} = I_{zy} \qquad \mathbf{16.2}$$

The set of six independent quantities will, for a given body, depend on the position and inclination of the reference. You should also understand that the reference may be established anywhere in space and need not be situated in the rigid body of interest.

---

* We use the same notation as was used for area moments of inertia. This is standard practice in mechanics. There need be no confusion in using these quantities if we keep the context of discussions clearly in mind.

There is an important invariance, which we mentioned in Chapter 9 but did not prove for the stress components at a point, that we can now easily demonstrate for the inertia components. We shall show that the sum of the mass moments of inertia for a set of orthogonal axes is independent of the orientation of the axes, and depends only on the position of the origin. Examine the sum of such a set of terms:

$$I_{xx} + I_{yy} + I_{zz} = \iiint_V (y^2 + z^2)\rho\, dv + \iiint_V (x^2 + z^2)\rho\, dv + \iiint_V (x^2 + y^2)\rho\, dv$$

Combining the integrals and rearranging, we get:

$$I_{xx} + I_{yy} + I_{zz} = \iiint_V 2(x^2 + y^2 + z^2)\rho\, dv = \iiint_V 2\,|\,\mathbf{r}\,|^2 \rho\, dv \qquad \textbf{16.3}$$

But the magnitude of the position vector from the origin to a particle is independent of the inclination of the reference at that point. *Thus the sum of the moments of inertia at a point in space for a given body clearly is an invariant.* This sum may then be considered to form a scalar field in space and to correspond to the bulk stress associated with a stress field for elastic bodies or to the pressure field associated with certain fluids.

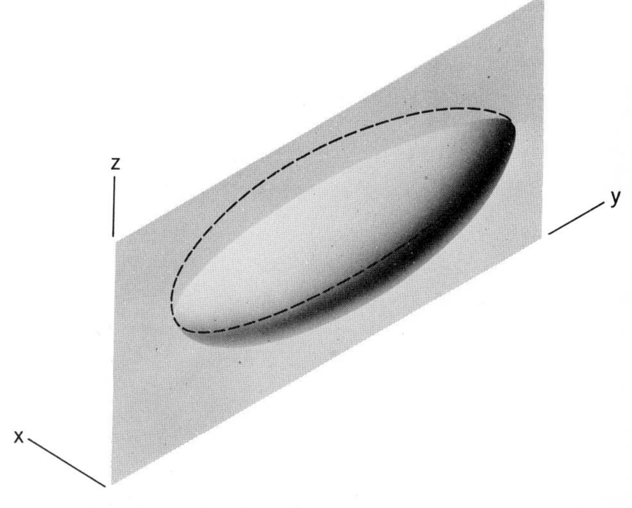

Fig. 16.2

It should be clear on inspection of the preceding formula that the moments of inertia must always exceed zero and that the products of inertia may have any value. Of interest is the case where one of the coordinate planes is a plane of symmetry for the mass distribution of the body. Such a plane is the zy plane shown in Fig. 16.2 cutting a body into two parts which are mirror images of each other. For the computation of I_{xz} each half will give a contribution of the same magnitude but of opposite sign. This is also true for I_{xy}. We can say that $I_{xy} = I_{xz} = 0$. But the term I_{zy} will have a positive value. Note that those products of inertia having x as an index are zero and that the x-coordinate axis is normal to the plane of symmetry. Thus we can conclude that if *two axes form a plane of symmetry for the mass distribution of a body, the products of inertia having as an index the coordinate which is normal to the plane of symmetry will be zero.*

We now illustrate the computation of moments and products of inertia.

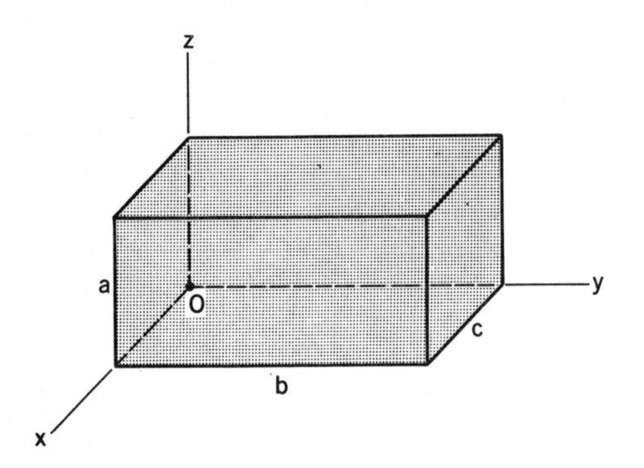

Fig. 16.3

EXAMPLE 16.1

Find the components of the inertia tensor of a rectangular body of uniform density ρ about point O for a reference xyz coincident with the edges of the block as shown in Fig. 16.3.

We first compute I_{xx}. Using volume elements $dv = dx\,dy\,dz$, we get:

$$I_{xx} = \int_0^a \int_0^b \int_0^c (y^2 + z^2)\rho\,dx\,dy\,dz$$

$$= \int_0^a \int_0^b (y^2 + z^2)c\rho\,dy\,dz = \int_0^a \left(\frac{b^3}{3} + z^2 b\right) c\rho\,dz$$

$$= \left(\frac{ab^3c}{3} + \frac{a^3bc}{3}\right)\rho = \frac{\rho V}{3}(b^2 + a^2) \quad \textbf{(a)}$$

where V is the volume of the body. Permuting the terms, we can get I_{yy} and I_{zz} by inspection as follows:

$$I_{yy} = \frac{\rho V}{3}(c^2 + a^2) \quad \textbf{(b)}$$

$$I_{zz} = \frac{\rho V}{3}(b^2 + c^2) \quad \textbf{(c)}$$

We next compute I_{xy}. Thus:

$$I_{xy} = \int_0^a \int_0^b \int_0^c xy\rho\,dx\,dy\,dz = \int_0^a \int_0^b \frac{c^2}{2} y\rho\,dy\,dz$$

$$= \int_0^a \frac{c^2b^2}{4}\rho\,dz = \frac{ac^2b^2}{4}\rho = \frac{\rho V}{4} cb \quad \textbf{(d)}$$

Permuting the terms, we get:

$$I_{xz} = \frac{\rho V}{4} ac \quad \textbf{(e)}$$

$$I_{yz} = \frac{\rho V}{4} ab \quad \textbf{(f)}$$

We accordingly have for the inertia tensor:

$$I_{ij} = \begin{pmatrix} \frac{\rho V}{3}(b^2 + a^2) & \frac{\rho V}{4} cb & \frac{\rho V}{4} ac \\ \frac{\rho V}{4} cb & \frac{\rho V}{3}(c^2 + a^2) & \frac{\rho V}{4} ab \\ \frac{\rho V}{4} ac & \frac{\rho V}{4} ab & \frac{\rho V}{3}(b^2 + c^2) \end{pmatrix} \quad \textbf{(g)}$$

EXAMPLE 16.2

Compute the components of the inertia tensor at the center of a solid sphere of uniform density ρ as shown in Fig. 16.4.

We shall first compute I_{yy}. Using spherical coordinates, we have:

$$I_{yy} = \int_0^R \int_0^{2\pi} \int_0^{\pi} [(r \sin\theta \cos\phi)^2 + (r\cos\theta)^2] \times \rho r^2 \sin\theta \, d\theta \, d\phi \, dr$$

$$= \int_0^R \int_0^{2\pi} [(r^2 \cos^2\phi)(\tfrac{4}{3}) + r^2(\tfrac{2}{3})]\rho r^2 \, d\phi \, dr$$

$$= \int_0^R \int_0^{2\pi} \frac{1}{3}(4\cos^2\phi + 2)\rho r^4 \, d\phi \, dr$$

$$= \int_0^R \frac{1}{3}(4\pi + 2\pi)\rho r^4 \, dr = \frac{2\pi\rho R^5}{5} \qquad \textbf{(a)}$$

Owing to symmetry about point O, we can say also:

$$I_{xx} = I_{zz} = \tfrac{2}{5}\pi\rho R^5 \qquad \textbf{(b)}$$

Because the coordinate planes are planes of symmetry for the mass distribution, the products of inertia are zero. Thus we get:

$$I_{jk} = \begin{pmatrix} \dfrac{2\pi\rho R^5}{5} & 0 & 0 \\ 0 & \dfrac{2\pi\rho R^5}{5} & 0 \\ 0 & 0 & \dfrac{2\pi\rho R^5}{5} \end{pmatrix} \qquad \textbf{(c)}$$

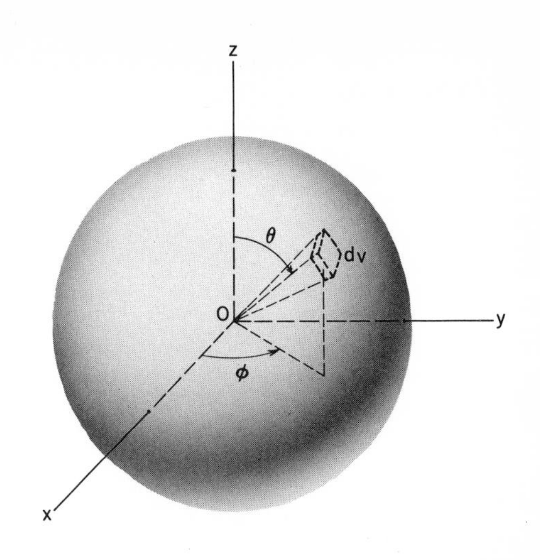

Fig. 16.4

16.3 The Relation of Mass Inertia Terms to Area Inertia Terms

As we pointed out in statics, and as may be apparent from the previous sections, we can derive the *second moment and the product of inertia of areas* from the mass inertia tensor.

To do this, consider a plate of constant thickness t and uniform density ρ (Fig. 16.5). A reference is picked so that the xy plane is one of the faces of this plate. The components of the inertia tensor are rewritten for convenience:

$$I_{xx} = \rho \iiint_V (y^2 + z^2)\, dv, \qquad I_{xy} = \rho \iiint_V xy \, dv$$

$$I_{yy} = \rho \iiint_V (x^2 + z^2)\, dv, \qquad I_{xz} = \rho \iiint_V xz \, dv \qquad \textbf{16.4}$$

$$I_{zz} = \rho \iiint_V (x^2 + y^2)\, dv, \qquad I_{yz} = \rho \iiint_V yz \, dv$$

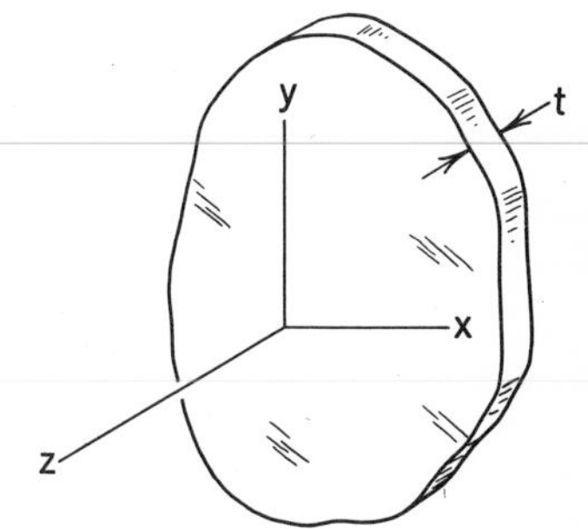

Fig. 16.5

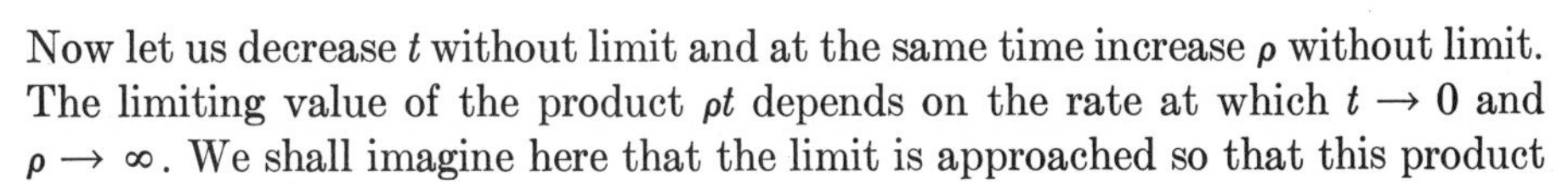

Now let us decrease t without limit and at the same time increase ρ without limit. The limiting value of the product ρt depends on the rate at which $t \to 0$ and $\rho \to \infty$. We shall imagine here that the limit is approached so that this product becomes unity. The maximum value of z in the above equations is t, so that as $t \to 0$ it must be the case that $z \to 0$. Now, replacing $\rho\, dv$ by $\rho t\, dA$ and observing the results of the above limiting process, we get:

$$I_{xx} = \iint_A y^2\, dA \quad \textbf{(a)} \qquad I_{xy} = \iint_A xy\, dA \quad \textbf{(d)}$$

$$I_{yy} = \iint_A x^2\, dA \quad \textbf{(b)} \qquad I_{xz} = 0 \quad \textbf{(e)} \qquad \textbf{16.5}$$

$$I_{zz} = \iint_A (x^2 + y^2)\, dA \quad \textbf{(c)} \qquad I_{yz} = 0 \quad \textbf{(f)}$$

Clearly, Eq. (c) is not an independent equation but the sum of Eqs. (a) and (b). It is the *polar moment of inertia* of the area as described in Chapter 8. We thus have the independent quantities $\iint y^2\, dA$, $\iint x^2\, dA$, and $\iint xy\, dA$, which are the second moments and product of inertia of the area of the face of the slab. We have succeeded, therefore, in deriving the familiar area moments and area product of inertia from the mass moment and products of inertia.

16.4 Translation of Coordinate Axes

In this section we will compute mass moment and product of inertia quantities for a reference xyz that is displaced under a translation from a reference $x'y'z'$ at the center of mass, for which the inertia terms are presumed known. Let us first compute the moment of inertia I_{zz}. Observing Fig. 16.6, we can formulate I_{zz} in the following way:

$$I_{zz} = \iiint_V (x^2 + y^2)\rho\, dv = \iiint_V [(x_c + x')^2 + (y_c + y')^2]\rho\, dv \qquad \textbf{16.6}$$

Carrying out the squares and rearranging, we have:

$$I_{zz} = \iiint_V (x_c^2 + y_c^2)\rho\, dv + 2\iiint_V x_c x'\, \rho\, dv + 2\iiint_V y_c y'\, \rho\, dv + \iiint_V (x'^2 + y'^2)\rho\, dv \qquad \textbf{16.7}$$

Note that the quantities bearing the subscript c are constant for the integration and may be extracted from under the integral sign. Thus:

$$I_{zz} = M[x_c^2 + y_c^2] + 2x_c \iiint_V x'\, dm + 2y_c \iiint_V y'\, dm + \iiint_V (x'^2 + y'^2)\rho\, dv \qquad \textbf{16.8}$$

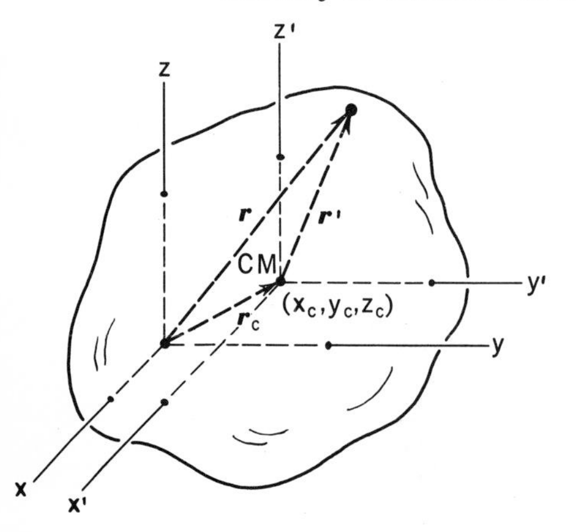

Fig. 16.6

where $\rho\, dv$ has been replaced in some terms by dm, and the integration $\iiint \rho\, dv$ has been evaluated as M, the total mass of the body. That the origin of the primed reference is the center of mass means that $\iiint x'\, dm = \iiint y'\, dm =$

$\iiint z'\,dm = 0$. The middle two terms drop out of the above expression, and we recognize the last expression to be $I_{z'z'}$. Thus the desired formula is:

$$I_{zz} = I_{z'z'} + M(x_c^2 + y_c^2) = I_{z'z'} + Md^2 \quad \textbf{16.9}$$

where d is the perpendicular distance between the z and z' axes. You may remember that the parallel-axis theorem for areas has this same form. Let us generalize from the above statement. *The moment of inertia of some body about any axis equals the moment of inertia of the body about a parallel axis that goes through the center of mass, plus the total mass times the perpendicular distance between the axes squared.*

It will be left for you to show that for products of inertia a similar relation can be reached. For I_{xy}, for example, we have:

$$I_{xy} = I_{x'y'} + Mx_cy_c \quad \textbf{16.10}$$

Here we must take care to put in the proper signs of x_c and y_c as measured from the xyz reference. Equations 16.9 and 16.10 comprise the well-known *parallel-axis theorems.* You can use them to advantage for bodies composed of simple familiar shapes, as we now illustrate.

EXAMPLE 16.3

Find I_{xx} and I_{xy} for the body shown in Fig. 16.7. Take ρ as constant for the body. Use the formulations for moments and products of inertia at the center of mass as given in Appendix VII.

We will consider first a solid rectangular prism having the outer dimensions given in Fig. 16.7, and we will then subtract the contribution of the cylinder and the rectangular block that have been cut away. Thus we have for the overall rectangular prism:

$$\begin{aligned}(I_{xx})_1 &= (I_{xx})_c + Md^2\\ &= \tfrac{1}{12}[(\rho)(20)(8)(15)](8^2 + 15^2)\\ &\quad + [(\rho)(20)(8)(15)](4^2 + 7.5^2)\\ &= 231{,}000\rho \qquad \textbf{(a)}\end{aligned}$$

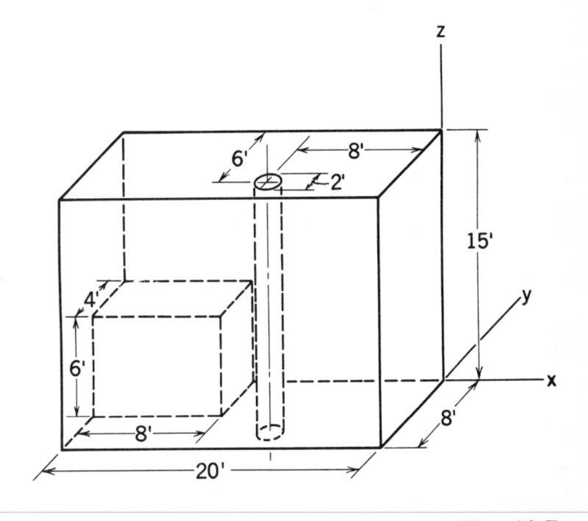

Fig. 16.7

From this we shall take away the contribution of the cylinder:

$$\begin{aligned}(I_{xx})_2 &= \tfrac{1}{12}[\rho\pi(1)^2(15)][3(1^2) + 15^2]\\ &\quad + [\rho\pi(1)^2(15)][6^2 + 7.5^2]\\ &= 5240\rho \qquad \textbf{(b)}\end{aligned}$$

Also we shall take away the contribution of the rectangular cutout:

$$\begin{aligned}(I_{xx})_3 &= \tfrac{1}{12}[(\rho)(8)(6)(4)][4^2 + 6^2]\\ &\quad + [(\rho)(8)(6)(4)][2^2 + 3^2]\\ &= 3330\rho \qquad \textbf{(c)}\end{aligned}$$

We get, accordingly:

$$I_{xx} = [231{,}000 - 5240 - 3330]\rho$$
$$= 222{,}000\rho \quad \textbf{(d)}$$

We do the same for I_{xy}. Thus:

$$(I_{xy})_1 = (I_{xy})_c + Mx_c y_c$$
$$= 0 + [\rho(20)(8)(15)](-4)(-10)$$
$$= 96{,}000\rho \quad \textbf{(e)}$$
$$(I_{xy})_2 = 0 + [\rho(\pi)(1^2)(15)](-8)(-6)$$
$$= 2260\rho \quad \textbf{(f)}$$
$$(I_{xy})_3 = 0 + [(\rho)(8)(6)(4)](-2)(-16)$$
$$= 6150\rho \quad \textbf{(g)}$$

Hence:

$$I_{xy} = (96{,}000 - 2260 - 6150)\rho = 87{,}600\rho \quad \textbf{(h)}$$

16.5 Transformation Properties of the Inertia Terms

Let us assume that the six moments of inertia are known for a given reference. What is the mass moment of inertia for an axis going through the origin of the reference and having the direction cosines l, m, and n relative to the axes of this reference? The axis is designated as kk in Fig. 16.8. From previous conclusions, we can say:

$$I_{kk} = \iiint_V [|\boldsymbol{r}|(\sin\phi)]^2 \rho\, dv \quad \textbf{16.11}$$

where ϕ is the angle between kk and $\boldsymbol{r}$. We shall now put $\sin^2\phi$ into a more useful form by considering the right triangle formed by the position vector $\boldsymbol{r}$ and the axis kk. This triangle is shown enlarged in Fig. 16.9. The side a of the triangle has a magnitude that can be given by the dot product of $\boldsymbol{r}$ and the unit vector $\boldsymbol{\varepsilon}_k$ along kk. Thus:

$$a = \boldsymbol{r}\cdot\boldsymbol{\varepsilon}_k = (x\boldsymbol{i} + y\boldsymbol{j} + z\boldsymbol{k})\cdot(l\boldsymbol{i} + m\boldsymbol{j} + n\boldsymbol{k}) \quad \textbf{16.12}$$

Hence:

$$a = lx + my + nz$$

Using the Pythagorean theorem, we can now give side b as:

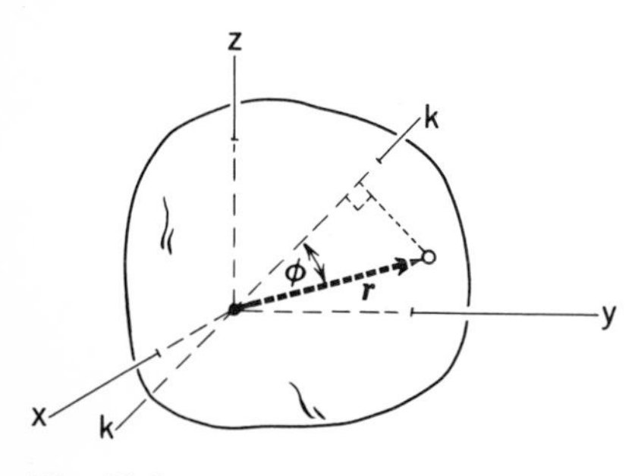

Fig. 16.8

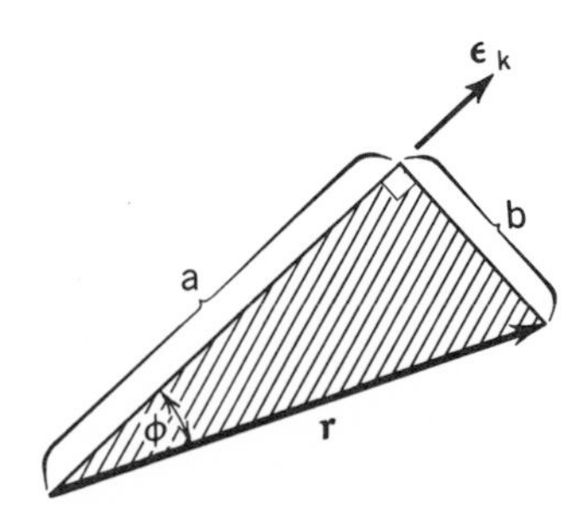

Fig. 16.9

$$b^2 = |\boldsymbol{r}|^2 - a^2 = (x^2 + y^2 + z^2) - (l^2x^2 + m^2y^2 + n^2z^2 + 2lmxy + 2lnxz + 2mnyz) \qquad 16.13$$

The term $\sin^2 \phi$ may next be given as:

$$\sin^2 \phi = \frac{b^2}{r^2} = \frac{(x^2 + y^2 + z^2) - (l^2x^2 + m^2y^2 + n^2z^2 + 2lmxy + 2lnxz + 2mnyz)}{(x^2 + y^2 + z^2)} \qquad 16.14$$

Substituting back into Eq. 16.11, we get on canceling terms:

$$I_{kk} = \iiint_V [(x^2 + y^2 + z^2) - (l^2x^2 + m^2y^2 + n^2z^2 + 2lmxy + 2lnxz + 2mnyz)]\rho\, dv$$

Since $l^2 + m^2 + n^2 = 1$, we can multiply the first bracketed expression in the integral by this sum:

$$I_{kk} = \iiint_V [(x^2 + y^2 + z^2)(l^2 + m^2 + n^2) - (l^2x^2 + m^2y^2 + n^2z^2 + 2lmxy + 2lnxz + 2mnyz)]\rho\, dv$$

Carrying out the multiplication and collecting terms, we get the relation:

$$I_{kk} = l^2 \iiint_V (y^2 + z^2)\rho\, dv + m^2 \iiint_V (x^2 + z^2)\rho\, dv + n^2 \iiint_V (x^2 + y^2)\rho\, dv - 2lm \iiint_V (xy)\rho\, dv - 2ln \iiint_V (xz)\rho\, dv - 2mn \iiint_V (yz)\rho\, dv$$

Referring back to the definitions presented by relations 16.1, we reach the desired transformation equation:

$$I_{kk} = l^2 I_{xx} + m^2 I_{yy} + n^2 I_{zz} - 2lm I_{xy} - 2ln I_{xz} - 2mn I_{yz} \qquad 16.15$$

Note that if we replace $-I_{xy}$, $-I_{xz}$, and $-I_{yz}$ with shear stresses τ_{xy}, τ_{xz}, and τ_{yz}, respectively, and replace I_{xx}, I_{yy}, and I_{zz} with σ_{xx}, σ_{yy}, and σ_{zz}, respectively, the above equation becomes identical to the transformation Eq. 9.2 for *normal stress* that we developed in statics.

Let us next compute the product of inertia for a pair of mutually perpendicular axes, Ok and Oq, as shown in Fig. 16.10. The direction cosines of Ok we will take as l, m, and n, while the direc-

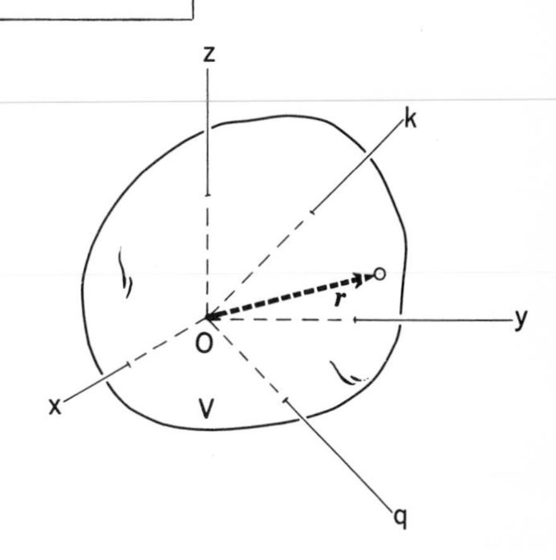

Fig. 16.10

tion cosines of Oq we will take as l', m', and n'. Since the axes are at right angles to each other, we know that:

$$\boldsymbol{\varepsilon}_k \cdot \boldsymbol{\varepsilon}_q = 0$$

$$\therefore\ ll' + mm' + nn' = 0 \qquad \textbf{16.16}$$

Noting that the coordinates of the mass element $\rho\, dv$ along the axes Ok and Oq are $\boldsymbol{r} \cdot \boldsymbol{\varepsilon}_k$ and $\boldsymbol{r} \cdot \boldsymbol{\varepsilon}_q$, respectively, we have for I_{kq}:

$$I_{kq} = \iiint_V (\boldsymbol{r} \cdot \boldsymbol{\varepsilon}_k)(\boldsymbol{r} \cdot \boldsymbol{\varepsilon}_q)\rho\, dv \qquad \textbf{16.17}$$

Using xyz components of $\boldsymbol{r}$ and the unit vectors, we have:

$$I_{kq} = \iiint_V [(x\boldsymbol{i} + y\boldsymbol{j} + z\boldsymbol{k}) \cdot (l\boldsymbol{i} + m\boldsymbol{j} + n\boldsymbol{k})] \times [(x\boldsymbol{i} + y\boldsymbol{j} + z\boldsymbol{k}) \cdot (l'\boldsymbol{i} + m'\boldsymbol{j} + n'\boldsymbol{k})]\rho\, dv \qquad \textbf{16.18}$$

Carrying out the dot products in the above integrand, we get the following result:

$$I_{kq} = \iiint_V (xl + ym + zn)(xl' + ym' + zn')\rho\, dv$$

Hence:

$$I_{kq} = \iiint_V (x^2ll' + y^2mm' + z^2nn' + xylm' + xzln' + yxml' + yzmn' + zxnl' + zynm')\rho\, dv \qquad \textbf{16.19}$$

Noting from Eq. 16.16 that $(ll' + mm' + nn')$ is zero, we may for convenience add the term, $(-x^2 - y^2 - z^2)(ll' + mm' + nn')$, to the integrand in the above equation. After canceling some terms, we have:

$$I_{kq} = \iiint_V (-x^2mm' - x^2nn' - y^2ll' - y^2nn' - z^2ll' - z^2mm' + xylm' + xzln' + yxml' + yzmn' + zxnl' + zynm')\rho\, dv \qquad \textbf{16.20}$$

Collecting terms and bringing the direction cosines outside the integrations, we get:

$$I_{kq} = -ll' \iiint_V (y^2 + z^2)\rho\, dv - mm' \iiint_V (x^2 + z^2)\rho\, dv - nn' \iiint_V (y^2 + x^2)\rho\, dv + (lm' + ml') \iiint_V xy\rho\, dv + (ln' + nl') \iiint_V xz\rho\, dv + (mn' + nm') \iiint_V yz\rho\, dv \qquad \textbf{16.21}$$

Noting the definitions in Eq. 16.1, we can state the desired transformation:

$$I_{kq} = -ll'I_{xx} - mm'I_{yy} - nn'I_{zz} + (lm' + ml')I_{xy} + (ln' + nl')I_{xz} + (mn' + nm')I_{yz} \qquad 16.22$$

Using Eqs. 16.15 and 16.22, we could find the moments and products of inertia for a new reference $x'y'z'$ rotated arbitrarily relative to reference xyz. And so once the values of these quantities are known for one reference at a point they are known for every reference at the point via the aforementioned transformation equations. Note, further, that if we replace the negative of the products of inertia (that is, I_{xy} and so on) by the corresponding shear stresses and replace the moments of inertia by corresponding normal stresses, Eq. 16.22 becomes identical to the equation corresponding to computation of shear stress exactly in the way that Eq. 16.15 becomes identical to the equation corresponding to the computation of normal stress. Thus we can conclude that the stresses for a new reference $x'y'z'$, rotated arbitrarily relative to an old reference xyz, may be found in terms of the stresses for the old reference in identically the same way as the inertia terms for a new reference $x'y'z'$ rotated relative to the old reference xyz. Accordingly, we say that the quantities

$$\begin{pmatrix} I_{xx} & (-I_{xy}) & (-I_{xz}) \\ (-I_{yx}) & I_{yy} & (-I_{yz}) \\ (-I_{zx}) & (-I_{zy}) & I_{zz} \end{pmatrix} \quad \text{and} \quad \begin{pmatrix} \sigma_{xx} & \sigma_{xy} & \sigma_{xz} \\ \sigma_{yx} & \sigma_{yy} & \sigma_{yz} \\ \sigma_{zx} & \sigma_{zy} & \sigma_{zz} \end{pmatrix}$$

transform at a point in identically the same manner. Furthermore we say that I_{xx}, I_{yy}, I_{zz}, $(-I_{xy})$, $(-I_{xz})$, and $(-I_{yz})$ are the *components* of the inertia tensor.

We may now define a symmetric* *second-order tensor as a set of components*

$$\begin{pmatrix} A_{11} & A_{12} & A_{13} \\ A_{21} & A_{22} & A_{23} \\ A_{31} & A_{32} & A_{33} \end{pmatrix}$$

which transforms with a rotation of axes according to the following equations. For the diagonal terms:

$$A_{kk} = l^2A_{11} + m^2A_{22} + n^2A_{33} + 2lmA_{12} + 2lnA_{13} + 2mnA_{23} \qquad 16.23\ \textbf{(a)}$$

* The word *symmetric* refers to the condition $A_{12} = A_{21}$ etc. that is required if the transformation equation is to have the form given. We can have nonsymmetric second-order tensors, but since they are less common in engineering work we shall not concern ourselves here with such possibilities.

For the off-diagonal terms:

$$A_{kj} = ll'A_{11} + mm'A_{22} + nn'A_{33} + (lm' + ml')A_{12} + (ln' + nl')A_{13} + (mn' + nm')A_{23} \qquad \textbf{16.23 (b)}$$

where l, m, n are direction cosines for the k direction and l', m', n' are direction cosines for the j direction.

You will learn that because of the common transformation law identifying certain quantities as tensors, there will be extremely important common characteristics for these quantities which set them apart from other quantities. Thus, in order to learn these common characteristics in an efficient way and to understand them better, we do become involved with tensors as an entity in the engineering sciences, physics, and applied mathematics. In addition to the stress and inertia tensors, you will soon be confronted with the strain tensor in your courses in strength of materials and in solid mechanics. And in electromagnetic theory and nuclear physics you will be introduced to the quadrupole tensor.†

In Sections 16.7 and 16.8 we shall initiate the study of certain characteristics of symmetric second-order tensors. Later, in your studies of fluid mechanics and strength of materials, other very important characteristics will be explored.

*16.6 Tensor Notation for Transformations

We shall now present a more compact notation that is almost universally used in more advanced studies for defining the transformation relations at a point characterizing tensor quantities. Instead of using l, m, and n as the direction cosines of any line k going through the origin of the xyz reference, we shall simply use the letter a with two subscripts. The first subscript identifies the line itself (in this case k), and the second subscript identifies the axis of the reference. Thus for line k, we have:

$$l = a_{kx}, \qquad m = a_{ky}, \qquad n = a_{kz} \qquad \textbf{16.24}$$

Equation 16.15 then can be given as:

$$I_{kk} = a_{kx}^2 I_{xx} + a_{ky}^2 I_{yy} + a_{kz}^2 I_{zz} + 2a_{kx}a_{ky}(-I_{xy}) + 2a_{kx}a_{kz}(-I_{xz}) + 2a_{kz}a_{ky}(-I_{zy}) \qquad \textbf{16.25}$$

---

† Vectors may be defined in terms of the way components of the vector for a new reference are related to the components of the old reference. Thus for any direction $\boldsymbol{k}$ we have for the vector $\boldsymbol{A}$:

$$A_k = lA_x + mA_y + nA_z \qquad \textbf{(a)}$$

where l, m, and n are the direction cosines of the $\boldsymbol{k}$ direction with the x, y, and z axes. Using Eq. (a), we can find components of vector $\boldsymbol{A}$ with respect to $x'y'z'$ rotated arbitrarily relative to xyz. Thus, all vectors must transform in accordance with Eq. (a) on rotation of the reference. It is obvious that the vector, as seen from this point of view, is a special, simple case of the second-order tensor. We say accordingly that vectors are *first-order tensors*.

As for scalars, there is clearly no change in value when there is a rotation of axes at a point. Thus:

$$T(x', y', z') = T(x, y, z) \qquad \textbf{(b)}$$

for $x'y'z'$ rotated relative to xyz. Scalars are a special form of tensor when considered from a transformation point of view. In fact they are called *zero-order tensors*.

This equation can then be written in the following compact form:

$$I_{kk} = \sum_j \sum_i a_{ki} a_{kj} I_{ij} \tag{16.26}$$

where i and j are summed over x, y, and z, respectively; when $i \neq j$, we must insert a minus sign for I_{ij}. Carry out this operation yourself to make sure you fully grasp the notation.

If the k axis is that of an x' axis of a new reference, we would replace k as a subscript by x'. A direction cosine such as $a_{x'x}$ is, then, the direction cosine between this x' axis and the x axis. Similarly, for a y' axis, we would replace k by y', etc. The term $a_{y'z}$ would then represent the direction cosine between the y' axis and the z axis. Thus, knowing the direction cosines, we can compute the various moments of inertia for the axes of a new reference by using Eq. 16.26 in the following forms:

$$\begin{aligned} I_{x'x'} &= \sum_j \sum_i a_{x'i} a_{x'j} I_{ij} \\ I_{y'y'} &= \sum_j \sum_i a_{y'i} a_{y'j} I_{ij} \\ I_{z'z'} &= \sum_j \sum_i a_{z'i} a_{z'j} I_{ij} \end{aligned} \tag{16.27}$$

In a similar manner, Eq. 16.22 can first be given as:

$$\begin{aligned} -I_{kq} = {} & a_{kx}a_{qx}I_{xx} + a_{ky}a_{qy}I_{yy} + a_{kz}a_{qz}I_{zz} + (a_{kx}a_{qy} + a_{ky}a_{qx})(-I_{xy}) \\ & + (a_{kx}a_{qz} + a_{kz}a_{qx})(-I_{xz}) + (a_{ky}a_{qz} + a_{kz}a_{qy})(-I_{yz}) \end{aligned} \tag{16.28}$$

and, using summation symbols as before, we can write:

$$-I_{kq} = \sum_j \sum_i a_{ki} a_{qj} I_{ij} \tag{16.29}$$

If k and q are the x' and y' axes, we need only replace k by x' and q by y'. Thus for a new reference $x'y'z'$ at the point of consideration, we have for the products of inertia:

$$\begin{aligned} -I_{x'y'} &= \sum_j \sum_i a_{x'i} a_{y'j} I_{ij} \\ -I_{x'z'} &= \sum_j \sum_i a_{x'i} a_{z'j} I_{ij} \\ -I_{y'z'} &= \sum_j \sum_i a_{y'i} a_{z'j} I_{ij} \end{aligned} \tag{16.30}$$

Actually, Eqs. 16.27 and 16.30 give the moments and products of inertia for the new reference $x'y'z'$ in terms of the moments and products of inertia for reference xyz and the direction cosines between the various axes of the two reference systems. We can simplify further by using notation that will represent all six of these equations. If we let k and q assume every combination of x', y', z', and if we remember to use minus signs for inertia terms with mixed indices, we can then express all six of Eqs. 16.27 and 16.30 as:

$$\boxed{I_{kq} = \sum_j \sum_i a_{ki} a_{qj} I_{ij}} \tag{16.31}$$

Second-order tensor quantities must satisfy transformation equations of this form. Higher-order tensors, which we will not discuss, are quantities that transform in the following way:*

$$I_{kpv} = \sum_i \sum_j \sum_s a_{ki}a_{pj}a_{vs}I_{ijs} \qquad \textbf{16.32}$$

The addition takes place over symbols i, j, and s, which are called *dummy* indices. Notice that they appear twice in a grouping of terms. We can make a further simplification by agreeing to sum over a repeated set of indices in a grouping of terms for a chosen set of letters such as i, j, q, and s. The above equations then become:

$$I_{kq} = a_{ki}a_{qj}I_{ij} \qquad \textbf{(a)}$$

$$I_{kpv} = a_{ki}a_{pj}a_{vs}I_{ijs} \qquad \textbf{(b)} \quad \textbf{16.33}$$

For more elaborate studies beyond the level of this course, you would learn tensor algebra and tensor calculus, which are generalizations of some of the vector algebra and vector calculus introduced in this course.

16.7 The Inertia Ellipsoid and Principal Moments of Inertia

Equation 16.15 gives the moment of inertia of a body about an axis k in terms of the direction cosines of that axis measured from an orthogonal reference with an origin O on the axis, and in terms of six inertia quantities for this reference. We wish to explore the nature of the variation of I_{kk} at a point O in space as the direction of k is changed (Fig. 16.11). To do this we will employ a geometric representation of inertia at a point that is developed in the following manner. Along the axis k we lay off as a distance the quantity OA given by the relation:

$$OA = \frac{d}{\sqrt{I_{kk}/M}} \qquad \textbf{16.34}$$

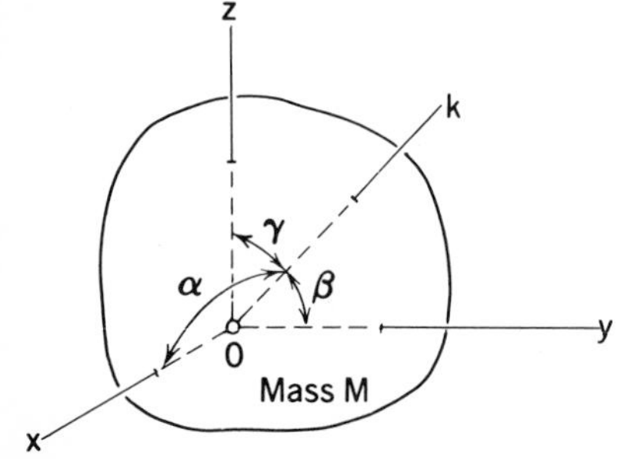

Fig. 16.11

where d is any arbitrary constant that has a dimension of length that will render OA dimensionless, as the reader may himself verify. The term $\sqrt{I_{kk}/M}$ is called the *radius of gyration* and is a generalization of the radius of gyration for areas studied in statics. To avoid confusion, this operation is shown in another diagram (Fig. 16.12), where the new ξ, η, ζ axes are *parallel* to x, y, z axes of the physical diagram. Considering all possible kirections of k, some surface will be formed about the point O' and this surface is related to the shape of the body

---

* In the other direction a first-order tensor or vector is identified by the transformation:

$$I_k = \sum_j a_{kj}I_j \qquad \textbf{(a)}$$

Note that this equation is the same as Eq. (a) of the footnote on page 552. As for a zeroth-order tensor or scalar, we get

$$I(x, y, z) = I(x', y', z') \qquad \textbf{(b)}$$

where there are not subscripts.

through Eq. 16.15. We can express the equation of this surface quite readily. Suppose we call ξ, η, ζ the coordinates of point A. Since $O'A$ is parallel to the line k and thus has the direction cosines l, m, and n that are associated with this line, we can say:

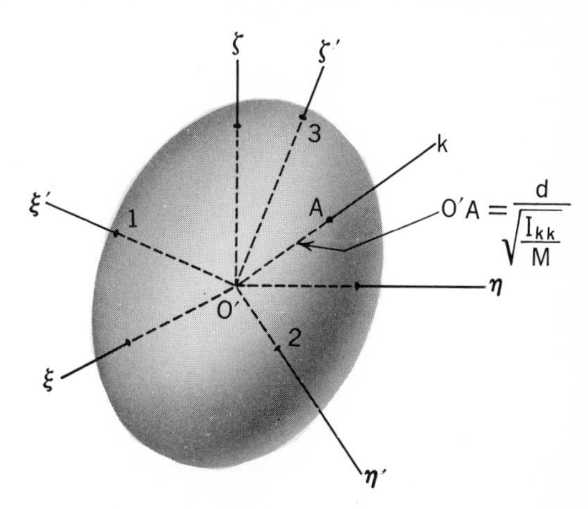

$$l = \frac{\xi}{O'A} = \frac{\xi}{d\sqrt{M/I_{kk}}}$$

$$m = \frac{\eta}{O'A} = \frac{\eta}{d\sqrt{M/I_{kk}}}$$

$$n = \frac{\zeta}{O'A} = \frac{\zeta}{d\sqrt{M/I_{kk}}} \qquad \textbf{16.35}$$

Fig. 16.12

Now replace the direction cosines in Eq. 16.15, using the above relations:

$$I_{kk} = \frac{\xi^2}{Md^2/I_{kk}} I_{xx} + \frac{\eta^2}{Md^2/I_{kk}} I_{yy} + \frac{\zeta^2}{Md^2/I_{kk}} I_{zz}$$

$$+ 2\frac{\xi\eta}{Md^2/I_{kk}}(-I_{xy}) + 2\frac{\xi\zeta}{Md^2/I_{kk}}(-I_{xz}) + 2\frac{\eta\zeta}{Md^2/I_{kk}}(-I_{yz}) \qquad \textbf{16.39}$$

We can see that I_{kk} cancels out of the preceding equation, leaving an equation involving the coordinates ξ, η, and ζ of the geometrical surface and the inertia terms of the body itself. Rearranging the terms, we then have:

$$\frac{\xi^2}{Md^2/I_{xx}} + \frac{\eta^2}{Md^2/I_{yy}} + \frac{\zeta^2}{Md^2/I_{zz}} + \frac{2\xi\eta}{Md^2}(-I_{xy})$$

$$+ \frac{2\xi\zeta}{Md^2}(-I_{xz}) + \frac{2\eta\zeta}{Md^2}(-I_{yz}) = 1 \qquad \textbf{16.37}$$

Considering analytic geometry, we know that the surface is that of an ellipsoid, and it is thus called the *ellipsoid of inertia*. We can conclude that the inertia tensor for any point of a body can be represented geometrically by such a second-order surface, and this surface may be thought of as analogous to the arrow used to represent a vector graphically. The size, shape, and inclination of the ellipsoid will vary for each point in space for a given body. Since all second-order tensors may be represented by second-order surfaces, you will, if you study elasticity, also encounter the ellipsoids of stress and strain.*

An ellipsoid has three orthogonal axes of symmetry, which have a common point at the center, O'. In the diagram, these are shown as $O'1$, $O'2$, and $O'3$. It has been pointed out that the shape and inclination of the ellipsoid of inertia depend on the mass distribution of the body about the *origin* of the xyz reference, and they have nothing to do with the choice of *the orientation of the* xyz (and hence, the $\xi\eta\zeta$) reference at the point. We can therefore imagine that the xyz

* See I. H. Shames, *Mechanics of Deformable Solids* (Englewood Cliffs, N.J.: Prentice-Hall, Inc., 1964), chap. 2.

reference (and hence the $\xi\eta\zeta$ reference) can be chosen so it has directions that coincide with the aforementioned symmetric axes, $O'1$, $O'2$, and $O'3$. If we call such references $x'y'z'$ and $\xi'\eta'\zeta'$, respectively, we know from analytic geometry that Eq. 16.37 becomes:

$$\frac{(\xi')^2}{Md^2/I_{x'x'}} + \frac{(\eta')^2}{Md^2/I_{y'y'}} + \frac{(\zeta')^2}{Md^2/I_{z'z'}} = 1 \qquad \textbf{16.38}$$

where ξ', η', and ζ' are the coordinates of the ellipsoidal surface relative to the new reference, and $I_{x'x'}$, $I_{y'y'}$, and $I_{z'z'}$ are mass moments of inertia of the body about the new axes. We can now draw several important conclusions from this geometrical construction and the accompanying equations. One of the above symmetrical axes of the ellipsoid is the longest distance from the origin to the surface of the ellipsoid, and another axis is the smallest distance from the origin to the ellipsoidal surface. Examining the definition in Eq. 16.34, we must conclude that the minimum moment of inertia for the point O must correspond to the axis having the maximum length, and the maximum moment of inertia must correspond to the axis having the minimum length. The third axis has some intermediate value that makes the sum of the moment of inertia terms equal the sum of the moment of inertia terms for all orthogonal axes at point O, in accordance with Eq. 16.3. In addition, Eq. 16.38 leads us to conclude that $I_{x'y'} = I_{y'z'} = I_{x'z'} = 0$. That is, the products of inertia of the mass about these axes must be zero. You probably have already realized that these axes are the *principal axes* of inertia at the point O.

Since the preceding operations could be carried out at any point in space for the body, we can conclude that *at each point there is a set of principal axes having the extreme values of moments of inertia for that point and having zero products of inertia. The orientation of these axes will vary continuously from point to point throughout space for the given body.*

All second-order tensor quantities have the properties discussed above for the inertia tensor. By transforming from the original reference to the principal reference, we change the inertia tensor representation from:

$$\begin{pmatrix} I_{xx} & (-I_{xy}) & (-I_{xz}) \\ (-I_{yx}) & I_{yy} & (-I_{yz}) \\ (-I_{zx}) & (-I_{zy}) & I_{zz} \end{pmatrix} \quad \text{to} \quad \begin{pmatrix} I_{x'x'} & 0 & 0 \\ 0 & I_{y'y'} & 0 \\ 0 & 0 & I_{z'z'} \end{pmatrix} \qquad \textbf{16.39}$$

In mathematical parlance, we have "diagonalized" the tensor by the preceding operations.

We have pointed out in the previous section that the principal axes at a point will correspond to axes for which the products of inertia are zero. Accordingly, if we have two orthogonal planes of symmetry at the point we can conclude from our earlier discussion in Section 16.2 that the products of inertia must be zero for a set of axes consisting of the line of intersection of the two planes and the pair of lines lying in the planes of symmetry and directed normal to the line of intersection at the point of interest. These axes clearly are the principal axes for the point.

16.8 Computation of Principal Moments of Inertia

We now turn to the problem of computing the principal moments of inertia and the directions of the principal axes for the case where we do not have planes of symmetry. It is unfortunate that a careful study of this important calculation is beyond the level of this text. However, we will present enough material to permit the computation of the principal moments of inertia and the directions of their respective axes.

The procedure that we will outline is that of extremizing the mass moment of inertia at a point where the inertia-tensor components are known for a reference xyz. This will be done by varying the direction cosines l, m, and n of an axis k so as to extremize I_{kk} as given by Eq. 16.15. We accordingly set the differential of I_{kk} equal to zero as follows:

$$\begin{aligned} dI_{kk} = {} & 2lI_{xx}\, dl + 2mI_{yy}\, dm + 2nI_{zz}\, dn \\ & -2lI_{xy}\, dm - 2mI_{xy}\, dl - 2lI_{xz}\, dn \\ & -2nI_{xz}\, dl - 2mI_{yz}\, dn - 2nI_{yz}\, dm = 0 \end{aligned} \qquad \textbf{16.40}$$

Collecting terms and canceling the factor 2, we get:

$$(lI_{xx} - mI_{xy} - nI_{xz})\, dl + (-lI_{xy} + mI_{yy} - nI_{yz})\, dm + (-lI_{xz} - mI_{yz} + nI_{zz})\, dn = 0 \qquad \textbf{16.41}$$

If the differentials dl, dm and dn were independent we could set their respective coefficients equal to zero to satisfy the equation. However, they are not independent because the equation:

$$l^2 + m^2 + n^2 = 1 \qquad \textbf{16.42}$$

must at all times be satisfied. Accordingly the differentials of the direction cosines must be related as follows:*

$$l dl + m dm + n dn = 0 \qquad \textbf{16.43}$$

We can of course consider any two differentials as independent. The third is then established in accordance with the equation above.

We shall now introduce the so-called *Lagrange multiplier* λ to facilitate the extremizing process. This constant is an arbitrary constant at this stage of the calculation. Multiplying Eq. 16.43 by λ and subtracting Eq. 16.43 from Eq. 16.42 we get when collecting terms:

$$\begin{aligned} & [(I_{xx} - \lambda)l - I_{xy}m - I_{xz}n]dl + [-I_{xy}l + (I_{yy} - \lambda)m - I_{yz}n]dm \\ & \qquad + [-I_{xz}l - I_{yz}m + (I_{zz} - \lambda)n]dn = 0 \end{aligned} \qquad \textbf{16.44}$$

Let us next consider that m and n are independent variables and consider the value of λ so chosen that the coefficient of dl is zero. That is,

$$(I_{xx} - \lambda)l - I_{xy}\, m - I_{xz}n = 0 \qquad \textbf{16.45}$$

With the first term of Eq. 16.44 disposed of in this way, we are left with differentials dm and dn, which are independent. Accordingly we can set their respective coefficients equal to zero in order to satisfy the equation. Hence we have in addition to Eq. 16.45 the following equations:

$$\begin{aligned} -I_{xy}l + (I_{yy} - \lambda)m - I_{yz}n &= 0 \\ -I_{xz}l - I_{yz}m + (I_{zz} - \lambda)n &= 0 \end{aligned} \qquad \textbf{16.46}$$

A necessary condition for the solution of a set of direction cosines l, m and n, from Eqs. 16.45 and 16.46, which does not violate Eq. 16.42† is that the determinant of these variables be zero.

---

* We are thus extremizing I_{kk} in the presence of a constraining equation.
† This precludes the possibility of a trivial solution $l = m = n = 0$.

Thus:

$$\begin{vmatrix} I_{xx} - \lambda & -I_{xy} & -I_{xz} \\ -I_{xy} & I_{yy} - \lambda & -I_{yz} \\ -I_{xz} & -I_{yz} & I_{zz} - \lambda \end{vmatrix} = 0 \qquad \textbf{16.47}$$

This results in a cubic equation for which we can show there are three real roots for λ. Substituting these roots into Eqs. 16.45 and 16.46, we can determine three direction cosines for each root. These are the direction cosines for the principal axes measured relative to xyz. We could get the principal moments of inertia next by substituting a set of these direction cosines into Eq. 16.15 and solving for I_{kk}. However, that is not necessary, since it can be shown that the three Lagrange multipliers *are* the principal moments of inertia.

It should be kept in mind that Eq. 16.47 resulted from the transformation properties of the inertia terms and accordingly can be used to give principal values for *any* second-order tensor. Thus for the stress tensor the equation

$$\begin{vmatrix} \tau_{xx} - \lambda & \tau_{xy} & \tau_{xz} \\ \tau_{yx} & \tau_{yy} - \lambda & \tau_{yz} \\ \tau_{zx} & \tau_{zy} & \tau_{zz} - \lambda \end{vmatrix} = 0 \qquad \textbf{16.48}$$

gives, for the roots λ, the principal stresses.

16.9 Closure

If quantities transform (i.e., change values when the reference is changed) in the same way, we may find certain common features of the quantities which are useful and physically meaningful. In this chapter, we have presented the inertia terms, and, by taking the negatives of certain of these quantities, we have shown that they transform, by a rotation of reference, in exactly the same way that the stress terms do. These transformation formulae, we pointed out, were the criteria for calling a set of quantities a tensor. Some of the useful common properties of tensor quantities that we then set forth are as follows:

1. The sum of the diagonal terms of the tensor (called the *trace*) is constant at a point for all orientations of the reference. This gives rise to such physically meaningful quantities as pressure (in fluid dynamics) and bulk stress (in elasticity).
2. While a vector can be represented graphically at a point by a directed line segment, a second-order tensor is representable at a point by a second-order surface such as an ellipsoid.
3. There are three mutually orthogonal directions at a point for which the nondiagonal terms of the tensor (shear stress, products of inertia, etc.) are zero, and the diagonal terms have their extreme values along two of these directions. These are the principal axes at the point.

There are other properties that we shall not discuss in this text. As you proceed in your studies of strength of materials and fluid mechanics, you will develop an increasingly stronger physical feel for many of the seemingly abstract concepts presented in this chapter. Meanwhile, you will find the inertia terms appearing continually as we study the motion of a rigid body in the next chapter.

PROBLEMS

1. [16.2] Compute I_{xx}, I_{yy}, I_{zz}, and I_{xy} for the homogeneous rectangular parallelepiped in Fig. 16.13.

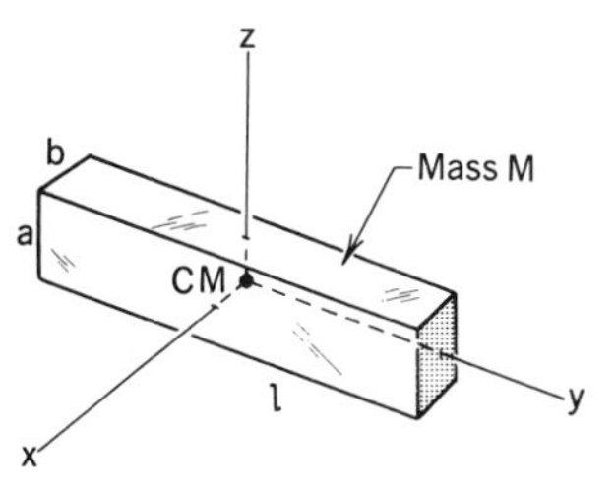

Fig. 16.13

2. [16.2] Shown in Fig. 16.14 is a uniform homogeneous slender rod of mass M. Compute I_{xx} and $I_{x'x'}$.

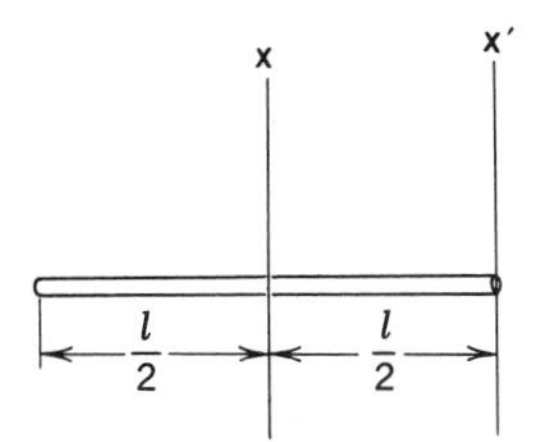

Fig. 16.14

3. [16.2] Find I_{zz} and I_{xx} for the homogeneous right circular cylinder of mass M in Fig. 16.15.

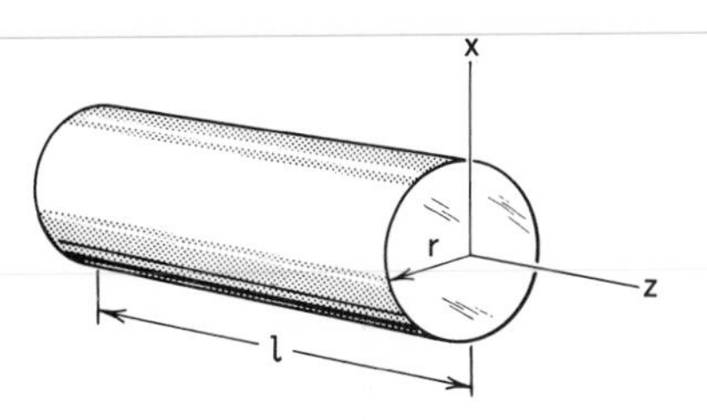

Fig. 16.15

4. [16.2] Compute I_{zz} for the homogeneous right circular cone in Fig. 16.16.

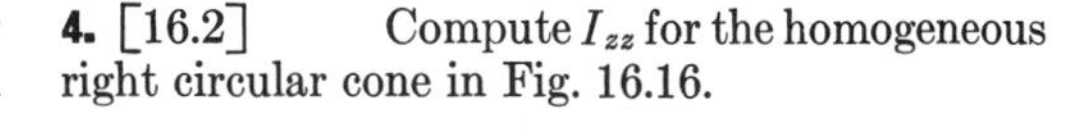

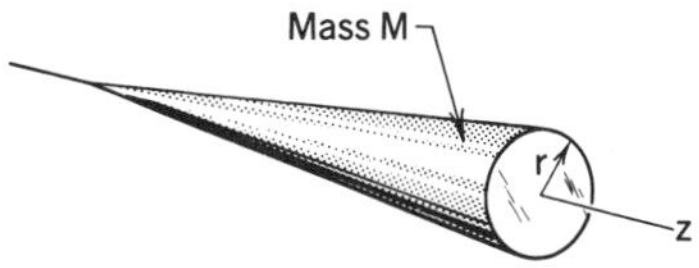

Fig. 16.16

5. [16.2] Compute I_{xy} for the thin homogeneous hoop of mass M in Fig. 16.17.

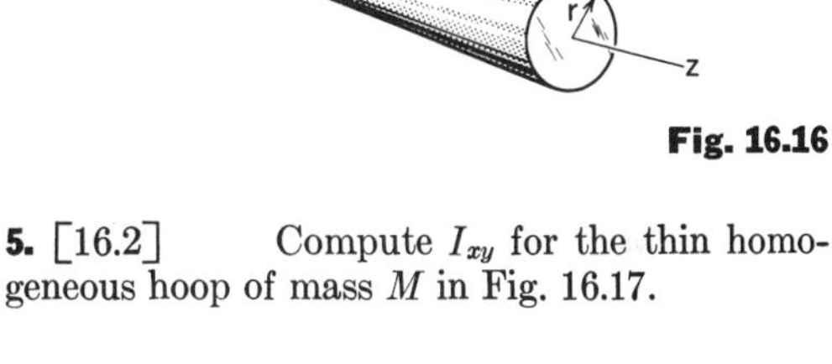

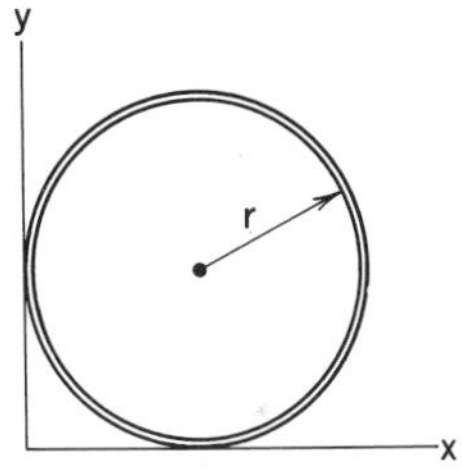

Fig. 16.17

6. [16.2] Compute the moment of inertia I_{BB} for the half-cylinder shown in Fig. 16.18. The body is homogeneous and has a mass M.

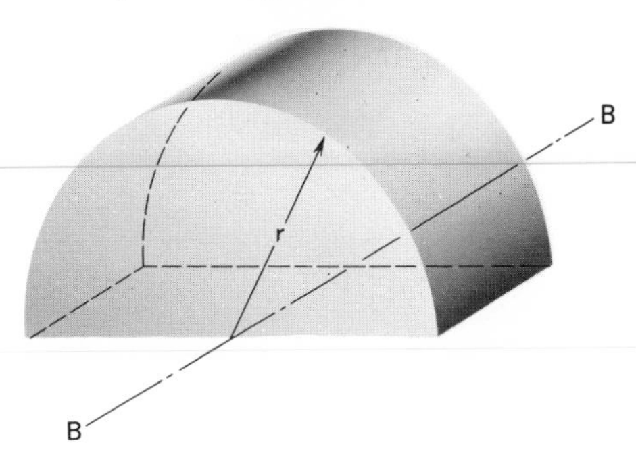

Fig. 16.18

7. [16.2] Shown in Fig. 16.19 is a body of revolution. The radial distance R of the boundary from the x axis is given as $R = 0.2x^2$. What is I_{xx} for a uniform density of 100 lbm/ft³?

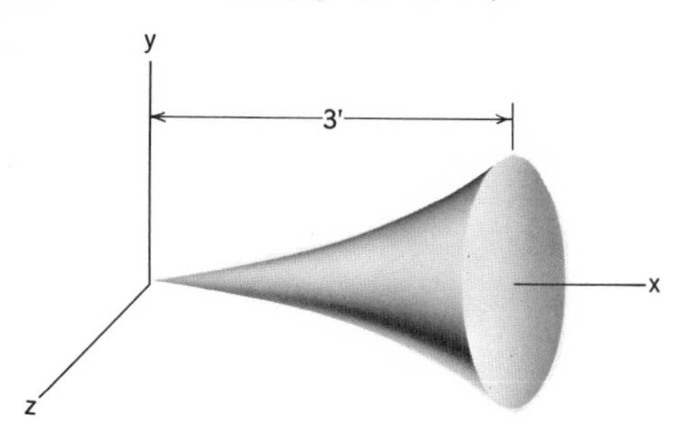

Fig. 16.19

8. [16.2] In Fig. 16.14 find I_{xx} and $I_{x'x'}$ for the thin rod for the case where the mass per unit length at the left end is 5 lbm/ft and increases linearly so that at the right end it is 8 lbm/ft. The rod is 20 ft in length.

9. [16.2] In Fig. 16.15 the density increases linearly in the z direction from a value of 100 lbm/ft³ at the left end to a value of 180 lbm/ft³ at the right end. Take $r = 3$ ft and $l = 15$ ft. Find I_{xx} and I_{zz}.

10. [16.2] In Fig. 16.16 the density increases as the square in the z direction from a value of 200 lbm/ft³ at the left end to a value of 400 lbm/ft³ at the right end. If $r = 2$ ft and the cone is 10 ft in length, find I_{zz}.

***11.** [16.2] A wire having the shape of a parabola is shown in Fig. 16.20. The curve is in the xy plane. If the mass of the wire is 0.3 lbm/ft, what are I_{yy}, I_{yz}, and I_{xz}?

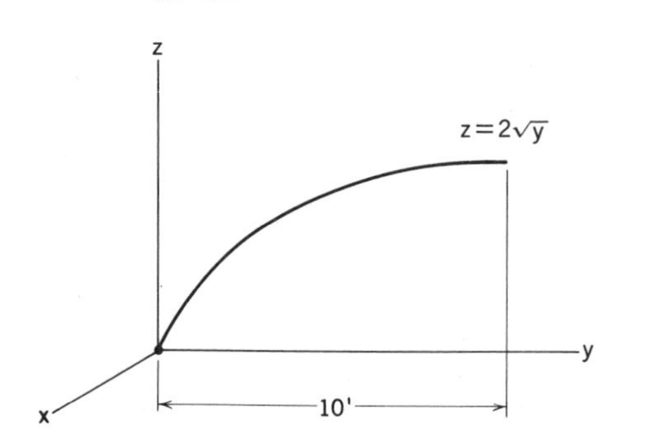

Fig. 16.20

***12.** [16.2] A uniform tetrahedron is shown in Fig. 16.21 having sides of length a, b, and c respectively and a mass M. Show that $I_{yz} = \frac{1}{20}Mac$.

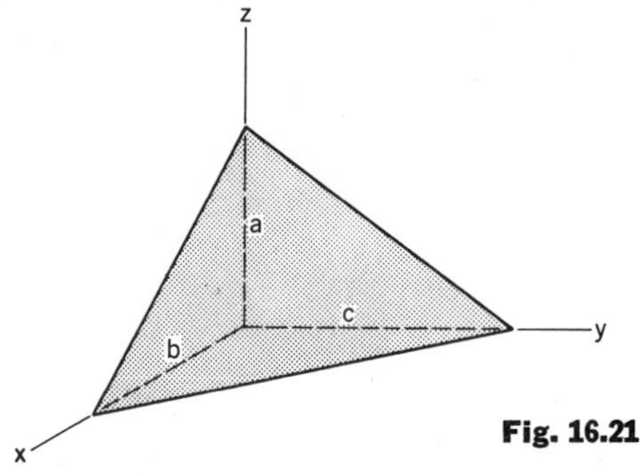

Fig. 16.21

In the remaining problems use the formulae for moments and products of inertia at the mass center to be found in Appendix V or a handbook.

13. [16.4] In Fig. 16.22, what are the moments and products of inertia for the xyz and $x'y'z'$ axes?

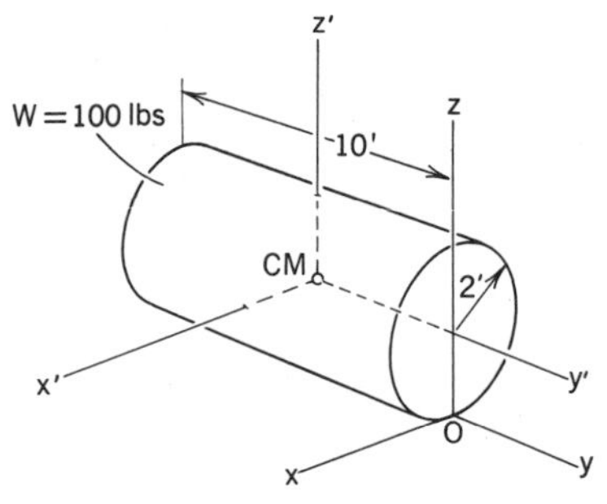

Fig. 16.22

14. [16.4] Shown in Fig. 16.23 is a uniform solid block. Compute the inertia tensor at the center of mass, at point a, and at point b for axes parallel to the xyz reference.

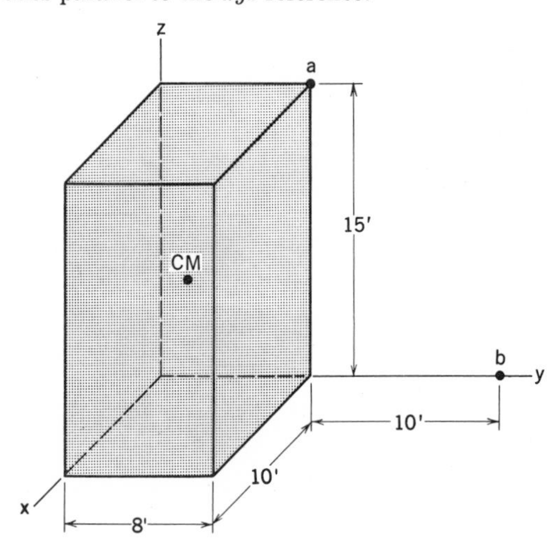

Fig. 16.23

15. [16.4] Using the results of Prob. 16.12, compute the products of inertia of the tetrahedron shown in Fig. 16.21 about centroidal axes parallel to the xyz reference shown.

16. [16.4] Determine $I_{xx} + I_{yy} + I_{zz}$ as a function of x, y, and z for all points in space for the uniform rectangular parallelepiped shown in Fig. 16.24. Note that xyz has its origin at the center of mass and is parallel to the sides.

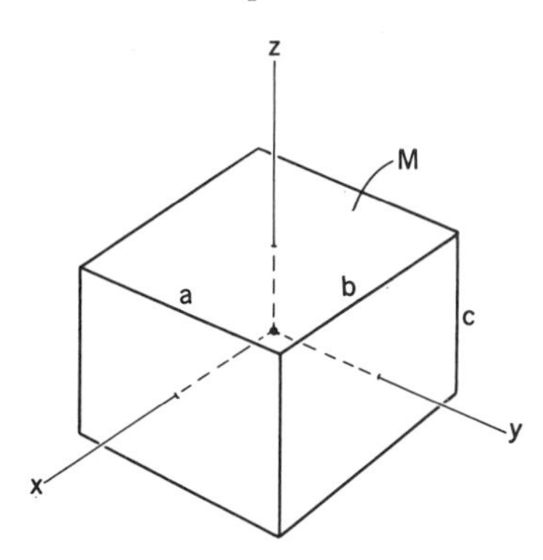

Fig. 16.24

17. [16.4] Shown in Fig. 16.25 is a cylinder having a conical cavity along axis AA and a cylindrical cavity oriented normal to AA. If the density of the material is 450 lbm/ft^3, what is I_{AA}?

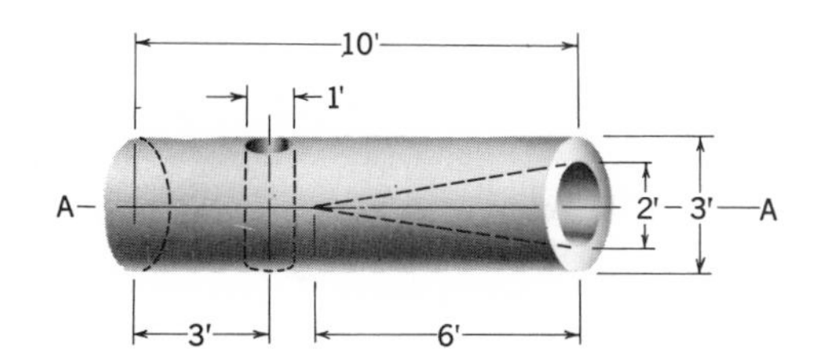

Fig. 16.25

18. [16.4] In Fig. 16.26 is a flywheel made of steel having a specific weight of 490 lb/ft³. What is the moment of inertia about its geometric axis? What is the radius of gyration?

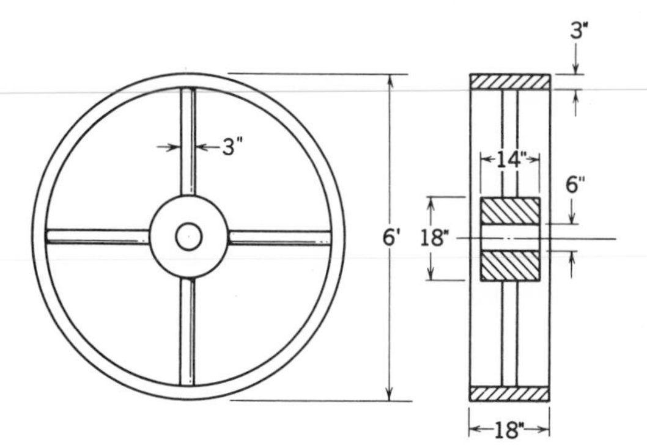

Fig. 16.26

19. [16.4] In Fig. 16.27, compute I_{yy} and I_{xy} for the right circular cylinder, which weighs 100 lb, and the square rod, which weighs 20 lb, when the two are joined together so that the rod is radial to the cylinder.

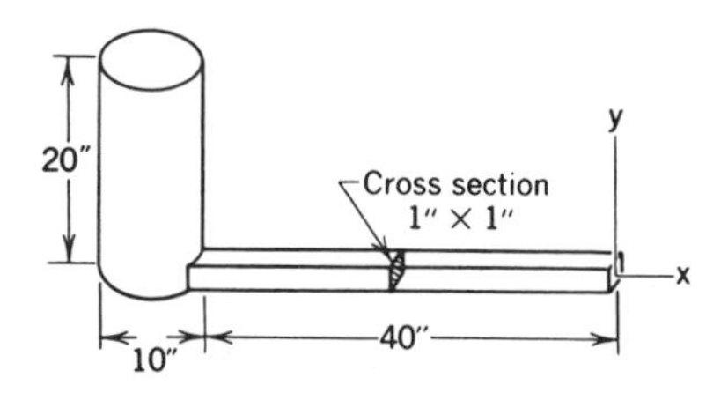

Fig. 16.27

20. [16.4] Compute the moments and products of inertia for the xy axes as shown in Fig. 16.28. The specific weight is 490 lb/ft³ throughout.

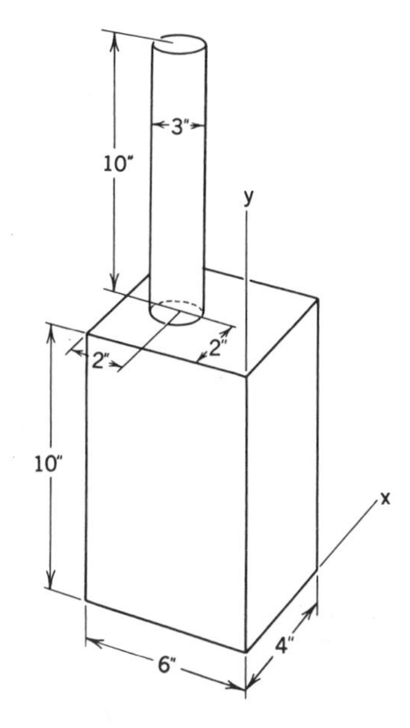

Fig. 16.28

21. [16.5] Find $I_{z'z'}$ for the cylinder shown in Fig. 16.29. The mass of the cylinder is 200 lbm.

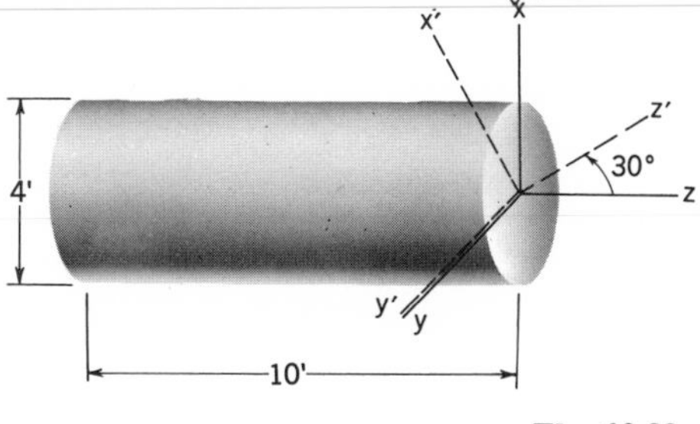

Fig. 16.29

22. [16.5] In the preceding problem find $I_{x'z'}$.

23. [16.5] In Prob. 1, the following data apply: $a = 6$ in., $b = 8$ in., $l = 20$ in., and the mass $M = 20$ lbm. Compute the mass moment of inertia about a main diagonal of the block.

24. [16.5] In Prob. 23 compute the product of inertia about xy' when y' is at an angle ot 30° to y and normal to x.

25. [16.5] A disc A is shown in Fig. 16.30 mounted on a shaft such that its normal is oriented 10° from the centerline of the shaft. The disc has a diameter of 2 ft, is 1 in. in thickness, and weighs 100 lb. Compute the moment of inertia of the disc about the centerline of the shaft.

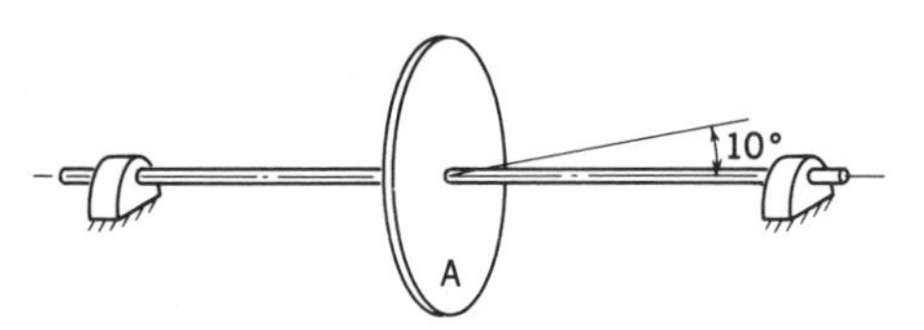

Fig. 16.30

26. [16.5] Shown in Fig. 16.31 is a plate of vanishingly small thickness t and a density ρ which becomes infinite such that $\rho t = 1$ in the limit. Show that Eq. 16.15 for $I_{x'x'}$ becomes identical with Eq. 8.14 for the moment of inertia of an area.

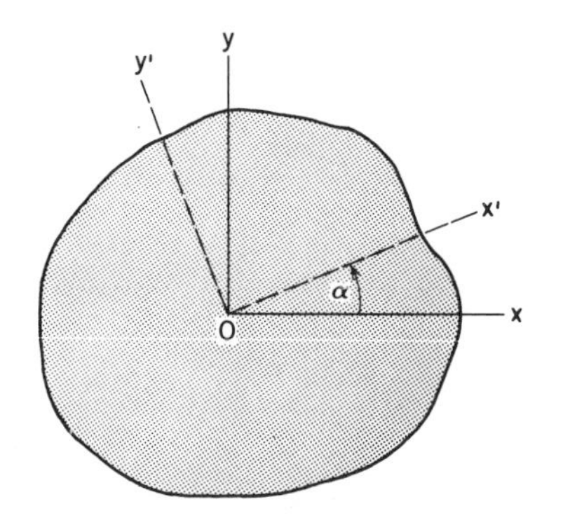

Fig. 16.31

27. [16.5] A gear B weighing 50 lb (see Fig. 16.32) rotates about axis CC. If the rod A weighs 5 lb/ft, compute the moment of inertia of A and B about the axis CC.

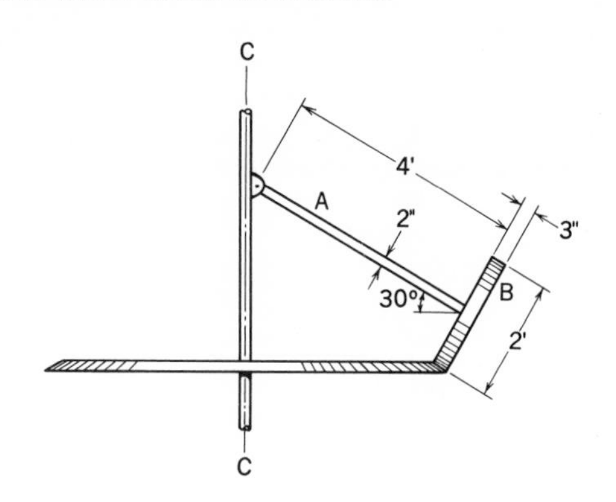

Fig. 16.32

28. [16.5] What is the normal stress on surface ABC for the element shown in Fig. 16.33?

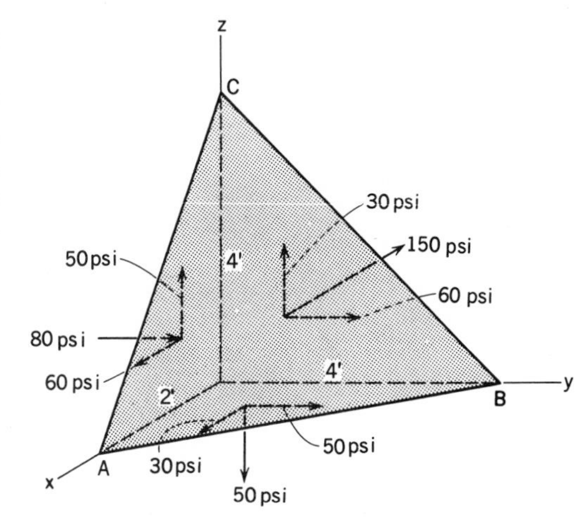

Fig. 16.33

29. [16.5] Shown in Fig. 16.34 is a solid sphere A of diameter 1 ft and weight 100 lb connected to the shaft BB by a solid rod weighing 2 lb/ft and having a diameter of 1 in. Compute $I_{z'z'}$ for the rod and ball.

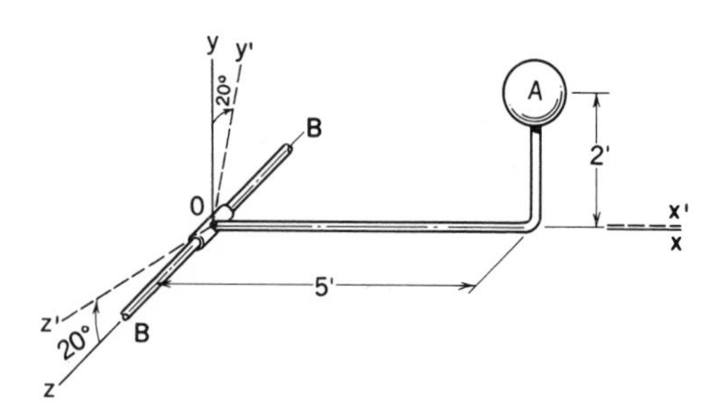

Fig. 16.34

30. [16.5] In the previous problem compute $I_{z'y'}$.

31. [16.6] The following array of numbers is a 3 × 3 matrix representing all the direction cosines between two sets of orthogonal axes xyz and $x'y'z'$. The position of the number in the matrix gives the subscripts to the term. Thus the particular row gives the first subscript, while the particular column gives the second subscript. If the first subscript refers to the sequence x', y', z', and the second subscript refers to the sequence xyz, (a) what is the direction cosine between the y and z' axes? (b) what is the direction cosine between the z and x' axes? (c) what relation must each row satisfy?

$$\begin{pmatrix} A & B & C \\ D & E & F \\ G & H & J \end{pmatrix}$$

32. [16.6] In a matrix representing direction cosines for two sets of orthogonal axes, such as the one given in Prob. 31, why must the inner product between columns be zero? That is, $AB + DE + GH = 0$, $AC + DF + GJ = 0$, and $BC + EF + HJ = 0$.

33. [16.6] By expanding Eq. 16.31, show how we may arrive at Eqs. 16.15 and 16.22.

34. [16.6] From the transformation Eq. 16.31, which is valid for all second-order tensors, develop Eq. 9.2 for normal stress at a point.

35. [16.6] In Fig. 16.36, give the matrix of direction cosines between the xyz and $x'y'z'$ axes.

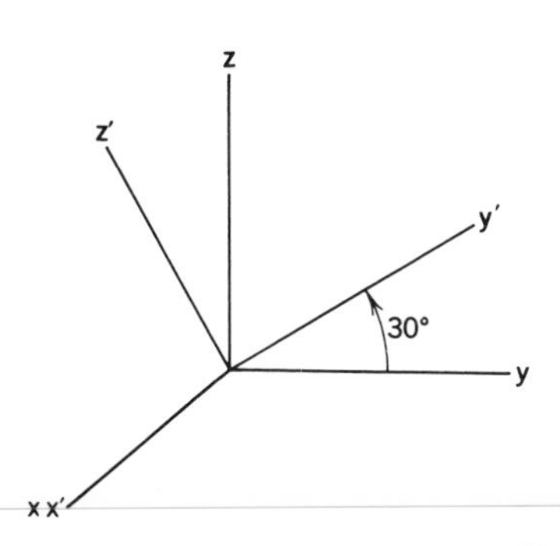

Fig. 16.35

36. [16.6] If in the above problem we have the following stresses:

$$\sigma_{xx} = 1000 \text{ psi}, \qquad \tau_{xy} = -500 \text{ psi}$$

$$\sigma_{yy} = -1000 \text{ psi}, \qquad \tau_{xz} = 1000 \text{ psi}$$

$$\sigma_{zz} = 0 \text{ psi}, \qquad \tau_{yz} = 800 \text{ psi}$$

compute $\tau_{x'z'}$ by using the general tensor transformation 16.31.

37. [16.6] Show that if the z axis at a point is a principal axis, then $I_{zx} = I_{zy} = 0$ for all positions of the x and y axes at the point. (Examine the computation of I_{zx} or I_{zy}, using data from a reference z, x_1, y_1, where x_1 and y_1 as well as z are principal axes at the point.)

38. [16.6] What is the defining equation for a vector using double index notation? Express the dot product of two vectors $\boldsymbol{A}$ and $\boldsymbol{B}$ in tensor notation.

39. [16.6] Which two of the following expressions are the same?

$$a_{ij}A_j, \qquad a_{ik}A_k, \qquad a_{ji}A_i$$

40. [16.7] In the development of the inertia ellipsoid, what is the effect of the arbitrary constant d in our results?

41. [16.7] What is the only case where a homogeneous body will have the same shape and orientation as the ellipsoid of inertia for some point in the body?

42. [16.8] In Prob. 29 compute the principal moments of inertia at the origin O for the bent rod and solid sphere. Find the direction cosines.

43. [16.8] In Prob. 66 of Chapter 8, you were asked to prove certain relations for principal moments of inertia for plane areas. As was pointed out at that time, two-dimensional stresses have the same relations as moments of inertia for areas, and so we rewrite the relations of the aforementioned problems in the following way for stresses:

$$(\sigma_{nn})_{\max} = \frac{\sigma_{xx} + \sigma_{yy}}{2} + \sqrt{\left(\frac{\sigma_{xx} - \sigma_{yy}}{2}\right)^2 + \tau_{xy}^2}$$

$$(\sigma_{nn})_{\min} = \frac{\sigma_{yy} + \sigma_{xx}}{2} - \sqrt{\left(\frac{\sigma_{xx} - \sigma_{yy}}{2}\right)^2 + \tau_{xy}^2}$$

For the given data: $\sigma_{xx} = 1$, $\sigma_{yy} = 1$, $\tau_{xy} = 1$, compute $(\sigma_{nn})_{\max}$ and $(\sigma_{nn})_{\min}$. Compute the principal stresses for the above data by using Eq. 16.48. Compare results.

44. [16.8] In Prob. 13 find the principal moments of inertia at point O. What are the direction cosines for the principal axes?

45. [16.8] In Prob. 14 find the principal moments of inertia at point b. What are the direction cosines for the principal axes?

46. [16.8] In Fig. 16.36 is shown a body of uniform density $\rho = 300$ lbm/ft^3. Explain why you can say on inspection that the x axis is a principal axis for point O. What are the principal moments of inertia for this body at O? Give the direction cosines for the principal axis relative to the xyz reference.

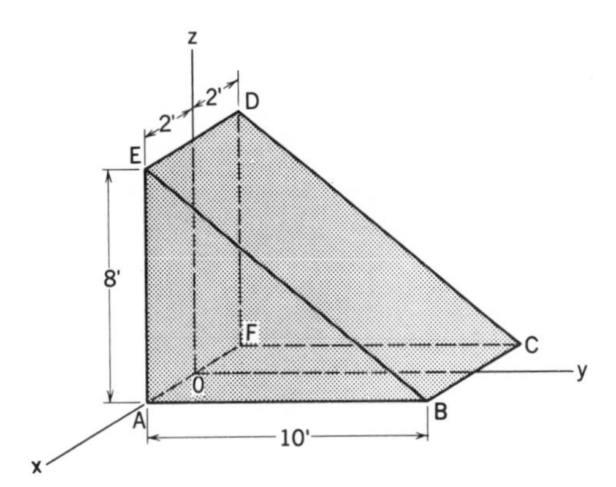

Fig. 16.36

47. [16.8] What are the principal axes at O (Fig. 16.37) for a uniform density ρ?

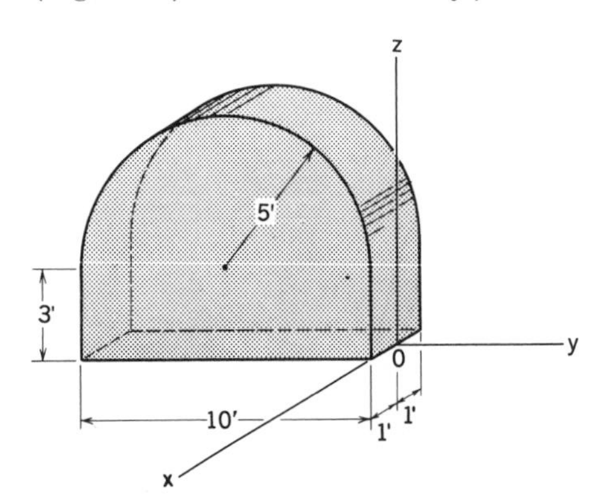

Fig. 16.37

***48.** [16.8] What are the principal moments of inertia at O for the body shown in Fig. 16.38? The density is uniform, having a value of 200 lbm/ft^3. Give the direction cosines of the principal axes relative to xyz.

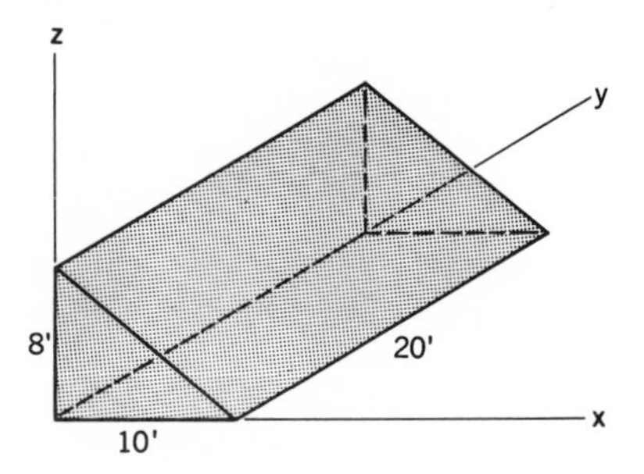

Fig. 16.38

49. [16.8] Carry out the determinant in Eq. 16.47 to form the following cubic equation for λ:

$$\lambda^3 - (I_{xx} + I_{yy} + I_{zz})\lambda^2 + (I_{xx}I_{yy} + I_{yy}I_{zz} + I_{zz}I_{xx} - I_{xz}^2 - I_{xy}^2 - I_{yz}^2)\lambda - (I_{xx}I_{yy}I_{zz} - I_{xx}I_{yz}^2 - I_{yy}I_{xz}^2 - I_{zz}I_{xy}^2 - 2I_{xy}I_{yz}I_{xz}) = 0$$

Explain why the coefficients of the λ^2 and λ terms as well as the last bracketed expression are independent of the orientation of xyz at the point. These quantities are called respectively the *first, second*, and *third tensor invariants* at a point and are denoted as I_I, II_I, and III_I respectively. Thus we have for the above equation:

$$\lambda^3 - \mathrm{I}_I\lambda^2 + \mathrm{II}_I\lambda - \mathrm{III}_I = 0$$

50. [16.8] Show that II_I in the preceding problem represents the sum of the minors along the main diagonal (left to right downward) of the determinant of the inertia tensor. Show that III_I is the determinant of the inertia tensor.

51. [16.8] What are the first, second, and third tensor invariants for the stress tensor?

52. [16.8] In Prob. 28 find the principal stresses and the principal axes.

Dr. Peter G. Glockner

17 Dynamics of Rigid Bodies

17.1 Introduction

In kinematics we learned that the motion of a rigid body at any time t can be considered to be a superposition of a translational motion and a rotational motion. The translational motion may have the actual instantaneous velocity of some point of the body, and the angular velocity of the rotation, $\boldsymbol{\omega}$, then has its axis of rotation through the chosen point. A convenient point is, of course, the center of mass of the rigid body. The translatory motion can then be found from particle dynamics. You will recall that the motion of the center of mass of any aggregate of particles (this includes a rigid body) is related to the total external force by the equation:

$$\boldsymbol{F} = M\dot{\boldsymbol{V}}_c \quad \textbf{17.1}$$

where M is the total mass of the aggregate. Integrating this equation, we get the motion of the center of mass. To ascertain fully the motion of the body, we must next find ω. As we saw in Chapter 14:

$$\boldsymbol{M} = \dot{\boldsymbol{H}} \quad \textbf{17.2}$$

for any system of particles where the point about which moments are to be taken may be (a) the mass center, (b) a point fixed in an inertial reference, or (c) a point accelerating toward the mass center. For any of these points, it will later be shown that the angular velocity vector $\boldsymbol{\omega}$ is involved in the above equation when it is applied to rigid bodies. Also, the inertia tensor will be involved as was indicated in the previous chapter. After we find the motion of the mass center from Eq. 17.1 and the angular velocity $\boldsymbol{\omega}$ from Eq. 17.2, we get the instantaneous motion by letting the entire body have the velocity $\boldsymbol{V}_c$ plus the angular velocity $\boldsymbol{\omega}$, with the axis of rotation going through the center of mass.

17.2 Moment of Momentum for a Rigid Body

As a first step toward developing useful forms of Eq. 17.2 for rigid-body motion, we now formulate the quantity $\boldsymbol{H}$ for a rigid body. You will recall that the velocity of a particle relative to a point A as seen from a reference XYZ is understood to mean the velocity of the particle relative to a reference having A as the origin and translating relative to XYZ. By the same token, the momentum of the body relative to point A as seen from XYZ is actually the momentum of the body relative to a reference $\xi\eta\zeta$ having A as an origin and translating with respect to XYZ. Although A can have any motion whatever in the preceding statement, we shall here only consider points A which are *fixed* in the rigid body or hypothetical massless extensions of the rigid body. We illustrate this in Fig. 17.1, where $\boldsymbol{V}'$ is the velocity of an element

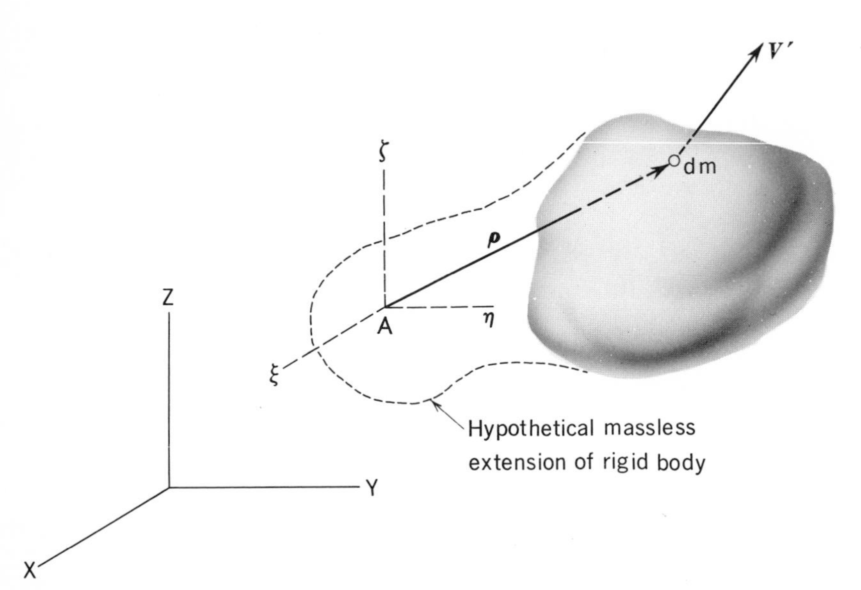

Fig. 17.1

dm as seen from reference $\xi\eta\zeta$ at A translating with respect to an inertial reference XYZ. The moment about point A of the momentum of the body relative to point A is accordingly:

$$d\boldsymbol{H}_A = \boldsymbol{\varrho} \times \boldsymbol{V}'\,dm = \boldsymbol{\varrho} \times \left(\frac{d\boldsymbol{\varrho}}{dt}\right)_{\xi\eta\zeta} dm \qquad 17.3$$

But since A is fixed in the body (or hypothetical massless extension of the body) the vector $\boldsymbol{\varrho}$ must be fixed in the body and accordingly $(d\boldsymbol{\varrho}/dt)_{\xi\eta\zeta}$ may be given as $\boldsymbol{\omega} \times \boldsymbol{\varrho}$, where $\boldsymbol{\omega}$ is the angular velocity of the body relative to $\xi\eta\zeta$. But since $\xi\eta\zeta$ translates with respect to XYZ, $\boldsymbol{\omega}$ is the angular velocity of the body relative to XYZ as well. Hence we can say:

$$d\boldsymbol{H}_A = \boldsymbol{\rho} \times (\boldsymbol{\omega} \times \boldsymbol{\rho})\, dm \qquad \textbf{17.4}$$

Quite often the point A used is simply the mass center [see Fig. 17.2]. We then have for an element dm:

$$d\boldsymbol{H}_C = \boldsymbol{\rho}_C \times (\boldsymbol{\omega} \times \boldsymbol{\rho}_C)\, dm \qquad \textbf{17.5}$$

It will be convenient to express Eq. 17.4 in terms of orthogonal components. For that purpose imagine a third reference xyz having the origin at A but having an arbitrary orientation relative to XYZ (see Fig. 17.3). Accordingly, we decompose each of the vectors in Eq. 17.3 into rectangular components in the $\boldsymbol{i}$,

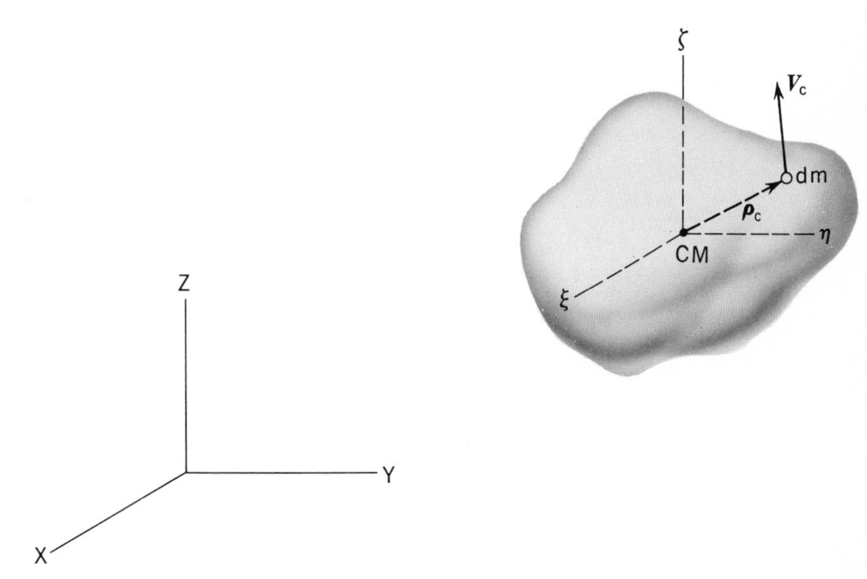

Fig. 17.2

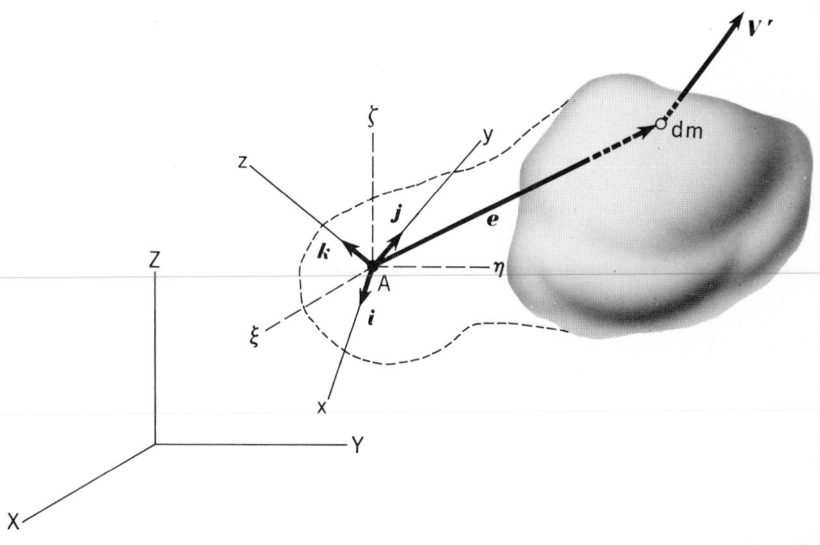

Fig. 17.3

$\boldsymbol{j}$, and $\boldsymbol{k}$ directions associated with the x, y, and z axes respectively. Thus:

$$d\boldsymbol{H}_A = (dH_A)_x\boldsymbol{i} + (dH_A)_y\boldsymbol{j} + (dH_A)_z\boldsymbol{k} \qquad \text{(a)}$$

$$\boldsymbol{\rho} = x\boldsymbol{i} + y\boldsymbol{j} + z\boldsymbol{k} \qquad \text{(b)}$$

$$\boldsymbol{\omega} = \omega_x\boldsymbol{i} + \omega_y\boldsymbol{j} + \omega_z\boldsymbol{k} \qquad \text{(c)} \qquad \textbf{17.6}$$

We then have for Eq. 17.4:

$$(dH_A)_x\boldsymbol{i} + (dH_A)_y\boldsymbol{j} + (dH_A)_z\boldsymbol{k} = dm\,(x\boldsymbol{i} + y\boldsymbol{j} + z\boldsymbol{k}) \times [(\omega_x\boldsymbol{i} + \omega_y\boldsymbol{j} + \omega_z\boldsymbol{k}) \times (x\boldsymbol{i} + y\boldsymbol{j} + z\boldsymbol{k})] \qquad \textbf{17.7}$$

Carrying out the cross products and collecting terms, we have:

$$(dH_A)_x = \omega_x(y^2 + z^2)\,dm - \omega_y xy\,dm - \omega_z xz\,dm \qquad \text{(a)}$$

$$(dH_A)_y = -\omega_x yx\,dm + \omega_y(x^2 + z^2)\,dm - \omega_z yz\,dm \qquad \text{(b)}$$

$$(dH_A)_z = -\omega_x zx\,dm - \omega_y zy\,dm + \omega_z(x^2 + y^2)\,dm \qquad \text{(c)} \qquad \textbf{17.8}$$

If we integrate the above relations for all the mass elements dm of the rigid body, we see that the components of the inertia tensor for point A appear. This gives us:

$$(H_A)_x = \omega_x I_{xx} - \omega_y I_{xy} - \omega_z I_{xz} \qquad \text{(a)}$$

$$(H_A)_y = -\omega_x I_{yx} + \omega_y I_{yy} - \omega_z I_{yz} \qquad \text{(b)}$$

$$(H_A)_z = -\omega_x I_{zx} - \omega_y I_{zy} + \omega_z I_{zz} \qquad \text{(c)} \qquad \textbf{17.9}$$

and we thus have components of the moment of momentum vector $\boldsymbol{H}$ for a rigid body about point A in terms of an arbitrary set of directions x, y, z at point A.

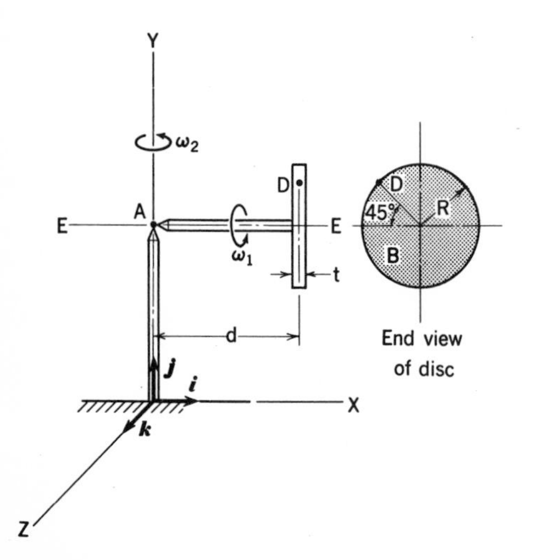

Fig. 17.4

EXAMPLE 17.1

In Fig. 17.4 is shown a disc B having a mass M rotating about centerline EE at a speed ω_1 while the centerline EE rotates about a vertical axis at an angular speed ω_2. Compute the angular momentum of the disc relative to the mass center and relative to point D.

The angular velocity of the disc relative to the center of mass equals the angular velocity relative to the ground reference and is given as:

$$\boldsymbol{\omega} = \omega_1\boldsymbol{i} + \omega_2\boldsymbol{j} \qquad \text{(a)}$$

For a set of axes at the center of mass parallel at time t to XYZ we have for the angular velocity components:

$$\omega_x = \omega_1, \quad \omega_y = \omega_2, \quad \omega_z = 0 \qquad \text{(b)}$$

The inertia tensor for these axes at the center of mass is:

$$I_{xx} = \frac{MR^2}{2}, \qquad I_{xy} = 0, \qquad I_{xz} = 0$$

$$I_{yx} = 0, \qquad I_{yy} = \frac{MR^2}{4}, \qquad I_{yz} = 0$$

$$I_{zx} = 0, \qquad I_{zy} = 0, \qquad I_{zz} = \frac{MR^2}{4} \qquad \textbf{(c)}$$

Hence from Eq. 17.9 we have:

$$(H_c)_x = \omega_1 I_{xx} = \frac{\omega_1 MR^2}{2}$$

$$(H_c)_y = \omega_2 I_{yy} = \frac{\omega_2 MR^2}{4}$$

$$(H_c)_z = 0 \qquad \textbf{(d)}$$

Note we have used principal axes here at the mass center, resulting in considerable simplification. Note also that the components of angular moments for such cases take on the appearance of components of linear moments with ω taking place of V and I taking place of M. The same thing will happen in Chapter 18 when we study the kinetic energy of a body relative to a point such as the mass center in the body.

We now compute the moment of momentum relative to point D of the disc. Clearly there is no change in $\boldsymbol{\omega}$. We use components again at D parallel at the instant of interest to the reference XYZ. The inertia tensor is now computed with the aid of the parallel axis theorems. Thus:

$$I_{xx} = \tfrac{1}{2}MR^2 + MR^2 = \tfrac{3}{2}MR^2$$

$$I_{xy} = 0$$

$$I_{xz} = 0$$

$$I_{yx} = 0$$

$$I_{yy} = \tfrac{1}{4}MR^2 + M(R \times 0.707)^2 = \tfrac{3}{4}MR^2$$

$$I_{yz} = M(R \times 0.707)^2 = \tfrac{1}{2}MR^2$$

$$I_{zx} = 0$$

$$I_{zy} = M(R \times 0.707)^2 = \tfrac{1}{2}MR^2$$

$$I_{zz} = \tfrac{1}{4}MR^2 + M(R \times 0.707)^2 = \tfrac{3}{4}MR^2$$

$$\textbf{(e)}$$

Now employing Eq. 17.9, we get:

$$(H_D)_x = \tfrac{3}{2}\omega_1 MR^2$$

$$(H_D)_y = \tfrac{3}{4}\omega_2 MR^2$$

$$(H_D)_z = -\tfrac{1}{2}\omega_2 MR^2 \qquad \textbf{(f)}$$

Let us consider point A for a moment. It is fixed in inertial space and is also at all times on the instantaneous axis of rotation of the disc. It could be considered then as a point on a massless hypothetical extension of the disc. Accordingly, we can employ Eq. 17.9 to compute $\boldsymbol{H}$ for this point. We shall leave this as an exercise.

17.3 Euler's Equations of Motion

We will now restrict points A further by considering only those points for which the equation $\boldsymbol{M} = \dot{\boldsymbol{H}}$ is valid—namely:

a. The mass center.

b. Points fixed at time t in inertial space (i.e., points having a zero acceleration at time t as seen from XYZ).

c. Points accelerating toward the mass center at time t as seen from XYZ.

Note points A have already been fixed in the rigid body (or massless hypothetical extension thereof). Accordingly, points along fixed axes may be used under restriction (b) above for $\boldsymbol{M} = \dot{\boldsymbol{H}}$.

It should also be noted that up to this time we have used xyz only to supply a set of orthogonal directions at a time t. That is, only the orientation of xyz at time t has been used. Actually, xyz could have additionally any arbitrary angular velocity $\boldsymbol{\Omega}$ relative to reference XYZ at time t.* This angular velocity does not affect in any way the calculation of the components $\boldsymbol{H}$ but will however enter into the calculation of the components of $\dot{\boldsymbol{H}}$. Accordingly, we can employ Eq. 15.13 to express Eq. 17.2 as follows:

$$\boldsymbol{M}_A = \left(\frac{d\boldsymbol{H}_A}{dt}\right)_{XYZ} = \left(\frac{d\boldsymbol{H}_A}{dt}\right)_{xyz} + \boldsymbol{\Omega} \times \boldsymbol{H}_A \qquad \textbf{17.10}$$

The idea now is to choose the reference xyz at A in such a way that $(d\boldsymbol{H}_A/dt)_{xyz}$ is most easily evaluated. With this accomplished the next step is to attempt the integration of the resulting differential equation.

With regard to attempts at integration it is to be pointed out at this early stage that the above equation is valid only as long as point A is one of the three qualified points discussed above. Clearly if A is the mass center Eq. 17.10 is valid at all times and may be integrated with respect to time provided the mathematics is not difficult. However, if for cases (b) and (c) point A qualifies only at time t, then Eq. 17.11 is valid only at time t and accordingly cannot be integrated. If, on the other hand, for case (b), the axis of rotation is fixed in inertial space (such as was the case in Example 14.15), then Eq. 17.11 is valid at all times for any point A along the axis of rotation and accordingly can be integrated. If, furthermore, the axis of rotation always goes through the chosen point A but does not have a fixed orientation in inertial space (see Fig. 17.4), we can again use the above equation at all times and attempt to integrate it with respect to time. The carrying out of such integrations may be quite difficult, however.†

Returning to Eq. 17.10, we may work directly with this equation selecting a reference xyz for each problem to yield the simplest working equation. On the

* xyz is chosen fixed in the body then clearly $\boldsymbol{\Omega} = \boldsymbol{\omega}$. Otherwise these angular velocities will be different.

† In Chapter 19 we will examine this case in some detail and will carry out integrations in the discussions of gyroscopic motion.

other hand, we can develop Eq. 17.10 further for certain classes of references xyz. For example, we could have xyz translate relative to XYZ. This would mean that $\mathbf{\Omega} = \mathbf{0}$ so that Eq. 17.10 would seem to be more simple for such cases. However, the body will be rotating relative to xyz and the moments and products of inertia will then be time functions. Since the computation of these terms as time functions is generally difficult, such an approach has limited value. On the other hand, the procedure of *fixing xyz* in the body does lead to very useful forms of Eq. 17.10 and we shall accordingly examine these equations with great care. Note first that the moments and products of inertia will be constants for this case and that $\mathbf{\Omega} = \boldsymbol{\omega}$. Hence we have:

$$\boldsymbol{M}_A = \left(\frac{d\boldsymbol{H}_A}{dt}\right)_{xyz} + \boldsymbol{\omega} \times \boldsymbol{H}_A \qquad \textbf{17.11}$$

Employing components for xyz and utilizing Eq. 17.9 we get on dropping the subscript A:

$$\begin{aligned} M_x\boldsymbol{i} + M_y\boldsymbol{j} + M_z\boldsymbol{k} = {} & (\dot{\omega}_x I_{xx} - \dot{\omega}_y I_{xy} - \dot{\omega}_z I_{xz})\boldsymbol{i} + (-\dot{\omega}_x I_{yx} + \dot{\omega}_y I_{yy} \\ & - \dot{\omega}_z I_{yz})\boldsymbol{j} + (-\dot{\omega}_x I_{zx} - \dot{\omega}_y I_{zy} + \dot{\omega}_z I_{zz})\boldsymbol{k} \\ & + (\omega_x I_{xx} - \omega_y I_{xy} - \omega_z I_{xz})(\boldsymbol{\omega} \times \boldsymbol{i}) \\ & + (-\omega_x I_{yx} + \omega_y I_{yy} - \omega_z I_{yz})(\boldsymbol{\omega} \times \boldsymbol{j}) \\ & + (-\omega_x I_{zx} - \omega_y I_{zy} + \omega_z I_{zz})(\boldsymbol{\omega} \times \boldsymbol{k}) \end{aligned} \qquad \textbf{17.12}$$

Carrying out the cross products, collecting terms, and expressing the vector Eq. 17.12 as scalar equations, we get:

$$\begin{aligned} M_x &= \dot{\omega}_x I_{xx} + \omega_y\omega_z(I_{zz} - I_{yy}) + I_{xy}(\omega_z\omega_x - \dot{\omega}_y) \\ &\quad - I_{xz}(\dot{\omega}_z + \omega_y\omega_x) - I_{yz}(\omega_y^2 - \omega_z^2) && \textbf{(a)} \\ M_y &= \dot{\omega}_y I_{yy} + \omega_z\omega_x(I_{xx} - I_{zz}) + I_{yz}(\omega_x\omega_y - \dot{\omega}_z) \\ &\quad - I_{yx}(\dot{\omega}_x + \omega_z\omega_y) - I_{zx}(\omega_z^2 - \omega_x^2) && \textbf{(b)} \\ M_z &= \dot{\omega}_z I_{zz} + \omega_x\omega_y(I_{yy} - I_{xx}) + I_{zx}(\omega_y\omega_z - \dot{\omega}_x) \\ &\quad - I_{zy}(\dot{\omega}_y + \omega_x\omega_z) - I_{xy}(\omega_x^2 - \omega_y^2) && \textbf{(c)} \end{aligned} \qquad \textbf{17.13}$$

These are indeed a formidable set of equations. However, if we choose reference xyz so that it coincides with the *principal axes* of the body at the center of mass, it is clear that the products of inertia are all zero in the above system of equations, and this enables us to simplify considerably. The resulting equations given below are the famous *Euler equations* of motion. Note that these equations relate the angular velocity and the angular acceleration to the moment of the external forces about the point A.

$$\begin{aligned} M_x &= I_{xx}\dot{\omega}_x + \omega_y\omega_z(I_{zz} - I_{yy}) && \textbf{(a)} \\ M_y &= I_{yy}\dot{\omega}_y + \omega_z\omega_x(I_{xx} - I_{zz}) && \textbf{(b)} \\ M_z &= I_{zz}\dot{\omega}_z + \omega_x\omega_y(I_{yy} - I_{xx}) && \textbf{(c)} \end{aligned} \qquad \textbf{17.14}$$

In both sets of Eqs. 17.13 and 17.14, we have three simultaneous first-order differential equations. If the motion of the body about point A is known, it is a simple matter to compute the required moments about point A. On the other hand, if the moments are known functions of time and the angular velocity is desired, we have the difficult problem of solving simultaneous nonlinear differential equations for the unknowns ω_x, ω_y, and ω_z. However, in practical problems, we often know some of the angular velocity and acceleration components from constraints or given data, so, with the restrictions mentioned earlier, we can sometimes integrate the equations readily. At other times we use them to solve for certain desired *instantaneous values* of the unknowns.

We shall now illustrate the use of Euler's equations. We shall also illustrate the use of Eq. 17.10 both in this next section and in Chapter 19.

17.4 Application of Euler's Equations

In this section we shall apply the Euler equations to a number of problems. Before taking up these problems, let us first carefully consider how to express the components $\dot{\omega}_x$, $\dot{\omega}_y$, and $\dot{\omega}_z$ for use in Euler's equations. First note that $\dot{\omega}_x$, $\dot{\omega}_y$, and $\dot{\omega}_z$ are time derivatives as seen from XYZ of the components of $\boldsymbol{\omega}$ along reference xyz. A procedure then is to express ω_x, ω_y, and ω_z first in a way that insures that these quantities are correctly stated over a time interval rather than at some instantaneous configuration. Once this is done, we can simply differentiate these scalar quantities with respect to time in this interval to get $\dot{\omega}_x$, $\dot{\omega}_y$, and $\dot{\omega}_z$.

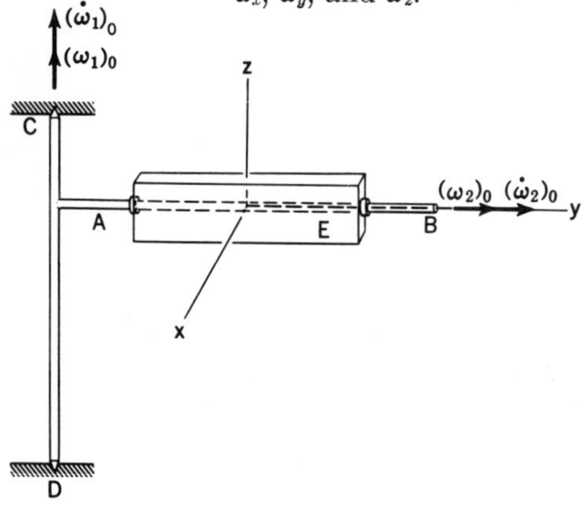

Fig. 17.5

To illustrate this, consider in Fig. 17.5 the case of a block E rotating about rod AB which in turn rotates about vertical axis CD. A reference xyz is fixed to the block at the center of mass so as to coincide with the principal axes of the block at the center of mass. When the block is vertical as shown, the angular speed and rate of change of angular speed relative to AB have the known values $(\omega_2)_0$ and $(\dot{\omega}_2)_0$, respectively. At that instant AB has an angular speed and rate of change of angular speed about axis CD of known values $(\omega_1)_0$ and $(\dot{\omega}_1)_0$, respectively. We can immediately give the angular velocity components at the instant shown as follows:

$$\omega_x = 0, \qquad \omega_y = (\omega_2)_0,$$
$$\omega_z = (\omega_1)_0$$

But to get the quantities $(\dot{\omega}_x)_0$, $(\dot{\omega}_y)_0$, and $(\dot{\omega}_z)_0$ for the instant of interest we must first express ω_x, ω_y, and ω_z as *general functions of time* in order to permit differentiation with respect to time.

To do this we have shown the system at some arbitrary time in Fig. 17.6. Note that the x axis is at some angle β from the horizontal. When β becomes zero, we arrive back at the configuration of interest, and ω_1, $\dot{\omega}_1$, ω_2, and $\dot{\omega}_2$ become

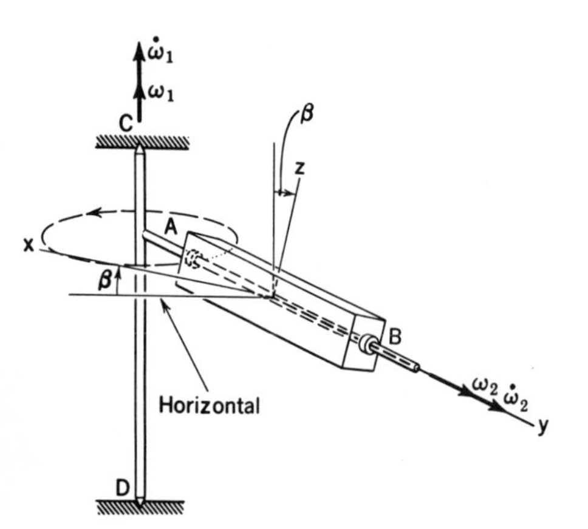

Fig. 17.6

known values $(\omega_1)_0$, $(\dot{\omega}_1)_0$, (ω_2), and $(\dot{\omega}_2)_0$ respectively. The angular velocity components for this arbitrary situation are:

$$\omega_x = \omega_1 \sin\beta, \qquad \omega_y = \omega_2, \qquad \omega_z = \omega_1 \cos\beta \qquad \textbf{17.15}$$

Since these relations are *generally* valid, we can differentiate them with respect to time and get:

$$\begin{aligned}\dot{\omega}_x &= \dot{\omega}_1 \sin\beta + \omega_1 \cos\beta\,\dot{\beta}\\ \dot{\omega}_y &= \dot{\omega}_2\\ \dot{\omega}_z &= \dot{\omega}_1 \cos\beta - \omega_1 \sin\beta\,\dot{\beta}\end{aligned} \qquad \textbf{17.16}$$

It should be clear upon inspecting the diagram that $\dot{\beta} = -\omega_2$, and so the above terms become:

$$\begin{aligned}\dot{\omega}_x &= \dot{\omega}_1 \sin\beta - \omega_1\omega_2 \cos\beta\\ \dot{\omega}_y &= \dot{\omega}_2\\ \dot{\omega}_z &= \dot{\omega}_1 \cos\beta + \omega_1\omega_2 \sin\beta\end{aligned} \qquad \textbf{17.17}$$

If we now let β become zero, we reach the configuration of interest and we get from Eqs. 17.15 and 17.16 the proper values of the angular velocity components and their time derivatives:

$$\begin{aligned}\omega_x &= 0, & \dot{\omega}_x &= -(\omega_1)_0(\omega_2)_0\\ \omega_y &= (\omega_2)_0, & \dot{\omega}_y &= (\dot{\omega}_2)_0\\ \omega_z &= (\omega_1)_0, & \dot{\omega}_z &= (\dot{\omega}_1)_0\end{aligned} \qquad \textbf{17.18}$$

Actually, we do not have to employ such a procedure for the evaluation of these quantities. There is a simple direct approach that can be used, but we must preface the discussion of this method by some general remarks about the time derivative of a vector $\boldsymbol{A}$, as seen from the XYZ axes, expressed in terms of components always parallel to the xyz reference, which moves relative to XYZ (Fig. 17.7). We can then say, considering $\boldsymbol{i}$, $\boldsymbol{j}$, and $\boldsymbol{k}$ as unit vectors for reference xyz:

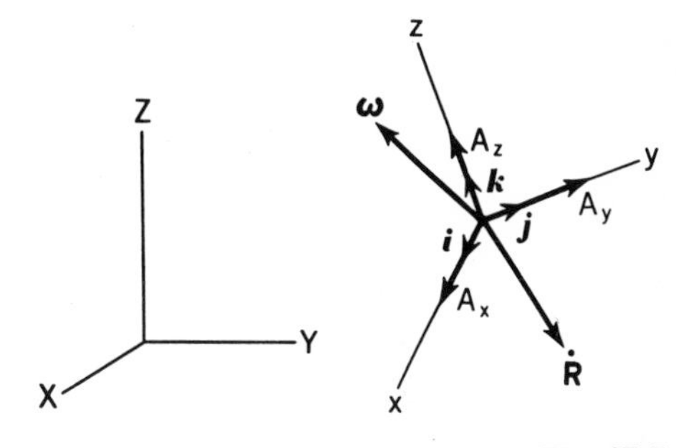

Fig. 17.7

$$\begin{aligned}\left(\frac{d\boldsymbol{A}}{dt}\right)_{XYZ} &= \frac{d}{dt_{XYZ}}(A_x\boldsymbol{i} + A_y\boldsymbol{j} + A_z\boldsymbol{k})\\ &= \dot{A}_x\boldsymbol{i} + \dot{A}_y\boldsymbol{j} + \dot{A}_z\boldsymbol{k} + A_x(\boldsymbol{\omega} \times \boldsymbol{i}) + A_y(\boldsymbol{\omega} \times \boldsymbol{j}) + A_z(\boldsymbol{\omega} \times \boldsymbol{k})\end{aligned} \qquad \textbf{17.19}$$

If we decompose the vector $(d\boldsymbol{A}/dt)_{XYZ}$ into components parallel to the xyz axes at time t and carry out the cross products on the right side in terms of xyz components, we get, after collecting terms and equating components:

$$\left[\left(\frac{d\boldsymbol{A}}{dt}\right)_{XYZ}\right]_x = \dot{A}_x + A_z\omega_y - A_y\omega_z \qquad \textbf{(a)}$$

$$\left[\left(\frac{d\boldsymbol{A}}{dt}\right)_{XYZ}\right]_y = \dot{A}_y + A_x\omega_z - A_z\omega_x \qquad \textbf{(b)}$$

$$\left[\left(\frac{d\mathbf{A}}{dt}\right)_{XYZ}\right]_z = \dot{A}_z + A_y\omega_x - A_x\omega_y \qquad \text{(c)} \quad \mathbf{17.20}$$

§17.4 We can learn an important lesson from these equations. If you take the time derivative of a vector $\mathbf{A}$ with respect to a reference XYZ and express the *components* of this vector parallel to the axes of a reference xyz rotating relative to XYZ (these are the terms on the left side of the above equations), the results are in general *not the same* as *first* taking the components of the vector $\mathbf{A}$ along the directions xyz and *then* taking time derivatives of these scalars. Thus:

$$\left[\left(\frac{d\mathbf{A}}{dt}\right)_{XYZ}\right]_x \neq \left[\frac{d(A_x)}{dt}\right]_{XYZ} \qquad \text{etc.}$$

Or, using the more usual notation, we get:

$$\left[\left(\frac{d\mathbf{A}}{dt}\right)_{XYZ}\right]_x \neq \dot{A}_x \qquad \mathbf{17.21}$$

How does this relate to our problem where we are considering $\dot{\omega}_x$, $\dot{\omega}_y$, and $\dot{\omega}_z$? Clearly, these are time derivatives of the components of the vector $\boldsymbol{\omega}$ along the moving xyz axes, and so they correspond to the terms on the right side of the above inequality. Let us then consider vector $\mathbf{A}$ to be $\boldsymbol{\omega}$ and examine Eq. 17.20:

$$\left[\left(\frac{d\boldsymbol{\omega}}{dt}\right)_{XYZ}\right]_x = \dot{\omega}_x + \omega_z\omega_y - \omega_y\omega_z$$

$$\left[\left(\frac{d\boldsymbol{\omega}}{dt}\right)_{XYZ}\right]_y = \dot{\omega}_y + \omega_x\omega_z - \omega_z\omega_x$$

$$\left[\left(\frac{d\boldsymbol{\omega}}{dt}\right)_{XYZ}\right]_z = \dot{\omega}_z + \omega_y\omega_x - \omega_x\omega_y \qquad \mathbf{17.22}$$

We see that terms on the right side cancel for the case, leaving us:

$$\left[\left(\frac{d\boldsymbol{\omega}}{dt}\right)_{XYZ}\right]_x = \dot{\omega}_x$$

$$\left[\left(\frac{d\boldsymbol{\omega}}{dt}\right)_{XYZ}\right]_y = \dot{\omega}_y$$

$$\left[\left(\frac{d\boldsymbol{\omega}}{dt}\right)_{XYZ}\right]_z = \dot{\omega}_z \qquad \mathbf{17.23}$$

We see that for the vector $\boldsymbol{\omega}$, i.e., the angular velocity of the xyz reference rela- to the XYZ reference, we have an exception to the rule stated earlier. Here is the one case where the derivative of a vector for one set of axes XYZ has components along the directions of another set of axes xyz rotating relative to XYZ which are equal to the simple time derivatives of the scalar components of the vector along the xyz directions. In other words, you can take the derivative of $\boldsymbol{\omega}$ first for XYZ axes and then take components along xyz, or you can take components along xyz first and then take simple time derivatives of the components, and the results are the same.

If we fully understand the exceptional nature of Eq. 17.23, *we can compute* $\dot{\omega}_x$, $\dot{\omega}_y$, *and* $\dot{\omega}_z$ *in a straightforward manner by simply determining* $(d\boldsymbol{\omega}/dt)_{XYZ}$ *and taking the components.* This is a step which we have practiced a great deal in kinematics. For instance, for the problem introduced at the outset of this discussion, we see by inspecting Fig. 17.5 that:

$$\boldsymbol{\omega} = \omega_2 \boldsymbol{j} + \omega_1 \boldsymbol{k}_1 \qquad \textbf{17.24}$$

where $\boldsymbol{k}_1$ is the unit vector in the fixed Z direction. Now differentiate with respect to time for the XYZ reference:

$$\dot{\boldsymbol{\omega}} = \dot{\omega}_2 \boldsymbol{j} + \omega_2 \dot{\boldsymbol{j}} + \dot{\omega}_1 \boldsymbol{k}_1 \qquad \textbf{17.25}$$

But $\boldsymbol{j}$ is fixed in a rigid body that is rotating with angular velocity $\omega_1 \boldsymbol{k}_1 + \omega_2 \boldsymbol{j}$. We then get:

$$\dot{\boldsymbol{\omega}} = \dot{\omega}_2 \boldsymbol{j} + \omega_2(\omega_1 \boldsymbol{k}_1 + \omega_2 \boldsymbol{j}) \times \boldsymbol{j} + \dot{\omega}_1 \boldsymbol{k}_1 \qquad \textbf{17.26}$$

When the xyz axes are parallel to the XYZ axes, the unit vector $\boldsymbol{k}$ becomes the same as the unit vector $\boldsymbol{k}_1$, and ω_1, ω_2, etc., become known values $(\omega_1)_0$, $(\omega_2)_0$, etc. We then get for that configuration:

$$\dot{\boldsymbol{\omega}}_0 = (\dot{\omega}_2)_0 \boldsymbol{j} - (\omega_1)_0(\omega_2)_0 \boldsymbol{i} + (\dot{\omega}_1)_0 \boldsymbol{k} \qquad \textbf{17.27}$$

The components of the above equation give the desired values of $\dot{\omega}_x$, $\dot{\omega}_y$, and $\dot{\omega}_z$ at the instant of interest. Thus we have:

$$\dot{\omega}_x = -(\omega_1)_0(\omega_2)_0$$

$$\dot{\omega}_y = (\dot{\omega}_2)_0$$

$$\dot{\omega}_z = (\dot{\omega}_1)_0$$

In most of the following examples we shall proceed by the second method discussed here.* We will find $\boldsymbol{\omega}$ as a general function of time in the form:

$$\boldsymbol{\omega} = \omega_x \boldsymbol{i} + \omega_y \boldsymbol{j} + \omega_z \boldsymbol{k} \qquad \textbf{17.28}$$

and then we will get $\dot{\omega}_x$, $\dot{\omega}_y$, and $\dot{\omega}_z$ at any time t_0 using the following formulations:

$$(\dot{\omega}_x)_{t_0} = \left\{\left[\left(\frac{d\boldsymbol{\omega}}{dt}\right)_{XYZ}\right]_x\right\}_{t_0} \qquad \textbf{(a)}$$

$$(\dot{\omega}_y)_{t_0} = \left\{\left[\left(\frac{d\boldsymbol{\omega}}{dt}\right)_{XYZ}\right]_y\right\}_{t_0} \qquad \textbf{(b)}$$

$$(\dot{\omega}_z)_{t_0} = \left\{\left[\left(\frac{d\boldsymbol{\omega}}{dt}\right)_{XYZ}\right]_z\right\}_{t_0} \qquad \textbf{(c)} \quad \textbf{17.29}$$

EXAMPLE 17.2

A cylinder rolls without slipping down an inclined plane (Fig. 17.8). What will be its angular velocity at any time t, assuming it starts from rest at $t = 0$?

---

* The instructor may, after examining Example 17.2 (which is a plane motion problem), go first to other simple special cases (including a detailed study of plane motion) in Section 17.6 before examining the three-dimensional problems starting with Example 17.3.

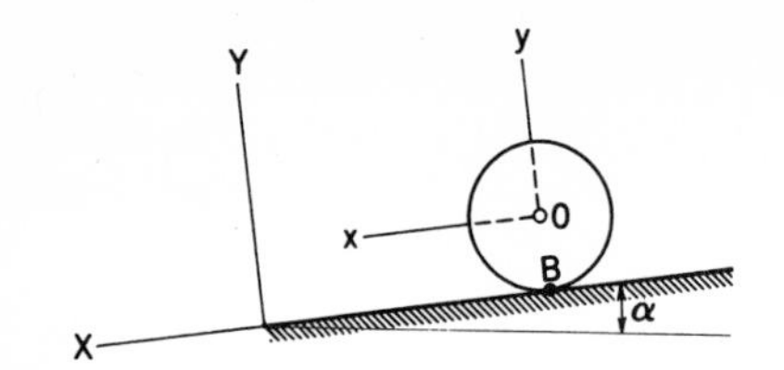

Fig. 17.8

We have solved this simple type of problem many times in the past (see, for instance, Example 14.16) using simpler and more restricted points of view. We shall take advantage of the simplicity of the problem here to illustrate the use of the Euler equations and method of approach that will characterize the more complex problems to be examined later.

Taking the ground as an inertial reference, we have indicated an XYZ reference fixed to the incline. We shall now solve the problem for two different viewpoints.

Viewpoint 1. We may readily establish a set of axes with an origin fixed at the mass center of the cylinder. The principal axes are composed of an axis along the longitudinal axis of symmetry of the cylinder and any pair of orthogonal lines in the center plane of the cylinder at right angles to the centerline. For convenience, we choose the directions xyz parallel to the inertial reference at $t = 0$, as shown in Fig. 17.8. We can now employ Euler's equation about the mass center. To compute the components of $\boldsymbol{M}$, we draw the free-body diagram of the cylinder in Fig. 17.9. Note that the friction force f is not known in terms of N, since we cannot assume that slippage is impending in order to use Coulomb's law of friction. The only nonzero moment component is M_z, which is equal to $-fr$. The Euler equations then become:

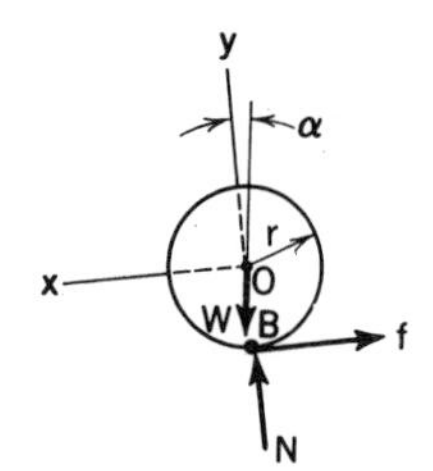

Fig. 17.9

$$0 = I_{xx}\dot{\omega}_x + \omega_y\omega_z(I_{zz} - I_{yy})$$
$$0 = I_{yy}\dot{\omega}_y + \omega_z\omega_x(I_{xx} - I_{zz})$$
$$-fr = I_{zz}\dot{\omega}_z + \omega_x\omega_y(I_{yy} - I_{xx}) \qquad \textbf{(a)}$$

It is apparent that $\omega_x = \omega_y = 0$ at all times. Thus only the last equation is useful:

$$-fr = I_{zz}\dot{\omega}_z \qquad \textbf{(b)}$$

We see that in this case the Euler equations have degenerated to the familiar $T = I\ddot{\theta}$ of elementary physics. In this equation, we have two unknowns, f and $\dot{\omega}_z$.

We may next write another equation for the translation of the mass center:

$$-f + W \sin \alpha = M\ddot{X} \qquad \textbf{(c)}$$

This, however, introduces another unknown, $\ddot{X}$, the acceleration of the mass center relative to the inertial reference.

We find a third equation without additional unknowns by employing kinematical considerations of the no-slipping condition. We can relate the acceleration of two points O and B in a very simple manner. Thus, employing Eq. 15.7, we have:

$$\boldsymbol{a}_0 = \boldsymbol{a}_B + \dot{\boldsymbol{\omega}} \times \boldsymbol{\varrho}_{BO} + \boldsymbol{\omega} \times (\boldsymbol{\omega} \times \boldsymbol{\varrho}_{BO})$$

Note (1) that $\boldsymbol{a}_0 = \ddot{X}\boldsymbol{i}$; (2) that the acceleration $\boldsymbol{a}_B$ must be in the y direction (as learned in analytic geometry and physics); and (3) that the direction of $\boldsymbol{\omega}$ and $\dot{\boldsymbol{\omega}}$ is in the z direction. Thus we get:

$$\ddot{X}\boldsymbol{i} = a_B\boldsymbol{j} + \dot{\omega}_z\boldsymbol{k} \times r\boldsymbol{j} + \omega_z\boldsymbol{k} \times (\omega_z\boldsymbol{k} \times r\boldsymbol{j})$$

$$\therefore\ \ddot{X}\boldsymbol{i} = a_B\boldsymbol{j} - r\dot{\omega}_z\boldsymbol{i} - r\omega_z^2\boldsymbol{j}$$

From this we see that:

$$\ddot{X} = -r\dot{\omega}_z \qquad \textbf{(d)}$$

a result that you most likely knew by inspection as a result of your earlier studies.

Now substitute for $\ddot{X}$ and f in Eq. (c), using Eqs. (d) and (b). This becomes:

$$\frac{I_{zz}\dot{\omega}_z}{r} + W \sin \alpha = -M\dot{\omega}_z r$$

Solving for $\dot{\omega}_z$, we have

$$\dot{\omega}_z = -\frac{Wr \sin \alpha}{I_{zz} + Mr^2} \qquad \textbf{(e)}$$

Note that on the right side we have all constants. Thus in this simple problem we can integrate directly:

$$\omega_z = -\frac{Wr \sin \alpha}{I_{zz} + Mr^2}\,t + C_1$$

Because $\omega_z = 0$ for $t = 0$, we have $C_1 = 0$. The desired result is:

$$\omega_z = -\frac{Wr \sin \alpha}{I_{zz} + Mr^2}\,t \qquad \textbf{(f)}$$

Viewpoint 2. Let us now consider as our point of interest the point B on the cylinder in contact with the incline at time t (Fig. 17.10). It should be clear from your studies in analytic geometry that this point accelerates toward the mass center and hence qualifies for the equation $\boldsymbol{M} = \dot{\boldsymbol{H}}$. We can then express Euler's equation for the point B at the time t positioned as shown in the diagram. As before, only one equation is non-trivial—the z' component. Observing Fig. 17.11, we can say:

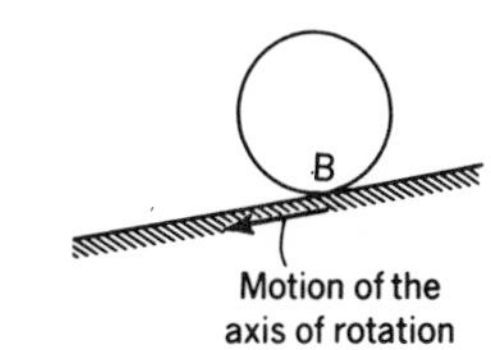

Fig. 17.10

$$-Wr \sin \alpha = I_{z'z'}\dot{\omega}_{z'} \qquad \textbf{(g)}$$

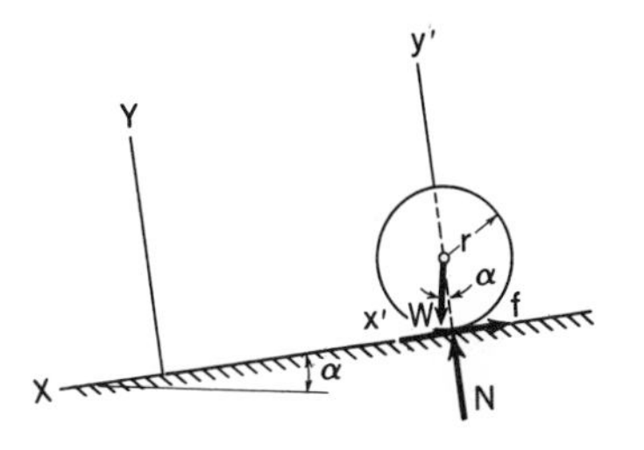

Fig. 17.11

Solving for $\dot{\omega}_{z'}$, we get:

$$\dot{\omega}_{z'} = -\frac{Wr \sin \alpha}{I_{z'z'}} \qquad \textbf{(h)}$$

An examination of the right side of this equation reveals that no matter where along the incline the point of contact is employed we will find the same terms for this equation. We can conclude that the acceleration of the cylinder is constant at all positions along the incline, and so we can integrate the above expression under these special circumstances. We get:

$$\omega_{z'} = -\frac{Wr \sin \alpha}{I_{z'z'}}\,t + C_1 \qquad \textbf{(i)}$$

When $t = 0$, $\omega_{z'} = 0$, so we see that $C_1 = 0$. Thus the angular velocity at any time is:

$$\omega_{z'} = -\frac{Wr \sin \alpha}{I_{z'z'}}\,t \qquad \textbf{(j)}$$

We must expect the same angular velocity for either analysis, since there is only one angular velocity at a given time associated with a body for a given reference. Actually, ω_z and $\omega_{z'}$ are the same, as we can see if we compare Eqs. (j) and (f), since by the parallel axis theorem for moments of inertia:

$$I_{z'z'} = I_{zz} + Mr^2 \tag{k}$$

Note that the point B used in viewpoint 2 is not only a point on the body accelerating toward the mass center as seen from XYZ; in addition it is a point of the cylinder coinciding with the axis of rotation at time t. If the cylinder were not uniform and had its mass center *off* the axis normal to the incline at the point of contact, we could not justify the use of Euler's equations for point B on the basis of viewpoint 2. We would have to use Eq. 14.39 for the point of contact.

The preceding problem was that of plane motion, presented here to illustrate most simply the manner of application of Newton's law, Euler's equation, and kinematics of rigid bodies, all used to compute certain quantities. We shall now apply this approach to three-dimensional problems so as to fully understand the general theory presented. Later we shall look at simplifications of the theory including a more thorough examination of the case of plane motion. These cases perhaps may best be understood and most effectively treated once a grasp of the three-dimensional problem has been developed.

EXAMPLE 17.3

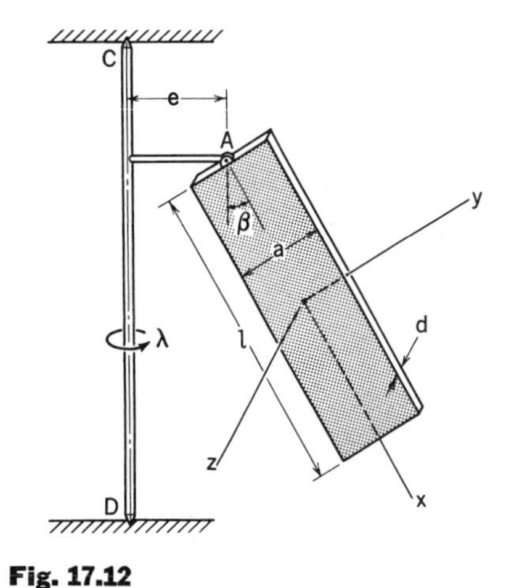

Fig. 17.12

A bar of metal is pinned to an extension of a shaft at A (Fig. 17.12). This shaft, noted as CD, rotates at a uniform speed of λ radians per second. What must the angle β be for the bar in the steady state when all oscillations have ceased? Also determine the forces at A for this condition.

Let us consider Euler's equations for the center of mass of the bar, where we have set up the principal axes xyz. To determine the moments about the center of mass, we next draw a free-body diagram of the bar (Fig. 17.13). The pin connector at A permits free rotation of the bar in the xy plane only, and thus couple components can be transmitted along the x and y directions. They are denoted as C_x and C_y, as shown in the free-body diagram. The angular speed of the bar about the center of mass, as seen from an inertial reference, is λ, and we can get the components along the principal axes as follows:

$$\boldsymbol{\omega} = \boldsymbol{\Omega} = -\lambda \cos\beta \boldsymbol{i} + \lambda \sin\beta \boldsymbol{j}$$

$$\therefore \omega_x = -\lambda\cos\beta, \quad \omega_y = \lambda\sin\beta, \quad \omega_z = 0$$

Since $\boldsymbol{\omega}$ is a constant vector, we have:

$$\dot{\boldsymbol{\omega}} = \mathbf{0}$$

$$\therefore \dot{\omega}_x = 0, \quad \dot{\omega}_y = 0, \quad \dot{\omega}_z = 0$$

Thus Euler's equations become:

$$M_x = 0$$

$$M_y = 0$$

$$M_z = (I_{yy} - I_{zz})\omega_x\omega_y = -(I_{yy} - I_{xx})\lambda^2 \sin\beta \cos\beta$$

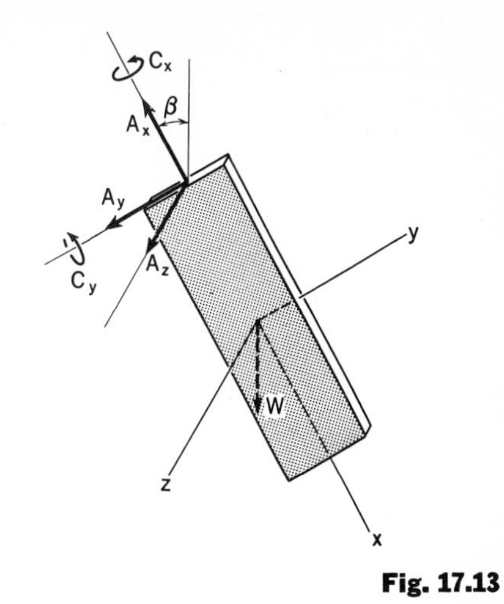

Fig. 17.13

From the free-body diagram, we see that $M_z = A_y(l/2)$, $M_x = -C_x$, and $M_y = A_z(l/2) - C_y$. The above equations can then be written as follows:

$$C_x = 0 \tag{a}$$

$$A_z \frac{l}{2} - C_y = 0 \tag{b}$$

$$A_y \frac{l}{2} = -(I_{yy} - I_{xx})\lambda^2 \sin\beta \cos\beta \tag{c}$$

From a consideration of the z component of Newton's law for the mass center, it is clear that A_z is zero, and so from Eq. (b) we see that $C_y = 0$. Equation (c) involves two unknowns, A_y and the angle β.

Consider next the component of Newton's law for the mass center in the vertical direction:

$$A_x \cos\beta - A_y \sin\beta - W = 0 \tag{d}$$

Since this introduces another unknown, A_x, we now have two equations, (c) and (d), with three unknowns.

Note that the center of mass is moving in a circle with a constant speed. We know then that it has an acceleration having the value $[e + (l/2)\sin\beta]\lambda^2$ radially toward the CD axis. Therefore, employing Newton's law in the radial direction, we have:

$$A_x \sin\beta + A_y \cos\beta = M\left(e + \frac{l}{2}\sin\beta\right)\lambda^2 \tag{e}$$

We now have three equations for three unknowns.

If we multiply Eq. (d) by $\sin\beta$ and Eq. (e) by $\cos\beta$ and subtract Eq. (e) from Eq. (d), we get, after replacing M by W/g:

$$-A_y = W\sin\beta - \left(e\cos\beta + \frac{l}{2}\sin\beta\cos\beta\right)\frac{W\lambda^2}{g} \tag{f}$$

Now replace A_y in Eq. (c), using Eq. (f):

$$\frac{l}{2}\left[W\sin\beta - \left(e\cos\beta + \frac{l}{2}\sin\beta\cos\beta\right)\frac{W\lambda^2}{g}\right] = (I_{yy} - I_{xx})\lambda^2 \sin\beta\cos\beta$$

Next divide through by $\cos\beta$. On rearranging the equation, we get:

$$\frac{Wl}{2}\tan\beta - \left[\frac{Wl^2}{4g} + (I_{yy} - I_{xx})\right]\lambda^2 \sin\beta = \frac{Wle\lambda^2}{2g}$$

We may solve such an equation by trial and error for β when the values of the various constants are known, and from Eqs. (f) and (e) we can determine the forces A_y and A_x.

In a later section, another approach will be presented for problems such as this one where the nature of the motion of the center of mass can be ascertained by inspection. This is the method of D'Alembert applied to rigid bodies.

EXAMPLE 17.4

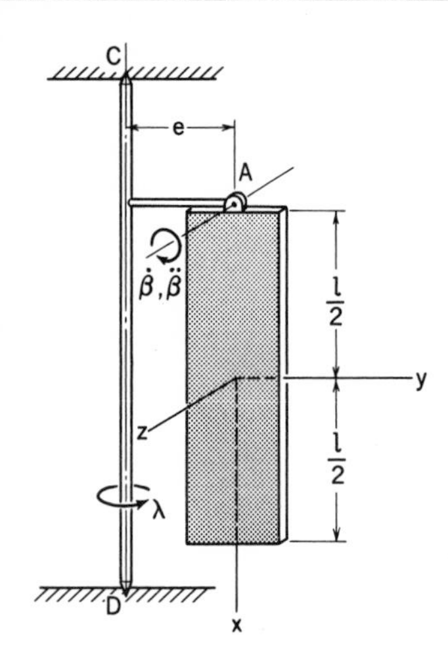

Fig. 17.14

In an apparatus similar to that of the preceding example, the metal bar is rotated about the pin at A by an internal mechanism at A such that when $\beta = 0$, $\dot{\beta}$ and $\ddot{\beta}$ are unknown. If the speed of the shaft CD is to remain a constant λ, compute the required torque about CD and the forces transmitted at A at the instant when the bar is passing through its vertical position, as shown in Fig. 17.14.

We again examine the free-body diagram of the bar (Fig. 17.15) to study the forces and couple-components at point A. (After computing these forces and couples, we will compute the desired torque about CD by using their reactions acting on CD). Note that since we no longer have a free hinge at A, we now have the possibility of a couple-component C_z. Additionally the angular velocities and accelerations for Euler's equations applied to the center of mass of the above body are:

$$\boldsymbol{\omega} = -\lambda\boldsymbol{i} - \dot{\beta}\boldsymbol{k}$$

$$\therefore\ \omega_x = -\lambda, \quad \omega_y = 0, \quad \omega_z = -\dot{\beta}$$

$$\dot{\boldsymbol{\omega}} = \frac{d}{dt}(-\lambda\boldsymbol{i}) + \frac{d}{dt}(-\dot{\beta}\boldsymbol{k}) = \boldsymbol{0} - \ddot{\beta}\boldsymbol{k} - \dot{\beta}\dot{\boldsymbol{k}}$$
$$= -\ddot{\beta}\boldsymbol{k} - \dot{\beta}\{(-\lambda\boldsymbol{i} - \dot{\beta}\boldsymbol{k}) \times \boldsymbol{k}\}$$
$$= -\ddot{\beta}\boldsymbol{k} - \dot{\beta}\lambda\boldsymbol{j}$$

$$\therefore\ \dot{\omega}_x = 0, \quad \dot{\omega}_y = -\lambda\dot{\beta}, \quad \dot{\omega}_z = -\ddot{\beta}$$

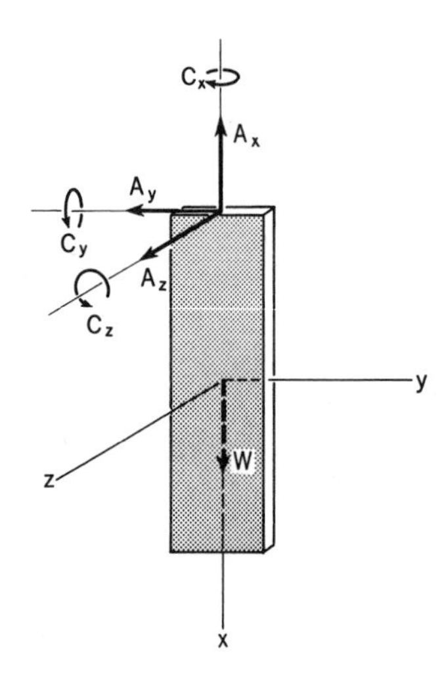

Fig. 17.15

Thus Euler's equations become:

$$C_x = 0 \tag{a}$$

$$C_y + A_z\frac{l}{2} = -\lambda\dot{\beta}I_{yy} + \lambda\dot{\beta}(I_{xx} - I_{zz}) \tag{b}$$

$$C_z + A_y\frac{l}{2} = -I_{zz}\ddot{\beta} \tag{c}$$

We see that C_x is zero, and we now have two equations with four unknowns, C_y, C_z, A_x, and A_y.

We must next employ Newton's laws for the center of mass. Accordingly, we will need the acceleration of the mass center relative to an inertial reference. To express this, it will be helpful to establish a reference $x'y'z'$ at A and fixed to the shaft CD. For convenience, $x'y'z'$ is chosen parallel to the xyz reference corresponding to the instant of interest, as shown in Fig. 17.16, where a convenient inertial reference XYZ has also been shown. Going back to earlier lessons in kinematics, we have:

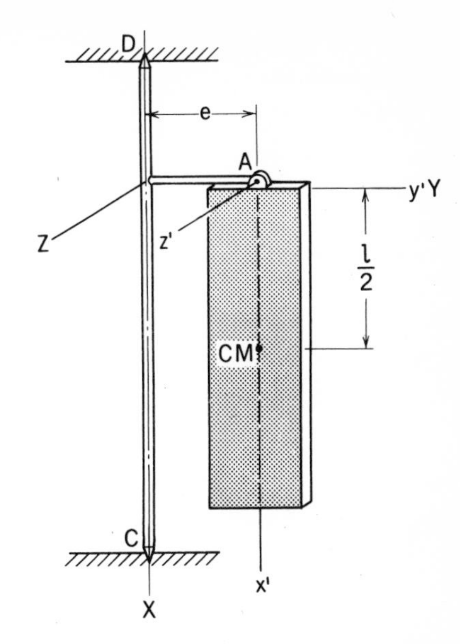

Fig. 17.16

A. *Motion of mass center relative to $x'y'z'$:*

$$\boldsymbol{\varrho} = \frac{l}{2}\,\boldsymbol{i}$$

$$\boldsymbol{V}_{x'y'z'} = -\dot{\beta}\boldsymbol{k} \times \frac{l}{2}\,\boldsymbol{i} = -\frac{l\dot{\beta}}{2}\,\boldsymbol{j}$$

$$\boldsymbol{a}_{x'y'z'} = -\frac{l}{2}\,\dot{\beta}^2\boldsymbol{i} - \frac{l}{2}\,\ddot{\beta}\boldsymbol{j} \quad \text{(using formulae for plane circular motion)}$$

B. *Motion of $x'y'z'$ relative to XYZ:*

$$\dot{\boldsymbol{R}} = -\lambda\boldsymbol{i} \times e\boldsymbol{j} = -e\lambda\boldsymbol{k}$$

$$\ddot{\boldsymbol{R}} = -e\lambda^2\boldsymbol{j} \quad \text{(using formulae for plane circular motion)}$$

$$\boldsymbol{\omega} = -\lambda\boldsymbol{i}$$

$$\dot{\boldsymbol{\omega}} = \boldsymbol{0}$$

Hence:

$$\boldsymbol{a}_{XYZ} = \boldsymbol{a}_{x'y'z'} + \ddot{\boldsymbol{R}} + 2\boldsymbol{\omega} \times \boldsymbol{V}_{x'y'z'} + \dot{\boldsymbol{\omega}} \times \boldsymbol{\varrho} + \boldsymbol{\omega} \times (\boldsymbol{\omega} \times \boldsymbol{\varrho})$$

$$= -\frac{l}{2}\,\dot{\beta}^2\boldsymbol{i} - \frac{l}{2}\,\ddot{\beta}\boldsymbol{j} - e\lambda^2\boldsymbol{j} + 2(-\lambda\boldsymbol{i}) \times \left(-\frac{l\dot{\beta}}{2}\,\boldsymbol{j}\right) + (-\lambda\boldsymbol{i}) \times \left[(-\lambda\boldsymbol{i}) \times \frac{l}{2}\,\boldsymbol{i}\right]$$

Collecting terms, we get:

$$\boldsymbol{a}_{XYZ} = -\frac{l}{2}\,\dot{\beta}^2\boldsymbol{i} - \left(\frac{l}{2}\,\ddot{\beta} + e\lambda^2\right)\boldsymbol{j} + \lambda l\dot{\beta}\boldsymbol{k}$$

Now we can use Newton's law for the center of mass. The scalar equations permit us to solve for A_x, A_y, and A_z. Thus:

$$A_x = \frac{Ml\dot{\beta}^2}{2} + W \qquad \textbf{(d)}$$

$$A_y = M\left(\frac{l}{2}\,\ddot{\beta} + e\lambda^2\right) \qquad \textbf{(e)}$$

$$A_z = M\lambda l\dot{\beta} \qquad \textbf{(f)}$$

It is a simple matter now to return to Eqs. (b) and (c) to evaluate C_y and C_z. All the forces and couples on the block are now determined at the instant of interest. Using the reactions to these forces and couples, and equating their moments about the axis CD with that of the required torque, T, for maintaining constant λ, we get:

$$A_z e + C_x = T$$

$$\therefore\ T = M\lambda l\dot{\beta}e$$

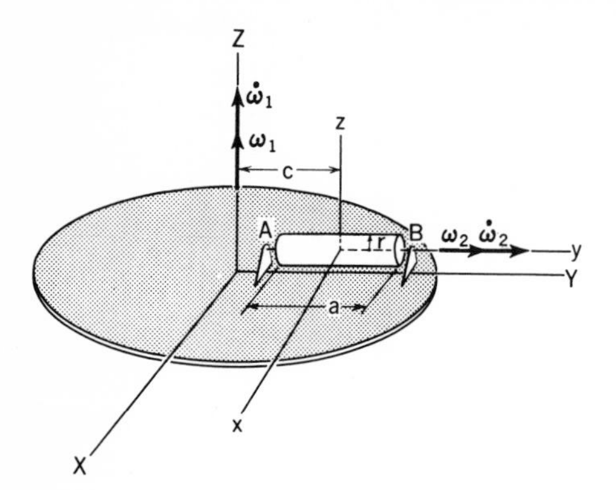

Fig. 17.17

EXAMPLE 17.5

A cylinder AB is rotating in bearings mounted on a platform (Fig. 17.17). The cylinder has an angular speed ω_2 and a rate of change of speed $\dot{\omega}_2$, both quantities being relative to the platform. The platform rotates with an angular speed ω_1 and has a rate of change of speed $\dot{\omega}_1$, both quantities being relative to the ground. Compute the moment of the supporting forces of the cylinder AB about the center of mass of the cylinder in terms of the above-mentioned quantities and the moments of inertia of the cylinder.

We shall do this problem by two methods, one using axes fixed to the body and using Euler's equations, and the other using axes fixed to the platform and using Eq. 17.10.

Method I: Reference fixed to cylinder. In Fig. 17.17, we have fixed axes xyz to the cylinder at the mass center. To get components of $\boldsymbol{M}$ parallel to the inertial reference, we consider the problem when the xyz reference is parallel to the XYZ reference. The angular velocity vector $\boldsymbol{\omega}$ for the body is then:

$$\boldsymbol{\omega} = \omega_1 \boldsymbol{k} + \omega_2 \boldsymbol{j} \tag{a}$$

and, by inspecting Fig. 17.17, we see that the angular acceleration of the body is:

$$\dot{\boldsymbol{\omega}} = \dot{\omega}_1 \boldsymbol{k} + \dot{\omega}_2 \boldsymbol{j} + \omega_1 \boldsymbol{k} \times \omega_2 \boldsymbol{j}$$

$$\therefore\ \dot{\boldsymbol{\omega}} = \dot{\omega}_1 \boldsymbol{k} + \dot{\omega}_2 \boldsymbol{j} - \omega_1 \omega_2 \boldsymbol{i} \tag{b}$$

Thus the angular velocity components and their time rates of change needed for Euler's equation are:

$$\omega_x = 0, \qquad \dot{\omega}_x = -\omega_1\omega_2$$

$$\omega_y = \omega_2, \qquad \dot{\omega}_y = \dot{\omega}_2$$

$$\omega_z = \omega_1, \qquad \dot{\omega}_z = \dot{\omega}_1$$

The Euler equations then become:

$$M_x = I_{xx}(-\omega_1\omega_2) + \omega_1\omega_2(I_{zz} - I_{yy}) \tag{c}$$

$$M_y = I_{yy}\dot{\omega}_2 + 0 \tag{d}$$

$$M_z = I_{zz}\dot{\omega}_1 + 0 \tag{e}$$

Since $I_{zz} = I_{xx}$, we see that $I_{xx}(-\omega_1\omega_2)$ cancels $\omega_1\omega_2 I_{zz}$ in Eq. (c), and we then have the desired result:

$$\boldsymbol{M} = -\omega_1\omega_2 I_{yy}\boldsymbol{i} + I_{yy}\dot{\omega}_2\boldsymbol{j} + I_{zz}\dot{\omega}_1\boldsymbol{k} \tag{f}$$

Method II: Reference fixed to platform. We shall now do this problem by having xyz at the mass center of the cylinder again, but now fixed to the platform. In other words, the cylinder rotates relative to the xyz reference with angular speed ω_2. Keeping this in mind, we can still refer to Fig. 17.17.

Obviously, we cannot use Euler's equations here and must return to Eq. 17.10:

$$\boldsymbol{M} = \left(\frac{d\boldsymbol{H}}{dt}\right)_{xyz} + \boldsymbol{\Omega} \times \boldsymbol{H} \tag{a}$$

Because the cylinder is a body of revolution about the y axis, the products of inertia I_{xy}, I_{xz}, and I_{yz} are always zero, and I_{xx}, I_{yy}, and I_{zz} are *constants*. Were these conditions not present, this method of approach would be very difficult, since we would have to ascertain the time derivatives of these inertia terms. Thus we see that:

$$\left(\frac{d\boldsymbol{H}}{dt}\right)_{xyz} = \frac{d}{dt_{xyz}}(H_x\boldsymbol{i} + H_y\boldsymbol{j} + H_z\boldsymbol{k})$$

$$= \frac{d}{dt_{xyz}}(0\boldsymbol{i} + I_{yy}\omega_2\boldsymbol{j} + I_{zz}\omega_1\boldsymbol{k})$$

$$= I_{yy}\dot{\omega}_2\boldsymbol{j} + I_{zz}\dot{\omega}_1\boldsymbol{k} \qquad \textbf{(b)}$$

Noting further that $\boldsymbol{\Omega} = \omega_1\boldsymbol{k}$ we have on substituting Eq. (b) into Eq. (a):

$$\boldsymbol{M} = I_{yy}\dot{\omega}_2\boldsymbol{j} + I_{zz}\dot{\omega}_1\boldsymbol{k} + \omega_1\boldsymbol{k} \times (H_x\boldsymbol{i} + H_y\boldsymbol{j} + H_z\boldsymbol{k})$$

$$= I_{yy}\dot{\omega}_2\boldsymbol{j} + I_{zz}\dot{\omega}_1\boldsymbol{k} + \omega_1\boldsymbol{k} \times (0\boldsymbol{i} + I_{yy}\omega_2\boldsymbol{j} + I_{zz}\omega_1\boldsymbol{k})$$

$$= -I_{yy}\omega_1\omega_2\boldsymbol{i} + I_{yy}\dot{\omega}_2\boldsymbol{j} + I_{zz}\dot{\omega}_1\boldsymbol{k} \qquad \textbf{(c)}$$

This equation is identical to the one obtained using method I.

EXAMPLE 17.6

A thin disc is mounted on a shaft so that its normal AA forms the angle α with the centerline of the shaft (Fig. 17.18). The shaft rotates with a uniform angular velocity of N rpm. Neglecting the mass of the shaft, compute the forces on the bearings at the time that the normal to the disc is in the plane of the paper.

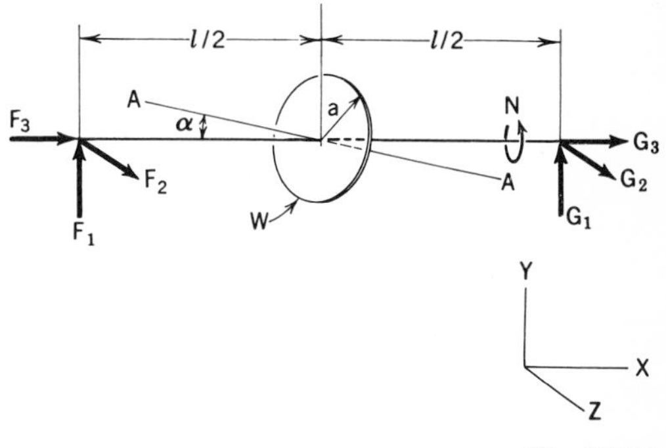

Fig. 17.18

In this problem, the center of mass of the body of interest happens to be a fixed point in an inertial reference. A set of principal axes, xyz, is chosen so that the x axis corresponds to the normal AA; the y axis is chosen as the intersection of the plane formed by the line AA and the centerline of the shaft and the plane of the disc; the z axis must then be in the plane of the disc, with a sense in accordance with the right-hand screw rule, and is by this construction parallel to the horizontal inertial Z axis (Fig. 17.19). We shall now decompose $\boldsymbol{\omega}$, the angular velocity of the body, into components parallel to the xyz axes. Thus, associating $\boldsymbol{i}$, $\boldsymbol{j}$, and $\boldsymbol{k}$ with these axes, we have at all times:

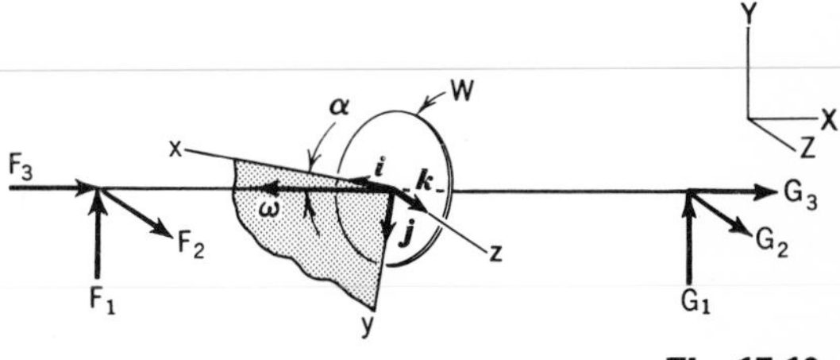

Fig. 17.19

$$\boldsymbol{\omega} = \frac{\pi N}{30}\cos\alpha\boldsymbol{i} + \frac{\pi N}{30}\sin\alpha\boldsymbol{j}$$

$$\therefore\ \omega_x = \frac{\pi N}{30}\cos\alpha$$

$$\omega_y = \frac{\pi N}{30}\sin\alpha$$

$$\omega_z = 0$$

Since the components are valid at all times, we can differentiate them with respect to time as explained in Section 17.4. Or, we can examine $\dot{\boldsymbol{\omega}}$ and then take components—the other approach of Section 17.4. Since the components for xyz are constants here, we see by the first approach that:

$$\dot{\omega}_x = 0, \quad \dot{\omega}_y = 0, \quad \dot{\omega}_z = 0 \tag{a}$$

Euler's equations of motion then become:

$$M_x = 0$$

$$M_y = 0$$

$$M_z = (I_{yy} - I_{xx})\left(\frac{\pi N}{30}\cos\alpha\right)\left(\frac{\pi N}{30}\sin\alpha\right) \tag{b}$$

It is shown in the appendix that $I_{xx} = \frac{1}{2}(W/g)a^2$ for a cylinder and, for a thin disc, that $I_{yy} = \frac{1}{4}(W/g)a^2$. The last of the above equations then becomes:

$$M_z = -\frac{1}{4}\frac{W}{g}a^2\left(\frac{\pi N}{30}\right)^2 \cos\alpha \sin\alpha \tag{c}$$

If α is very small, $\cos\alpha$ may be taken as unity and $\sin\alpha$ may be taken as α. Then we can say:

$$M_z = -\frac{1}{4}\frac{W}{g}\left(\frac{\pi N}{30}\right)^2 \alpha a^2 \tag{d}$$

Thus as a result of Euler's equations, we know that the bearing reactions must exert only this moment component about the center of mass.

Next examine Newton's law for the mass center. Since the center of mass is stationary, we can say:

$$\begin{aligned} F_1 + G_1 &= W, \quad \therefore F_1 = W - G_1 \quad &(1)\\ F_2 + G_2 &= 0, \quad \therefore F_2 = -G_2 \quad &(2)\\ F_3 + G_3 &= 0, \quad \therefore F_3 = -G_3 \quad &(3) \end{aligned} \tag{e}$$

In considering the moments of external forces about the x axis, we clearly see that only F_2 and G_2 can make a contribution (since all other forces intersect the x axis). But F_2 and G_2 form a couple, according to Eq. (e) (2). Since $M_x = 0$ from Euler's equations, it is clear that $F_2 = G_2 = 0$. Next, taking moments about the z axis and substituting into Eq. (d), we get:

$$-F_1\frac{l}{2} + G_1\frac{l}{2} = -\frac{1}{4}\frac{W}{g}\left(\frac{\pi N}{30}\right)^2 \alpha a^2 \tag{f}$$

Rearranging, we have:

$$F_1 - G_1 = \frac{1}{2}\frac{W}{gl}\left(\frac{\pi N}{30}\right)^2 \alpha a^2 \tag{g}$$

We also have Eq. (e) (1):

$$F_1 + G_1 = W \tag{h}$$

Adding Eqs. (g) and (h) we have the solution for F_1:

$$F_1 = \frac{W}{2} + \frac{1}{4}\frac{W}{gl}\left(\frac{\pi N}{30}\right)^2 \alpha a^2 \tag{i}$$

Subtracting Eq. (g) from Eq. (h), we have the solution for G_1:

$$G_1 = \frac{W}{2} - \frac{1}{4}\frac{W}{gl}\left(\frac{\pi N}{30}\right)^2 \alpha a^2 \qquad \text{(j)}$$

It is useful to consider the above forms as being composed of a static part, $W/2$, due to the weight, and a dynamic part, $(W/4gl)(\pi N/30)^2\alpha a^2$, due to the motion. The forces G_3 and F_3 remain undetermined from this analysis, although we know they are equal and opposite. The reactions to the solved forces are then the desired results.

Note that dynamic parts of the forces F_1 and G_1 rotate with the angular speed of the shaft and remain normal to the axis of the shaft.* We can represent such forces by a *phasor* diagram similar to the kind you may be using in your circuit courses for alternating current and voltage. This is shown in Fig. 17.20 for force $(G_1)_D$, wherein vector $(G_1)_D$ rotates with angular speed ω in the YZ plane. The projection of $(G_1)_D$ along the Y and Z axes at any time t then gives the dynamic force components that the bearing G must develop at the time t in the directions of these axes.

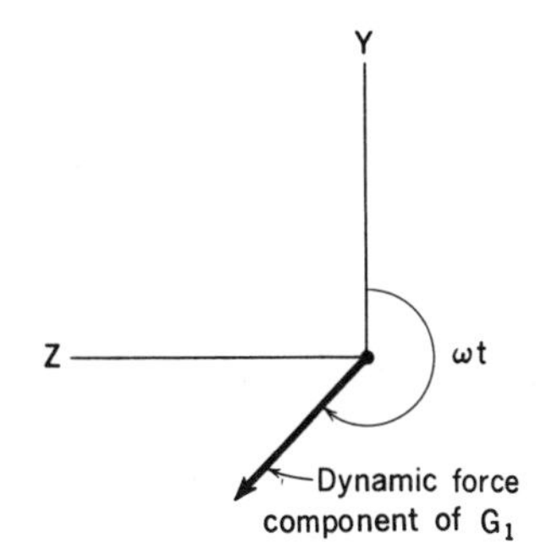

Fig. 17.20

*17.5 Balancing

In the last sample problem, we found that rotating forces are developed on the bearings because of the misalignment of the disc as it is incorporated in the angle α. From Fig. 17.20 it is clear that in any given direction normal to the shaft centerline, this misalignment results in a force on the bearing that varies harmonically with time at a frequency corresponding to the angular rotation of the shaft. Such forces may induce large vibrations in the structure or support if a natural frequency or multiple of the natural frequency is reached in these bodies.† When a shaft creates rotating forces on the bearings by virtue of its own rotation, the shaft is said to be *unbalanced*.

We shall now set forth the criteria for the condition of balance in a shaft, as well as the computations needed for achieving balance in a shaft under certain circumstances. Consider some arbitrary rigid body rotating with angular speed ω and a rate of change of speed $\dot{\omega}$ about axis AB (Fig. 17.21). The center of mass is a distance r from the axis. We shall set up equations for determining the supporting forces at the bearings. Consider point a on the axis of rotation at the bearing A and establish a set of axes xyz (not necessarily principal axes) fixed to the rotating body with the z axis corresponding to the axis of

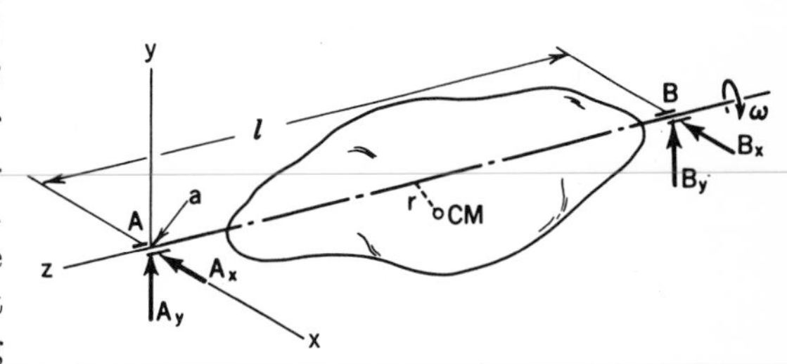

Fig. 17.21

* This should be clear when you realize that turning the whole system in Fig. 17.19 (including reference XYZ) about the axis of rotation to any arbitrary orientation for study will yield the same results for F_1 and G_1 provided we do not include W.

† Natural frequencies will be discussed in detail in Chapter 20.

rotation. The x and y axes may be chosen for convenience. Using the moment of momentum equations (a) and (b) in Eq. 17.13 and including only dynamic forces, we get:

$$B_y l = I_{yz}\omega_z^2 - I_{xz}\dot{\omega}_z \quad \textbf{(a)}$$

$$B_x l = -I_{zx}\omega_z^2 - I_{yz}\dot{\omega}_z \quad \textbf{(b)} \quad \textbf{17.30}$$

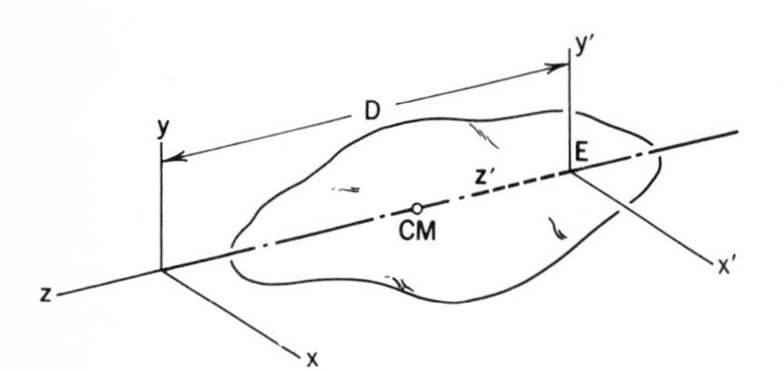

Fig. 17.22

You may have been asked to show in Problem 37 of Chapter 16 that with z as a principal axis at a point, all products of inertia involving the z axis are zero at this point. From the above equations, we can therefore conclude that if the axis of rotation is a principal axis at bearing A, the dynamic forces at bearing B are zero.

Next we will show that if in addition the center of mass lies along the axis of rotation, this axis is a principal axis for all points along its line of action. In Fig. 17.22, a set of axes $x'y'z'$ parallel to the xyz axes has been set up at an arbitrary point E along the axis of rotation. We can see from the arrangement of the axes that for any element of the body dm:

$$y' = y, \qquad x' = x, \qquad z' = z + D \quad \textbf{17.31}$$

where D may be any distance. Also we know for the xyz reference that:

$$I_{xz} = \int xz\,dm = 0, \qquad I_{yz} = \int yz\,dm = 0 \quad \textbf{17.32}$$

and if the center of mass is along the centerline, we can say:

$$y_c M = \int y\,dm = \int y'\,dm = 0$$

$$x_c M = \int x\,dm = \int x'\,dm = 0 \quad \textbf{17.33}$$

We will now show that products of inertia involving the z' axis at E are zero under these conditions, and consequently that the z' axis is a principal axis at E. Substituting from Eqs. 17.31 into 17.32, we get:

$$\int x'(z' - D)\,dm = 0 \quad \textbf{(a)}$$

$$\int y'(z' - D)\,dm = 0 \quad \textbf{(b)}$$

If we carry out the multiplication in the integrand of Eqs. (a) and (b), we get:

$$\int x'z'\,dm - D\int x'\,dm = 0 \quad \textbf{(c)}$$

$$\int y'z'\,dm - D\int y'\,dm = 0 \quad \textbf{(d)}$$

As a result of Eq. 17.33, the second integral of Eqs. (c) and (d) is zero, and we conclude that the products of inertia $I_{x'z'}$ and $I_{y'z'}$ are zero. Accordingly, the axis of rotation must be a principal axis at E.

With this in mind, let us return to the problem of balancing and express the moment of momentum equations for a point along the axis of rotation at bearing B. For dynamic forces, we get:

$$-A_y l = I_{y'z}\omega_z^2 - I_{x'z'}\dot{\omega}_z \quad \text{(a)}$$

$$-A_x l = -I_{z'x'}\omega_z^2 - I_{y'z'}\dot{\omega}_z \quad \text{(b)} \qquad \mathbf{17.34}$$

If the z axis is a principal axis at bearing A (or, for that matter, along any point of the axis of rotation) and if the center of mass is on the axis of rotation, it is clear from the preceding discussion that $I_{y'z'}$ and $I_{x'z'}$ are zero. The dynamic forces at bearing A, therefore, are zero. The rotating system is thus balanced.

We can now conclude that *for a rotating system to be dynamically balanced, it is necessary and sufficient* (*a*) *that at some point along the axis of rotation this axis is a principal axis and* (*b*) *that the center of mass is along the axis of rotation.*

EXAMPLE 17.7

A rotating member carries two weights, $W_1 = 5$ lb and $W_2 = 8$ lb, at radial distances $r_1 = 1$ ft and $r_2 = 1\frac{1}{2}$ ft, respectively. The weights and a reference xyz fixed to the shaft are shown in Fig. 17.23. They are to be balanced by two other weights W_3 and W_4, which are to be placed in the balancing planes A and B, respectively. If the weights are placed in these planes at a distance of 1 ft from the axis of rotation, determine the value of these weights and their position relative to the xyz reference.

We have two unknown weights and two unknown angles, i.e., four unknowns, to evaluate in this problem. The condition that the mass center be on the centerline yields the following relations:*

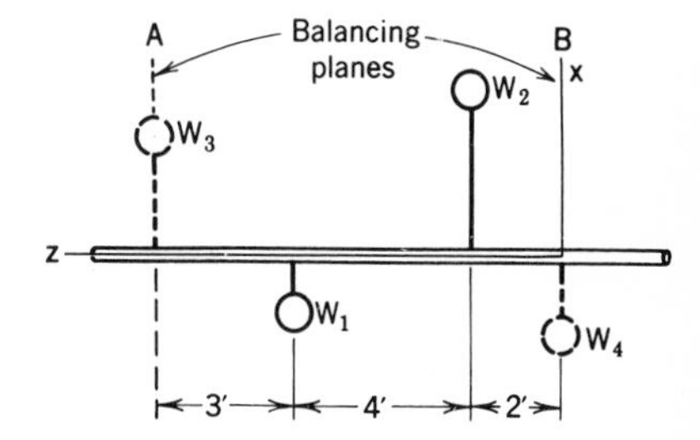

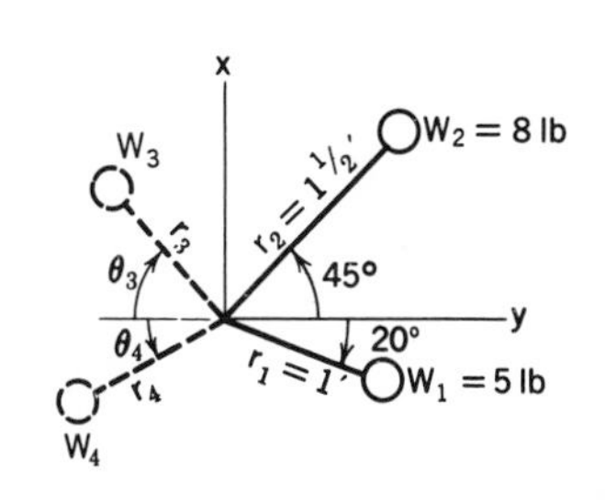

Fig. 17.23

$\int y\, dm = 0$:

$$\frac{W_1}{g} r_1 \cos 20° + \frac{W_2}{g} r_2 \cos 45° - \frac{W_3}{g} r_3 \cos\theta_3 - \frac{W_4}{g} r_4 \cos\theta_4 = 0$$

$\int x\, dm = 0$:

$$-\frac{W_1}{g} r_1 \sin 20° + \frac{W_2}{g} r_2 \sin 45° + \frac{W_3}{g} r_3 \sin\theta_3 - \frac{W_4}{g} r_4 \sin\theta_4 = 0$$

---

* We are considering the weights to be particles in this discussion. In some homework problems you will be asked to balance rotating systems for which the particle model will not be proper. You will then have to carry out integrations and/or employ the formulae and transfer theorems for first moments of inertia and products of inertia.

When the numerical values of r_1, r_2, etc., are inserted, these equations become:

$$W_3 \cos\theta_3 + W_4 \cos\theta_4 = 13.16 \qquad \textbf{(a)}$$

$$W_3 \sin\theta_3 - W_4 \sin\theta_4 = -6.75 \qquad \textbf{(b)}$$

Now consider the products of inertia I_{yz} and I_{xz} to be zero for the xyz reference which is positioned so that yx is in the balancing plane B:

$\underline{I_{xz} = 0:}$

$$\frac{W_1}{g}(6)(-r_1 \sin 20°) + \frac{W_2}{g}(2)(r_2 \sin 45°) + \frac{W_3}{g}(9)(r_3 \sin\theta_3) = 0 \qquad \textbf{(c)}$$

$\underline{I_{yz} = 0:}$

$$\frac{W_1}{g}(6)(r_1 \cos 20°) + \frac{W_2}{g}(2)(r_2 \cos 45°) + \frac{W_3}{g}(9)(-r_3 \cos\theta_3) = 0 \qquad \textbf{(d)}$$

Eqs. (c) and (d) may be put in the form:

$$9W_3 \sin\theta_3 = -6.74 \qquad \textbf{(e)}$$

$$9W_3 \cos\theta_3 = 45.2 \qquad \textbf{(f)}$$

Dividing Eq. (f) into Eq. (e), we get:

$$\tan\theta_3 = -0.1495$$

$$\theta_3 = 171.5° \text{ or } 351.5°$$

and so from Eq. (e):

$$W_3 = -\frac{6.74}{9}\frac{1}{\sin\theta_3} = 5.06 \text{ lb}$$

In order to have a positive weight W_3, we chose θ_3 to be 351.5° rather than 171.5°, and now we return to Eqs. (a) and (b). We can then say, on substituting known values of W_3 and θ_3:

$$W_4 \cos\theta_4 = 13.16 - 5.00 = 8.16 \qquad \textbf{(g)}$$

$$W_4 \sin\theta_4 = 6.75 - 0.75 = 6.00 \qquad \textbf{(h)}$$

Dividing Eq. (g) into Eq. (h), we get:

$$\tan\theta_4 = 0.735$$

$$\theta_4 = 36.3° \text{ or } 216.3°$$

Hence from Eq. (g), we have:

$$W_4 = 8.16/\cos\theta_4 = 10.1 \text{ lb}$$

if we use $\theta_4 = 36.3°$ rather than 216.3° to prevent a negative W_4. The final orientation of the balanced system is shown in Fig. 17.24.

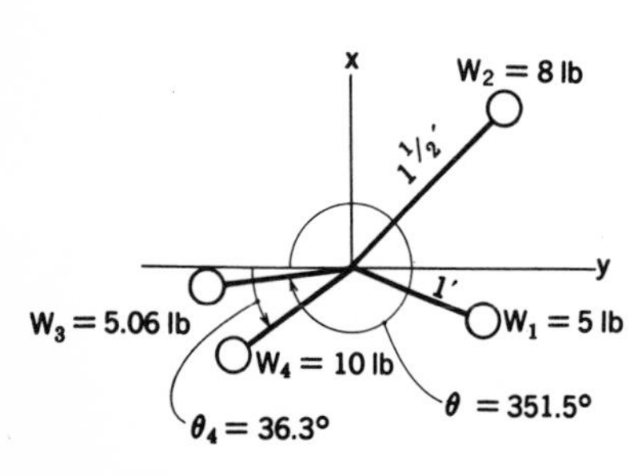

Fig. 17.24

17.6 Simplifications of Euler's Equations

You may have noticed that the components of Euler's equations in Eq. 17.14 or the more general form in Eq. 17.13 frequently degenerate to the form $T = I\dot{\omega}$, which you know from elementary courses in physics. We shall now point out three important classes of problems where this takes place.

Case 1. *Rotation about a Stationary Axis.* Shown In Fig. 17.25 is an arbitrary rigid body rotating about an axis that is fixed in an inertial reference. We may use any point along this axis to employ the relation $\boldsymbol{M} = \dot{\boldsymbol{H}}$. In this case, we have set up an xyz reference fixed to the body at O, with the z axis coinciding with the axis of rotation. These *need not* be principal axes for our purposes.

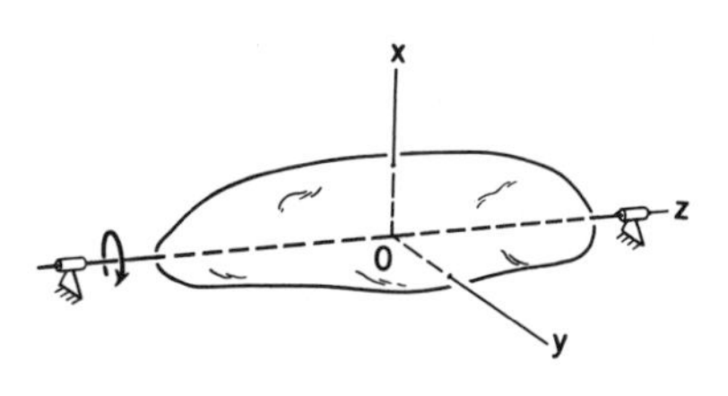

Fig. 17.25

Owing to the constraints of the shaft by bearings, the angular velocity $\boldsymbol{\omega}$ has only one nonzero component, ω_z. Now examine Eq. 17.13(c). You immediately see that all terms but the first are zero on the right-hand side of the equation. Thus this equation becomes $M_z = I_{zz}\dot{\omega}_z$, which is the simple familiar form.

The above special case of Euler's equations may be put into the following form:

$$\ddot{\theta} = \frac{M_z}{I_{zz}} \qquad \textbf{17.35}$$

This form is identical with Eq. 12.8, namely $\ddot{x} = F/m$, the equation for rectilinear translation of a particle investigated in Chapter 12. At that time we considered cases where F was a function of time, a function of speed, and so on for the purposes of integrating the equation of motion. Since there is no change in the mathematical aspects of the problem when we consider the corresponding equation for pure rotation, we shall merely consider one example here and shall leave as exercises the study of various other problems whose analyses were set forth in Chapter 12.

EXAMPLE 17.8

Shown in Fig. 17.26 as curve A is an idealized torque versus angular speed curve for a shunt, direct-current motor. The motor drives a pump which has a resisting torque versus speed curve shown in the diagram as curve B. Find the angular speed of the system as a function of time, after starting, over the range of speeds given in the diagram. Take the moment of inertia of motor, connecting shaft, and pump to be I.

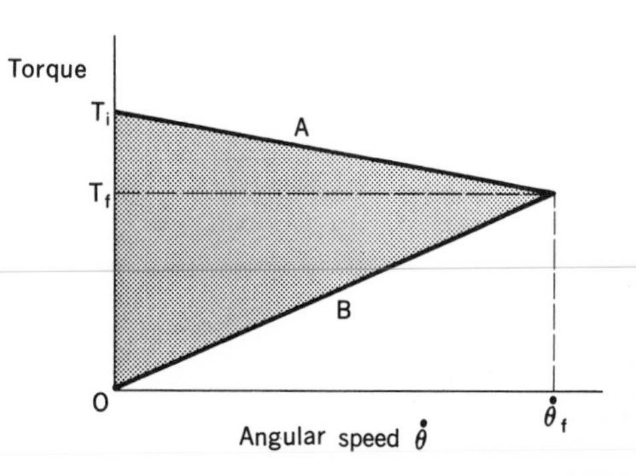

Fig. 17.26

The net torque on the system can be readily deduced from the diagram to be:

$$T = T_i - \frac{\dot{\theta}}{\dot{\theta}_f}(T_i - T_f) - \frac{\dot{\theta}}{\dot{\theta}_f}T_f$$

$$= T_i - \frac{\dot{\theta}}{\dot{\theta}_f}(T_i) = T_i\left(1 - \frac{\dot{\theta}}{\dot{\theta}_f}\right) \qquad \textbf{(a)}$$

We get accordingly for Euler's equation:

$$I\frac{d\dot{\theta}}{dt} = T_i\left(1 - \frac{\dot{\theta}}{\dot{\theta}_f}\right) \tag{b}$$

Separating the variables, we have:

$$\frac{I\,d\dot{\theta}}{T_i\left(1 - \dfrac{\dot{\theta}}{\dot{\theta}_f}\right)} = dt \tag{c}$$

Integrating, we get:

$$-\frac{I}{T_i}\left[\ln\left(1 - \frac{\dot{\theta}}{\dot{\theta}_f}\right)\right](\dot{\theta}_f) = t + C$$

where C is a constant of integration. Rearranging terms, we have:

$$\ln\left(1 - \frac{\dot{\theta}}{\dot{\theta}_f}\right) = -\frac{T_i}{I\dot{\theta}_f}(t + C) \tag{d}$$

When $t = 0$, $\dot{\theta} = 0$. Submitting Eq. (d) to this condition, we find that $C = 0$. Thus we have for $\dot{\theta}$:

$$\dot{\theta} = \dot{\theta}_f\{1 - \exp\left[-\left(T_i/I\dot{\theta}_f\right)t\right]\} \tag{e}$$

Case 2. *Plane Motion.* Consider a body that is moving so that each particle of the body forms trajectories parallel to a common plane (Fig. 17.27). This means that the rotation vector $\boldsymbol{\omega}$ for the body must be perpendicular to this common plane. For the desired simplification, choose a reference that is fixed to the body at the mass center in such a way that the z axis is normal to the plane of motion and thus in the direction of $\boldsymbol{\omega}$. This reference *need not* be the principal reference at the mass center. Examining Eq. 17.13(c) and noting that ω_y and ω_x are zero by the constraining action of the plane, we clearly see that this equation again degenerates to the familiar form, $M_z = I_{zz}\dot{\omega}_z$.

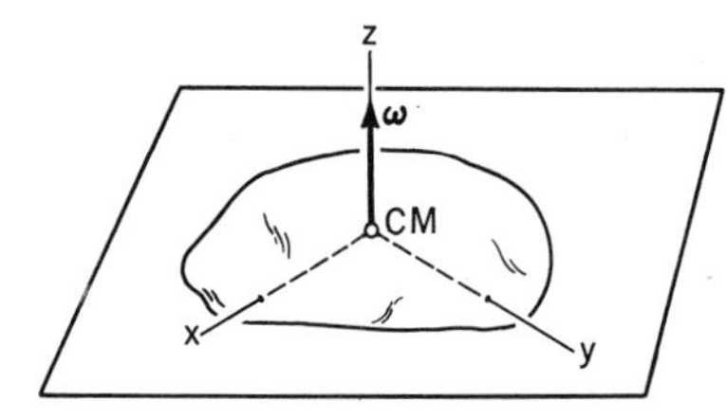

Fig. 17.27

If the body has a stationary point at time t, then the axis of rotation must be normal to the plane through this point. The equation $M_z = I_{zz}\dot{\omega}_z$ applies also for this axis at time t, with M_z and I_{zz} taken about this axis. If this axis is fixed, we have Case (1) again, and we can integrate the aforementioned equation with respect to time as described in the previous case.

EXAMPLE 17.9

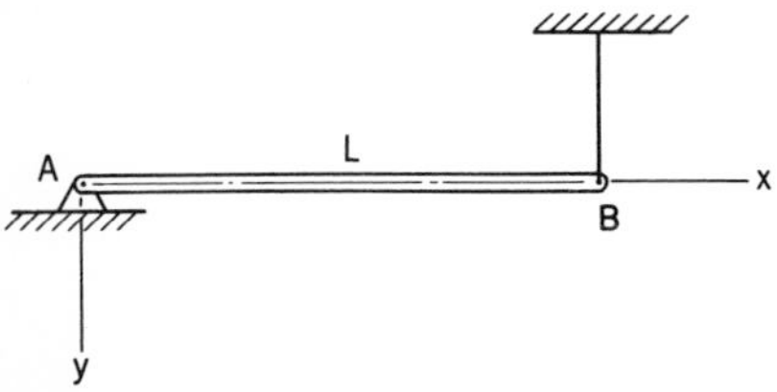

Shown in Fig. 17.28 is a uniform rod of weight W supported by a pin connection at A and a wire at B. What is the force on pin A at the instant that the wire is released? What is the force at A when the rod has rotated 45°?

A free-body diagram of the rod is shown in Fig. 17.29 at the instant that the wire is released at B. Euler's equation about the axis of rotation at A gives us:

Fig. 17.28

$$\frac{WL}{2} = I\ddot{\theta} = \frac{1}{3}\left(\frac{W}{g}\right) L^2\ddot{\theta}$$

$$\therefore \ddot{\theta} = \frac{3}{2}\frac{g}{L} \qquad \text{at time } t = 0. \qquad \textbf{(a)}$$

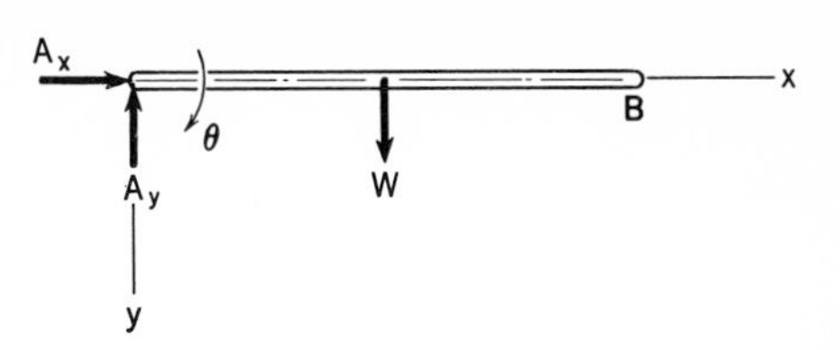

Fig. 17.29

Using simple kinematics of plane circular motion, we can now give the acceleration of the mass center as follows at $t = 0$:

$$\ddot{x} = 0, \qquad \ddot{y} = \frac{L}{2}\ddot{\theta} = \tfrac{3}{4}g \qquad \textbf{(b)}$$

Now express Newton's law for the mass center:

$$\frac{W}{g}\ddot{x} = A_x, \qquad \frac{W}{g}\ddot{y} = W - A_y$$

Accordingly at time $t = 0$ we have:

$$A_x = 0, \qquad A_y = \tfrac{1}{4}W \qquad \textbf{(c)}$$

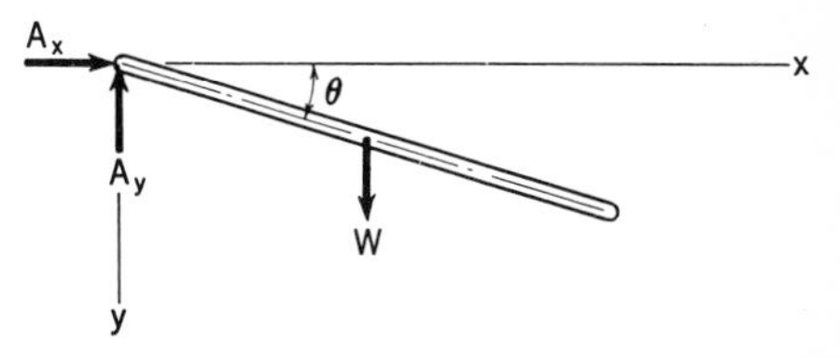

Fig. 17.30

Thus we see that at the first instant there is a upward force of $\frac{1}{4}W$ on the left support.

We next express Euler's equation for the rod at any arbitrary position θ. Observing Fig. 17.30, we get:

$$\frac{WL}{2}\cos\theta = \frac{1}{3}\frac{W}{g}L^2\ddot{\theta}$$

$$\therefore \ddot{\theta} = \frac{3}{2}\frac{g}{L}\cos\theta \qquad \textbf{(d)}$$

Consequently, at $\theta = 45°$ we have:

$$\ddot{\theta} = (1.5)(0.707)\frac{g}{L} = 1.06\frac{g}{L} \qquad \textbf{(e)}$$

We shall also need $\dot{\theta}$, and accordingly we now rewrite Eq. (d) as follows:

$$\ddot{\theta} = \left(\frac{d\dot{\theta}}{d\theta}\right)(\dot{\theta}) = \frac{3}{2}\frac{g}{L}\cos\theta \qquad \textbf{(f)}$$

Separating variables, we get:

$$\dot{\theta}\,d\dot{\theta} = \frac{3}{2}\frac{g}{L}\cos\theta\,d\theta$$

Integrating:

$$\frac{\dot{\theta}^2}{2} = \frac{3}{2}\frac{g}{L}\sin\theta + C$$

When $\theta = 0$, $\dot{\theta} = 0$ and accordingly $C = 0$. We get:

$$\dot{\theta}^2 = 3\frac{g}{L}\sin\theta \qquad \textbf{(g)}$$

At the instant of interest we have for $\dot{\theta}^2$:

$$\dot{\theta}^2 = 3\frac{g}{L}(0.707) = 2.12\frac{g}{L} \qquad \textbf{(h)}$$

We can now give the acceleration component of the center of mass for $\theta = 45°$ directed normal to the rod and along the rod. These quantities are, respectively:

$$a_1 = \frac{L}{2}\ddot{\theta} = \frac{L}{2}\left(1.06\,\frac{g}{L}\right) = 0.53g$$

$$a_2 = \frac{L}{2}(\dot{\theta})^2 = \frac{L}{2}\left(2.12\,\frac{g}{L}\right) = 1.06g \qquad \textbf{(i)}$$

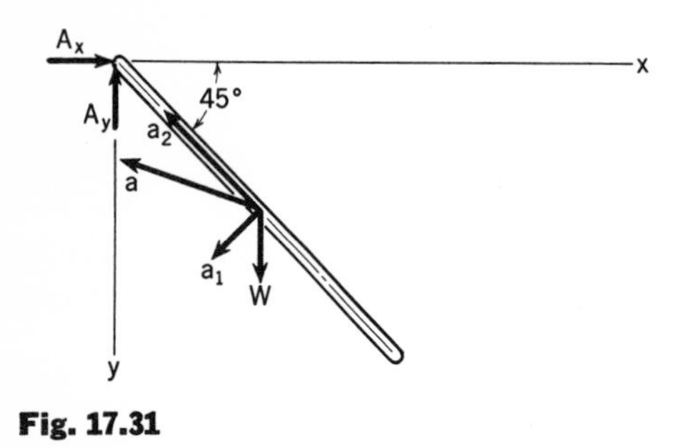

Fig. 17.31

These components have been shown in Fig. 17.31. Now, employing Newton's law for the mass center, we have:

$$A_x = \frac{W}{g}(-a_1 \sin 45° - a_2 \cos 45°)$$

$$\therefore\ A_x = -1.125W$$

$$-A_y + W = \frac{W}{g}(-a_2 \sin 45° + a_1 \cos 45°)$$

$$= -0.375W$$

$$\therefore\ A_y = 1.375W \qquad \textbf{(j)}$$

EXAMPLE 17.10

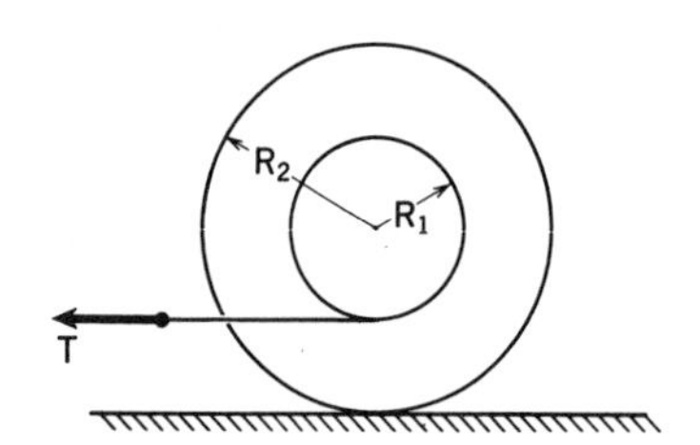

Fig. 17.32

Shown in Fig. 17.32 is a stepped cylinder having a mass of 100 lbm and a radius of gyration k of 1 ft. The radii R_1 and R_2 are respectively 1 ft and 2 ft. A pull T equal to 40 lb is exerted on the rope attached to the inner cylinder. What is the ensuing motion? The coefficients of static and dynamic friction between cylinder and ground are, respectively, 0.1 and 0.08.

A free-body diagram of the body is shown in Fig. 17.33. Let us assume first that there is no slipping at the contact surface. We have then pure rotation about the contact point O and we can say:

$$T(R_2 - R_1) = \left[\left(\frac{W}{g}\right)(k)^2 + \frac{W}{g}R_2^2\right]\ddot{\theta} \qquad \textbf{(a)}$$

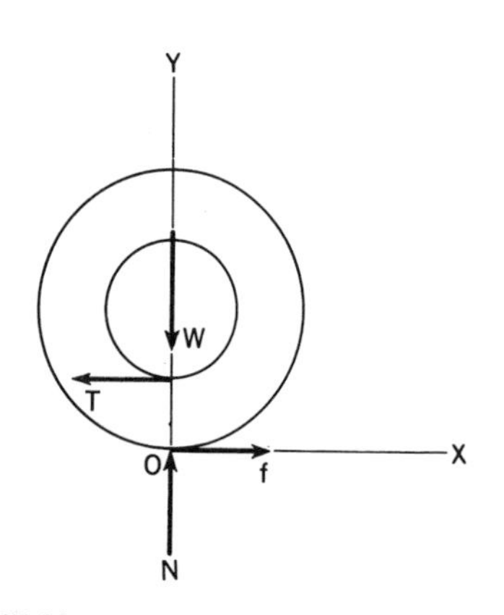

Fig. 17.33

wherein we have used the transfer theorem for moments of inertia. Inserting numerical values, we can solve directly for $\ddot{\theta}$ at the instant that the force T is applied. Thus:

$$40 = \frac{500}{g}\ddot{\theta}$$

$$\therefore\ \ddot{\theta} = \frac{2}{25}g \qquad \textbf{(b)}$$

Now employ Newton's law for the mass center. In the x direction we get:

$$-T + f = -\frac{W}{g}R_2\ddot{\theta} \qquad \textbf{(c)}$$

Inserting numerical values, we get:

$$-40 + f = -\frac{100}{g}(2)\left(\frac{2}{25}g\right) = -16$$

$$\therefore f = 24 \text{ lb} \tag{d}$$

Thus for no slipping we must be able to develop a friction force of 24 lb. The maximum friction force that we can have, however, is, according to Coulomb's law:

$$f_{max} = W\mu_s = (100)(0.1) = 10 \text{ lb} \tag{e}$$

Accordingly, we must conclude that there *is* slipping present, and we must re-examine the problem on this basis.

Using $\mu_d = 0.08$, we now take f to be 8 lb and employ Euler's equation for the mass center. We then have (see Fig. 17.33):

$$fR_2 - TR_1 = \frac{W}{g} k^2\ddot{\theta} \tag{f}$$

Inserting numerical values, we get for $\ddot{\theta}$:

$$\ddot{\theta} = -7.74 \text{ rad/sec}^2 \tag{g}$$

Now, using Newton's law in the x direction for the mass center, we get:

$$-T + f = \frac{W}{g}\ddot{X} \tag{h}$$

Inserting numerical values, we get for $\ddot{X}$:

$$\ddot{X} = -(32)\left(\frac{32.2}{100}\right) = -10.30 \text{ ft/sec}^2 \tag{i}$$

Thus the cylinder has a linear acceleration of 10.30 ft/sec² and an angular acceleration of 7.74 rad/sec² in the clockwise direction. Equations (g) and (i) are valid at all times, so we can integrate them to get θ and X at any time t.

EXAMPLE 17.11

Shown in Fig. 17.34 are a cylinder and a block connected by an inextensible cable. The block weighs 100 lb and the cylinder weighs 200 lb with a radius of gyration of 1 ft. If the coefficient of static friction for all contact surfaces is 0.3 and the coefficient of dynamic friction for all contact surfaces is 0.2, what is the acceleration of the block when the system is released from the configuration shown? The rope can unwind from the cylinder.

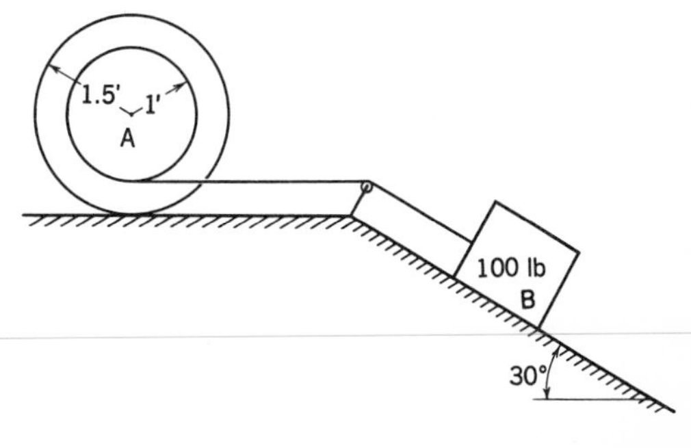

Fig. 17.34

Free-body diagrams have been shown for both bodies in Fig. 17.35. A decision must now be made as to whether the system moves at all. We can decide this quickly by considering the body B. It is clear, on inspection, that:

$$N_B = 100 \cos 30° = 86.6 \text{ lb}$$

The largest friction force possible is $\mu_s N_B = (0.3)(86.6) = 26$ lb. This cannot withstand the component of the force of gravity down the incline equal to $(100)(\sin 30°) = 50$ lb. Thus there will be a tension T developed on the rope and the wheel A will have to move, resulting in a downward motion of the system.

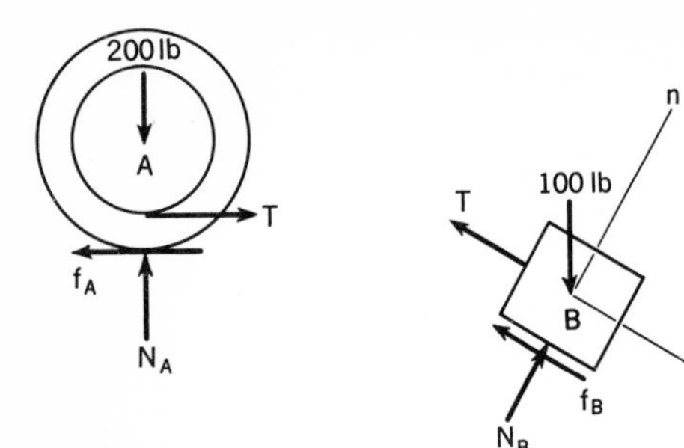

Fig. 17.35

Let us assume that wheel A rolls without slipping. We have from Euler's equation at the point of contact:

$$T(1.5 - 1) = \left(\frac{200}{g}\,1^2 + \frac{200}{g}\,1.5^2\right)\ddot{\theta}$$

$$\therefore\ T = 40.4\ddot{\theta} \tag{a}$$

From Newton's law applied to the mass center of the cylinder, we have:

$$N_A = 200 \tag{b}$$

$$T - f_A = \frac{200}{g}\,\ddot{x} = \frac{200}{g}\,(1.5\ddot{\theta}) \tag{c}$$

We have here three unknowns, T, f_A, $\ddot{\theta}$ for the two equations (a) and (c). Accordingly, considering the free body of the block we have from Newton's law:

$$100 \sin 30° - (0.2)(100 \cos 30°) - T = \left(\frac{100}{g}\right)(\ddot{s})$$

Noting from kinematical considerations that $\ddot{s} = 0.5\ddot{\theta}$, we get for the above equation:

$$32.7 - T = 1.55\ddot{\theta} \tag{d}$$

We can now solve for $\ddot{\theta}$ from Eqs. (a) and (d). Thus eliminating T from Eq. (d), we get:

$$32.7 - 40.4\ddot{\theta} = 1.55\ddot{\theta}$$

$$\therefore\ \ddot{\theta} = 0.780 \text{ rad/sec}^2 \tag{e}$$

From Eq. (a) we have for T:

$$T = (40.4)(0.780) = 31.5 \text{ lb} \tag{f}$$

Now go to Eq. (c) to compute f_A and thus to verify whether there is indeed rolling without slipping. We get:

$$f_A = T - 9.32\ddot{\theta} = 31.5 - (9.32)(0.780) = 24.2 \text{ lb}$$

Can such a force be developed? The answer is yes, because the maximum force of friction according to Coulomb's law is:

$$f_{\max} = (\mu_s)(N_A) = (0.3)(200) = 60 \text{ lb}$$

The block accordingly accelerates at the rate $(0.5)(\ddot{\theta}) =$ 0.390 ft/sec² down the inclined plane.

EXAMPLE 17.12

A rigid rod, AB, slides against a frictionless wall and floor (Fig. 17.36). The rod has a weight W and is made to move to the right in the plane of the paper by a force P as shown at B. What is the initial angular acceleration of the rod if the initial inclination of the rod is θ_0?

Since this is a case of plane motion, we can use the simplified relation about an axis normal to the plane of motion at the center of mass:

$$M_z = I_{zz}\dot{\omega}_z = I_{zz}\ddot{\theta} \tag{a}$$

Putting in the proper moments and using $(M/12)l^2$ as I_{zz}, we have for this equation:

$$P\frac{l}{2}\sin\theta - F_B\frac{l}{2}\cos\theta + F_A\frac{l}{2}\sin\theta = \frac{M}{12}l^2\ddot{\theta} \qquad \textbf{(b)}$$

We have here three unknowns, F_B, F_A, and $\ddot{\theta}$, so we must consider other possible equations. The motion of the center of mass may be used for this purpose:

$$P - F_A = \frac{W}{g}(a_c)_X \qquad \textbf{(c)}$$

$$F_B - W = \frac{W}{g}(a_c)_Y \qquad \textbf{(d)}$$

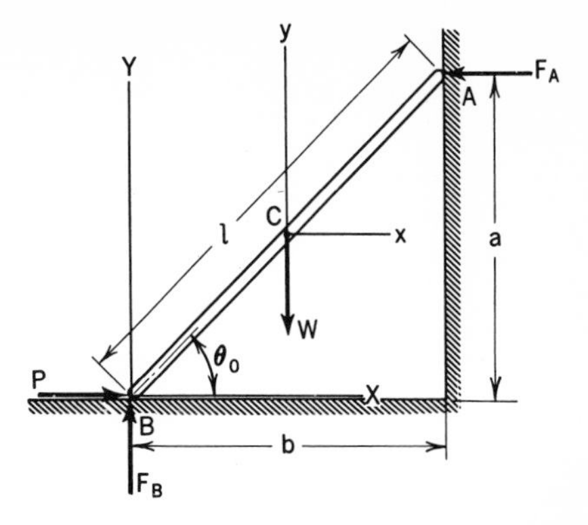

Fig. 17.36

Two more equations have been set forth, but we do not know $(a_c)_X$ and $(a_c)_Y$, i.e., the acceleration components of the center of mass. Let us next turn to kinematical considerations. The acceleration of the mass center can be given in terms of the acceleration of point B, by employing Eq. 15.7:

$$\boldsymbol{a}_C = \boldsymbol{a}_B + \dot{\boldsymbol{\omega}} \times \boldsymbol{\rho}_{BC} + \boldsymbol{\omega} \times (\boldsymbol{\omega} \times \boldsymbol{\rho}_{BC}) \qquad \textbf{(e)}$$

In rectangular components we get:

$$(a_C)_X\boldsymbol{i} + (a_C)_Y\boldsymbol{j}$$
$$= a_B\boldsymbol{i} + \ddot{\theta}\boldsymbol{k} \times \left(\frac{l}{2}\sin\theta\boldsymbol{j} + \frac{l}{2}\cos\theta\boldsymbol{i}\right)$$
$$+ \dot{\theta}\boldsymbol{k} \times \left[\dot{\theta}\boldsymbol{k} \times \left(\frac{l}{2}\sin\theta\boldsymbol{j} + \frac{l}{2}\cos\theta\boldsymbol{i}\right)\right] \qquad \textbf{(f)}$$

Considering the Y scalar equation we have for $(a_C)_Y$:

$$(a_C)_Y = \ddot{\theta}\frac{l}{2}\cos\theta - \dot{\theta}^2\frac{l}{2}\sin\theta \qquad \textbf{(g)}$$

We can get $(a_C)_X$ by similarly considering points C and A of the rod. Thus:

$$\boldsymbol{a}_C = \boldsymbol{a}_A + \dot{\boldsymbol{\omega}} \times \boldsymbol{\rho}_{AC} + \boldsymbol{\omega} \times (\boldsymbol{\omega} \times \boldsymbol{\rho}_{AC}) \qquad \textbf{(h)}$$

$$\therefore\ (a_C)_X\boldsymbol{i} + (a_C)_Y\boldsymbol{j}$$
$$= a_A\boldsymbol{j} + \ddot{\theta}\boldsymbol{k} \times \left(-\frac{l}{2}\sin\theta\boldsymbol{j} - \frac{l}{2}\cos\theta\boldsymbol{i}\right)$$
$$+ \dot{\theta}\boldsymbol{k} \times \left[\dot{\theta}\boldsymbol{k} \times \left(-\frac{l}{2}\sin\theta\boldsymbol{j} - \frac{l}{2}\cos\theta\boldsymbol{i}\right)\right] \qquad \textbf{(i)}$$

Considering now the X scalar equation, we then have:

$$(a_C)_X = \ddot{\theta}\frac{l}{2}\sin\theta + \dot{\theta}^2\frac{l}{2}\cos\theta \qquad \textbf{(j)}$$

Substituting the acceleration components from Eqs. (g) and (j) into Eqs. (c) and (d), respectively, we get, with Eq. (b), a system of three simultaneous equations in three unknowns. They are:

$$P - F_A = \frac{Wl}{2g}(\ddot{\theta}\sin\theta + \dot{\theta}^2\cos\theta) \qquad \textbf{(k)}$$

$$F_B - W = \frac{Wl}{2g}(\ddot{\theta}\cos\theta - \dot{\theta}^2\sin\theta) \qquad \text{(l)}$$

$$P\sin\theta - F_B\cos\theta + F_A\sin\theta = \frac{Ml}{6}\ddot{\theta} \qquad \text{(m)}$$

In Eq. (m) note that we have canceled out $l/2$. Solving for F_A and F_B in Eqs. (k) and (l), respectively, and substituting into Eq. (m), we then get the equation:

$$P\sin\theta - \left[W + \frac{Wl}{2g}(\ddot{\theta}\cos\theta - \dot{\theta}^2\sin\theta)\right]\cos\theta$$
$$+ \left[P - \frac{Wl}{2g}(\ddot{\theta}\sin\theta + \dot{\theta}^2\cos\theta)\right]\sin\theta = \frac{Ml}{6}\ddot{\theta}$$

Collecting and rearranging the terms, we have:

$$\left[\frac{Wl}{2g}(\cos^2\theta + \sin^2\theta) + \frac{Ml}{6}\right]\ddot{\theta} = 2P\sin\theta - W\cos\theta$$

Noting that $(\cos^2\theta + \sin^2\theta)$ is unity and replacing M by W/g, we have finally:

$$\ddot{\theta} = \frac{3}{2}\frac{g}{Wl}(2P\sin\theta - W\cos\theta) \qquad \text{(n)}$$

Substituting the initial value of θ, we get the initial acceleration:

$$\ddot{\theta}_0 = \frac{3}{2}\frac{g}{Wl}(2P\sin\theta_0 - W\cos\theta_0) \qquad \text{(o)}$$

Note from Eq. (n) that the angular acceleration does not depend on the angular velocity (the $\dot{\theta}$ terms canceled) and so we did not have to specify the initial angular velocity of the bar. Since the integration of θ as a function of time from Eq. (n) is difficult and involves elliptic integrals, we have restricted ourselves to instantaneous values of acceleration.

Before leaving this problem it should be pointed out that we could have handled the kinematics needed in the analysis by locating the instantaneous center of rotation and considering pure rotation about this point. Clearly the intersection of perpendiculars from A and B is this center of rotation for this case.

EXAMPLE 17.13

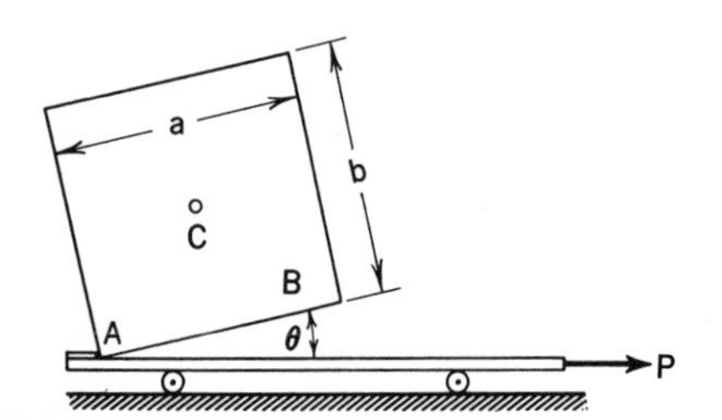

Fig. 17.37

Body B is a homogeneous block of weight W that is carried by a cart whose mass we shall neglect (Fig. 17.37). Find the value of the force P needed to bring the box to the condition of impending tipping, and, with double this value for P, determine the angular acceleration of the block at the instant when it is tipped at angle θ_0 and has an angular velocity $\dot{\theta}_0$.

To establish the force P needed to tip the box, we show the block as a free-body diagram, with the supporting force concentrated at the edge A as a consequence of the condition of impending tipping

(Fig. 17.38). In this limiting condition, there is a zero angular velocity and a zero angular acceleration. Employing Euler's equation at the mass center C in a direction normal to the plane of motion, we have for this condition:

$$A_x \frac{b}{2} - A_y \frac{a}{2} = 0$$

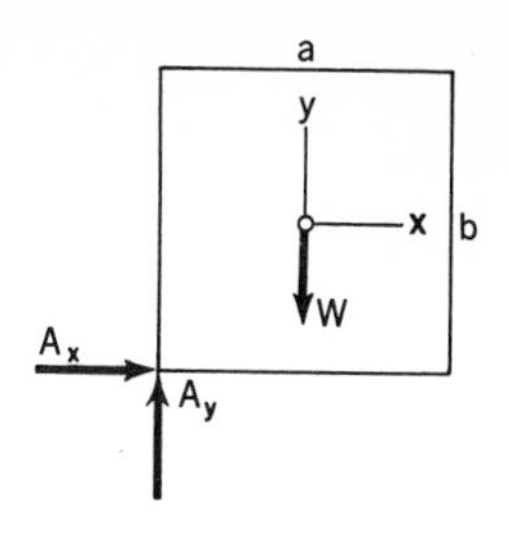

Fig. 17.38

Since the cart has negligible mass, it is clear that $A_x = P$ and so the above equation then becomes:

$$P = \frac{a}{b} A_y \qquad \textbf{(a)}$$

Since there is no acceleration of the mass center in the vertical direction, we have from Newton's law:

$$A_y - W = 0 \qquad \textbf{(b)}$$

Substituting for A_y in Eq. (b) using Eq. (a), we get for the required force P:

$$P = \frac{a}{b} W \qquad \textbf{(c)}$$

Next consider the second part of the problem, for which the value of P is to be taken as $2(a/b)W$. The free-body diagram for this case is shown in Fig. 17.39. Euler's equation in the z direction for the mass center now becomes:

$$(A_Y \sin\theta_0)\left(\frac{b}{2}\right) - (A_Y \cos\theta_0)\left(\frac{a}{2}\right) + \left(\frac{2Wa}{b}\cos\theta_0\right)\frac{b}{2} + \left(\frac{2Wa}{b}\sin\theta_0\right)\frac{a}{2} = I_{zz}\ddot{\theta}_0$$

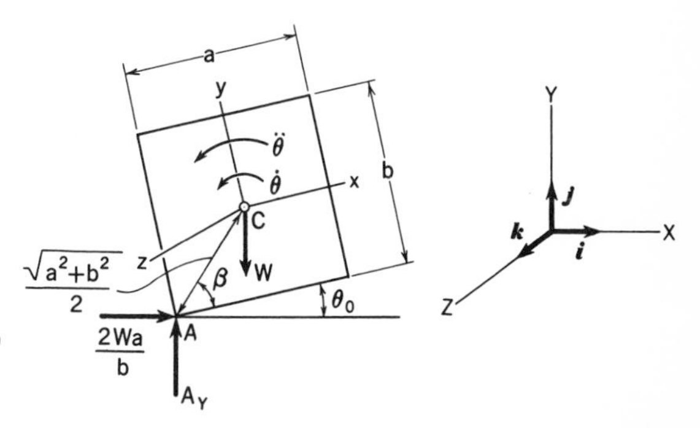

Fig. 17.39

Canceling and collecting terms:

$$A_Y\left(\frac{b}{2}\sin\theta_0 - \frac{a}{2}\cos\theta_0\right) + aW\cos\theta_0 + \frac{a^2}{b}W\sin\theta_0 = I_{zz}\ddot{\theta}_0 \qquad \textbf{(d)}$$

There are two unknowns, A_Y and $\ddot{\theta}_0$, in this equation. Employing Newton's law for the mass center in the Y direction, we get:

$$A_Y - W = \frac{W}{g}(a_c)_Y \qquad \textbf{(e)}$$

Since this introduces a further unknown, we shall use kinematics to relate $(a_c)_Y$ and $\ddot{\theta}_0$. To do this relate the accelerations of points C and A. Thus:

$$\boldsymbol{a}_C = \boldsymbol{a}_A + \dot{\boldsymbol{\omega}} \times \boldsymbol{\rho}_{AC} + \boldsymbol{\omega} \times (\boldsymbol{\omega} \times \boldsymbol{\rho}_{AC}) \qquad \textbf{(f)}$$

Using components parallel to the XYZ reference, we have:

$$(a_C)_X\boldsymbol{i} + (a_C)_Y\boldsymbol{j} = (a_A)\boldsymbol{i} + \ddot{\theta}_0\boldsymbol{k} \times \frac{\sqrt{a^2+b^2}}{2} \times [\cos(\theta_0+\beta)\boldsymbol{i} + \sin(\theta_0+\beta)\boldsymbol{j}]$$

$$+ \dot{\theta}_0 \boldsymbol{k} \times \left\{ \dot{\theta}_0 \boldsymbol{k} \times \frac{\sqrt{a^2 + b^2}}{2} \times [\cos(\theta_0 + \beta)\boldsymbol{i} + \sin(\theta_0 + \beta)\boldsymbol{j}] \right\} \quad \text{(g)}$$

Taking the Y scalar equation, we get:

$$(a_C)_Y = \frac{\sqrt{a^2 + b^2}}{2} \times [\ddot{\theta}_0 \cos(\theta_0 + \beta) - \dot{\theta}_0^2 \sin(\theta_0 + \beta)] \quad \text{(h)}$$

Now substitute for $(a_c)_Y$ in Eq. (e) from Eq. (h) and solve for the force A_Y:

$$A_Y = W + W \frac{\sqrt{b^2 + a^2}}{2g} \times [\ddot{\theta}_0 \cos(\theta_0 + \beta) - \dot{\theta}_0^2 \sin(\theta_0 + \beta)] \quad \text{(i)}$$

Finally, substituting for A_Y in Eq. (d) using Eq. (i), we get:

$$\left\{ \frac{W}{2} + W \frac{\sqrt{b^2 + a^2}}{4g} [\ddot{\theta}_0 \cos(\theta_0 + \beta) - \dot{\theta}_0^2 \sin(\theta_0 + \beta)] \right\} \times (b \sin\theta_0 - a \cos\theta_0) + aW \cos\theta_0 + \frac{a^2}{b} W \sin\theta_0 = I_{zz}\ddot{\theta}_0$$

Solving for $\ddot{\theta}_0$, we get the desired result:

$$\ddot{\theta}_0 = \frac{\frac{W}{4g}\sqrt{b^2 + a^2}\,\dot{\theta}_0^2 \sin(\theta_0 + \beta)[b \sin\theta_0 - a \cos\theta_0]}{W \frac{\sqrt{b^2 + a^2}}{4g} \cos(\theta_0 + \beta)[b \sin\theta_0 - a \cos\theta_0] - I_{zz}} - \frac{\frac{W}{2}\left(a \cos\theta_0 + \frac{2a^2 + b^2}{b} \sin\theta_0\right)}{W \frac{\sqrt{b^2 + a^2}}{4g} \cos(\theta_0 + \beta)[b \sin\theta_0 - a \cos\theta_0] - I_{zz}} \quad \text{(j)}$$

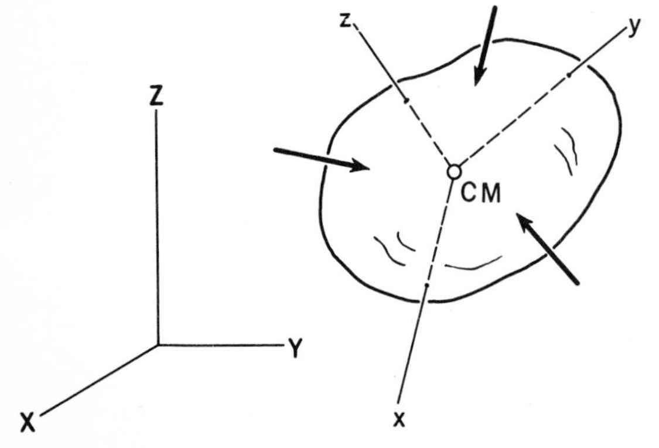

Fig. 17.40

Case 3. Body in Space with Zero Angular Velocity. Suppose we now consider a body in space that is acted on by forces at a time when it has zero angular velocity relative to an inertial reference (Fig. 17.40). We set up any reference fixed at the mass center and, with $\omega_x = \omega_y = \omega_z = 0$ at the time t, Eq. 17.13 becomes:

$$\begin{aligned} M_x &= \dot{\omega}_x I_{xx} - I_{xy}\dot{\omega}_y - I_{xz}\dot{\omega}_z \\ M_y &= \dot{\omega}_y I_{yy} - I_{yz}\dot{\omega}_z - I_{yx}\dot{\omega}_x \\ M_z &= \dot{\omega}_z I_{zz} - I_{zx}\dot{\omega}_x - I_{zy}\dot{\omega}_y \end{aligned} \quad \textbf{17.36}$$

If we restrict this xyz reference to the principal axes, we see that the resulting Euler's equations all attain the simple form:

$$M_x = I_{xx}\dot{\omega}_x, \qquad M_y = I_{yy}\dot{\omega}_y, \qquad M_z = I_{zz}\dot{\omega}_z \tag{17.37}$$

which are applicable only at the instant that corresponds to the time when $\boldsymbol{\omega} = \mathbf{0}$.

17.7 D'Alembert's Principle for Rigid Bodies

In Chapter 12 we employed the D'Alembert principle and the method of virtual work to solve problems involving simply-interconnected bodies having constraints that limited the motion of each body to that of rectilinear translation. The rules of particle dynamics were applied, since the bodies had no rotation. At this time, we shall extend the method to bodies which may rotate and thus require the use of rigid-body dynamics. It should be understood that the procedure of this section is an alternative to what we have presented thus far, an alternative which for some problems may be considered by some engineers to be a quicker and more direct method of approach.

Let us then reformulate the D'Alembert principle. You will recall from earlier work in particle dynamics that we considered the term $-m\boldsymbol{a}$ to be a force—the so-called D'Alembert force. In this way we can consider that the combination of the external forces on the particle plus the D'Alembert force forms a null vector. This, in turn, permits the formulations of statics to be applied to these forces as a means of reaching the equations of motion. For instance, to guarantee that the total external forces and the force $-m\boldsymbol{a}$ form a null vector, we can set the total moment of these forces about any point in space equal to zero. We would in this way be giving the equations of motion for the particle.

In the case of a rigid body we can say in a similar manner:

$$\sum_i \boldsymbol{F}_i + (-M\boldsymbol{a}^*) = \mathbf{0} \tag{17.38}$$

where $\sum \boldsymbol{F}_i$ is the sum of the external forces, M is the total mass of the body, and $\boldsymbol{a}^*$ is to represent the acceleration vector of the center of mass. Thus the total external force and the D'Alembert force for the mass center form a null vector for a rigid body.

Furthermore, we can express the moment of momentum equation about the center of mass in the following manner:

$$\sum_i \boldsymbol{M}_i + (-\dot{\boldsymbol{H}}^*) = \mathbf{0} \tag{17.39}$$

where we again use the superscript asterisk to indicate the mass center. We can consider that the term $(-\dot{\boldsymbol{H}}^*)$ is a couple-moment which we shall call the D'Alembert couple.

The technique is now to consider acting on the rigid body the external force $\sum \boldsymbol{F}_i$, the D'Alembert force $(-M\boldsymbol{a})$, and the D'Alembert couple with moment $(-\dot{\boldsymbol{H}}^*)$. The sum of such a force system, if Eq. 17.38 is to be satisfied, is still a null vector. Additionally the total moment of this force system about the mass center, if Eq. 17.39 is to be satisfied, is also a null vector. Two factors now should be understood. First, by satisfying Eqs. 17.38 and 17.39 we are satisfying the equations of motion. Second, by having the sum of these forces and couples be zero and by having the sum of moments of these forces and couples be zero about a point (the mass center here) we are spelling out the equations of equilibrium for a rigid body acted on by such a system of forces. Thus, knowing that the body is in "equilibrium" under the aforementioned system of forces, we can use *other* formulations of statics for stating this, and in this way we have other routes to arrive at the equations of motion.

The procedure to follow is to enter the vectors $-M\boldsymbol{a}^*$ and $-\dot{\boldsymbol{H}}^*$ in the free-body diagram. To identify these as the D'Alembert force and couple we have used dashed lines to draw the vectors as shown in Fig. 17.41, where the vectors $\boldsymbol{a}^*$ and $\dot{\boldsymbol{H}}^*$ have been also shown to the lower right. In using *vector* equations the minus signs are needed to give the proper sense to the D'Alembert vectors. For such purposes, then, we have a force system $\boldsymbol{F}_1, \boldsymbol{F}_2, \cdots, \boldsymbol{F}_n, -M\boldsymbol{a}^*, -\dot{\boldsymbol{H}}^*$ satisfying equation of "equilibrium."

If we use *components* for the D'Alembert quantities, we proceed as has been shown in Fig. 17.42. Thus the quantities Ma_x^*, $(\dot{\boldsymbol{H}}^*)_x$, etc. in the free-body diagram represent *magnitudes*. We achieve the proper sign for the D'Alembert quantities, when expressing scalar equations, by taking into account the *sense* of the arrows associated with these quantities in the free-body diagram. Thus, from our work in statics, we can set equal to zero the sum of the components

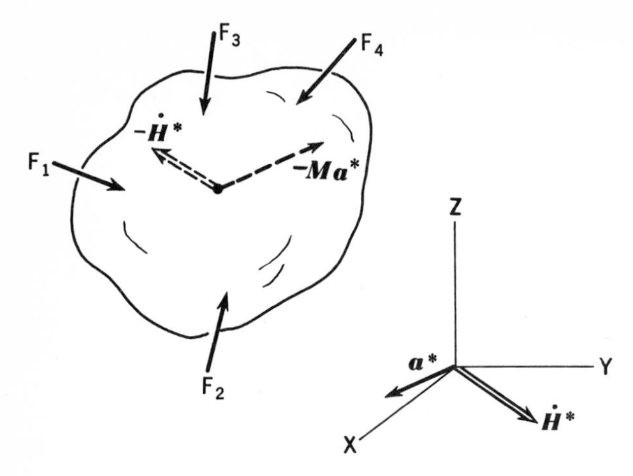

Fig. 17.41

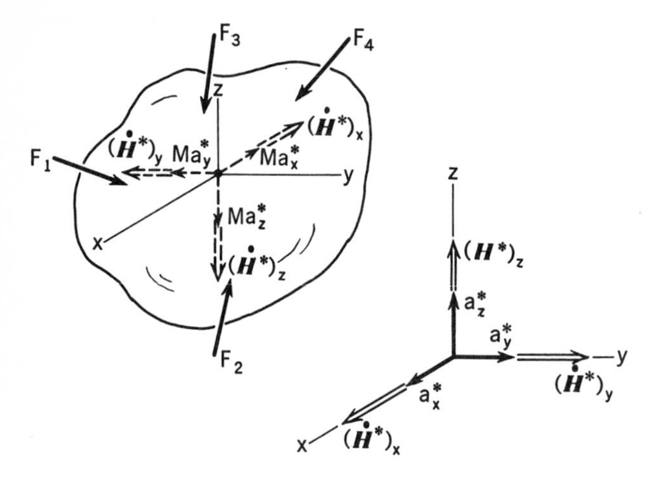

Fig. 17.42

of the force system shown in convenient directions and set equal to zero moments of this system about convenient axes. If the resulting scalar equations are independent we can consider that "equilibrium" of the force system has been insured. And, more importantly, we insure that the equations of motion of the rigid body have been properly stated.

For the special case of plane motion where the axis of rotation has a direction coinciding with a principal axis of inertia at the mass center (see Fig. 17.43), we have for $\dot{H}^*$ the simple expression $I_{zz}\,\dot{\omega}_z$ where I_{zz} is the principal moment of inertia of the body about the z axis at the mass center. The sense of $I_{zz}\,\dot{\omega}_z$ in the free-body diagram is opposite to the assumed or known direction of $\dot{\omega}_z$, as has been shown in the diagram.

We now illustrate the use of the D'Alembert principle in the following examples.

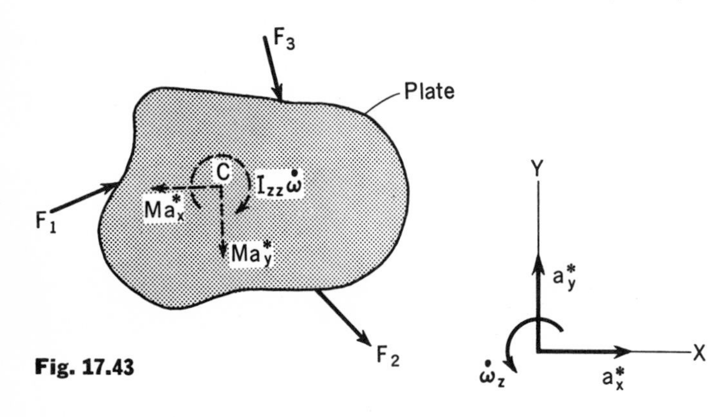

Fig. 17.43

EXAMPLE 17.14

We shall do Example 17.10 using the D'Alembert approach. Thus in Fig. 17.44(a) we have shown the stepped cylinder with the D'Alembert force and the D'Alembert couple applied. Notice that the directions of the D'Alembert force and couple have been taken opposite to the acceleration vector $\boldsymbol{a}^*$ and angular acceleration vector $\dot{\boldsymbol{\omega}}$ shown in Fig. 17.44(b).

To get the equation of motion we may first sum the forces acting on the indicated free body of the cylinder as follows:

$\sum F_x = 0$:

$$-T + f + Ma^* = 0 \tag{a}$$

$\sum F_y = 0$:

$$N - W = 0 \tag{b}$$

Next, taking moments about the center of mass O, we have:

$\sum M_0 = 0$:

$$R_2 f - R_1 T - I_{zz}\dot{\omega} = 0 \tag{c}$$

For the no-slipping condition we can relate a^* and $\dot{\omega}$ as follows:

$$a^* = R_2\dot{\omega} \tag{d}$$

We have here four unknowns, f, N, a^* and $\dot{\omega}$, which can be solved from the four equations. We leave it to the reader to demonstrate that the results for $\dot{\omega}$ and a^* from these equations are identical to the result given in Example 17.10.

We shall now demonstrate that we can take moments about any point P [see Fig. 17.44(c)] rather than the center of mass to get an equation consistent with the set given above. Thus, taking moments of the force system about P, we get:

$$T(d - R_1) - Ma^*d - f(d - R_2) + (W - N)e - I_{zz}\dot{\omega} = 0 \tag{e}$$

Clearly $(W - N)e = 0$ in accordance with Eq. (b). Combining terms, we get:

$$(T - Ma^* - f)d - TR_1 + fR_2 - I_{zz}\dot{\omega} = 0 \tag{f}$$

The first term is zero because of Eq. (a), and the resulting equation is identical with Eq. (c). Thus we could have used Eq. (e) for any point P rather than Eq. (c) for the mass center. This method thus offers considerable flexibility, which at times may be convenient.

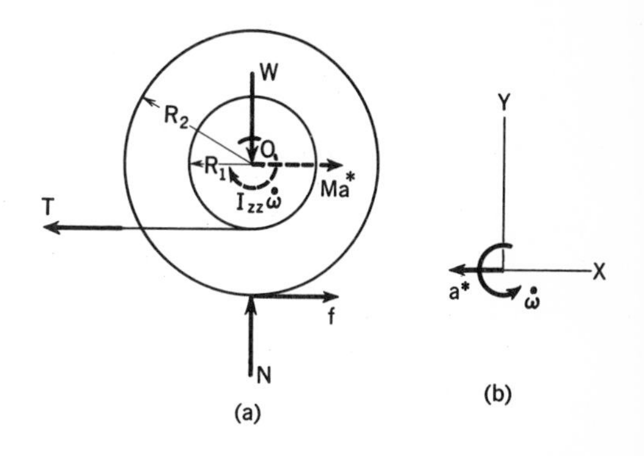

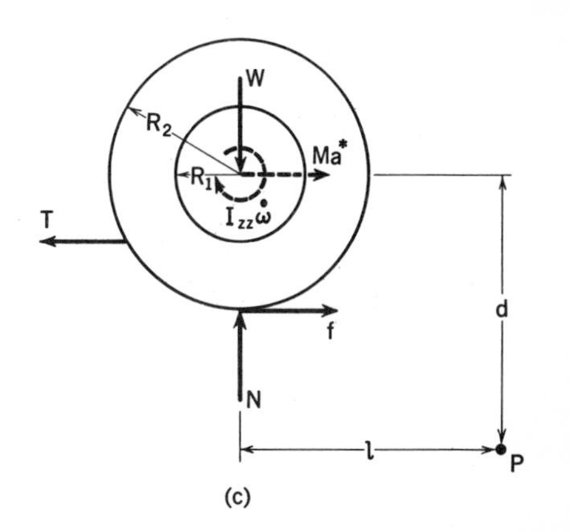

Fig. 17.44

*EXAMPLE 17.15

Shown in Fig. 17.45 is a rod AB rotating at constant speed ω about the vertical axis AD. If the bearing and pin connection at A are frictionless, what is the correct angle θ for this motion? The weight of AB is W and the length is L. Assume that the rod is quite thin.

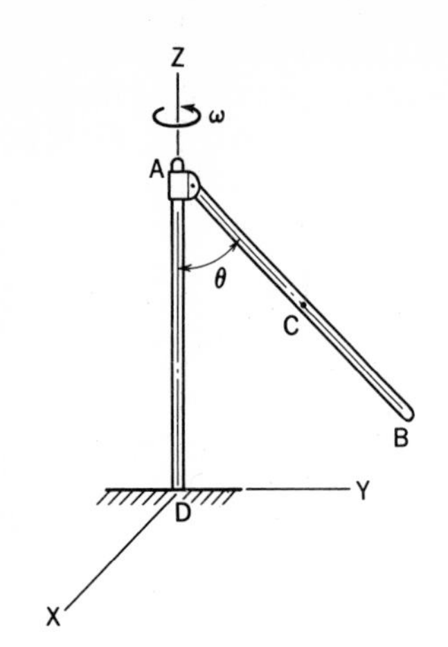

Fig. 17.45

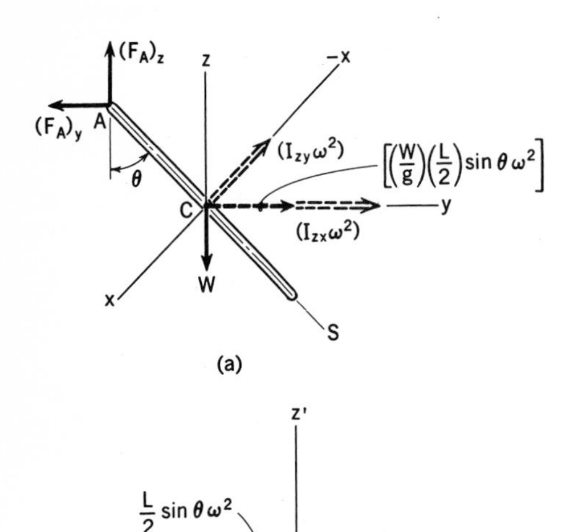

Fig. 17.46

To get the D'Alembert torque we fix a reference xyz at C [see Fig. 17.46(b)]. We can express $\boldsymbol{H}^*$ as follows:

$$\dot{\boldsymbol{H}}^* = \left(\frac{d\dot{\boldsymbol{H}}^*}{dt}\right)_{XYZ} = \left(\frac{d\dot{\boldsymbol{H}}^*}{dt}\right)_{xyz} + \boldsymbol{\Omega} \times \boldsymbol{H}^*$$

$$= \frac{d}{dt_{xyz}}\left(-\omega I_{xz}\boldsymbol{i} - \omega I_{yz}\boldsymbol{j} + \omega I_{zz}\boldsymbol{k}\right) + \boldsymbol{\Omega} \times \boldsymbol{H}^*$$

$$= \boldsymbol{0} + \omega \boldsymbol{k} \times (H_x^*\boldsymbol{i} + H_y^*\boldsymbol{j} + H_z^*\boldsymbol{k})$$

$$= \omega H_x^*\boldsymbol{j} - \omega H_y^*\boldsymbol{i}$$

wherein we have employed Eq. 17.9. Hence:

$$(\dot{\boldsymbol{H}}^*)_x = -\omega H_y^*$$

$$(\dot{\boldsymbol{H}}^*)_y = \omega H_x^*$$

$$(\dot{\boldsymbol{H}}^*)_z = 0$$

Employing Eq. 17.9 again:

$$(\dot{\boldsymbol{H}}^*)_y = I_{yz}\omega^2$$

$$(\dot{\boldsymbol{H}}^*)_y = -I_{zx}\omega^2$$

$$(\dot{\boldsymbol{H}}^*)_z = 0 \qquad \textbf{(a)}$$

It should be clear, furthermore, that the acceleration vector for the center of mass is:

$$\boldsymbol{a}^* = -\left(\frac{L}{2}\sin\theta\right)\omega^2\boldsymbol{j} \qquad \textbf{(b)}$$

The above quantities have been shown in Fig. 17.46(b). The corresponding D'Alembert couples and forces have been shown with opposite senses in Fig. 17.46(a).

We can now consider the free body in Fig. 17.46(a) to be in "equilibrium." To get the desired information—that is, the value θ—we set equal to zero moments of the indicated force system about axes at A parallel to the x and y axes, respectively. Thus:

$\sum (M_x)_A = 0$:

$$-W\frac{L}{2}\sin\theta + \left(\frac{W}{g}\frac{L}{2}\sin\theta\,\omega^2\right)\frac{L}{2}\cos\theta - I_{yz}\omega^2 = 0 \qquad \textbf{(c)}$$

$\sum (M_y)_A = 0$:

$$I_{zx}\omega^2 = 0 \qquad \textbf{(d)}$$

We next compute the products of inertia at the mass center. Using s as the distance from the mass center along the centerline of the rod, we have:

$$I_{zy} = 2\int_0^{L/2} (s\sin\theta)(-s\cos\theta)\,\frac{W/g}{L}\,ds$$

$$= -\sin\theta\cos\theta\,\frac{W/g}{L}\,\frac{L^3}{12} = -\frac{WL^2}{12g}\sin\theta\cos\theta \qquad \textbf{(e)}$$

$$I_{zx} = 2\int_0^{L/2} (-s\cos\theta)(0)\,\frac{W/g}{L}\,ds = 0 \qquad \textbf{(f)}$$

As a result of $I_{zx} = 0$, Eq. (d) is identically satisfied. Substituting for I_{zy} in Eq. (c) using Eq. (e), we get on cancelling terms:

$$-g \sin \theta + \tfrac{2}{3}\, \omega^2 L \sin \theta \cos \theta = 0 \qquad \text{(g)}$$

The solutions for θ are:

$$\sin \theta = 0 \qquad \text{(h)}$$

$$\cos \theta = \frac{3}{2} \frac{g}{\omega^2 L} \qquad \text{(i)}$$

The first solution (h) we can recognize, from our work in Chapter 10, as an unstable case, and accordingly result (i) is the one with physical meaning for us here.

The D'Alembert principle can be used to advantage when applied to a system of rigid bodies, each of which moves in plane motion such that there are few degrees of freedom. For such problems we can use the method of virtual work as developed in Chapter 10 for statics problems, since the applied forces and D'Alembert forces satisfy the same equations for a dynamical system of bodies as do the applied forces alone for a system of bodies in equilibrium. We illustrate the procedure in the following example.

EXAMPLE 17.16

Shown in Fig. 17.47 is a cylinder connected to a weight by an inextensible cord that runs over a tiny pulley, whose mass we can neglect. As the weight falls, it causes the cylinder to rotate about its axis. When the weight is released from rest, what is the angular acceleration of the cylinder and the linear acceleration of the weight?

We will first use the D'Alembert principle for each of the bodies separately, and then we will show how we can, with the aid of virtual work, handle the whole system. In Fig. 17.48(b) we have shown the assumed direction of a_y of the block and $\dot{\omega}_z$ of the cylinder and in Fig. 17.48(a) we have drawn free-body diagrams of the bodies, including the D'Alembert forces corresponding to the assumed directions of $\dot{\omega}_z$ and a_y. To determine quickly the desired unknowns a_y and $\dot{\omega}_z$, for the cylinder we shall set the moments about the centerline equal to zero and for the suspended weight we shall set the sum of the forces equal to zero. We get:

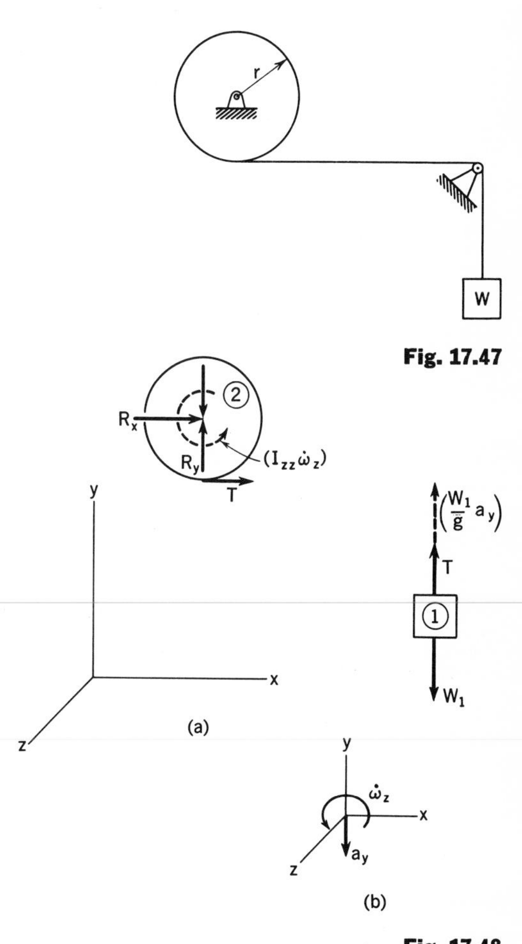

Fig. 17.47

Fig. 17.48

$$Tr - I_{zz}\dot{\omega}_z = 0 \qquad \text{(a)}$$

$$-W_1 + T + \frac{W_1}{g} a_y = 0 \qquad \text{(b)} \qquad \textbf{17.40}$$

Multiplying Eq. (b) by r and subtracting Eq. (b) from Eq. (a), we can eliminate the unknown force T and get the following equation:

$$-W_1 r + \frac{W_1}{g} r a_y + I_{zz}\dot{\omega}_z = 0 \qquad \textbf{17.41}$$

Although we can now relate a_y and $\dot{\omega}_z$ by kinematics and easily solve both quantities, we shall instead show how we may reach this equation by a more direct approach. In Fig. 17.49 we shall consider the bodies as a system and include in the free-body diagram only external forces and the D'Alembert forces and couples.

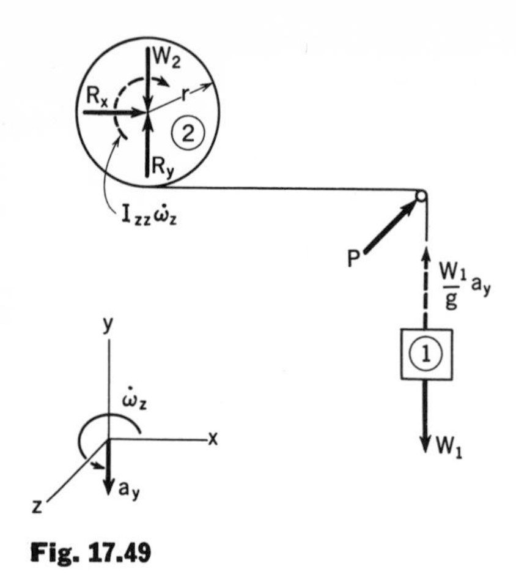

Fig. 17.49

Note that the force P from the small pulley acting on the cord is external to the system and must be included. This system of bodies clearly has one degree of freedom. Since the forces shown are in "equilibrium," we can give the system a virtual displacement and equate the virtual work to zero. Thus we give body (1) a displacement δy downward. Body (2) must rotate an angle $\delta\theta$, which is equal to $\delta y/r$. Hence we have:

$$W_1\delta y - \left(\frac{W_1}{g}\, a_y\right)\delta y - (I_{zz}\dot{\omega}_z)\,\frac{\delta y}{r} = 0$$

(With no friction, it is clear that P cannot do work.) Canceling δy and multiplying by r, we have:

$$W_1 r - \frac{W_1}{g}\, a_y r - I_{zz}\dot{\omega}_z = 0 \qquad \textbf{(c)}$$

which is precisely the same equation that we developed earlier by considering the separate free bodies. If friction forces are present, they are to be considered as active forces, as you will recall from Chapter 10.

---

*17.8 Necessary and Sufficient Conditions for Equilibrium of a Rigid Body

In this chapter we have employed Newton's law at the mass center as well as the equation $\boldsymbol{M} = \dot{\boldsymbol{H}}$ and Euler's equations for rigid bodies. We can now go back to our work in Chapter 5 and put on firm ground the fact that $\boldsymbol{M} = \boldsymbol{0}$ and $\boldsymbol{F} = \boldsymbol{0}$ are necessary and sufficient conditions for equilibrium of a rigid body. (You will recall we accepted these equations for statics at that time by intuition, pending a proof to come later.) We will first prove that these equations are necessary.

A particle is in equilibrium, you will recall, if it is stationary or moving with constant speed along a straight line in inertial space. To be in a state of equilibrium every point in a rigid body must accordingly be moving at uniform speeds along straight lines in inertial space. The rigidity requirement thus limits a rigid body in equilibrium to translational motion along a straight line at constant speed in inertial space. This means that $\dot{\boldsymbol{V}}_C = \boldsymbol{0}$ and $\boldsymbol{\omega} = \boldsymbol{0}$ for equilibrium and so, from Newton's law and Euler's equations, we see that $\boldsymbol{F} = \boldsymbol{M} = \boldsymbol{0}$ are necessary conditions for equilibrium.

For the sufficiency proof we go the other way. We start with the conditions $\boldsymbol{F} = \boldsymbol{M} = \boldsymbol{0}$* and show that there must be equilibrium. More specifically, we will start with a body in equilibrium at time t and apply a force system satisfying the preceding conditions. We address ourselves to the question—does the body stay in a state of equilibrium or not? According to Newton's law there will be no change in the velocity of the mass center since $\boldsymbol{F} = \boldsymbol{0}$. And with $\boldsymbol{\omega} = \boldsymbol{0}$ at time t Euler's equations indicate, for $\boldsymbol{M}_c = \boldsymbol{0}$, that $\dot{\omega}_x = \dot{\omega}_y = \dot{\omega}_z = 0$. Thus, the angular velocity must remain zero. With the velocity of the center of mass constant, and with $\dot{\boldsymbol{\omega}} = \boldsymbol{0}$ in inertial space we know that the body remains in equilibrium. Thus if a body is initially in equilibrium the condition $\boldsymbol{F} = \boldsymbol{0}$ and $\boldsymbol{M} = \boldsymbol{0}$ is sufficient for maintaining equilibrium.

* We have shown in statics that if $\boldsymbol{F} = \boldsymbol{0}$ and $\boldsymbol{M} = \boldsymbol{0}$ about some point in inertial space, then $\boldsymbol{M} = \boldsymbol{0}$ about any point in inertial space.

17.9 Closure

In this chapter we have set forth the general equations of the motion of rigid bodies. We examined various kinds of three-dimensional motions and then studied certain interesting special cases—particularly the case of plane motion. The following is a capsule representation of the various levels of generality, arranged from the more general to the most restrictive formulations.

Equation $\boldsymbol{M} = \dot{\boldsymbol{H}}$:

This equation is valid for the motion of *any system of particles.* $\boldsymbol{H}$ is the moment, about any of the following points, of the momentum relative to any of these points, as seen from an inertial reference, and $\boldsymbol{M}$ is the total moment of all external forces about any of these points:

1. A point fixed in the inertial reference.
2. The mass center of the system of particles.
3. A point having an acceleration that is directed toward or away from the mass center.

Euler's equations of motion:

$$M_x = I_{xx}\dot{\omega}_x + \omega_y\omega_z\,(I_{zz} - I_{yy})$$

$$M_y = I_{yy}\dot{\omega}_y + \omega_z\omega_x\,(I_{xx} - I_{zz})$$

$$M_z = I_{zz}\dot{\omega}_z + \omega_x\omega_y\,(I_{yy} - I_{xx})$$

These are a specific form of the relation $\boldsymbol{M} = \dot{\boldsymbol{H}}$ applicable for a *rigid body* in which the directions of the vector components are fixed to the rigid body and form principal axes for the three points mentioned in the more general relation. For Euler's equations, these points have the added restrictions:

1. The body has, at time t, its axis of rotation through the the point.
2. No further restrictions for the center of mass.
3. The body has, at time t, its axis of rotation through the point.

The moment of momentum equations simplify to the elementary form $T = I\dot{\omega}$ (which we learned in physics) for:

a. Pure rotation about an axis fixed in inertial space if moments are taken about the axis of rotation.

b. Plane motion if moments are taken about the normal to the plane of motion at the mass center.

c. The case for which $\boldsymbol{\omega}$ is instantaneously zero.

In the following chapter we shall examine energy considerations for rigid bodies, and then in Chapter 19 we will bring our full knowledge of rigid-body dynamics to bear on the interesting problems of motion about a fixed point, with a view toward carrying out useful integrations for various classes of such problems.

PROBLEMS

1. [17.2] Compute the moment of momentum of the disc about point A in Example 17.1.

2. [17.2] A uniform cylinder C of radius 1 ft and thickness 3 in. (Fig. 17.50) rolls without slipping at its center plane on the platform B such that the centerline of CD makes 2 revolutions per second relative to the platform. What is the angular momentum vector for the cylinder about the center of mass of the cylinder? The cylinder weighs 64.4 lb.

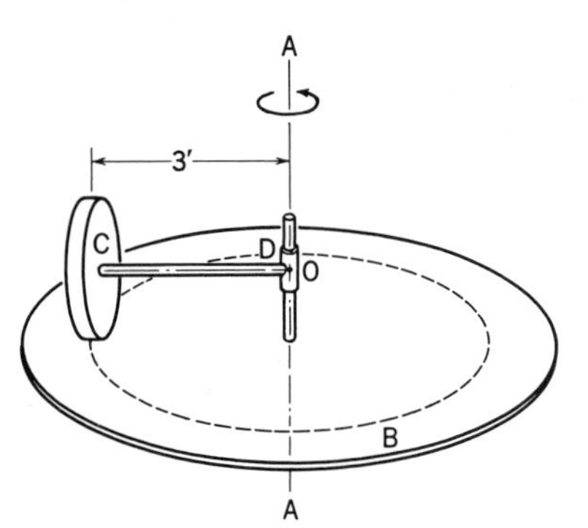

Fig. 17.50

3. [17.2] In the previous problem find the moment of momentum of the disc about the stationary point O along the vertical axis AA.

4. [17.2] A platform rotates at an angular speed of ω_1, while mounted on the platform is a cylinder of radius r and length a which rotates relative to the platform at an angular speed of ω_2 (Fig. 17.51). When the axis of the cylinder is collinear with the stationary Y axis, what is the angular momentum vector of the cylinder about the center of mass of the cylinder? The mass of the cylinder is M.

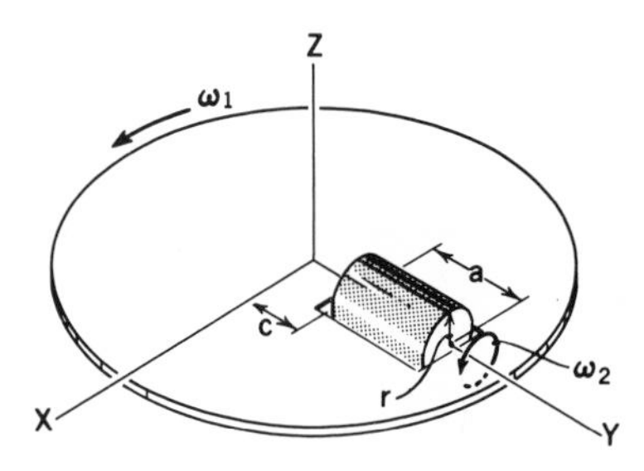

Fig. 17.51

5. [17.2] A disc A in Fig. 17.52 rotates relative to an inclined shaft CD at the rate ω_2 of 3 rad/sec while shaft CD rotates about FE at the rate ω_1 of 4 rad/sec relative to the ground. What is the angular momentum of the disc about the mass center as seen from the rod DC? What is the angular momentum of the disc about the mass center as seen from the ground? What is the angular momentum about point D as seen from the ground? The disc weighs 64.4 lb.

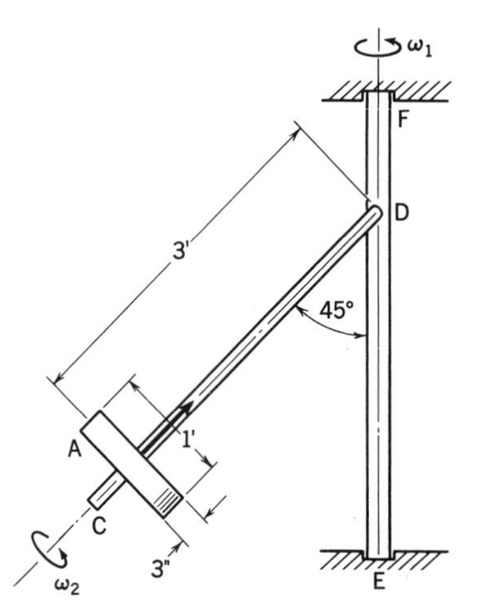

Fig. 17.52

6. [17.2] A 50-lb disc with a beveled edge is shown in Fig. 17.53 rolling without slipping on surface B so that its centerline makes 5 revolutions per second around the vertical axis Y. What is the angular momentum of the disc about point A? The disc has a thickness of 1 in.

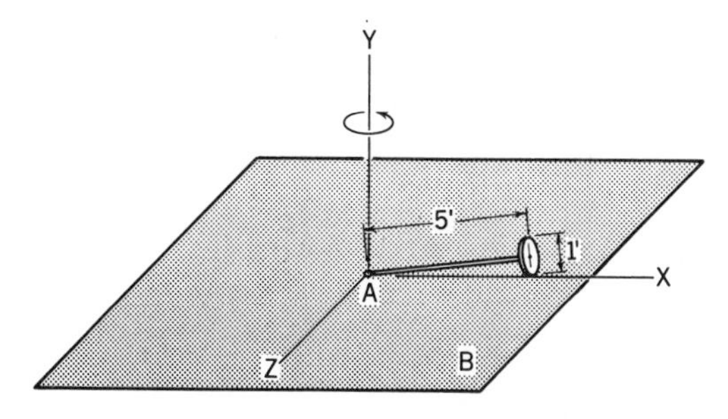

Fig. 17.53

7. [17.2] What is the moment of momentum vector about the center of mass of a homogeneous rectangular parallelepiped rotating with an angular velocity of 10 rad/sec about a main diagonal? The sides of the rectangular parallelepiped are 1 ft, 2 ft, and 4 ft, as shown in Fig. 17.54, and the weight is 4000 lb.

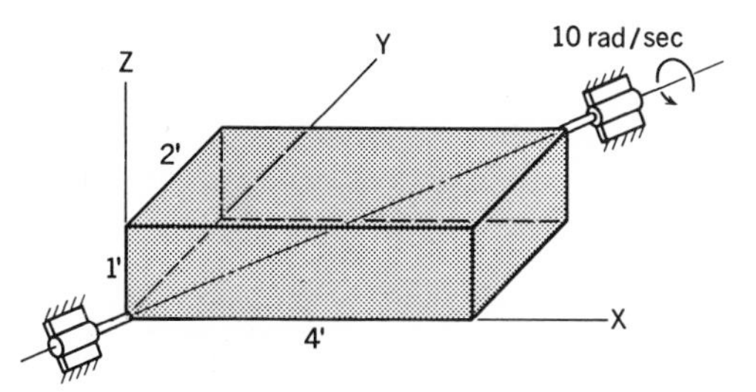

Fig. 17.54

8. [17.2] A cone B weighing 20 lb rolls without slipping inside a conical cavity C (Fig. 17.55). The cone has a length of 10 ft. The centerline of the cone rotates with an angular speed ω_1 of 5 rad/sec about the Y axis. Compute the moment of momentum about the center of mass of the body.

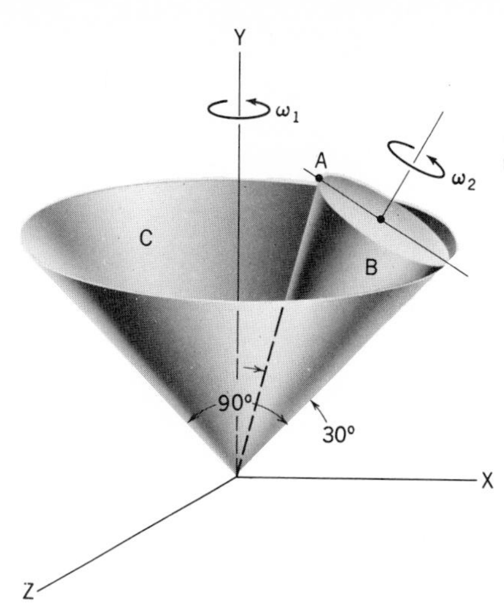

Fig. 17.55

9. [17.2] In the previous problem compute the moment of momentum of the cone about point A shown in Fig. 17.55.

10. [17.2] Shown in Fig. 17.56 is a device consisting of a disc G and two masses E and F protruding from the disc. The disc and masses are rotating freely with angular speed ω_2 of 3 rad/sec relative to the horizontal shaft which, in turn, rotates freely with angular speed ω_1 of 2 rad/sec relative to the ground. If bodies E and F have weights of 4 ounces and if the disc has a weight of 20 lb, what is the moment of momentum of the disc and attached masses about point O?

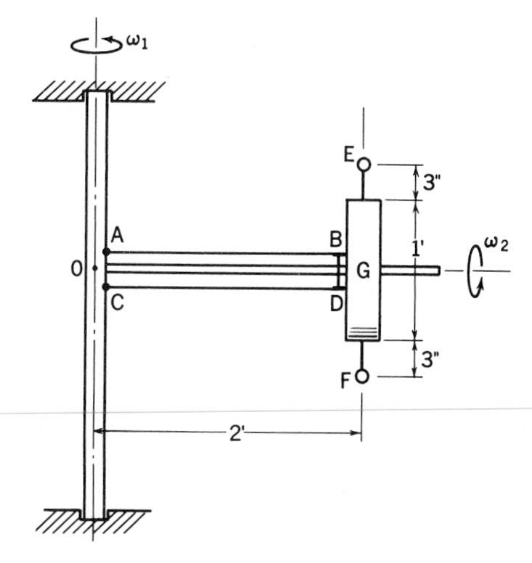

Fig. 17.56

11. [17.4] In the previous problem consider that cords AB and CD draw the disc G toward the vertical axis a distance of 6 in., and an internal electromagnet of the disc draws the masses E and F in toward the horizontal centerline a distance of 2 in. each. Explain why there cannot be a change in the total moment of momentum relative to the ground of the disc and attached masses due to this action. Compute the changes in ω_1 and ω_2 respectively as a result of this action.

12. [17.4] Shown in Fig. 17.57 is a cylinder made up of two semicylinders A and B weighing 15 lb and 30 lb, respectively. If the cylinder has a diameter of 3 in., what is the angular acceleration when released from a stationary configuration at the position shown? Assume no slipping.

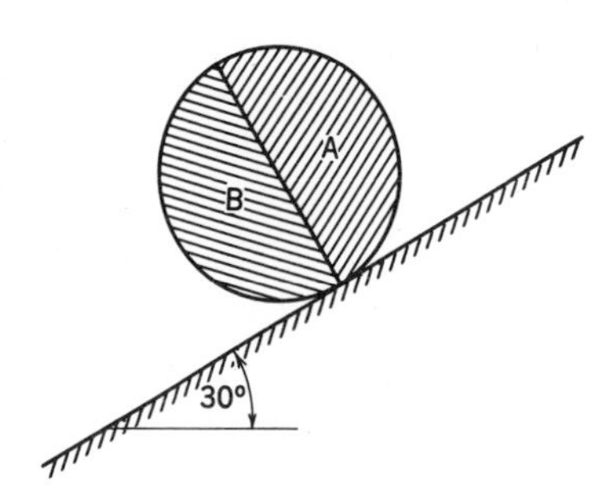

Fig. 17.57

13. [17.4] A semi-cylinder A is shown in Fig. 17.58. The diameter of A is 1 ft and the weight is 100 lb. What is the angular acceleration of A at the position shown, if at this instant it has an angular velocity of 2 rad/sec?

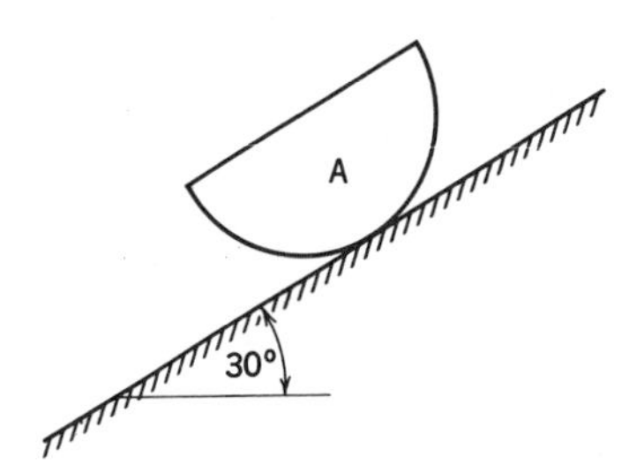

Fig. 17.58

14. [17.4] In Fig. 17.59, a slender rod is pinned to a shaft rotating at an angular speed ω of 10 rad/sec. The rod weighs 50 lb. What is the tension in the cord AB, whose mass we can neglect?

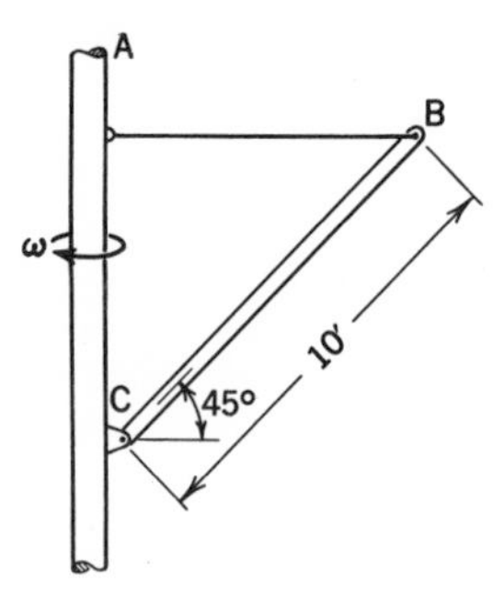

Fig. 17.59

15. [17.4] In Fig. 17.60, a thin disc weighing 322 lb rotates at a speed ω_2 of 100 rad/sec. It is mounted on a platform which rotates at ω_1 of 20 rad/sec. The radius R of the disc is 4 ft. Compute the bearing reactions at A and B. Neglect the mass of the shaft supporting the disc and assume that bearing A retains the system in the radial direction.

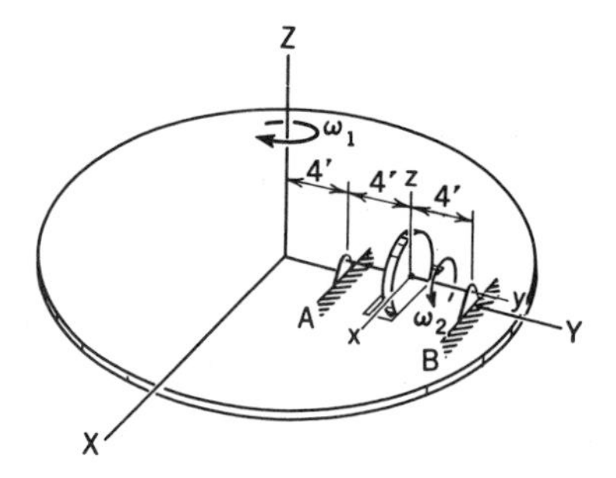

Fig. 17.60

16. [17.4] Consider the above problem. (a) If a torque of 50 lb-ft is applied to the shaft AB when it is collinear with the Y axis, what is the angular acceleration of the disc at that position? (b) Does this torque affect the bearing reactions at the instant of application?

17. [17.4] Do Prob. 15 for a set of axes xyz at the center of mass of the disc but not attached to the disc. That is, the disc rotates with angular speed ω_1 relative to xyz in a direction along the y axis.

18. [17.4] The thin disc in Fig. 17.61 rotates with an angular speed of $\omega_1 = 10$ rad/sec and has a rate of change of speed $\dot{\omega}_1$ relative to the bearings AB (bearing A holds the shaft in the direction AB). These bearings are mounted on platform DE, which swings downward with an angular speed of $\omega_2 = 5$ rad/sec about the connector D. Connector D is held on a shaft FG which rotates at an angular speed of $\omega_3 = 2$ rad/sec. What is the moment from the bearings about the center of the disc at the instant that DE makes a right angle with GF and what is the value of $\dot{\omega}_1$ at this instant? The disc has a radius of 1 ft, weighs 32.2 lb, and rotates freely in the bearings.

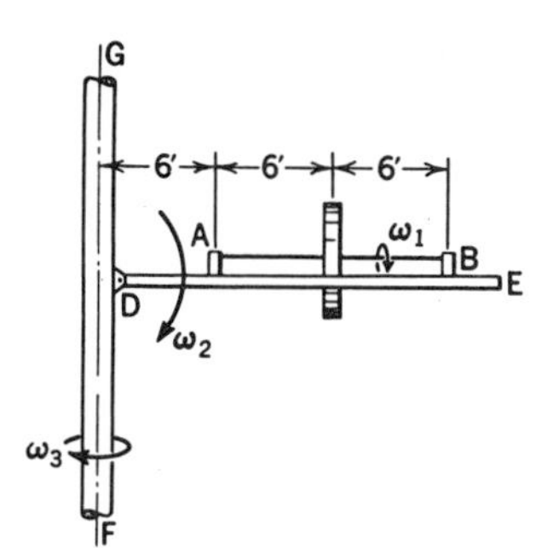

Fig. 17.61

19. [17.4] The disc in the preceding problem has the given velocities when DE is perpendicular to FG. At that position the following angular accelerations also apply:

(1) arm DE accelerates at 3 rad/sec² relative to shaft FG,

(2) shaft FG accelerates at 10 rad/sec² relative to the ground.

Compute the moment of the bearings at this position about the center of the disc and determine $\dot{\omega}_1$.

20. [17.4] A propeller-driven airplane is at the bottom of a loop of radius 2000 ft and traveling at 350 mi/hr. The propeller consists of 2 identical blades at right angles, weighs 322 lb, has a radius of gyration of 2 ft about its axis of rotation, and is rotating at 1200 rpm. If the propeller rotates counterclockwise as viewed from the rear of the plane, compute the torques coming onto the propeller at the bearings from the motion if one blade is vertical and the other is horizontal at the time of interest.

21. [17.4] A thin disc weighing 32.2 lb rotates on rod AB at a speed of 100 rad/sec in a clockwise direction looking from B to A (Fig. 17.62). The radius of the disc is 1 ft and it is located 10 ft from the centerline of the shaft CD, to which rod AB is fixed. Shaft CD rotates at 50 rad/sec in a counterclockwise direction as one looks from C to D. Find the tensile force, bending moment, and shear force on rod AB at the end A due to the disc.

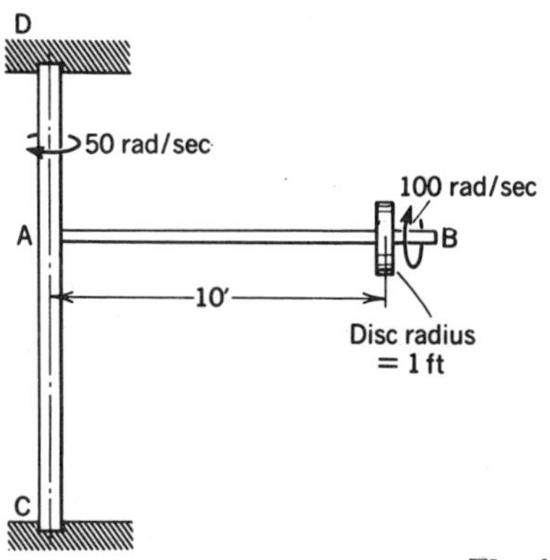

Fig. 17.62

22. [17.4] Do Prob. 21 using a reference xyz at the mass center of the disc such that the disc rotates about the x axis of this reference with the indicated speed of 100 rad/sec.

23. [17.4] In Fig. 17.63, a disc and a cylinder are mounted on a shaft. The disc has been mounted eccentrically so that the center of mass is $\frac{1}{2}$ in. from the centerline of the shaft. If the shaft rotates at 1750 rpm, compute the static and the dynamic loads on the supports.

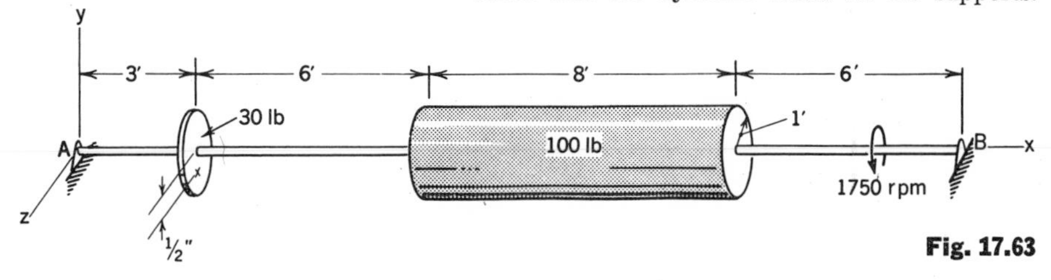

Fig. 17.63

24. [17.4] Shown in Fig. 17.64 is a shaft rotating with constant angular speed ω of 5 rad/sec. The protruding arms have a weight of 3 lb/ft. Compute the bearing reactions at A and B at the instant shown. The shaft without arms weighs 40 lb.

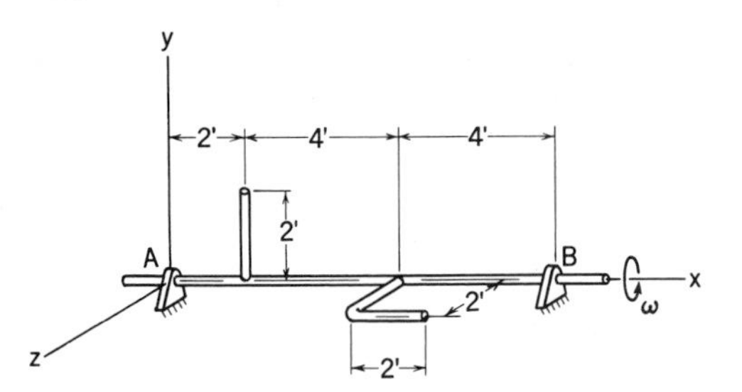

Fig. 17.64

25. [17.4] A disc is shown in Fig. 17.65 mounted off-center at B on a shaft CD which rotates with angular speed ω. The disc weighs 50 lb and has a diameter of 6 ft. What are the bearing forces at the configuration shown for an angular speed ω of 10 rad/sec and an angular acceleration of 2 rad/sec^2? Neglect the weight of the shaft.

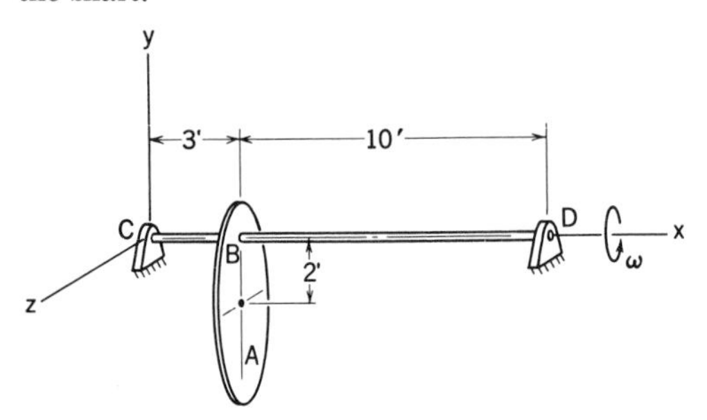

Fig. 17.65

26. [17.4] In Fig. 17.66 is shown a shaft supported by bearings A and B and rotating at a speed ω of 3 rad/sec. Identical blocks C and D weighing 30 lb each are attached to the shaft by light structural members. What are the bearing reactions if we neglect the weight of the shaft.

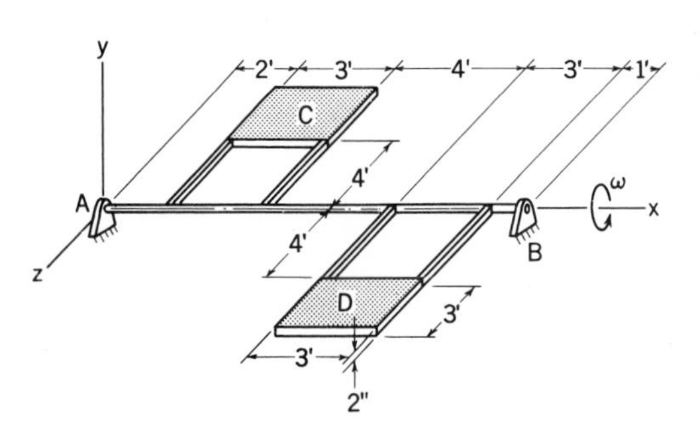

Fig. 17.66

27. [17.4] A vertical shaft is shown in Fig. 17.67 rotating with angular speed ω of 5 rad/sec in bearings A and D. A uniform plate B weighing 50 lb is attached to the shaft as is a disc C weighing 30 lb as shown in the diagram. What are the bearing reactions at the configuration shown? The shaft weighs 20 lb and the thickness of disc and plate is 2 in.

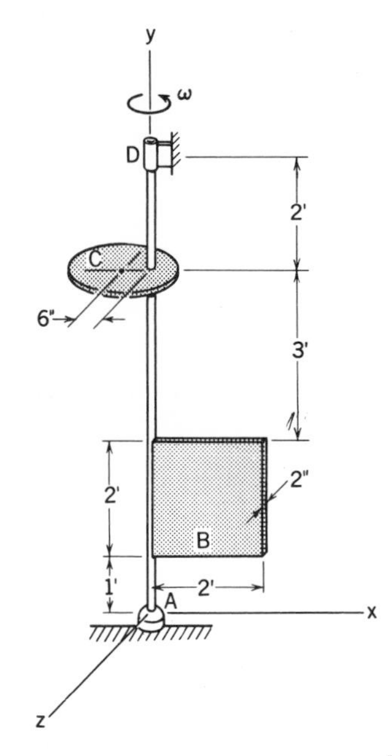

Fig. 17.67

28. [17.4] A uniform wooden panel is shown in Fig. 17.68 supported by bearings A and B. A 100-lb weight is connected by an inextensible cable to the panel at point G over a light pulley D. If the system is released from rest at the configuration shown, what is the angular acceleration of the panel and what are the forces at the bearings? The panel weighs 60 lb.

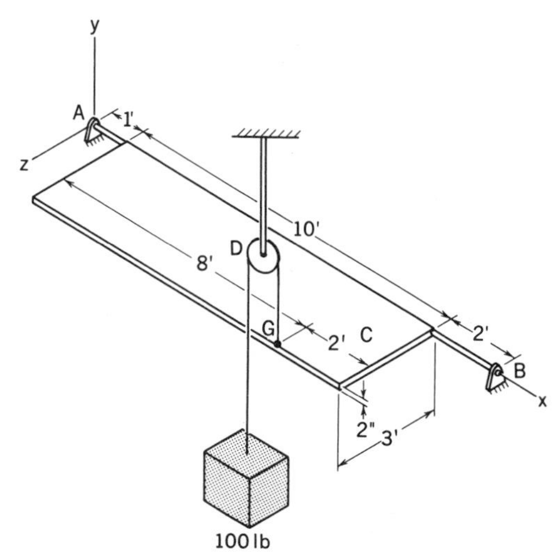

Fig. 17.68

29. [17.4] Do preceding problem when there is a frictional torque at the bearings of 10 ft-lb and the moment of inertia of the pulley is 10 lbm-ft² with radius 1 ft.

30. [17.4] In Fig. 17.69, a thin rectangular plate weighing 25 lb rotates at a uniform speed of 20 rad/sec about axis AB. What are the dynamic loads on the bearings when the plate is in the XY plane of the inertial reference? The plate is restrained in the Y direction at bearing A only. [*Hint*: Use components of the forces at A and B parallel to the XYZ reference.]

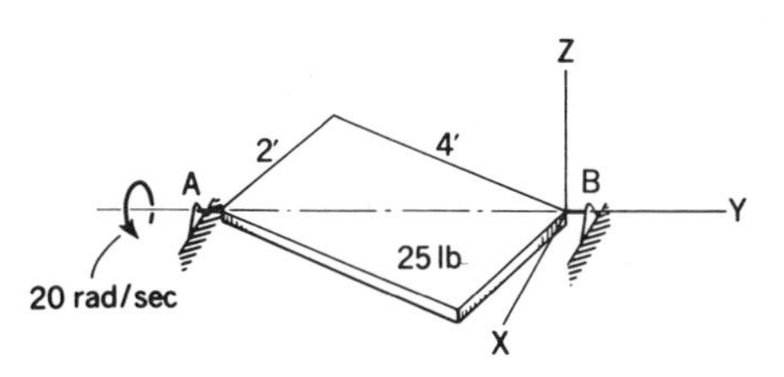

Fig. 17.69

31. [17.4] If a torque of 30 lb-ft in the direction of rotation is applied to the shaft on which the plate in the above problem rotates, what is the angular acceleration at the instant of application of the torque? What are the bearing reactions at this instant? The plate is in the XY plane when the torque is applied and has an angular velocity of 20 rad/sec.

32. [17.4] Explain how the roll of a ship can be stabilized by the action of a rapidly spinning gyroscope (Fig. 17.70).

Fig. 17.70

33. [17.4] In Fig. 17.71, a thin disc has its axis inclined to the vertical by an angle θ and rolls without slipping with an angular speed ω_1 about the supporting rod hinged at B. If $l = 10$ ft, $r = 2$ ft, $\theta = 45°$, and $\omega_1 = 10$ rad/sec, compute the angular velocity of the rod BC about OO. If the disc weighs 40 lb, what is the total moment about point B from all forces acting on the system? Neglect the mass of the rod OC. [*Hint*: Use a reference xyz at B when two of the axes are in the plane of OO and OC.]

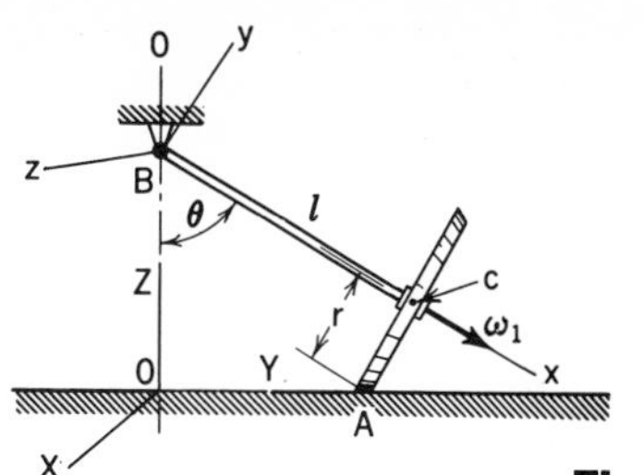

Fig. 17.71

34. [17.4] Do Prob. 33 using axes xyz chosen so that the disc rotates relative to this reference with an angular speed ω_1 directed along the x axis of this reference.

35. [17.4] The turbine in a ship is parallel to the longitudinal axis of the ship and is rotating at a rate of 800 rpm counterclockwise as viewed from stern to bow (Fig. 17.72). The turbine weighs 50 tons and has radii of gyration at the mass center of 3 ft about axes normal to the centerline, and 1 ft about the centerline. The ship has a pitching motion, which is approximately sinusoidal, given by the equation:

$$\theta = 0.3 \sin \frac{2\pi}{15} t \text{ rad}$$

The amplitude of the pitching is thus 0.3 rad and the period is 15 sec. Determine the moment as a function of time coming onto the bearings of the ship, resulting from the motion of the turbine, using axes fixed to the *ship* at the center of mass of the turbine.

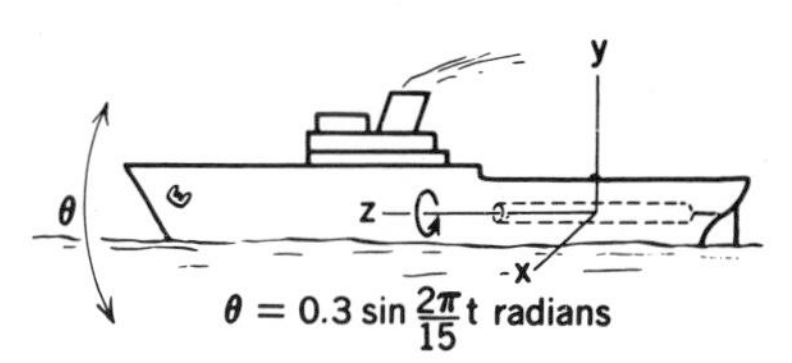

Fig. 17.72

36. [17.4] Do the above problem using Euler's equations.

37. [17.5] Balance the system in planes A and B in Fig. 17.73 at a distance 1 ft from centerline. Use two weights.

38. [17.5] Using Fig. 17.73, balance the system by using a weight in plane A of $1\frac{1}{2}$ lb and a weight in plane B of 1 lb. You may choose suitable radii in these planes.

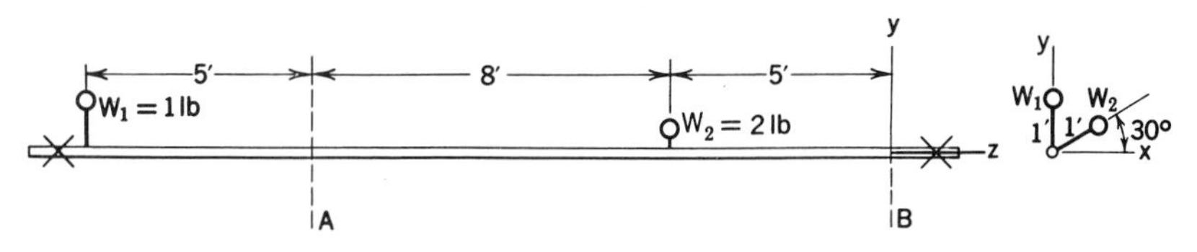

Fig. 17.73

39. [17.5] Balance the shaft described in Prob. 23 using balancing planes 5 ft from bearing A and 3 ft from bearing B, respectively. The balancing masses each weigh 3 lb and may be taken as particles. Give the proper position of these balancing masses in these planes.

40. [17.5] Balance the shaft described in Prob. 23 by removing a small chunk of metal from each of the end faces of the 100-lb cylinder at a position 10 in. from the shaft centerline. What are the weights of these chunks and what are their orientations?

41. [17.5] In Prob. 24 balance the rotating system by properly placing 8-lb spherical masses in balancing planes 1 ft from the bearings A and B. Assume that the balancing masses are particles.

42. [17.5] Balance the system given in Prob. 25 using two rods, each weighing 10 lb/ft having a diameter of 2 in., attached normally to the shaft at position 1 ft from bearing C and 2 ft from bearing D. The diameter of the shaft is 2 in. Determine the lengths of these rods and their inclination.

43. [17.5] Balance the system given in Prob. 26 by attaching rods, each weighing 10 lb/ft and having a diameter of 3 in., normal to the shaft at position 1 ft from bearing A and at the center of the shaft. Determine the lengths of these rods and their orientation.

44. [17.6] Shown in Fig. 17.74 is a shaft and disc of steel having a density of 453 lbm/ft³. A constant torque T of 50.0 lb-ft is applied as shown. After 2 minutes, what is the angular velocity of the system? How many revolutions have been made during this interval? Neglect friction of the bearings.

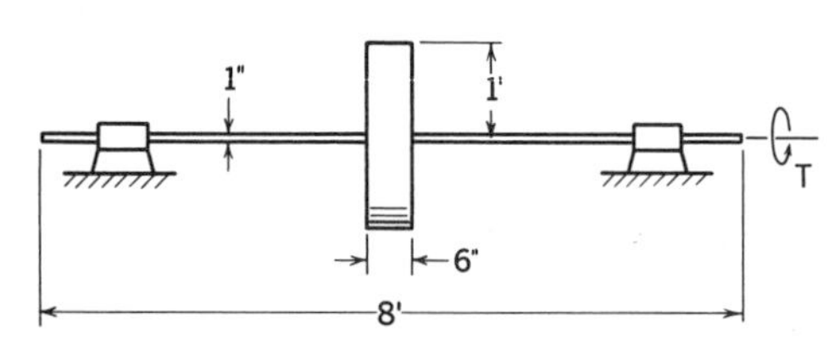

Fig. 17.74

45. [17.6] In the preceding problem, include windage and bearing friction losses by assuming that they are proportional to angular speed $\dot{\theta}$. It is known that the disc will halve its speed after 5 minutes from a speed of 300 RPM when there is no external applied torque.

46. [17.6] Shown in Fig. 17.75 is a motor B driving a gear C which connects with gear D to driven device A. The top system of motor, shaft, and gear has a moment of inertia I_1 about the axis of rotation of 3 lbm ft² while the bottom system of device A and gear D has a moment of inertia about its axis of rotation of I_2 equal to 1 lbm ft². If motor B develops a net torque given as:

$$T = 300 - 0.02t^2 \text{ in-lb},$$

what is the angular speed of gear D 6 seconds after starting from a stationary configuration? How many revolutions has it undergone during this time interval?

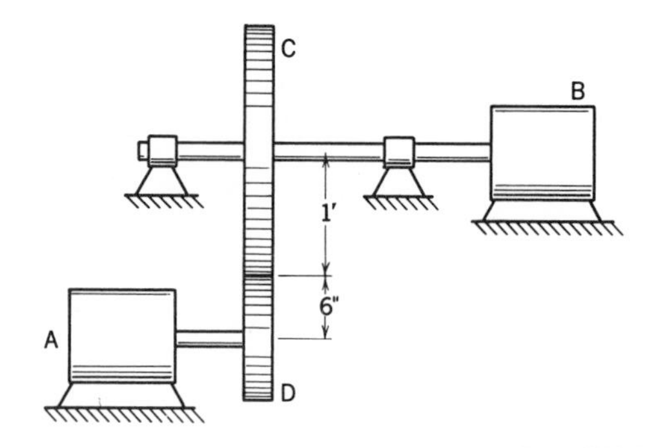

Fig. 17.75

47. [17.6] In Fig. 17.76 is shown a uniform cylinder of radius $R = 2$ ft and mass M of 5 slugs. The springs shown are identical, each having a spring constant K of 50 lb/in. If the cylinder is turned 10° from its indicated equilibrium position and released, what will the angular speed be when it has rotated 15°?

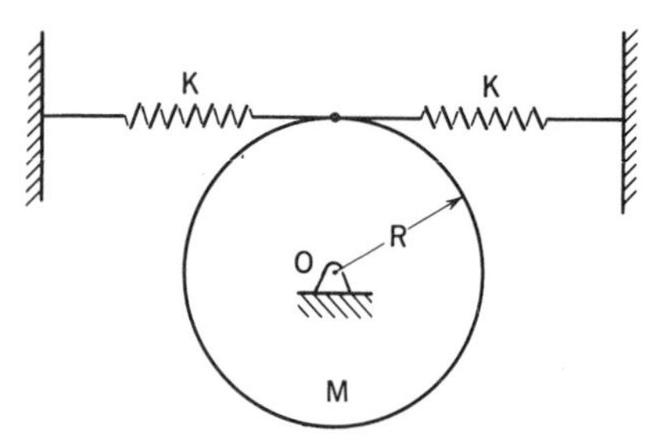

Fig. 17.76

48. [17.6] In Fig. 17.77 a device is restrained from rotating by 2 identical springs each having a spring constant K equal to 10 lb/in. The device has a mass of 500 lbm and a radius of gyration of 2 ft. If $r = 3$ ft and $W_1 = 100$ lb, what is the angular speed of the device after 3 seconds? How much has it rotated during this time? Take $R = 4$ ft.

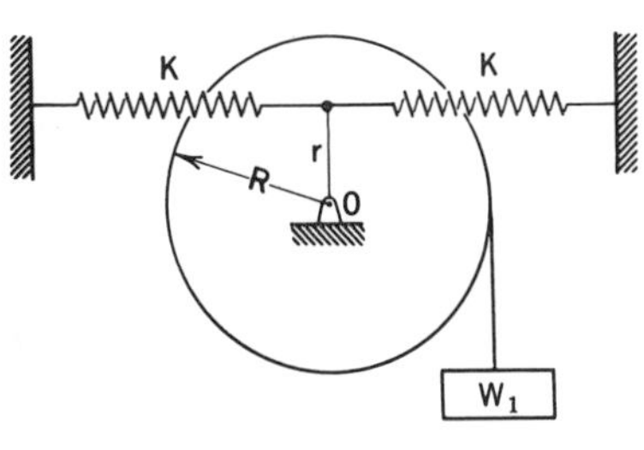

Fig. 17.77

49. [17.6] Shown in Fig. 17.78 is a stepped cylinder having a moment of inertia I about its axis of rotation. If the spring is unstretched in the position shown, what is the amount of rotation for short time interval t after the system is released from the configuration shown?

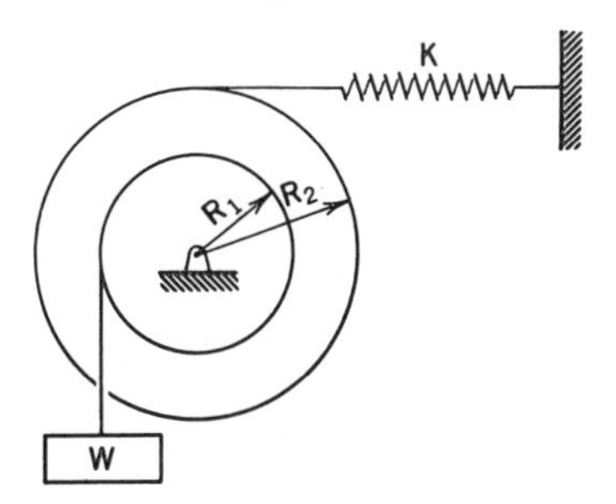

Fig. 17.78

50. [17.6] In Fig. 17.79, a slender rod weighing 32.2 lb is held by a frictionless pin at A and by a spring having a spring constant of 50 lb/in. at B. If point B of the rod is depressed 1 in. at $t = 0$ from the static equilibrium position, what will its speed be when $t = 0.02$ sec?

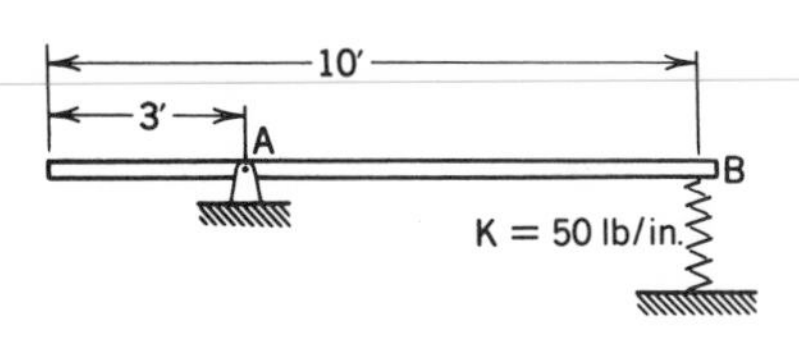

Fig. 17.79

51. [17.6] Shown in Fig. 17.80 are two discs E and F of diameter 1 ft rotating in frictionless bearings. Disc F weighs 100 lb and rotates with angular speed ω_1 of 10 rad/sec while disc E weighs 30 lb and rotates with angular speed ω_2 of 5 rad/sec. Neglecting the angular momentum of the shafts, what is the total angular momentum of the system relative to the ground? Consider that the discs are forced together along the axis of rotation. What is the common angular velocity when friction has reduced relative motion between the disc to zero? Do you expect that there has been a change in kinetic energy?

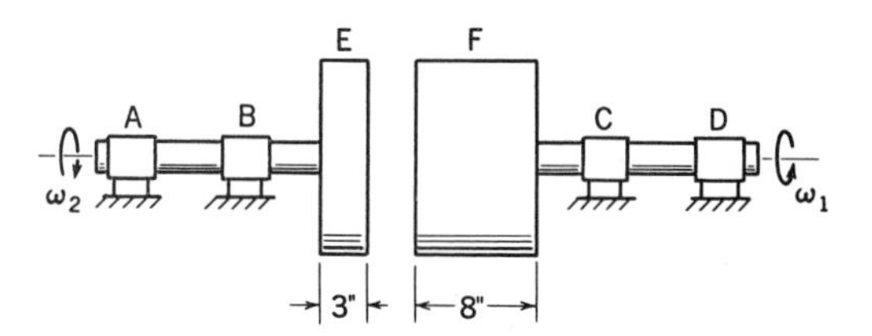

Fig. 17.80

52. [17.6] In the previous problem if $\mu_s = 0.2$ between the discs, and it takes 30 seconds for them to reach the same angular speed, what is the constant normal force required to bring the discs together in such a manner?

53. [17.6] Cylinder A in Fig. 17.81 has an angular speed ω_1 of 3 rad/sec when it is lowered onto cylinder B, which has an angular speed ω_2 of 5 rad/sec before contact is made. What are the final angular velocities of the cylinders resulting from friction at the surfaces of contact? Take the mass of A to be 500 lbm and of B to be 400 lbm. If $\mu = 0.3$ for the contact surface of the cylinders and if the normal force transmitted from A to B is 600 lb, how long does it take for the cylinders to reach a constant speed?

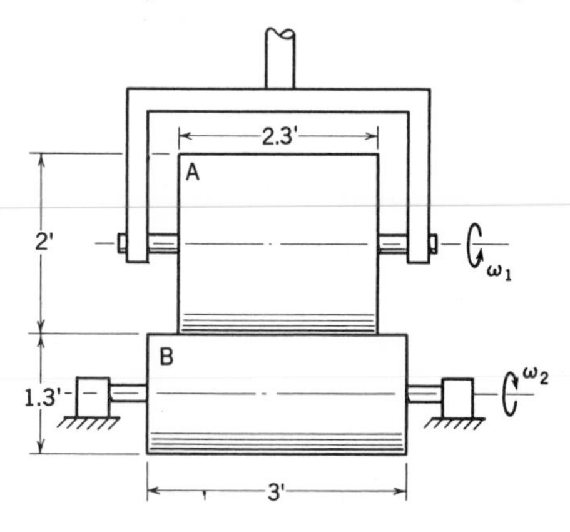

Fig. 17.81

54. [17.6] In Prob. 53, is angular momentum conserved relative to the ground for the action? Explain. Is kinetic energy conserved relative to the ground as a result of the action described? Explain.

55. [17.6] We have shown in Section 17.6 that pure rotation is mathematically identical with rectilinear translation. And, just as we have springs giving linear restoring torques in rectilinear motion problems, we have "torsional springs" that give linear restoring torques for pure rotational motion. A shaft, such as is shown in Fig. 17.82, if not twisted excessively and if having negligible inertia, will supply such a restoring torque to the angular motion of the disc. We accordingly have the concept of a torsional spring constant K_t given as torque per radian of twist. What is the total, equivalent, torsional spring constant for the system in Fig. 17.83?

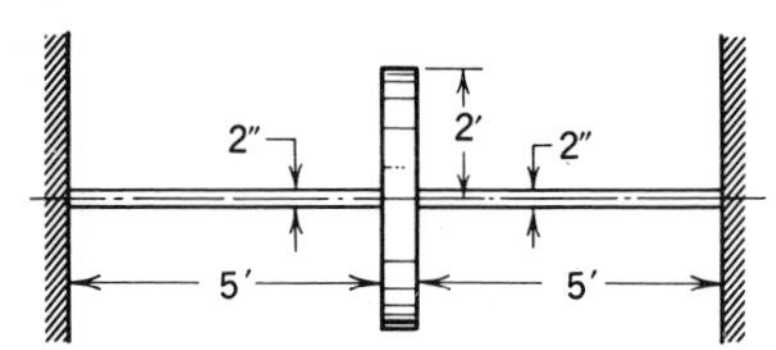

Fig. 17.82

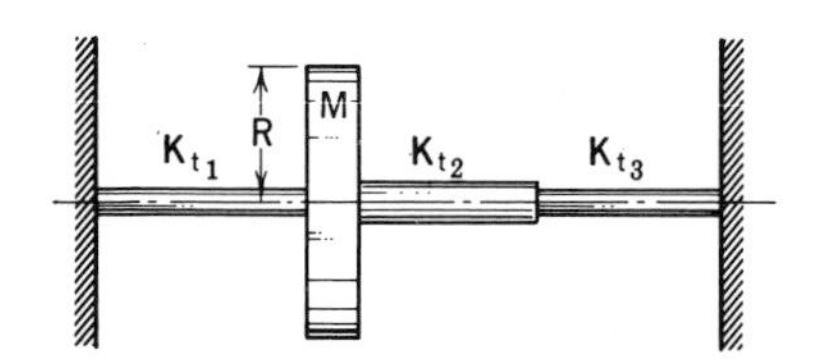

Fig. 17.83

56. [17.6] We know from strength of materials that the amount of twist θ induced by torque M_z on a uniform circular shaft in the elastic range is given as:

$$\theta = \frac{M_z L}{GJ}$$

where G is the shear modulus, L is the length of shaft, and J is the polar moment of inertia of the cross section. For the shaft shown in Fig. 17.82 compute the equivalent torsional spring constant on the disc. Take $G = 15 \times 10^6$ psi. If the disc is given an angular velocity of 0.1 rad/sec, how much will it rotate before it reaches its first zero angular speed? The disc weighs 50 lb. Neglect the mass of the shaft.

57. [17.6] In Fig. 17.84, a constant force of 100 lb is exerted on a rope wrapped around a 50-lb cylinder. What is the motion of the cylinder? Neglect initial frictional effects by the support.

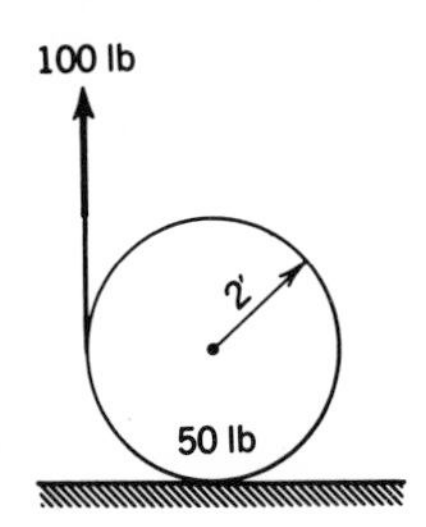

Fig. 17.84

58. [17.6] In Fig. 17.85, a cylinder 2 ft in diameter and weighing 200 lb is made to roll up an inclined surface so that the center has an acceleration of 15 ft sec². What force P, applied to a ring of negligible mass fastened to the cylinder and having a diameter of 1 ft, is required for this acceleration?

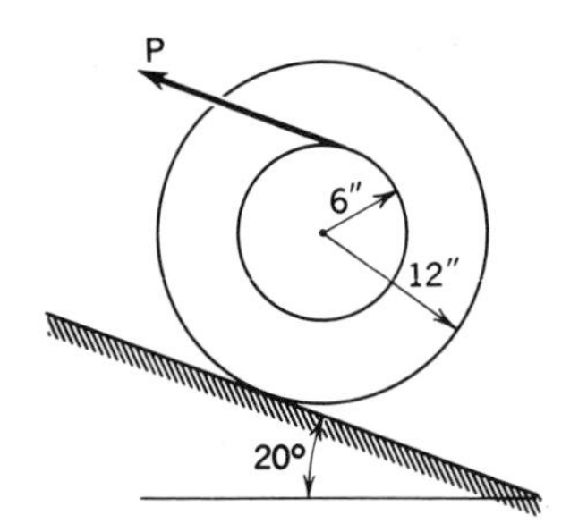

Fig. 17.85

59. [17.6] Shown in Fig. 17.86 is a vehicle moving down a 30° incline with the wheels locked. The vehicle is decelerating at the rate of 6 ft/sec². If the vehicle (plus occupants) weighs 5000 lb with the center of gravity as shown, what are the normal and friction forces on the wheels?

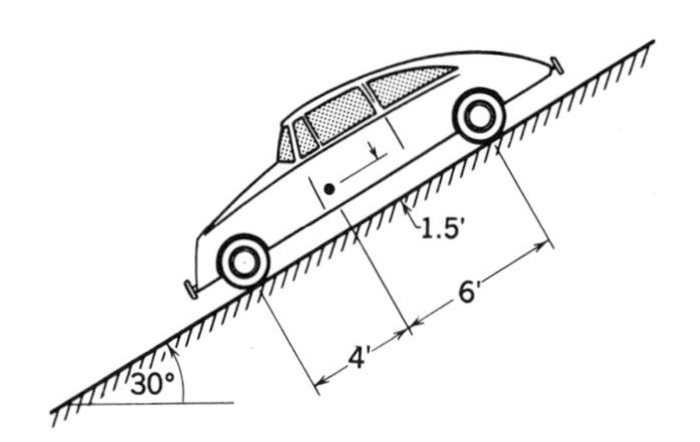

Fig. 17.86

60. [17.6] The cylinder shown in Fig. 17.87 weighs 100 lb and has a radius of gyration of 0.82 ft. What is the minimum coefficient of friction at A that will prevent the body from moving? If we use half this coefficient of friction, what is the acceleration of point O at the instant that the cylinder is released from rest?

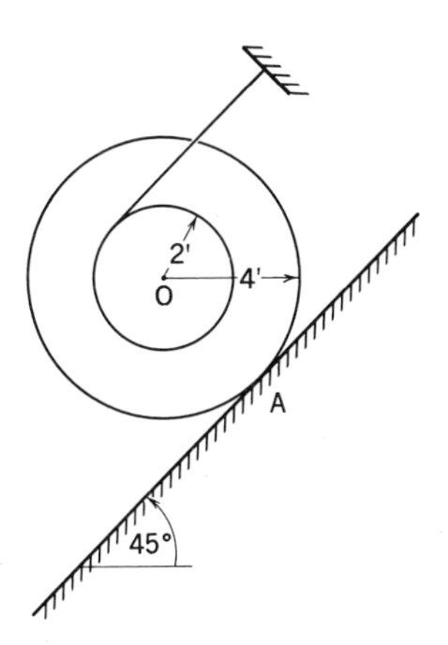

Fig. 17.87

61. [17.6] Shown in Fig. 17.88 is a stepped cylinder on an incline with an inextensible cord wrapped around the inner cylinder. If $\mu_s = 0.1$ and the tension T on the cord at the instant that the cylinder is released from the position shown is 100 lb, what is the initial angular acceleration? What is the acceleration of the mass center? Use the following data:

$$W = 300 \text{ lb}$$

$$\text{radius of gyration} = 3 \text{ ft}$$

$$R_1 = 2 \text{ ft}$$

$$R_2 = 4 \text{ ft}$$

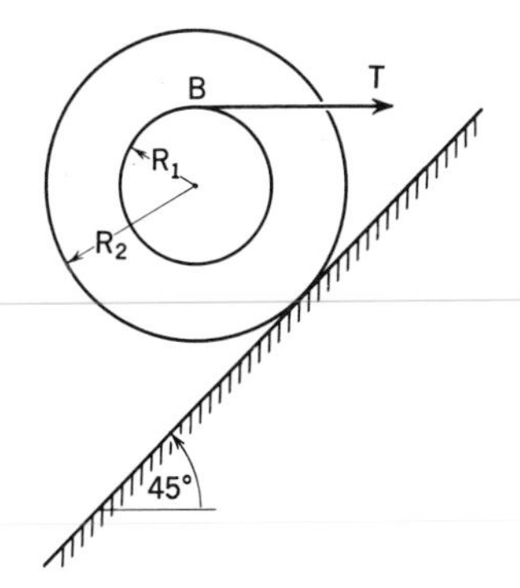

Fig. 17.88

62. [17.6] Shown in Fig. 17.89 is a plate supported at A and B. The plate weighs 3 lb/ft^2. What are the force components at B at the instant support A is removed?

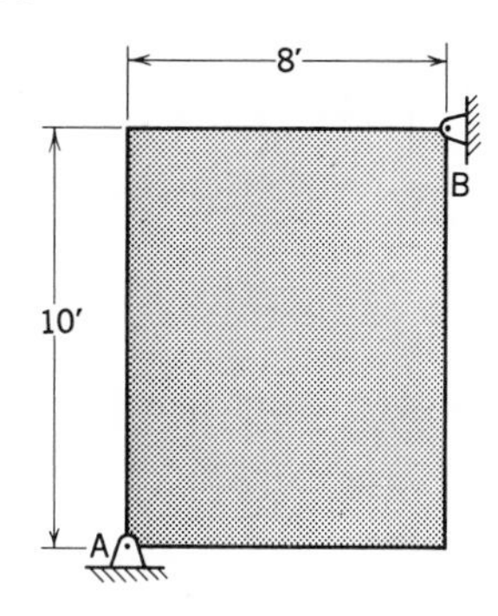

Fig. 17.89

63. [17.6] In Fig. 17.90, when the uniform bar is horizontal the spring at C is extended 3 in. If the bar weighs 50 lb, what is the force at B when support A is removed suddenly? Compute the angular velocity of the bar after 2 sec. The spring constant is 50 lb/inch.

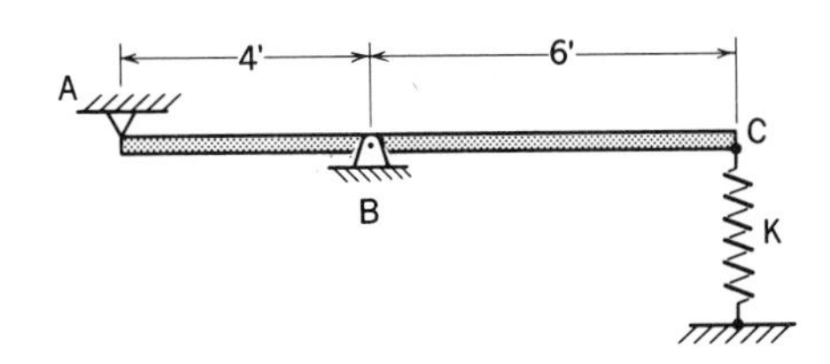

Fig. 17.90

64. [17.6] The cylinder shown in Fig. 17.91 is acted on by a 100-lb force as shown. At the contact point A there is viscous friction such that the friction force is given as:

$$f = 0.05V_A$$

where V_A is the velocity of the cylinder at the contact point. The weight of the cylinder is 30 lb and the radius of gyration is 1 ft. Set up a differential equation for finding the position of O as a function of time.

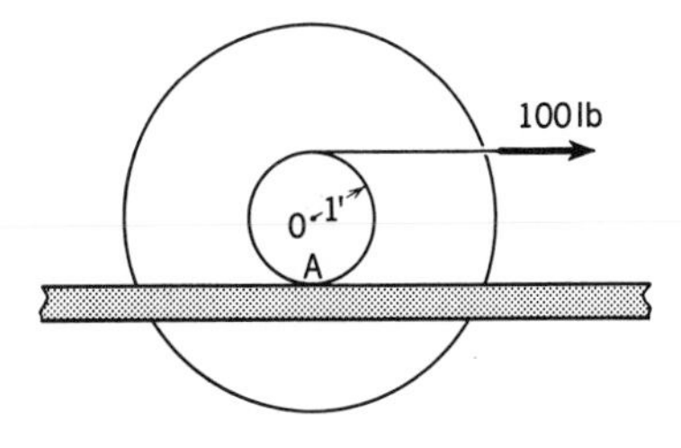

Fig. 17.91

65. [17.6] A solid semicylinder of weight W and radius R is released from rest from the position shown in Fig. 17.92. What is the friction force at that instant?

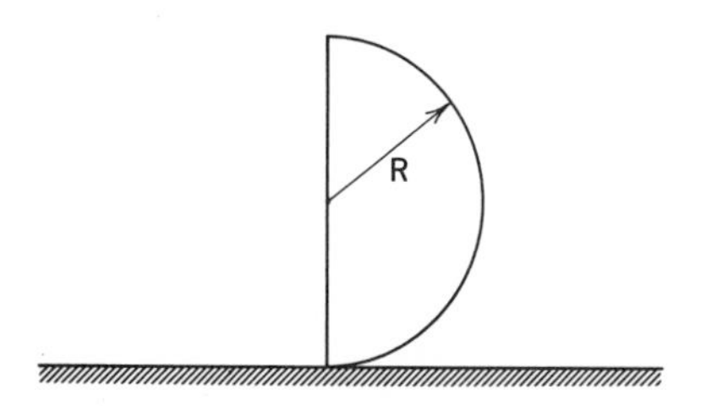

Fig. 17.92

66. [17.6] Shown in Fig. 17.93 is a bar of weight W equal to 100 lb on a horizontal surface S at the instant that a force P equal to 60 lb is applied. Find the center of rotation at the instant that the force P is applied if the coefficient of friction μ equals 0.2. The length of the bar is 10 ft.

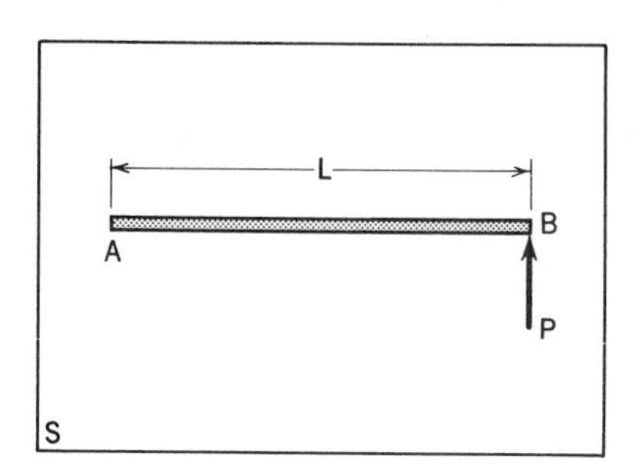

Fig. 17.93

67. [17.6] If the rod shown in Fig. 17.94 is released from rest at the configuration shown, what are the supporting forces at A and B at that instant? The rod weighs 100 lb and is 10 ft long. The coefficient of friction is 0.2 for all surface contacts.

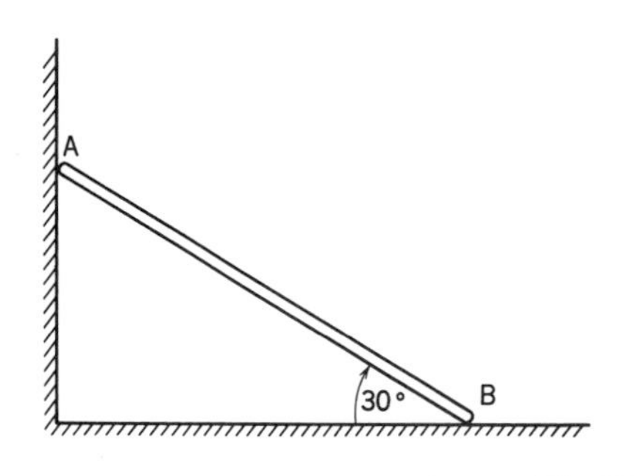

Fig. 17.94

68. [17.6] Do the above problem for the case where end A is moving downward at a speed of 10 ft/sec at the instant shown.

69. [17.6] In Prob. 67 first find by inspection the instantaneous center of rotation for the rod. What are the magnitude and direction of the acceleration vector for the axis of rotation at the instant the rod is released?

70. [17.6] Rod AB is released from the configuration shown in Fig. 17.95. What are the supporting forces at this instant if we neglect friction? The rod weighs 200 lb and is 20 ft in length.

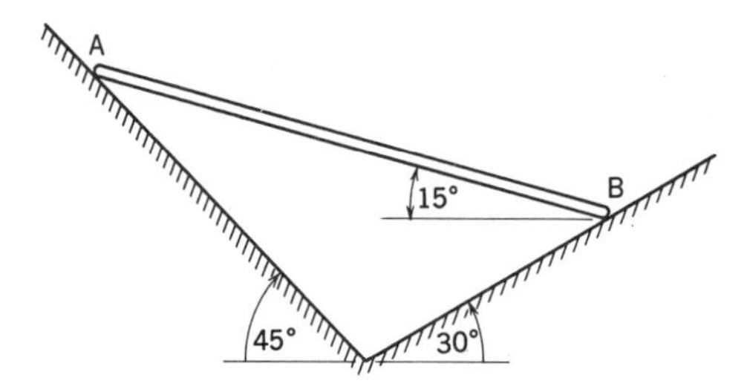

Fig. 17.95

71. [17.6] A rod AB of length 15 ft and weight 100 lb is shown (Fig. 17.96) directly after it has been released from rest. AC and BD are wires. Compute the tension of these wires at the instant shown.

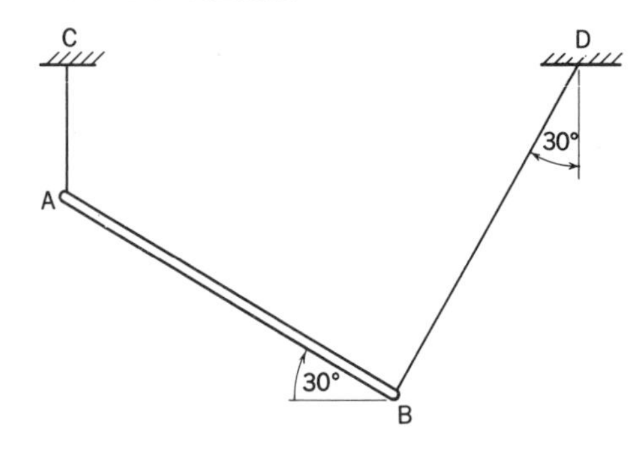

Fig. 17.96

72. [17.6] Shown in Fig. 17.97 is a rod AB of length 20 ft and weight 200 lb at the instant it has been released from rest. AC is a weightless wire and the incline at B is frictionless. What is the tension in the wire at this instant?

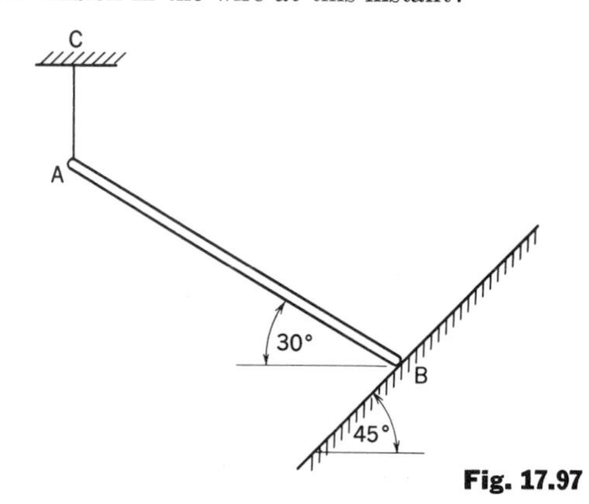

Fig. 17.97

73. [17.6] The cart in Fig. 17.98 is moving at 15 ft/sec and is accelerating at a rate of 30 ft/sec². A thin rod weighing 30 lb and having a length of 10 ft is swinging about pin A. What must its angular acceleration be if it has an angular velocity of 10 rad/sec and is at a position of $\theta = 30°$ when the cart has the data given?

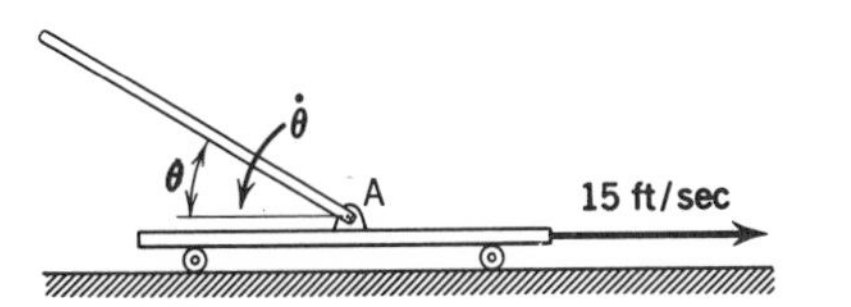

Fig. 17.98

74. [17.6] A crude cart is shown in Fig. 17.99. A horizontal force component P_x of 100 lb is applied to the cart. The coefficient of friction between wheels and ground is 0.6. If $D = 3$ ft and $d = 7$ ft, what is the acceleration of the cart to the right? The wheels weigh 50 lb each. Neglect friction in the axle bearings. The total weight of cart with load is 322 lb.

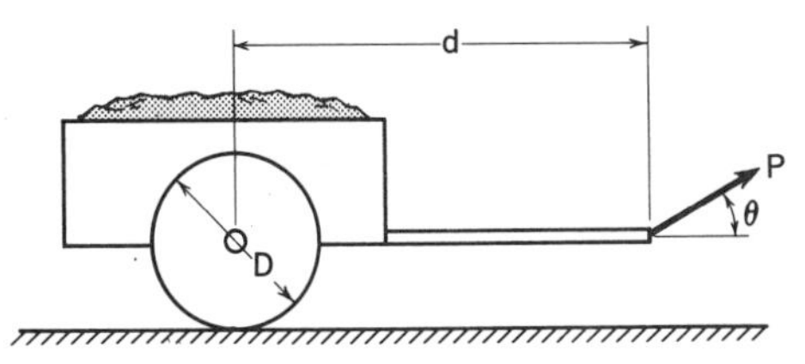

Fig. 17.99

75. [17.6] What minimum force component P_x is required to cause the cart in the previous problem to move so that the wheels slip rather than roll without slipping? What is the acceleration of the cart for this condition?

76. [17.6] An automobile shown in Fig. 17.100 develops a constant torque of 100 in-lb on the rear wheels. The car loaded weighs 4000 lb with the center of gravity as shown. What is the speed the car will reach at the end of 1 mile if we neglect the rotational inertia of the wheels and wind resistance? What is the maximum possible speed of the vehicle for unlimited torque if $\mu_s = 0.6$? Find the supporting forces from the ground for this case. The diameter of the wheel is 2 ft.

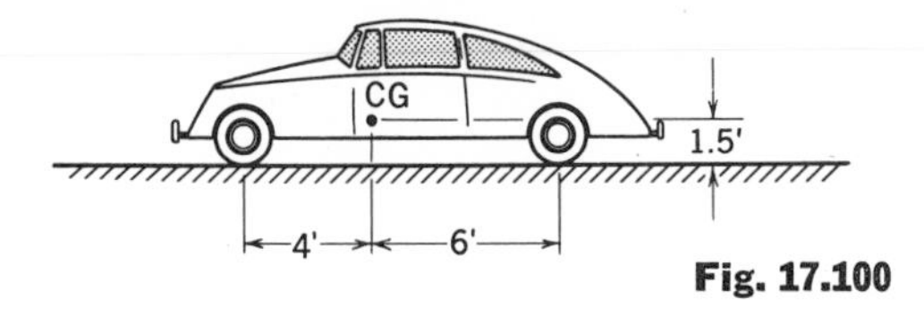

Fig. 17.100

77. [17.6] Work the first part of the previous problem for the case where the inertia of the wheels is taken into account. Take the weight of each wheel to be 30 lb and the radius of gyration to be 11 in.

78. [17.6] Shown in Fig. 17.101 is a system of interconnected gears. Gear B rotates about a fixed axis and gear D is stationary. If a torque T of 20 in.-lb is applied to gear B at the configuration shown, what is the angular acceleration of the gear A? Gear A has a mass of 3 lbm while gear B has a mass of 10 lbm. The system is in a vertical orientation relative to the ground. What force is transmitted to the stationary gear D?

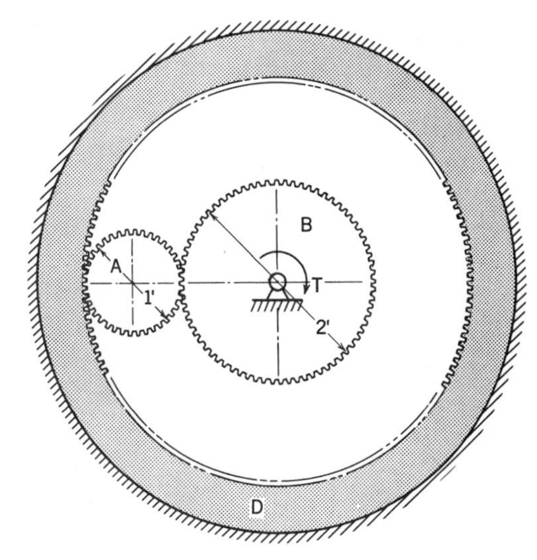

Fig. 17.101

79. [17.6] In the preceding problem, assume that the system of gears is oriented horizontal to the ground and that there are no friction losses. What is the angular speed of gear A 10 seconds after a constant torque of 2 lb-ft is applied to gear B?

80. [17.6] In Prob. 78, assume that the system of gears is oriented horizontal to the ground and that there is no friction. What is the angular speed of gear A 5 seconds after a torque is applied that increases linearly with time at the rate of 5 lb-ft/sec during the interval of interest?

81. [17.6] Shown in Fig. 17.102 is an electric motor D driving gears C, B, and device A. The diameters of gears C and B are 6 in. and 16 in., respectively. The mass of A is 200 lbm. The mass and radius of gyration of the motor armature and gear C are respectively 50 lb and 8 in. The mass of B is 20 lbm. If a constant torque of 60 lb-ft is developed in the motor, what distance does the device A travel in 2 seconds? Neglect the inertia of the small wheels under A.

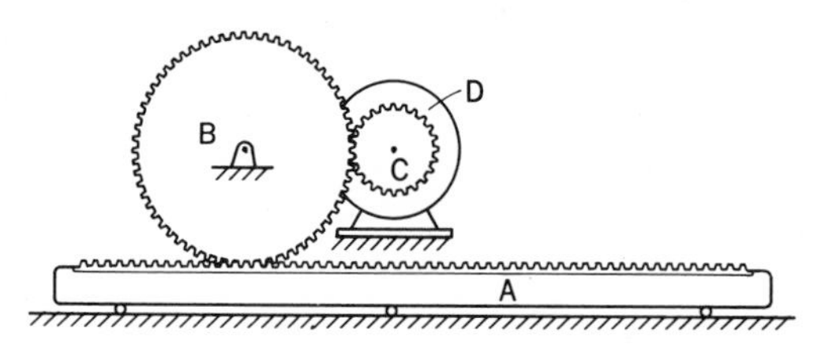

Fig. 17.102

82. [17.6] Do the preceding problem for a torque which increases linearly with time at the rate of 30 ft-lb/sec during the first 2 seconds. Take the torque to be zero at $t = 0$.

83. [17.6] A bar C weighing 100 lb rolls on cylinders A and B, each weighing 50 lb (Fig. 17.103). What is the acceleration of bar C when the 20-lb load is applied as shown?

84. [17.6] In the previous problem what position of the bar relative to the wheels does slipping first occur after the load is applied? Take $\mu_s = 0.8$ for the bottom contact surface and $\mu_s = 0.1$ for the contact surface between bar and cylinders.

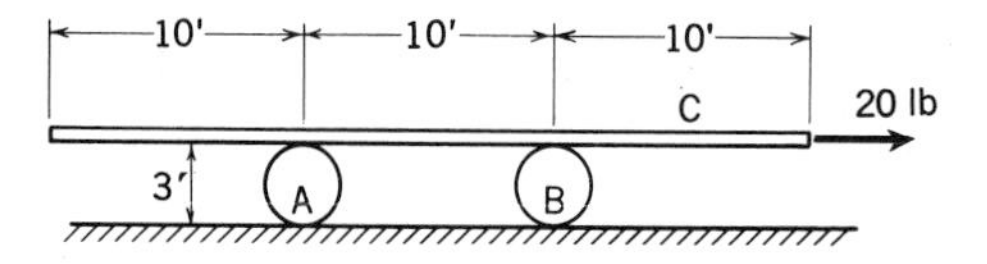

Fig. 17.103

85. [17.6] A plunger A is shown in Fig. 17.104 connected to two identical gears B and C, each weighing 10 lb. The plunger weighs 40 lb. How far does the plunger drop in 1 second if released from rest?

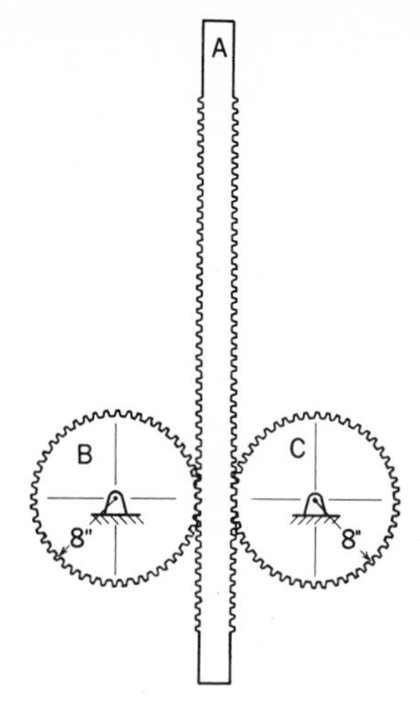

Fig. 17.104

86. [17.6] A platform B, of weight 30 lb and carrying block A of weight 100 lb, rides on gears D and E as shown in Fig. 17.105. If each gear weighs 30 lb, what distance will the upper system move in 1 second after the application of a 100-lb force as shown?

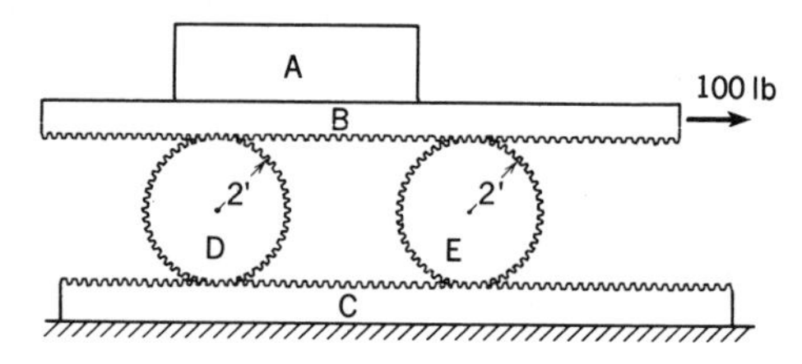

Fig. 17.105

87. [17.6] A steam roller is shown going up a 5° grade in Fig. 17.106. Wheels A have a radius of gyration of 1.5 ft and a weight each of 500 lb, while roller B has a radius of gyration of 1 ft and a weight of 5,000 lb. The vehicle minus wheels and roller has a weight of 7,000 lb with a center of mass shown in the diagram as $C.M.$ If the steam roller is to accelerate at the rate of 1 ft/sec^2, what torque must be developed by the drive wheels A? What torque must the engine develop?

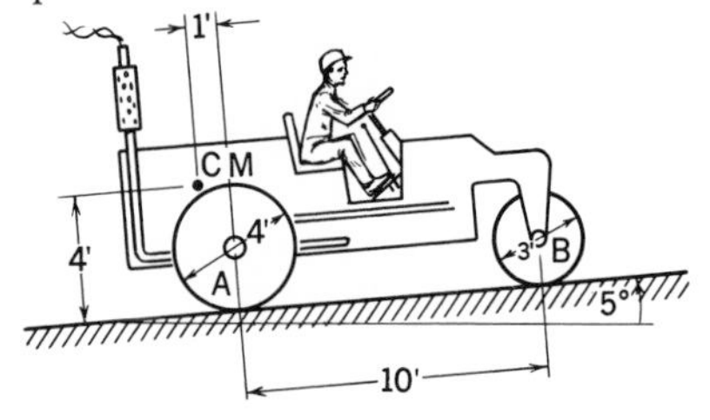

Fig. 17.106

88. [17.6] In the preceding problem what is the maximum acceleration up the incline, assuming that the machine could develop unlimited torque? Take $\mu = 0.6$.

89. [17.6] A cylinder weighing 100 lb with a radius of 1 ft moving on a conveyor is allowed to roll down the conveyor, which is moving with a uniform speed of 10 ft/sec (Fig. 17.107).

(a) How far down will the cylinder descend in 2 sec?

(b) If the conveyor belt is given a constant acceleration of 2 ft/sec/sec at the instant the cylinder is released, how far will it move in 3 sec?

(c) What acceleration is required of the belt to keep the cylinder at a constant elevation?

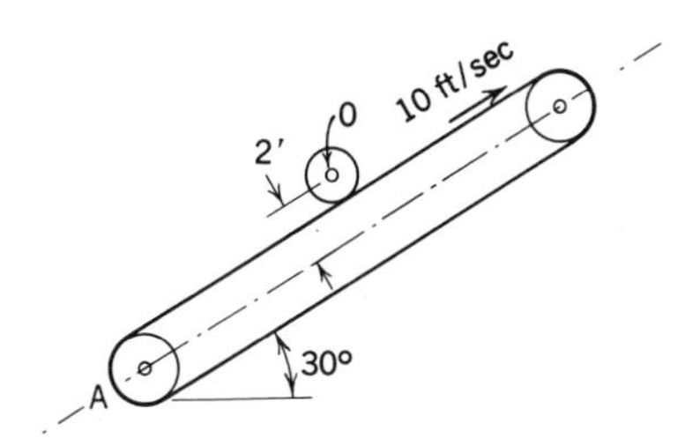

Fig. 17.107

90. [17.6] In Fig. 17.108, a cylinder weighing 100 lb with a radius of 1 ft rests on an incline, which is rotating at $\frac{1}{2}$ rad/sec. It is released when the incline is at position θ equal to 30°. If the cylinder is 20 ft from the bottom, A, at the instant of release, what is the initial acceleration of the center of the cylinder along the incline?

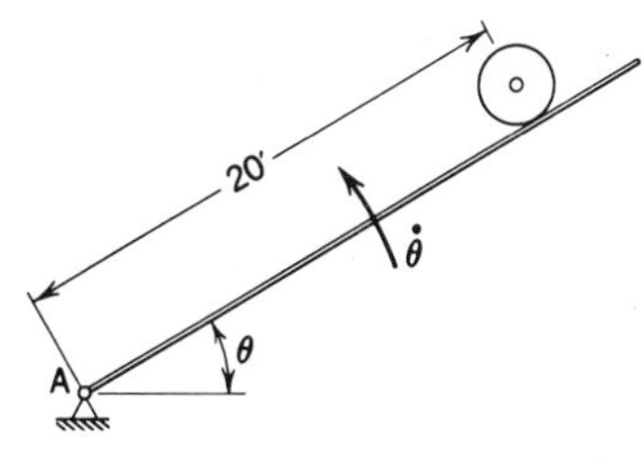

Fig. 17.108

91. [17.6] In Prob. 89, the cylinder is 20 ft from A and the conveyor is increasing its inclination at $\frac{1}{10}$ rad/sec. The conveyor belt is moving at 2 ft/sec along the conveyor frame. If the cylinder is released when the inclination is 30°, what is the initial acceleration of O along the conveyor (a) if the belt has a uniform speed along the conveyor frame of 2 ft/sec? (b) if the belt has a rate of change of speed of 4 ft/sec² and a speed of 2 ft/sec along the conveyor frame at the instant of interest?

92. [17.7] Do Prob. 60 using the D'Alembert principle.

93. [17.7] Do Prob. 62 using the D'Alembert principle.

94. [17.7] Do Prob. 65 using the D'Alembert principle.

95. [17.7] Do Prob. 76 using the D'Alembert principle.

96. [17.7] Do Prob. 90 using the D'Alembert principle.

97. [17.7] Do Prob. 14 using the D'Alembert principle.

98. [17.7] In Fig. 17.109, two identical bars, each weighing 20 lb, hang freely from the vertical. A force of 10 lb is applied at the center of the upper bar AB. What are the angular accelerations of the bars?

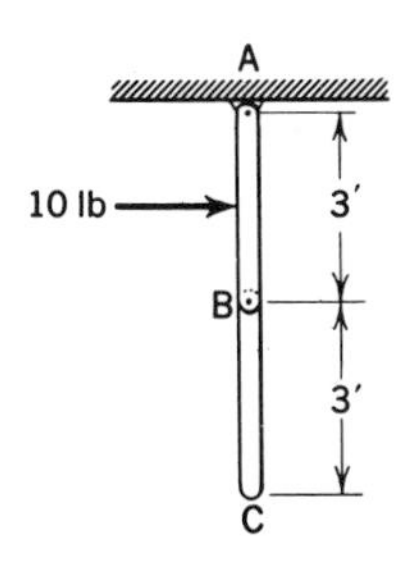

Fig. 17.109

99. [17.7] Identical bars AB and BC are pinned together by frictionless pins (Fig. 17.110). Each is 5 ft in length and weighs 20 lb. A force of 100 lb is exerted at C when the bars are inclined at 60°. What is the angular acceleration of the bars?

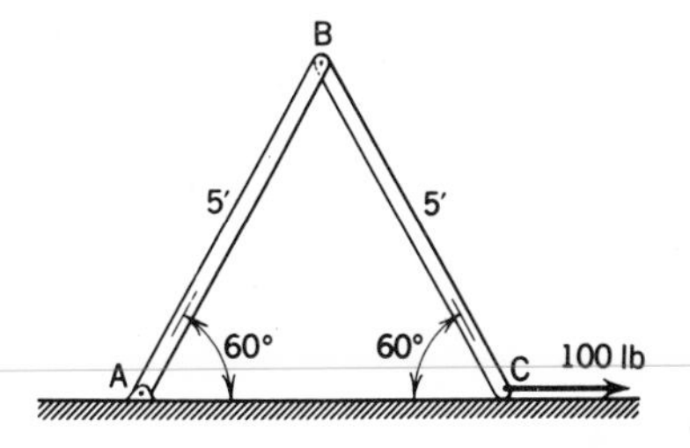

Fig. 17.110

100. [17.7] Do Prob. 78 using the D'Alembert principle and the method of virtual work.

101. [17.7] Do Prob. 87 using the D'Alembert principle and the method of virtual work.

18 Energy Considerations for Rigid Bodies

18.1 Kinetic Energy of a Rigid Body

In the last chapter, we studied Newton's law and the moment of momentum equations for a rigid body. We will now consider how to use energy methods as an alternative in handling rigid-body dynamics problems.

First, we will derive a convenient expression for the kinetic energy of a rigid body. We have already found (Section 13.7) that the kinetic energy of an aggregate of particles relative to any reference is the sum of two parts, which we will here list again:

a. The kinetic energy of a hypothetical particle that has a mass equal to the total mass of the system and a motion corresponding to that of the mass center of the system, plus

b. The kinetic energy of the particles relative to the mass center, as seen from the given reference.

Mathematically, this was given as:

$$KE = \frac{1}{2}M\,|\,\dot{\boldsymbol{r}}_c\,|^2 + \frac{1}{2}\sum_{i=1}^{n} m_i\,|\,\dot{\boldsymbol{\rho}}_i\,|^2 \qquad \mathbf{18.1}$$

where ϱ_i is the displacement vector from the mass center to the ith particle.

Let us now consider the above equation as applied to a rigid body which is a special "aggregate of particles" (Fig. 18.1). In such a case, the velocity of any particle relative to the mass center becomes:

$$\dot{\varrho}_i = \omega \times \varrho_i \qquad \textbf{18.2}$$

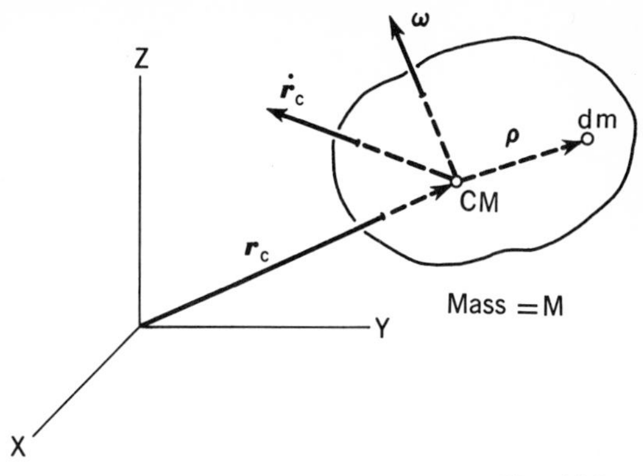

Fig. 18.1

where ω is the angular velocity of the body relative to reference XYZ in which we are computing the kinetic energy. The discrete particles of mass m_i become a continuum of infinitesimal particles each of mass dm, and the summation in Eq. 18.1 then becomes an integration. Thus we may say for the rigid body replacing $|\dot{r}_c|^2$ by V_c^2:

$$KE = \tfrac{1}{2}MV_c^2 + \tfrac{1}{2}\iiint_M |\omega \times \varrho|^2\, dm \qquad \textbf{18.3}$$

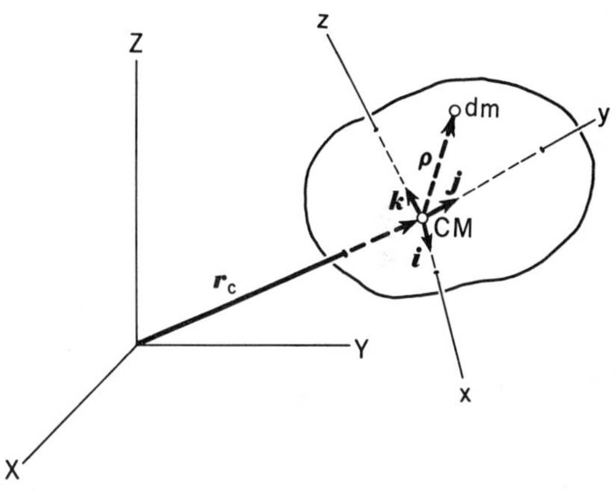

Fig. 18.2

where ϱ represents the displacement vector from the center of mass to any element of mass dm. Let us now choose a set of orthogonal directions xyz at the center of mass, so we can carry out the above integration in terms of the scalar components of ω and ϱ. This has been illustrated in Fig. 18.2. We may first express the integral in Eq. 18.3 in the following manner:

$$\iiint |\omega \times \varrho|^2\, dm = \iiint (\omega \times \varrho)\cdot(\omega \times \varrho)\, dm \qquad \textbf{18.4}$$

Inserting the scalar components, we get:

$$\iiint |\omega \times \varrho|^2\, dm = \iiint [(\omega_x \boldsymbol{i} + \omega_y \boldsymbol{j} + \omega_z \boldsymbol{k}) \times (x\boldsymbol{i} + y\boldsymbol{j} + z\boldsymbol{k})]$$
$$\cdot [(\omega_x \boldsymbol{i} + \omega_y \boldsymbol{j} + \omega_z \boldsymbol{k}) \times (x\boldsymbol{i} + y\boldsymbol{j} + z\boldsymbol{k})]\, dm$$

Carrying out first the cross products and then the dot product in the integrand and collecting terms, we may form the following relation:

$$\iiint |\omega \times \varrho|^2\, dm = \omega_x^2 \iiint (z^2 + y^2)\, dm + \omega_y^2 \iiint (x^2 + z^2)\, dm$$
$$+ \omega_z^2 \iiint (x^2 + y^2)\, dm - 2\omega_x\omega_z \iiint xz\, dm$$
$$- 2\omega_y\omega_z \iiint yz\, dm - 2\omega_x\omega_y \iiint xy\, dm \qquad \textbf{18.5}$$

You will recognize that the integrals are the components of the inertia tensor for the xyz reference. Thus:

$$\iiint_M |\boldsymbol{\omega} \times \boldsymbol{\rho}|^2 \, dm = I_{xx}\omega_x^2 + I_{yy}\omega_y^2 + I_{zz}\omega_z^2 - 2\omega_x\omega_z I_{xz} - 2\omega_y\omega_z I_{yz} - 2\omega_x\omega_y I_{xy} \quad \mathbf{18.6}$$

We can now give the kinetic energy of a rigid body in the following form:

$$KE = \tfrac{1}{2}MV_c^2 + \tfrac{1}{2}[I_{xx}\omega_x^2 + I_{yy}\omega_y^2 + I_{zz}\omega_z^2 - 2\omega_x\omega_y I_{xy} - 2\omega_x\omega_z I_{xz} - 2\omega_y\omega_z I_{yz}] \quad \mathbf{18.7}$$

Since the dot product $\boldsymbol{\omega} \cdot \boldsymbol{H}_c$ equals the large bracketed set of terms, as you can readily demonstrate using Eq. 17.9, a more compact form for the kinetic energy of a rigid body is:

$$KE = \tfrac{1}{2}MV_c^2 + \tfrac{1}{2}(\boldsymbol{\omega} \cdot \boldsymbol{H}_c) \quad \mathbf{18.8}$$

Note that the first expression on the right side of the above equation gives the kinetic energy of translation of the rigid body while the second expression gives the kinetic energy of rotation of the rigid body about its center of mass. If principal axes are chosen, Eq. 18.7 becomes:

$$KE = \tfrac{1}{2}MV_c^2 + \tfrac{1}{2}(I_{xx}\omega_x^2 + I_{yy}\omega_y^2 + I_{zz}\omega_z^2) \quad \mathbf{18.9}$$

Note that for this condition the kinetic energy terms for rotation have the same form as the kinetic energy term that is due to translation, with the moment of inertia corresponding to mass and angular velocity corresponding to linear velocity.

18.2 Kinetic Energy of a Body in Pure Rotation

In the last section, we computed the kinetic energy of a rigid body that has any motion in terms of the motion of and about the mass center and the inertia tensor at the mass center. We will now consider the special case of a body that has at time t a pure rotation in some reference XYZ about an instantaneous axis of rotation. We will compute the kinetic energy at time t for the reference, using the inertia tensor components of the body at any position O along the axis of rotation, as is shown in Fig. 18.3. The kinetic energy of the body at this instant relative to XYZ can then be evaluated as:

$$KE = \tfrac{1}{2}\iiint_M V^2 \, dm = \tfrac{1}{2}\iiint_M |\boldsymbol{\omega} \times \boldsymbol{r}|^2 \, dm \quad \mathbf{18.10}$$

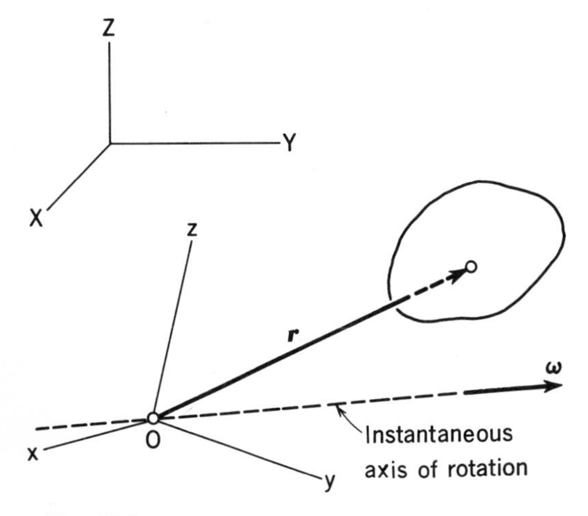

Fig. 18.3

By selecting any reference xyz that has its origin

at O at time t, we can evaluate the above integral in terms of components along these axes to get:

$$KE = \tfrac{1}{2}(\omega_x^2 I_{xx} + \omega_y^2 I_{yy} + \omega_z^2 I_{zz} - 2\omega_x\omega_y I_{xy} - 2\omega_x\omega_z I_{xz} - 2\omega_y\omega_z I_{yz}) = \tfrac{1}{2}(\boldsymbol{\omega}\cdot\boldsymbol{H}_0) \qquad \textbf{18.11}$$

where $\boldsymbol{H}_0$ is the moment of momentum about O, as seen from XYZ.

If the xyz axes coincide with the principal axes of the body at O, we have:

$$KE = \tfrac{1}{2}(I_{xx}\omega_x^2 + I_{yy}\omega_y^2 + I_{zz}\omega_z^2) \qquad \textbf{18.12}$$

In freshman physics we learned that the kinetic energy of a body rotating about a fixed axis, as shown in Fig. 18.4, is given as:

$$KE = \frac{I\omega^2}{2} \qquad \textbf{18.13}$$

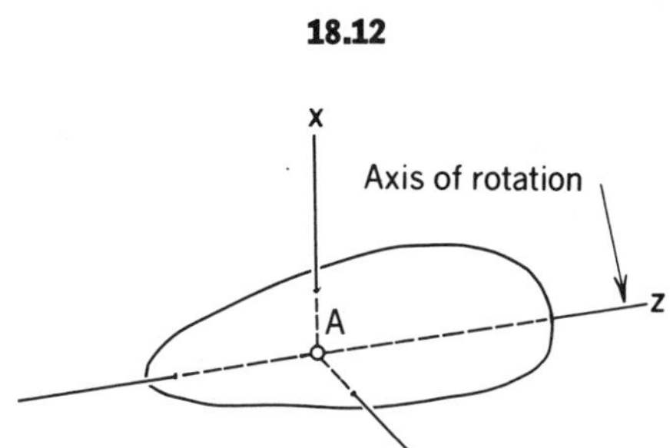

Fig. 18.4

Let us see how the general equation for kinetic energy of rotation degenerates to this result. Consider any point A along the axis of rotation and set up a reference xyz so that the z axis coincides with the axis of rotation. Clearly, $\omega_x = \omega_y = 0$. Thus, going to Eq. 18.11, we have:

$$KE = \tfrac{1}{2}\omega_z^2 I_{zz} \qquad \textbf{18.14}$$

which corresponds to the formula from physics.

EXAMPLE 18.1

Compute the kinetic energy of the crank system at the configuration shown in Fig. 18.5. Piston A weighs 2 lb, rod AB is 2 ft long and weighs 5 lb, and flywheel C weighs 100 lb with a radius of gyration of 1.2 ft. The radius r is 1 ft. At the instant of interest piston A moves to the right at a speed V of 10 ft/sec.

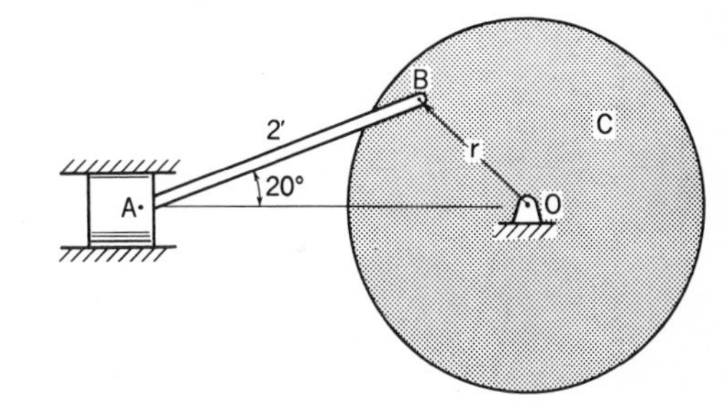

Fig. 18.5

We have here a translatory motion (piston A), a plane motion (rod AB) and a pure rotation (flywheel C). Thus for piston A we have for the kinetic energy:

$$(KE)_A = \frac{1}{2}MV^2 = \frac{1}{2}\left(\frac{2}{32.2}\right)(10^2) = 3.10 \text{ ft-lb} \qquad \textbf{(a)}$$

As for the rod AB we must first enter into kinematical considerations. For this purpose we have shown rod AB again in Fig. 18.6, where V_A is the known velocity of point A and V_B is the velocity vector for point B oriented at an angle α. We can readily find α for the configuration of interest by trigonometric considerations of triangle ABO. To do this we use the law of sines to first compute the angle β. Thus:

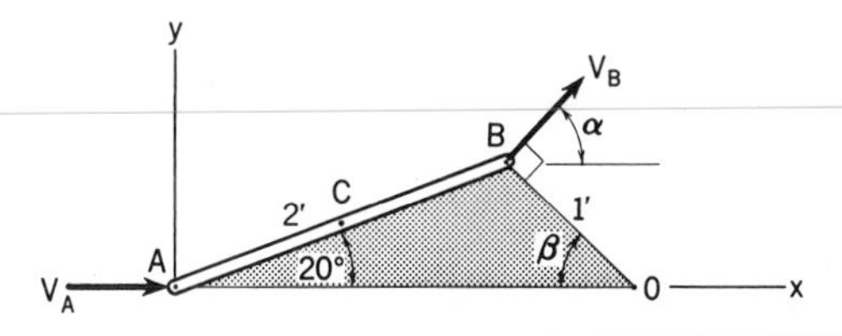

Fig. 18.6

$$\frac{2}{\sin\beta} = \frac{1}{\sin 20°}$$

$$\therefore\ \beta = 43.2° \qquad \textbf{(b)}$$

Because V_B is at right angles to OB, we have for the

angle α:

$$\alpha = 90° - \beta = 46.8° \qquad \textbf{(c)}$$

From kinematics of a rigid body we can now say:

$$\boldsymbol{V}_B = \boldsymbol{V}_A + (\omega_{AB}\boldsymbol{k}) \times \boldsymbol{\rho}_{AB}$$

$$V_B(\cos\alpha\boldsymbol{i} + \sin\alpha\boldsymbol{j}) = 10\boldsymbol{i} + \omega_{AB}\boldsymbol{k} \times (2\cos 20°\boldsymbol{i} + 2\sin 20°\boldsymbol{j})$$

$$V_B(0.684\boldsymbol{i} + 0.730\boldsymbol{j}) = 10\boldsymbol{i} + 1.88\omega_{AB}\boldsymbol{j} - 0.684\omega_{AB}\boldsymbol{i} \qquad \textbf{(d)}$$

From this we solve for ω_{AB} and V_B. Thus:

$$V_B = 10.52 \text{ ft/sec}$$

$$\omega_{AB} = 4.1 \text{ rad/sec} \qquad \textbf{(e)}$$

To get the velocity of the mass center C we proceed as follows:

$$\boldsymbol{V}_C = \boldsymbol{V}_A + (\omega_{AB}\boldsymbol{k}) \times \boldsymbol{\rho}_{AC}$$

$$\therefore \boldsymbol{V}_C = 10\boldsymbol{i} + 4.1\boldsymbol{k} \times (0.94\boldsymbol{i} + 0.342\boldsymbol{j})$$

$$= 10\boldsymbol{i} + 3.85\boldsymbol{j} - 1.40\boldsymbol{i} = 8.60\boldsymbol{i} + 3.85\boldsymbol{j} \qquad \textbf{(f)}$$

We can now give $(KE)_{AB}$, the kinetic energy of the rod. Noting that the only nonzero component of $\boldsymbol{\omega}_{AB}$ is the z direction, we have:

$$(KE)_{AB} = \tfrac{1}{2}M_{AB}V_c^2 + \tfrac{1}{2}I_{zz}\omega_{AB}^2$$

$$= \frac{1}{2}\left(\frac{5}{32.2}\right)(8.60^2 + 3.85^2)$$

$$+ \frac{1}{2}\left(\frac{1}{12}\frac{5}{32.2}2^2\right)(4.1^2)$$

$$= 7.37 \text{ ft-lb} \qquad \textbf{(g)}$$

Finally we consider the flywheel C. The angular speed ω_C can easily be computed using V_B of Eq. (e). Thus:

$$\omega_C = \frac{10.52}{1} = 10.52 \text{ rad/sec} \qquad \textbf{(h)}$$

Accordingly, we get for $(KE)_C$:

$$(KE)_C = \frac{1}{2}\left(\frac{100}{32.2}\right)(1.2^2)(10.52^2) = 247 \text{ ft-lb} \qquad \textbf{(i)}$$

The total kinetic energy of the system may now be given as:

$$KE = (KE)_A + (KE)_{AB} + (KE)_C$$

$$= 3.10 + 7.37 + 247 = 257 \text{ ft-lb} \qquad \textbf{(j)}$$

EXAMPLE 18.2

Compute the kinetic energy of a right circular cone shown in Fig. 18.7 rolling without slipping such that the centerline rotates about the Z axis at a rate ω_1 of 2 radians per second. The height h of the cone is 2 ft and the radius r at the base is $\frac{1}{2}$ ft. The weight W of the cone is 100 lb.

Our first step is to compute the total angular velocity of the cone. Because of the no-slipping condition we know that the axis of rotation lies along the line of contact. Accordingly $\boldsymbol{\omega}$ must be in the negative Y direction at the instant of interest for this case. We can then say:

$$\omega_1 \boldsymbol{k} - \omega_2 (\cos \alpha \boldsymbol{j} + \sin \alpha \boldsymbol{k}) = -\omega \boldsymbol{j}$$

$$\therefore\ 2\boldsymbol{k} - \omega_2(0.969\boldsymbol{j} + 0.243\boldsymbol{k}) = -\omega \boldsymbol{j}$$

We can now solve for ω_2 and ω from the above equation. Thus:

$$\omega_2 = 8.24 \text{ rad/sec}$$

$$\omega = 7.98 \text{ rad/sec} \qquad \textbf{(a)}$$

As a next step we compute the velocity of the mass center C. Accordingly, we have:

$$\boldsymbol{V}_C = \boldsymbol{V}_B + \boldsymbol{\omega} \times \boldsymbol{\rho}_{BC}$$

$$\therefore\ \boldsymbol{V}_C = \boldsymbol{0} + (-7.98\boldsymbol{j}) \times (\tfrac{3}{4}h)(\cos \alpha \boldsymbol{j} + \sin \alpha \boldsymbol{k})$$

$$= -(7.98)(\tfrac{3}{4})(2)(0.243\boldsymbol{i}) = -2.91\boldsymbol{i} \text{ ft/sec} \qquad \textbf{(b)}$$

Choosing a principal set of axes xyz at C, we now compute moments of inertia of the body, employing formulae to be found in the appendix. Thus:

$$I_{xx} = I_{zz} = \frac{3}{20}\frac{W}{g_0}\left(r^2 + \frac{h^2}{4}\right) = \frac{3}{20}\left(\frac{100}{32.2}\right)\left(\frac{1}{4} + \frac{4}{4}\right)$$

$$= 0.583 \text{ slug-ft}^2$$

$$I_{yy} = \frac{3}{10}\frac{W}{g_0} r^2 = \frac{3}{10}\left(\frac{100}{32.2}\right)\left(\frac{1}{4}\right)$$

$$= 0.233 \text{ slug-ft}^2 \qquad \textbf{(c)}$$

The kinetic energy of the body may now be computed using Eq. 18.7.

$$KE = \frac{1}{2}\left(\frac{100}{g_0}\right)(2.91^2)$$

$$+ \tfrac{1}{2}[0.583\omega_x^2 + 0.233\omega_y^2 + 0.583\omega_z^2]$$

Noting that

$$\omega_x = 0$$

$$\omega_y = -7.98 \cos \alpha = -7.73 \text{ rad/sec}$$

$$\omega_z = 7.98 \sin \alpha = 1.945 \text{ rad/sec} \qquad \textbf{(d)}$$

we get:

$$KE = 13.12 + 8.05 = 21.2 \text{ ft-lb} \qquad \textbf{(e)}$$

If we choose point B to set up principal axes (point B always lies along the axes of rotation), we proceed as follows. The principal moments of inertia at B are computed as:

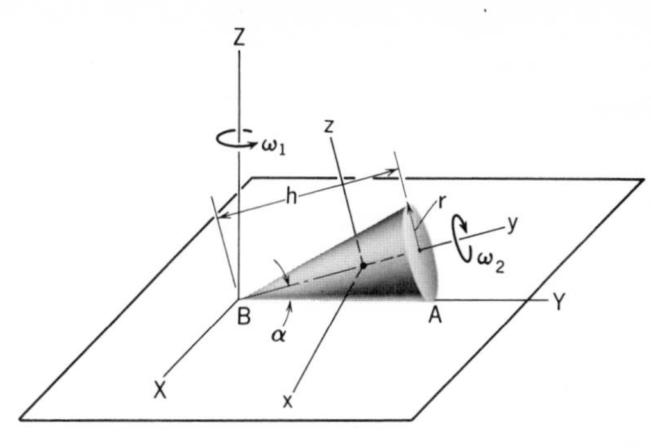

Fig. 18.7

$$I_{xx} = I_{zz} = \frac{3}{5}\left(\frac{W}{g_0}\right)\left(\frac{1}{4}r^2 + h^2\right) = \frac{3}{5}\left(\frac{100}{32.2}\right)\left(\frac{1}{16} + 4\right)$$

$$= 7.57 \text{ slugs-ft}^2$$

$$I_{yy} = \frac{3}{10}\frac{W}{g_0}r^2 = \left(\frac{3}{10}\right)\left(\frac{100}{32.2}\right)\left(\frac{1}{4}\right)$$

$$= 0.233 \text{ slug-ft}^2 \quad \textbf{(f)}$$

Employing Eq. 18.12, the kinetic energy becomes:

$$KE = \tfrac{1}{2}[(7.57)\omega_x^2 + (0.233)\omega_y^2 + (7.57)\omega_z^2]$$

$$= 21.2 \text{ ft-lb} \quad \textbf{(g)}$$

18.3 Energy Formulations for Conservative Systems

The preceding formulations may be used most effectively in problems involving only conservative forces. You will recall from Chapter 13 that under such conditions the law of conservation of mechanical energy is valid for motion relative to an *inertial reference for any aggregate of particles.*

Having computed the kinetic energy of a rigid body, we will next compute the potential energy of a rigid body due to gravity so that we will be able to employ the conservation of mechanical energy equation effectively for rigid bodies. Using some arbitrary datum plane parallel to the ground and denoting the elevation to the particles from the datum plane with the symbol z, as shown in Fig. 18.8, we can then say for any aggregate of particles:

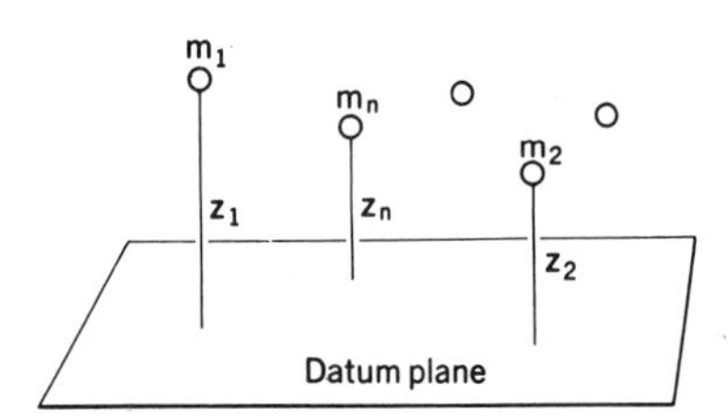

Fig. 18.8

$$PE = \sum_i m_i g z_i \qquad \textbf{18.15}$$

and for a rigid body, this becomes:

$$PE = \iiint_M gz\,dm \qquad \textbf{18.16}$$

Taking g as constant, we see that the potential energy of the rigid body can be given as:

$$PE = g\iiint_M z\,dm = gMz_c = Wz_c \qquad \textbf{18.17}$$

and thus we need only consider the position of the mass center in computing potential energies due to gravity. We shall now consider several examples that illustrate the rule of conservation of mechanical energy in the case of rigid bodies.

EXAMPLE 18.3

A cylinder of radius a rolls with no slipping from a position of rest down an incline of angle β (Fig. 18.9). After the center has descended a height of h, what is the angular velocity of the cylinder?

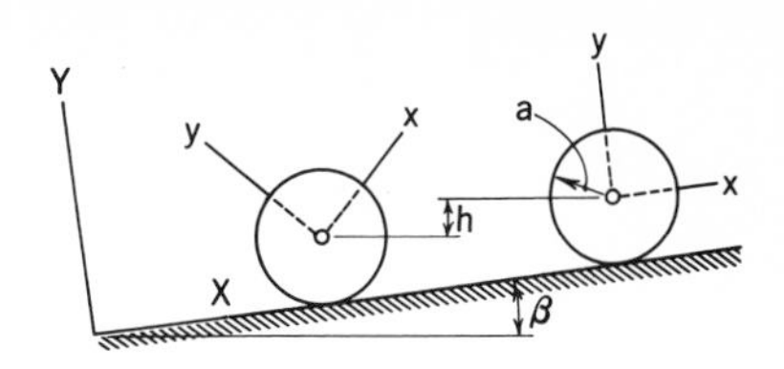

Fig. 18.9

Although a friction force is present, it does no work at any time, since it is never moving as a result of the no-slipping requirement. The normal forces from the plane also do no work, leaving only the action of gravity, which we know stems from a conservative force field. Clearly we may apply the conservation of mechanical energy principle.

A principal set of axes fixed to the body at the mass center has been shown. Using the final position of the mass center as the datum for potential energy and noting that ω_x and ω_y are zero, we have for the conservation of mechanical energy.

$$0 + Mgh = [\tfrac{1}{2}M\dot{X}^2 + \tfrac{1}{2}I_{zz}\omega_z^2] + 0 \qquad \textbf{(a)}$$

Here we have two unknowns in the equation, ω_z and $\dot{X}$. By employing the no-slipping condition at the point of contact, B, we will introduce a second equation.

$$\dot{X} = -\omega_z a$$

$$\therefore\ \dot{X}^2 = \omega_z^2 a^2 \qquad \textbf{(b)}$$

Substituting into Eq. (a) and solving for ω_z, we get:

$$\omega_z = \left[\frac{Mgh}{\frac{1}{2}(Ma^2 + I_{zz})}\right]^{1/2} \qquad \textbf{(c)}$$

We could have chosen points along the line of contact on the incline at the initial and final positions for computing kinetic energies, since the body is instantaneously in rotation about these lines. Consequently, by choosing principal axes as shown in Fig. 18.10, we can compute the kinetic energies from Eq. 18.12. We can then say:

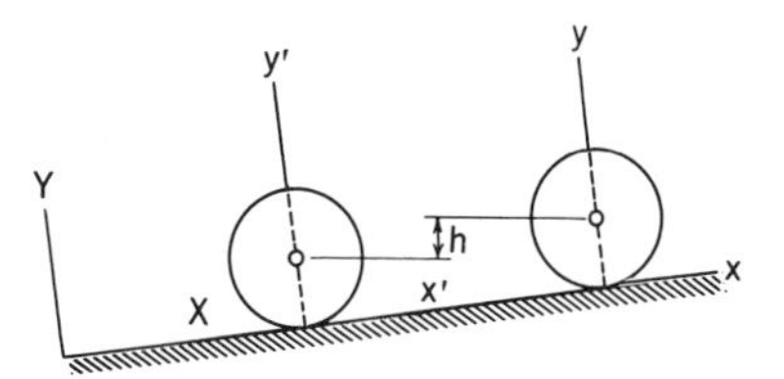

Fig. 18.10

$$0 + Mgh = \tfrac{1}{2}\omega_{z'}^2 I_{z'z'} + 0$$

$$\therefore\ \omega_{z'} = \left(\frac{Mgh}{\frac{1}{2}I_{z'z'}}\right)^{1/2} \qquad \textbf{(d)}$$

Using the transfer theorem for moments of inertia, we see that the angular velocities ω_z and $\omega_{z'}$ are equal, as was to be expected.

In the previous problem we considered a single rigid body. Clearly, we may also consider the conservation theorem for a system of rigid bodies if the connections between these bodies are frictionless and if only conservative external and internal forces perform work on the bodies. The next example illustrates such a case.

EXAMPLE 18.4

Two rods AB and BD are of equal length l and are connected by a frictionless pin at B (Fig. 18.11). Rod AB is held to the vertical wall by a frictionless

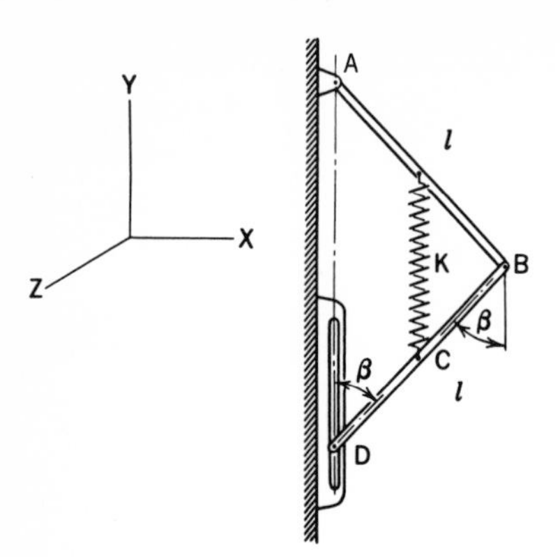

Fig. 18.11

pin connection at A, and BD rides in a frictionless slot at D. The rods each have a weight W and are connected at their midpoints by a spring having a spring constant K. When the bars make an angle β_0 with the vertical wall, the spring is unstretched. If the system is released from such a configuration, what will be the angular velocity of the bars when the bars have reached an angle β with the vertical?

Since only conservative forces are acting on this system, we can use the conservation of mechanical energy theorem. Furthermore, the motion is confined to plane XY. A quick observation reveals that since pin D moves along a straight line AD and since the bars are of equal length, an isosceles triangle is always maintained and both bars have the same angular variation $d\beta/dt$.

Let us accordingly compute the kinetic energy of the bars in terms of β and $\dot{\beta}$. Bar AB is at all times in pure rotation about an axis parallel to Z at fixed point A, so we may say:

$$(KE)_{AB} = \tfrac{1}{2}(I_{zz})_A\dot{\beta}^2 \tag{a}$$

Since bar BD is in plane motion, we can say:

$$(KE)_{BD} = \frac{1}{2}\frac{W}{g}V_c^2 + \frac{1}{2}(I_{zz})_c\dot{\beta}^2 \tag{b}$$

We shall next determine V_c^2 in terms of β and $\dot{\beta}$ by kinematical considerations. Note first that the velocity $\boldsymbol{V}_B$ of point B is easily computed in terms of β and $\dot{\beta}$ by considering the rotation of bar AB. Furthermore, we can say, using this $\boldsymbol{V}_B$:

$$\boldsymbol{V}_c = \boldsymbol{V}_B + \boldsymbol{\omega}_{BD} \times \boldsymbol{\rho}_{BC} \tag{c}$$

If the angular variation $\dot{\beta}$ is a negative number (as it will be for this problem), the proper angular velocity vector for AB is $\dot{\beta}\boldsymbol{k}$ and the correct angular velocity vector for BD is $-\dot{\beta}\boldsymbol{k}$. The same formulations will result if a positive $\dot{\beta}$ is considered, as you can readily reason out yourself by using the previous diagram. Equation (c) thus becomes for this problem:

$$\boldsymbol{V}_c = \dot{\beta}\boldsymbol{k} \times (l\sin\beta\boldsymbol{i} - l\cos\beta\boldsymbol{j}) + (-\dot{\beta}\boldsymbol{k}) \times \left(-\frac{l}{2}\sin\beta\boldsymbol{i} - \frac{l}{2}\cos\beta\boldsymbol{j}\right) \tag{d}$$

Carrying out the cross products, we have:

$$\mathbf{V}_c = \dot{\beta}l\sin\beta\boldsymbol{j} + \dot{\beta}l\cos\beta\boldsymbol{i} + \frac{\dot{\beta}l\sin\beta}{2}\boldsymbol{j} - \frac{\dot{\beta}l\cos\beta}{2}\boldsymbol{i}$$

Collecting terms we get:

$$\boldsymbol{V}_c = \tfrac{3}{2}\beta l\sin\dot{\beta}\boldsymbol{j} + \tfrac{1}{2}\dot{\beta}l\cos\beta\boldsymbol{i}$$

The quantity V_c^2 is then:

$$V_c^2 = \frac{\dot{\beta}^2l^2}{4}(9\sin^2\beta + \cos^2\beta)$$

$$= \frac{\dot{\beta}^2l^2}{4}(1 + 8\sin^2\beta) \tag{e}$$

The kinetic energy for bar BD in accordance with Eq. (b) is then:

$$(KE)_{BD} = \frac{\dot{\beta}^2 l^2 W}{g}\left(\frac{1}{8} + \sin^2\beta\right) + \frac{1}{2}(I_{zz})_c\dot{\beta}^2 \qquad \textbf{(f)}$$

Simple trigonometric considerations give the stretch in the spring, δ, for an angle β as:

$$\begin{aligned}\delta &= (\tfrac{3}{2}l\cos\beta - \tfrac{3}{2}l\cos\beta_0) - (\tfrac{1}{2}l\cos\beta - \tfrac{1}{2}l\cos\beta_0)\\ &= l\,(\cos\beta - \cos\beta_0) \qquad \textbf{(g)}\end{aligned}$$

and thus the potential energy of the spring is:

$$(PE)_{\text{spring}} = \tfrac{1}{2}K\delta^2 = \tfrac{1}{2}Kl^2(\cos\beta - \cos\beta_0)^2 \qquad \textbf{(h)}$$

Finally, we must compute the potential energy change due to gravity. Using the position of the center of mass of AB at β_0 as the datum, we have for the bar AB:

$$(PE_{\text{gravity}})_{AB} = W\left(\frac{l}{2}\cos\beta_0 - \frac{l}{2}\cos\beta\right) \qquad \textbf{(i)}$$

Also for bar BD we have, using the position of its center of mass at β_0 as the datum:

$$(PE)_{BD} = W(\tfrac{3}{2}l\cos\beta_0 - \tfrac{3}{2}l\cos\beta) \qquad \textbf{(j)}$$

The conservation of mechanical energy can now be employed. At position β_0, we have no kinetic and no potential energy of the system and thus can say:

$$\begin{aligned}0 &= \frac{1}{2}(I_{zz})_A\dot{\beta}^2 + \frac{\dot{\beta}^2 l^2 W}{g}\left(\frac{1}{8} + \sin^2\beta\right) + \frac{1}{2}(I_{zz})_c\dot{\beta}^2\\ &\quad + W\frac{l}{2}(\cos\beta_0 - \cos\beta) + \frac{3}{2}Wl(\cos\beta_0 - \cos\beta)\\ &\quad + \tfrac{1}{2}Kl^2(\cos\beta - \cos\beta_0)^2\end{aligned}$$

Collecting terms and rearranging, we have:

$$\begin{aligned}&\left[\frac{1}{2}(I_{zz})_A + \frac{1}{2}(I_{zz})_c + \frac{Wl^2}{g}\left(\frac{1}{8} + \sin^2\beta\right)\right]\dot{\beta}^2\\ &\qquad = [2Wl - \tfrac{1}{2}Kl^2(\cos\beta - \cos\beta_0)]\\ &\qquad\qquad \times(\cos\beta - \cos\beta_0) \qquad \textbf{(k)}\end{aligned}$$

Solving for $\dot{\beta}$ and taking the negative root as pointed out earlier, we get:

$$\dot{\beta} = -\left[\frac{[2Wl - \frac{1}{2}Kl^2(\cos\beta - \cos\beta_0)](\cos\beta - \cos\beta_0)}{(I_{zz})_A/2 + (I_{zz})_c/2 + (Wl^2/g)(\frac{1}{8} + \sin^2\beta)}\right]^{1/2}$$

EXAMPLE 18.5

Shown in Fig. 18.12 is a disc of radius r equal to $\frac{1}{2}$ ft and weight W of 100 lb. The disc is made to roll over the edge AC and then down the inclined plane F without slipping. The disc is constrained by a rod AB of length $= 2$ ft held at A by a frictionless ball-joint connection. Neglecting the mass of the rod,

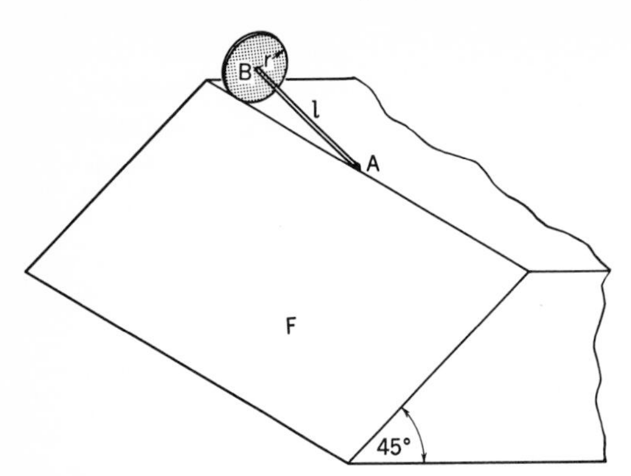

Fig. 18.12

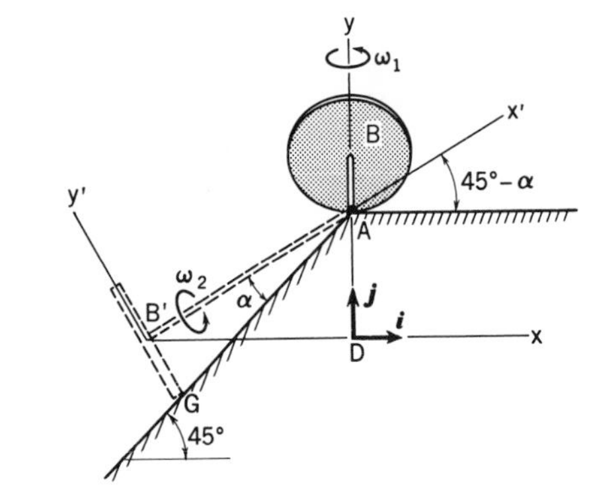

Fig. 18.13

what is the maximum angular speed that the disc can attain about the centerline of rod AB?

We have here a problem involving three-dimensional motion. Since the only force performing work is that of gravity, we can use the principle of conservation of mechanical energy. Clearly the maximum angular speed will be developed when the disc is at its lowest position. In Fig. 18.13 we have shown a side view of the disc at its starting position and at a position of maximum kinetic energy. The change in potential energy will first be computed. Note first that:

$$\tan \alpha = \frac{\frac{1}{2}}{2} = 0.250$$

$$\therefore \alpha = 14.05^\circ \tag{a}$$

The vertical distance of descent BD for the center of mass (see Fig. 18.13) can then be given as:

$$\begin{aligned}\overline{BD} &= l \sin \alpha + l \cos (45^\circ + \alpha) \\ &= 2(0.243 + 0.514) = 1.514 \text{ ft}\end{aligned} \tag{b}$$

The change in potential energy is:

$$\Delta(PE) = (1.514)(100) = 151.4 \text{ ft-lb} \tag{c}$$

Since the initial kinetic energy is zero, we can equate the maximum kinetic energy to the above change in potential energy. For this purpose we shall now enter into kinematical considerations.

The angular velocity of the centerline of the rod will be denoted as ω_1. At the instant of interest ω_1 is directed along the y direction, as shown in Fig. 18.13. The angular velocity of the disc about the rod we call ω_2 as shown in Fig. 18.13. Noting that the total angular velocity vector must lie along GA we get on summing the projections of ω_1 and ω_2 along a direction normal to GA:

$$-\omega_2 \sin \alpha + \omega_1 \cos 45^\circ = 0$$

$$\therefore \omega_1 = 0.345\, \omega_2 \tag{d}$$

Now, using principal axes $x'y'z'$ at B' as shown in the diagram, we may express the kinetic energy as:

$$\begin{aligned}KE &= \tfrac{1}{2}MV_B^2 + \tfrac{1}{2}I_{x'x'}\omega_{x'}^2 + \tfrac{1}{2}I_{y'y'}\omega_{y'}^2 + \tfrac{1}{2}I_{z'z'}\omega_{z'}^2 \\ &= \tfrac{1}{2}M\{l \cos (45^\circ - \alpha)\omega_1\}^2 \\ &\quad + \tfrac{1}{2}Mr^2[\omega_2 + \omega_1 \sin (45^\circ - \alpha)]^2 \\ &\quad + \tfrac{1}{4}Mr^2[\omega_1 \cos (45^\circ - \alpha)]^2 + \tfrac{1}{4}Mr^2(0)^2\end{aligned}$$

Collecting terms and putting in numerical values:

$$\begin{aligned}KE = \frac{1}{2}\left(\frac{100}{g_0}\right)\{&[2(0.859)\omega_1]^2 \\ &+ \tfrac{1}{4}(\omega_2 + 0.514\omega_1)^2 + \tfrac{1}{4}(0.859\omega_1)^2\}\end{aligned} \tag{e}$$

Replacing ω_1 by employing Eq. (d), we get:

$$KE = \frac{1}{2}\left(\frac{100}{g_0}\right)\{[(2)(0.859)(0.345\omega_2)]^2$$

$$+ \tfrac{1}{4}[\omega_2 + (0.514)(0.345)\omega_2]^2$$
$$+ \tfrac{1}{4}[(0.859)(0.345)(\omega_2)]^2\}$$
$$= 1.118\omega_2^2 \qquad \textbf{(f)}$$

Equating the above quantity with ΔPE from Eq. (c), we reach the desired result. Thus:

$$1.118\omega_2^2 = 151.4$$
$$\therefore \omega_2 = 11.6 \text{ rad/sec} \qquad \textbf{(g)}$$

---

*EXAMPLE 18.6

Shown in Fig. 18.14 is a uniform solid cylindrical rod AB connected to frictionless slider bearings which move along rods FC and ED. At B there is a ball-joint connection and at A there is a pin connection as illustrated in the diagram. If we neglect the mass and dimensions of the slider bearings, what is the velocity of connector B when, after being released from a state of rest at the position shown, it drops a distance of 8 ft? (This position is shown dashed.) The diameter of the rod is 2 in. and its weight is 100 lb.

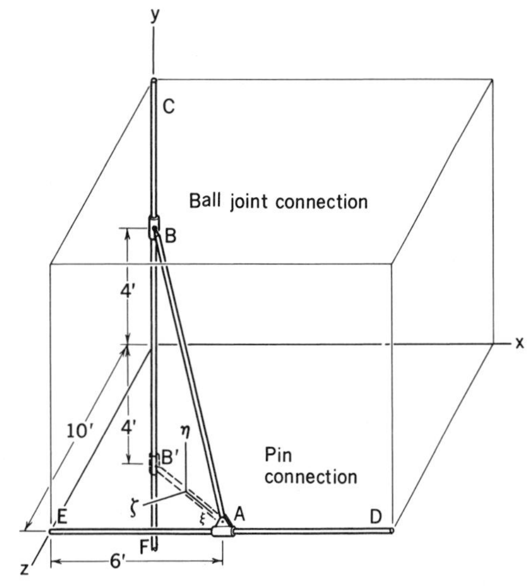

Fig. 18.14

Since the only force that does work is gravity, we can employ the conservation of mechanical energy principle. Clearly there is a loss in potential energy of $(100)(4) = 400$ ft-lb to be converted into kinetic energy.

Let us first examine the constraint on the velocity developed by the pin connection at A*. Clearly, rotation of bar AB in the plane EAB is permitted by the pin, and rotation is possible about the axis of ED as a result of the bearing itself. Those planes have been indicated as planes I and II in Fig. 18.15 for the configuration of interest for the problem. These planes are at right angles to each other and have unit normals given as follows:

Plane I:

$$\boldsymbol{n}_{\text{I}} = \frac{\overrightarrow{A'E} \times \overrightarrow{A'B'}}{(A'E)(A'B')} = \frac{(-6\boldsymbol{i}) \times (-6\boldsymbol{i} - 4\boldsymbol{j} - 10\boldsymbol{k})}{(6)(\sqrt{6^2 + 4^2 + 10^2})}$$

$$= \frac{24\boldsymbol{k} - 60\boldsymbol{j}}{(6)(12.3)} = -0.813\boldsymbol{j} + 0.325\boldsymbol{k}$$

Plane II:

$$\boldsymbol{n}_{\text{II}} = \boldsymbol{i} \qquad \textbf{(a)}$$

We now introduce plane III, which is normal respectively to planes I and II. Clearly we must preclude the possibility of a rotation component normal to plane III, since otherwise the pin connection would offer no rotational constraint whatsoever for rod $B'A'$. The unit normal vector for plane III is:

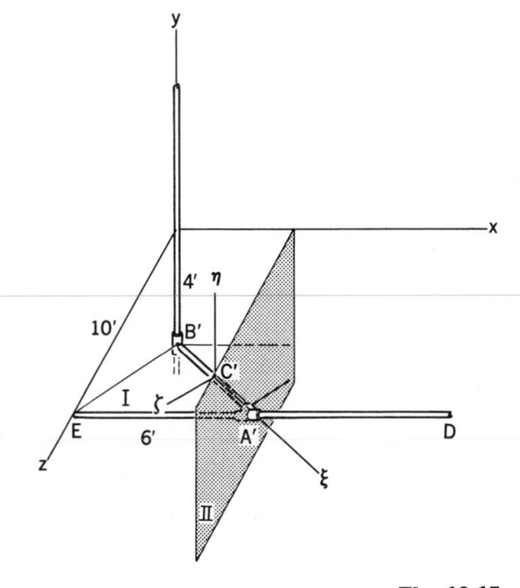

Fig. 18.15

* This kind of constraint was also discussed in Example 15.10.

$$n_{III} = n_I \times n_{II} = (-0.813j + 0.325k) \times i$$

$$\therefore n_{III} = 0.813k + 0.325j \qquad \textbf{(b)}$$

We can, accordingly, require that:

$$\omega \cdot n_{III} = 0$$

$$\therefore 0.325\omega_y + 0.813\omega_z = 0 \qquad \textbf{(c)}$$

We shall need to know the speed $V_{C'}$ of the center of mass. As can readily be seen by inspection of Fig. 18.15, we can give $V_{C'}$ in terms of $V_{A'}$ and $V_{B'}$ in the following simple manner:

$$V_{C'} = -\tfrac{1}{2}V_{A'}i - \tfrac{1}{2}V_{B'}j \qquad \textbf{(d)}$$

Furthermore, we can relate $V_{A'}$ and $V_{B'}$ to ω by the following equation from kinematics of rigid bodies:

$$V_{A'} = V_{B'} + \omega \times \rho_{A'B'}$$

which becomes:

$$-V_{A'}i = -V_{B'}j + (\omega_x i + \omega_y j + \omega_z k) \times (-6i - 4j - 10k)$$

The resulting scalar equations are:

$$-V_{A'} + 10\omega_y - 4\omega_z = 0 \qquad \textbf{(e)}$$

$$V_{B'} + 6\omega_z - 10\omega_x = 0 \qquad \textbf{(f)}$$

$$4\omega_x - 6\omega_y = 0 \qquad \textbf{(g)}$$

Enough for kinematics.

We now establish reference axes $\xi\eta\zeta$ at the center of mass at the configuration of interest (see Fig. 18.15) such that ξ is along the centerline of the rod and ζ is in plane I. Since these are principal axes, we have for kinetic energy of the rod:

$$KE = \tfrac{1}{2}MV_{C'}^2 + \tfrac{1}{2}I_{\xi\xi}\omega_\xi^2 + \tfrac{1}{2}I_{\eta\eta}(\omega_\eta^2 + \omega_\zeta^2) \qquad \textbf{(h)}$$

where we have used the fact that $I_{\eta\eta} = I_{\zeta\zeta}$. The angular velocity component ω_ξ is determined in terms of ω_x, ω_y, and ω_z as follows:

$$\omega_\xi = \omega \cdot \hat{\rho}_{B'A'} = (\omega_x i + \omega_y j + \omega_z k) \cdot \frac{6i + 4j + 10k}{12.3}$$

$$= 0.488\omega_x + 0.325\omega_y + 0.814\omega_z \qquad \textbf{(i)}$$

Also note that:

$$(\omega_\eta^2 + \omega_\zeta^2) = \omega^2 - \omega_\xi^2 = \omega_x^2 + \omega_y^2 + \omega_z^2 - (0.488\omega_x)^2 - (0.325\omega_y)^2 - (0.814\omega_z)^2 - 2(0.488)(0.325)\omega_x\omega_y - 2(0.488)(0.814)\omega_x\omega_z - 2(0.325)(0.814)\omega_y\omega_z$$

This becomes:

$$(\omega_\eta^2 + \omega_\zeta^2) = 0.760\omega_x^2 + 0.894\omega_y^2 + 0.335\omega_z^2 - 0.317\omega_x\omega_y - 0.795\omega_x\omega_z - 0.528\omega_y\omega_z \qquad \textbf{(j)}$$

Substituting from Eqs. (d), (i), and (j) into Eq. (h)

and equating the kinetic energy to the loss in potential energy, we get:

$$400 = \frac{1}{2}\left(\frac{100}{g}\right)\left(\frac{V_{A'}^2}{4} + \frac{V_{B'}^2}{4}\right)$$

$$+ \tfrac{1}{2}I_{\xi\xi}(0.488\omega_x + 0.325\omega_y + 0.814\omega_z)^2$$

$$+ \tfrac{1}{2}I_{\eta\eta}(0.760\omega_x^2 + 0.894\omega_y^2 + 0.335\omega_z^2$$

$$- 0.317\omega_x\omega_y - 0.795\omega_x\omega_z - 0.528\omega_y\omega_z)$$

Inserting the proper values for $I_{\xi\xi}$ and $I_{\eta\eta}$, we get, on collecting terms:

$$0.388V_{A'}^2 + 0.388V_{B'}^2 + 14.85\omega_x^2 + 17.49\omega_y^2 + 6.54\omega_z^2$$

$$- 6.14\omega_x\omega_y - 10.32\omega_y\omega_z$$

$$- 15.52\omega_x\omega_z = 400 \qquad \textbf{(k)}$$

Replacing $V_{A'}$ and $V_{B'}$ using Eqs. (e) and (f), we get:

$$0.388(10\omega_y - 4\omega_z)^2 + 0.388(-6\omega_z + 10\omega_x)^2$$

$$+ 14.85\omega_x^2 + 17.49\omega_y^2 + 6.54\omega_z^2 - 6.14\omega_x\omega_y$$

$$- 10.32\omega_y\omega_z - 15.52\omega_x\omega_z = 400 \qquad \textbf{(l)}$$

Collecting terms, we have:

$$53.6\omega_x^2 + 56.3\omega_y^2 + 26.9\omega_z^2 - 6.14\omega_x\omega_y$$

$$- 41.3\omega_y\omega_z - 62.1\omega_x\omega_z = 400 \qquad \textbf{(m)}$$

Now replace ω_z using Eq. (c) and ω_x using Eq. (g). Thus, collecting terms, we get:

$$279\omega_y^2 = 400 \qquad \textbf{(n)}$$

$$\therefore\ \omega_y = \pm 1.192 \text{ rad/sec}$$

From Eqs. (c) and (g) we get the other angular velocity components:

$$\omega_x = \pm 1.798 \text{ rad/sec}$$

$$\omega_z = \pm 0.477 \text{ rad/sec}$$

By physical reasoning we choose the lower of the set of signs in the preceding results. We then have the desired result $V_{B'}$ by employing Eq. (f). Thus:

$$V_{B'} = 10\omega_x - 6\omega_z = -17.98 + 2.86 = -15.12 \text{ ft/sec}$$

In the preceding examples we were able to solve for the desired unknown by a direct use of the energy equation. It must be remembered that this equation is a scalar equation and only one unknown can be determined from it. Thus, if the preceding problems had more than one degree of freedom, we would not be able to proceed with the simple use of the conservation of mechanical energy principle only. Newton's law, or the work-energy relation to be examined in the next section, for one or more of the bodies would have to be used in conjunction with the mechanical energy conservation statement.

18.4 Work-Energy Relations

We can extend the work-energy relation presented for a single particle to the case of a rigid body by summing these relations for all elements in the rigid body. In this way, we will be able to formulate energy relations for rigid bodies that are valid for conservative as well as for nonconservative forces. In Section 10.3 we saw that the virtual work of internal forces is zero for rigid bodies, and you should be able to show as an exercise by a similar argument that if Newton's third law is satisfied the work done by internal forces is always zero for any actual rigid body motion. We then compute the work done on a rigid body in moving from configuration I to configuration II by summing the work terms for all the external forces. Thus for the body shown in Fig. 18.16 we can express the work between I and II in the following manner:

$$(\text{work})_{\text{I,II}} = \int_{\substack{\text{I} \\ \text{path 1}}}^{\text{II}} \boldsymbol{F}_1 \cdot d\boldsymbol{s}_1 + \int_{\substack{\text{I} \\ \text{path 2}}}^{\text{II}} \boldsymbol{F}_2 \cdot d\boldsymbol{s}_2 + \cdots + \int_{\substack{\text{I} \\ \text{path } n}}^{\text{II}} \boldsymbol{F}_n \cdot d\boldsymbol{s}_n \qquad \textbf{18.18}$$

where, we must remember, the dot products of *nonconservative* forces are to be integrated over the *actual paths* along which the *points of application on the rigid body move,* taking into account variation of direction or magnitude of these forces along the paths.

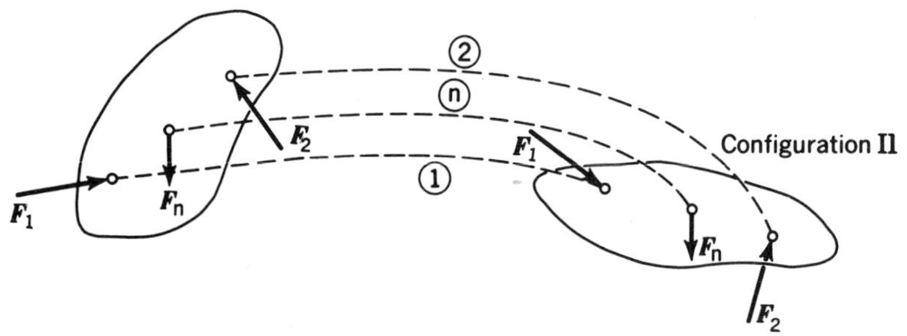

Fig. 18.16

Although we can treat couples as sets of discrete forces in the above manner, it is often useful to take advantage of the special properties of couples and to treat them separately. We have already shown in Chapter 10 that a torque rotating through an angle $\Delta\theta$ about its axis does work in the amount $T\ \Delta\theta$. Consider the more general case of the work done by a couple-moment $\boldsymbol{M}$ acting on a rigid body that moves from configuration I to II. Shown in Fig. 18.17 is the body at configuration I at time t. Using Chasle's theorem, we choose some point O along the line of action of either force of the couple and assume that the body has at the time t a velocity of translation $\boldsymbol{V}_o$. The axis of rotation of the body, then, must be considered as going through point O, as shown. The angular velocity vector $\boldsymbol{\omega}$ for time t is shown along this axis of rotation. Using this description of the motion,

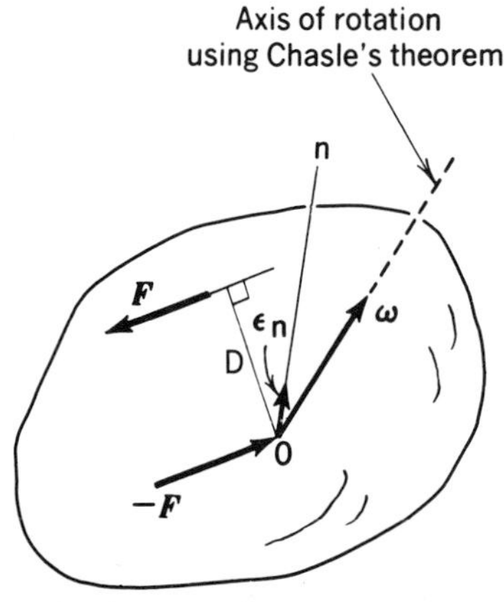

Fig. 18.17

we can say that the differential change in configuration during an elapse of time dt is a translational displacement $\boldsymbol{V}_o\, dt$ and a rotation $\boldsymbol{\omega}\, dt$. Clearly, we need only consider the rotation in order to evaluate the work done by the couple during this interval. The perpendicular to the line of action of $\boldsymbol{F}$ is drawn from O and is shown as D. It is easily seen that with this viewpoint only force $\boldsymbol{F}$ does work. We compute the work by first multiplying the component of the angular velocity in the direction *normal* to the plane of the couple by dt to get the differential rotation of the force $\boldsymbol{F}$ *in the plane of the couple* during the time interval dt. Thus:

$$d\theta = \boldsymbol{\omega}\cdot\boldsymbol{\varepsilon}_n\, dt$$

where $\boldsymbol{\varepsilon}_n$ is the unit vector normal to the plane of the couple. The rotations of the force stemming from the other orthogonal components of the angular velocity give the force no displacement whatsoever in the direction of the force; thus there is no work produced by the force from these rotations. By multiplying $d\theta$ by D, therefore, we get the only displacement in the direction of the force, and by multiplying by $|\boldsymbol{F}|$ we get the work during the time interval dt. Thus:

$$dW_K = |\boldsymbol{F}|\, D\, \boldsymbol{\omega}\cdot\boldsymbol{\varepsilon}_n\, dt$$

Since variations of the magnitude and direction of $\boldsymbol{F}$ and $\boldsymbol{\omega}$ during dt only bring in second-order terms, they are neglected in the above formulation. But $|\boldsymbol{F}|\, D$ is the magnitude of the couple-moment, that is, $|\boldsymbol{M}|$, and $\boldsymbol{\omega}\cdot\boldsymbol{\varepsilon}_n$ can be given as $|\boldsymbol{\omega}| \cos(\boldsymbol{\omega}, \boldsymbol{\varepsilon}_n)$, or, since $\boldsymbol{M}$ and $\boldsymbol{\varepsilon}_n$ are collinear, as $|\boldsymbol{\omega}| \cos(\boldsymbol{\omega}, \boldsymbol{M})$. Thus we can rewrite the above equation as:

$$dW_K = |\boldsymbol{M}|\, |\boldsymbol{\omega}| \cos(\boldsymbol{\omega}, \boldsymbol{M})\, dt$$

and, from the definition of the dot product, we then have the result:

$$dW_K = \boldsymbol{M}\cdot\boldsymbol{\omega}\, dt \qquad \textbf{18.19}$$

In going from configuration I to II, we can integrate the above expression:

$$W_{\text{I–II}} = \int_{\text{I}}^{\text{II}} \boldsymbol{M}\cdot\boldsymbol{\omega}\, dt \qquad \textbf{18.20}$$

The couple-moment $\boldsymbol{M}$ and $\boldsymbol{\omega}$ may have variations in going from I to II that must be accounted for during integration. You should be able to see how the simpler relation $T\,\Delta\theta$ is formulated from the more general Eq. 18.20.

We thus have formulations for ascertaining the work done by forces and couples. For the conservative forces, we know from Chapter 13 that we can use a quantity that is minus the change in potential energy from I to II as the work done by the conservative force from I to II without having to specify the path taken.

Using this information for computing work, we can then say for any rigid body:

work done by forces and couples from I to II

$$= \text{change in } KE \text{ from I to II} \qquad \textbf{18.21}$$

where we employ on the right side of the equation the formulations 18.7, 18.11, or any of the appropriate simplifications. In addition, we can extend this equation to include systems of rigid bodies.

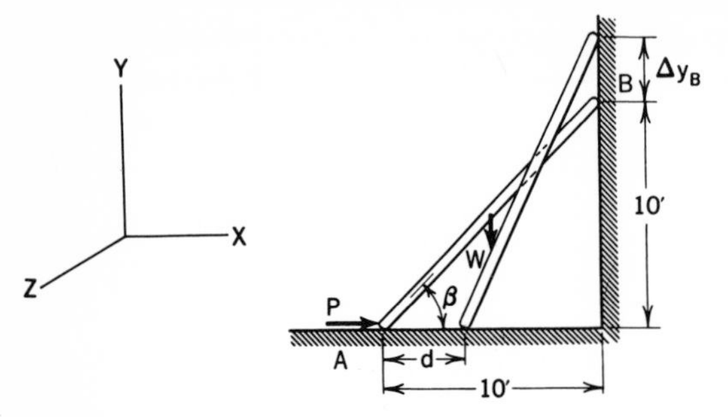

Fig. 18.18

EXAMPLE 18.7

A constant force P is exerted on a rod of weight W (Fig. 18.18). The rod is supported by frictionless walls. If the rod starts from a position of rest when $\beta = 45°$, as shown in the diagram, what is its angular speed $\dot{\beta}$ when the end A has moved a distance $d = 5$ ft?

Here we have a rigid body undergoing plane motion. By considering a set of axes at the center of mass where the z axis corresponds to the direction normal to the plane, we see that the expression for kinetic energy, Eq. 18.7, becomes:

$$KE = \tfrac{1}{2}MV_c^2 + \tfrac{1}{2}I_{zz}\omega_z^2 \qquad \textbf{(a)}$$

since $\omega_x = \omega_y = 0$. For a zero initial kinetic energy, the work-energy relation then becomes:

$$\text{work of forces } P \text{ and } W = \tfrac{1}{2}MV_c^2 + \tfrac{1}{2}I_{zz}\dot{\beta}^2 \qquad \textbf{(b)}$$

We must determine the distance that the weight W is raised and use kinematical relations to determine V_c in terms of $\dot{\beta}$ at the configuration corresponding to $d = 5$ ft. To find how far W is raised, we utilize the fact that the rod has a constant length, and from Fig. 18.18 it is clear that:

$$(10 - d)^2 + (10 + \Delta y_B)^2 = 200$$

Substituting for $d = 5$ ft and solving for Δy_B, we get:

$$\Delta y_B = 3.25 \text{ ft} \qquad \textbf{(c)}$$

Consequently, W rises one-half this value, i.e., 1.625 ft. Next, consider the rod in the configuration of interest shown in Fig. 18.19. We see by inspection that the velocity of the mass center can be given in terms of the velocity of the ends A and B:

$$\boldsymbol{V}_c = \frac{V_A}{2}\,\boldsymbol{i} + \frac{V_B}{2}\,\boldsymbol{j} \qquad \textbf{(d)}$$

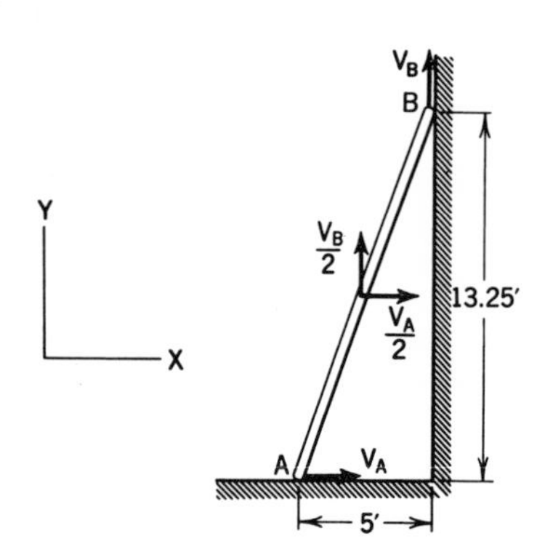

Fig. 18.19

Using Chasle's theorem to relate the velocity of the mass center and point A, we get:

$$\boldsymbol{V}_c = \frac{V_A}{2}\,\boldsymbol{i} + \frac{V_B}{2}\,\boldsymbol{j} = V_A\boldsymbol{i} + \dot{\beta}\boldsymbol{k} \times (2.5\boldsymbol{i} + 6.62\boldsymbol{j}) \qquad \textbf{(e)}$$

Solving, we find that $V_B/2 = 2.5\dot{\beta}$ and $V_A/2 = 6.62\dot{\beta}$. From Eq. (d) we then have:

$$V_c^2 = (2.5^2 + 6.62^2)\dot{\beta}^2 = 50\dot{\beta}^2 \qquad \textbf{(f)}$$

Using results (c) and (f), we can now reconsider Eq. (b):

$$5P - 1.625W = \frac{1}{2}\frac{W}{g}(50\dot{\beta}^2) + \frac{1}{2}(I_{zz})_c\dot{\beta}^2 \qquad \textbf{(g)}$$

With $(I_{zz})_c = 16.7(W/g)$ we can solve for $\dot{\beta}$ in the following manner:

$$\dot{\beta} = \left(4.83\,\frac{P}{W} - 1.57\right)^{1/2}$$

Before leaving this problem, we should point out that the angular velocity of the rod can be related to the velocity of the mass center in another effective manner. By extending perpendicular lines from the velocity vectors at A and B, as shown in Fig. 18.20, we locate the instantaneous center of rotation for the motion. It is then immediately apparent that:

$$V_B = 5\dot{\beta} \qquad \text{and} \qquad V_A = 13.25\dot{\beta}$$

and thus we say:

$$V_c^2 = \left(\frac{V_B}{2}\right)^2 + \left(\frac{V_A}{2}\right)^2 = (2.5^2 + 6.62^2)\dot{\beta}^2 = 50\dot{\beta}^2$$

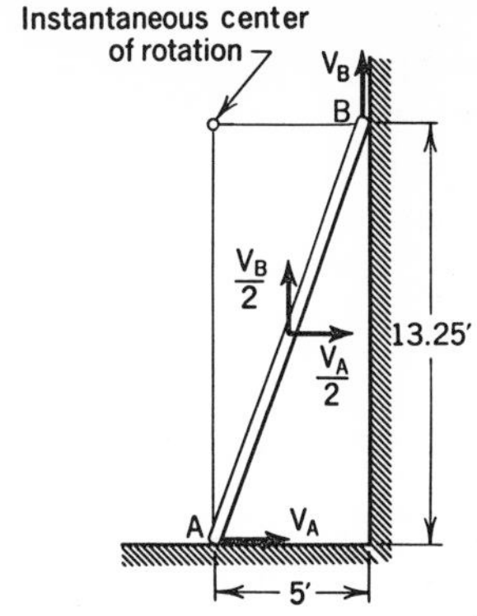

Fig. 18.20

*EXAMPLE 18.8

Suppose in Example 18.6 a 100-lb force acts at slider bearing B and a frictional force of 20 lb acts at slider bearing A. This has been shown in Fig. 18.21. What is the velocity of slider bearing A when B has dropped 8 ft?

We may use the formulation of Example 18.6 for the kinetic energy. All we need do is to compute the work done by the 100-lb force and the friction force. Clearly the contribution from the applied force is:

$$(W_{1-2})_{\text{I}} = (100)(8) = 800 \text{ ft-lb} \qquad \textbf{(a)}$$

To compute the work of the friction force, note that the slider bearing on which it acts moves to the right along ED, reaching an extreme position when $B'A'$ is in the horizontal plane xz as shown dashed in the diagram. The bearing A then starts to move back so that when B has dropped 8 ft, it returns to the starting position. The distance traveled is clearly $2\overline{AA'}$, and the work done by friction is then:

$$(W_{1-2})_{\text{II}} = -(20)(\overline{AA'}) \qquad \textbf{(b)}$$

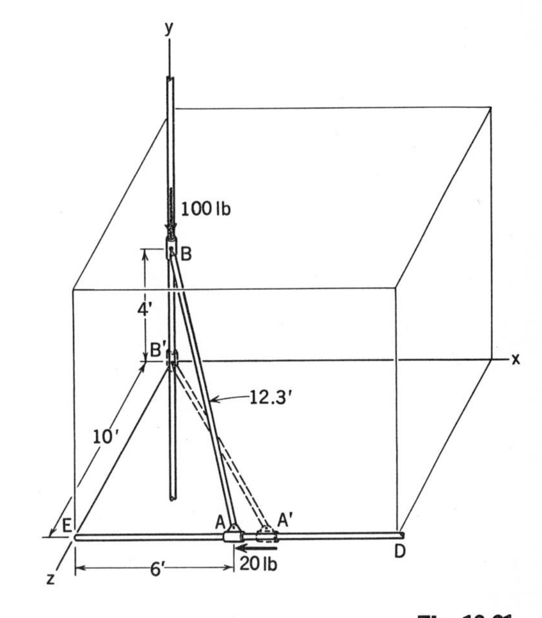

Fig. 18.21

To get $\overline{AA'}$ we note from the diagram that:

$$(EB')^2 + (EA')^2 = (12.3)^2$$

$$\therefore\ 10^2 + (6 + \overline{AA'})^2 = (12.3)^2 \qquad \textbf{(c)}$$

Solving for $\overline{AA'}$, we get:

$$\overline{AA'} = 1.21 \text{ ft} \qquad \textbf{(d)}$$

Hence:

$$(W_{1-2})_{\text{II}} = -24.2 \text{ ft-lb} \qquad \textbf{(e)}$$

The total work done including gravity is then:

$$(W_{1-2}) = 800 - 24.2 + 400 = 1176 \text{ ft-lb} \qquad \textbf{(f)}$$

Equating the work done with the change in kinetic energy, we get, using the left side of Eq. (n) of Example 18.6 for the latter:

$$279\omega_y^2 = 1176$$

$$\therefore \omega_y = \pm 2.05 \text{ rad/sec} \quad \textbf{(g)}$$

Using the kinematical results of Example 18.6, it is now a simple matter to evaluate ω_x and ω_z and then to get V_A. The final result is:

$$V_A = -53.4 \text{ ft/sec} \quad \textbf{(h)}$$

In the previous problems we considered the application of Eq. 18.21 to an individual rigid body. We may also employ this equation for a system of interconnected rigid bodies. In this regard, it is to be pointed out that for connectors that are frictionless and inextensible there is zero net work done by forces arising from such connectors. If there is friction present, there will again be no net work done by forces at connectors, provided there is no slippage between the various contact surfaces at the connectors. (Why?) In the following example, we consider a system of two interconnected bodies.

EXAMPLE 18.9

Shown in Fig. 18.22 is a drum A connected by an inextensible cord to a 200-lb block on a 30° incline. A flywheel B is connected to the drum. The combined weight of drum and flywheel is 400 lb, with a radius of gyration of 1.5 ft. The diameter D of the drum is 2 ft and the coefficient of dynamic friction between the block and inclined surface is 0.3. There is a frictional torque T on the drum-flywheel system of 5 lb-ft when it is rotating. What is the speed of the block when a 100-lb horizontal force is applied, as shown in the diagram, after the block has moved 10 ft down the incline starting from a stationary configuration?

The force system that will perform work consists of the resisting torque at the drum-flywheel, the force of friction along the incline, the 100-lb applied force, and the force of gravity. We shall compute each contribution separately for simplicity.

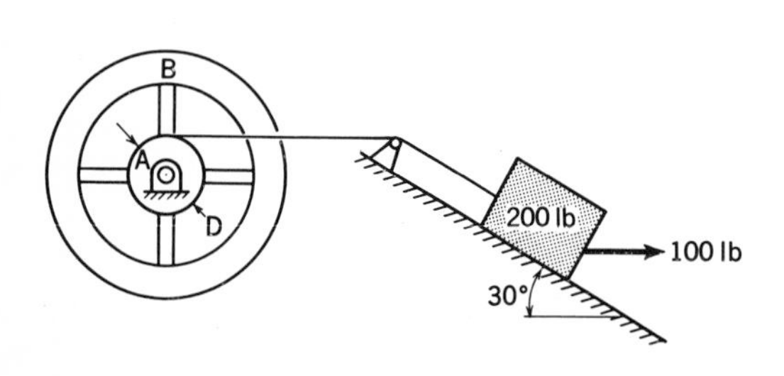

Fig. 18.22

(a) Resisting torque:

$$(W_{1-2})_T = -\int_1^2 T\,d\theta = -(T)\left(\frac{10}{\pi D_{\text{drum}}}\right)(2\pi)$$

$$= -50 \text{ ft-lb} \quad \textbf{(a)}$$

(b) Friction:

$$(W_{1-2})_f = -\int_1^2 \text{f}\,ds$$

$$= -(0.3)(200\cos 30° - 100\sin 30°)(10)$$

$$= -370 \text{ ft-lb} \quad \textbf{(b)}$$

(c) Applied force:

$$(W_{1-2})_F = (100)(\cos 30°)(10) = 866 \text{ ft-lb} \quad \textbf{(c)}$$

(d) Gravity:

$$(W_{1-2})_g = (200)(10 \sin 30°) = 1000 \text{ ft-lb} \quad \textbf{(d)}$$

The net work done during the interval of interest is then:

$$W_{1-2} = -50 - 370 + 866 + 1000 = 1446 \text{ ft-lb} \quad \textbf{(e)}$$

Using the work-energy relation, we have:

$$1446 = \frac{1}{2}\left(\frac{200}{g_0}\right)V^2 + \frac{1}{2}\left(\frac{400}{g_0}k^2\right)\omega^2 \quad \textbf{(f)}$$

Noting that $\omega = V/D/2 = V$, we get:

$$1446 = \left[\frac{1}{2}\left(\frac{200}{g_0}\right) + \frac{1}{2}\left(\frac{400}{g_0}1.5^2\right)1^2\right]V^2 \quad \textbf{(g)}$$

Solving for V, we get:

$$V = 9.2 \text{ ft/sec} \quad \textbf{(h)}$$

18.5 Closure

We have covered in the last two chapters the salient features of Newton's law and its derived concepts of linear momentum, moment of momentum, and energy, as they pertain to rigid bodies. You will recall that in Chapter 17, we considered cases where the axis of rotation of a body goes through a fixed point at all times but does not have a fixed orientation in inertial space. The mathematical difficulties of the problem, however, prevented us from integrating these equations, although we employed them at times to determine forces, angular accelerations, and certain instantaneous values of angular velocity. In the next chapter, we shall examine this problem again and shall set forth further concepts and definitions that are helpful in the analysis of the general nature of this complex motion. And, in certain of the cases to be studied, we shall have the opportunity of employing the energy considerations of this chapter.

PROBLEMS

In the following problems, neglect friction unless otherwise instructed.

1. [18.2] Shown in Fig. 18.23 is a uniform solid cylinder of radius 2 ft and weight 200 lb. It rolls without slipping down a 45° incline and drags the 100-lb block B with it. What is the kinetic energy of the system if block B is moving at a speed of 10 ft/sec? Neglect the mass of connecting agents between the bodies.

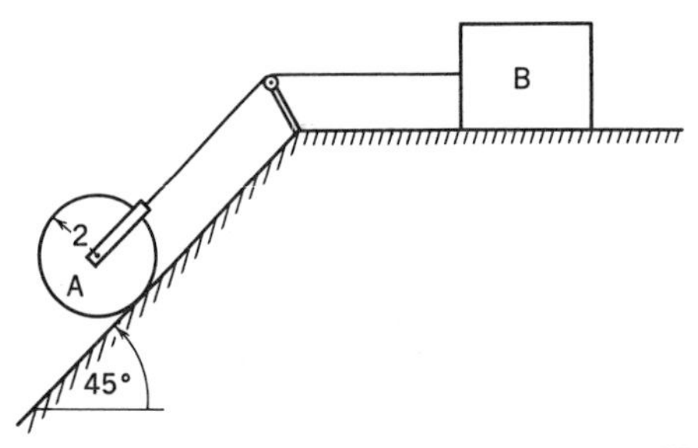

Fig. 18.23

2. [18.2] A pulley system is shown in Fig. 18.24. Sheave A weighs 50 lb and has a radius of gyration of 1.6 ft. Sheave B weighs 30 lb and has a radius of gyration of 1 ft. If the 100-lb weight is falling at a speed of 10 ft/sec, what is the kinetic energy of the system?

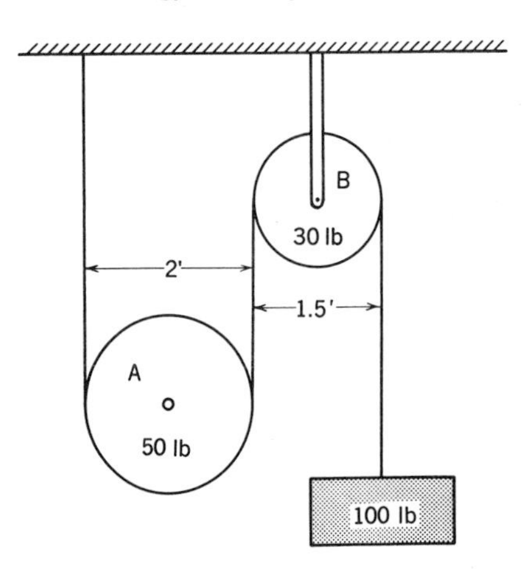

Fig. 18.24

3. [18.2] Shown in Fig. 18.25 is a steam roller weighing 5 tons. Wheel A weighs 1 ton and has a radius of gyration of 1.3 ft. Drive-wheels B have a total mass of 1000 lb and a radius of gyration of 3 ft. If the steam roller is coasting at a speed of 5 ft/sec with motor disconnected, what is the total kinetic energy of the system?

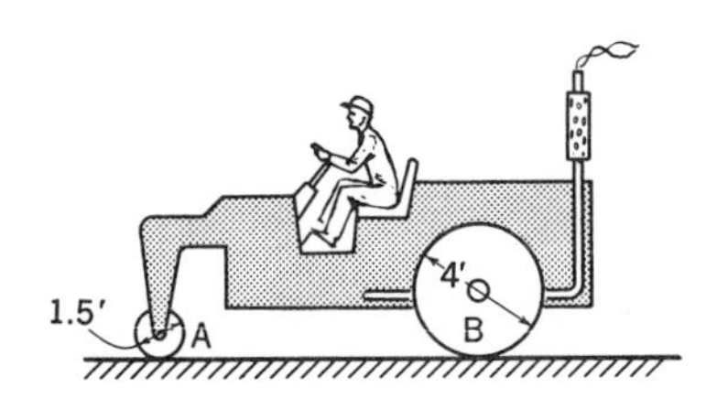

Fig. 18.25

4. [18.2] What is the kinetic energy of a propellor having a radius of gyration of 2 ft and weighing 40 lb, when it is rotating at 500 rpm relative to the airplane, which moves at a speed of 200 mi/hr?

5. [18.2] Considering the connecting rod AB to be a slender rod weighing 2 lb, compute its kinetic energy for the data given in Fig. 18.26.

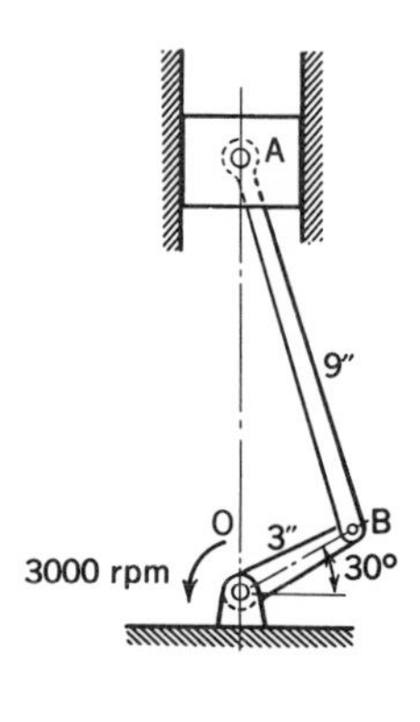

Fig. 18.26

6. [18.2] Shown in Fig. 18.27 are two slender rods CD and EA pinned together at B. Rod EA is rotating at a speed ω equal to 2 rad/sec. Rod CD rides in a vertical slot at D. For the configuration shown in the diagram, compute the kinetic energy of the rods.

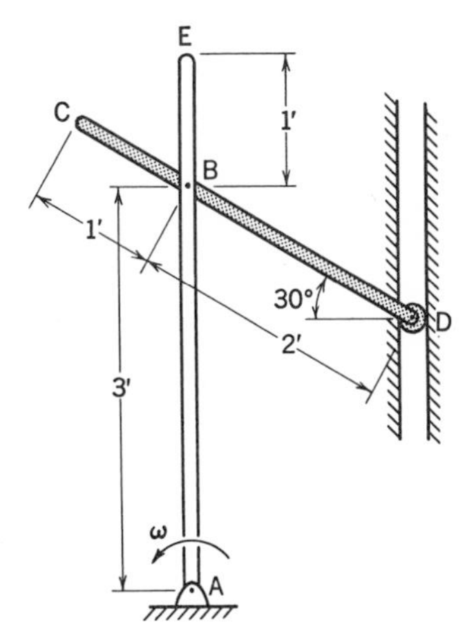

Fig. 18.27

7. [18.2] A rod AB (Fig. 18.28) rotates at a rate ω of 2 rad/sec. It carries a uniform block C at B. Corner D of block C slides on an inclined surface. If C weighs 30 lb and BA weighs 10 lb, compute the kinetic energy of the system at the configuration shown.

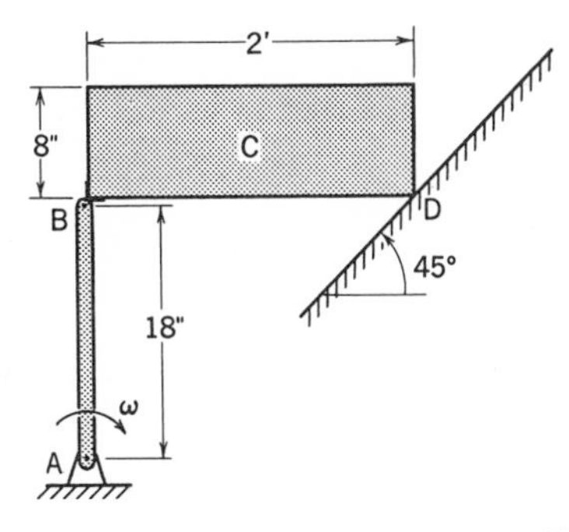

Fig. 18.28

8. [18.2] Identical rods CB and AB (Fig. 18.29) are pinned together at B. Rod BC is pinned to a block D weighing 50 lb. Each rod is 2 ft in length and weighs 10 lb. Rod BA rotates counterclockwise at a constant speed ω of 3 rad/sec. Compute the kinetic energy of the system when BA is oriented (a) at an angle of 60° with the vertical and (b) at an angle of 90° with the vertical (latter position is shown dashed in the diagram).

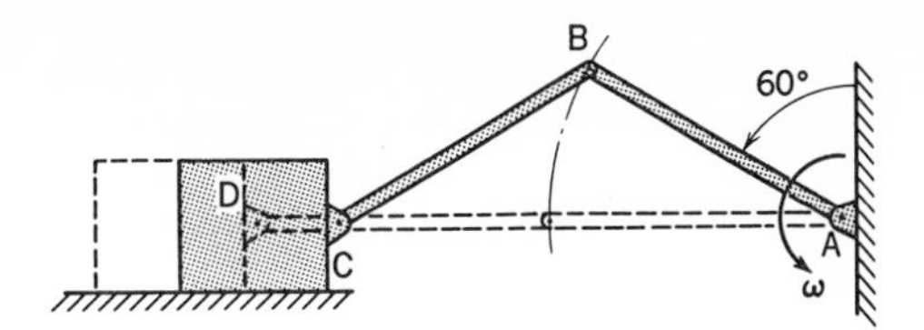

Fig. 18.29

9. [18.2] Shown in Fig. 18.30 is a uniform cylinder C, weighing 10 lb, to which is pinned a rod AB, weighing 15 lb. If end B of the rod is moving upward along the vertical wall at a speed of 10 ft/sec, what is the kinetic energy of the system? Assume C rolls without slipping.

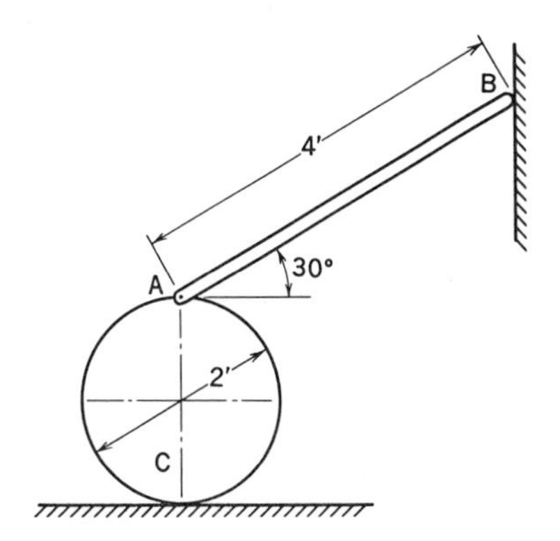

Fig. 18.30

10. [18.2] Gear E (see Fig. 18.31) rotates at an angular speed ω of 5 rad/sec and drives four smaller "floating" gears A, B, C, and D, which roll within stationary gear F. What is the kinetic energy of the system if gear E weighs 50 lb and each of the small gears weighs 10 lb?

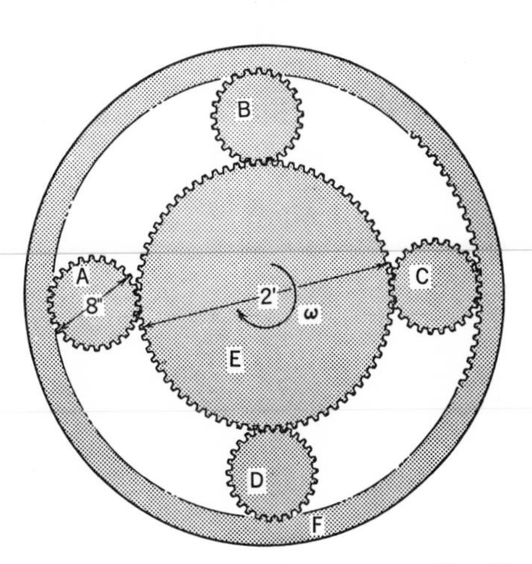

Fig. 18.31

11. [18.2] What is the kinetic energy of the system shown in Fig. 18.32? Wedge A moves to the left at a speed V of 3 ft/sec. The wheels on which A rides roll without slipping at the contact surfaces of both A and the ground support. The wheels are identical. Each weighs 5 lb and each has a radius of gyration of 0.8 ft. Wedge A weighs 50 lb and wedge B weighs 150 lb.

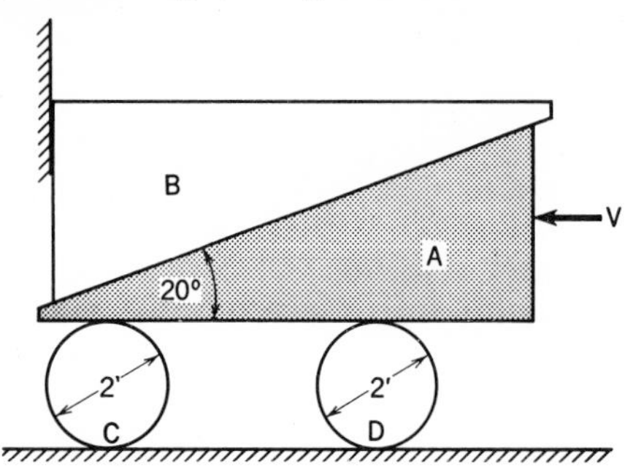

Fig. 18.32

12. [18.2] Find the kinetic energy of the rotating system described in Prob. 24 of Chap. 17. The diameter of the shaft is 2 in.

13. [18.2] Find the kinetic energy of the rotating system described in Prob. 25 of Chap. 17. The shaft weighs 20 lb with a diameter of 2 in.

14. [18.2] Find the kinetic energy of the rotating system described in Prob. 27 of Chap. 17. Diameter of shaft is 0.3 ft and of C is 2 ft.

15. [18.2] Shown in Fig. 18.33 is a gear A whose centerline rotates about axis MM at an angular speed ω_1 of 3 rad/sec. The mean diameter of the gear is 1 ft. If the gear has a mass of 10 lb and a radius of gyration 0.8 ft, what is the kinetic energy of the gear?

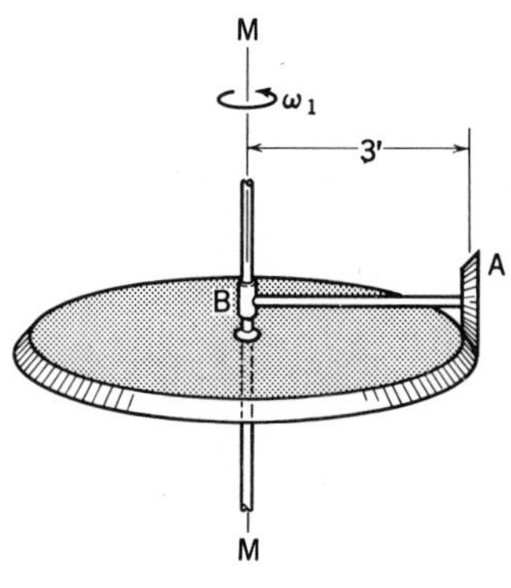

Fig. 18.33

16. [18.2] A thin disc weighing 100 lb is suspended from a vehicle moving at a speed of 30 ft/sec (Fig. 18.34). If the disc and its support rotate in the plane of the page (i.e., ZY plane) at an angular speed of 5 rad/sec, compute the kinetic energy of the disc.

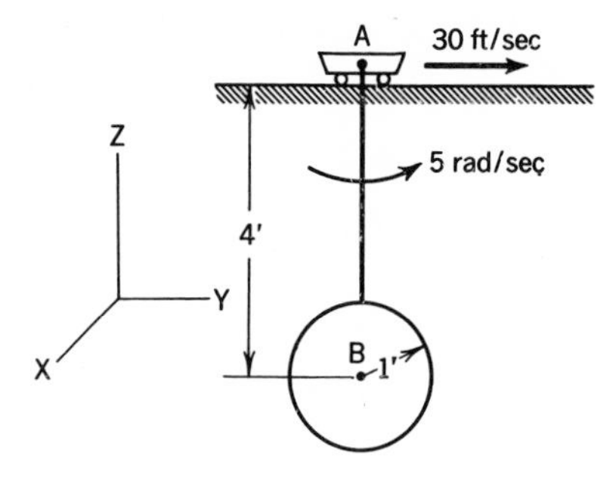

Fig. 18.34

17. [18.2] Find the kinetic energy of the cylinder shown in Fig. 17.17 rotating at a speed $\omega_2 = 5$ rad/sec relative to a platform, which rotates at a speed $\omega_1 = 3$ rad/sec relative to the ground. The cylinder weighs 100 lb. The following data are to be used:

$$c = 3 \text{ ft}$$

$$a = 4 \text{ ft}$$

$$r = \tfrac{1}{2} \text{ ft}$$

18. [18.2] Compute the kinetic energy of the disc in Prob. 5 of Chapter 17 relative to the rod and relative to the ground.

19. [18.2] Compute the kinetic energy of the disc and attached masses E and F for Prob. 10 of Chapter 17.

20. [18.2] In Prob. 6 of Chapter 17 compute the kinetic energy of the disc.

21. [18.2] In Prob. 8 of Chapter 17 compute the kinetic energy of the cone.

22. [18.2] Compute the kinetic energy of the propeller in Prob. 20 of Chapter 17.

23. [18.2] Compute the kinetic energy of the disc in Prob. 21 of Chapter 17.

24. [18.2] Compute the kinetic energy of the disc of Prob. 33 Chapter 17.

25. [18.2] At time t the body B has an instantaneous axis of rotation going through point P as shown in Fig. 18.35. At point P, this axis has the following set of direction cosines relative to the principal axes of the body at that point: $l = 0.4$, $m = 0.3$, and $n = 0.866$. Furthermore, it is known at that point that the principal moments of inertia are:

$$I_{xx} = 100 \text{ slugs-ft}^2$$

$$I_{yy} = 300 \text{ slugs-ft}^2$$

$$I_{zz} = 50 \text{ slugs-ft}^2$$

Compute the kinetic energy of the body if it is rotating at an angular speed of 20 rad/sec.

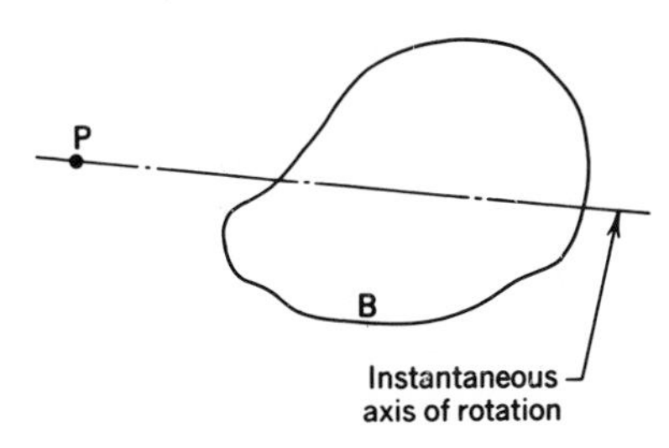

Fig. 18.35

26. [18.2] In Fig. 18.36, a homogeneous rectangular parallelepiped weighing 200 lb rotates at 20 rad/sec about a main diagonal held by bearings A and B, which are mounted on a vehicle moving at a speed of 50 ft/sec. What is the kinetic energy of the rectangular parallelepiped?

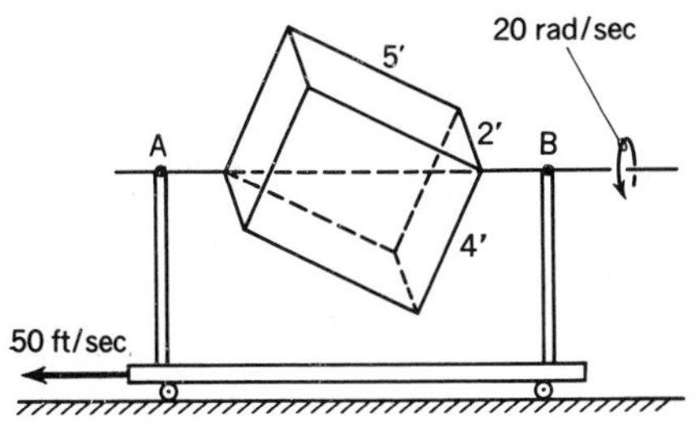

Fig. 18.36

27. [18.2] A cylinder weighing 200 lb is shown in Fig. 18.37 attached to a shaft such that the centerlines of cylinder and shaft intersect at 45°. If the shaft rotates at a speed ω of 10 rad/sec, what is the kinetic energy of the cylinder?

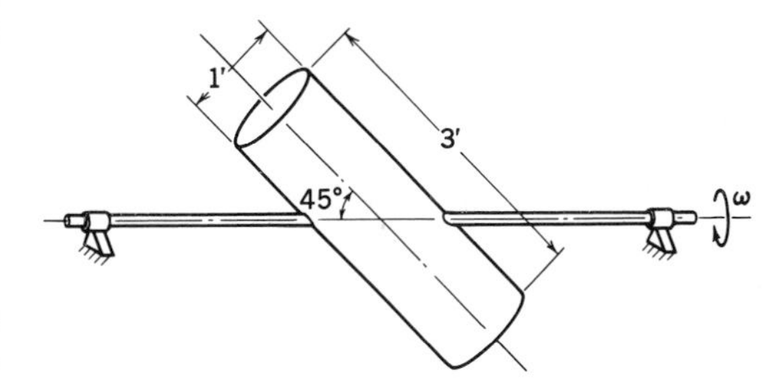

Fig. 18.37

28. [18.3] A uniform cylinder of radius r and weight W_1 is shown in Fig. 18.38. A weight W_2, which we shall consider a particle because of its small physical dimensions, is placed at G a distance a from O, the center of the disc, such that OG is vertical. What is the angular velocity of the cylinder when, after it is released from rest, the point G reaches its lowest elevation, as shown at the right? The cylinder rolls without slipping.

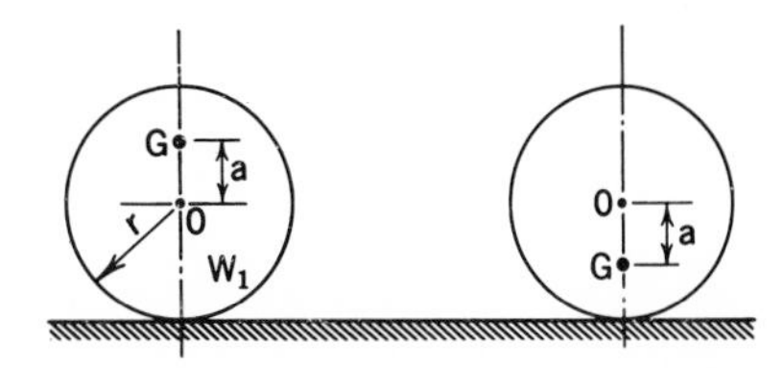

Fig. 18.38

29. [18.3] A homogeneous solid cylinder of radius 1 ft is shown in Fig. 18.39 with a fine wire held fixed at A and wrapped around the cylinder. If the cylinder is released from rest, what will its velocity be when it has dropped 10 ft?

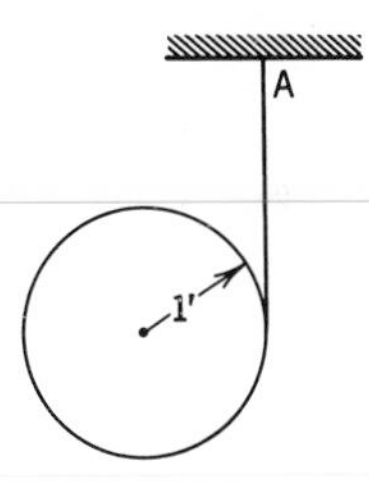

Fig. 18.39

30. [18.3] In Fig. 18.40, three identical bars, each of length l and weight W, are connected to each other and a wall by smooth pins at A, B, C, and D. A spring having spring constant K is connected to the center of bar BC at E and to a pin at F, which is free to slide in the slot. Compute the angular speed $\dot{\theta}$ as a function of time if the system is released from rest when AB and DC are at right angles to the wall. The spring is unstretched at the outset of the motion. Neglect friction.

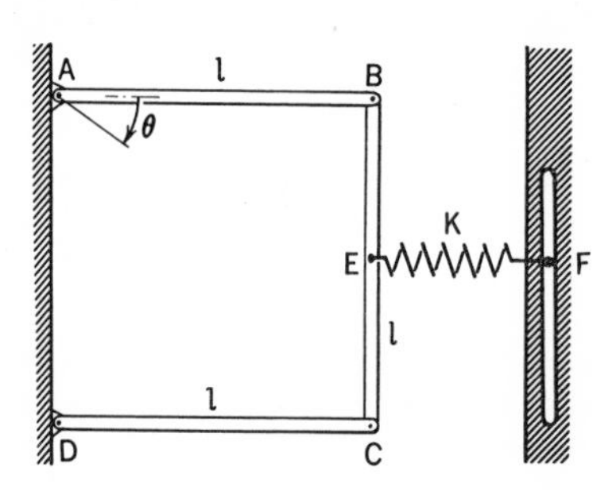

Fig. 18.40

31. [18.3] A 15-lb weight is suspended from a light cord wrapped around a cylinder of radius 2 ft and weight 100 lb (Fig. 18.41). What is the angular velocity of the cylinder after it has started from rest and rolled without slipping a distance of 10 ft? State assumptions.

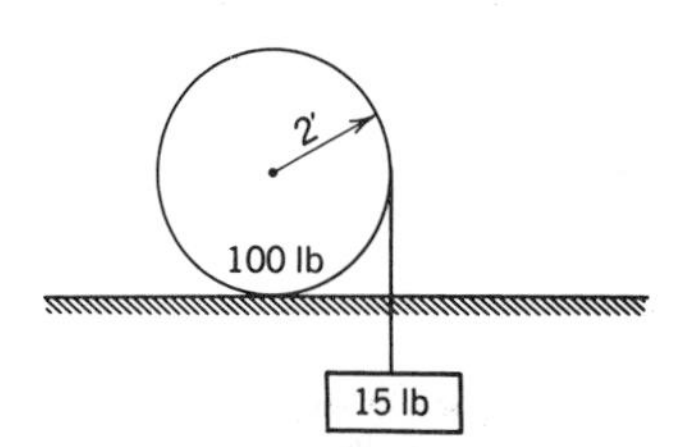

Fig. 18.41

32. [18.3] A weight W is released from rest (see Fig. 18.42) and slides down the inclined rod. It comes to rest in a position such that the spring at the bottom, having a spring constant K_1 of 1 lb/in., is compressed 2 in. A second spring having a spring constant K_2 of 0.2 lb/in. is originally horizontal and unstretched. Determine the weight W of this body.

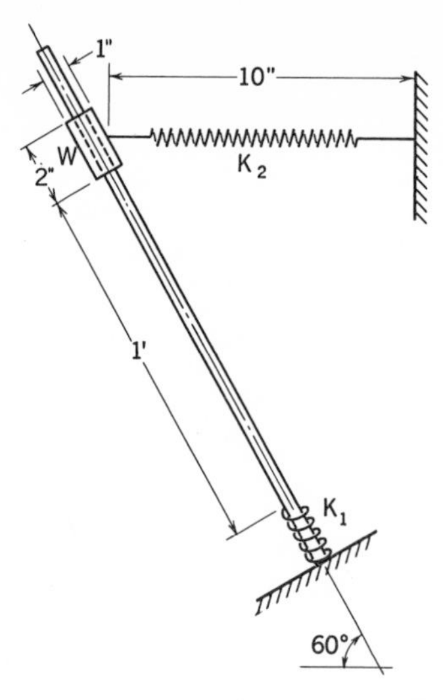

Fig. 18.42

33. [18.3] Using energy methods, set up the differential equation of motion for the thin rod which is constrained in Fig. 18.43 to move in the plane of the page. The rod has a length l and a weight W and is connected at A to a spring having spring constant K. Neglect friction at the hinge. Limit the analysis to small motion.

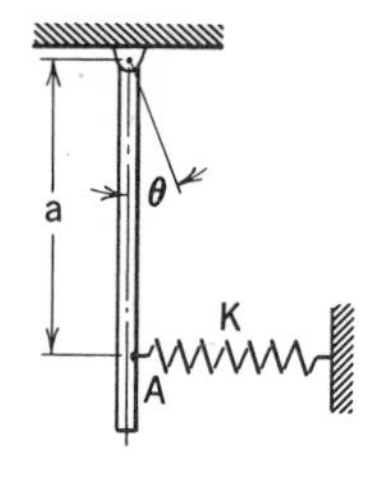

Fig. 18.43

34. [18.3] Four identical rods, each of length $l = 4$ ft and weight 20 lb, are connected at the frictionless pins A, B, C, and D in Fig. 18.44. A spring of spring constant $K = 30$ lb/in. connects pins B and C, and a weight W_2 of 100 lb is supported at pin D. The system is released from a configuration where $\theta = 45°$. If the spring is not compressed at that configuration, compute the maximum deflection of the weight W_2.

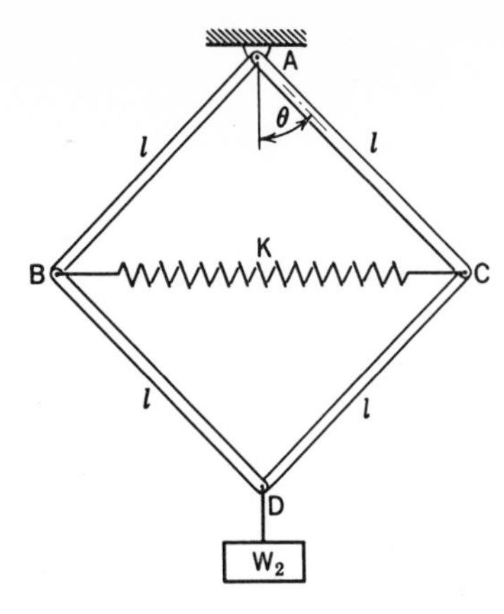

Fig. 18.44

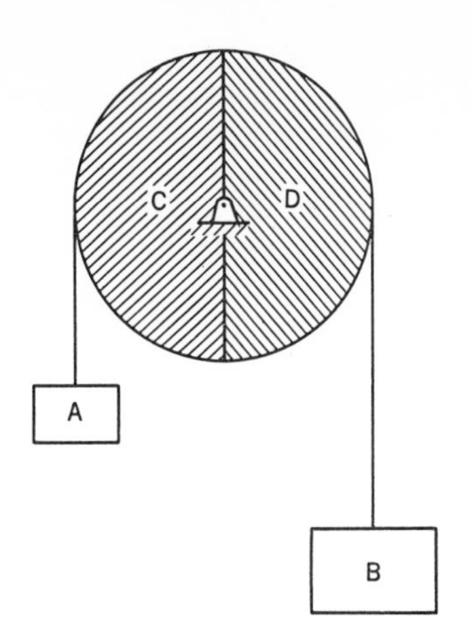

Fig. 18.46

35. [18.3] A body A weighing 1 lb (see Fig. 18.45) is released from a stationary position wherein a spring having a spring constant K of 50 lb/inch is compressed 4 in. What is the maximum height that A will reach? At what position x does it reach this maximum height? Neglect friction.

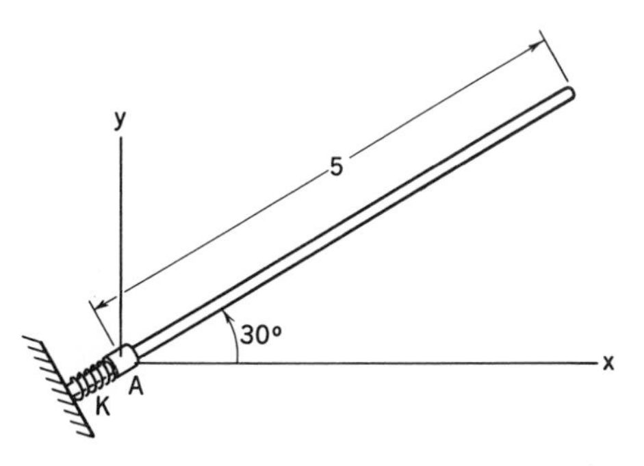

Fig. 18.45

36. [18.3] In Fig. 18.46 is shown a cylinder of diameter 2 ft composed of 2 semicylinders C and D weighing 50 lb and 80 lb, respectively. Bodies A and B weighing 20 lb and 50 lb, respectively, are connected by a light flexible cable that runs over the cylinder. If the system is released from rest for the configuration shown, what is the speed of B when the cylinder has rotated 90°?

37. [18.3] Shown in Fig. 18.47 is a cylinder weighing 100 lb and with a 2-ft diameter. The radius of gyration for the axis through O is 1.3 ft. What is the angular speed of the disc after it has moved from contact point A to contact B?

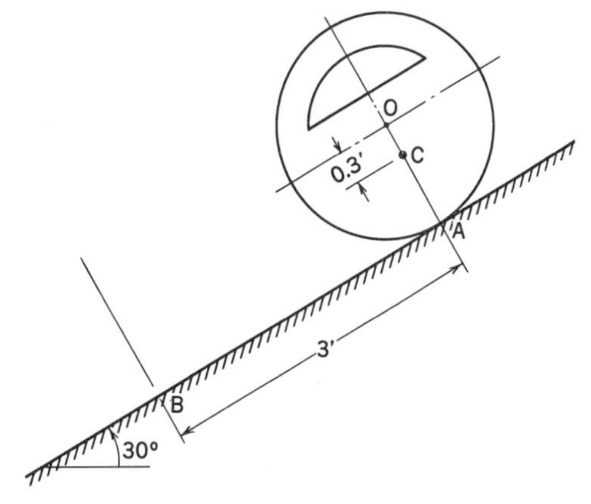

Fig. 18.47

38. [18.3] A rod AB of weight 20 lb and length 5 ft is shown in Fig. 18.48 in a stationary configuration. If the surfaces are frictionless, what is the speed of end B after it has moved 2 ft to the right?

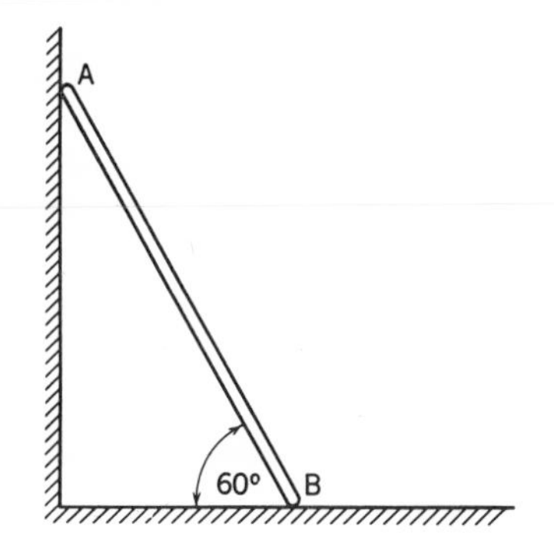

Fig. 18.48

39. [18.3] A 10-ft rod AB weighing 50 lb is guided at A by a slot (see Fig. 18.49) and at B by a horizontal surface. Neglecting the mass of the slider at A, what is the speed of B when A has moved 3 ft along the slider after starting from a rest configuration shown in the diagram?

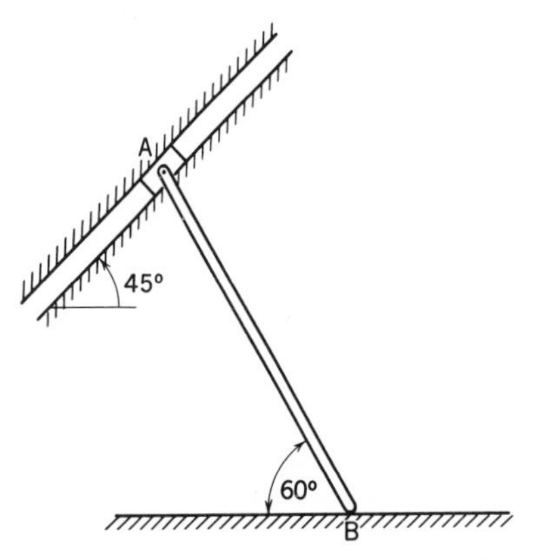

Fig. 18.49

40. [18.3] Shown in Fig. 18.50 is a stepped cylinder having radii of 2 ft for the smaller portion and 4 ft for the larger portion. A rectangular block A weighing 50 lb is welded to the cylinder at B. The spring constant K is 1 lb/in. If the system is released from a configuration of rest, what is the angular speed of the cylinder after it has rotated 90°? The radius of gyration for the stepped cylinder is 3 ft and its mass is 80 lb. The spring is unstretched in the position shown.

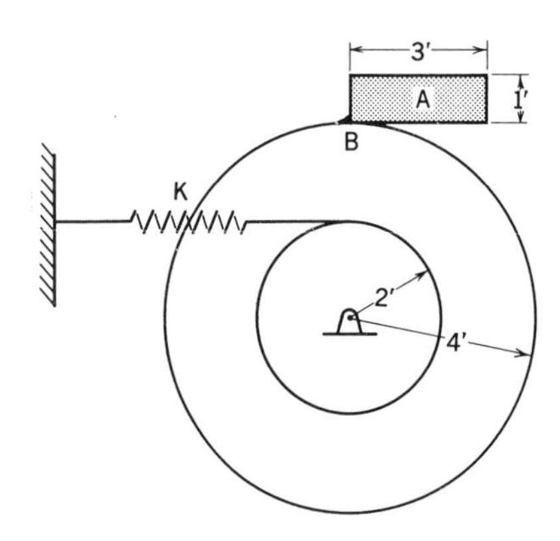

Fig. 18.50

41. [18.3] Shown in Fig. 18.51 is a stepped cylinder weighing 100 lb and having a radius of gyration of 4 ft. A 50-lb block A is welded to the cylinder as shown. If the spring is unstretched in the configuration shown and has a spring constant K of 0.5 lb/in., what is the angular speed of the cylinder after it rotates 90°? Assume the cylinder rolls without slipping.

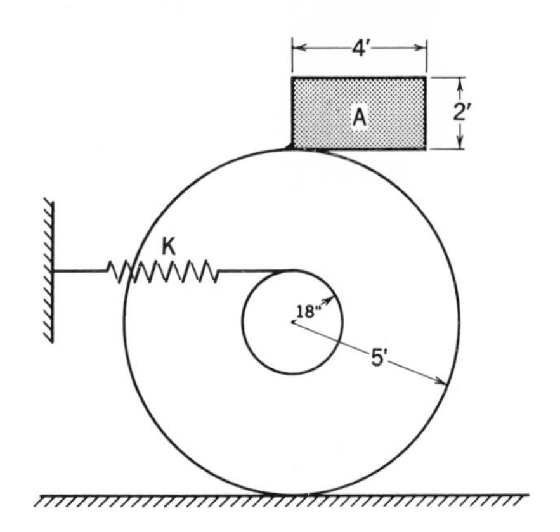

Fig. 18.51

42. [18.3] In Fig. 18.52, a right circular cone of weight 32.2 lb, height 4 ft, and cone angle 20° is allowed to roll without slipping on a plane surface inclined at an angle of 30° to the horizontal. The cone is started from rest when the line of contact is parallel to the X axis. What is the angular speed of the centerline of the cone when it has its maximum kinetic energy?

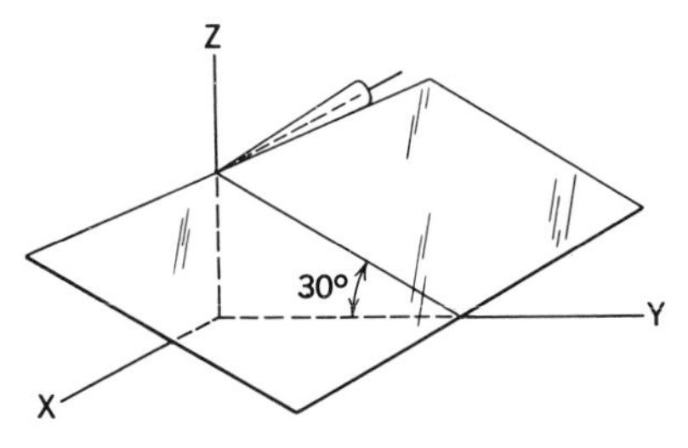

Fig. 18.52

***43.** [18.3] Shown in Fig. 18.53 is a solid uniform rod AB connected to slider bearings A and B which move in a frictionless manner along the indicated guide rods. The rod has a mass of 150 lbm and a diameter of 2 in. At connection A there is a pin connection and at B there is a ball-joint connection. If A moves down at a speed of 10 ft/sec, what is the kinetic energy of the rod? Neglect energy of the slider bearings.

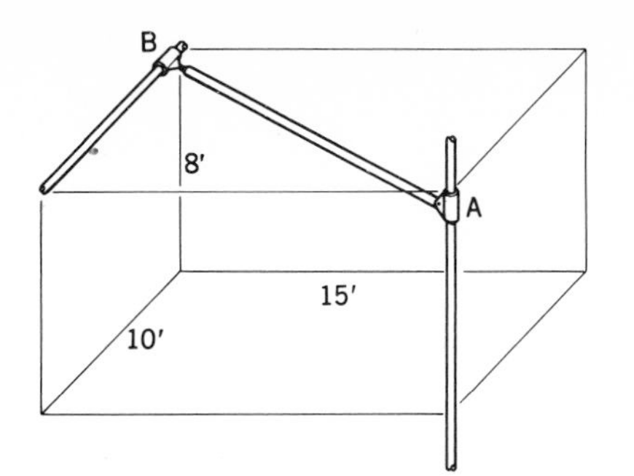

Fig. 18.53

*44. [18.3] In Prob. 43 find the kinetic energy of the rod after A has descended 2 ft.

*45. [18.3] In Prob. 9 find the kinetic energy of AB if it is released to a configuration where the cylinder has rotated 15°.

46. [18.3] A solid uniform block A (see Fig. 18.54) moves along two frictionless angle-iron supports at a speed of 20 ft/sec. One of the supports is inclined at an angle of 20° from the horizontal at B and causes the block to rotate about its front lower edge as it moves to the right of B. What is the speed of the block after it moves 1 ft to the right of B (measured horizontally)? The block weighs 100 lb.

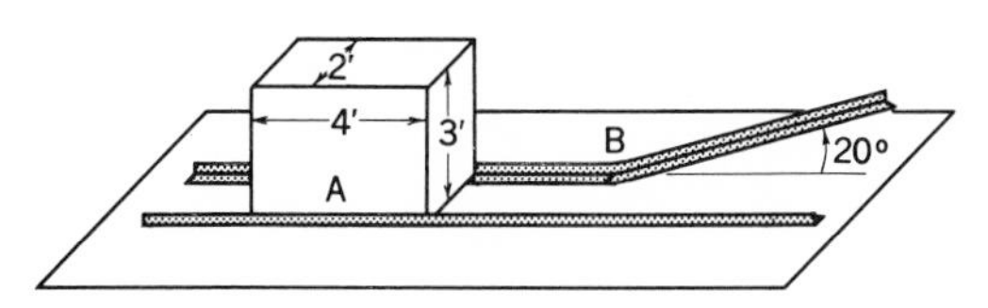

Fig. 18.54

*47. [18.3] In the previous problem, will the block reach an instantaneous zero motion and then slide back, or will it tip over onto face A?

*48. [18.3] Shown in Fig. 18.55 are the top and front views of a support A welded to a vertical shaft C. Plate A supports with three light rods a disc B that can rotate about C and move along C. If the disc B is given, by an impact torque, an instantaneous angular speed of 1 rad/sec, what is the angular speed of B after it has rotated 10°? Disc B weighs 80 lb.

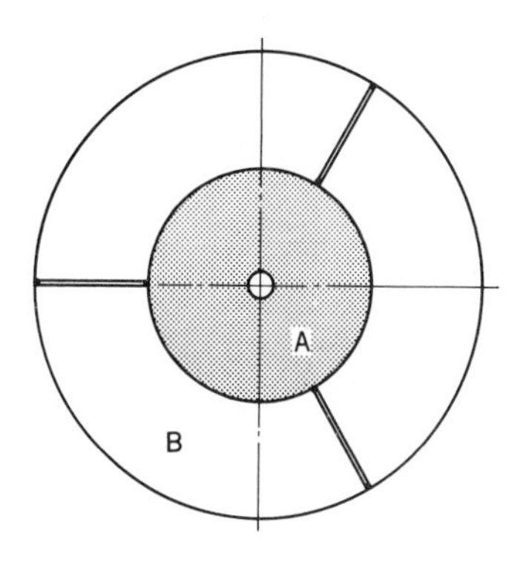

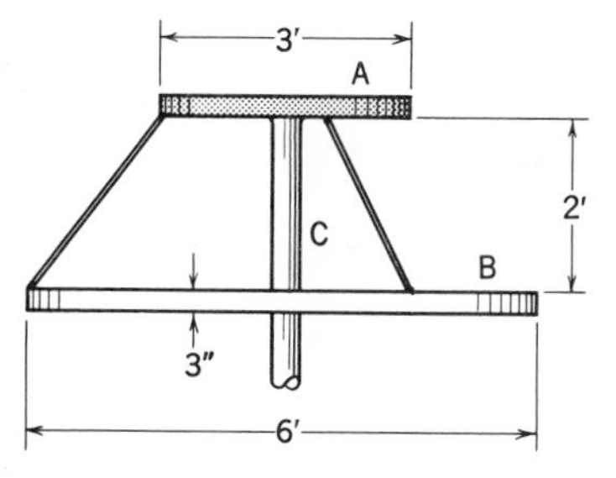

Fig. 18.55

*49. [18.3] In the previous problem, if disc B is rotated 20° and then released, what is the maximum angular speed reached by the disc?

50. [18.4] A windlass is shown in Fig. 18.56. The rotating part weighs 75 lb and has a radius of gyration of 1 ft. When the suspended weight of 20 lb is dropping at a speed of 20 ft/sec, a 100-lb force is applied to the level at A. This applies the brake shoe at B, where there is a coefficient of friction of 0.5. How far will the 20-lb weight drop before stopping?

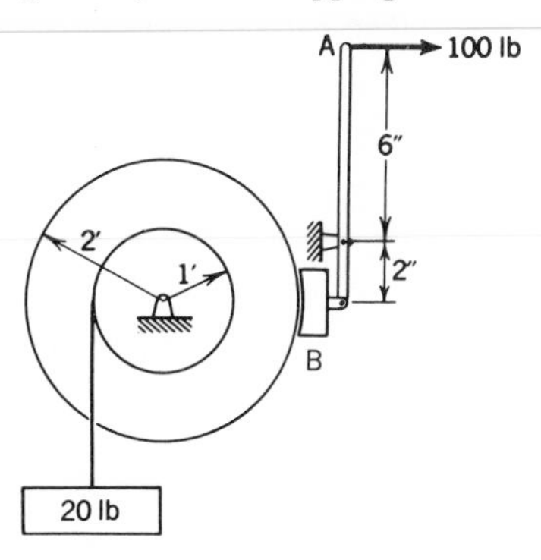

Fig. 18.56

51. [18.4] Neglecting the weight of the cable in Fig. 18.57, find the speed of the 100-lb weight after it has moved 5 ft along the incline from a position of rest. The coefficient of friction along the incline is 0.3.

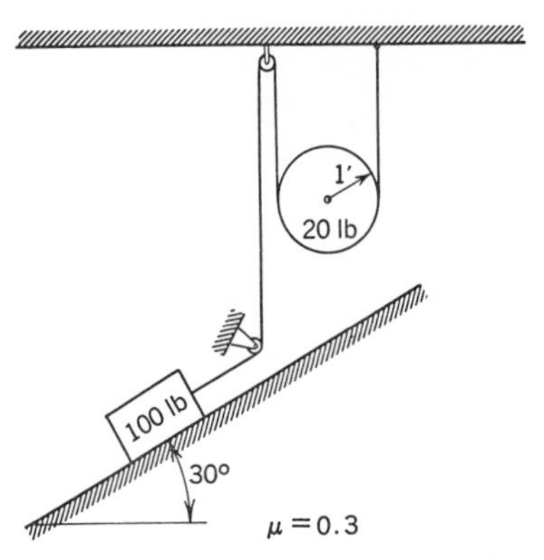

Fig. 18.57

52. [18.4] A belt weighing 10 lb is mounted over two pulleys of diameter 1 ft and 2 ft, respectively, as is shown in Fig. 18.58. The radius of gyration and weight for pulley A are 6 in. and 50 lb, respectively, and for pulley B are 9 in. and 200 lb, respectively. A constant torque of 20 lb-in. is applied to pulley A. After 30 revolutions of pulley A, what will its angular speed be if the system starts from rest? There is no slipping between belts and pulleys, and pulley B turns freely.

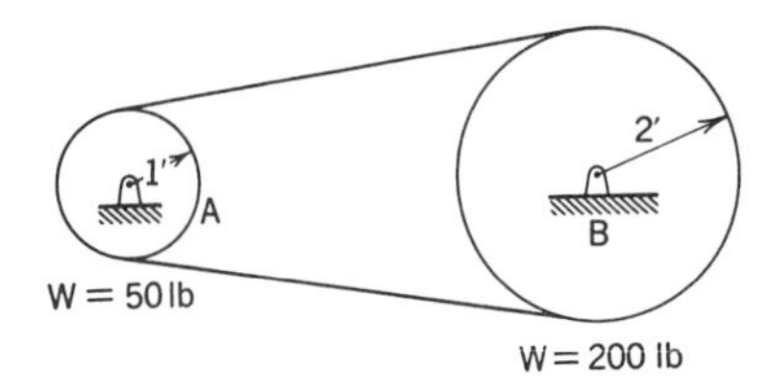

Fig. 18.58

53. [18.4] A stepped disc is shown in Fig. 18.59. A constant torque T of 20 ft-lb is applied at a configuration where the spring is unstretched. If there is rolling without slipping, what is the speed of the center of the stepped cylinder after one-half revolution? Disc weighs 322 lb with a radius of gyration of 3 ft. K is .02 lb/ft.

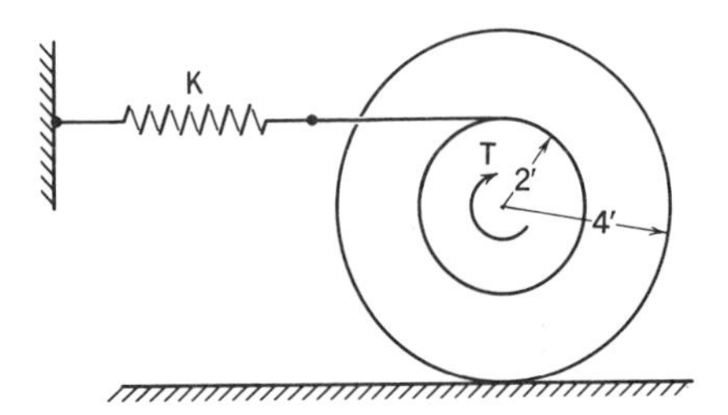

Fig. 18.59

54. [18.4] Do the preceding problem for the case where the torque is given as:

$$T = 25 + 2\theta \text{ ft-lb}$$

where θ in radians is the amount of rotation of the cylinder from its initial configuration.

55. [18.4] A stepped cylinder (Fig. 18.60) is released from a rest configuration where the spring is in a stretched condition of 8 in. A constant force F of 80 lb acts on the cylinder, as shown, maintaining a fixed direction at all times. The cylinder weighs 322 lb and has a radius of gyration of 3 ft. What is the speed of O after it has moved 2 ft? The spring constant K is 20 lb/ft.

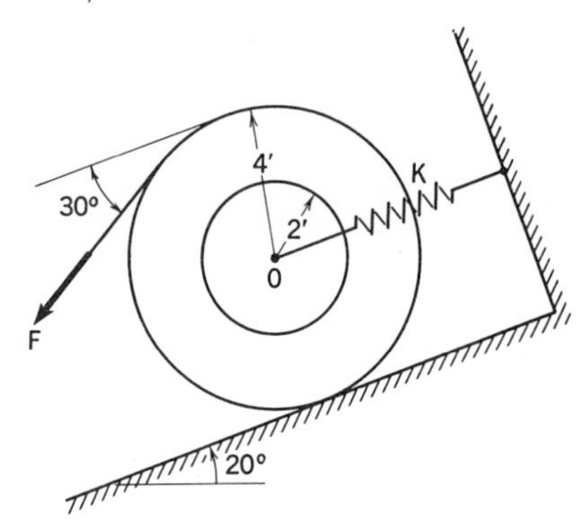

Fig. 18.60

56. [18.4] Do the preceding problem for the case where the spring is nonlinear, having the requirement of $10\delta^2$ lb for the deflection of δ ft.

57. [18.4] Shown in Fig. 18.61 is a square-threaded screw of diameter 2 in. and inclined 45° to the horizontal. The pitch of the thread is 0.2 in. and it is single-threaded. A body A weighing 64.4 lb and having a radius of gyration of 1 ft screws onto the shaft. A torque T of 30 ft-lb is applied to A as shown. What is the angular speed of A after 3 revolutions starting from a rest configuration? Neglect friction.

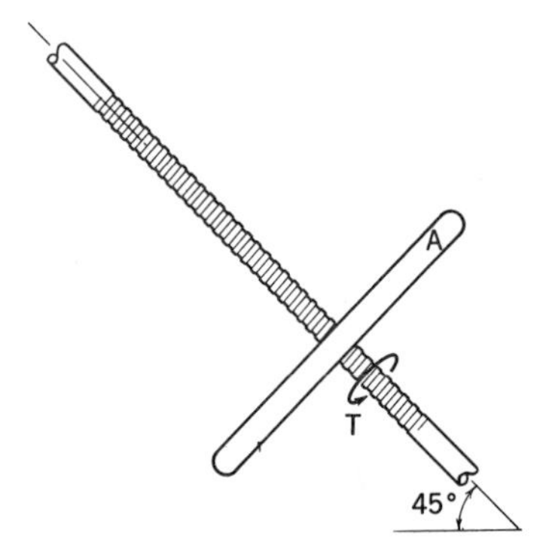

Fig. 18.61

58. [18.4] A disc A weighing 64.4 lb screws onto a square-threaded shaft as shown in Fig. 18.62. The diameter of the thread is 2 in. and the pitch of the thread is 0.2 in. The screw is single-threaded. If the coefficient of friction is 0.02, what is the speed of descent of the disc after it moves down 1 ft? The diameter of the disc is 2 ft.

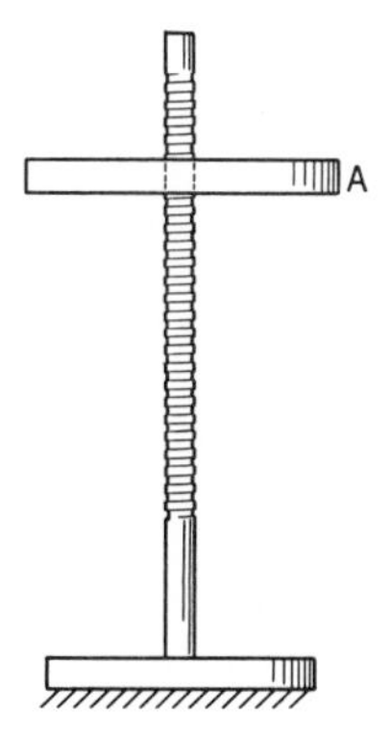

Fig. 18.62

59. [18.4] Shown in Fig. 18.63 is a conveyor moving a weight W of 64.4 lb. Cylinders A and B have a diameter of 1 ft and weight 32.2 lb each. Also they each have a radius of gyration of 0.8 ft. Rollers C, D, E, F, and G each have a diameter of 3 in., weigh 10 lb each, and have a radius of gyration of 2 in. What constant torque will increase the speed of W from 1 ft/sec to 3 ft/sec in 5 ft of travel? There is no slipping at any of the rollers and drums. The belt weighs 25 lb.

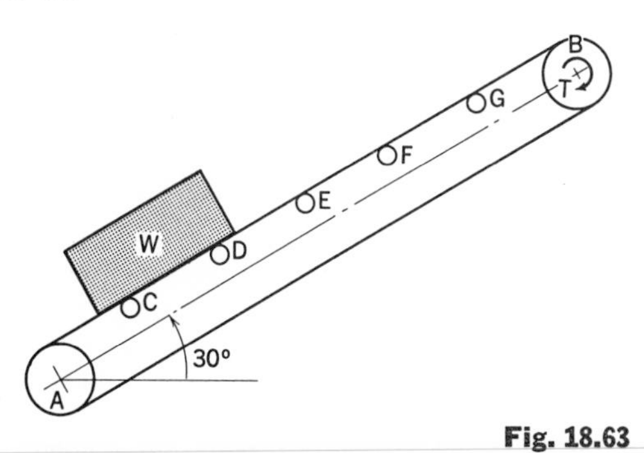

Fig. 18.63

60. [18.4] In the previous problem, if the weight W and belt system were allowed to move so that the weight moves to the left a distance of 5 ft, what is the speed of the weight if the system starts from rest and there is no resisting torque applied to the drums? Assume there is no slipping at the rollers and drums.

61. [18.4] A weight W of 96.6 lb (see Fig. 18.64) is being lowered by a rope running over a light frictionless pulley A and around a post having a diameter D of 2 ft and developing a coefficient of dynamic friction with the rope of 0.3. A constant force F of 10 lb acts on the rope as shown. Neglecting the mass of the rope, what increase in speed is developed by the system for a movement of 5 ft after motion has started?

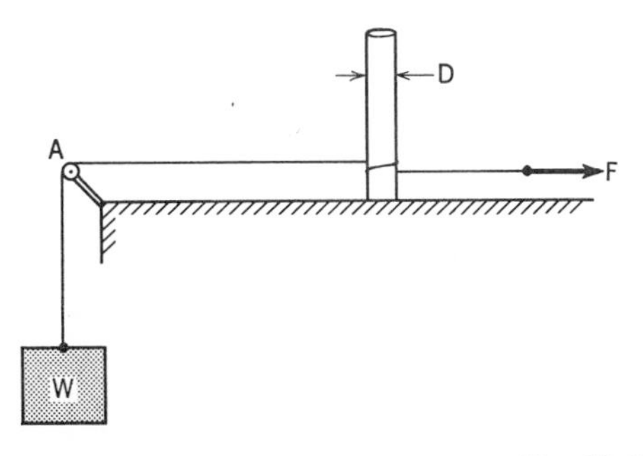

Fig. 18.64

62. [18.4] A weight W_1 (see Fig. 18.65) is held by a light flexible wire. The wire runs over a stationary semicylinder of radius R equal to 1 ft. A pulley weighing 32.2 lb and having a radius of gyration of unity rides on the wire carrying a weight W_2 of 15.1 lb. If W_1 weighs 128.8 lb and the coefficient of friction for the semicylinder and wire is 0.2, what is the drop in the weight W_1 for an increase in speed of 5 ft/sec of weight W_1 starting from rest? The diameter d of the small pulley is 1 ft.

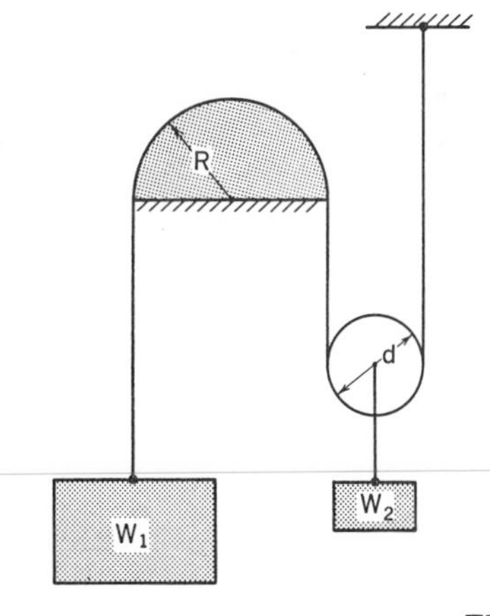

Fig. 18.65

63. [18.4] In Prob. 3, assume the steam roller is pulled by a 500-lb force and develops a torque on its drive wheels of 200 ft-lb. What is the increase in speed after it moves 5 ft?

64. [18.4] A tractor weighing with driver 3000 lb is shown in Fig. 18.66. If a torque of 200 ft-lb is developed on the drive wheels by the motor, what is the speed of the tractor after it moves 10 ft? The large drive wheels each weigh 200 lb and have a diameter of 3 ft and a radius of gyration of 2 ft. The small wheels each weigh 40 lb and have a diameter of 1 ft with a radius of gyration of 0.8 ft.

Fig. 18.66

65. [18.4] A force F of 100 lb acts on block A in Fig. 18.67 weighing 96.6 lb. Block A rides on identical uniform cylinders B and C, each weighing 64.4 lb and having a radius of 1 ft. If there is no slipping, what is the speed of A after it moves 3 ft?

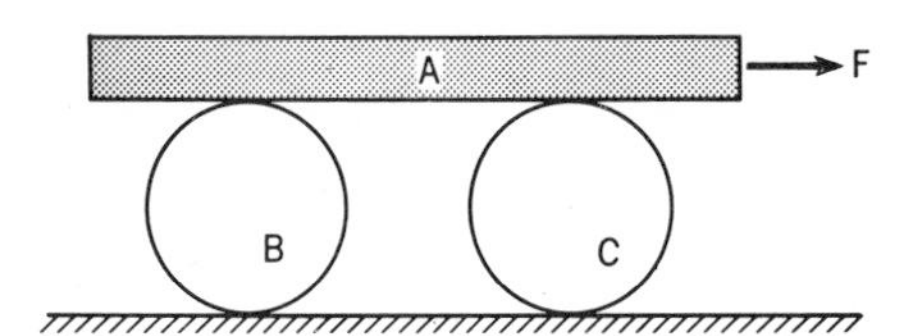

Fig. 18.67

66. [18.4] In Fig. 18.68 the linkage system rests on a frictionless plane. The lengths AB, BF, and so on are each 2 ft and the bars, all of the same stock, weigh 5 lb/ft. A force F of 100 lb is applied at D. What is the speed of D after it moves 1 ft? The system is stationary at the configuration shown.

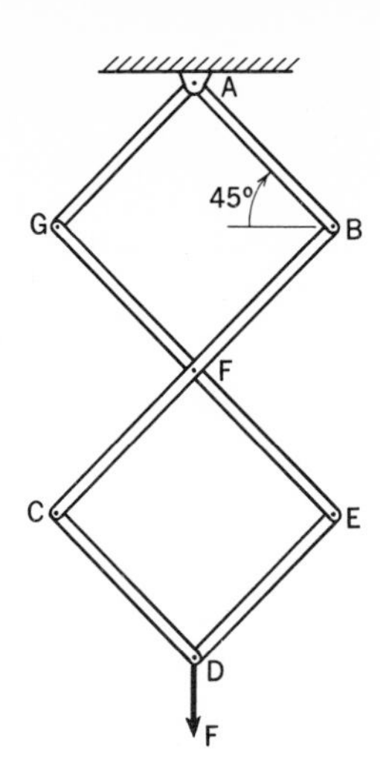

Fig. 18.68

67. [18.4] Do the preceding problem for the case where the system is in a vertical plane.

68. [18.4] In Fig. 18.69, two identical members, AB and BC, are pinned together at B. Also member BC is pinned to the wall at C. Each member weighs 32.2 lb and is 20 ft long. A spring having a spring constant $K = 20$ lb/ft is connected to the centers of the members. A force $P = 100$ lb is applied to member AB at A. If initially the members are inclined 45° to the ground and the spring is unstretched, what is $\dot{\beta}$ after A has moved 2 ft?

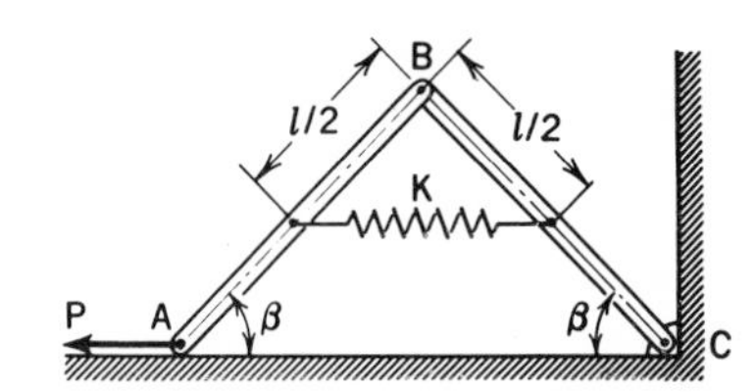

Fig. 18.69

69. [18.4] In Fig. 18.70, a stepped cylinder weighing 30 lb with a radius of gyration of 1 ft is connected to a 50-ft chain weighing 100 lb. The chain hangs down from the horizontal surface a distance of 10 ft when the system is released. Determine the speed of the chain when 30 additional feet of chain have come off the horizontal surface. The coefficient of friction between the chain and the horizontal surface is 0.2, and the smaller diameter of the stepped cylinder is 4 in.

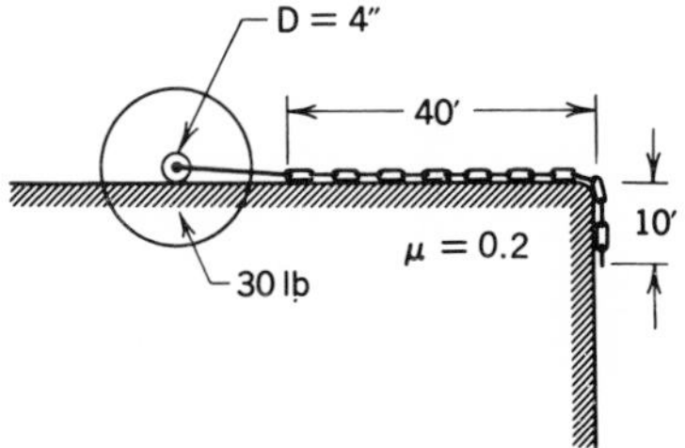

Fig. 18.70

70. [18.4] A flexible cord of total length 50 ft and weighing 50 lb is pinned to a wall and is wrapped around a cylinder having a radius of 4 ft and weighing 30 lb as shown in Fig. 18.71. A 50-lb force is applied to the end of the cord. What is the speed of the cylinder after the end of the cord has moved 10 ft? The system starts from rest in the configuration shown in the diagram. Neglect potential energy considerations arising from the sag of the upper cord.

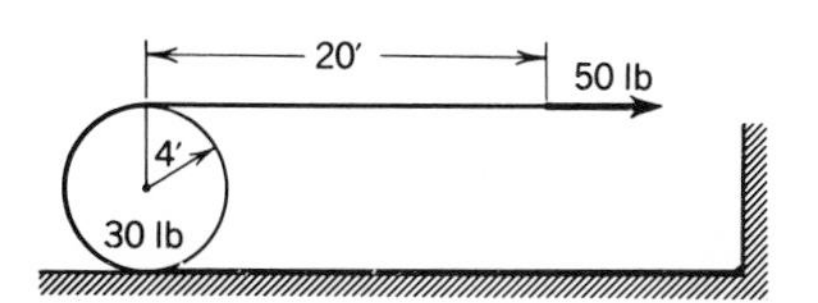

Fig. 18.71

71. [18.4] In Prob. 5 suppose that there exists an average pressure of 20 psia in the cylinder. What is the rpm after the crankshaft has rotated 60° from position shown? The crank rod OB weighs 1 lb and has a radius of gyration of 2 in. The diameter of the piston is 4 in. and its weight is 8 ounces. The crankshaft is rotating at 3000 rpm at position shown.

72. [18.4] A uniform block A weighing 64.4 lb is pulled by a force P of 50 lb as shown in Fig. 18.72. The block moves along the rails on small light wheels. One rail descends at an angle of 15° at point B. If the force P always remains horizontal, what is the speed of the block after it has moved 5 ft in the horizontal direction? The block is stationary at the position shown. Assume the block does not tilt forward.

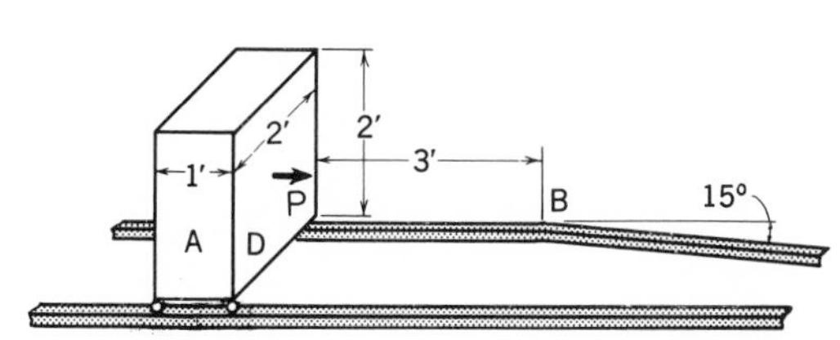

Fig. 18.72

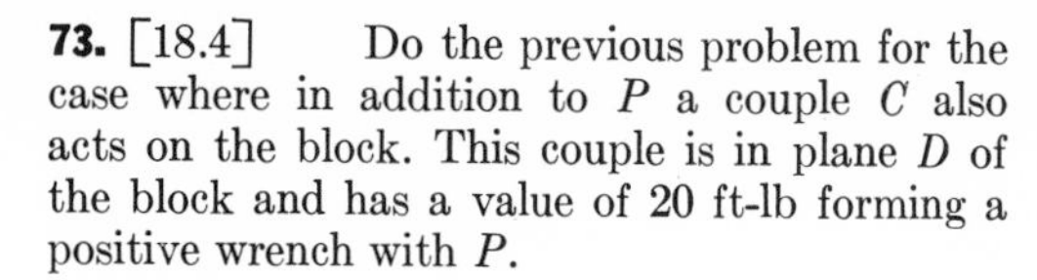

73. [18.4] Do the previous problem for the case where in addition to P a couple C also acts on the block. This couple is in plane D of the block and has a value of 20 ft-lb forming a positive wrench with P.

74. [18.4] In Prob. 43 find the kinetic energy of the system if it is dropped from a condition of rest to a configuration where A has descended 2 ft. There are friction forces of 5 lb and 3 lb at bearings B and A, respectively.

***75.** [18.4] A rod weighing 20 lb is guided by two slider bearings A and B (see Fig. 18.73). Bearing A has a ball-joint connection with the rod and bearing B has a pin-joint connection with the rod. A force F of 10 lb acts on bearing A. What is the speed of A after it has moved 8 in.? The system is stationary for the configuration shown.

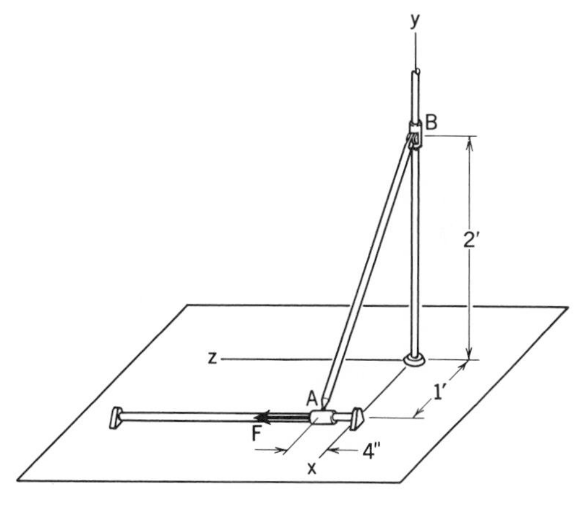

Fig. 18.73

19 Motion of a Body about a Fixed Point

19.1 Introduction

In Chapters 17 and 18, we developed equations that permitted us to compute the linear and angular acceleration of rigid-body motions. We examined a number of classes of problems for which it is often possible, once these accelerations are expressed, to describe the velocity and position variations with time by pursuing rather straightforward integration procedures. These problems generally fell into three classes: pure translation, rotation about a fixed axis, and plane motion. Cases of bodies rotating about a *fixed point* for which the axis of rotation is not fixed have come up in the problems, but you will recall that in these cases the motion was either partially or fully known and you had the relatively easy task of computing the reactions or certain instantaneous values of acceleration. In this chapter, we will examine more carefully the motion of selected rigid bodies constrained to have a point fixed in inertial reference (Fig. 19.1). This will lead to an examination of a very important device—the gyro-

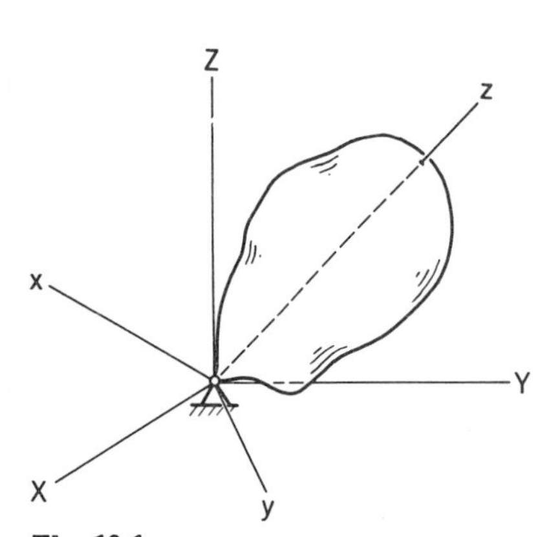

Fig. 19.1

scope. As a first step, we shall set forth an effective method of locating a rigid body in space constrained so that one point is fixed.

19.2 Euler Angles

We shall now set forth certain angles which have the very desirable dual properties of orienting a rigid body having one point fixed in a reference and, in addition, giving by the specification of their time derivatives the angular velocity of the body in this reference. (Clearly, ω_x, ω_y and ω_z are not quantities which when integrated with respect to time describe the orientation of a rigid body in space.) By doing so we will be better able to integrate the moment of momentum equation for rigid bodies and to treat more effectively many interesting problems.

Accordingly, consider a rigid body shown in Fig. 19.2 fixed at point O. To reach the configuration shown we shall start with the body in a position indicated in Fig. 19.3 and we shall specify a sequence of three rotations in the following manner.

1. Keeping a reference xyz fixed in the body, rotate the body about the Z axis through an angle ψ shown in Fig. 19.4.

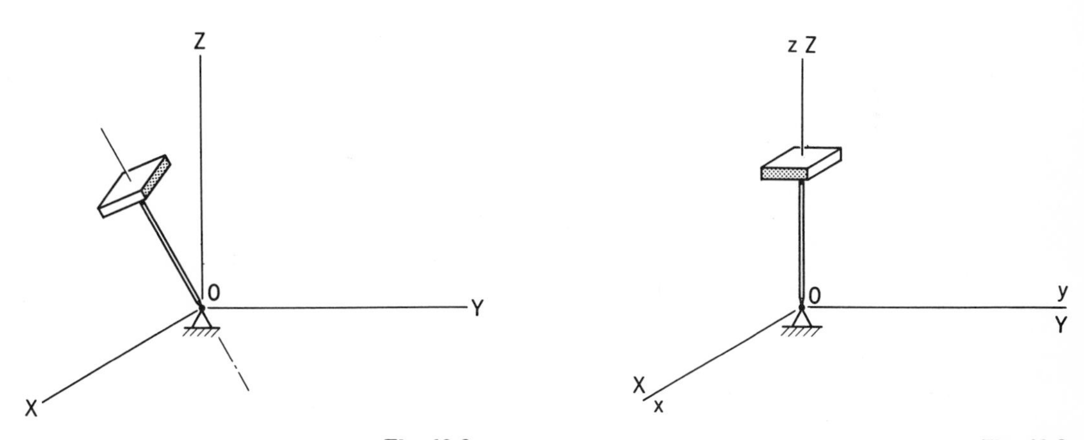

Fig. 19.2

Fig. 19.3

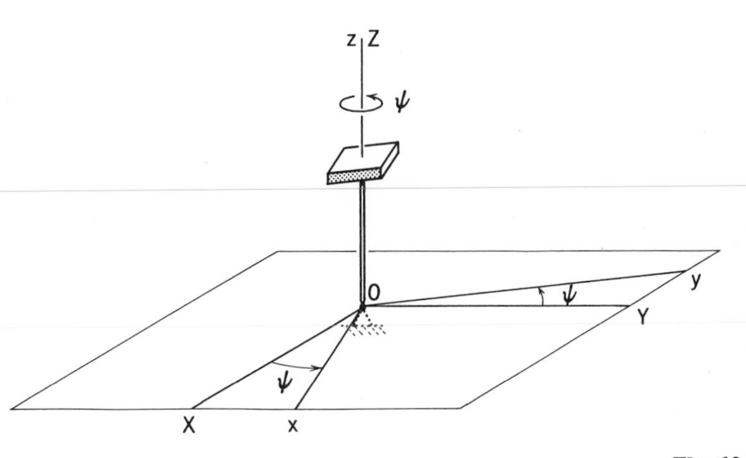

Fig. 19.4

2. Now rotate the body about the x axis through an angle θ to reach the configuration in Fig. 19.5. Note that the z, Z, and y axes form a plane I normal to the XY plane and normal consequently to the x axis. The axis of rotation for this rotation (x axis) is called the *line of nodes*.
3. Finally, rotate the body an angle ϕ about the z axis. We provide the option here of detaching the xyz reference from the body for this movement (see Fig. 19.6), in which case the body rotates an angle ϕ relative to xyz, and the x axis remains collinear with the line of nodes. Or, we can permit the reference xyz to remain fixed in the body (see Fig. 19.7), in which case we may use components of $\boldsymbol{M}$, and $\boldsymbol{\omega}$, along these axes in employing Euler's equations.

We thus arrive at the desired orientation. Positive rotations in each case are those taken as counterclockwise as one looks to the origin O along the axis of rotation. (Thus we have instituted three positive rotations here.)

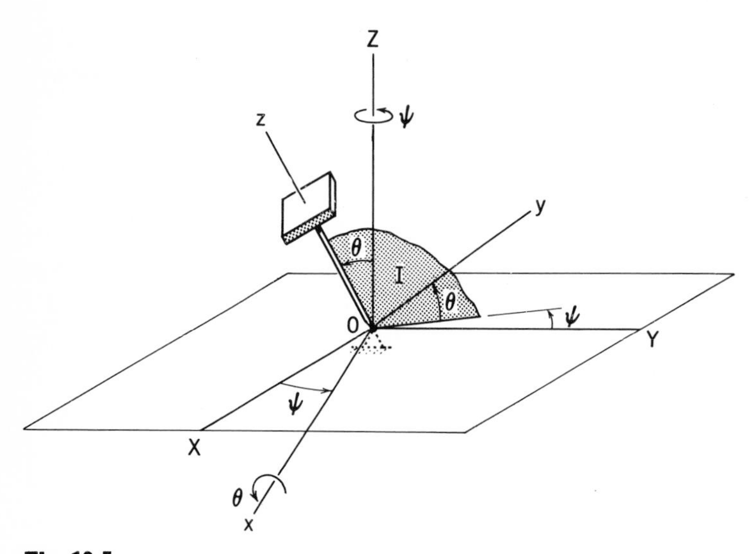

Fig. 19.5

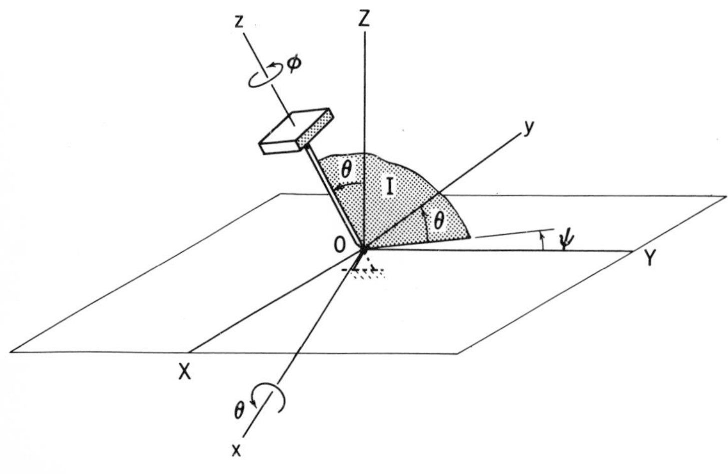

Fig. 19.6

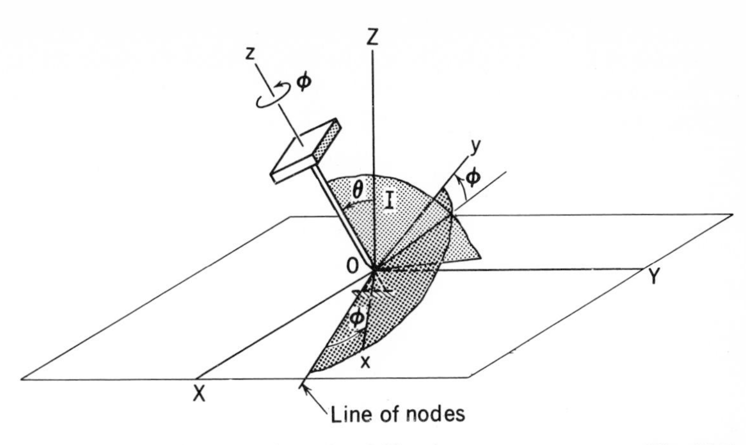

Fig. 19.7

We call these angles the *Euler angles* and we assign the following names.

ψ = the angle of precession,

θ = the angle of nutation,

ϕ = the angle of spin.

Furthermore, the z axis is usually called the *body axis* and the Z axis is often called the *axis of precession.*

We have shown that the position of a body moving with one point fixed can be established by three rotations given in a certain sequence. For an infinitesimal change in position, this would mean a rotation $d\psi$ about the Z axis, $d\theta$ about the line of nodes, and $d\phi$ about the body axis z. Because these rotations are infinitesimal, they may be construed as vectors, and the order mentioned above is no longer required. The limiting ratios of these changes in angles with respect to time give rise to three angular velocity vectors (Fig. 19.8), which we express in the following manner:

$\dot{\boldsymbol{\psi}}$, directed along the Z axis;

$\dot{\boldsymbol{\theta}}$, directed along the line of nodes;

$\dot{\boldsymbol{\phi}}$, directed along the z body axis.

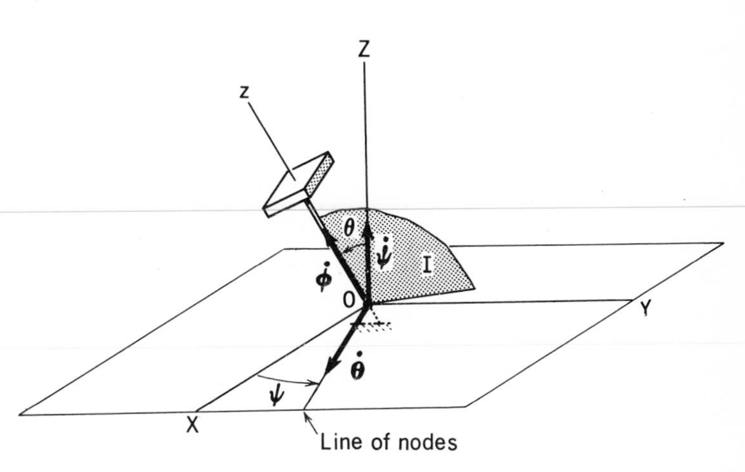

Fig. 19.8

Note that the nutation velocity vector $\dot{\boldsymbol{\theta}}$ is always normal to plane I and consequently it is always normal to the spin velocity vector $\dot{\boldsymbol{\phi}}$ and the precession velocity vector $\dot{\boldsymbol{\psi}}$. However, the spin velocity vector $\dot{\boldsymbol{\phi}}$ will generally *not* be at right angles with the precession velocity $\dot{\boldsymbol{\psi}}$ and so this system of angular velocity vectors generally is *not* an orthogonal system.

Finally, it should be clear that the reference xyz moves with the body during precession and nutation motion of the body, but we may choose that it not move (relative to XYZ) during a spin rotation. Hence, while the body has the angular velocity $\dot{\boldsymbol{\phi}} + \dot{\boldsymbol{\psi}} + \dot{\boldsymbol{\theta}}$ at any time t, the reference xyz would have for the aforestated condition an angular velocity, denoted as $\boldsymbol{\Omega}$, equal to $\dot{\boldsymbol{\psi}} + \dot{\boldsymbol{\theta}}$. The velocity of the disc relative to xyz is accordingly $\dot{\phi}\boldsymbol{k}$ for this case. To illustrate how such a reference xyz can be chosen in a physical problem consider Fig. 19.9. A gimbal G is shown moving relative to XYZ with point O fixed at all times. The gimbal moves in such a way that its midplane is coplanar with the Z axis at all times, forming plane I as shown in the diagram. The centerline of the gimbal can rotate about the Z axis with angular speed $\dot{\psi}$ and can simultaneously have a varying value for angle θ. Mounted in the gimbal is a disc D rotating relative to G at an angular speed $\dot{\phi}$. If we choose a reference xyz fixed to the gimbal such that z is along the axis of the disc D as shown, and such that the y axis is in the aforementioned plane I, we have a situation where xyz corresponds exactly, in a physical situation, to the reference xyz we have set forth in the discussion. Clearly, the x axis here is the line of nodes and $\boldsymbol{\Omega}$ is simply the angular velocity of the gimbal. In problems where no gimbal exists to simplify the choice of xyz we often take the y axis to be coplanar both with the body axis z and the axis of precession Z, so that the x axis then becomes the line of nodes.

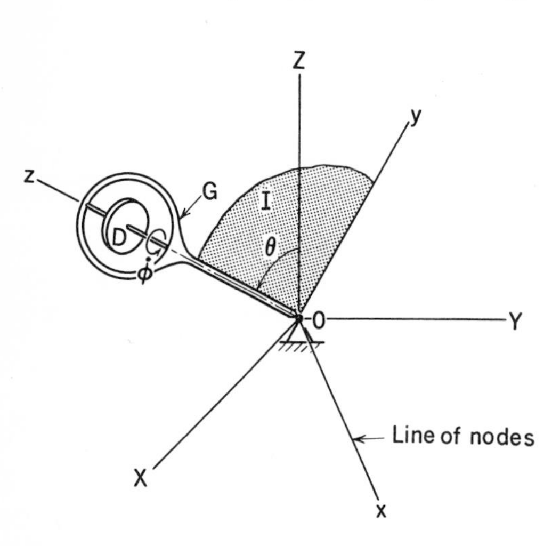

Fig. 19.9

19.3 Equations of Motion

Consider next a body having a shape such that, at any point along the body axis z, the moments of inertia for axes normal to the body axis have the same value for all directions at that point. Such would, of course, be true for the special case of a body of revolution having the z axis as the axis of symmetry.* We shall consider the motion of such a body about a fixed point O along the axis z (see Fig. 19.10). Reference xyz, as explained in the previous section, has the same nutation and precession motion as the body but will be chosen such that the body rotates with an angular speed $\dot{\phi}$ relative to it. Since the reference is not fixed to the body we cannot use Euler's equations but must go back to the equation $\boldsymbol{M} = \dot{\boldsymbol{H}}$, which when carried out in terms of components parallel to the xyz reference becomes:

$$\boldsymbol{M} = \left(\frac{d\boldsymbol{H}}{dt}\right)_{xyz} + \boldsymbol{\Omega} \times (H_x\boldsymbol{i} + H_y\boldsymbol{j} + H_z\boldsymbol{k}) \qquad \textbf{19.1}$$

Since the xyz axes remain at *all times* principal axes we have:

* You will be asked to show in Prob. 27 that, if I_{xx}, I_{yy}, and I_{zz} are principal axes and $I_{xx} = I_{yy} = I'$, then $I_{x'x'} = I_{y'y'} = I'$ for *any* axes x', y' formed by rotating xyz about the z axis. Thus, homogeneous cylinders having regular cross sections such as squares or octagons would meet the requirements of this section.

$$H_x = I'\omega_x, \qquad H_y = I'\omega_y, \qquad H_z = I\omega_z \qquad \textbf{19.2}$$

where I is the moment of inertia about the axis of symmetry and I' is the moment of inertia about an axis normal to the axis of symmetry at O. Considering Fig. 19.10 we see by inspection that the angular velocity of the body relative to XYZ is at *all times* given by components parallel to xyz as follows:

$$\omega_x = \dot{\theta} \qquad \textbf{(a)}$$

$$\omega_y = \dot{\psi} \sin\theta \qquad \textbf{(b)}$$

$$\omega_z = \dot{\phi} + \dot{\psi} \cos\theta \qquad \textbf{(c)} \qquad \textbf{19.3}$$

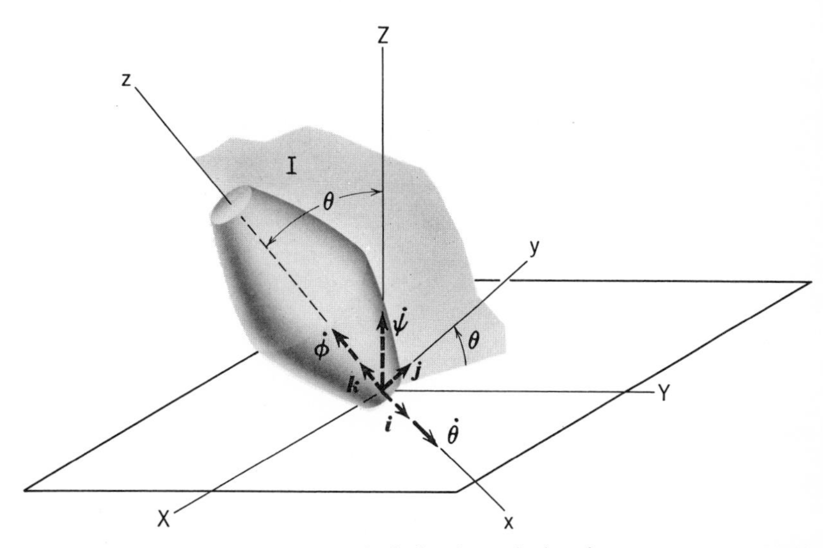

Fig. 19.10

Hence, the components of the angular momentum and their time derivatives are:

$$(H_x) = I'\dot{\theta}, \qquad \dot{H}_x = I'\ddot{\theta}$$

$$(H_y) = I'\dot{\psi}\sin\theta, \qquad \dot{H}_y = I'(\ddot{\psi}\sin\theta + \dot{\psi}\dot{\theta}\cos\theta)$$

$$(H_z) = I(\dot{\phi} + \dot{\psi}\cos\theta), \qquad \dot{H}_z = I(\ddot{\phi} + \ddot{\psi}\cos\theta - \dot{\psi}\dot{\theta}\sin\theta) \qquad \textbf{19.4}$$

As for the angular velocity of reference xyz we have:

$$\mathbf{\Omega} = \dot{\theta}\mathbf{i} + \dot{\psi}\sin\theta\mathbf{j} + \dot{\psi}\cos\theta\mathbf{k} \qquad \textbf{19.5}$$

Consequently we have

$$\mathbf{\Omega} \times \mathbf{i} = -\dot{\psi}\sin\theta\mathbf{k} + \dot{\psi}\cos\theta\mathbf{j}$$

$$\mathbf{\Omega} \times \mathbf{j} = \dot{\theta}\mathbf{k} - \dot{\psi}\cos\theta\mathbf{i}$$

$$\mathbf{\Omega} \times \mathbf{k} = -\dot{\theta}\mathbf{j} + \dot{\psi}\sin\theta\mathbf{i} \qquad \textbf{19.6}$$

Substituting the results from Eqs. 19.4 and 19.6 into Eq. 19.1, we get:

$$\begin{aligned} M_x\mathbf{i} + M_y\mathbf{j} + M_z\mathbf{k} = {} & I'\ddot{\phi}\mathbf{i} + I'(\ddot{\psi}\sin\theta + \dot{\psi}\dot{\theta}\cos\theta)\mathbf{j} \\ & + I(\ddot{\phi} + \ddot{\psi}\cos\theta - \dot{\psi}\dot{\theta}\sin\theta)\mathbf{k} \\ & + I'\dot{\theta}(-\dot{\psi}\sin\theta\mathbf{k} + \dot{\psi}\cos\theta\mathbf{j}) \\ & + I'\dot{\psi}\sin\theta(\dot{\theta}\mathbf{k} - \dot{\psi}\cos\theta\mathbf{i}) \\ & + I(\dot{\phi} + \dot{\psi}\cos\theta)(-\dot{\theta}\mathbf{j} + \dot{\psi}\sin\theta\mathbf{i}) \end{aligned} \qquad \textbf{19.7}$$

The corresponding scalar equations are:

$$M_x = I'\ddot{\theta} + (I - I')(\dot{\psi}^2 \sin\theta\cos\theta) + I\dot{\phi}\dot{\psi}\sin\theta \qquad \text{(a)}$$

$$M_y = I'\ddot{\psi}\sin\theta + 2I'\dot{\theta}\dot{\psi}\cos\theta - I(\dot{\phi} + \dot{\psi}\cos\theta)\dot{\theta} \qquad \text{(b)}$$

$$M_z = I(\ddot{\phi} + \ddot{\psi}\cos\theta - \dot{\psi}\dot{\theta}\sin\theta) \qquad \text{(c)} \qquad \mathbf{19.8}$$

The above equations are valid for the motion of a homogeneous body having $I_{xx} = I_{yy} = I'$ moving about a point on the axis of symmetry fixed in inertial space. It should be clear that these equations are also applicable for motion about the center of mass for such bodies. Note that the equations are nonlinear and except for certain special cases are very difficult to integrate. They are, of course, very useful as they stand when computer methods are to be employed.

As a special case we shall now consider a motion involving a constant nutation angle θ, a constant spin speed $\dot{\phi}$, and a constant precession speed $\dot{\psi}$. Such a motion is termed *steady precession.*

To determine the torque $\boldsymbol{M}$ for a given steady precession we set $\dot{\theta}$, $\ddot{\phi}$, and $\ddot{\psi}$ equal to zero in Eq. 19.8. Accordingly we get the following result:

$$M_x = [I(\dot{\phi} + \dot{\psi}\cos\theta) - I'\dot{\psi}\cos\theta]\dot{\psi}\sin\theta \qquad \text{(a)}$$

$$M_y = 0 \qquad \text{(b)}$$

$$M_z = 0 \qquad \text{(c)} \qquad \mathbf{19.9}$$

We see that for such a motion, we require a *constant torque about the line of nodes* as given by Eq. (a). Noting that $\dot{\phi} + \dot{\psi}\cos\theta = \omega_z$ from Eq. 19.3(c), this torque may be given as:

$$M_x = (I\omega_z - I'\dot{\psi}\cos\theta)\dot{\psi}\sin\theta \qquad \mathbf{19.10}$$

Examining Fig. 19.10, we can conclude that for the body to maintain a constant spin speed $\dot{\phi}$ about its body axis (i.e., relative to xyz) while the body axis (and also xyz) is rotating at constant speed about the Z axis at a fixed angle θ, one requires a constant torque having a value dependent on the motion of the body as well as the values of the moments of inertia of the body, and having a direction always normal to the body and precession axes (i.e., normal to plane I). Intuitively you may feel that such a torque should cause a rotation about its own axis (the so-called *torque-axis*) and should thereby change θ. Instead the torque causes a rotation $\dot{\psi}$ of the body axis about an axis *normal* to the torque axis. As an example, consider the special case where θ has been chosen as 90° for motion of a disc about its center of mass (see Fig. 19.11). According to Eq. 19.10 we have as a required torque for a steady precession the result:

$$M_x = I\omega_z\dot{\psi} = I\dot{\phi}\dot{\psi} \qquad \mathbf{19.11}$$

Here the proper torque about the line of nodes maintains a steady rotation of the spin axis z

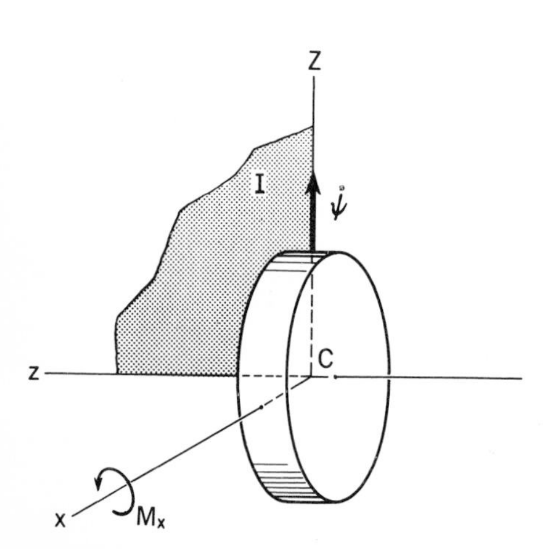

Fig. 19.11

about an axis (the Z axis), which is at *right angles* both to the torque and the spin axis. Because of this rather unexpected phenomenon, toy manufacturers have developed various gyroscopic devices to surprise and delight children (as well as their parents). Here is yet another case where relying solely on intuition may lead one to highly erroneous conclusions.*

It should be strongly pointed out that steady precessions are not easily initiated. One must have, at the start, simultaneously the proper precession and spin speeds as well as the proper θ for the given applied torque. If these conditions are not properly met initially, a complicated motion ensues. We shall consider one example of such a motion later in this chapter when we consider the spinning top.

We shall now consider a series of problems designed to acquaint the student with various practical devices in gyrodynamics.

EXAMPLE 19.1

Shown in Fig. 19.12 is a *single-degree-of-freedom gyro*. The spin axis of disc E is held by a gimbal A which can rotate about bearings C and D. These bearings are supported by the gyro case which in turn is generally clamped to the vehicle to be guided. If the gyro case rotates about a vertical axis (i.e., normal to its base) while the rotor is spinning, the gimbal A will tend to rotate about CD in an attempt to align with the vertical. When gimbal A is restrained by a set of torsional springs S with a combined torsional spring constant given as K_t, the gyro is called a *rate gyro*. If the rotation of the gyro case is constant and the gimbal A assumes a fixed orientation relative to the vertical as a result of the restraining springs and a damper (not shown), we have a case of regular precession. The rotation of the gyro case gives the precession speed $\dot{\psi}$ about the precession axis which clearly is the vertical axis. The nutation angle θ is then the orientation of gimbal A (i.e., the z axis) with the Z axis.

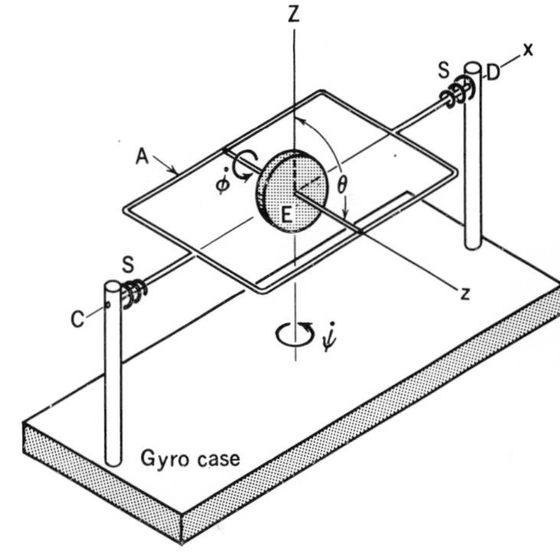

Single degree of freedom gyro

Fig. 19.12

Given the following data:

$$I = 3 \times 10^{-4} \text{ slugs-ft}^2$$

$$I' = 1.5 \times 10^{-4} \text{ slugs-ft}^2$$

$$\dot{\phi} = 20{,}000 \text{ rad/sec}$$

$$K_t = 4.95 \text{ ft-lb/rad}$$

$$\dot{\psi} = 1 \text{ rad/sec}$$

what is θ for the condition of steady precession?

Choosing reference xyz here is a simple matter. We need merely attach the reference to the gimbal A. The normal to plane I (i.e., the plane of z and Z) is simply the axis CD of the gimbal, and so CD must at all times be collinear with the line of nodes. Accordingly, the x axis is easily established as has been

* In Problem 4, you will be asked to set forth with the aid of hints a physical argument for this action.

shown in the diagram. Thus we have for Eq. 19.9(a):

$$M_x = K_t\left(\frac{\pi}{2} - \theta\right)$$

$$= [I(\dot{\phi} + \dot{\psi}\cos\theta) - I'\dot{\psi}\cos\theta]\dot{\psi}\sin\theta \quad \textbf{(a)}$$

Putting in numerical values, we have:

$$(4.95)\left(\frac{\pi}{2} - \theta\right) = [3 \times 10^{-4}(2 \times 10^4 + \cos\theta) - 1.5 \times 10^{-4}\cos\theta]\sin\theta$$

$$\therefore\ 4.95 \times 10^4\left(\frac{\pi}{2} - \theta\right) = (6 \times 10^4 + 1.5\cos\theta)\sin\theta$$

We can neglect the term $(1.5 \cos\theta)$ and so we have:

$$4.95\left(\frac{\pi}{2} - \theta\right) = 6\sin\theta$$

$$\therefore\ \left(\frac{\pi}{2} - \theta\right) = 1.210\sin\theta \quad \textbf{(b)}$$

Solving by trial and error, we get:

$$\theta = 43° \quad \textbf{(c)}$$

The way the rate gyro is used in practice is to maintain θ close to 90° by a small motor. The torque M_x developed to maintain this angle is measured, and from Eq. 19.9(a) we have available the proper $\dot{\psi}$ which tells us of the rate of rotation of the gyro case and hence the rate of rotation of the vehicle about an axis normal to the gyro case. Now $\dot{\psi}$ need not be constant as was the case in this problem. If it does not vary very rapidly, the results from Eq. 19.9(a) can be taken as instantaneously valid even though the equation, strictly speaking, stems from steady precession where $\dot{\psi}$ should be constant.

EXAMPLE 19.2

Shown in Fig. 19.13 is a *two-degree-of-freedom gyroscope*. The rotor E is held by a gimbal A, which is turn is held by a gimbal C such that the axes bb of the rotor and aa of the gimbal C are at right angles to each other. Gimbal C is held by bearings c supported by the gyro case. Axes cc and aa must always be at right angles to each other, as can easily be seen from the diagram. This kind of suspension of the motor is called a *Cardan suspension*. If the bearings are frictionless, a torque cannot be transmitted from the gyro case to the rotor.* The disc is said to be torque-free for this case.

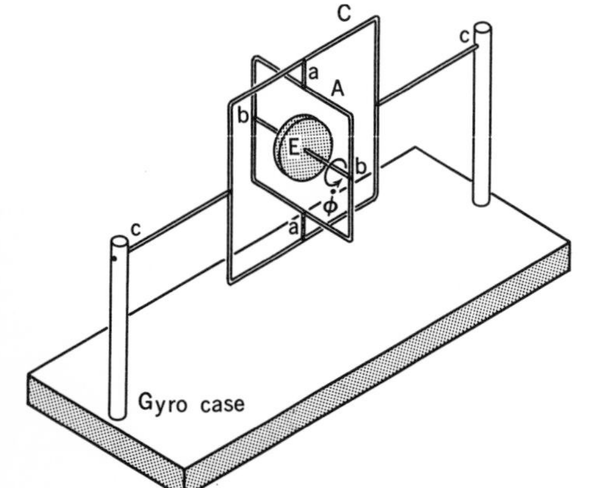

Two-degree of freedom gyro

Fig. 19.13

If the rotor is given a rapid spin velocity in a given direction in inertial space (such as toward the North Star), then for the ideal case of frictionless bearings the rotor will maintain this direction even though the gyro case is given rapid and complicated motions in inertial space, since no torque can be transmitted to the rotor to alter the direction of its angular momentum. Thus the two-dimensional gyro gives a fixed direction in inertial space for purposes of

* That is, except for the singular situation where the gimbal axes are coplanar.

guidance of a vehicle such as a missile. In use, the gyro case is rigidly fixed to the frame of the missile and measurements of the orientation of the missile are accomplished by having pickoffs mounted between the gyro case and the outer gimbal and between the outer and inner gimbals. We shall investigate the characteristics of torque-free motion of this kind in a more general way in Section 19.5.

The presence of some friction in the gyro bearings is, of course, inevitable. It is the counteraction of this friction when this is possible and, when not, the accounting of its action, that is of much concern to the gyro engineer. Suppose that the gyro has been given a motion such that the axis *bb* (see Fig. 19.14) has an angular speed ω_1 about axis *cc* of 0.1 rev/sec while maintaining a fixed orientation of 85° with axis *cc*. The gyro case is stationary and the spin speed $\dot{\phi}$ of the disc relative to gimbal *A* is 10,000 rpm. What torque is developed on the rotor? From what bearings must such a torque arise? The radius of gyration for the disc is 2 in. for the axis of symmetry and 1.5 in. for the transverse axes. The mass of the disc is 1 lbm.

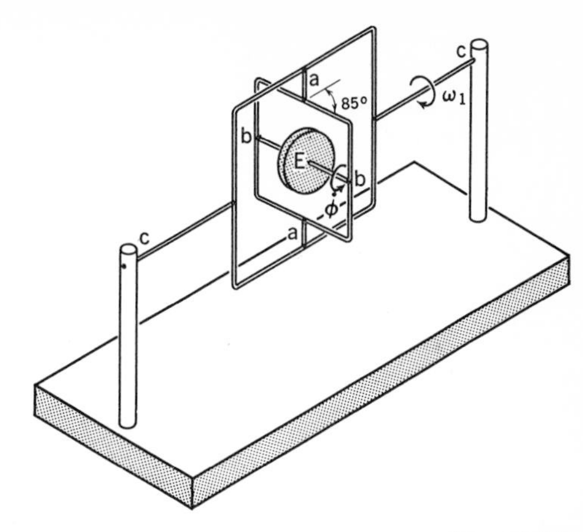

Fig. 19.14

We have here a case of steady precession motion. The precession axis is clearly *cc* and the precession speed is 0.10 rps. The nutation angle θ is 85°. A constant torque M_x is required to maintain this motion where the x axis now clearly corresponds to *aa*. We can solve for M_x as follows:

$$M_x = \{I[\dot{\phi} + \dot{\psi}\cos\theta] - I'\dot{\psi}\cos\theta\}\dot{\psi}\sin\theta$$

$$= \left\{\frac{1}{32.2}\left(\frac{2}{12}\right)^2\left[10{,}000\,\frac{2\pi}{60} + (0.1)(2\pi)\cos 85°\right]\right.$$

$$\left. - \frac{1}{32.2}\left(\frac{1.5}{12}\right)^2 (0.1)(2\pi)\cos 85°\right\}$$

$$\times (0.1)(2\pi)\sin 85°$$

$$= 0.564 \text{ ft-lb}$$

Thus, bearings along the *a-a* axis interconnecting the two gimbals are developing the frictional torque.

In the preceding examples we employed the results developed for steady precession. In the following example we again have a steady precession problem, but we shall proceed from the basic equation, $\boldsymbol{M} = \dot{\boldsymbol{H}}$. You will be asked to solve a number of problems by going back to first principles in this manner.

EXAMPLE 19.3

Shown in Fig. 19.15(a) is a thin disc *A* weighing 100 lb mounted on a shaft light *BC* about which it is free to rotate. The shaft is connected by a clevis connection at *B* to a vertical shaft which is rotating at a constant angular speed ω_1 of 2 rad/sec. If the disc rolls without slipping, what is the force developed by the ground on the disc?

A reference xyz is fixed to bar BC as shown in Fig. 19.15(a). Accordingly, the disc rotates with speed ω_2 relative to xyz. This reference rotates with angular speed ω_1 about the vertical axis BE. We shall first compute the total angular velocity $\boldsymbol{\omega}$ of the disc relative to the ground. Noting that the line of contact is in the direction BD, we form the angular velocity vector diagram as shown in Fig. 19.15(b). From this diagram we get the following results:

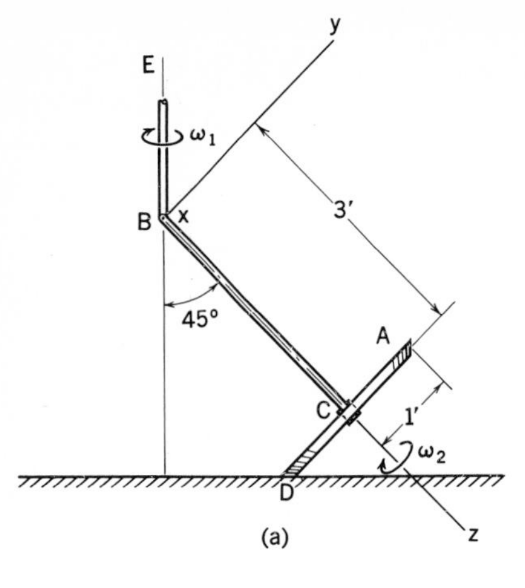

(a)

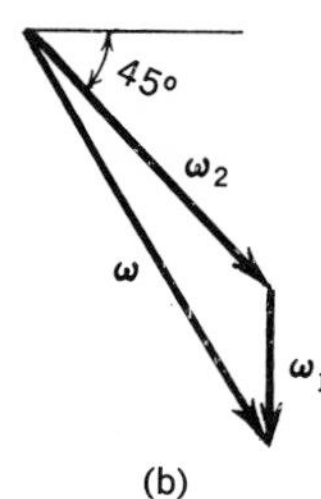

(b)

Fig. 19.15

$$\omega_2 = 2.83 \text{ rad/sec} \qquad \omega = 4.46 \text{ rad/sec} \qquad \textbf{(a)}$$

Now let us consider the equation $\boldsymbol{M} = \dot{\boldsymbol{H}}$ about stationary point B. Noting that the moments of inertia of the disc about B are constant as seen from xyz at all times, and that xyz are principal axes we get:

$$\boldsymbol{M} = \left(\frac{d\boldsymbol{H}}{dt}\right)_{xyz} + \boldsymbol{\Omega} \times \boldsymbol{H} = I'\dot{\omega}_x\boldsymbol{i} + I'\dot{\omega}_y\boldsymbol{j} + I\dot{\omega}_z\boldsymbol{k}$$
$$+ I'\omega_x\boldsymbol{\Omega} \times \boldsymbol{i} + I'\omega_y\boldsymbol{\Omega} \times \boldsymbol{j} + I\omega_z\boldsymbol{\Omega} \times \boldsymbol{k} \qquad \textbf{(b)}$$

Furthermore, the components of $\boldsymbol{\omega}$ along xyz are constant with time so that the first three terms on the right side of the above equation are zero. And noting that

$$\boldsymbol{\Omega} = -\omega_1 \sin 45°\boldsymbol{j} + \omega_1 \cos 45°\boldsymbol{k}$$
$$= -1.414\boldsymbol{j} + 1.414\boldsymbol{k} \qquad \textbf{(c)}$$

we have for $\boldsymbol{M}$:

$$\boldsymbol{M} = (I'\omega_x)(1.414\boldsymbol{k} + 1.414\boldsymbol{j}) + (I'\omega_y)(-1.414\boldsymbol{i}) + (I\omega_z)(-1.414\boldsymbol{i})$$

Inserting values for I' and I and noting that $\omega_x = 0$, $\omega_y = -1.414$ and $\omega_z = 4.24$, we get:

$$\boldsymbol{M} = \left(\frac{1}{4}\frac{100}{32.2}1^2 + \frac{100}{g_0}3^2\right)(-1.414)(-1.414\boldsymbol{i})$$
$$+ \left(\frac{1}{2}\frac{100}{32.2}1^2\right)(4.24)(-1.414\boldsymbol{i})$$
$$= 48.2\boldsymbol{i} \qquad \textbf{(d)}$$

Now employing the free body diagram in Fig. 19.16 and equating moments of the force system about the x axis at B we get:*

$$48.2 = 3 \cos 45°W - (3 \sin 45° - 1 \cos 45°)N$$
$$\therefore\ N = 116 \text{ lb.}$$

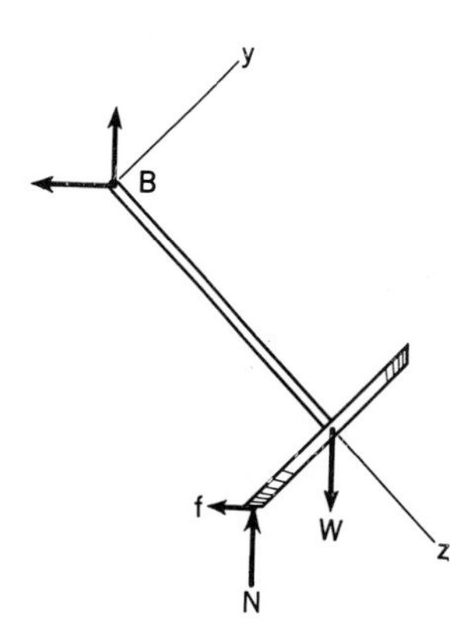

Fig. 19.16

Had we desired to employ the steady precession equations, we would have arrived at the xyz reference above by placing the y axis in plane I—i.e., in the plane formed by body axis z and the axis of rotation BE. The x axis would then be the line of modes.

A considerably enlarged force can be developed by the disc on the ground as a result of the gyroscopic action when BC is horizontal. Devices for milling and

* We are neglecting frictional effects at the contact surface in the radial direction.

crushing are developed to take advantage of this effect.

In the final example of this series we examine a case where we do not have steady precession. Hence we must go back to the basic equation $\boldsymbol{M} = \dot{\boldsymbol{H}}$.

---

*EXAMPLE 19.4

We shall now explain the operation of the *gyro-compass*, a very interesting device that gives the direction to the geometric north pole (not the magnetic north pole). Essentially, it is a gyroscope whose symmetric axis (z axis) is confined to motion parallel to the surface of the earth (which we shall take as a sphere) by gravitational action on what we call a pendulous weight W (see Fig. 19.17). Note that we are observing the gyro-compass in this diagram at various portions in the Southern Hemisphere from a viewpoint above the north pole, thus exposing the pendulous weight to view. The compass is not necessarily "pointing north" in the figure.

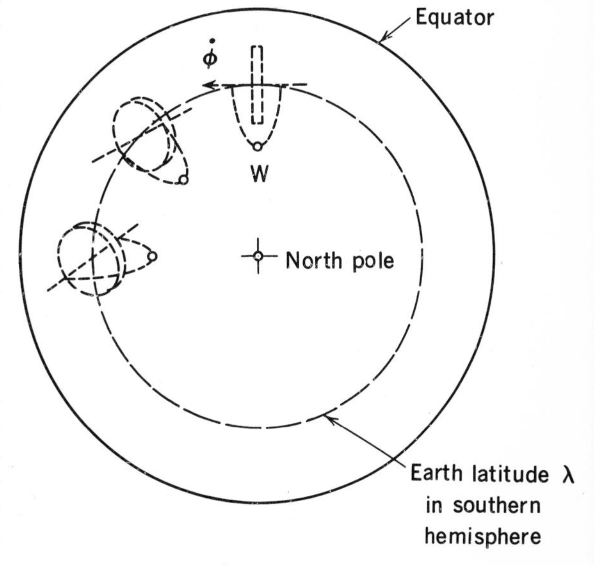

Fig. 19.17

For simplicity, we shall consider a gyro-compass at a fixed position on the earth's surface. The body axis z of the gyro-compass can rotate in plane T tangent to the earth's surface as shown in Fig. 19.18, where the z axis is at an angle α with the tangent to the meridian line. Since the angle α may vary with time, we have a possible angular velocity vector $\dot{\boldsymbol{\alpha}}$ with a direction normal to the plane T. The y axis is a radial line from the center of the earth at O and therefore is at all times collinear with $\dot{\boldsymbol{\alpha}}$. The x axis then is chosen to form a right-hand triad and is in plane T. An inertial reference XYZ is chosen at the center of the earth so that the Z axis is along the south-north axis. Clearly, the gyroscope, in addition to its spin velocity $\dot{\boldsymbol{\phi}}$ along z and its swinging motion $\dot{\boldsymbol{\alpha}}$ along y, also has a precession velocity $\dot{\boldsymbol{\psi}}$ along Z, where $\dot{\boldsymbol{\psi}}$ is the angular velocity of the earth, a constant vector of small magnitude. For convenience, another Z axis has been set up at the gyroscope. The angle between Z and the tangent to the meridian designated as λ is just the latitude of the position of the gyro-compass. Note that the nutation velocity $\dot{\boldsymbol{\theta}}$ is not conveniently given here explicitly. (It is actually a function of α and $\dot{\alpha}$.)

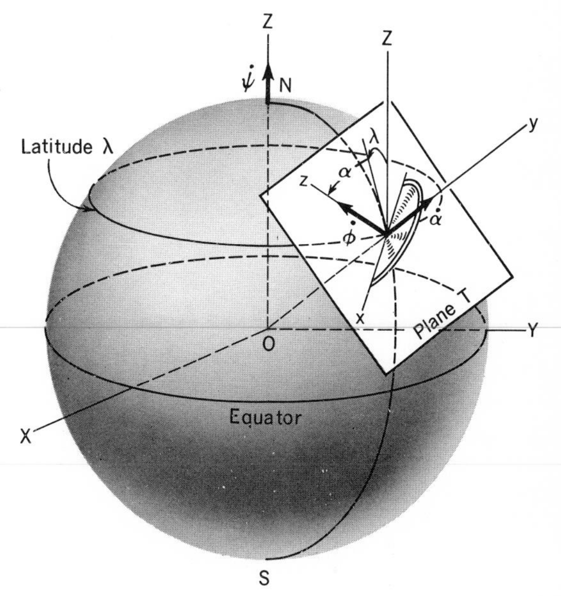

Fig. 19.18

Since we have chosen a set of axes xyz that is not fixed to the body, we must return to the equation $\boldsymbol{M} = \dot{\boldsymbol{H}}_c$, which, when carried out in terms of components parallel to xyz, becomes:

$$\boldsymbol{M} = \left(\frac{d\boldsymbol{H}_c}{dt}\right)_{xyz} + \boldsymbol{\Omega} \times \boldsymbol{H}_c$$

$$= (\dot{\boldsymbol{H}}_c)_x\boldsymbol{i} + (\dot{\boldsymbol{H}}_c)_y\boldsymbol{j} + (\dot{\boldsymbol{H}}_c)_z\boldsymbol{k}$$

$$+ (H_c)_x\dot{\boldsymbol{i}} + (H_c)_y\dot{\boldsymbol{j}} + (H_c)_z\dot{\boldsymbol{k}} \qquad \textbf{(a)}$$

Note that xyz are principal axes at all times and that we have:

$$(H_c)_x = I'\omega_x, \quad (H_c)_y = I'\omega_y, \quad (H_c)_z = I\omega_z \tag{b}$$

Considering Fig. 19.18, we see that the angular velocity components of the disc are easily established by inspection to be *at all times*:

$$\omega_x = -\dot{\psi}\cos\lambda\sin\alpha \tag{c}$$

$$\omega_y = \dot{\alpha} + \dot{\psi}\sin\lambda \tag{d}$$

$$\omega_z = \dot{\phi} + \dot{\psi}\cos\lambda\cos\alpha \tag{e}$$

Thus we have for the components of the moments of momentum:

$$(H_c)_x = -I'(\dot{\psi}\cos\lambda\sin\alpha) \tag{f}$$

$$(H_c)_y = I'(\dot{\alpha} + \dot{\psi}\sin\lambda) \tag{g}$$

$$(H_c)_z = I(\dot{\phi} + \dot{\psi}\cos\lambda\cos\alpha) \tag{h}$$

The angular velocity components of xyz are seen to be

$$\Omega_x = -\dot{\psi}\cos\lambda\sin\alpha \tag{i}$$

$$\Omega_y = \dot{\alpha} + \dot{\psi}\sin\lambda \tag{j}$$

$$\Omega_z = \dot{\psi}\cos\lambda\cos\alpha \tag{k}$$

We can now write Eq. (a) as:

$$\begin{aligned} M_x\boldsymbol{i} + M_y\boldsymbol{j} + M_z\boldsymbol{k} = {} & I'\frac{d}{dt}(-\dot{\psi}\cos\lambda\sin\alpha)\boldsymbol{i} \\ & + I'\frac{d}{dt}(\dot{\alpha} + \dot{\psi}\sin\lambda)\boldsymbol{j} \\ & + I\frac{d}{dt}(\dot{\phi} + \dot{\psi}\cos\lambda\cos\alpha)\boldsymbol{k} \\ & - I'\dot{\psi}\cos\lambda\sin\alpha(-\Omega_y\boldsymbol{k} + \Omega_z\boldsymbol{j}) \\ & + I'(\dot{\alpha} + \dot{\psi}\sin\lambda)(\Omega_x\boldsymbol{k} - \Omega_z\boldsymbol{i}) \\ & + I(\dot{\phi} + \dot{\psi}\cos\lambda\cos\alpha) \\ & \times(-\Omega_x\boldsymbol{j} + \Omega_y\boldsymbol{i}) \end{aligned} \tag{l}$$

Next consider the external moments acting on the disc. Only a torque keeping the z axis in the plane T is present and it is in the x direction; therefore, $M_z = M_y = 0$. We shall thus consider the y and z components of the above equation. Substituting from Eqs. (i), (j), and (k) we get, after collecting terms:

$$\begin{aligned} 0 = {} & I'\ddot{\alpha} - I'(\dot{\psi}\cos\lambda\sin\alpha)(\dot{\psi}\cos\lambda\cos\alpha) \\ & + I(\dot{\phi} + \dot{\psi}\cos\lambda\cos\alpha)(\dot{\psi}\cos\lambda\sin\alpha) \end{aligned} \tag{m}$$

$$\begin{aligned} 0 = {} & I(\ddot{\phi} - \dot{\psi}\dot{\alpha}\cos\lambda\sin\alpha) \\ & + I'\dot{\psi}\cos\lambda\sin\alpha(\dot{\alpha} + \dot{\psi}\sin\lambda) \\ & - I'(\dot{\alpha} + \dot{\psi}\sin\lambda)(\dot{\psi}\cos\lambda\sin\alpha) \end{aligned} \tag{n}$$

As has been noted, $\dot{\psi}$ is small and so we shall drop terms containing $\dot{\psi}^2$. The above equations then simplify to:

$$I'\ddot{\alpha} + I\dot{\phi}\dot{\psi}\cos\lambda\sin\alpha = 0 \qquad \textbf{(o)}$$

$$I(\ddot{\phi} - \dot{\psi}\dot{\alpha}\cos\lambda\sin\alpha) = 0 \qquad \textbf{(p)}$$

Equation (p) shows that $\ddot{\phi}$ is a term of small value, since $\dot{\psi}\dot{\alpha}\cos\lambda\sin\alpha$ will be small; we can therefore consider $\dot{\phi}$ to be approximately constant. Looking at Eq. (o), we see that the coefficient of $\sin\alpha$ is then a constant and that this equation is of the form:

$$\ddot{\alpha} + C\sin\alpha = 0 \qquad \textbf{(q)}$$

where:

$$C = \frac{I\dot{\phi}\dot{\psi}\cos\lambda}{I'}$$

You may recognize this equation as that corresponding to the swinging pendulum. Thus the axis of the disc oscillates symmetrically about the meridian. The northerly direction is then at the mid-position of swing. Since $\dot{\psi}$ is small, it is necessary that the spin $\dot{\phi}$ be large so that the frequency of oscillation is kept high enough to make the readings more readily usable. With small initial values of α_0 and $\dot{\alpha}_0$, α (and $\dot{\alpha}$) will remain small, and, replacing $\sin\alpha$ by α in Eq. (q), we can say for such a case that the frequency of oscillation of the z axis about the meridian is:

$$f = \frac{1}{2\pi}\sqrt{\frac{I\dot{\phi}\dot{\psi}\cos\lambda}{I'}} \qquad \textbf{(r)}$$

*19.4 Euler's Equations

It will be convenient to be able to use Euler's equations in connection with motion about a fixed point. This requires that reference xyz be fixed in the body. Accordingly, we have shown a body moving about a fixed point in Fig. 19.19 with reference $x'y'z'$ corresponding to the reference we have used up to now. That is, x' is the line of nodes and y' is in plane I containing axes z and Z. The reference xyz, however, is fixed to the body and is shown at time t rotated an angle ϕ about the z axis measured from reference $x'y'z'$.

For Euler's equations we shall need ω_x, ω_y, and ω_z expressed in a form that is valid at any time t. Accordingly, the angular velocities $\dot{\psi}$, $\dot{\phi}$, and $\dot{\theta}$ have been shown in the diagram with $\dot{\psi}$ decomposed with orthogonal components along y' and z. We can then express ω_x, ω_y, and ω_z at any time as follows:

$$\omega_x = \dot{\theta}\cos\phi + \dot{\psi}\sin\theta\sin\phi \qquad \textbf{(a)}$$

$$\omega_y = -\dot{\theta}\sin\phi + \dot{\psi}\sin\theta\cos\phi \qquad \textbf{(b)}$$

$$\omega_z = \dot{\phi} + \dot{\psi}\cos\theta \qquad \textbf{(c)} \quad \textbf{19.12}$$

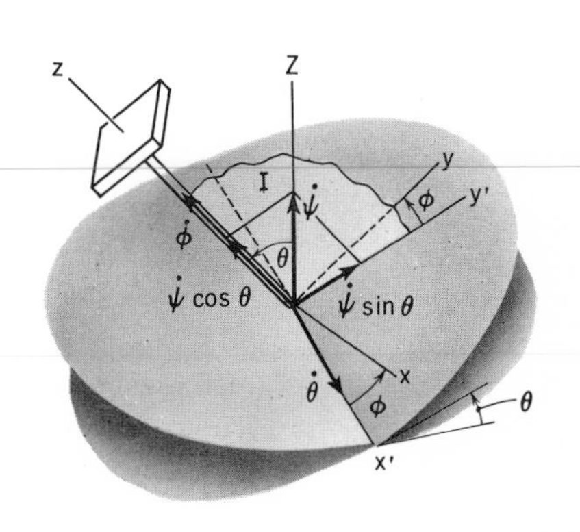

Fig. 19.19

And because these relations are valid at any time t, we have for $\dot{\omega}_x$, $\dot{\omega}_y$, and $\dot{\omega}_z$ the relations:

$$\dot{\omega}_x = \frac{d}{dt}(\dot{\theta}\cos\phi + \dot{\psi}\sin\theta\sin\phi) \qquad \text{(a)}$$

$$\dot{\omega}_y = \frac{d}{dt}(-\dot{\theta}\sin\phi + \dot{\psi}\sin\theta\cos\phi) \qquad \text{(b)}$$

$$\dot{\omega}_z = \frac{d}{dt}(\dot{\phi} + \dot{\psi}\cos\theta) \qquad \text{(c)} \quad \mathbf{19.13}$$

We may thus employ the above results in the familiar Euler's equations of motion about a fixed point or the center of mass.

*19.5 Torque-free Motion

We shall now consider *torque-free motion* for a body having $I_{xx} = I_{yy} = I'$ along the body axis. An example of a device which can approach such motion is the two-degree-of-freedom gyroscope described in Example 19.2.

Let us now examine the equations of torque-free motion. First consider the general relation:

$$\boldsymbol{M} = \dot{\boldsymbol{H}} \qquad \mathbf{19.14}$$

Since $\boldsymbol{M}$ is zero, $\boldsymbol{H}$ must be constant. Thus:

$$\boldsymbol{H} = \boldsymbol{H}_0 \qquad \mathbf{19.15}$$

where $\boldsymbol{H}_0$ is the initial moment of momentum either about a fixed point or about the mass center. Let us arrange the system so that the Z axis coincides with the direction of $\boldsymbol{H}_0$. This simplifies the problem and still does not detract from the generality of our conclusions. Using Fig. 19.19, we can then express $\boldsymbol{H}_0$ in terms of its x, y, and z components in the following way:

$$\boldsymbol{H}_0 = H_0\sin\theta\sin\phi\boldsymbol{i} + H_0\sin\theta\cos\phi\boldsymbol{j} + H_0\cos\theta\boldsymbol{k} \qquad \mathbf{19.16}$$

For principal axes, we may also state:

$$\boldsymbol{H}_0 = I'\omega_x\boldsymbol{i} + I'\omega_y\boldsymbol{j} + I\omega_z\boldsymbol{k} \qquad \mathbf{19.17}$$

Comparing Eqs. 19.16 and 19.17, we then have:

$$\omega_x = \frac{H_0\sin\theta\sin\phi}{I'} \qquad \text{(a)}$$

$$\omega_y = \frac{H_0\sin\theta\cos\phi}{I'} \qquad \text{(b)}$$

$$\omega_z = \frac{H_0\cos\theta}{I} \qquad \text{(c)} \quad \mathbf{19.18}$$

By using the preceding formulations for ω_x, ω_y, and ω_z, we can write Euler's equations in a form that includes the constant H_0 in the following way:

$$I'\frac{d}{dt}\left[\frac{H_0\sin\theta\sin\phi}{I'}\right] + \frac{I-I'}{II'}H_0^2\sin\theta\cos\theta\cos\phi = 0 \qquad \text{(a)}$$

$$I' \frac{d}{dt}\left[\frac{H_0 \sin\theta \cos\phi}{I'}\right] + \frac{I' - I}{I'I} H_0^2 \sin\theta \cos\theta \sin\phi = 0 \qquad \textbf{(b)}$$

$$I \frac{d}{dt}\left[\frac{H_0 \cos\theta}{I}\right] = 0 \qquad \textbf{(c)} \qquad \textbf{19.19}$$

From Eq. 19.19(c) it is then clear that:

$$\frac{H_0 \cos\theta}{I} = \text{const.} \qquad \textbf{19.20}$$

Thus, since H_0 and I are constant, we can conclude from this equation that the *nutation angle* is a fixed angle θ_0. Now consider Eq. 19.19(b), using the fact that $\theta = \theta_0$. Canceling H_0 and carrying out the differentiation, we get:

$$-\sin\theta_0 \sin\phi\, \dot{\phi} + \frac{I' - I}{I'I} H_0 \sin\theta_0 \cos\theta_0 \sin\phi = 0$$

$$\therefore\ \dot{\phi} = \frac{I' - I}{I'I} H_0 \cos\theta_0 \qquad \textbf{19.21}$$

Thus the *spin speed*, $\dot{\phi}$, is constant.

To get the precession speed, $\dot{\psi}$, we equate the right sides of Eqs. 19.12(c) and 19.18(c), which are expressions for ω_z:

$$\dot{\phi} + \dot{\psi} \cos\theta_0 = \frac{H_0 \cos\theta_0}{I} \qquad \textbf{19.22}$$

Substituting for $\dot{\phi}$ from Eq. 19.21 and solving for $\dot{\psi}$, we get:

$$\dot{\psi} = \frac{H_0}{I} - H_0 \frac{I' - I}{I'I}$$

Collecting terms, we have:

$$\dot{\psi} = \frac{H_0}{I}\left[1 - \frac{I' - I}{I'}\right] = \frac{H_0}{I'} \qquad \textbf{19.23}$$

The results of the discussion for torque-free motion of the body of revolution may then be given as:

$$\theta = \theta_0 \qquad \textbf{(a)}$$

$$\dot{\psi} = \frac{H_0}{I'} \qquad \textbf{(b)}$$

$$\dot{\phi} = \frac{I' - I}{I'I} H_0 \cos\theta_0 \qquad \textbf{(c)} \qquad \textbf{19.24}$$

Hence, if a body of revolution is torque-free—as, for example, in the case illustrated in Fig. 19.20, where the center of mass is fixed—and has initially an angular momentum vector $\boldsymbol{H}_0$ in the direction

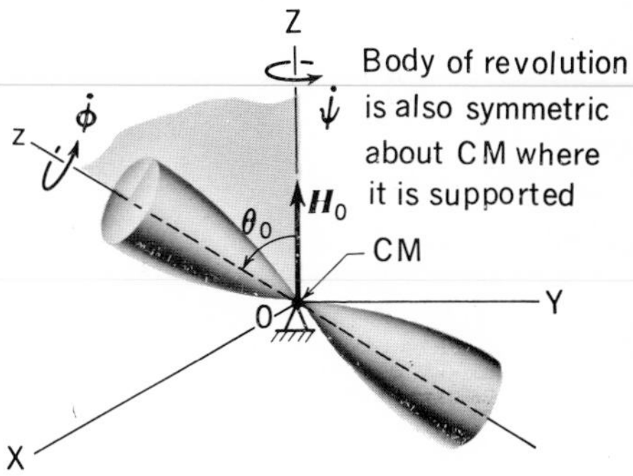

Body of revolution is also symmetric about CM where it is supported

Fig. 19.20

we have chosen for the Z axis, then the angular momentum $\boldsymbol{H}$ is constant and equals $\boldsymbol{H}_0$. Furthermore, the body will have a motion that consists of a constant angular velocity of the centerline about the Z axis (precession) at a fixed inclination θ_0 from Z, plus a constant spin speed $\dot{\phi}$ about the centerline. Thus two angular velocity vectors, $\dot{\boldsymbol{\psi}}$ and $\dot{\boldsymbol{\phi}}$, are present, and the total angular velocity $\boldsymbol{\omega}$ is at an inclination of ϵ from the Z axis (see Fig. 19.21) and precesses with angular speed $\dot{\psi}$ about the Z axis. This must be true, since the direction of one component, $\dot{\boldsymbol{\phi}}$, rotates in this manner while the other component, $\dot{\boldsymbol{\psi}}$, is fixed in the Z direction. The vector $\boldsymbol{\omega}$, then, may be considered to sweep out a cone, as is illustrated in Fig. 19.21.

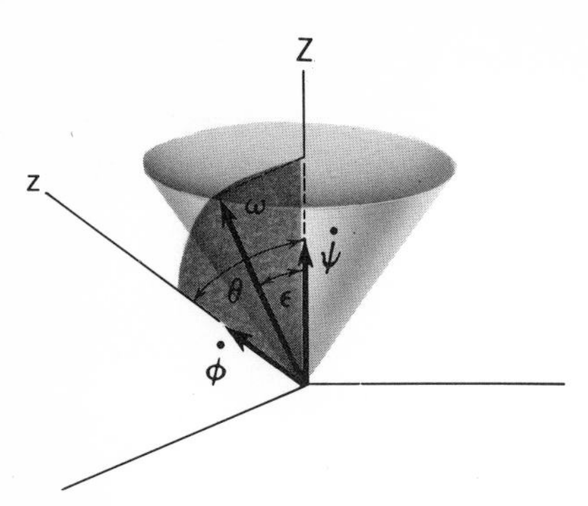

Fig. 19.21

We now illustrate the use of the basic formulations for torque-free motion.

EXAMPLE 19.5

Shown in Fig. 19.22 is a cylindrical space capsule in orbit. A quarter section of the cylinder can be opened about AB to a test configuration as shown in Fig. 19.23. At the earth's surface the end plates of the capsule each have a weight of 300 lb and the cylindrical portion weighs 1800 lb. In the closed configuration the center of mass of the capsule is at the geometric center.

If the capsule is in a test configuration (Fig. 19.23) with a total angular speed ω of 2 rad/sec in the z direction in inertial space, what will be the precession axis for the capsule and its rate of precession when door C is closed?

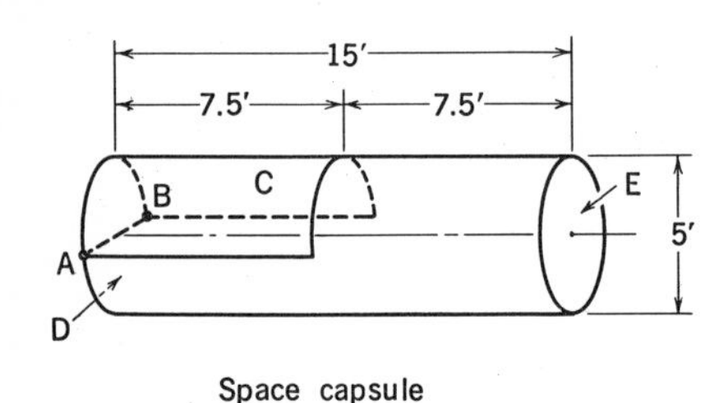

Fig. 19.22

In changing configuration there is a zero net torque on the system so that $\boldsymbol{H}_C$, the angular momentum about the center of mass, is not changed. As a first step we shall compute $\boldsymbol{H}_C$ using data for the test configuration. For this we shall need the position of the center of mass.

A reference xyz has been fixed to the system as shown in Fig. 19.23 and the system has been decomposed into simple portions in Fig. 19.24, for convenience in carrying out ensuing calculations. Employing handbook formulae for positions of centroids, we have:

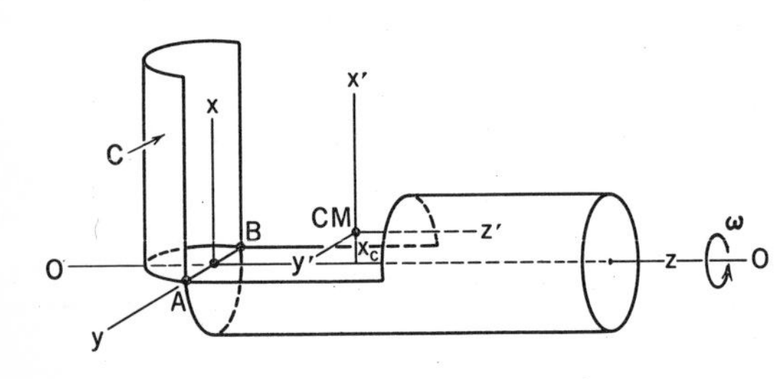

Fig. 19.23

$$\frac{2400}{g_0}\boldsymbol{r}_C = \sum_{i=1}^{6} M_i(\boldsymbol{r}_C)_i$$

$$= \frac{450}{g_0}\left(\frac{15}{4}\boldsymbol{i} - \frac{5}{\pi}\boldsymbol{k}\right) + \frac{150}{g_0}$$

$$\times\left[-(0.424)\left(\frac{5}{2}\right)(\boldsymbol{k})\right]$$

$$+ \frac{150}{g_0}\left[-(0.424)\left(\frac{5}{2}\right)\boldsymbol{i}\right]$$

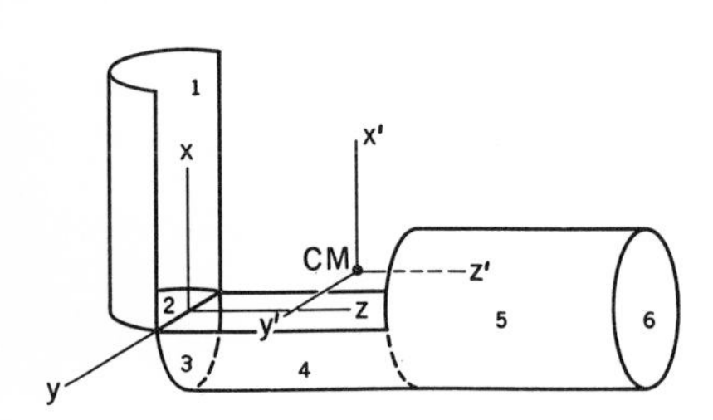

Fig. 19.24

$$+\frac{450}{g_0}\left(\frac{15}{4}\boldsymbol{k}-\frac{5}{\pi}\boldsymbol{i}\right)$$

$$+\frac{900}{g_0}\left(\frac{3}{4}\right)(15)\boldsymbol{k}+\frac{300}{g_0}(15)\boldsymbol{k}$$

$$\therefore\ \boldsymbol{r}_C = 6.44\boldsymbol{k} + 0.338\boldsymbol{i}\text{ ft} \qquad \textbf{(a)}$$

To get $\boldsymbol{H}_C$ we next set up a second reference $x'y'z'$ at the centroid as shown in Figs. 19.23 and 19.24. In accordance with Eq. 17.9 we have for $\boldsymbol{H}_C$, on noting that the only nonzero component of $\boldsymbol{\omega}$ is in the z' direction:

$$\boldsymbol{H}_C = -I_{x'z'}\omega\boldsymbol{i} - I_{y'z'}\omega\boldsymbol{j} + I_{z'z'}\omega\boldsymbol{k} \qquad \textbf{(b)}$$

To compute $I_{z'z'}$ we proceed as follows, using the decomposed capsule sections of Fig. 19.24 and employing transfer theorems for moments of inertia:

$$(I_{z'z'})_1 = \frac{1}{4}\left(\frac{450}{g_0}\right)\left(2.5^2+\frac{7.5^2}{6}\right)$$

$$+\frac{450}{g_0}(3.75-0.338)^2$$

$$= 217$$

$$(I_{z'z'})_2 = \frac{1}{8}\left(\frac{150}{g_0}\right)(2.5^2)+\frac{150}{g_0}(0.338)^2$$

$$= 8.96$$

$$(I_{z'z'})_3 = \left\{\frac{1}{4}\left(\frac{150}{g_0}\right)(2.5)^2-\frac{150}{g_0}[(0.424)(2.5)]^2\right\}$$

$$+\frac{150}{g_0}[0.338+(0.424)(2.5)]^2$$

$$= 11.16$$

$$(I_{z'z'})_4 = \left\{\frac{1}{2}\left(\frac{450}{g_0}\right)(2.5)^2-\frac{450}{g_0}\left(\frac{5}{\pi}\right)^2\right\}$$

$$+\frac{450}{g_0}\left(0.388+\frac{5}{\pi}\right)^2$$

$$= 60.3$$

$$(I_{z'z'})_5 = \frac{900}{g_0}(2.5)^2+\frac{900}{g_0}(0.338)^2$$

$$= 177.9$$

$$(I_{z'z'})_6 = \frac{1}{2}\left(\frac{300}{g_0}\right)(2.5)^2+\frac{300}{g_0}(0.338)^2$$

$$= 30.2$$

Accordingly, we have for $I_{z'z'}$:

$$I_{z'z'} = \sum_{i=1}^{6}(I_{zz})_i = 506\text{ slugs-ft}^2 \qquad \textbf{(c)}$$

By proceeding in a similar fashion we compute $I_{z'x'}$ and $I_{z'y'}$. Thus:

$$I_{z'x'} = -3.29 \text{ slugs-ft}^2$$

$$I_{z'y'} = 0$$

From Eq. (b) we have for $\boldsymbol{H}_C$:

$$\boldsymbol{H}_C = 329\omega\boldsymbol{i} + 506\omega\boldsymbol{k}$$
$$= 658\boldsymbol{i} + 1012\boldsymbol{k} \qquad \textbf{(d)}$$

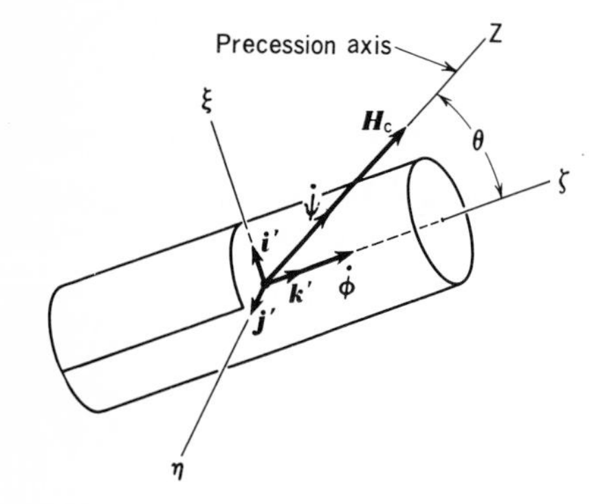

Fig. 19.25

Since the precession axis is collinear with $\boldsymbol{H}_C$, we have thus established this axis (Z axis), as is shown in Fig. 19.25. A reference $\xi\eta\zeta$ has been set up at the center of mass for the closed configuration. The body axis ζ remains at a fixed angle θ with the Z axis and precesses about it with an angular speed $\dot{\psi}$ given in accordance with Eq. 19.24(b) as:

$$\dot{\psi} = \frac{H_C}{I_{\xi\xi}}$$

$$= \frac{\sqrt{658^2+1012^2}}{\frac{1}{2}\left(\frac{1800}{g_0}\right)\left(2.5^2+\frac{15^2}{6}\right)+2\left(\frac{1}{4}\right)\left(\frac{300}{g_0}\right)(2.5^2)+2\left(\frac{300}{g_0}\right)(7.5)^2}$$

$$= 0.526 \text{ rad/sec} \qquad \textbf{(e)}$$

We can now state that the body axis will precess around an axis collinear with $\boldsymbol{H}_C$ as given by Eq. (d) with a speed of 0.526 rad/sec. However, we are unable to determine θ and $\dot{\phi}$ with what information we now have available. Needed is more information as to the way the door was closed. Thus, knowing how much net work was done in the configuration change, we can, from the work energy relations, write another equation and hence compute θ and $\dot{\phi}$. We shall present a number of problems with such information available in the homework exercises.

Upon further consideration, we can make a simple model of this motion. Imagine that we have a fixed cone of the shape just described, and a second cone of half angle β corresponding to the angle between the z and $\boldsymbol{\omega}$ directions (Fig. 19.26). This second cone is rotated about its axis of symmetry with the spin speed $\dot{\phi}$, and the condition of no slipping is imposed between the cones. The line of contact between the cones, then, forms the instantaneous axis of rotation for the moving cone and is thus the direction of the resultant angular velocity of the moving cone, which includes as components $\dot{\boldsymbol{\phi}}$, and $\dot{\boldsymbol{\psi}}'$—the latter a precessional motion imposed by the no-slipping condition. It would appear that the mechanical model portrays the motion of the physical case. We would be assured of this if we knew that the *magnitude* of the resultant angular velocity of the cone $\boldsymbol{\omega}'$ corresponds to $\boldsymbol{\omega}$ of the physical problem and that the precession velocities are equal for both systems. We know now that:

a. $\dot{\boldsymbol{\phi}}$ is the same for both device and physical case.

b. The direction of resultant angular velocity is the same for both cases.

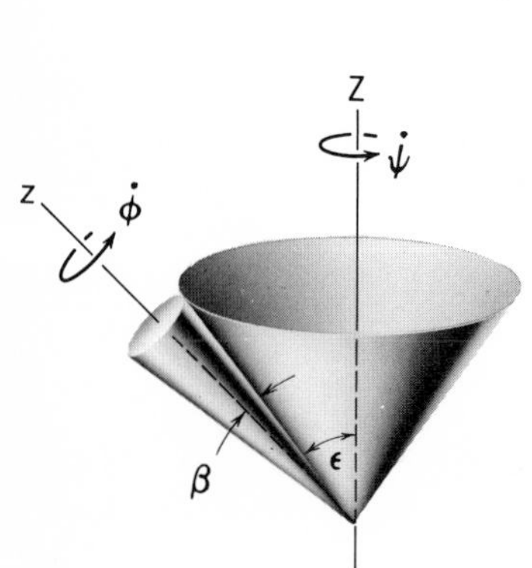

Fig. 19.26

c. The direction of the precession velocity must be the same for both cases, i.e., the Z direction.

This is shown in Fig. 19.27. Note that $\dot{\phi}$ is the same in both the physical case and the mechanical model and that the directions of $\boldsymbol{\omega}$ and $\boldsymbol{\omega}'$ as well as $\dot{\boldsymbol{\psi}}$ and $\dot{\boldsymbol{\psi}}'$ are respectively the same for both diagrams. Accordingly, when we consider the construction of the parallelogram of vectors, we see that the vectors $\boldsymbol{\omega}$ and $\boldsymbol{\omega}'$ as well as $\dot{\boldsymbol{\psi}}$ and $\dot{\boldsymbol{\psi}}'$ must necessarily be respectively equal for both the physical case and the model.

We shall now investigate more carefully the relation between the senses of rotation for corresponding angular velocities between the model and the physical case for various classes of geometries of the physical body.

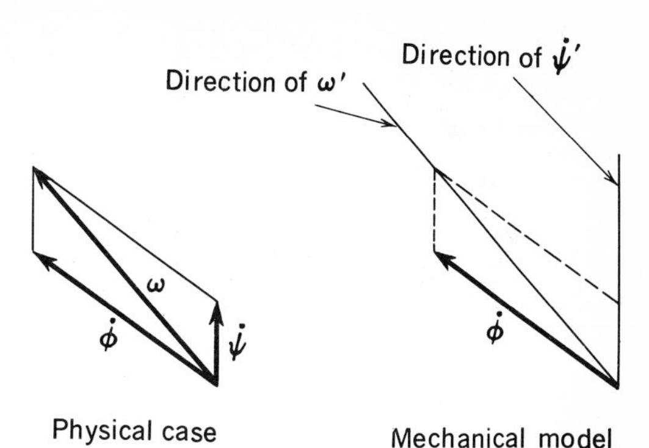

Fig. 19.27

1. $I' > I'$. From Eq. 19.24(c), we see that when θ_0 is less than $\pi/2$ radians, $\dot{\phi}$ is positive for this case. This means that the spin must be counterclockwise as one looks along the z axis toward the origin. From Eq. 19.24(b), we see that $\dot{\psi}$ is positive and thus counterclockwise as one looks toward the origin along Z. It is clear from these stipulations that the rolling-cone model shown earlier gives the proper motion for this case. The motion is termed *regular precession*.

2. $I < \text{I}'$. Here the spin $\dot{\phi}$ will be negative for a nutation angle less than 90°. However, the precession $\dot{\phi}$ must still be positive according to Eq. 19.24(b). The rolling-cone model as thus far presented clearly cannot give these proper senses, but if the moving cone is inside the stationary cone (Fig. 19.28) we have motion that is consistent with the relations in Eq. 19.24. Such motion is called *retrograde precession*.

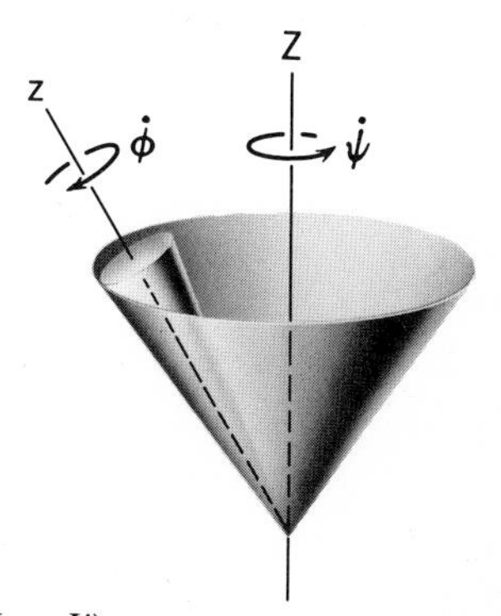

Fig. 19.28

Let us now examine Eq. 19.24 for the special case where $I = I'$. Here the spin velocity $\dot{\boldsymbol{\phi}}$ must be zero, leaving only one angular motion, $\dot{\boldsymbol{\psi}}$ the precession. This motion is about the Z axis, so the direction of angular velocity $\boldsymbol{\omega}$ corresponds to $\boldsymbol{H}_0$. Since this is a body of revolution, the condition for this case ($I = I'$) means that the moments of inertia for the x, y, and z axes are mutually equal, and we can verify from Eq. 16.15 that *all* axes inclined to the xyz reference have the same moment of inertia I (and are therefore all principal axes at the point). Thus the body, if homogeneous, would be that of a sphere, a cube, any regular polyhedron, or, in general, any body that possesses point symmetry. *No matter how we launch this body, the angular momentum* $\boldsymbol{H}$ *will be equal to* $I\boldsymbol{\omega}$ *and will thus always coincide with the direction of angular velocity* $\boldsymbol{\omega}$. This may also be shown analytically as follows:

$$\boldsymbol{H} = H_x\boldsymbol{i} + H_y\boldsymbol{j} + H_z\boldsymbol{k} \qquad \textbf{19.25}$$

For principal axes, we have:

$$\boldsymbol{H} = \omega_x I_{xx}\boldsymbol{i} + \omega_y I_{yy}\boldsymbol{j} + \omega_z I_{zz}\boldsymbol{k} \qquad \textbf{19.26}$$

If $I_{xx} = I_{yy} = I_{zz} = I$, we have for the above:

$$\boldsymbol{H} = I(\omega_x\boldsymbol{i} + \omega_y\boldsymbol{j} + \omega_z\boldsymbol{k}) = I\boldsymbol{\omega} \qquad \textbf{19.27}$$

indicating that $\boldsymbol{H}$ and $\boldsymbol{\omega}$ must be collinear.

There are two other situations in which the direction of $\boldsymbol{H}$ and the direction of $\boldsymbol{\omega}$ are collinear. Examining Eq. 19.24, we thus see that if θ_0 is 90°, then $\dot{\phi}$ is zero, leaving only $\dot{\psi}$ as a rotation about the Z axis, which for the analysis corresponds to the direction of $\boldsymbol{H}$. This case corresponds to a proper "drop kick" or "place kick" of a football (Fig. 19.29(a)).

The other case consists of $\theta_0 = 0$. This means that $\dot{\boldsymbol{\phi}}$ and $\dot{\boldsymbol{\psi}}$ have the same direction—that is, along the Z direction, which then means that $\boldsymbol{\omega}$ and $\boldsymbol{H}$ again are collinear. This case corresponds to a good football pass (Fig. 19.29(b)). *For all other motions of bodies where* $I_{xx} \neq I_{yy}$, *the angular velocity vector* $\boldsymbol{\omega}$ *will not have the direction of angular momentum* $\boldsymbol{H}_0$.

We can now draw these conclusions for torque-free motion. *If a body of revolution is given an initial motion that has a moment of momentum vector* $\boldsymbol{H}_0$ *and the axis of symmetry is inclined at an angle* θ_0 *to the direction of this vector, the axis of symmetry of the body must precess about the fixed*

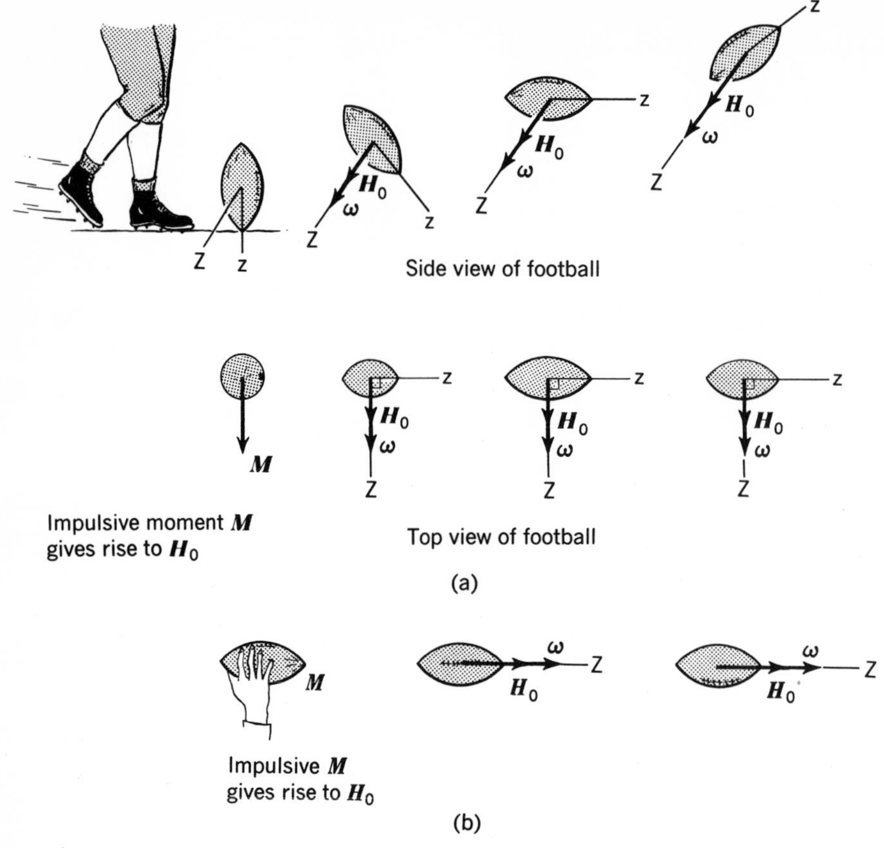

Fig. 19.29 *$\boldsymbol{H}$ direction and maintain the same angle θ_0 with $\boldsymbol{H}$. For an initial θ_0 and $\boldsymbol{H}_0$, the spin velocity about the axis of symmetry and the precession velocity about the direction $\boldsymbol{H}$ are then uniquely determined by the equations in 19.24.*

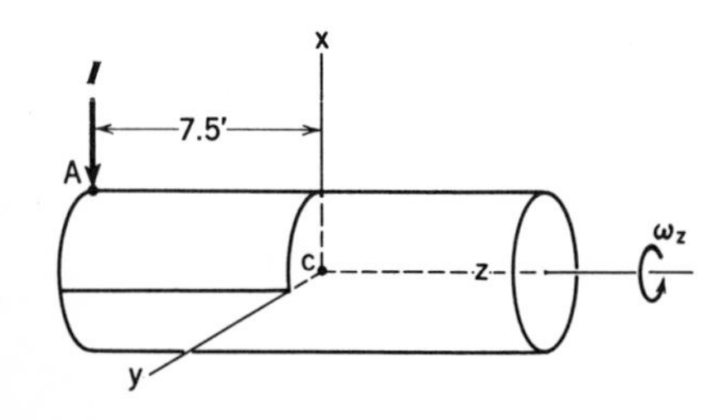

Fig. 19.30

EXAMPLE 19.6

The space capsule of Example 19.5 is shown again in Fig. 19.30 rotating about its axis of symmetry z in inertial space with an angular speed ω_z of 2 rad/sec. As a result of an impact with a meteorite, it is given an impulse $\boldsymbol{I}$ of 20 lb-sec at position A as shown in the diagram. Ascertain the post-impact motion.

The impact will give the cylinder an angular momentum component $(H_C)_y$ at the configuration shown given as:

$$(H_C)_y = (20)(7.5) = 150 \text{ slugs-ft}^2/\text{sec} \qquad \textbf{(a)}$$

Accordingly, the total angular momentum vector after impact is:

$$\boldsymbol{H}_C = I_{zz}\omega_z\boldsymbol{k} + 150\boldsymbol{j} = 916\boldsymbol{k} + 150\boldsymbol{j} \qquad \textbf{(b)}$$

Since the ensuing motion is torque-free, we have thus established the direction of the precession axis (Z), this has been shown in Fig. 19.31. Furthermore, the total angular velocity of the capsule is now given as:

$$\boldsymbol{\omega} = \omega_z\boldsymbol{k} + \omega_y\boldsymbol{j} = 2\boldsymbol{k} + \frac{(H_C)_y}{I_{yy}}\boldsymbol{j}$$

$$= 2\boldsymbol{k} + \frac{150}{2290}\boldsymbol{j} = 2\boldsymbol{k} + 0.0653\boldsymbol{j} \qquad \textbf{(c)}$$

We can now make good use of the cone model representing the motion. Accordingly in Fig. 19.31 we have shown two cones, one about the z axis (this is the moving cone) and one about the Z axis (this is the stationary cone). The line of contact between the cones coincides with the total angular velocity vector $\boldsymbol{\omega}$. We can easily compute the angles θ and ϵ using Eqs. (b) and (c). Thus:

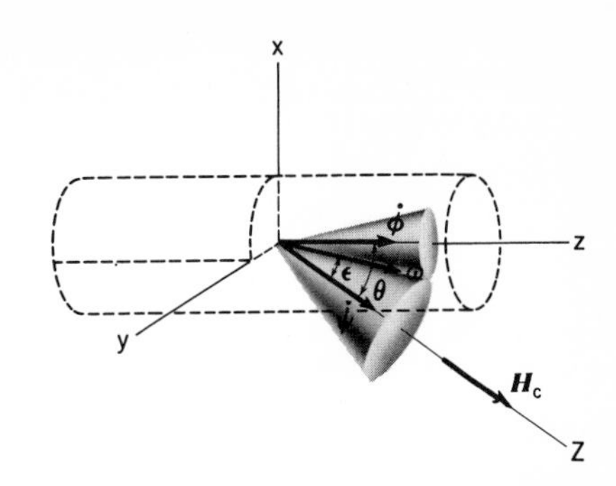

Fig. 19.31

$$\tan\theta = \frac{H_y}{H_z} = \frac{150}{916} = 0.1638$$

$$\therefore \theta = 9.30^\circ$$

$$\epsilon = \theta - \tan^{-1}\frac{\omega_y}{\omega_z} = 9.30^\circ - \tan^{-1}\frac{0.0653}{2}$$

$$\therefore \epsilon = 7.42^\circ$$

In Fig. 19.32 we have shown ω, $\dot\phi$, and $\dot\psi$ in the yz plane. Knowing $\dot\phi$, ω, ϵ, and θ, it is a simple matter to compute $\dot\psi$. Thus, using the law of sines, we get:

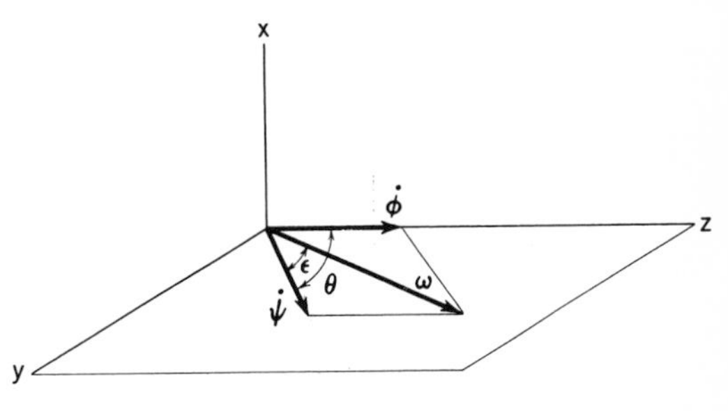

Fig. 19.32

$$\frac{\dot\psi}{\sin(\theta-\epsilon)} = \frac{\omega}{\sin\theta}$$

$$\therefore \dot\psi = \frac{\sin(\theta-\epsilon)\omega}{\sin\theta} = \frac{(0.0326)(2^2 + 0.0653^2)^{1/2}}{0.1618} = 0.405$$

Thus we can say that the body continues to spin at 2 rad/sec about its axis but now the axis precesses about the indicated Z direction at the rate of 1.592 rad/sec.

19.6 Symmetric Spinning Top under the Action of Gravity

We shall evaluate the motion of a body of revolution moving about a fixed point when there is a moment due to gravity about that point. Accordingly, a spinning body of revolution, shown in Fig. 19.33 with point O fixed, will serve as an illustration of the problem to be studied. The reference xyz is fixed in the body.

Let us first consider Euler's equations. Since the gravity force goes through z axis, M_z equals zero. Also, since $I_{xx} = I_{yy} = I'$, the z component of Euler's equation should prove relatively simple. Thus, using I for I_{zz}, we have:

$$I\frac{d\omega_z}{dt} = I\frac{d}{dt}(\dot\phi + \dot\psi\cos\theta) = 0 \qquad \textbf{19.28}$$

Hence we see that:

$$\dot\phi + \dot\psi\cos\theta = \omega_z = \text{const.} = \beta \qquad \textbf{19.29}$$

That is, the total angular velocity component along the body centerline does not change and may be considered an initial condition of the motion given as β.

Another useful relation may be developed from the fact that the gravity force is parallel to the Z axis and has therefore a zero moment about it. Thus:

$$M_Z = 0 \qquad \textbf{19.30}$$

Using the general relation $\boldsymbol{M} = \dot{\boldsymbol{H}}$, we see immediately that the component of $\dot{\boldsymbol{H}}$ along the Z axis must be zero, and so:

$$H_Z = \text{const.} = K \qquad \textbf{19.31}$$

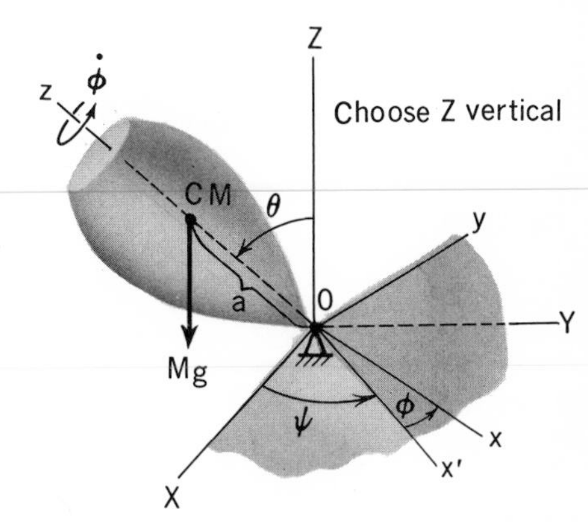

Fig. 19.33

This is another constant determined by initial conditions. To bring in desirable variables, we shall express H_Z in terms of the components of $\boldsymbol{H}$ along the x, y, and z directions. From Fig. 19.19 we see that:

a. Projection of H_x along Z direction $= H_x \sin\phi \sin\theta$

b. Projection of H_y along Z direction $= H_y \cos\phi \sin\theta$

c. Projection of H_z along Z direction $= H_z \cos\theta$ **19.32**

The total component of $\boldsymbol{H}$ along Z is then:

$$H_x \sin\phi \sin\theta + H_y \cos\phi \sin\theta + H_z \cos\theta = K \tag{19.33}$$

Since xyz are principal axes, H_x, H_y, and H_z are $I'\omega_x$, $I'\omega_y$, and $I\omega_z$, respectively. Using Eq. 19.12 for the angular velocity components, we then have:

$$I'(\dot\theta\cos\phi + \dot\psi\sin\theta\sin\phi)\sin\phi\sin\theta + I'(-\dot\theta\sin\phi + \dot\psi\sin\theta\cos\phi)\cos\phi\sin\theta + I(\dot\phi + \dot\psi\cos\theta)\cos\theta = K \tag{19.34}$$

The above equation simplifies to:

$$I'\dot\psi\sin^2\theta + I(\dot\phi + \dot\psi\cos\theta)\cos\theta = K \tag{19.35}$$

Noting that $(\dot\phi + \dot\psi\cos\theta)$ in this equation is the constant β, we then have, as a result of the two momentum considerations, the following equation with two unknown variables, $\dot\psi$ and θ

$$I'\dot\psi\sin^2\theta + I\beta\cos\theta = K \tag{19.36}$$

We may make good use now of energy considerations because we have here a system for which the only work done is that by gravity—a conservative force field. This provides the additional equation, since the potential energy, which is $Mga\cos\theta$, with the fixed point as a datum, plus the kinetic energy, $(I'/2)(\omega_x^2+\omega_y^2) + (I/2)\omega_z^2$, must be conserved. Thus:

$$\frac{I'}{2}(\omega_x^2 + \omega_y^2) + \frac{I}{2}\omega_z^2 + Mga\cos\theta = E \tag{19.37}$$

where E is the total energy. Again replacing ω_x, ω_y, and ω_z, using Eq. 19.12, we get:

$$\frac{I'}{2}[(\dot\theta\cos\phi + \dot\psi\sin\theta\sin\phi)^2 + (-\dot\theta\sin\phi + \dot\psi\sin\theta\cos\phi)^2] + \frac{I}{2}\beta^2 + Mga\cos\theta = E \tag{19.38}$$

Carrying out the algebra and canceling cross-products from squaring, we have:

$$\frac{I'}{2}(\dot\theta^2\cos^2\phi + \dot\psi^2\sin^2\theta\sin^2\phi + \dot\theta^2\sin^2\phi + \dot\psi^2\sin^2\theta\cos^2\phi) + \frac{I}{2}\beta^2 + Mga\cos\theta = E \tag{19.39}$$

Simplifying the bracket by combining terms and multiplying through by 2, we get the desired equation:

$$I'(\dot\theta^2 + \dot\psi^2\sin^2\theta) + I\beta^2 + 2Mga\cos\theta = 2E \tag{19.40}$$

Now we may combine Eqs. 19.36 and 19.40 by first solving for $\dot\psi$ in the former. That is:

$$\dot\psi = \frac{K - I\beta\cos\theta}{I'\sin^2\theta} \tag{19.41}$$

Thus, if we can determine θ as a function of time, we can integrate this equation to get ψ as a function of time. Now substitute for $\dot\psi$ in Eq. 19.40 using the preceding equation:

$$I'\left[\dot\theta^2 + \frac{(K - I\beta\cos\theta)^2}{(I')^2\sin^2\theta}\right] + I\beta^2 + 2Mga\cos\theta = 2E$$

Divide through by I', multiply by $\sin^2\theta$, and rearrange:

$$\dot\theta^2\sin^2\theta = \sin^2\theta\left[\frac{1}{I'}(2E - I\beta^2) - \frac{2Mga}{I'}\cos\theta\right] - \left[\frac{K}{I'} - \frac{I\beta\cos\theta}{I'}\right]^2 \tag{19.42}$$

This equation is of the form:

$$\dot{\theta}^2 \sin^2\theta = \sin^2\theta\,[C_1 - C_2\cos\theta] - [C_3 - C_4\cos\theta]^2 \qquad \textbf{19.43}$$

where C_1, C_2, C_3, and C_4 are constants whose values are:

$$C_1 = \frac{1}{I'}(2E - I\beta^2) \qquad \textbf{(a)}$$

$$C_2 = \frac{2Mga}{I'} \qquad \textbf{(b)}$$

$$C_3 = \frac{K}{I'} \qquad \textbf{(c)}$$

$$C_4 = \frac{I\beta}{I'} \qquad \textbf{(d)} \quad \textbf{19.44}$$

To simplify the equation, we introduce a new dependent variable, u, so that:

$$u = \cos\theta \qquad \textbf{19.45}$$

This means that $\dot{u} = -\dot{\theta}\sin\theta$ and $\dot{\theta}^2 = \dot{u}^2/\sin^2\theta$. Thus the left side of Eq. 19.43 becomes $\dot{u}^2$. Charging $\sin^2\theta$ to $1 - \cos^2\theta$ on the right side of 19.43 and then changing variables we get the following differential equation, which depicts the motion in terms of u:

$$\left(\frac{du}{dt}\right)^2 = (1 - u^2)(C_1 - C_2u) - (C_3 - C_4u)^2 \qquad \textbf{19.46}$$

Separating variables for this first-order differential equation in u and setting up the integration, we have the following quadrature:

$$t = \int_{u(o)}^{u(t)} \frac{du}{[(1 - u^2)(C_1 - C_2u) - (C_3 - C_4u)^2]^{1/2}} \qquad \textbf{19.47}$$

19.7 An Examination of Expected Nutation Velocity of the Top

We could presumably integrate the above equation to determine t as a function of u and then find θ as a function of time (Eq. 19.45). From Eq. 19.41 we could also find ψ as a function of time, and, finally, from Eq. 19.29 we could find ϕ. For this case, therefore, we could determine the motion for a given body of revolution, with initial conditions embodied in the constants β, K, and E. However, the integral is not an easy one to evaluate and results in so much mathematical complexity that the computations obscure important general salient features of the motion. Thus, instead of proceeding in the way we have just outlined, we shall use Eq. 19.46 to deduce in a general way some important features of the motion.

Since the right side of Eq. 19.46 is a cubic, there are in general three values of u, which reduce it to zero. This equation tells us that for those values of u, the time derivative of u and thus of θ is zero*. Hence at these values of u, the nutation velocity of the centerline of the body is changing its sense. We shall therefore examine the roots of the right side of Eq. 19.46. We accordingly denote the right side of this equation as $f(u)$. That is:

$$\left(\frac{du}{dt}\right)^2 = f(u) = (1 - u^2)(C_1 - C_2u) - (C_3 - C_4u)^2 \qquad \textbf{19.48}$$

What approximately is the plot of $f(u)$ versus u? The term of highest degree in the function $f(u)$ is C_2u^3, and this term will be dominant for the large values of u. Thus for a large and positive u, C_2u^3 is positive, and $f(u)$ must also be positive. For large negative values of u,

* The time derivitive of θ need not be zero here for the case where $\theta = 0$.

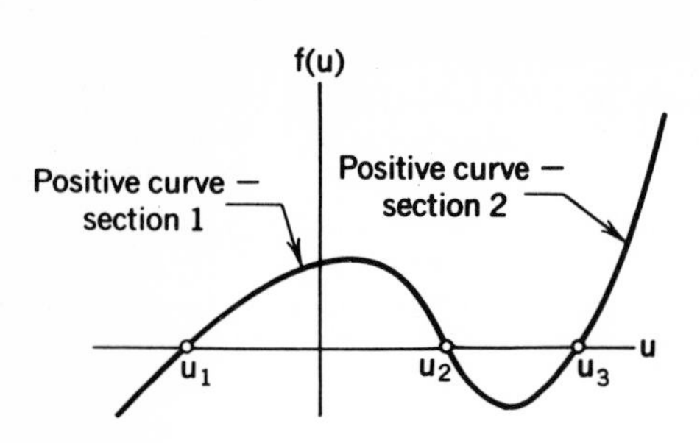

Fig. 19.34

C_2u^3 is negative, and $f(u)$, too, is negative. Also, for the case of three real roots, the curve intersects the u axis three times. With this information, we can thus draw the possible cubic curve in Fig. 19.34.

The three roots of $f(u)$ have been shown as u_1, u_2, and u_3. Let us try to position these roots approximately. All physically meaningful u's must lie between $+1$ and -1, since $\cos\theta$ does not have a meaningful value below -1 and above $+1$. Therefore, u_0, which corresponds to the initial condition, must lie within these bounds. Also, since $(du/dt)_0$, which corresponds to the initial nutation velocity, must be real, $f(u)_0$ must be equal to or greater than zero (see Eq. 19.48). This means that between $u = +1$ and $u = -1$, either positive curve-section 1 or positive curve-section 2 of $f(u)$ (see Fig. 19.34) must be present. Next examine $f(u)$ for $u = \pm 1$. This becomes:

$$f(u)_{\pm 1} = -[C_3 - C_4(\pm 1)]^2 \qquad \textbf{19.49}$$

It is clear that $f(u)_{\pm 1}$ must be negative or zero. This fact eliminates the possibility that curve-section 2 is in the region under consideration, since it is bordered only on one side by a negative region. Thus it could not satisfy the condition requiring it to have a negative or zero value at both $u = +1$ and $u = -1$ and a positive value or zero value somewhere in between these extremes. Thus curve-section 1 is the correct curve-section between $u = +1$ and $u = -1$, as has been shown in Fig. 19.35. From this curve, we may make the following deductions for the roots of $f(u)$:

$$-1 \leq u_1 \leq u_2$$
$$u_1 \leq u_2 \leq +1$$
$$+1 \leq u_3 < \infty \qquad \textbf{19.50}$$

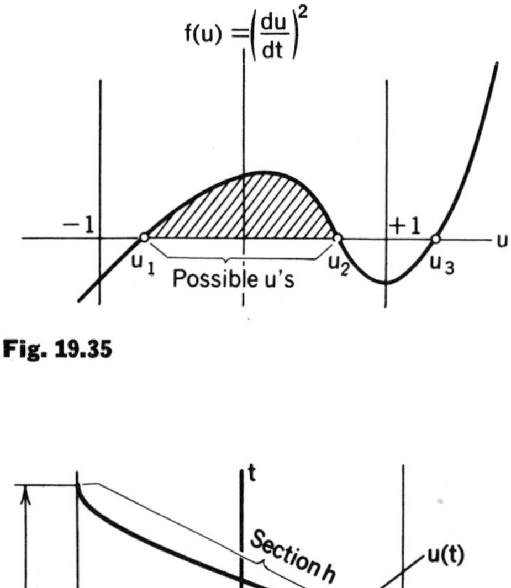

Fig. 19.35

We can now make certain statements about the behavior of nutation for the spinning top. Since u_3 in general exceeds unity, it has no physical meaning for us, so we drop it. Thus, in the general case, there will be *two roots* of $f(u)$ that have physical meaning. Furthermore, for real values of (du/dt) and thus for physically possible motions, it is necessary that $f(u)$ itself be positive. We see, then, that the possible values of u must lie between u_1 and u_2, as shown in Fig. 19.35. *This means that there will be two θ's—θ_1 and θ_2—that correspond to the roots u_1 and u_2, between which the axis of the top will be confined in its nutation.* If there is only one root in the region between ± 1, the curve-section is tangent to the u axis. The top will not nutate but will remain at a fixed angle θ_0 from the vertical. This was the condition, you will remember, in the steady precession examined in a previous section.

We can now prove, from the equations thus far developed, that $u(t)$—and consequently $\theta(t)$—is a periodic function of time. To do this, we examine u as plotted against time (Fig. 19.36). Note that we start with an initial value, u_0, in between the extremes, u_1 and u_2, and that the curve $u(t)$, never exceeds the limitations, u_1 and u_2, as developed earlier. Since $f(u)$ and hence (du/dt) is zero at the extreme positions of u_1 and u_2, the curve $u(t)$ must be tangent to the limiting lines at these extreme positions, as is shown in Fig. 19.36. There can be no other positions where the slope is zero in the ut plane, since:

$$\left(\frac{du}{dt}\right)^2 = f(u)$$

$$\therefore \frac{du}{dt} = \pm\sqrt{f(u)} \qquad \textbf{19.51}$$

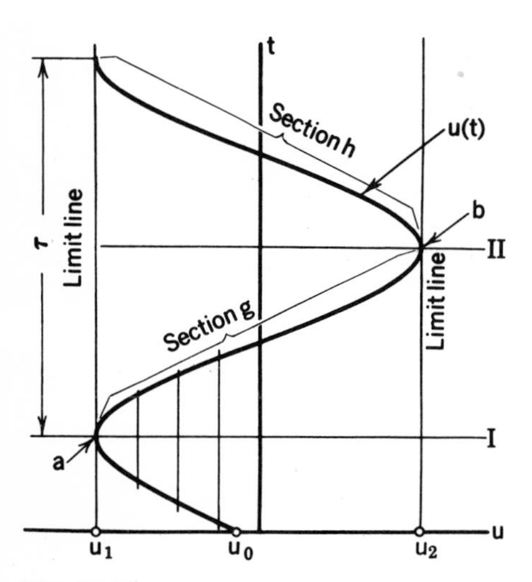

Fig. 19.36

and we know that $f(u)$ can be zero only at the extremes u_1 and u_2, where limit lines have been established. Note also from the above equation that for any given value of u in between the extremes there are two slopes of equal magnitude but of opposite signs. With this information, let us focus our attention on the point a having coordinates (u_1, t_a). It is clear that du/dt must be positive after passing t_a and remain positive* until the other extreme, u_2, is reached at b, where it becomes again zero. The slope du/dt is negative, on the other hand, on approaching point (u_1, t_a). For each value of u, the curves on each side of the point a have slopes equal in magnitude and opposite in sign, as we saw in Eq. 19.51. This means that the curve section beyond t_a is a mirror image about the horizontal axis I at a of the curve section before t_a. We can go through the same argument at point b, using axis II. That is, section g is a mirror image of section h about II. Thus, we can conclude that the curve is periodic, the period τ being the time required to go from one extreme, u_1, to the other extreme, u_2, and back to u_1.

If $\cos\theta$ varies periodically, it can only mean that θ must vary periodically. Using the more familiar representation of the horizontal axis for t, we have shown $\theta(t)$ in Fig. 19.37. You should not make the mistake of concluding that this curve is sinusoidal; it is merely periodic.

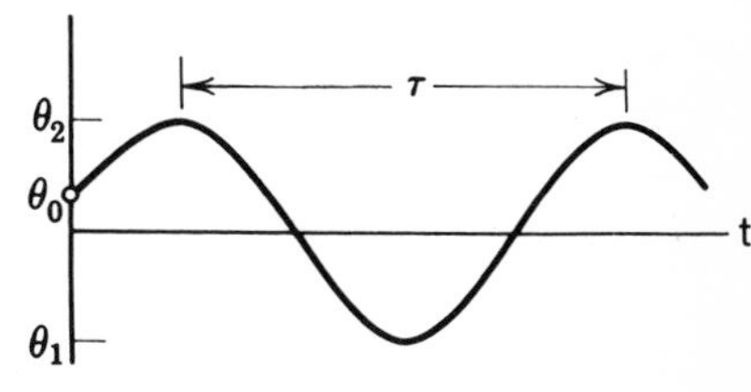

Fig. 19.37

Thus we see that in the general case of the spinning top, the axis of symmetry will bob periodically up and down between two limiting angles.

19.8 The Precession and Spin of the Top

Now let us turn to the other aspects of the motion. The precession speed, $\dot{\psi}$, has been shown (Eq. 19.41) to be:

$$\dot{\psi} = \frac{K - I\beta\cos\theta}{I'\sin^2\theta} \qquad 19.52$$

We can rewrite the above equation as:

$$\dot{\psi} = \frac{\beta I}{I'\sin^2\theta}\left(\frac{K}{I\beta} - \cos\theta\right) \qquad 19.53$$

The variations of θ and $\dot{\psi}$ give the motion of the body axis z. Therefore, to help illustrate the nutation and precession, we may imagine that the z axis is tracing out a path on a spherical surface whose center is at the fixed point O. With this device, let us examine certain possible motions of z in accordance with Eq. 19.53 and the conclusions of the previous section.

Case 1. Consider the motion for the following situation:

$$\frac{K}{I\beta} < (\cos\theta)_{\max}$$

or

$$\frac{K}{I\beta} < (\cos\theta)_{\min}$$

We can see by inspecting Eq. 19.53 for this case that $\dot{\psi}$ cannot be zero at any time. The precession angle, therefore, changes secularly in a sense which depends on the geometry and initial conditions of the body. Figure 19.38 illustrates this case.

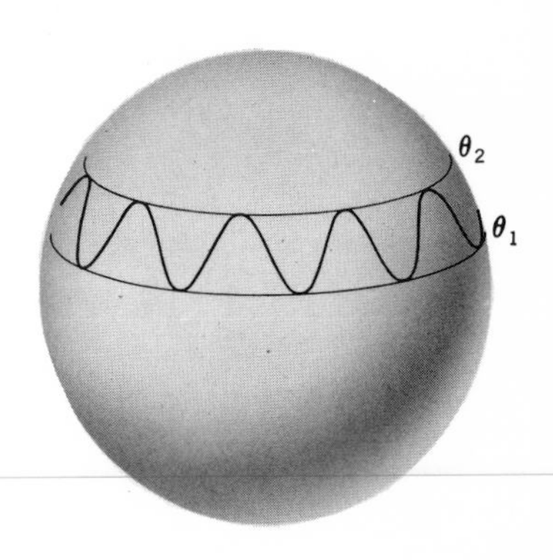

Fig. 19.38

Case 2. Consider next the case where:

$$(\cos\theta)_{\min} < \frac{K}{I\beta} < (\cos\theta)_{\max}$$

* To become negative, du/dt would have to be zero between a and b, which, as we have shown, is not possible.

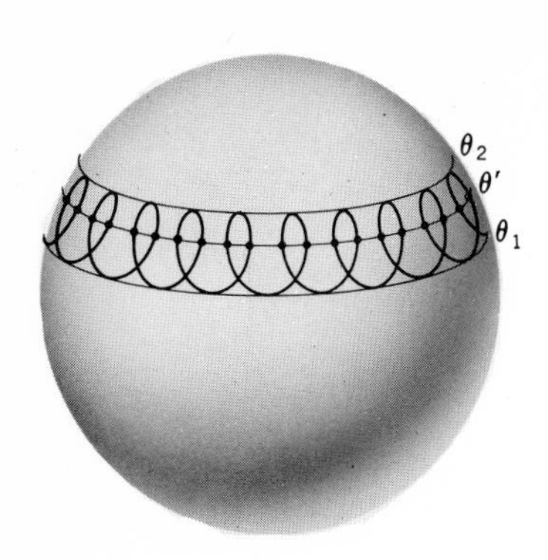

Fig. 19.39

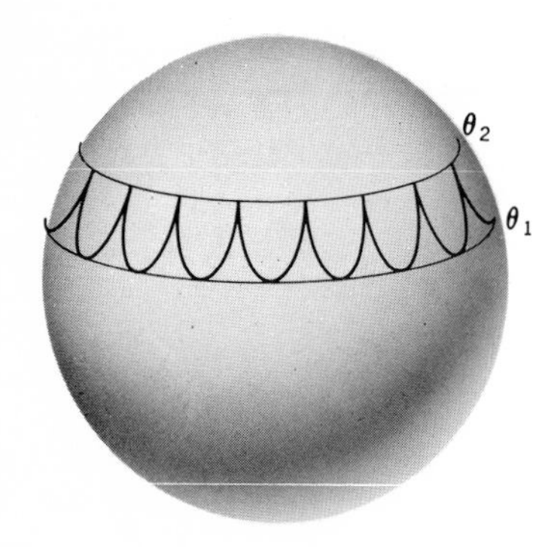

Fig. 19.40

In this case, Eq. 19.53 indicates that $\dot{\psi}$ can periodically have zero velocity at one value of θ within the extremes of nutation. This means that there will be reversals of precessional motion, as is shown in Fig. 19.39. Points on the curve shown at the nutation angle, θ', represent positions of zero velocity of precession. It can be shown that despite this reversal effect, there will always be a net precession per cycle of nutation angle.

Case 3. We consider finally the possibility that $K/I\beta$ will equal one of the extreme values of u. This would mean that $\dot{\psi}$ must be zero at that extreme. We could achieve this condition by initiating the motion with a zero precession velocity and a zero nutation velocity. Physically, the spinning top is "dropped" at time $t = 0$, and the z axis periodically returns to the original θ where there exist zero nutation and precession. The precession must, according to Eq. 19.53, always be of one sign, and the motion will be that in Fig. 19.40.

The extreme at which the stationary points occur must be the θ_2, i.e., the smaller angle. We can see this clearly if we examine the energy Eq. 19.40, which we shall consider in the following form:

$$I'\,[\dot{\theta}^2 + \dot{\psi}^2 \sin^2 \theta] + 2Mga \cos \theta = 2E - I\beta^2$$

where the right side is obviously a constant. At the stationary point, the kinetic energy term on the left is zero but increases in value directly thereafter. However, since the right side of the above equation is a constant, the potential energy term, $2Mga \cos \theta$, must decrease in value. This in turn means that θ is increasing in value after the stationary point. Thus the *axis must begin to drop* after being at the stationary position, and only the smaller θ, which we call θ_2, can have the stationary points, as was illustrated in Fig. 19.40.

As for the spin $\dot{\phi}$, we simply note from Eq. 19.29 that it will not be uniform in speed if there is any nutational motion present.

19.9 Closure

We have considered the motion of a rigid body having a fixed point. In the final chapter of this text we shall for the most part go back to particle mechanics to consider the motion of particles confined by certain constraints to move about a fixed point in a small domain. This is the work on vibrations (alluded to in Chapter 12) which we have held in abeyance so as to take full advantage of course work in differential equations. We shall also briefly consider rigid body motion in the neighborhood of a fixed point. The point, however, will not be part of the rigid body as was the case in the present chapter.

PROBLEMS

1. [19.2] In Fig. 19.41, the Z axis coincides initially with the centerline of the block. The block is given the following rotations in the sequence listed: (a) $\psi = 30°$, (b) $\theta = 45°$, (c) $\phi = 20°$. What are the projections of the centerline OA along the XYZ axes in the final position?

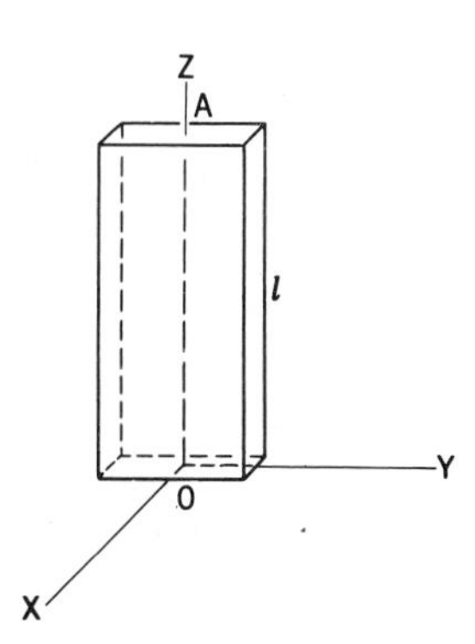

Fig. 19.41

2. [19.2] A disc A of mean diameter 1 ft rolls without slipping (see Fig. 19.42) so that its centerline rotates an angular speed ω_1 of 2 rad/sec about the Z axis. What are the precession, nutation, and spin angular velocity components?

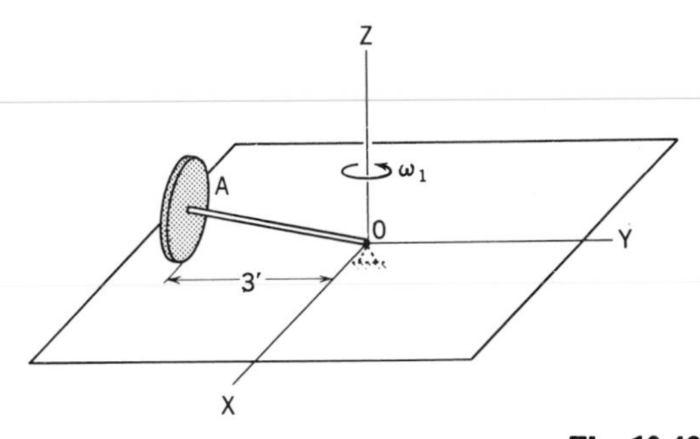

Fig. 19.42

3. [19.2] A body has the following components of angular velocity:

$$\dot{\phi} = 10 \text{ rad/sec}$$

$$\dot{\theta} = 5 \text{ rad/sec}$$

$$\dot{\psi} = 2 \text{ rad/sec}$$

when the following Euler angles are known to be:

$$\phi = 45° \qquad \theta = 30°$$

What is the magnitude of the total angular velocity?

4. [19.3] Using vectors to represent $\boldsymbol{M}$ and $\boldsymbol{H}$, explain using a simple vector diagram why the precession axis for steady precession must always be at right angles to the torque axis. [*Hint*: Consider the body at times dt apart.]

5. [19.3] If the disc shown in Fig. 19.43 were to be undergoing regular precession as shown, what would have to be the spin velocity $\dot{\phi}$? The disc weighs 20 lb. Neglect the mass of the rod.

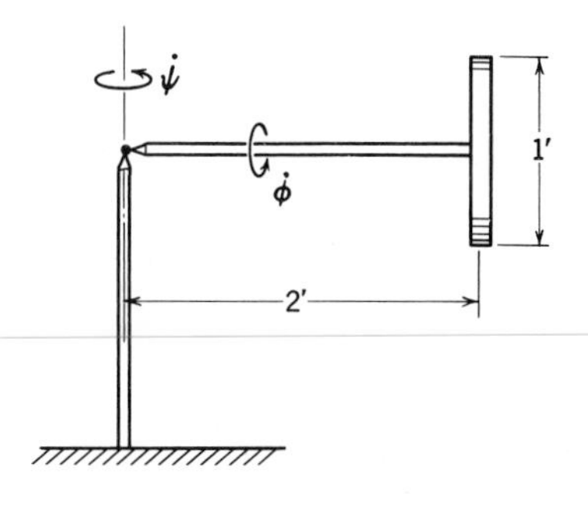

Fig. 19.43

6. [19.3] In the preceding problem, explain how you institute such a motion. Would you get the steady precession if for the computed $\dot{\phi}$ you merely released the disc from a horizontal configuration of the disc centerline?

7. [19.3] A 20-lb cylinder having a radius of 1 ft and a length of $\frac{1}{4}$ ft is connected by a 2-ft rod to a fixed point O where there is a ball-joint connector (Fig. 19.44). The cylinder spins about its own centerline at a speed of 50 rad/sec. What torque about O is required for the cylinder to precess uniformly at a rate of $\frac{1}{2}$ rad/sec about the Z axis at an inclination of 45° to the Z axis? (Compute the torque when the centerline of the cylinder is in the XZ plane.)

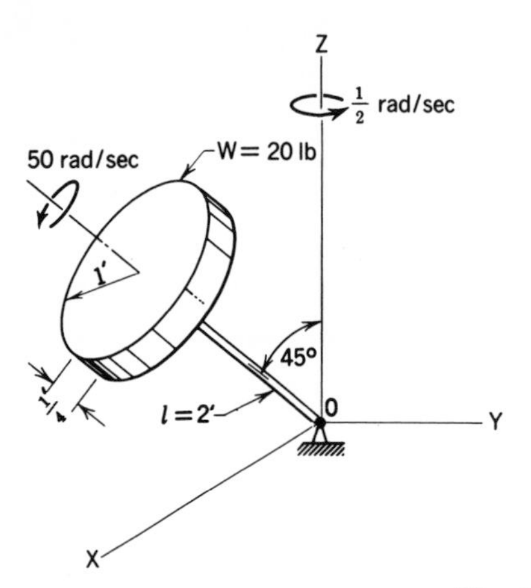

Fig. 19.44

8. [19.3] In Fig. 19.45, the centerline of the rod rotates uniformly in a horizontal plane with a constant torque of 20 in.-lb applied about O. Each cylinder weighs 50 lb and has a radius of 1 ft. The discs rotate on a bar AB with a speed ω_1 of 5000 rpm. Bar AB is held at O by a ball-joint connection. The applied torque is always perpendicular to AB and can only rotate about the vertical axis. What is the precession speed of the system?

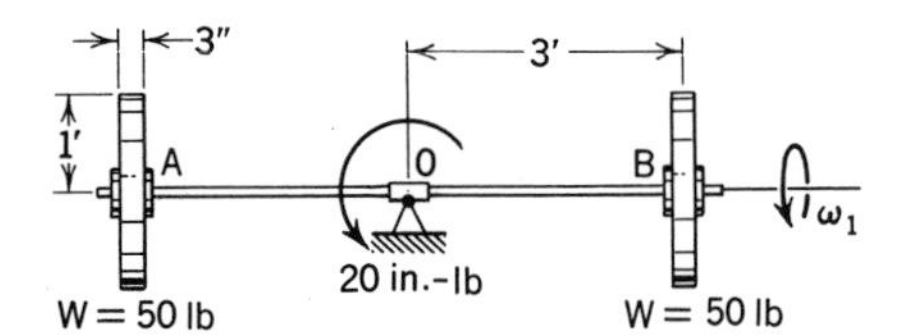

Fig. 19.45

9. [19.3] (a) In the above problem, consider the disc at B to have an angular speed of 5000 rpm and the disc at A to have a speed of 2500 rpm. What is the precession speed for the condition of steady precession?

(b) If the disc at A and the disc at B have angular speeds of 5000 rpm in opposite directions, what is the initial motion of the system when a torque perpendicular to AB is suddenly applied?

10. [19.3] Shown in Fig. 19.46 is a single-degree-of-freedom gyro mounted on a vehicle moving at constant speed V of 100 ft/sec on a track which is coplanar and is circular, having a mean radius of 200 ft. The disc weighs 1 lb and has a radius of 2 in. It is turning at a speed of 20,000 rpm relative to the gimbal. If the gimbal maintains a rotated position of 15° with the horizontal, what is the equivalent torsional spring constant about axis AA for the gimbal suspension?

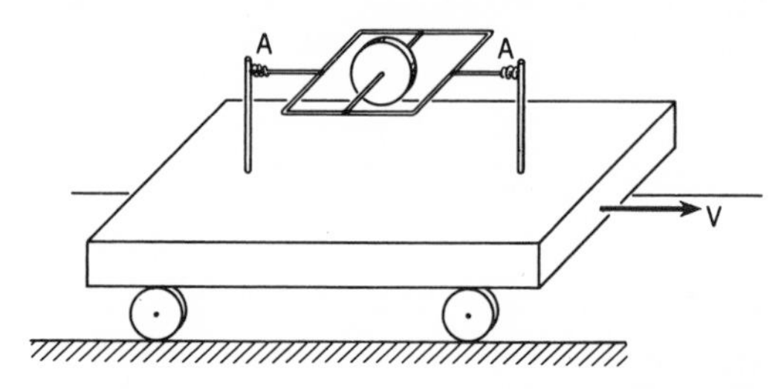

Fig. 19.46

11. [19.3] In the preceding problem suppose that the speed of the vehicle were adjusted to 50 ft/sec—i.e., half its given speed. What would then be the position of the gimbal for steady-state precession?

12. [19.3] A plate (see Fig. 19.47) is rotating about shaft CD at a constant speed ω of 2 rad/sec. A single-degree-of-freedom gyro is mounted on the plate. It has mounted on it through a gimbal a disc of weight 12 ounces and radius 2 in. The disc has a rotational speed of 10,000 rpm relative to the gimbal. If the gimbal is to be maintained parallel to the plate, what torque is required? If the bearings are frictionless, explain how this torque is developed. What is the direction of the line of nodes?

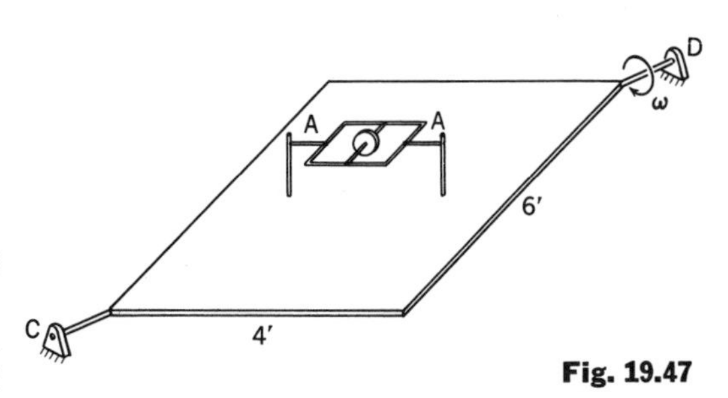

Fig. 19.47

13. [19.3] Two identical single-degree-of-freedom gyros are mounted on faces of a rectangular parallelepiped as shown in Fig. 19.48. The block is rotating at constant speed ω of 25 rad/sec about a shaft connected to the block at hinges E and F. If each disc weighs 8 ounces, has a radius of 2 in., and is rotating at a constant speed of 15,000 rpm relative to the block, what torques are needed to keep the gimbals parallel at all times to the faces A and B, respectively? Specify the direction of the torques.

14. [19.3] In Fig. 19.48 suppose that the block rotates about a diagonal from corner H to corner N rather than about the shaft EF as shown. If the angular speed about the diagonal is 3 rad/sec clockwise as one looks from H to N, what torque would have to be developed about axes ca for each gyro if the gimbals remain parallel to the faces A and B, respectively? The disc of each gyro has a radius of 2 in., weighs 1 lb, and rotates at a speed of 15,000 rpm relative to the block. Give the direction of the line of nodes for each gyro, using the edges of the block for directions of a set of orthogonal axes.

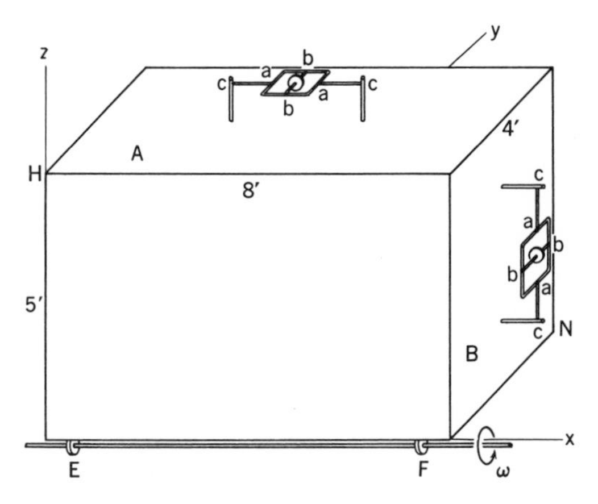

Fig. 19.48

15. [19.3] Shown in Fig. 19.49 are two discs A and B which roll without slipping at their midplanes. Light shafts cd and ef connect the discs to a centerpost which rotates at an angular speed ω_1 of 2 rad/sec. If each disc weighs 20 lb, what total force downward is developed by the discs on the ground support? Work directly with $\boldsymbol{M} = \dot{\boldsymbol{H}}$.

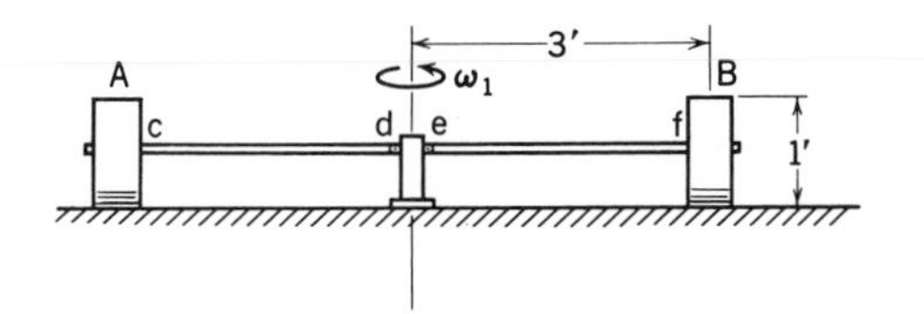

Fig. 19.49

16. [19.3] Shown in Fig. 19.50 are discs A and B rolling without slipping at their centerlines against an upper surface D. Each disc weighs 40 lb and each spins about a shaft which connects to a centerpost E rotating at an angular speed ω_1. If a total of 20 lb is developed upward on D, what is ω? Work directly with $\boldsymbol{M} = \dot{\boldsymbol{H}}$.

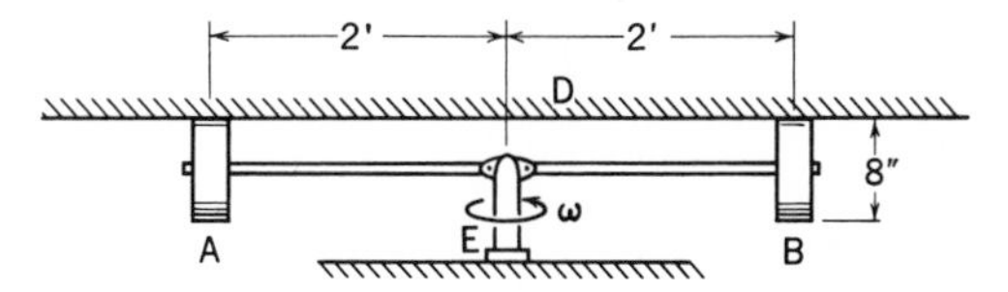

Fig. 19.50

17. [19.3] Shown in Fig. 19.51 is a disc spinning about its centerline with speed $\dot{\phi}$ while the centerline is precessing uniformly at fixed angle θ about the vertical axis. The mass of the disc is M. Show that such a state of regular precession is possible if:

$$\omega_z^2 > \frac{4I'Mgl}{I^2}$$

Also show that there are, for every θ, two possible precession speeds. In particular, show that as ω_z gets very large, the following precessional speeds are possible:

$$\dot{\psi}_1 = \frac{I\omega_z}{I' \cos\theta}, \qquad \dot{\psi}_2 = \frac{Mgl}{I\omega_z}$$

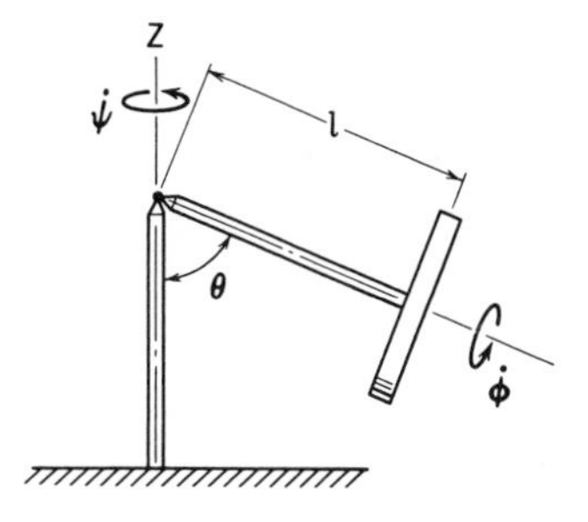

Fig. 19.51

18. [19.3] Do Example 17.15 using the results of this chapter.

19. [19.4] Do Example 19.3 using Euler's equations of motion.

20. [19.4] Do Prob. 15 using Euler's equations of motion.

21. [19.4] Do Prob. 16 using Euler's equations of motion.

22. [19.4] Develop Eqs. (o) and (p) of Example 19.4 for the gyro-compass, using Euler's equations for a convenient set of axes fixed in the disc.

23. [19.4] What is the frequency of a gyrocompass having a disc of radius 3 in. and weight 5 lb with a length of 1 in. if it has a spin of 15,000 rpm; (a) when it is at the equator? (b) when it is at Toledo, Spain (40° north latitude)?

24. [19.5] In Fig. 19.52, two identical thin discs, each weighing 100 lb and having a radius of 2 ft, are connected to a light rod of length 8 ft. The rod is free to rotate in a frictionless bearing at its center, and this bearing is mounted on a frictionless ball joint, as shown at O. A set of principal axes xyz has been fixed in the body at O. If the centerline of the system has an angular speed of 10 rad/sec about the Z axis and remains at 45° from the Z axis at all times, what must the spin about the centerline be if no external influences other than gravity and the supporting force at O are present?

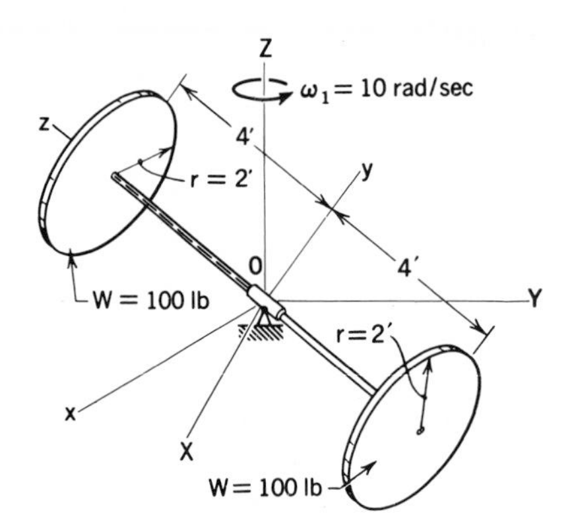

Fig. 19.52

25. [19.5] A football is thrown so it has an angular momentum of $\boldsymbol{H} = H_0(l\boldsymbol{i} + m\boldsymbol{j} + n\boldsymbol{k})$, and the axis of symmetry has at some instant an orientation given as $\boldsymbol{\varepsilon} = l'\boldsymbol{i} + m'\boldsymbol{j} + n'\boldsymbol{k}$. The football will "wobble" about some axis of fixed direction. What is this axis and at what angle will the centerline of the football move about this axis?

26. [19.5] In the above problem, take $l = 0.4$, $n = 0.4$, $m = 0.766$ and $l' = 0$, $m' = 0.6$, $n' = 0.8$. If $H_0 = 0.05$ slug ft²/sec and the principal moments of inertia are $I_{zz} = \frac{1}{4}$ lbm-ft² and $I_{xx} = I_{yy} = \frac{1}{2}$ lbm-ft², what is the rate of spin of the football about its centerline and the rate of precession of the centerline about the $\boldsymbol{H}$ axis?

27. [19.5] A uniform prism having a square cross section is shown in Fig. 19.53. Prove that $I_{\eta\eta}$ for any angle θ equals $I_{xx} = I_{yy}$. Thus, in order to use $I' = I_{xx} = I_{yy}$ as was done in the development in Section 19.5, the body need not be a body of revolution. Show in general that if $I_{xx} = I_{yy}$ and if xyz are principal axes, then $I_{\eta\eta} = I_{xx} = I_{yy}$.

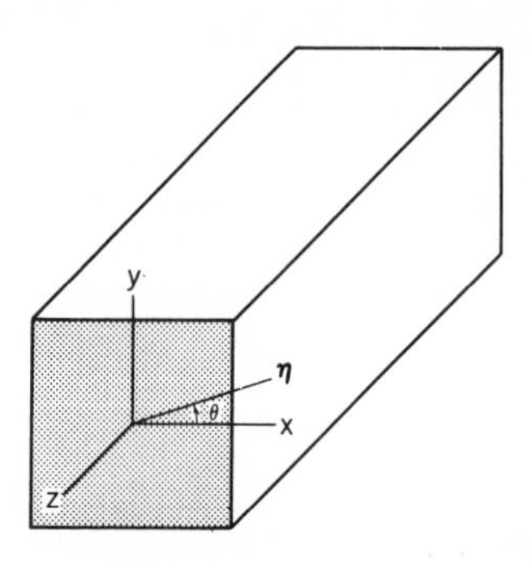

Fig. 19.53

28. [19.5] Shown in Fig. 19.54 is an object representing dynamically a space device. It is made of three homogeneous blocks A, B, and C each of density 50 lbm/ft³. Blocks A and C are hinged along aa and bb. At the configuration shown, the system is in orbit and is rotating about axis parallel to RR at a speed of 3 rad/sec. The block C is then closed by an internal mechanism. What are the precession axis and rate of precession?

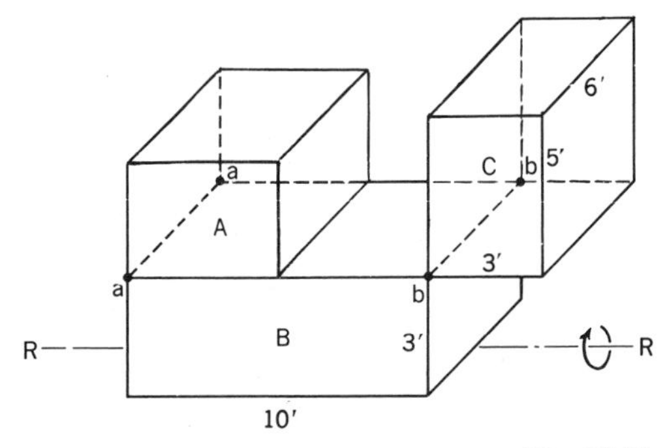

Fig. 19.54

29. [19.5] A dynamical model of a device in orbit is shown in Fig. 19.55. It consists of a 2000-lbm cylindrical shell A of uniform thickness and a disc B rotating relative to the cylinder at a speed ω_2 of 5000 rad/min. The disc B is 1 ft in diameter and has a mass of 100 lbm. The cylinder is rotating at a speed ω_1 of 10 rad/min about axis DD in inertial space. If the shaft FF about which B rotates is made to line up with DD by an internal mechanism, what is the axis of precession for the system and the rate of precession? Neglect the mass of all bodies except the disc B and the shell.

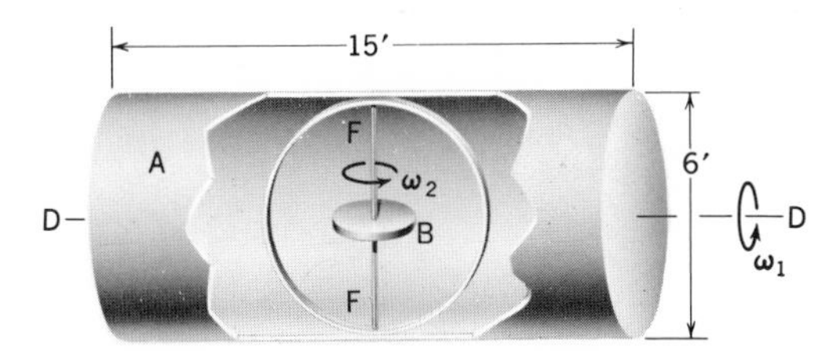

Fig. 19.55

30. [19.5] Suppose you know how much energy is required to change the configuration in Example 19.5 and Probs. 28 and 29. Explain how you could then solve for θ and ϕ.

***31.** [19.5] In Example 19.5, if 20 ft-lb of work is done on the system when going from a test configuration to a closed configuration, compute the nutation angle θ and the spin velocity $\dot{\phi}$.

***32.** [19.5] In Prob. 28, if 10 ft-lb of mechanical energy is added to the bodies from a battery in the closure process, determine the nutation angle θ and the spin velocity $\dot{\phi}$.

***33.** [19.5] In Prob. 29, compute $\dot{\phi}$ of casing and the amount of energy that must have been added to the mechanical system if final ω_2 is 8000 rad/min.

34. [19.5] A projectile is shot out of a weapon in such a manner that it has an angular velocity $\boldsymbol{\omega}$ at an angle α from the centerline as it leaves the weapon (Fig. 19.56). Using the cone model, draw a picture depicting the ensuing motion. Denote θ on this diagram and indicate the direction of $\boldsymbol{H}$.

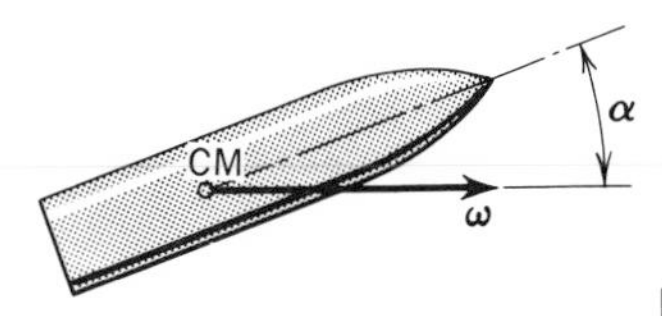

Fig. 19.56

35. [19.5] In the above problem, assume that the spin $\dot{\phi}$ about the axis of symmetry is known. Set up formulations leading to the evaluation of the rate of precession of z about $\boldsymbol{H}$ and the angle between z and $\boldsymbol{H}$.

36. [19.5] A space capsule is shown in Fig. 19.57 rotating about its axis of symmetry in inertial space with an angular speed ω_1 of 2 rad/sec. As a result of an impact with a meteorite at point A an impulse $\boldsymbol{I}$ of 40 lb-sec is developed. Find the axis of precession and the precession velocity for post-impact motion. What are the spin velocity and nutation angle? The mass of the capsule is 3000 lbm. The radius of gyration for the axis of symmetry is 2 ft while the radius of gyration for transverse axes at the center of mass is 2.5 ft.

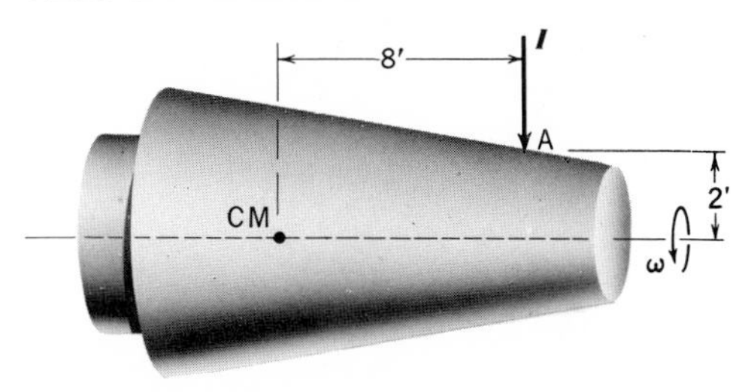

Fig. 19.57

37. [19.5] Do the preceding problem for the case where $\boldsymbol{I}$ is inclined to the right an angle of 45°.

38. [19.5] A rocket casing is shown in Fig. 19.58 in orbit. The casing has a spin of 5 rad/sec about its axis of symmetry. The axis of symmetry is oriented 30° from the precession axis as shown in the diagram. What is the angular momentum of the casing? Take the mass of the casing as 2000 lbm. It has a radius of gyration of 2 ft about the axis of symmetry and a radius of gyration about transverse axes at its center of mass of 3 ft.

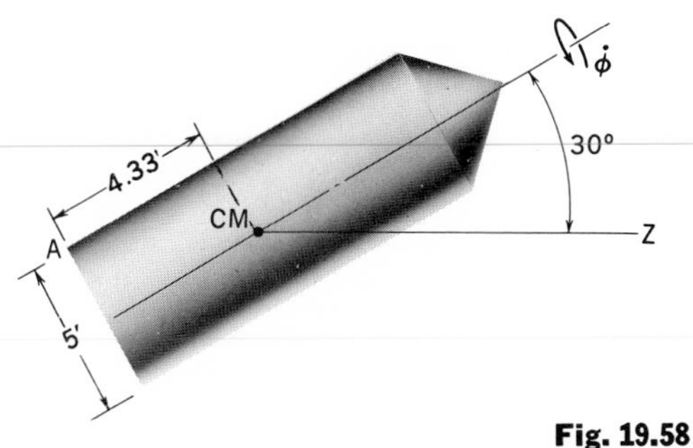

Fig. 19.58

39. [19.5] In the preceding problem assume that an impact in the vertical direction is developed at point A as a result of an impact with a meteorite. If the impulse from the impact is 30 lb-sec, what are the new precession axis and the rate of precession after impact?

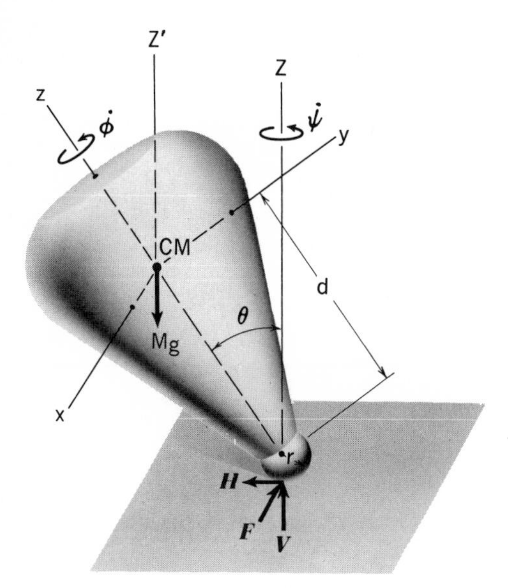

Fig. 19.59

***40.** [19.9] Shown in Fig. 19.59 is a top with a spherical tip of radius r riding on a rough surface which develops a vertical force V and horizontal force components H and F. As every boy knows, the top will generally tend to rise so that its body axis lines up with the vertical axis. We shall now show for certain circumstances that the top must rise.

A reference xyz is chosen at the center of mass not fixed to the body but oriented with the x axis perpendicular to the plane of z and Z and hence parallel to the ground. Show that the component of $\boldsymbol{H}$ in the Z direction is given at all times as:

$$H_Z = I\omega_z \cos\theta + I'\dot{\psi}\sin^2\theta$$

Accordingly, about the Z' axis at the center of mass we can say:

$$\frac{d}{dt}(I\omega_z \cos\theta + I'\dot{\psi}\sin^2\theta) = Fd\sin\theta \qquad (1)$$

Also, considering $\boldsymbol{M} = \dot{\boldsymbol{H}}$ along the z direction, show that:

$$I\dot{\omega}_z = -Fr\sin\theta \qquad (2)$$

and, eliminating F between (1) and (2), show that

$$I\left(\frac{d}{r} + \cos\theta\right)\omega_z + I'\dot{\psi}\sin^2\theta = \text{const.}$$

(This is known as Jellet's integral.) Next show that

$$\dot{\theta} = -\frac{\left(\frac{d}{r} + \cos\theta\right)Fr - I'\ddot{\psi}\sin\theta}{I\omega_z - 2I'\dot{\psi}\cos\theta}$$

Show that the top will rise if ω_z is large and $I > I'$, and if d/r, F, and r are large while θ is small.

20 Vibrations

20.1 Introduction

You will recall that in Chapter 12 we indicated we would defer a more general examination of particle motion about a fixed point till the very end of the text in order to take full advantage of any course work that the student might be undertaking in differential equations. Accordingly, we shall now continue the work begun in Chapter 12.

20.2 Free Vibration

Let us begin by reiterating what we have done earlier leading to the study of vibrations. Recall that we examined the case of a particle in rectilinear translation acted on either by a constant force, a force given as a function of time, a force that is a function of speed, or, finally, a force that is a function of position. In each case we could separate the variables and effect a quadrature to arrive at the desired algebraic equations, including constants of integration. In particular we considered, as a special case of a force given as a function of position, the linear restoring force resulting from the action (or equivalent action) of a spring. Thus for the mass-spring system shown in Fig. 20.1 the differential equation of motion was shown to be:

$$\frac{d^2x}{dt^2} + \frac{K}{m}x = 0 \tag{20.1}$$

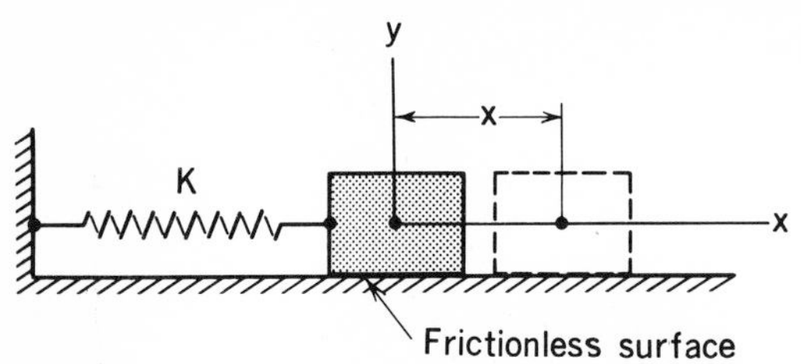

Fig. 20.1

where K is the spring constant and where x is measured from the static equilibrium position of the mass. You will now recognize this from your studies in mathematics as a second-order, linear differential equation with constant coefficients.

Instead of rearranging the equation to effect a quadrature, as we did in the previous case,* we shall take a more general viewpoint toward the solving of differential equations.

To solve a differential equation, we must find a function of time, $x(t)$, which when substituted into the equation satisfies the equation, i.e., reduces it to an identity. We can either guess at $x(t)$ or use a formal procedure. You have learned in your differential equations course that the most general solution of the above equation will consist of a linear combination of two functions that cannot be written as multiples of each other (i.e., the functions are linearly independent). There will also be two arbitrary constants of integration. Thus $C_1 \cos \sqrt{K/m}\, t$ and $C_2 \sin \sqrt{K/m}\, t$ will satisfy the equation, as we can readily demonstrate by substitution, and are independent in the manner described. We can therefore say:

$$x = C_1 \cos \sqrt{\frac{K}{m}}\, t + C_2 \sin \sqrt{\frac{K}{m}}\, t \qquad \textbf{20.2}$$

where C_1 and C_2 are the aforementioned constants of integration to be determined by the initial conditions.

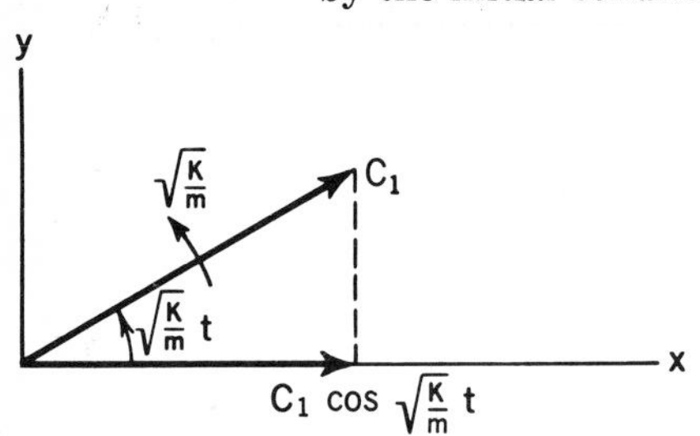

Fig. 20.2

We may conveniently represent each of the above functions by employing rotating vectors of magnitudes that correspond to the coefficients of the functions. This has been shown in Fig. 20.2 where, if the vector C_1 rotates counterclockwise with an angular velocity of $\sqrt{K/m}$ radians per unit time and if C_1 lies along the x axis at time $t = 0$, the projection of this vector along the x axis represents one of the functions of Eq. 20.2—namely $C_1 \cos \sqrt{K/m}\, t$. Vectors used in this manner are called *phasors*.†

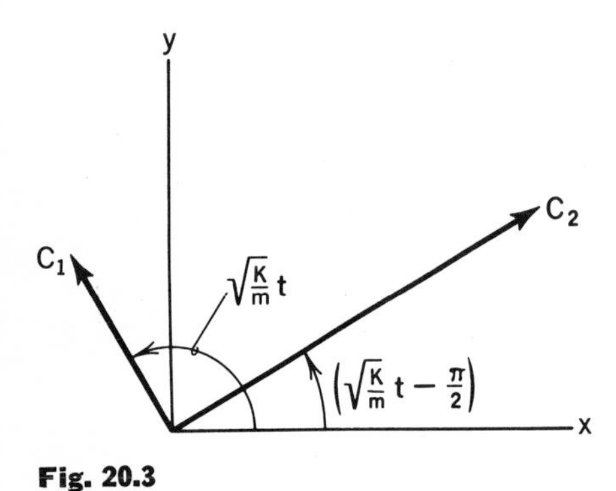

Fig. 20.3

Consider now the function $C_2 \sin \sqrt{K/m}\, t$, which we can replace by $C_2 \cos (\sqrt{K/m}\, t - \pi/2)$, as we learned in elementary trigonometry. The phasor representation for this function, therefore, would be a vector of magnitude C_2 that rotates with angular velocity $\sqrt{K/m}$ and that is out of phase by $\pi/2$ with the phasor C_1 (Fig. 20.3). It is clear that since vectors C_1 and C_2 rotate at the same angular speed, we can represent the combined contribution by simply summing the vectors

* Recall that this can be done by replacing d^2x/dt^2 by $(dV/dx)(dx/dt)$, which is simply $V(dV/dx)$.

† Recall that phasors were also discussed in Example 17.6.

C_1 and C_2 and considering the projection of the resulting single vector along the x axis. This is shown in Fig. 20.4 where vector C_3 replaces the vectors C_1 and C_2. Now we can say:

$$C_3 = \sqrt{C_1^2 + C_2^2}, \qquad \beta = \tan^{-1}\frac{C_2}{C_1} \qquad \textbf{20.3}$$

Since C_1 and C_2 are arbitrary constants, C_3 and β are also arbitrary constants. Consequently, we can replace the solution given by Eq. 20.2 by another equivalent form:

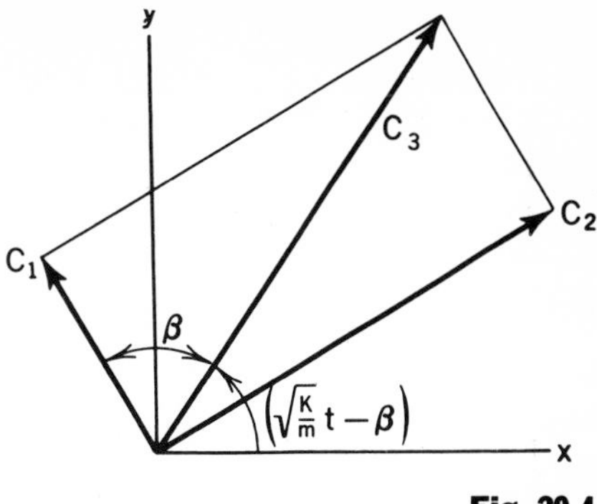

Fig. 20.4

$$x = C_3 \cos\left(\sqrt{\frac{K}{m}}\,t - \beta\right) \qquad \textbf{20.4}$$

From this form, you probably recognize that the motion of the body is *harmonic motion*. In studying this type of motion, we shall use the following definitions:

Cycle. The cycle is that portion of a motion (or series of events in the more general usage) which, when repeated, forms the motion. On the phasor diagrams, this would be the motion associated with one revolution of the rotating vector.

Frequency. The number of cycles per unit time is the frequency. It is equal to $\sqrt{K/m}/2\pi$ for the above motion, since $\sqrt{K/m}$ has units of radians per unit time. Sometimes $\sqrt{K/m}$ is termed the *natural frequency* of the system in radians per unit time or, when divided by 2π, in cycles per unit time.

Period. The period, τ, is the time of one cycle, and is therefore the reciprocal of frequency. That is:

$$\tau = \frac{2\pi}{\sqrt{K/m}} \qquad \textbf{20.5}$$

Amplitude. The largest displacement attained by the body during a cycle is the amplitude. In this case, the amplitude corresponds to the coefficient C_3.

Phase angle. The phase angle is the angle between the phasor and the x axis when $t = 0$, i.e., the angle β.

A plot of the motion as a function of time is presented in Fig. 20.5, where these various quantities are shown graphically.

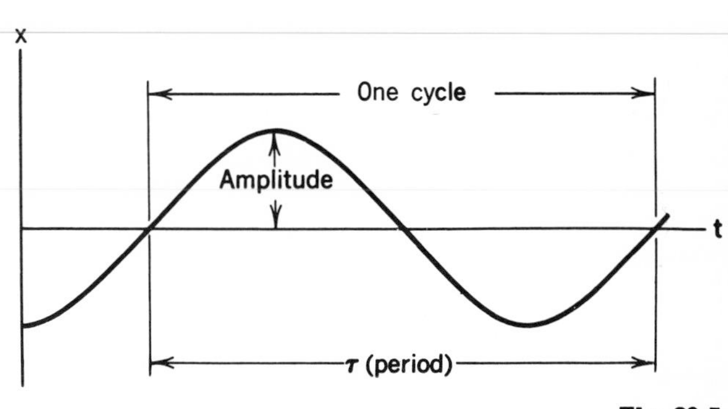

Fig. 20.5

It is usually easier to use the earlier form of solution, Eq. 20.2, rather than Eq. 20.4 in satisfying initial conditions. Accordingly, the position and velocity can be given as:

$$x = C_1 \cos \sqrt{\frac{K}{m}}\, t + C_2 \sin \sqrt{\frac{K}{m}}\, t$$

$$V = -C_1 \sqrt{\frac{K}{m}} \sin \sqrt{\frac{K}{m}}\, t + C_2 \sqrt{\frac{K}{m}} \cos \sqrt{\frac{K}{m}}\, t \qquad \textbf{20.6}$$

The initial conditions to be applied to these equations are:

$$\text{when } t = 0, \quad x = x_0, \quad V = V_0$$

Substituting, we get:

$$x_0 = C_1, \qquad V_0 = C_2 \sqrt{\frac{K}{m}}$$

Therefore, the motion is given as:

$$x = x_0 \cos \sqrt{\frac{K}{m}}\, t + \frac{V_0}{\sqrt{K/m}} \sin \sqrt{\frac{K}{m}}\, t \qquad \textbf{(a)}$$

$$V = -x_0 \sqrt{\frac{K}{m}} \sin \sqrt{\frac{K}{m}}\, t + V_0 \cos \sqrt{\frac{K}{m}}\, t \qquad \textbf{(b)} \quad \textbf{20.7}$$

We can generalize from these results by noting that any agent supplying a linear restoring force for all motions of a mass can take the place of the spring in the preceding computations. We must remember, however, that to behave this way the agent must have negligible mass. Thus we can associate with such agents an *equivalent spring constant* K_e, which we can ascertain if we know the static deflection δ permitted by the agent on application of some known force F. We can then say:

$$K_e = \frac{F}{\delta} \qquad \textbf{20.8}$$

Once we determine the equivalent spring constant, we immediately know that the natural frequency of the system is $(1/2\pi)\sqrt{K_e/m}$ cycles per unit time. This is the number of cycles the system will repeat in a unit time if some initial disturbance is imposed on the mass. Note that this natural frequency depends only on the "stiffness" of the system and on the mass of the system and is not dependent on the amplitude of the motion.*

We shall now consider several problems in which we can apply what we have just learned about harmonic motion.

EXAMPLE 20.1

A mass weighing 10 lb is placed on the spring shown in Fig. 20.6 and is released very slowly, extending the spring a distance of 2 inches. What is the natural

* Actually, when the amplitude gets comparatively large, the spring ceases to be linear, and the motion does depend on the amplitude. Our results do not apply for such a condition.

frequency of the system? If the mass is given a velocity instantaneously of 5 ft/sec down from the equilibrium position, what is the equation for displacement as a function of time?

The spring constant is immediately available by the equation:

$$K = \frac{F}{\delta} = \frac{10 \text{ lb}}{2 \text{ in.}} = 5 \text{ lb/in.}$$

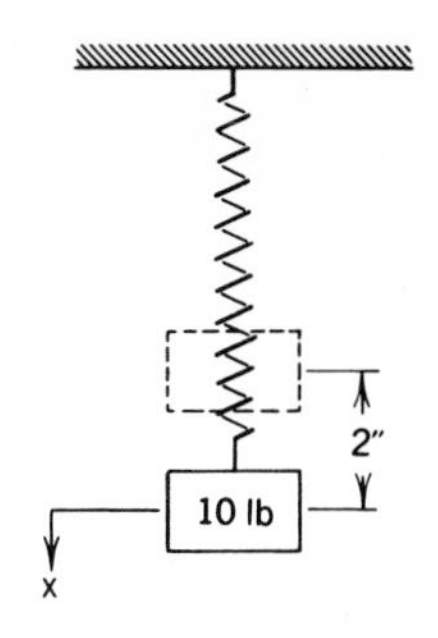

Fig. 20.6

The equation of motion for the mass can be written for a reference whose origin is at the loaded equilibrium position shown in the diagram. Thus:

$$m \frac{d^2x}{dt^2} = W - K(x + \delta)$$

where δ is the distance from the unextended position of the spring to the origin of the reference. However, from our initial equation, $\delta = F/K = W/K$. Therefore, we have:

$$m \frac{d^2x}{dt^2} = W - K\left(x + \frac{W}{K}\right) = -Kx$$

and the equation becomes:

$$\frac{d^2x}{dt^2} + \frac{K}{m} x = 0 \qquad \textbf{(a)}$$

Thus, as we showed in a somewhat different manner in Section 12.5, the motion will proceed about the position of static equilibrium, which is an extended position of the spring, in precisely the same manner it did in the discussion where the static-equilibrium position and the unextended position of the spring happened to coincide. This conclusion follows from the fact that Eq. (a) is the same as Eq. 20.1.

Accordingly, we can use the results stemming from our main discussion. Employing the notation ω_n as the natural frequency in units of radians per unit time, we have:

$$\omega_n = \sqrt{\frac{K}{m}} = \sqrt{\frac{5 \text{ lb/in.}}{10 \text{ lb}/g \text{ ft/sec}^2}} = \sqrt{\frac{(5)(32)}{10}\left(\frac{\text{ft}}{\text{in. sec}^2}\right)}$$

$$= \sqrt{\frac{(5)(32)}{10}\left(\frac{12 \text{ in.}}{\text{ft}}\right)\left(\frac{\text{ft}}{\text{in. sec}^2}\right)} = 13.9 \text{ rad/sec}$$

The motion is now given by the equation.

$$x = C_1 \sin 13.9t + C_2 \cos 13.9t$$

$$\dot{x} = 13.9C_1 \cos 13.9t - 13.9C_2 \sin 13.9t$$

From the specified initial conditions, we know that when $t = 0$, $x = 0$ and $\dot{x} = 5$. Therefore, the constants of integration become:

$$C_2 = 0, \qquad C_1 = \frac{5}{13.9} = 0.359$$

The desired equation, then, is:

$$x = 0.359 \sin 13.9t \text{ ft}$$

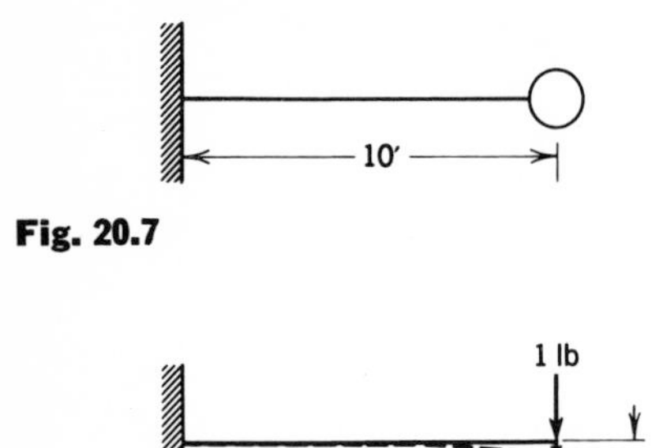

Fig. 20.7

Fig. 20.8

EXAMPLE 20.2

In Fig. 20.7, a body weighing 5 lb is positioned on the end of a slender cantilever beam whose mass we can neglect in considering the motions of the body at its end.

If we know the geometry and the composition of the cantilever beam, and if the deflection involved is small, we can compute from strength of materials the deflection of the end of the beam that results from a vertical load there. In this case, suppose we have computed a deflection of 0.5 in. for a force of 1 lb (see Fig. 20.8). What would be the natural frequency of the body weighing 5 lb for small oscillations in the vertical direction?

Because the motion is restricted to small amplitudes, we may consider the mass to be translating in the vertical direction in the same manner as the mass on the spring in the previous case. The formulations of this section are once again applicable. The equivalent spring is found to be:

$$K_e = \frac{F}{\delta} = \frac{1}{0.5} = 2 \text{ lb/in.}$$

The natural frequency for a 5-lb weight at the end of the cantilever is then:

$$\omega_n = \sqrt{\frac{(2)(12)(32)}{5}} = 12.4 \text{ rad/sec}$$

20.3 Torsional Vibration

We showed in Section 17.6 that for a body constrained to rotate about an axis fixed in inertial space Euler's equation simplified to the elementary form:

$$I_{zz}\dot{\omega}_z = I_{zz}\ddot{\theta} = M_z \qquad \textbf{20.9}$$

Numerous homework problems were presented involving the determination of $\dot{\theta}$ and θ for applied torques which either were constant, varied with time, varied with speed $\dot{\theta}$, or, finally, varied with position θ. The analyses paralleled very closely corresponding cases for rectilinear translation. Primarily the approach was that of separation of variables and then that of carrying out one or more quadratures.

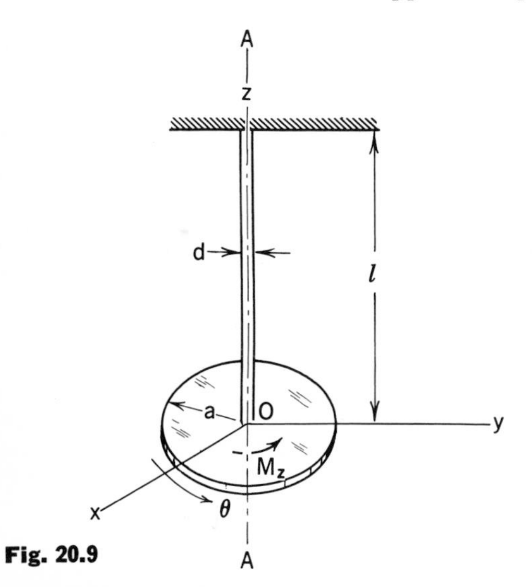

Fig. 20.9

Paralleling the case of the linear restoring force in rectilinear translation is the important case where M_z is a linear restoring torque. For example, consider a circular disc attached to the end of a light shaft as shown in Fig. 20.9. Note that the upper end of the shaft is fixed. If the disc is twisted by an external agent about the centerline AA of the shaft, the disc will rotate essentially as a rigid body, while the shaft, since it is so much thinner and longer, will twist and supply a restoring torque on the disc that tries to bring the disc back to its initial position. In considering the possible motions of such a system disturbed in the aforementioned manner, we idealize the problem by *lumping* all elastic action into the shaft and all inertial effects into the disc. We know from strength of materials that for a circular shaft of constant cross section the amount of twist θ induced by torque M_z is, in the elastic range of deformation, given as:

$$\theta = \frac{M_z L}{GJ} \tag{20.10}$$

where G is the shear modulus of the shaft material, J is the polar moment of inertia of the shaft cross section, and L is the length of the shaft. We can set forth the concept of a torsional spring constant K_t given as:

$$K_t = \frac{M_z}{\theta} \tag{20.11}$$

For the case at hand we have for K_t:

$$K_t = \frac{GJ}{L} \tag{20.12}$$

Thus the thin shaft has the same role in this discussion as the light linear spring of the previous section. Employing Eq. 20.11 for M_z and using the proper sign to ensure that we have a restoring action, we can express Eq. 20.9 as follows:

$$\ddot{\theta} + \frac{K_t}{I_{zz}}\theta = 0 \tag{20.13}$$

Notice that the above equation is identical in form to Eq. 20.1. Accordingly, all the conclusions developed in that discussion apply with the appropriate changes in notation. Thus the disc, once disturbed by being given an angular motion, will have a torsional natural oscillation frequency of $\sqrt{K_t/I_{zz}}$ radians per unit time. The equation of motion for the disc is:

$$\theta = C_1 \cos\sqrt{\frac{K_t}{I_{zz}}}\,t + C_2 \sin\sqrt{\frac{K_t}{I_{zz}}}\,t \tag{20.14}$$

where C_1 and C_2 are constants of integration to be determined from initial conditions. Thus for $\theta = \theta_0$ and $\dot{\theta} = \dot{\theta}_0$ at $t = 0$ we have:

$$\theta = \theta_0 \cos\sqrt{\frac{K_t}{I_{zz}}}\,t + \frac{\dot{\theta}_0}{\sqrt{K_t/I_{zz}}} \sin\sqrt{\frac{K_t}{I_{zz}}}\,t \tag{20.15}$$

In the example just presented the linear restoring torque stemmed from a long thin shaft. There may be other agents that can develop a linear restoring torque on a system otherwise free to rotate about an axis fixed in inertial space. We then talk about an equivalent torsional spring constant. We shall illustrate such cases in the following examples.

EXAMPLE 20.3

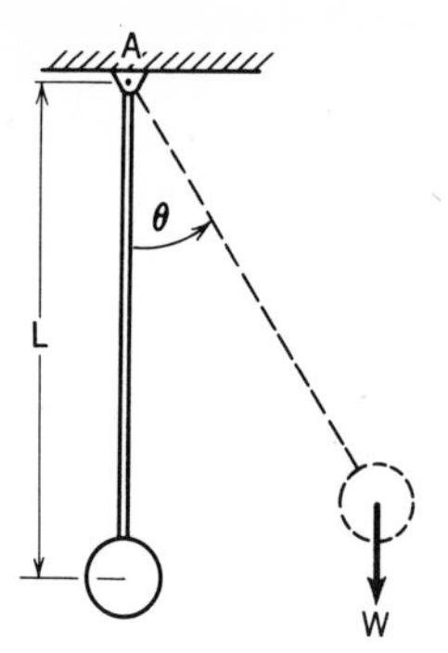

Fig. 20.10

What are the equation of motion and the natural frequency of oscillation for small amplitude of a simple plane pendulum shown in Fig. 20.10? The pendulum rod may be considered massless.

Because the pendulum bob is small compared to the radius of curvature of its possible trajectory of motion, we may consider it as a particle. The pendulum has one degree of freedom and we can use θ as the independent coordinate. Notice from the diagram that there is a restoring torque about point A developed by gravity given as:

$$M_z = -WL \sin \theta \qquad \textbf{(a)}$$

where W is the weight of the bob. If the amplitude of the motion θ is very small, we can replace $\sin \theta$ by θ and so for this case we have a linear restoring torque given as:

$$M_z = -WL\theta \qquad \textbf{(b)}$$

and we have an equivalent torsional spring constant for the system given as:

$$K_t = WL \qquad \textbf{(c)}$$

The equation of possible small-amplitude motions for the pendulum is given as:

$$-WL\theta = (ML^2)\ddot{\theta} \qquad \textbf{(d)}$$

where we have used the moment-of-momentum equation about the fixed point A. Rearranging terms, we get:

$$\ddot{\theta} + \frac{WL}{ML^2}\theta = 0 \qquad \textbf{(e)}$$

Noting that $W = Mg$, we have:

$$\ddot{\theta} + \frac{g}{L}\theta = 0 \qquad \textbf{(f)}$$

Accordingly the natural frequency of oscillation is:

$$\omega_n = \sqrt{\frac{g}{L}} \text{ rad/sec} \qquad \textbf{(g)}$$

The equation of motion for this system is:

$$\theta = C_1 \cos \sqrt{\frac{g}{L}}\, t + C_2 \sin \sqrt{\frac{g}{L}}\, t \qquad \textbf{(h)}$$

where C_1 and C_2 are computed from known conditions at some time t_0.

EXAMPLE 20.4

A stepped disc is shown in Fig. 20.11 supporting a weight W_1 while being constrained by a linear spring having a spring constant K. The mass of the stepped disk is M and the radius of gyration about its geometric axis is k. What is the equation of motion for the system if the disc is rotated a small angle θ_0 counterclockwise from its static-equilibrium configuration and then suddenly released from rest? Assume the cord holding W_1 is weightless and perfectly flexible.

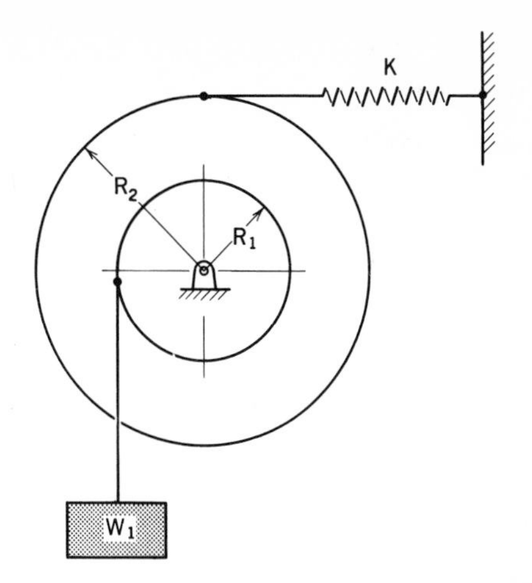

Fig. 20.11

If we measure θ from the static-equilibrium position as shown in Fig. 20.12(a) it means that the spring is stretched an amount $R_2(\theta + \theta_0)$ wherein θ_0 is the amount of rotation induced by the weight W_1 to reach the static-equilibrium configuration. Consequently, applying the simplified Euler equation to the stepped disc about the axis of rotation, we get:

$$R_1 T - KR_2^2(\theta + \theta_0) = Mk^2\ddot{\theta} \qquad \textbf{(a)}$$

Next consider the suspended weight W_1. Clearly we have only translation for this body, for which Newton's law gives us:

$$-T + W_1 = \frac{W_1}{g} R_1\ddot{\theta} \qquad \textbf{(b)}$$

where we have made the assumption that the cord is always taut and is inextensible. We may replace T in Eq. (a) using Eq. (b) as follows:

$$R_1 W_1 - \frac{W_1}{g} R_1^2\ddot{\theta} - KR_2^2(\theta + \theta_0) = Mk^2\ddot{\theta} \qquad \textbf{(c)}$$

Rearranging terms, we get:

$$\left(Mk^2 + \frac{W_1}{g} R_1^2\right)\ddot{\theta} + KR_2^2\theta = R_1 W_1 - KR_2^2\theta_0 \qquad \textbf{(d)}$$

Considering the static-equilibrium configuration of the system, it is clear on summing moments about the axis of rotation that the right side of the above equation is zero. Accordingly we have for Eq. (d):

$$\ddot{\theta} + \frac{KR_2^2}{Mk^2 + (W_1/g)R_1^2}\theta = 0 \qquad \textbf{(e)}$$

We can say immediately that the natural torsional frequency of the system is given as:

$$\omega_n = \sqrt{\frac{KR_2^2}{Mk^2 + (W_1/g)R_1^2}} \text{ rad/sec} \qquad \textbf{(f)}$$

The equation of motion is then:

$$\theta = C_1 \cos\sqrt{\frac{KR_2^2}{Mk^2 + (W_1/g)R_1^2}}\,t + C_2 \sin\sqrt{\frac{KR_2^2}{Mk^2 + (W_1/g)R_1^2}}\,t \qquad \textbf{(g)}$$

Submitting Eq. (g) to the initial conditions we get:

$$\theta = \theta_0 \cos\sqrt{\frac{KR_2^2}{Mk^2 + (W_1/g)R_1^2}}\,t \qquad \textbf{(h)}$$

We could have reached Eq. (e) more directly by noting that, when θ is measured from the equilibrium configuration, the weight W_1 is already counteracted by the stretch $R_2\theta_0$ of the spring and accordingly only force $-R_2K\theta$ from further stretch of the spring and

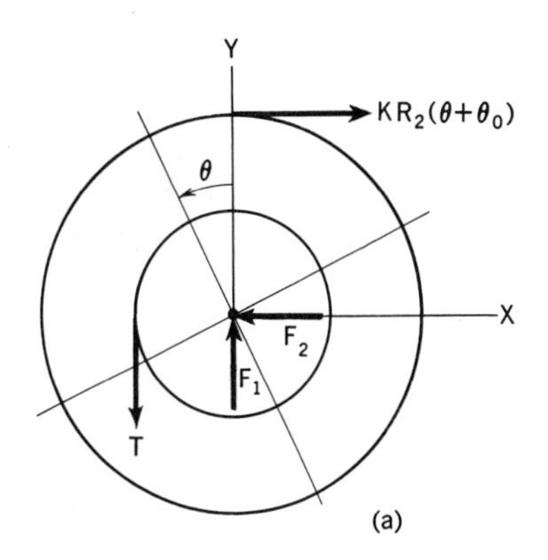

(a)

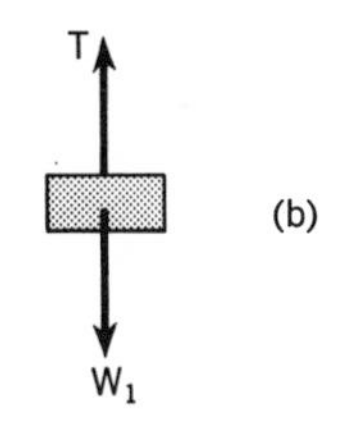

(b)

Fig. 20.12

the inertial force $-(W_1/g)R_1\ddot{\theta}$ of the hanging weight need be considered. Thus, using the simplified Euler equation, we have from this viewpoint:

$$-KR_2\theta - \frac{W_1}{g}R_1^2\ddot{\theta} = Mk^2\ddot{\theta} \tag{i}$$

Rearranging, we have:

$$\ddot{\theta} + \frac{KR_2}{Mk^2 + (W_1/g)R_1^2}\theta = 0 \tag{j}$$

Accordingly we arrive at very same differential equations in a more direct manner. We can again conclude as in Example 20.1 that when the coordinate is measured from an equilibrium configuration we can forget about contributions of forces and torques that are present for the equilibrium configuration and include only new forces and torques developed when there is a departure from the equilibrium configuration.

*20.4 Examples of Other Free-Oscillating Motions

In the previous sections we have examined the rectilinear translation of a rigid body under the action of a linear restoring force as well as the pure rotation of a rigid body under the action of a linear restoring torque. In this section we shall first examine a body with one degree of freedom undergoing *plane motion* governed by a differential equation of motion of the form given in the previous section. The dependent variable for such a case varies harmonically with time, and we have a vibratory plane motion. Consider the following example.

EXAMPLE 20.5

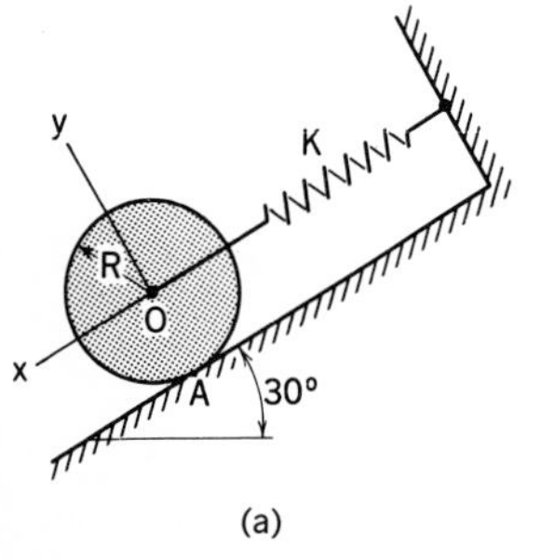

W
f
N
(b)

Fig. 20.13

Shown in Fig. 20.13(a) on an inclined plane is a uniform cylinder maintained in a position of equilibrium by a linear spring having a spring constant K. If the cylinder rolls without slipping, what is the equation of motion when it is disturbed from its equilibrium position?

We have here a case of plane motion about a configuration of equilibrium. We shall measure the displacement x of the center of mass from the equilibrium position and accordingly will need to consider only those forces and torques developed as the cylinder departs from this position. Accordingly we have for Newton's law for the mass center [see Fig. 20.13(b)]:

$$-f - Kx = M\ddot{x} \tag{a}$$

Now employ the simplified Euler equation about the geometric axis of the cylinder at O. Using θ to measure the rotation of the cylinder about this axis from the equilibrium configuration, we get:

$$fR = \tfrac{1}{2}MR^2\ddot{\theta} \tag{b}$$

Noting from kinematics that $\ddot{x} = R\ddot{\theta}$ as a result of the no-slipping condition, we have for the above equation:

$$fR = \frac{1}{2} MR^2 \left(\frac{\ddot{x}}{R}\right)$$

$$\therefore f = \tfrac{1}{2} M\ddot{x} \qquad \textbf{(c)}$$

Substituting for f in Eq. (a) using the above result, we have:

$$-\tfrac{1}{2} M\ddot{x} - Kx = M\ddot{x}$$

$$\therefore \ddot{x} + \frac{2}{3}\frac{K}{M} x = 0 \qquad \textbf{(d)}$$

We could also have arrived at the above differential equation by noting that we have instantaneous pure rotation about the line of contact A as a result of the no-slipping condition. Thus the simplified Euler equation can be used as follows:

$$-KxR = \tfrac{3}{2} MR^2\ddot{\theta} \qquad \textbf{(e)}$$

Noting as before that $\ddot{\theta} = \ddot{x}/R$, we get

$$-KxR = \frac{3}{2} MR^2 \frac{\ddot{x}}{R}$$

$$\therefore \ddot{x} + \frac{2}{3}\frac{K}{M} x = 0 \qquad \textbf{(f)}$$

Thus, for small oscilations we can consider this problem as one of pure rotation about a *fixed* axis of rotation and not need to get involved in a more general plane motion analysis such as is given at the outset. You will have the opportunity of making such simplifications for certain of the homework problems.

We may integrate the differential equation to give us:

$$x = x_0 \cos \sqrt{\frac{2}{3}\frac{K}{M}}\, t + \frac{\dot{x}_0}{\sqrt{\frac{2}{3} K/M}} \sin \sqrt{\frac{2}{3}\frac{K}{M}}\, t \qquad \textbf{(g)}$$

where x_0 and $\dot{x}_0$ are respectively the initial position and speed of the center of mass. Since $\theta = x/R$ (we have here only one degree of freedom as a result of the no-slipping condition), we have for θ from Eq. (d):

$$\theta = \frac{x_0}{R} \cos \sqrt{\frac{2}{3}\frac{K}{M}}\, t + \frac{\dot{x}_0}{R\sqrt{\frac{2}{3} K/M}} \sin \sqrt{\frac{2}{3}\frac{K}{M}}\, t \qquad \textbf{(h)}$$

In the next example we shall consider a vibratory motion as seen from a *noninertial* reference. Other such problems will be presented in the homework problems.

EXAMPLE 20.6

Shown in Fig. 20.14(a) is a vertical rod AC rotating at uniform angular speed ω. At the end A of this rod is pinned a second rod AB of length L and weight W. The rod AB rotates about the vertical axis along

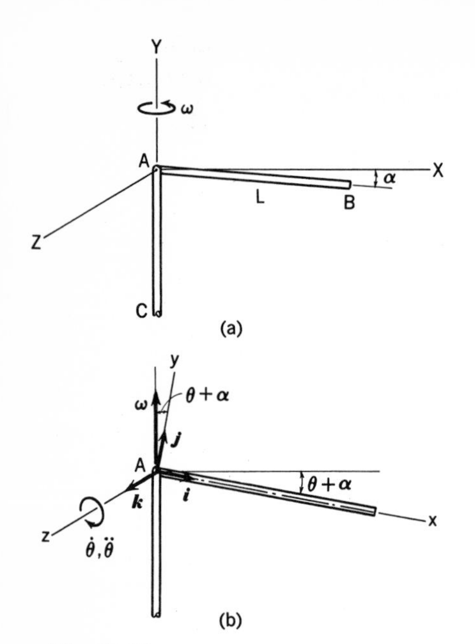

Fig. 20.14

with rod AC while remaining at a fixed angle α with the horizontal plane XZ. Suppose the rod AB is disturbed from this motion so as to have a varying inclination with the XZ plane. What is the nature of the possible variation of this inclination if the angular speed ω is kept constant?

In Fig. 20.14(b) we have shown the rod at some position $\alpha + \theta$ from the XZ plane. We have fixed a reference xyz in the rod with A as the origin. Since point A is fixed in inertial space, we may use Euler's equations of motion. The angular velocity of reference xyz is:

$$\boldsymbol{\omega} = \omega \cos(\theta + \alpha)\boldsymbol{j} - \omega \sin(\theta + \alpha)\boldsymbol{i} + \dot{\theta}\boldsymbol{k} \qquad \text{(a)}$$

Thus:

$$\omega_x = -\omega \sin(\theta + \alpha)$$
$$\omega_y = \omega \cos(\theta + \alpha)$$
$$\omega_z = \dot{\theta} \qquad \text{(b)}$$

Since these are valid at any time t, we may differentiate with respect to time t to get:

$$\dot{\omega}_x = -\omega \cos(\theta + \alpha)\, \dot{\theta}$$
$$\dot{\omega}_y = -\omega \sin(\theta + \alpha)\, \dot{\theta}$$
$$\dot{\omega}_z = \ddot{\theta} \qquad \text{(c)}$$

Accordingly we have for Euler's equation about the z axis

$$0 = I_{zz}\ddot{\theta} + \omega^2 \cos(\theta + \alpha) \sin(\theta + \alpha)[I_{yy} - I_{xx}] \qquad \text{(d)}$$

Neglecting I_{xx}, we get:

$$I_{zz}\ddot{\theta} + I_{yy}\omega^2 \cos(\theta + \alpha) \sin(\theta + \alpha) = 0 \qquad \text{(e)}$$

Noting that:

$$\cos(\theta + \alpha) \sin(\theta + \alpha) = \tfrac{1}{2} \sin[(2)(\theta + \alpha)],$$

we have:

$$I_{zz}\ddot{\theta} + \frac{I_{yy}\omega^2}{2} \sin[(2)(\theta + \alpha)] = 0 \qquad \text{(f)}$$

For small angles α and θ we can replace $\sin 2(\theta + \alpha)$ by $2(\theta + \alpha)$. We then get, on replacing $\ddot{\theta}$ by $(d^2/dt^2)(\theta + \alpha)$:

$$I_{zz} \frac{d^2(\theta + \alpha)}{dt^2} + I_{yy}\omega^2(\theta + \alpha) = 0 \qquad \text{(g)}$$

We have next, on rearranging the equation and letting $\theta + \alpha = \beta$:

$$\ddot{\beta} + \frac{I_{yy}\omega^2}{I_{zz}} \beta = 0 \qquad \text{(h)}$$

The solution of this equation is:

$$\beta = \beta_0 \cos \sqrt{\frac{I_{yy}}{I_{zz}}}\, \omega t + \frac{\dot{\beta}_0}{\sqrt{(I_{yy}/I_{zz})}\, \omega} \sin \sqrt{\frac{I_{yy}}{I_{zz}}}\, \omega t \qquad \text{(i)}$$

Now, going back to the original notation, we get:

$$\theta + \alpha = (\theta_0 + \alpha)\cos\sqrt{\frac{I_{yy}}{I_{zz}}}\,\omega t + \frac{\dot{\theta}_0}{\sqrt{(I_{yy}/I_{zz})}\,\omega}\sin\sqrt{\frac{I_{yy}}{I_{zz}}}\,\omega t \qquad \text{(j)}$$

where θ_0 is the angular displacement from the steady-state configuration α at time $t = 0$ and $\dot{\theta}_0$ is the angular speed about the x axis at time $t = 0$. Thus for small steady-state angle α and for small disturbances we will get an oscillatory motion of the rod AB as seen from a noninertial reference rotating with rod AC, provided we maintain a constant angular speed ω.

---

*20.5 Energy Methods

Up to now the procedure has been primarily to work with Newton's law in reaching the differential equation of interest. There is an alternative approach to the handling of free-vibration problems that may be very useful in dealing with simple systems and in setting up approximate calculations for more complex systems. Suppose it is known for a one-degree-of-freedom system that only linear restoring forces and torques do work during possible motions of the system. Then the agents developing such forces are conservative agents and may be considered to store potential energy. You will recall from Section 13.3 that the total mechanical energy for such systems is conserved. Thus we have:

$$P.E. + K.E. = \text{const.} \qquad \textbf{20.16}$$

Also we know from our present undertakings that the system must oscillate harmonically when disturbed and then allowed to move freely with only the linear restoring agents doing work. Thus if κ is the independent coordinate measured from the static-equilibrium configuration, we have:

$$\kappa = A\sin(\omega_n t + \alpha) \qquad \textbf{20.17}$$

Also we have:

$$\dot{\kappa} = A\omega_n\cos(\omega_n t + \alpha) \qquad \textbf{20.18}$$

Now at the instant when $\kappa = 0$ we are at the static-equilibrium position and the potential energy of the system is a minimum. Since the total mechanical energy must be conserved at all times once such a motion is under way, it is also clear that the kinetic energy must be at a maximum at that instant. If we take the lowest potential energy as zero, then we have for the total mechanical energy simply the maximum kinetic energy. Also when the body is undergoing a change in direction of its motion at the outer extreme position, the kinetic energy is zero instantaneously and accordingly the potential energy must be a maximum and equal to the total mechanical energy of the system. Thus we can equate the maximum potential energy with the maximum kinetic energy.

$$[K.E.]_{\max} = [P.E.]_{\max} \qquad \textbf{20.19}$$

In computing the $[K.E.]_{\max}$ we will involve $(\dot{\kappa})_{\max}$ and hence $A\omega_n$, while for the $[P.E.]_{\max}$ we will involve $(\kappa)_{\max}$ and hence A. In this way we can set up quickly an equation for ω_n, the natural frequency of the system. For example, if we have the simple linear mass-spring system of Fig. 20.1, we can say:

$$[P.E.] = \tfrac{1}{2}Kx^2$$

$$\therefore\ [P.E.]_{\max} = \tfrac{1}{2}K(x_{\max})^2 = \tfrac{1}{2}KA^2$$

where we have made use of our knowledge that $x = A \sin(\omega_n t + \alpha)$. And, noting that $\dot{x} = A\omega_n \cos(\omega_n t + \beta)$, we have:

$$[K.E.]_{\max} = \tfrac{1}{2}M(\dot{x}_{\max})^2 = \tfrac{1}{2}M[A\omega_n]^2$$

Now, equating these expressions, we get:

$$\tfrac{1}{2}KA^2 = \tfrac{1}{2}M[A\omega_n]^2$$

$$\therefore\ \omega_n = \sqrt{\frac{K}{M}}$$

which is the expected result. We next illustrate this approach in a more complex problem.

EXAMPLE 20.7

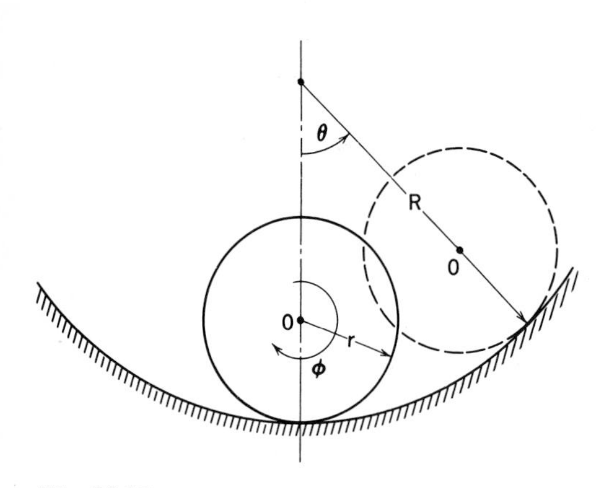

Fig. 20.15

A cylinder of radius r and weight W rolls without slipping along a circular path of radius R as shown in Fig. 20.15. Compute the natural frequency for small oscillation.

We have here a system with one degree of freedom. We can use ϕ, the angle of rotation of the cylinder about its axis of symmetry, as the independent coordinate, or we may use θ as shown in the diagram. To relate these variables for no slipping we may conclude, on observing the motion of point O, that for small rotation:

$$(R - r)\theta = r\phi$$

$$\therefore\ \theta = \frac{r}{R - r}\phi \qquad \textbf{(a)}$$

The only force that does work during the possible motions of the system is the force of gravity W. The torque developed by W about the point of contact for a given θ is easily determined by examining Fig. 20.16 to be:

$$\text{torque} = Wr \sin\theta = Wr \sin\left(\frac{r}{R - r}\phi\right) \qquad \textbf{(b)}$$

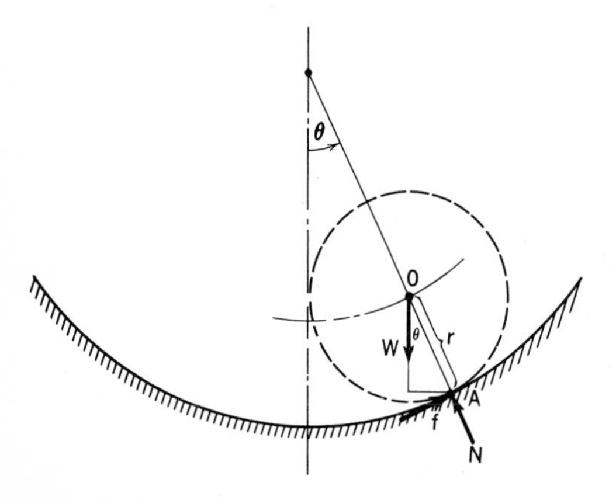

Fig. 20.16

This is a restoring torque and if we limit ourselves to small oscillations it becomes $W[r^2\phi/(R - r)]$—clearly a linear restoring torque. We can accordingly employ the energy formulation of this section. The motion may be considered to be given as follows:

$$\theta = C \sin(\omega_n t + \beta)$$

or

$$\phi = \frac{R - r}{r} C \sin(\omega_n t + \beta) \qquad \textbf{(c)}$$

Expressing the maximum kinetic and potential energies, we have using C for θ_{max}:

$$[P.E.]_{max} = W(R - r)(1 - \cos\theta_{max})$$

$$= W(R - r)(1 - \cos C) \qquad \textbf{(d)}$$

$$[K.E.]_{max} = \frac{1}{2}\frac{W}{g}(R - r)^2\dot{\theta}^2_{max} + \frac{1}{4}\frac{W}{g}r^2\dot{\phi}^2_{max}$$

$$= \frac{1}{2}\frac{W}{g}(R - r)^2(C\omega_n)^2 + \frac{1}{4}\frac{W}{g}r^2 \times \left(\frac{R - r}{r}C\omega_n\right)^2 \qquad \textbf{(e)}$$

Expanding $\cos C$ into a power series and retaining the first two terms $(1 - C^2/2)$, we then get, on equating the right sides of the above equations:

$$W(R - r)\frac{C^2}{2} = \frac{W}{2g}\left[(R - r)^2 + \frac{(R - r)^2}{2}\right]\omega_n^2 C^2$$

$$\therefore \omega_n = \sqrt{\frac{g}{\frac{3}{2}(R - r)}} \qquad \textbf{(f)}$$

20.6 Linear Restoring Force and a Force Varying Sinusoidally with Time

We shall now consider the case of a sinusoidal force acting on a spring-mass system (Fig. 20.17). The sinusoidal force has a frequency of ω (not to be confused with ω_n, the natural frequency) and an amplitude of F_0. At time $t = 0$, the mass will be assumed to have some known velocity and position, and we will investigate the ensuing motion.

Measuring the position x from the unextended position of the spring, we have for Newton's law:

$$m\frac{d^2x}{dt^2} = -Kx + F_0 \sin\omega t \qquad \textbf{20.20}$$

Rearranging so that the dependent variable and its derivatives are on the left-hand side of the equation and dividing through by m, we get the standard form:

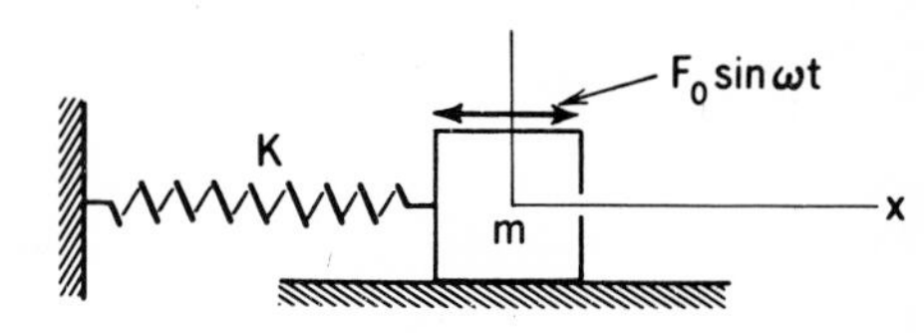

Fig. 20.17

$$\frac{d^2x}{dt^2} + \frac{K}{m}x = \frac{F_0}{m}\sin\omega t \qquad \textbf{20.21}$$

If the right-hand side is zero in such an arrangement, the equation is termed *homogeneous*. This was the equation studied in the previous section. If any function of t or constant appears on the right side, as in the above case, the equation is *nonhomogeneous*.

As pointed out in Section 12.5, the general solution of a nonhomogeneous differential equation of this type is found by getting the general solution of the corresponding homogeneous equation and then finding some *particular solution* which satisfies the full equation. The sum of these solutions, then, is the general solution of the equation. Often the solution for the homogeneous equation is termed the *complementary solution.*

In this case, we have already ascertained the complementary solution:

$$x_c = C_1 \sin \sqrt{\frac{K}{m}}\, t + C_2 \cos \sqrt{\frac{K}{m}}\, t \qquad \textbf{20.22}$$

To get a particular solution x_p, we can see by inspection that a function of the form $x_p = C_3 \sin \omega t$ will give a solution if the constant C_3 is chosen properly. Substituting this function into Eq. 20.21, we thus have:

$$-C_3\omega^2 \sin \omega t + \frac{K}{m} C_3 \sin \omega t = \frac{F_0}{m} \sin \omega t$$

Clearly, the value of C_3 must be:

$$C_3 = \frac{F_0/m}{K/m - \omega^2} \qquad \textbf{20.23}$$

We can now express the general solution of the differential equation at hand:

$$x = C_1 \sin \sqrt{\frac{K}{m}}\, t + C_2 \cos \sqrt{\frac{K}{m}}\, t + \frac{F_0/m}{K/m - \omega^2} \sin \omega t \qquad \textbf{20.24}$$

Note that there are two arbitrary constants which are determined from the initial conditions of the problem. Do not use the results of Eq. 20.7 for these constants, since *we must now include the particular solution in ascertaining the constants.* When $t = 0$, $x = x_0$ and $\dot{x} = \dot{x}_0$, and we have these conditions for Eq. 20.24:

$$x_0 = C_2$$

$$\dot{x}_0 = C_1 \sqrt{\frac{K}{m}} + \frac{F_0/m}{K/m - \omega^2}\, \omega \qquad \textbf{20.25}$$

Solving for the constants, we get:

$$C_2 = x_0$$

$$C_1 = \frac{\dot{x}_0}{\sqrt{K/m}} - \frac{\omega F_0/m}{(K/m - \omega^2)\sqrt{K/m}} \qquad \textbf{20.26}$$

Returning to Eq. 20.24, notice that we have the superposition of two harmonic motions—one with a frequency equal to $\sqrt{K/m}$, the natural frequency ω_n of the system, and the other with a frequency of the "driving function," i.e., the nonhomogeneous part of the equation. The frequencies ω and ω_n are not the same in the general case. The phasor representation then shows that since the rotating vectors have different angular speeds, the resulting motion cannot be represented by a single phasor and hence the motion is not harmonic. The two parts of the motion are termed the *transient* and the *steady state,* having frequencies ω_n and ω, respectively. With the introduction of friction (next section), we will see that the transient part of the motion dies out while the steady state persists as long as there is a disturbance present.

Let us now consider the steady-state part of the motion. Dividing numerator and denominator by K/m, we have for this motion which we denote as x_p:

$$x_p = \frac{F_0/K}{1 - (\omega^2 m/K)} \sin \omega t = \frac{F_0/K}{1 - (\omega/\omega_n)^2} \sin \omega t \qquad \textbf{20.27}$$

Since ω, the driving frequency, can be varied, we shall study the variation of the magnitude

$$\left| \frac{1}{1 - (\omega/\omega_n)^2} \right|$$

with ω/ω_n, shown plotted in Fig. 20.18. As the forcing frequency approaches the natural frequency,

$$\left| \frac{1}{1 - (\omega/\omega_n)^2} \right|$$

goes to infinity and thus the amplitude of the forced vibration approaches infinity. This is the condition of *resonance.* Under such circumstances friction, which we neglect here but which is always present, may limit the amplitude. If not, when very large amplitudes are developed, the properties of the restoring element do not remain linear, so that the theory which predicts infinite amplitudes is inapplicable. Thus the linear, frictionless formulations cannot yield correct amplitudes at resonance in real problems. The condition of resonance, however, does indicate that large amplitudes are to be expected. Furthermore these amplitudes can be dangerous, since the large stresses that will be found in parts of the restoring system as well as in the moving body may result in disastrous failures. It is therefore important in most situations to avoid resonance. If a disturbance corresponding to the natural frequency is present and cannot be eliminated, we may find it necessary to change either the stiffness or the mass of a system in order to avoid resonance.

From Fig. 20.18 we can conclude that the amplitude will become small as the frequency of the disturbance becomes very high. Also, considering the

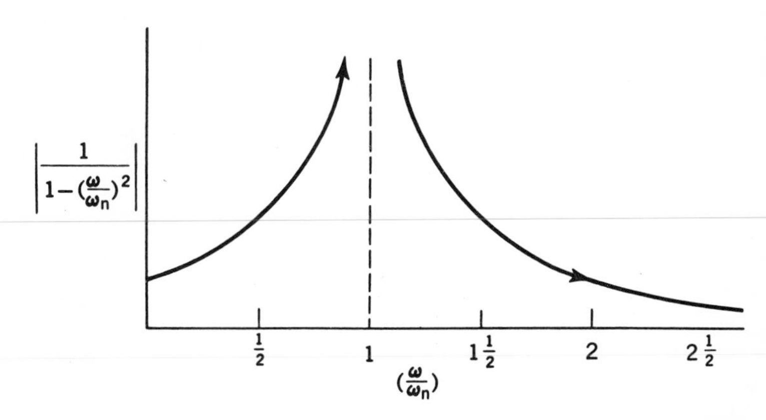

Fig. 20.18

amplitude for steady-state motion, (Eq. 20.23), we see that below resonance the sign of this expression is positive, and above resonance it is negative, indicating that below resonance the motion is in phase with the disturbance and above resonance the motion is directly out of phase with the disturbance.

EXAMPLE 20.8

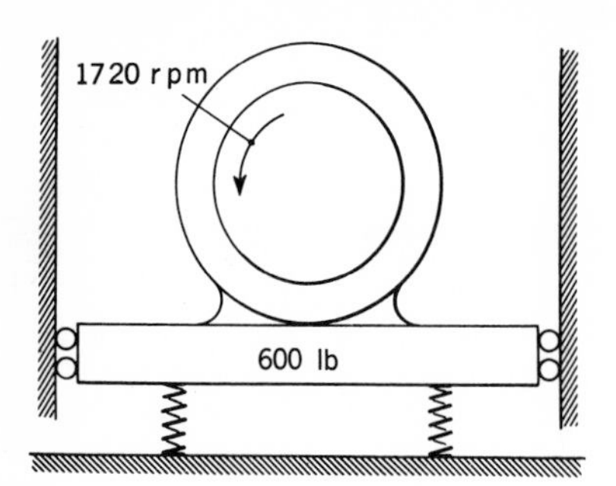

Fig. 20.19

A motor mounted on springs is constrained by the rollers to move only in the vertical direction (Fig. 20.19). The assembly weighs 600 lb and when placed carefully on the springs causes a deflection of 0.1 in. Because of an unbalance in the rotor, a disturbance results that is approximately sinusoidal in the vertical direction with a frequency equal to the angular speed of the rotor. The amplitude of this disturbance is 30 lb when the motor is rotating at 1720 rpm. What is the steady-state motion of this system under these circumstances if we neglect the mass of the springs, the friction, and the inertia of the rollers?

The spring constant for the system is:

$$K = \frac{600}{0.1} = 6000 \text{ lb/in.}$$

and the natural frequency becomes:

$$\omega_n = \sqrt{\frac{(6000)(12)(32)}{600}} = \sqrt{3840}$$

$$= 62 \text{ rad/sec or } 9.86 \text{ cycles/sec}$$

The steady-state motion is:

$$x_p = \frac{F_0/K}{1 - (\omega/\omega_n)^2} \sin \omega t$$

$$= \frac{30/6000}{1 - [1720/(9.86)(60)]^2} \sin 2\pi \frac{1720}{60} t$$

$$= -0.00067 \sin 180t \text{ in.}$$

Note that the driving frequency is above the natural frequency. In starting up motors and turbines, we must sometimes go through a natural frequency of the system, and it is wise to get through this zone as quickly as possible to prevent large amplitudes from building up.

EXAMPLE 20.9

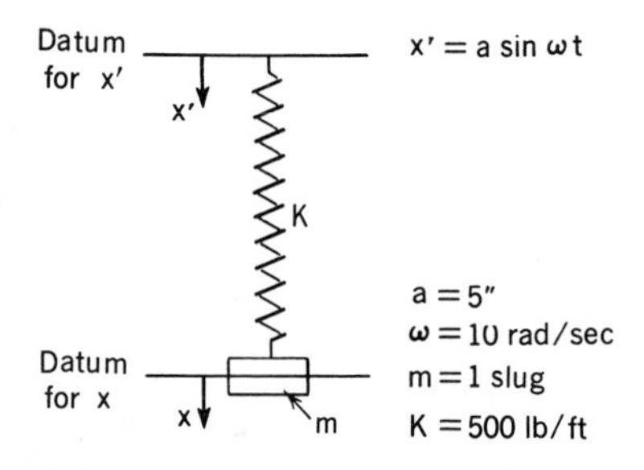

Fig. 20.20

A mass on a spring is shown in Fig. 20.20. The support of the spring at x' is made to move with harmonic motion in the vertical direction by some external agent. This motion is expressed as $a \sin \omega t$. If at $t = 0$ the mass is displaced in a downward position a distance of 1 in. and if it has a speed downward of 3 in./sec, what is the position of the mass at $t = 5$ sec? Take $a = 5$ in., $\omega = 10$ rad/sec, $K = 500$ lb/ft, and $m = 1$ slug.

Let us express Newton's law for the mass. Note that the extension of the spring is given as $x - x'$. Hence:

$$m \frac{d^2x}{dt^2} = -K(x - x')$$

Replacing x' by the known function of time, we get, upon rearranging the terms:

$$\frac{d^2x}{dt^2} + \frac{K}{m}x = \frac{Ka}{m}\sin\omega t$$

This is the same form as Eq. 20.21 for the case where the disturbance is exerted on the mass directly. The solution, then, is:

$$x = C_1 \sin\sqrt{\frac{K}{m}}\,t + C_2\cos\sqrt{\frac{K}{m}}\,t + \frac{a}{1-(\omega/\sqrt{K/m})^2}\sin\omega t$$

Putting in the numerical values of $\sqrt{K/m}$ etc., we have:

$$x = C_1 \sin 22.4t + C_2 \cos 22.4t + 6.25 \sin 10t \text{ in.}$$

Now impose the initial conditions. We have:

$$1 = C_2$$

$$3 = 22.4C_1 + (6.25)(10) \qquad \therefore\; C_1 = -2.65$$

The motion, then, is given as:

$$x = -2.65 \sin 22.4t + \cos 22.4t + 6.25 \sin 10t \text{ in.}$$

When $t = 5$ sec, the position of the mass relative to the lower datum is given as:

$$(x)_5 = -2.65 \sin (22.4)(5) + \cos (22.4)(5) + 6.25 \sin 50 = 1.174 \text{ in.}$$

You may approximate the setup of this problem profitably with an elastic band supporting a small body as shown in Fig. 20.21. By oscillating the free end of the band with varying frequency from low frequency to high frequency, you can demonstrate the rapid change of phase between the disturbance and the excited motion as you pass through resonance. Thus at low frequencies both motions will be in phase and at frequencies well above resonance the motion will be close to being 180° out of plane. Without friction this change, according to the mathematics, is discontinuous, but with the presence of friction, i.e., in a real case, there is actually a smooth although sometimes rapid transition between both extremes.

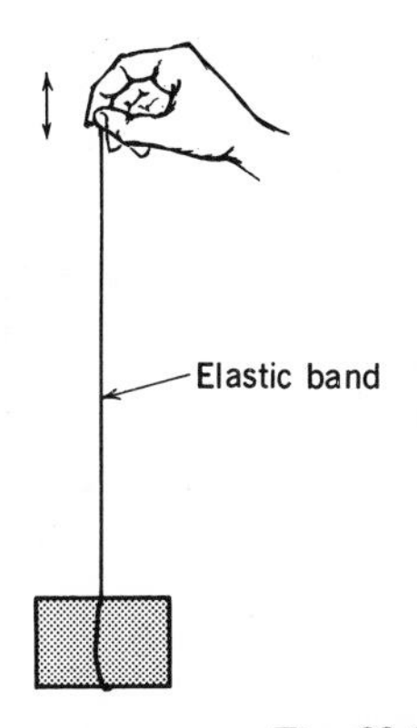

Fig. 20.21

20.7 Linear Restoring Force with Viscous Damping

We shall now consider the case in which a special type of friction is present. In the chapters on statics, you will recall, we considered coulomb or dry friction for the cases of sliding and impending motion. This force was proportional to the normal force at the interface of contact and dependent on the material of the bodies. At this time, we shall consider the case of bodies separated from each other by a thin film of fluid.

As we learned in Chapter 9 the frictional force is now independent of the material of the bodies but depends on the nature of the fluid and, as computations of Chapter 9 show, is proportional for a given fluid to the relative velocity of the two bodies separated by the film. Thus:

$$f = -c\left(\frac{dx}{dt}\right)_{\text{rel.}} \tag{20.28}$$

where c is called the *coefficient of damping*. The minus sign indicates that the frictional force opposes the motion, i.e., must always have the opposite sign of the velocity.

In Fig. 20.22 is shown the mass-spring model with damping present. We shall investigate possible motions consistent with a set of given initial conditions. The differential equation of motion is:

$$m\frac{d^2x}{dt^2} = -Kx - c\frac{dx}{dt}$$

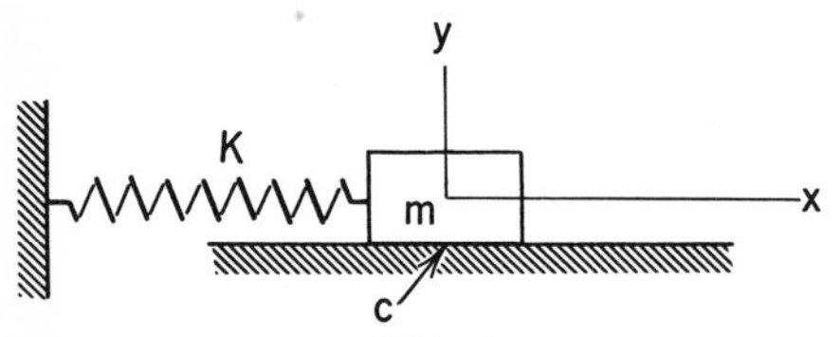

Fig. 20.22

In standard form, we get:

$$\frac{d^2x}{dt^2} + \frac{c}{m}\frac{dx}{dt} + \frac{K}{m}x = 0 \tag{20.29}$$

This is a homogeneous, second-order, differential equation with constant coefficients. We shall expect two independent functions with two arbitrary constants to form the general solution to this equation. Because of the presence of the first derivative in the equation, we cannot use sines or cosines for trial solutions, since the first derivative changes their form and prevents a cancellation of the time function. Instead, we use e^{pt} where p is determined so as to satisfy the equation. Thus:

$$x = C_1e^{pt}$$

Substituting, we get:

$$C_1p^2e^{pt} + \frac{c}{m}C_1pe^{pt} + \frac{K}{m}C_1e^{pt} = 0$$

Canceling out C_1e^{pt}, we get:

$$p^2 + \frac{c}{m}p + \frac{K}{m} = 0$$

Solving for p, we write:

$$p = \frac{-c/m \pm \sqrt{(c/m)^2 - 4K/m}}{2} = -\frac{c}{2m} \pm \sqrt{\left(\frac{c}{2m}\right)^2 - \frac{K}{m}} \tag{20.30}$$

It will be helpful to consider three cases here.

Case A.

$$\frac{c}{2m} > \sqrt{\frac{K}{m}}$$

Here the value p is real. Using both possible values of p and employing C_1 and C_2 as arbitrary constants, we get:

$$x = C_1 \exp\{[-(c/2m) + \sqrt{(c/2m)^2 - K/m}]t\} + C_2 \exp\{[-(c/2m) - \sqrt{(c/2m)^2 - K/m}]t\} \quad \textbf{20.31}$$

Rearranging terms in Eq. 20.31 we get the following standard form of solution:

$$x = \exp[-(c/2m)]\{C_1 \exp[\sqrt{(c/2m)^2 - K/m}\,t] + C_2 \exp[-\sqrt{(c/2m)^2 - K/m}\,t]\} \quad \textbf{20.32}$$

Since $c/2m > \sqrt{(c/2m)^2 - K/m}$, we see from the above equation that as the time t increases, the motion can only be that of an exponential of decreasing amplitude. Thus, there can be no oscillation. The motion is illustrated in Fig. 20.23 and is called *overdamped* motion.

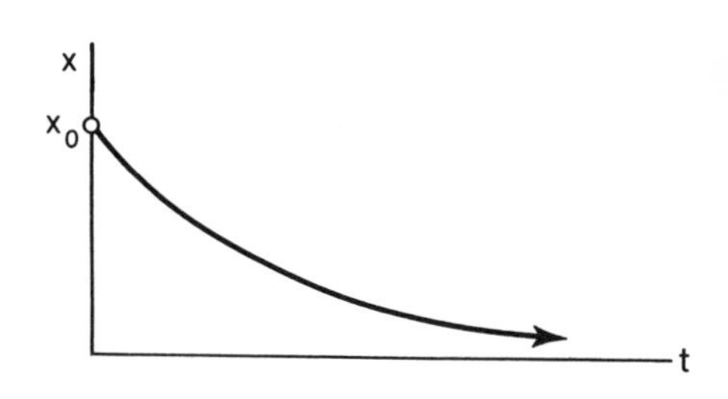

Fig. 20.23

Case B.

$$\frac{c}{2m} < \sqrt{\frac{K}{m}}$$

This means that we have a negative quantity under the root in Eq. 20.30. Extracting $\sqrt{-1} = i$, we can then write p as follows:

$$p = -\frac{c}{2m} \pm i\sqrt{\frac{K}{m} - \left(\frac{c}{2m}\right)^2}$$

The solution then becomes:

$$x = \exp[-(c/2m)t]\{C_1 \exp[i\sqrt{K/m - (c/2m)^2}\,t] + C_2 \exp[-i\sqrt{K/m - (c/2m)^2}\,t]\} \quad \textbf{20.33}$$

From complex-number theory, we know that $e^{i\theta}$ may be replaced by $\cos\theta + i\sin\theta$ and thus the above equation can be put in the form:

$$x = \exp[-(c/2m)t]\left\{C_1\left[\cos\sqrt{\frac{K}{m} - \left(\frac{c}{2m}\right)^2}\,t + i\sin\sqrt{\frac{K}{m} - \left(\frac{c}{2m}\right)^2}\,t\right] + C_2\left[\cos\sqrt{\frac{K}{m} - \left(\frac{c}{2m}\right)^2}\,t - i\sin\sqrt{\frac{K}{m} - \left(\frac{c}{2m}\right)^2}\,t\right]\right\} \quad \textbf{20.34}$$

Collecting terms and replacing sums and differences of arbitrary constants by other arbitrary constants, we get the result:

$$x = \exp[-(c/2m)t]\left[C_3 \cos\sqrt{\frac{K}{m} - \left(\frac{c}{2m}\right)^2}\,t + C_4 \sin\sqrt{\frac{K}{m} - \left(\frac{c}{2m}\right)^2}\,t\right] \quad \textbf{20.35}$$

The quantity in brackets represents a harmonic motion which has a frequency less than the free undamped natural frequency of the system. The exponential term to the left of the brackets, then, serves to decrease continually the amplitude of this motion. A plot of the displacement against time for this case is illustrated in Fig. 20.24, where the upper envelope corresponds in form to the exponential function $e^{-(c/2m)t}$.

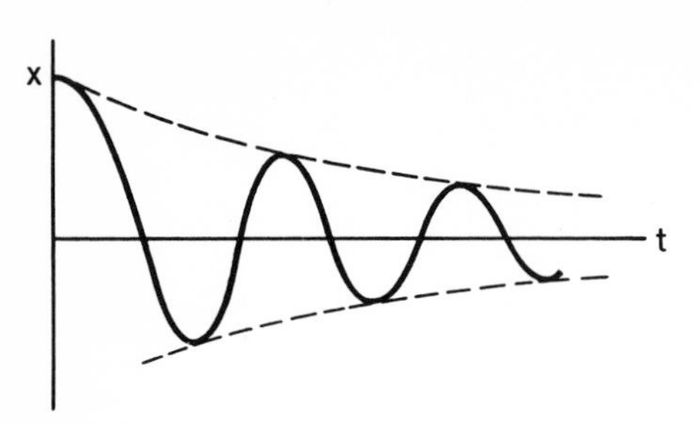

Fig. 20.24

Case C.

$$\frac{c}{2m} = \sqrt{\frac{K}{m}}$$

Since this is the dividing line between the overdamped case and one in which oscillation is possible, the motion is termed a *critically damped motion*. We have here identical roots for p given as:

$$p = -\frac{c}{2m} \qquad \textbf{20.36}$$

and accordingly for such a case the general solution to Eq. 20.29 is then:

$$x = (C_1 + C_2t)\, e^{-(c/2m)t} \qquad \textbf{20.37}$$

First we see from this equation that we do *not* have an oscillatory motion. Also you will recall from the calculus that as t goes to infinity an exponential of the form e^{-At}, with A a positive constant, goes to zero faster than Ct goes to infinity. Accordingly Fig. 20.23 can be used to picture the plot of x versus t for this case.

The damping constant for this case is called the *critical* damping constant and is denoted as c_{cr}. The value of c_{cr} clearly is:

$$c_{cr} = 2\sqrt{Km} \qquad \textbf{20.38}$$

In all the above cases for damped free vibration, the remaining step for a complete evaluation of the solution is to compute the arbitrary constants from the initial conditions of the particular problem. Note that in discussing damped motion we shall consider the "natural frequency" of the system to be that of the corresponding undamped case and shall refer to the actual frequency of the motion as the frequency of free, damped motion.

*20.8 Linear Restoring Force, Viscous Damping, and a Harmonic Disturbance

In the problem shown in Fig. 20.25 we include disturbing function, $F_0 \cos \omega t$. The differential equation in the standard form then becomes:

$$\frac{d^2x}{dt^2} + \frac{c}{m}\frac{dx}{dt} + \frac{K}{m}x = \frac{F_0}{m}\cos \omega t \qquad \textbf{20.39}$$

This is now a nonhomogeneous equation. The general solution will be the homogeneous solution worked out in the previous section, plus any particular solution of Eq. 20.39, which we shall consider at this time.

Since there is a first derivative on the left side of the equation, we cannot expect a particular solution of the form $D \sin \omega t$ to go through. Instead, from the method of *undetermined coefficients* we shall try the following:

$$x_p = D \sin \omega t + E \cos \omega t \qquad \textbf{20.40}$$

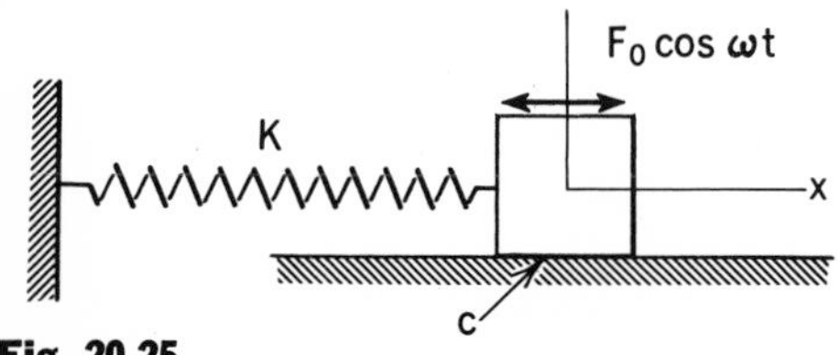

Fig. 20.25

The constants D and E are to be adjusted to facilitate a solution. Substituting into the differential equation, we write:

$$-D\omega^2 \sin \omega t - E\omega^2 \cos \omega t + \frac{c}{m}\omega D \cos \omega t - \frac{c}{m}\omega E \sin \omega t$$

$$+ \frac{K}{m} D \sin \omega t + \frac{K}{m} E \cos \omega t = \frac{F_0}{m} \cos \omega t$$

Collecting the terms, we have:

$$\left(-D\omega^2 - \frac{c}{m}\omega E + \frac{K}{m} D\right) \sin \omega t + \left(-\frac{F_0}{m} - E\omega^2 + \frac{c}{m}\omega D + \frac{K}{m} E\right) \cos \omega t = 0$$

We set each coefficient equal to zero and thus get two simultaneous equations in the unknowns E and D:

$$-D\omega^2 - \frac{\omega c}{m} E + \frac{K}{m} D = 0$$

$$-\frac{F_0}{m} - E\omega^2 + \frac{\omega c}{m} D + \frac{K}{m} E = 0$$

Rearranging and replacing K/m by ω_n^2, we get

$$D(\omega^2 - \omega_n^2) + E\left(\frac{\omega c}{m}\right) = 0$$

$$D\left(-\frac{\omega c}{m}\right) + E(\omega^2 - \omega_n^2) = -\frac{F_0}{m}$$

Using Cramer's rule, we see that the constants D and E become:

$$D = \frac{\begin{vmatrix} 0 & \omega c/m \\ -F_0/m & \omega^2 - \omega_n^2 \end{vmatrix}}{\begin{vmatrix} \omega^2 - \omega_n^2 & \omega c/m \\ -\omega c/m & \omega^2 - \omega_n^2 \end{vmatrix}} = \frac{(F_0/m)(\omega c/m)}{(\omega^2 - \omega_n^2)^2 + (\omega c/m)^2}$$

$$E = \frac{\begin{vmatrix} \omega^2 - \omega_n^2 & 0 \\ -\omega c/m & -F_0/m \end{vmatrix}}{\begin{vmatrix} \omega^2 - \omega_n^2 & \omega c/m \\ -\omega c/m & \omega^2 - \omega_n^2 \end{vmatrix}} = \frac{(F_0/m)(\omega_n^2 - \omega^2)}{(\omega^2 - \omega_n^2)^2 + (\omega c/m)^2}$$

The entire solution can then be given as:

$$x = x_c + \frac{(F_0/m)(\omega_n^2 - \omega^2)}{(\omega^2 - \omega_n^2)^2 + (\omega c/m)^2} \cos \omega t + \frac{F_0 \omega c/m^2}{(\omega^2 - \omega_n^2)^2 + (\omega c/m)^2} \sin \omega t \qquad \textbf{20.41}$$

The constants of integration are present in the complementary solution x_c and are determined by the initial condition to which the entire solution given above is subject.

The complementary solution here is a transient in the true sense of the word, since it dies out in the manner explained in the preceding section. The particular

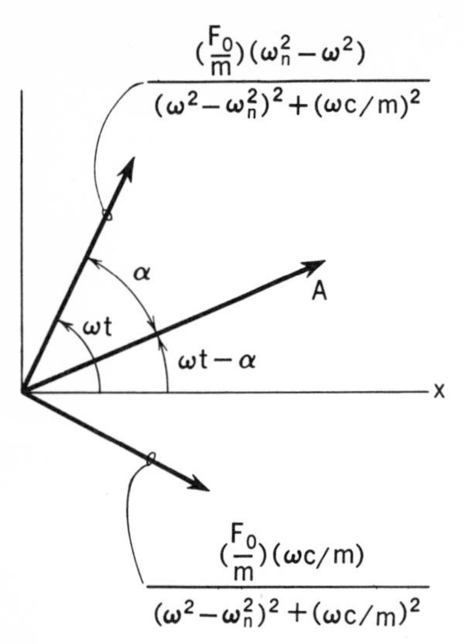

Fig. 20.26

solution is a harmonic motion with the same frequency as the disturbance. Only the amplitude of this motion is affected by the damping present. Note that, mathematically, the amplitude of the steady-state motion cannot become infinite with damping present unless F_0 becomes infinite.

As a next step, examine the steady-state solution, which we write in the following way:

$$x_p = \frac{(F_0/m)(\omega_n^2 - \omega^2)}{(\omega^2 - \omega_n^2)^2 + (\omega c/m)^2}\cos\omega t + \frac{(F_0/m)(\omega c/m)}{(\omega^2 - \omega_n^2)^2 + (\omega c/m)^2}\sin\omega t \qquad \textbf{20.42}$$

We can represent the above formulation in a phasor diagram as shown in Fig. 20.26. It should be clear that we can give x_p in the following form:

$$x_p = A\cos(\omega t - \alpha) \qquad \textbf{20.43}$$

where the amplitude A is given as:

$$A = \left\{\left[\frac{(F_0/m)(\omega^2 - \omega_n^2)}{(\omega^2 - \omega_n^2)^2 + (\omega c/m)^2}\right]^2 + \left[\frac{(F_0/m)(\omega c/m)}{(\omega^2 - \omega_n^2)^2 + (\omega c/m)^2}\right]^2\right\}^{1/2}$$

$$= \frac{F_0}{m}\frac{\sqrt{(\omega^2 - \omega_n^2)^2 + (\omega c/m)^2}}{(\omega^2 - \omega_n^2)^2 + (\omega c/m)^2} = \frac{F_0/m}{\sqrt{(\omega^2 - \omega_n^2)^2 + (\omega c/m)^2}}$$

$$= \frac{F_0}{\sqrt{(m\omega^2 - K)^2 + (\omega c)^2}} \qquad \textbf{20.44}$$

and where α, the phase angle, is given as:

$$\alpha = \tan^{-1}\left\{\frac{(F_0/m)(\omega c/m)}{(\omega^2 - \omega_n^2)^2 + (\omega c/m)^2}\cdot\frac{(\omega^2 - \omega_n^2)^2 + (\omega c/m)^2}{(F_0/m)(\omega_n^2 - \omega^2)}\right\}$$

$$= \tan^{-1}\frac{\omega c}{K - m\omega^2} \qquad \textbf{20.45}$$

We may express the amplitude A in another form by dividing numerator and denominator by K and by recalling from Eq. 20.38 that the ratio $2\sqrt{Km}/c_{cr}$ is unity. Thus we get:

$$A = \frac{F_0/K}{\sqrt{\left[\left(\frac{\omega}{\omega_n}\right)^2 - 1\right]^2 + \frac{1}{K^2}\left(\frac{2\sqrt{Km}}{c_{cr}}\right)^2(\omega c)^2}}$$

$$= \frac{\delta_{st}}{\sqrt{\left[\left(\frac{\omega}{\omega_n}\right)^2 - 1\right]^2 + \left[2\left(\frac{c}{c_{cr}}\right)\left(\frac{\omega}{\omega_n}\right)\right]^2}} \qquad \textbf{20.46}$$

where $F_0/K = \delta_{st}$ is the so-called static deflection. The term

$$\frac{1}{\sqrt{\left[\left(\frac{\omega}{\omega_n}\right)^2 + 1\right]^2 + \left[2\left(\frac{c}{c_{cr}}\right)\left(\frac{\omega}{\omega_n}\right)\right]^2}}$$

is called the *magnification factor*. It is a dimensionless factor giving the amplitude of steady-state motion per unit static deflection. Accordingly this factor for a given system is useful for examining the effects of frequency changes or damping changes on the steady-state vibration amplitude. A plot of the magnification factor versus ω/ω_n for various values of c/c_{cr} is shown in Fig. 20.27. We see from

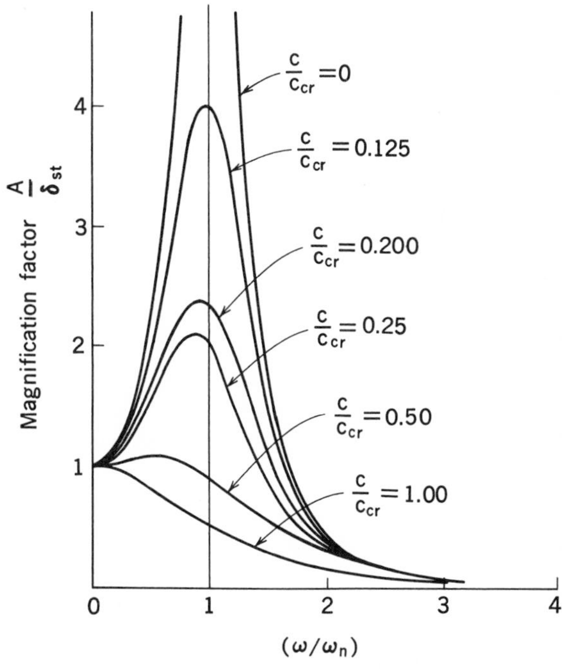

Fig. 20.27

this plot that small vibrations result when ω is kept far from ω_n and also when the damping is large. Additionally, note that maximum amplitude does not occur at resonance but actually at frequencies somewhat below resonance. Only when the damping goes to zero does the maximum amplitude occur at resonance. However, for light damping we can usually consider that when $\omega/\omega_n = 1$ we have an amplitude very close to the maximum amplitude possible for the system.

EXAMPLE 20.10

A *vibrating* table is a machine which can be given harmonic oscillatory motion over a range of amplitudes and frequencies. It is used as a test apparatus for imposing a desired sinusoidal motion on a device.

In Fig. 20.28 is shown a vibrating table with a device bolted to it. The device has in it a body B of mass 16.1 lbm supported by two springs each of stiffness equal to 30 lb/in. and a dashpot having a damping constant c equal to 6 lb/ft/sec. If the table

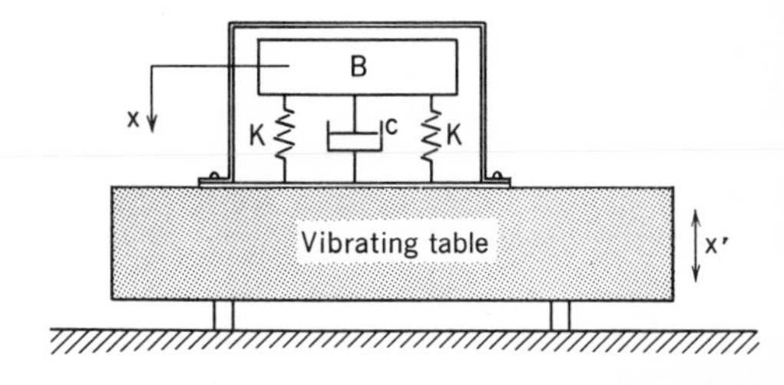

Fig. 20.28

has been adjusted for a vertical motion x' given as sin $40t$ in./sec, compute the following:

1. The steady-state amplitude of motion for body B.
2. The maximum number of g's acceleration that body B is subjected to.
3. The maximum and minimum forces that body B exerts on the vibrating table.

Measuring the vertical position of body B from the static-equilibrium position with coordinate x, we have from Newton's law:

$$M\ddot{x} + c(\dot{x} - \dot{x}') + K(x - x') = 0 \tag{a}$$

Using $P \sin \omega t$ to represent x' for now, we have:

$$\ddot{x} + \frac{c}{M}\dot{x} + \frac{K}{M}x = \frac{cP\omega}{M}\cos \omega t + \frac{KP}{M}\sin \omega t \tag{b}$$

Letting $cP\omega = F_1$ and $KP = F_2$, we have:

$$\ddot{x} + \frac{c}{M}\dot{x} + \frac{K}{M}x = \frac{F_1}{M}\cos \omega t + \frac{F_2}{M}\sin \omega t \tag{c}$$

Using a phasor-diagram representation, we can combine the forcing functions into one expression as follows:

$$\left(\frac{F_1}{M}\cos \omega t + \frac{F_2}{M}\sin \omega t\right) = \frac{\sqrt{F_1^2 + F_2^2}}{M}\cos(\omega t - \alpha)$$

$$= \frac{R}{M}\cos(\omega t - \alpha)$$

where $\alpha = \tan^{-1}(F_2/F_1)$. Thus we have:

$$\ddot{x} + \frac{c}{M}\dot{x} + \frac{K}{M} = \frac{R}{M}\cos(\omega t - \alpha) \tag{d}$$

Except for the phase angle α, Eq. (d) is identical in form to Eq. 20.39. Clearly if we are interested only in the steady-state amplitude, the phase angle α is of no consequence. Hence we can use the result given by Eq. 20.44 with R taking the place of F_0. Thus for the amplitude A of mass B we have:

$$A = \frac{R}{\sqrt{(M\omega^2 - K)^2 + (\omega c)^2}} \tag{e}$$

The following numerical values apply:

$$M = \tfrac{1}{2}\text{ slug}; \quad K = (12)(60)\text{ lb/ft}; \quad \omega = 40\text{ rad/sec}$$

$$c = 6\text{ lb/ft/sec}; \qquad P = \tfrac{1}{12}\text{ ft}$$

$$R = \sqrt{F_1^2 + F_2^2} = [(40cP)^2 + (KP)^2]^{1/2}$$

$$= \{[(40)(6)(\tfrac{1}{12})]^2 + [(12)(60)(\tfrac{1}{12})]^2\}^{1/2} = 63.1$$

Hence we have for A:

$$A = \frac{63.1}{\sqrt{(800 - 720)^2 + [(40)(6)]^2}}$$

$$= 0.25\text{ ft} = 3\text{ in.} \tag{f}$$

To get the maximum acceleration for body B we compute $|(\ddot{x}_p)|_{max}$. Thus we have:

$$|(\ddot{x}_p)|_{max} = \omega^2 A$$

$$= (1600)(0.25) = 400 \text{ ft/sec}^2$$

$$= \frac{400}{32.2} g\text{'s} = 12.41 \; g\text{'s} \qquad \textbf{(g)}$$

The maximum force transmitted to the body by the springs and dashpot is established clearly when the body B has its greatest acceleration in the upward direction. We have for the maximum force F_B:

$$F_B = W_B + \frac{W_B}{g_0}(\ddot{x}_p)_{max}$$

$$= 16.1 + (\tfrac{1}{2})(400) = 216 \text{ lb} \qquad \textbf{(h)}$$

If there were no spring-dashpot system between B and the vibratory table, the maximum force transmitted to B would be:

$$F_B = W_B + \left(\frac{W_B}{g_0}\right)(\ddot{x})_{max}$$

$$= 16.1 + (\tfrac{1}{2})[(\tfrac{1}{12})(40)^2] = 149.3 \text{ lb} \qquad \textbf{(i)}$$

We see from Eq. (f) that the amplitude of the induced motion on B is three times what it would be if there were no spring-damping system present to separate B from the table. And from Eqs. (h) and (i) we see that the presence of the spring-damping system has resulted in a considerable *increase* in force acting on body B. Now the use of springs and dashpots for suspending or packaging equipment is generally for the purpose of reducing—not increasing—the amplitude of motion and forces acting on the suspended body. The reason for the increase in these quantities for the disturbing frequency of 40 rad/sec is the fact that the natural frequency of the system is 37.8 rad/sec and putting us just above resonance. To protect the body B for disturbances of 40 rad/sec we must use considerably softer springs.

As an exercise at the end of the chapter you will be asked to compute K for permitting only a maximum of $\frac{1}{4}$ in. vibration for this problem.

20.9 Oscillatory Systems with Multi-Degrees of Freedom

We will concern ourselves here with a very simple system that has two degrees of freedom, and we will be able to generalize from this simple case. In the system of masses shown in Fig. 20.29, the masses are equal, as are the spring constants of the outer springs. We neglect friction, windage, etc. How can we describe the motion of the masses subsequent to any imposed set of initial conditions?

We first express Newton's law for each mass. To do this, imagine the masses at any position x_1, x_2 measured from the equilibrium configuration, and then compute the forces. Assume for convenience that $x_1 > x_2$. The spring K_2 is in compression for this supposition, and hence it

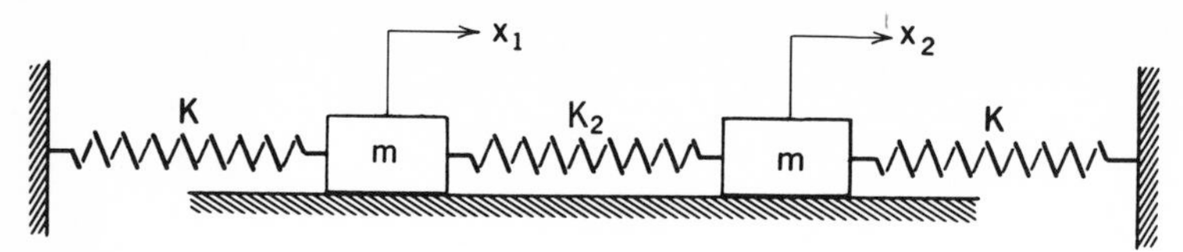

Fig. 20.29

produces a negative force on the mass at x_1 and a positive force on the mass at x_2. The equations of motion then are:

$$m\frac{d^2x_1}{dt^2} = -Kx_1 - K_2(x_1 - x_2) \qquad \textbf{(a)}$$

$$m\frac{d^2x_2}{dt^2} = -Kx_2 + K_2(x_1 - x_2) \qquad \textbf{(b)} \qquad \textbf{20.47}$$

If you imagine that the masses are at any other nontrivial position, you will still arrive at the above equations.

Since the dependent variables appear in both differential equations, they are termed *simultaneous* differential equations. We rearrange the equations to the following standard form:

$$\frac{d^2x_1}{dt^2} + \frac{K}{m}x_1 + \frac{K_2}{m}(x_1 - x_2) = 0 \qquad \textbf{(a)}$$

$$\frac{d^2x_2}{dt^2} + \frac{K}{m}x_2 - \frac{K_2}{m}(x_1 - x_2) = 0 \qquad \textbf{(b)} \qquad \textbf{20.48}$$

Finding a solution is equivalent to finding two functions of time $x_1(t)$ and $x_2(t)$, which when substituted into Eqs. 20.48 (a) and (b) reduce each equation to an identity. Only second derivatives and zeroth derivatives appear in these equations, and we would thus expect that sine or cosine functions of time would yield a possible solution. And since both x_1 and x_2 appear in the same equation, these time functions must be of the same form. A trial solution, therefore, might be:

$$x_1 = C_1 \sin(pt + \alpha) \qquad \textbf{(a)}$$

$$x_2 = C_2 \sin(pt + \alpha) \qquad \textbf{(b)} \qquad \textbf{20.49}$$

where C_1, C_2, α, and p are as yet undetermined. Substituting into Eq. 20.48 and canceling out the time function, we get:

$$-C_1p^2 + \frac{K}{m}C_1 + \frac{K_2}{m}(C_1 - C_2) = 0 \qquad \textbf{(a)}$$

$$-C_2p^2 + \frac{K}{m}C_2 - \frac{K_2}{m}(C_1 - C_2) = 0 \qquad \textbf{(b)} \qquad \textbf{20.50}$$

Rearranging the above equations, we write:

$$\left(-p^2 + \frac{K}{m} + \frac{K_2}{m}\right)C_1 - \frac{K_2}{m}C_2 = 0 \qquad \textbf{(a)}$$

$$-\frac{K_2}{m}C_1 + \left(-p^2 + \frac{K}{m} + \frac{K_2}{m}\right)C_2 = 0 \qquad \textbf{(b)} \qquad \textbf{20.51}$$

One way of insuring the satisfaction of this equation is to have $C_1 = 0$ and $C_2 = 0$. This means, from Eqs. 20.49 (a) and (b), that x_1 and x_2 are always zero, which corresponds to the static equilibrium position. While this is a valid solution, since this static equilibrium is a possible motion, the result is trivial. We now ask: Is there a means of satisfying these equations without setting C_1 and C_2 equal to zero?

To answer this, solve for C_1 and C_2, in terms of the coefficients, as if they were unknowns in the above equations. Using Cramer's rule, we then have:

$$C_1 = \frac{\begin{vmatrix} 0 & -K_2/m \\ 0 & -p^2 + K/m + K_2/m \end{vmatrix}}{\begin{vmatrix} -p^2 + K/m + K_2/m & -K_2/m \\ -K_2/m & -p^2 + K/m + K_2/m \end{vmatrix}}$$

$$C_2 = \frac{\begin{vmatrix} -p^2 + K/m + K_2/m & 0 \\ -K_2/m & 0 \end{vmatrix}}{\begin{vmatrix} -p^2 + K/m + K_2/m & -K_2/m \\ -K_2/m & -p^2 + K/m + K_2/m \end{vmatrix}} \qquad \textbf{20.52}$$

Notice that the determinant in the numerator is in each case zero. If the denominator is other than zero, we must have the trivial solution $C_1 = C_2 = 0$, the significance of which we have just discussed. A *necessary* condition for a nontrivial solution is that the denominator also be zero, for then we get the indeterminate form 0/0 for C_1 and C_2. Clearly, C_1 and C_2 can then have possible values other than zero, and so the required condition for a nontrivial solution is:

$$\begin{vmatrix} -p^2 + K/m + K_2/m & -K_2/m \\ -K_2/m & -p^2 + K/m + K_2/m \end{vmatrix} = 0 \qquad \textbf{20.53}$$

Carrying this out, we get:

$$\left(-p^2 + \frac{K}{m} + \frac{K_2}{m}\right)^2 = \left(\frac{K_2}{m}\right)^2 \qquad \textbf{20.54}$$

Taking the roots of both sides, we have:

$$-p^2 + \frac{K}{m} + \frac{K_2}{m} = \pm\frac{K_2}{m} \qquad \textbf{20.55}$$

Two values of p^2 satisfy the necessary condition we have imposed. If we use the positive roots, the values of p are:

$$p_1 = \sqrt{\frac{K}{m}}$$

$$p_2 = \sqrt{\frac{K}{m} + \frac{2K_2}{m}} \qquad \textbf{20.56}$$

where p_1 and p_2 are found for the plus and minus cases, respectively, of the right side of Eq. 20.55.

Let us now return to Eqs. 20.51 (a) and (b) to ascertain what further restrictions we may have to impose to ensure a solution, since these equations form the criterion for acceptance of a set of functions as solutions. Employing $\sqrt{K/m}$ for p in Eq. 20.51 (a), we have:

$$\left(-\frac{K}{m} + \frac{K}{m} + \frac{K_2}{m}\right)C_1 - \left(\frac{K_2}{m}\right)C_2 = 0 \qquad \textbf{20.57}$$

From this we see that when we use this value of p it is necessary that $C_1 = C_2$ to satisfy the equation. The same conclusions can be reached by employing Eq. 12.51(b). We can now state a permissible solution to the differential equation. Using A as the amplitude in place of $C_1 = C_2$, we have:

$$x_1 = A \sin\left(\sqrt{\frac{K}{m}}\,t + \alpha\right) \qquad \textbf{(a)}$$

$$x_2 = A \sin\left(\sqrt{\frac{K}{m}}\,t + \alpha\right) \qquad \textbf{(b)} \qquad \textbf{20.58}$$

If we examine the second value of p, we find that for this value it is required that $C_1 = -C_2$. Thus if we use B for C_1, and use β as the arbitrary value in the sine function, another possible solution is:

$$x_1 = B \sin\left(\sqrt{\frac{K}{m} + \frac{2K_2}{m}}\,t + \beta\right)$$

$$x_2 = -B \sin\left(\sqrt{\frac{K}{m} + \frac{2K_2}{m}}\,t + \beta\right) \qquad \textbf{20.59}$$

Let us consider each of these solutions. In the first case, the motions of both masses are in phase with each other, have the same amplitude, and thus move together with simple harmonic motion with a natural frequency $\sqrt{K/m}$. For this motion, the center spring is not extended or compressed, and, since the mass of the spring has been neglected, it has no effect on this motion. This explains why the natural frequency has such a simple formulation.

The second possible independent solution is one in which the amplitudes are equal for both masses but the masses are 180° out of phase. Each mass oscillates harmonically with a natural frequency greater than the preceding motion. Since the masses move in opposite directions in the manner described, the center of the middle spring must be stationary for this motion. It is as if each mass were vibrating under the action of a spring of constant K and the the action of half the length of a spring with a spring constant K_2 (Fig 20.30), which explains why the natural frequency for this motion is $\sqrt{(K + 2K_2)/m}$. (It will be left for you to demonstrate in an exercise that halving the length of the spring doubles the spring constant.)

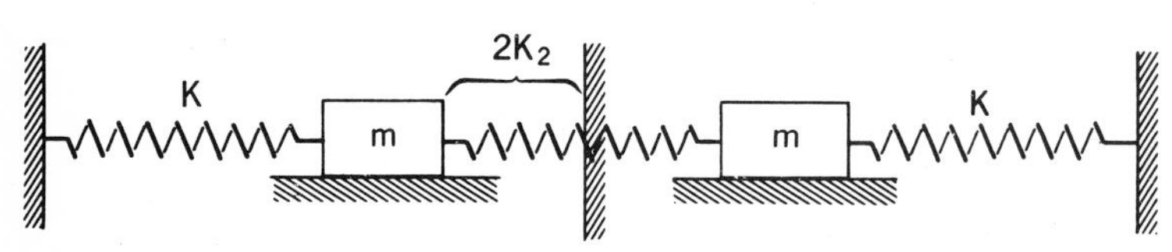

Fig. 20.30

Each of these motions is called a natural *mode*. The first mode refers to the motion of lower natural frequency, and the second mode identifies the one with the higher natural frequency. It is known from differential equations that the general solution is the sum of the two solutions presented:

$$\begin{aligned} x_1 &= \left[A \sin\left(\sqrt{\frac{K}{m}}\,t + \alpha\right)\right] + \left[B \sin\left(\sqrt{\frac{K}{m} + \frac{2K_2}{m}}\,t + \beta\right)\right] \\ x_2 &= \left[A \sin\left(\sqrt{\frac{K}{m}}\,t + \alpha\right)\right] + \left[-B \sin\left(\sqrt{\frac{K}{m} + \frac{2K_2}{m}}\,t + \beta\right)\right] \end{aligned}$$

first mode of motion — second mode of motion **20.60**

Four constants are yet to be determined: A, B, α, and β. These are the constants of integration and are determined by the initial conditions of the motion—that is, the velocity and position of each mass at time $t = 0$.

From this discussion we can make the following conclusions. The general motion of the system under study is the superposition of two modes of motion of harmonic nature that have distinct natural frequencies with amplitudes and phase angles that are evaluated to fit the initial conditions. Thus the basic modes are the "building blocks" of the general free motion.

If the masses, as well as the springs, were unequal, the analysis would still produce two natural frequencies and mode shapes, but these would not be as simple as the special case we have worked out nor, perhaps, as intuitively obvious.

As we discussed in the first paragraph of this section, two natural frequencies correspond to the two degrees of freedom. In the general case of n degrees of freedom, there will be n natural frequencies, and the general free vibrations will be the superposition of n modes of motion that have proper amplitudes and are phased together in such a way that they satisfy $2n$ initial conditions.

A similar, although more complicated, argument can be carried out for the case of damping. Also, when disturbances are present, more elegant procedures are available which are beyond the scope of this text. However, it should be pointed out that the natural frequencies from the type of analysis carried out in this section, i.e., without inclusion of damping, give the engineer the potentially dangerous frequencies that may have to be avoided in the disturbances. For if a disturbing frequency or a multiple of it coincides with one of the natural frequencies of the system, large vibrations can occur that may possibly induce large stresses and thus cause a machine element to fail.

20.10 Electric Circuit Analogue for a Mechanical System

We will now show that the differential equations of motion of the systems of masses and springs studied earlier have the same form as the differential equations describing the flow of charge through certain lumped electrical circuits. The particular circuit having the desired equation is termed the *analogue of the mechanical system*. Although the mechanical systems we have presented are usually solvable, a given system could well be too complex for direct mathematical treatment. It may then be profitable to build the electrical analogue and study the characteristics of the mechanical system by conveniently varying voltages, resistances, etc. of the electrical analogue.*

Another reason for examining circuits here is to be sure that you are well aware of the analogue, so that the techniques you will later learn for solving circuit problems, such as those in operational mathematics and possibly linear graph theory, will be available for solving mechanical systems.

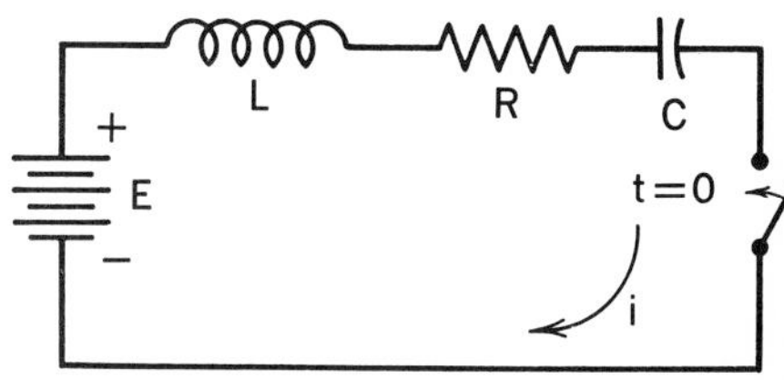

As an introduction, consider the simple lumped series circuit in Fig. 20.31. Here we have a battery of constant voltage E,† an induction coil with inductance L, a resistor of resistance R, a capacitor of capacitance C, and a switch that represents the time $t = 0$ when it is closed. Kirchhoff's second law, as you undoubtedly learned in physics, states, that for a clockwise direction:

Fig. 20.31

$$E - L\frac{di}{dt} - iR - \frac{1}{C}\int_0^t i\,dt = 0 \qquad \textbf{20.61}$$

If we replace i, the current, by dq/dt, the rate of change of the charge with respect to time, we have:

$$E - L\frac{d^2q}{dt^2} - R\frac{dq}{dt} - \frac{q}{C} = 0 \qquad \textbf{20.62}$$

This is a second-order differential equation which when put into standard form is:

$$\frac{d^2q}{dt^2} + \frac{R}{L}\frac{dq}{dt} + \frac{1}{LC}q = \frac{E}{L} \qquad \textbf{20.63}$$

This equation looks like Eq. 20.39, for the case where the driving function is a constant. The mechanical system for Eq. 20.39 is shown in Fig. 20.32 and the equation is presented again as:

$$\frac{d^2x}{dt^2} + \frac{c}{m}\frac{dx}{dt} + \frac{K}{m}x = \frac{F_0}{m} \qquad \textbf{20.64}$$

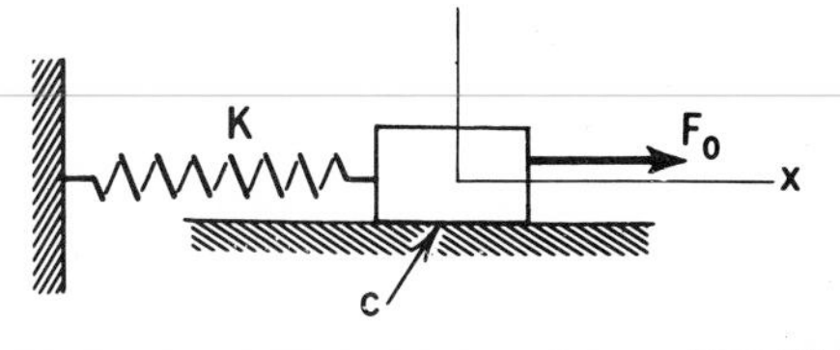

Fig. 20.32

Comparing the terms of the two systems, we can set up the following table of electrical and mechanical counterparts.

---

* For more information on analogue computer techniques see W. W. Soroka, *analog Methods in Computation and Simulation* (New York: McGraw-Hill Book Company, 1954).

† The voltage E, a scalar, is not to be confused with the potential field $\mathbf{E}$, a vector, which we studied in Chapter 12. It corresponds to V, the voltage, which is termed E for a battery source.

Mechanical system	*Electrical system*
F_0	E
x	$q = \int i\,dt$
$dx/dt = V$	$dq/dt = i$
$d^2x/dt^2 = a$	$d^2q/dt^2 = di/dt$
m	L
c	R
K	$1/C$

If both systems are given the same type of initial disturbances, the subsequent velocity variation of the mechanical system will be similar to the variation of the current in the electrical system. An example of a set of analogous initial conditions would be:

Mechanical system	*Electrical system*
when F is suddenly applied,	when switch is suddenly closed,
$t = 0$	$t = 0$
$x = 0$	$q = 0$
$\dot{x} = 0$	$i = 0$

We could observe the current in an equivalent circuit with a meter or some recording device for such a disturbance, and thus ascertain what is to be expected of the velocity in the mechanical system. Finally, we can conclude that the concepts of critical damping, resonances, degrees of freedom, and so on carry over to circuit analysis.

EXAMPLE 20.11

Work out an electrical analogue for the system we studied in Section 20.9 that has two masses and three springs and two degrees of freedom. The diagram (Fig. 20.33) and the equations are repeated here.

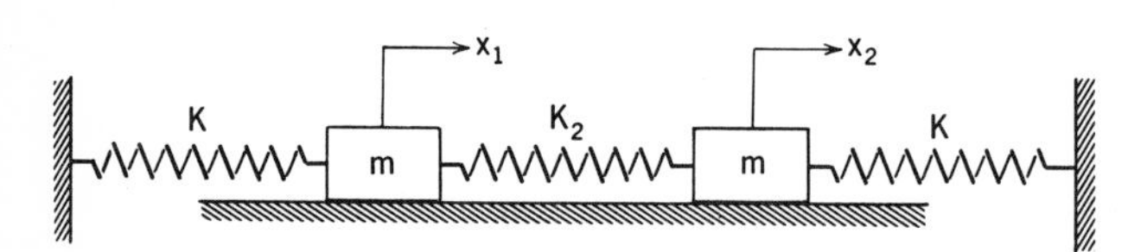

Fig. 20.33

$$\frac{d^2x_1}{dt^2} + \frac{K}{m}x_1 + \frac{K_2}{m}(x_1 - x_2) = 0 \quad \textbf{(a)}$$

$$\frac{d^2x_2}{dt^2} + \frac{K}{m}x_2 - \frac{K_2}{m}(x_1 - x_2) = 0 \quad \textbf{(b)}$$

Using the table of equivalences, we find that the analogue circuit would have the equations:

$$\frac{d^2q_1}{dt_2} + \frac{1}{LC}q_1 + \frac{1}{LC_2}(q_1 - q_2) = 0 \quad \textbf{(c)}$$

$$\frac{d^2q_2}{dt^2} + \frac{1}{LC}q_2 - \frac{1}{LC_2}(q_1 - q_2) = 0 \quad \textbf{(d)}$$

Multiplying through by L in each equation and replacing the q's by q $i\ dt$, we have:

$$L\left(\frac{di_1}{dt}\right) + \frac{1}{C}\int i_1\,dt + \frac{1}{C_2}\int i_1\,dt - \frac{1}{C_2}\int i_2\,dt = 0 \quad \textbf{(e)}$$

$$L\left(\frac{di_2}{dt}\right) + \frac{1}{C}\int i_2\,dt - \frac{1}{C_2}\int i_1\,dt + \frac{1}{C_2}\int i_2\,dt = 0 \quad \textbf{(f)}$$

Going back to Kirchoff's law, we see that we have two loops with a common capacitor C_2. The circuit is shown in Fig. 20.34.

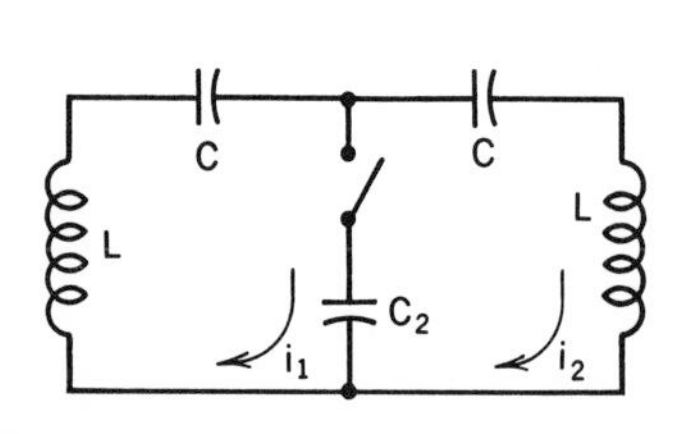

Fig. 20.34

20.11 Closure

This introductory study of vibrations brings to a close the present study of particle and rigid-body mechanics. As you progress to the study of deformable media in your courses in solid and fluid mechanics you will find that particle mechanics and, to a lesser extent rigid-body mechanics, will form cornerstones for these disciplines. And in your studies involving the design of machines and the performance of vehicles you will find rigid-body mechanics indispensible.

It should be realized, however, that we have by no means said the last word on particle and rigid-body mechanics. More advanced studies will emphasize the variational approach introduced in statics. With the use of the calculus of variations, such topics as Hamilton's principle, Lagrange's equation, and Hamilton–Jacobi theory will be presented and you will then see a greater unity between mechanics and other areas of physics such as electromagnetic theory and wave mechanics. Also the special theory of relativity will most surely be considered.*

Finally, in your studies of modern physics you will come to more fully understand the limitations of classical mechanics when you are introduced to quantum mechanics.

* These topics and others are treated in the author's text *Variational Mechanics* which will be Vol. III of this series.

PROBLEMS

1. [20.2] (a) Show that the spring constant is doubled if the length of the spring is halved.

(b) Show that two springs having spring constants K_1 and K_2 have a combined spring constant of $K_1 + K_2$ when connected in parallel, and have a combined spring constant whose reciprocal is $1/K_1 + 1/K_2$ when combined in series, as shown in Fig. 20.35.

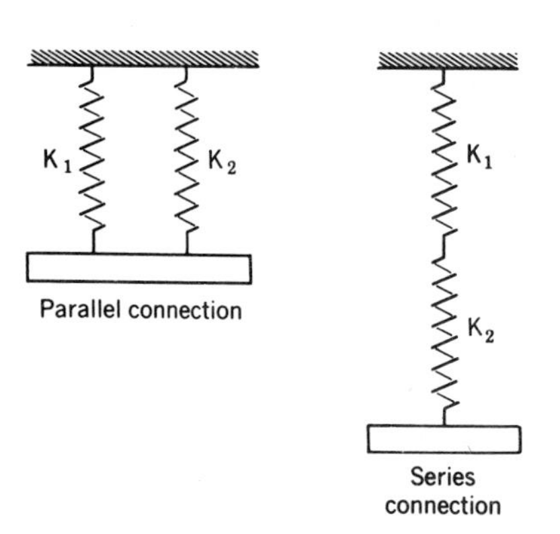

Fig. 20.35

2. [20.2] If a 5-lb weight causes an elongation of 2 in. when suspended from the end of a spring, determine the natural frequency of the mass and spring system.

3. [20.2] For small oscillations, what is the natural frequency of the system in Fig. 20.36? (Neglect the mass of the rod.)

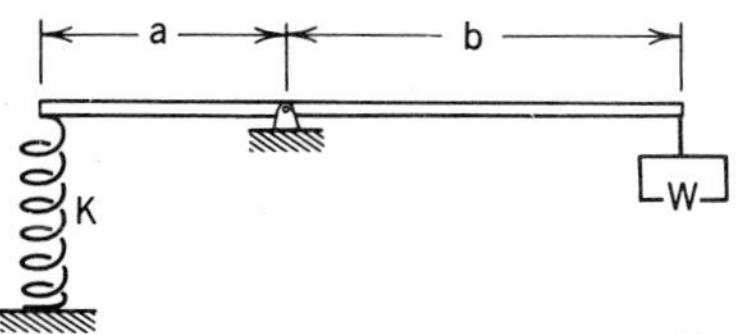

Fig. 20.36

4. [20.2] A rod is supported by two rotating grooved wheels (Fig. 20.37). The contact surfaces have a coefficient of friction of μ. Explain how the rod will oscillate in the horizontal direction if it is disturbed in that direction. Compute the natural frequency of the system.

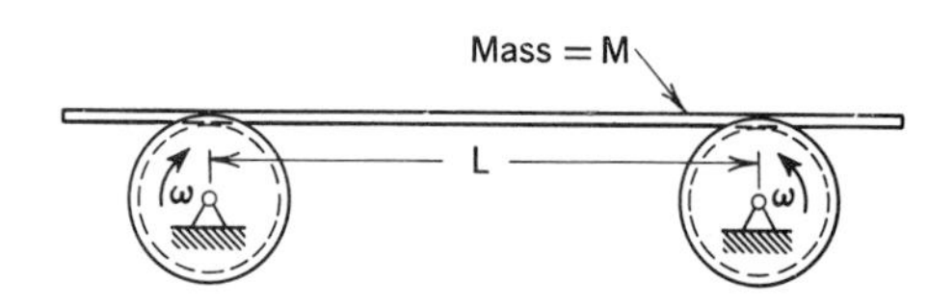

Fig. 20.37

5. [20.2] A mass is held so it just makes contact with a spring, as is shown in Fig. 20.38. If the mass is released suddenly from this position, give the amplitude, frequency, and the center position of the motion.

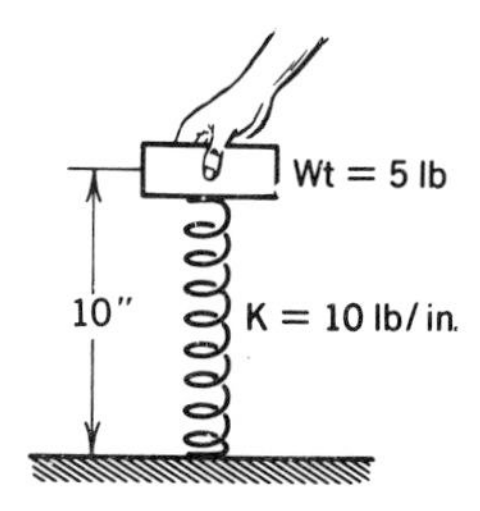

Fig. 20.38

6. [20.2] A mass is held by three springs (Fig. 20.39). Assume the rolling friction on the floor is negligible, as are the inertial effects of the rollers. The spring constants are:

$$K_1 = 30 \text{ lb/in.}$$

$$K_2 = 20 \text{ lb/in.}$$

$$K_3 = 10 \text{ lb/in.}$$

Determine the natural frequency of the system. If the mass is deflected 2 in. and then released, determine the displacement from equilibrium after 3 sec. Finally determine the *total* distance traveled during this time.

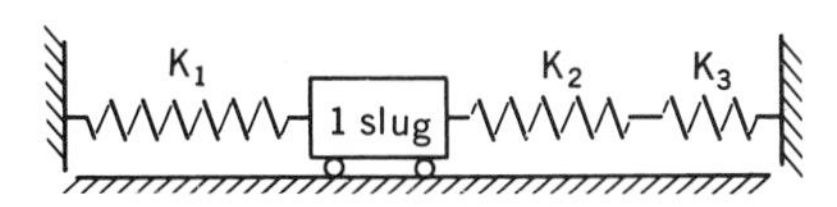

Fig. 20.39

7. [20.2] What is the natural frequency of motion for block A for small oscillation (Fig. 20.40)? Consider BC to have negligible mass and body A to be a particle. It is known that when body A is attached to the rod there is a static deflection of 1 in. and that the spring constant K_1 is 10 lb/in. Body A weighs 25 lb.

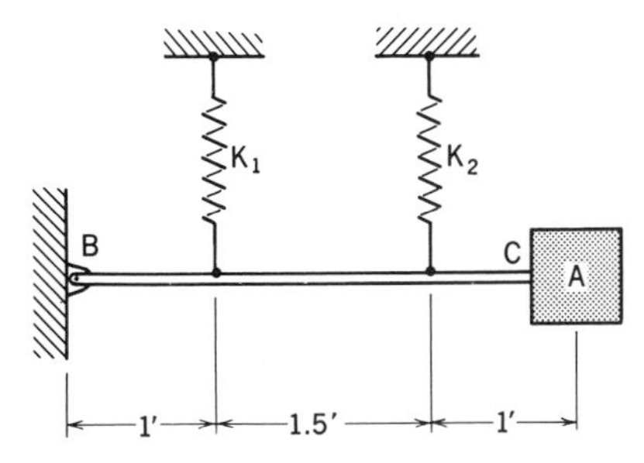

Fig. 20.40

8. [20.2] If bar ABC in Fig. 20.41 is of negligible mass, what is the natural frequency of free oscillation of the block for small amplitude of motion? The springs are identical, having a spring constant K of 25 lb/in. The weight of the block is 10 lb. The springs are unstretched when AB is oriented vertically as shown in the diagram.

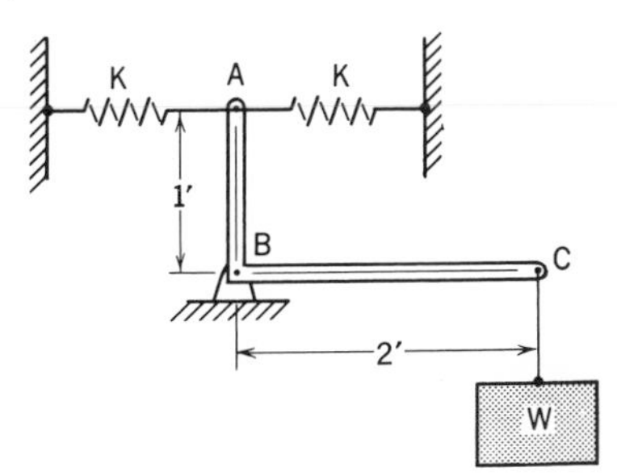

Fig. 20.41

9. [20.2] Do the previous problem for the case where the springs are stretched 1 in. when AB is vertical.

10. [20.2] Find the natural frequency of motion of body A (see Fig. 20.42) for small motion of rod BD when we neglect the inertial effects of rod BD. Spring constant K_2 is 5 lb/in. and spring constant K_1 is 10 lb/in. The weight of block A is 40 lb. Neglect friction everywhere.

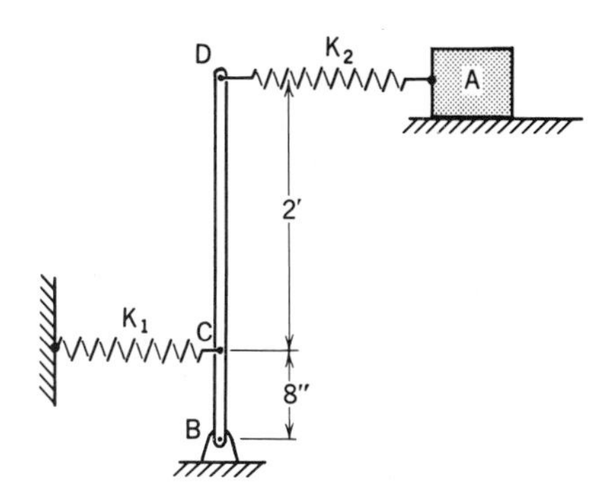

Fig. 20.42

11. [20.2] What are the differential equation of motion about the static-equilibrium configuration and the natural frequency of motion of body A for small motion of BC (Fig. 20.43)? Neglect inertial effects from BC. The following data apply:

$$K_1 = 15 \text{ lb/in.}$$

$$K_2 = 20 \text{ lb/in.}$$

$$K_3 = 30 \text{ lb/in.}$$

$$W_A = 30 \text{ lb}$$

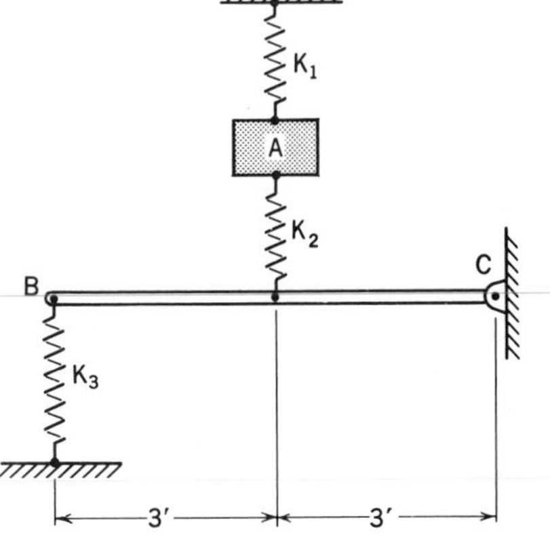

Fig. 20.43

12. [20.2] A horizontal platform (Fig. 20.44) is rotating with a uniform angular speed of ω rad/sec. On the platform is a rod CD on which slides a cylinder A having weight W. The cylinder is connected to C through a linear spring having a spring constant K. What is the equation of motion for A relative to the platform after it has been disturbed? What is the natural frequency of oscillation?

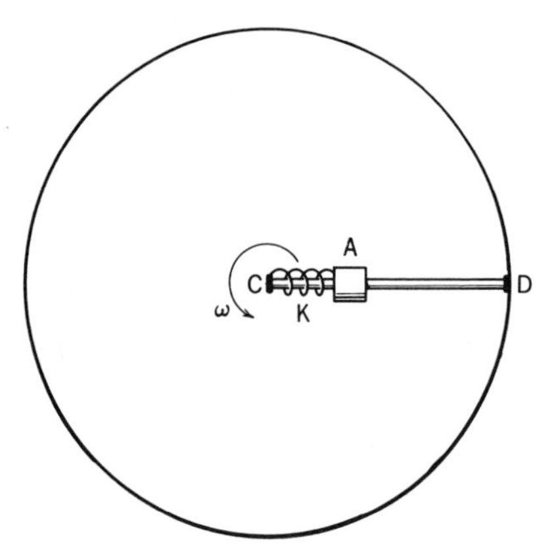

Fig. 20.44

13. [20.2] Shown in Fig. 20.45 is a rigid body A resting on a spring with stiffness K equal to 50 lb/in. A lead pad B falls onto the block A with a speed on impact of 20 ft/sec. If the impact is perfectly plastic, what are the frequency and amplitude of the motion of the system, provided the lead pad sticks to A at all times? Take $W_A = 30$ lb and $W_B = 5$ lb.

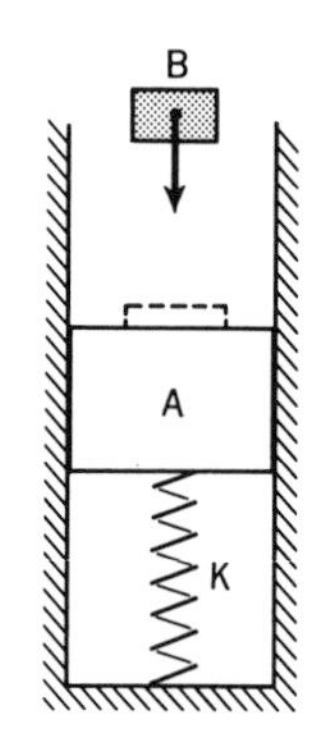

Fig. 20.45

14. [20.2] A small sphere of weight 5 lb. is held by taut elastic cords as shown in Fig. 20.46. If it takes 50 lb of force to cause an elongation of 1 in. for each cord, what is the natural frequency of small oscillation of the weight in a transverse direction? Also determine the natural frequency of the weight in a direction along the cord for small oscillations. Neglect the mass of the cord. The tension in the cord in the configuration shown is 100 lb.

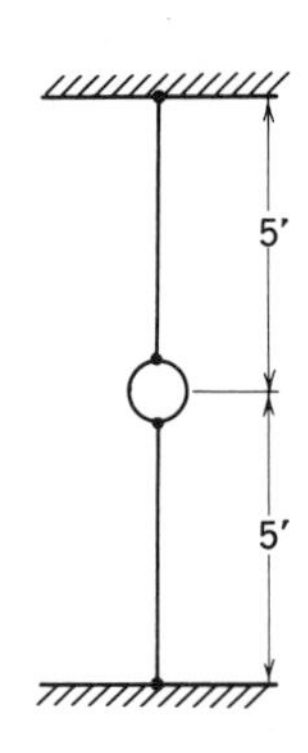

Fig. 20.46

15. [20.2] Body A in Fig. 20.47 weighs 100 lb. It is connected to a spring having a spring constant K_1 of 20 lb/in. At the right of A is a second spring having a spring constant K_2 of 50 lb/in. Body A is moved 6 in. to the left from the configuration of static equilibrium shown in the diagram, and it is released from rest. What is the period of oscillation for the body?

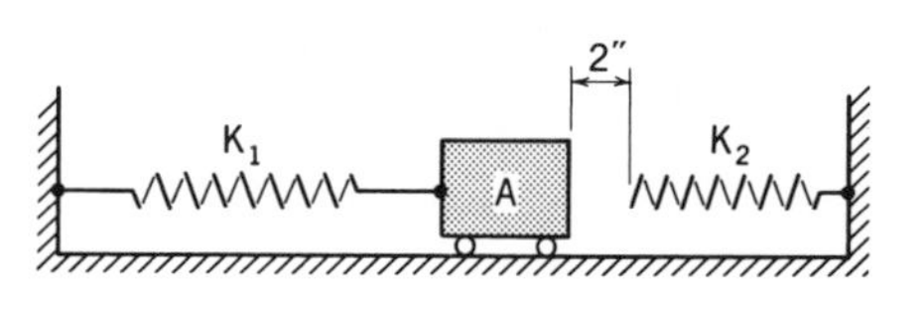

Fig. 20.47

16. [20.2] Body A, weighing 50 lb (Fig. 20.48), has a speed of 20 ft/sec to the left. If there is no friction, what is the period of oscillation of the body for the following data:

$$K_1 = 20 \text{ lb/in.}$$

$$K_2 = 10 \text{ lb/in.}$$

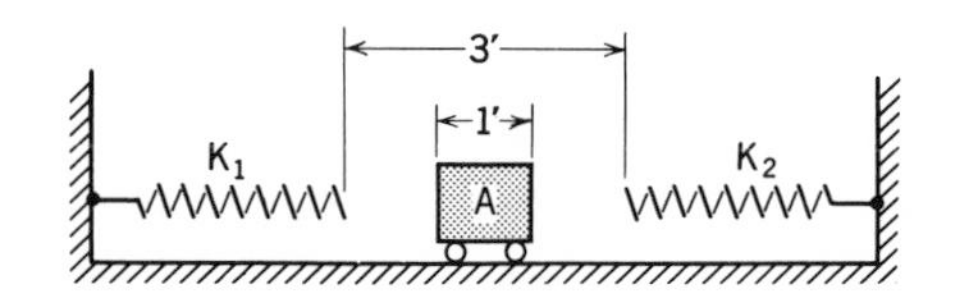

Fig. 20.48

17. [20.3] In Fig. 20.49, what is the equivalent torsional spring constant on the disc from the shafts? The modulus of elasticity G for the shafts is 15×10^6 psi. What is the natural frequency of the system? If the disc is twisted 10° and then released, what will its angular position be in 1 sec? Neglect the mass of the shafts. The disc weighs 32.2 lb.

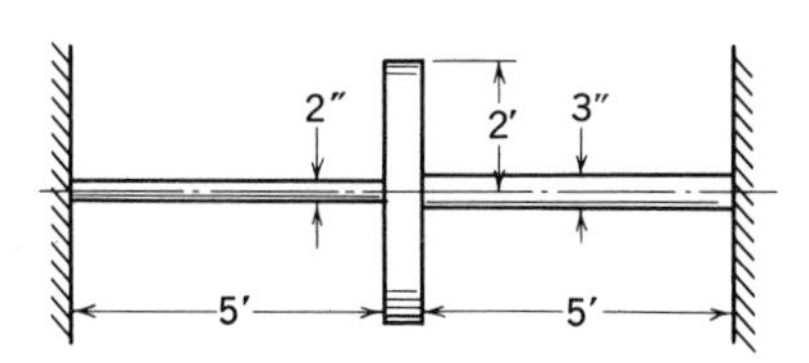

Fig. 20.49

18. [20.3] What is the equivalent spring constant for small oscillations about the shaft AB in Fig. 20.50? Neglect all mass except the block at B, which weighs 100 lb. The modulus of elasticity for the shaft is 15×10^6 psi. What is the natural frequency of the system for torsional oscillation of small amplitude?

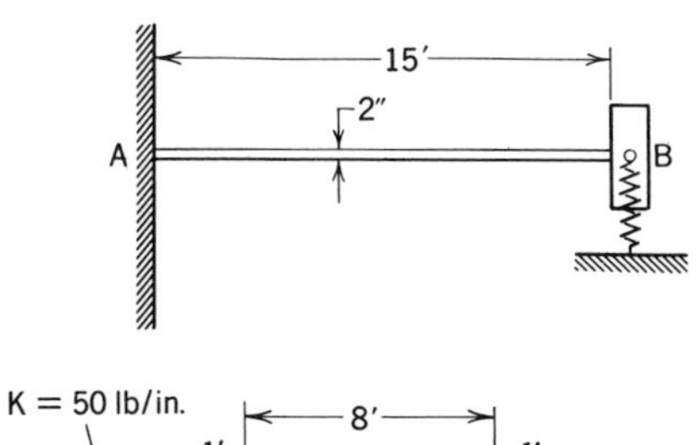

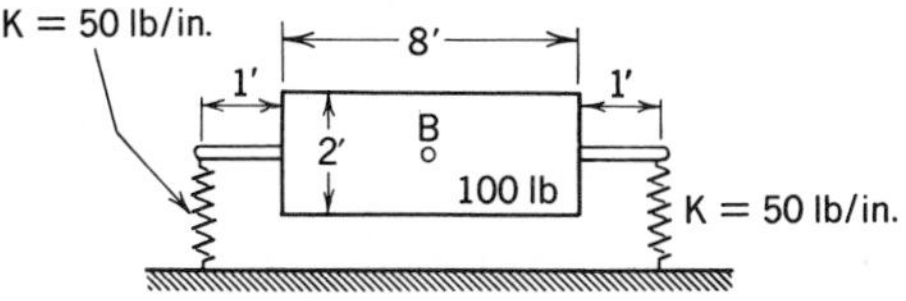

Fig. 20.50

19. [20.3] What is the natural frequency for small oscillations of the compound pendulum shown in Fig. 20.51?

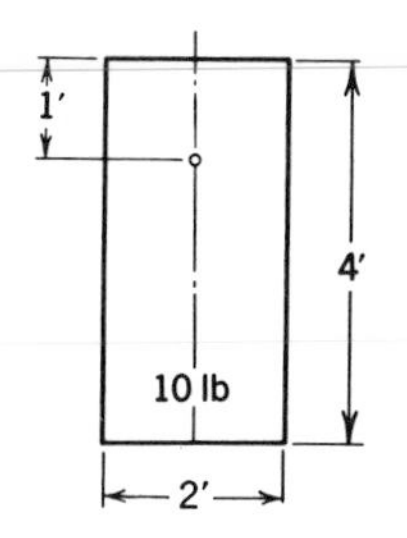

Fig. 20.51

20. [20.3] In Fig. 20.52, a slender rod weighing 32.2 lb is held by a frictionless pin at A and by a spring having a spring constant of 50 lb/in. at B.

(a) What is the natural frequency of oscillation for small vibrations?

(b) If point B of the rod is depressed 1 in. at $t = 0$ from the static-equilibrium position, what will its position be when $t = 0.02$ sec?

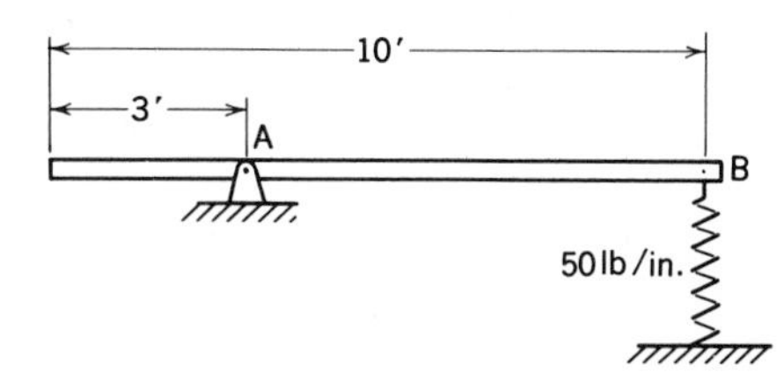

Fig. 20.52

21. [20.3] What is the natural frequency of the pendulum shown in Fig. 20.53 for small oscillations, taking into account the inertia of the rod whose mass we take as m? Also consider the bob to be a sphere of diameter D and mass M rather than a particle.

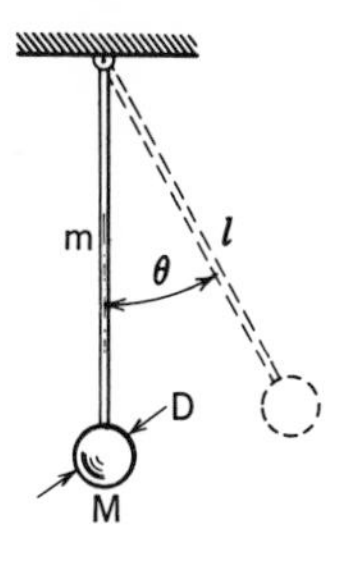

Fig. 20.53

22. [20.3] In Fig. 20.54, a cylinder of mass M and radius R is connected to identical springs and rotates without friction about O. For small oscillations, what is the natural frequency? The cord supporting W_1 is wrapped around the cylinder.

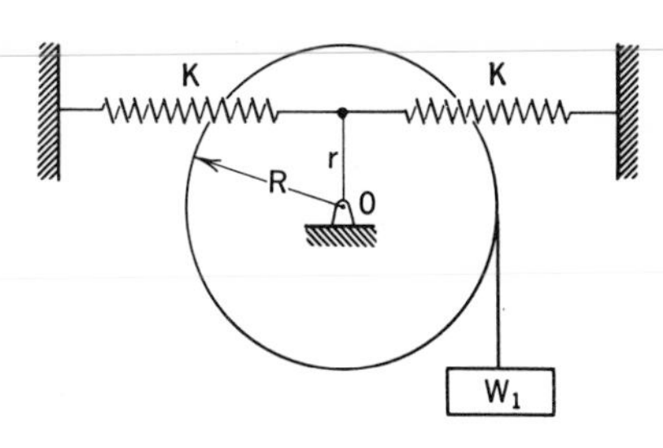

Fig. 20.54

23. [20.3] In Prob. 7 do not consider body A to be a particle and compute the natural frequency of the system for small vibrations. Take the dimension of A to be that of a 6-in. cube.

24. [20.3] Gears A and B weighing 50 lb and 80 lb, respectively, are fixed to supports C and D as shown in Fig. 20.55. If the shear modulus for the shafts is 15×10^6 psi, what is the natural frequency of oscillation for the system?

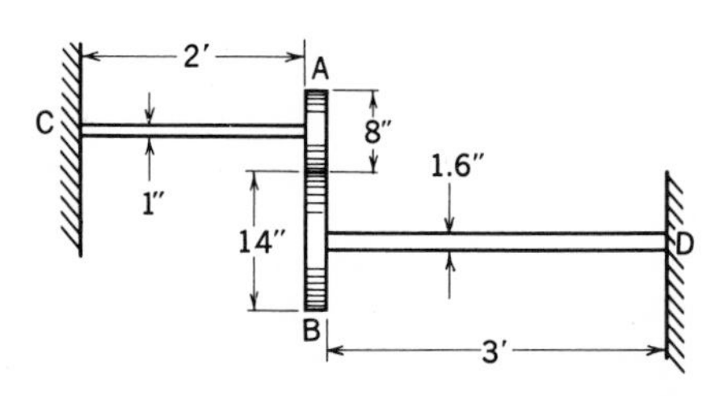

Fig. 20.55

25. [20.3] A plate A weighing 200 lb is attached to a rod CD as shown in Fig. 20.56. If at the instant that the rod CD is torsionally unstrained, the plate has an angular speed of 0.2 rad/sec about the centerline of CD, what is the amplitude of twist developed by the rod? Take $G = 10 \times 10^6$ psi for the rod.

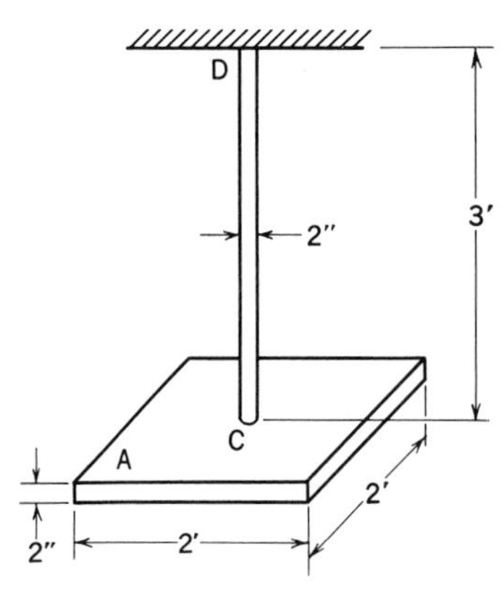

Fig. 20.56

26. [20.3] A block having a uniform density of 300 lb/ft^3 is suspended by a fixed shaft of length 3 ft as shown in Fig. 20.57. If the area of the top surface of the block is to be 5 ft^2, what are the values of a and b for an extreme value of natural torsional frequency of the system? The shear modulus for the shaft is 15×10^6 psi. Compute the natural frequency for the extreme case. Is this a maximum or a minimum value of the natural frequency?

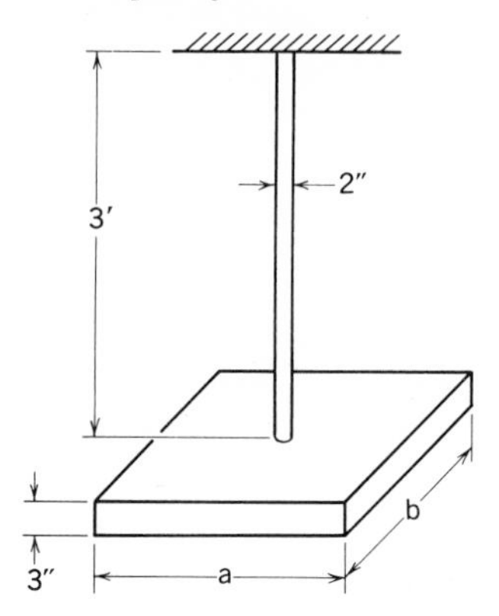

Fig. 20.57

27. [20.3] What is the natural frequency of torsional vibration for the stepped cylinder shown in Fig. 20.58? The mass of the cylinder is 100 lbm and the radius of gyration is 18 in. The following data also apply:

$$D_1 = 1 \text{ ft}$$
$$D_2 = 2 \text{ ft}$$
$$K_1 = 5 \text{ lb/in.}$$
$$K_2 = 10 \text{ lb/in.}$$
$$W_A = 40 \text{ lb}$$

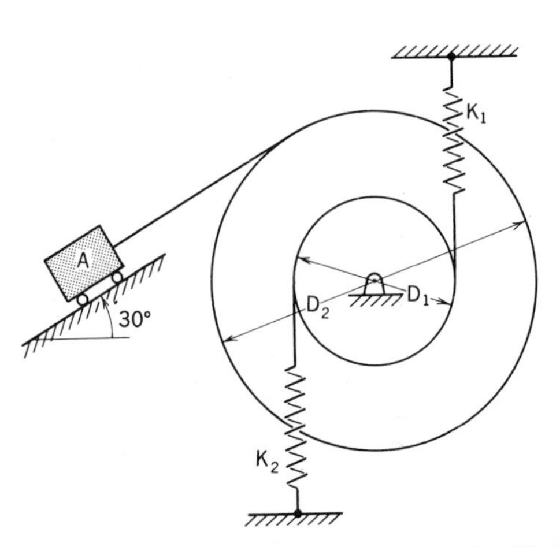

Fig. 20.58

28. [20.3] A disc A weighing 100 lb with a radius of gyration of 18 in. about its axis of symmetry is shown in Fig. 20.59. Note that the center of gravity does not coincide with the geometric center. What is the amplitude of oscillation and frequency of oscillation if, at the instant that the center of gravity is directly below B, the disc is rotating at a speed of 0.01 rad/sec?

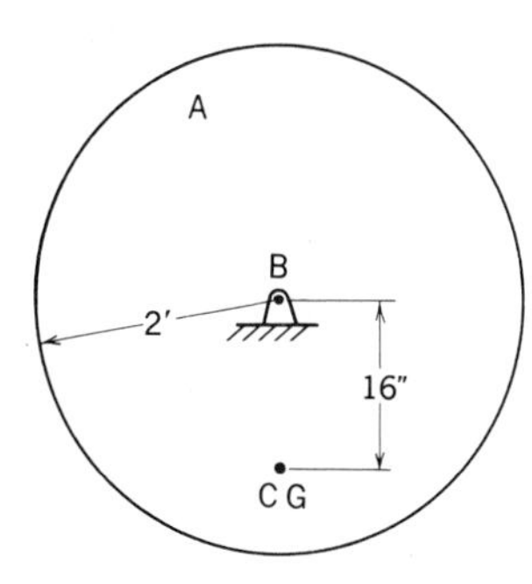

Fig. 20.59

29. [20.3] A disc B is suspended by a flexible wire as shown in Fig. 20.60. The tension in the top wire is 1000 lb. If the disc is observed to have a period of lateral oscillation of 0.2 sec for very small amplitude, and a period of torsional oscillation of 5 sec, what is the radius of gyration of the disc about its geometric axis? The torsional spring constant for the wires is 13 lb-in./rad.

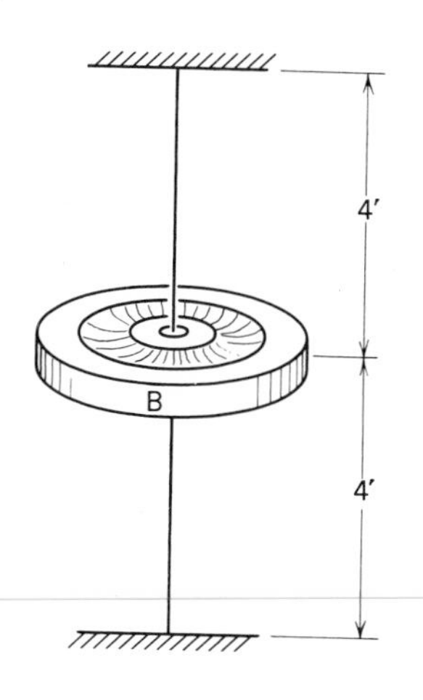

Fig. 20.60

30. [20.3] In Fig. 20.61, a uniform bar of length L and weight W is suspended by strings. What is the differential equation of motion for small torsional oscillation about the center of mass at C? What is the natural frequency?

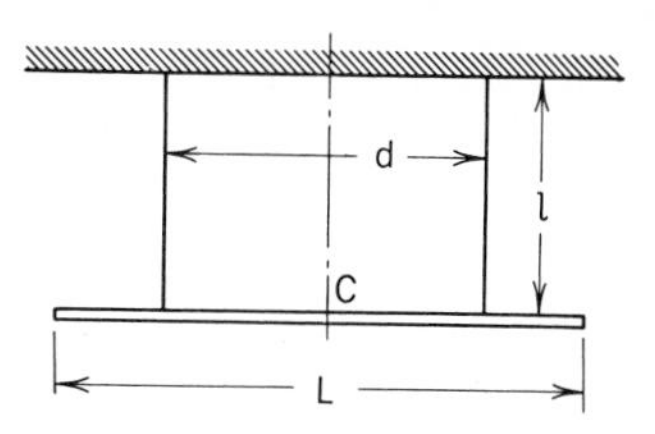

Fig. 20.61

31. [20.3] Two discs are forced together as shown in Fig. 20.62 such that at the point of contact a normal force of 50 lb is transmitted from one disc to the other. Disc A weighs 200 lb and has a radius of gyration of 1.4 ft while disc B weighs 50 lb and has a radius of gyration of 1 ft. What is the natural frequency of oscillation for the system, if disc A is rotated 10° counterclockwise and then released? The center of gravity of B coincides with the geometric center.

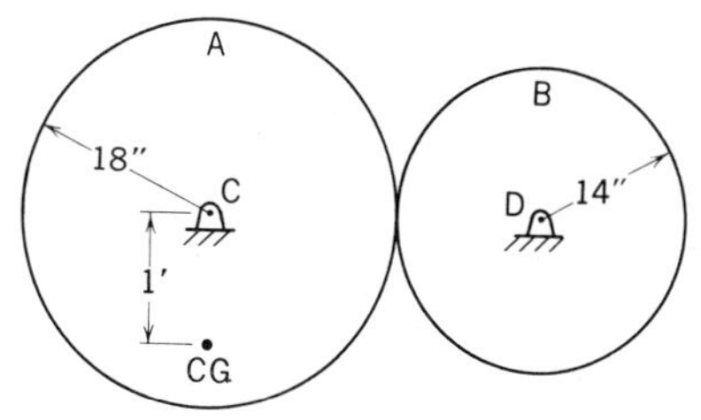

Fig. 20.62

32. [20.3] In the previous problem find the minimum coefficient of friction for no slipping between the discs.

33. [20.4] A cylinder of diameter 3 ft is shown in Fig. 20.63. The center of gravity of the cylinder is 1 ft from the geometric center and the radius of gyration is 2 ft. What is the natural frequency of oscillation for small vibrations without slipping? The cylinder weighs 50 lb.

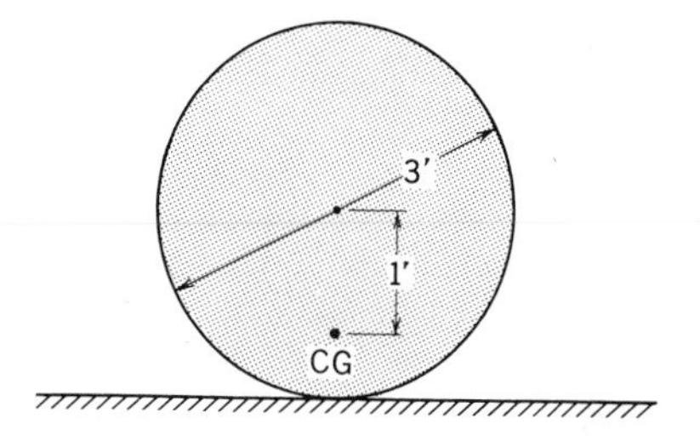

Fig. 20.63

34. [20.4] A stepped cylinder is shown in Fig. 20.64 maintained along the incline by a spring having a spring constant K. What is the formulation for the natural frequency of oscillation for the system? What is the maximum friction force? Take the weight of the cylinder as W and the radius of gyration about the geometric centerline O as k.

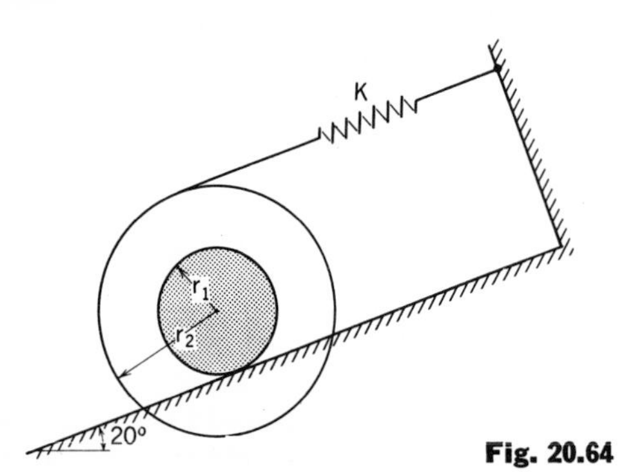

Fig. 20.64

35. [20.4] In the preceding problem the following data apply:

$$r_1 = 1 \text{ ft}$$

$$r_2 = 2 \text{ ft}$$

$$K = 10 \text{ lb/in.}$$

$$W = 30 \text{ lb}$$

$$k = 1.8 \text{ ft}$$

$$\mu = 0.3$$

What is the maximum amplitude of translation of O for the no-slipping condition?

36. [20.4] Two masses are attached to a light rod as shown in Fig. 20.65. The rod rides on a frictionless horizontal rail. If $M_1 = 100$ lbm and $M_2 = 30$ lbm, what is the natural frequency of oscillation of the system if a small impulsive torque is applied to the system when it is in a rest configuration? Consider the masses as particles.

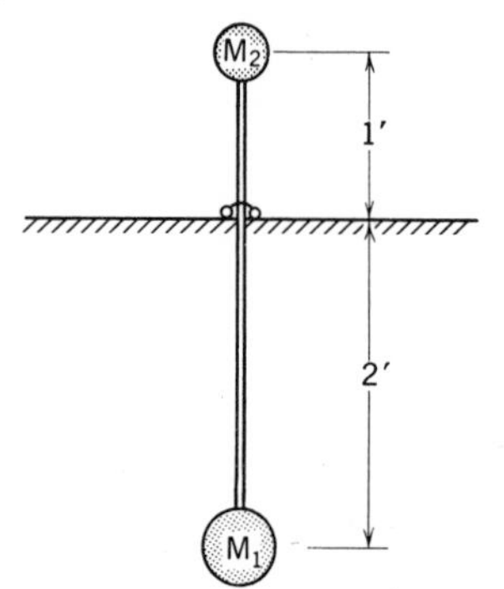

Fig. 20.65

***37.** [20.4] In the preceding problem formulate the differential equation for the rotation of the bar for large amplitudes.

38. [20.4] A rod of length L and mass M is suspended from a frictionless roller as shown in Fig. 20.66. If a small impulsive torque is applied to the rod when it is in a state of rest, what is the natural frequency of oscillation about this state of rest?

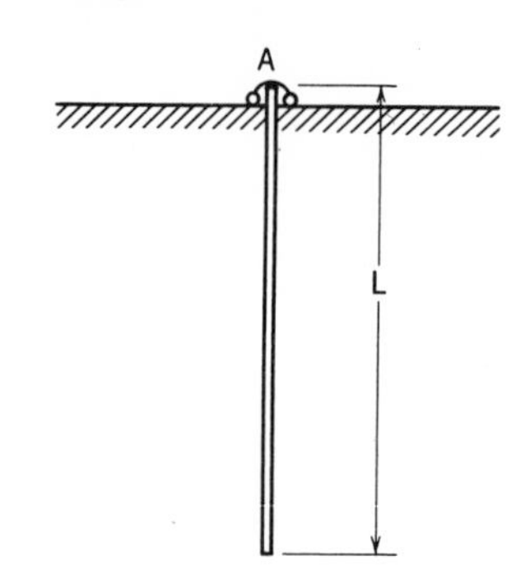

Fig. 20.66

39. [20.5] Do Prob. 7 by energy methods.

40. [20.5] Do Prob. 8 by energy methods.

41. [20.5] Do Prob. 22 by energy methods.

42. [20.5] Do Prob. 27 by energy methods.

43. [20.5] A manometer is shown in Fig. 20.67. If the mercury has a length L in the tube, what is the formulation for the natural frequency of movement of the mercury?

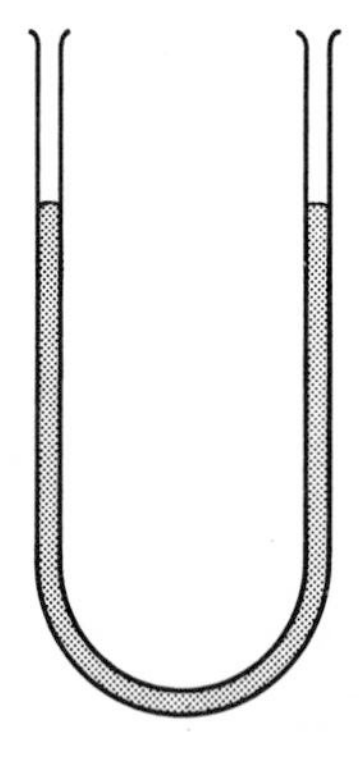

Fig. 20.67

44. [20.5] A cylinder rolls without slipping along a circular path (see Fig. 20.68). For small oscillations, what is the natural frequency? The mass of the cylinder is M.

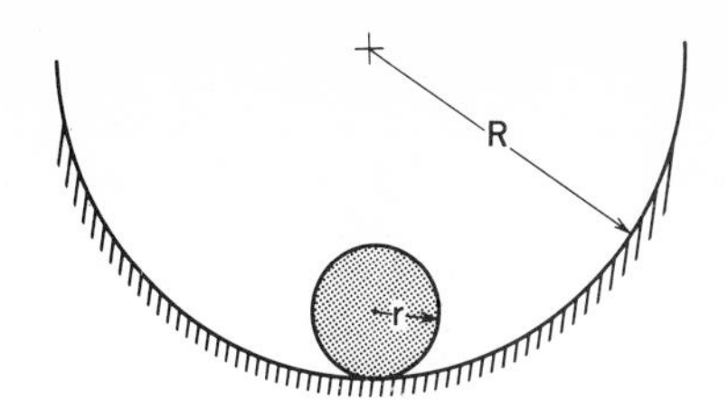

Fig. 20.68

45. [20.5] Shown in Fig. 20.69 is a stepped cylinder which rides on a circular path. For small oscillations, what is the natural frequency? Take the radius of gyration about the geometric axis O as k and the weight of the cylinder as W.

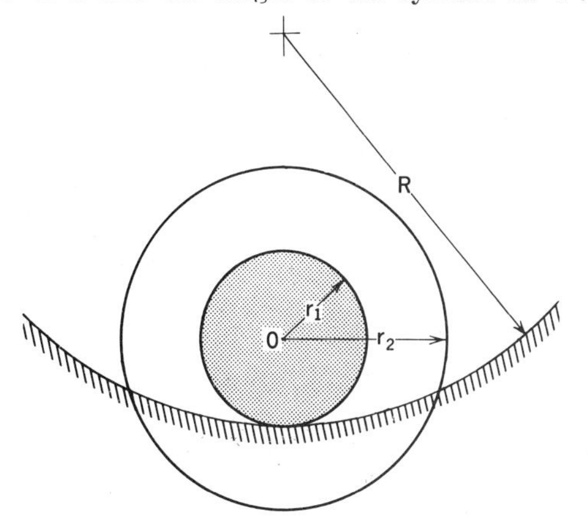

Fig. 20.69

46. [20.6] In Prob. 6, a sinusoidal force having an amplitude of 5 lb and a frequency of $10/\pi$ cycles/sec acts on the body in the direction of the springs. What is the steady-state amplitude of the motion of the body?

47. [20.6] In the preceding problem, the following initial conditions are present:

(a) The initial position of the body is 3 in. to the right of the static-equilibrium position.

(b) The initial velocity is zero.

(c) At $t = 0$, the sinusoidal disturbing force has a value of 5 lb in the positive direction.

Find the position of the body after 3 sec.

48. [20.6] Suppose in Prob. 47 that the sinusoidal force with amplitude of 5 lb has a value of 3 lb at $t = 0$. Find the position of the body after 3 sec.

49. [20.6] A sinusoidal force of amplitude 5 lb and of frequency $1/2\pi$ cycles/sec acts on a body having a mass of one slug (Fig. 20.70). Meanwhile, the wall moves with a motion given as 0.3 cos t in. For a spring constant $K = 50$ lb/in., what is the amplitude of the steady-state motion?

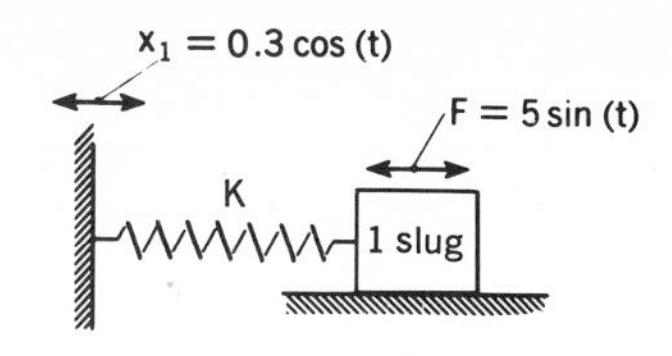

Fig. 20.70

50. [20.6] A torque $T = A \sin \omega t$ is applied to the disc as shown in Fig. 20.71. Express the solution for the transient torsional motion and the steady-state torsional motion, using arbitrary constants of integration. Take the shear modulus of elasticity of the shaft as G.

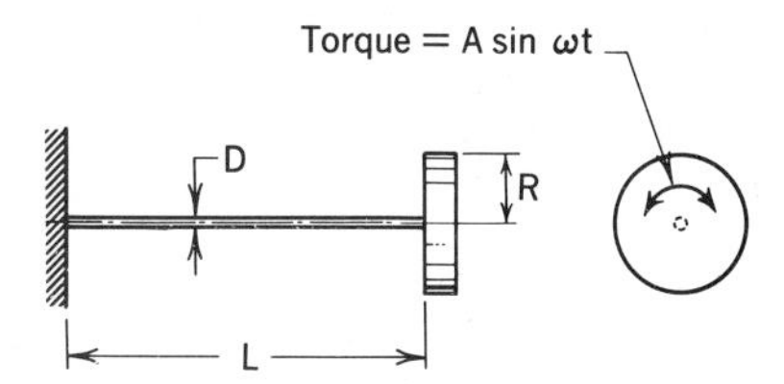

Fig. 20.71

51. [20.6] A *vibrograph* (see Fig. 20.72) is a device for measuring the amplitude of vibration in a given direction. The apparatus is bolted to the machine to be tested, as shown in the diagram. A so-called seismic mass M in the vibrograph rides along a rod CD under constraint of a linear spring of spring constant K. If the machine being tested has a harmonic motion $\bar{x}$ of frequency ω in the direction of C-D, then M will have a steady-state oscillatory frequency also of ω. The motion of M relative to the vibrograph is given as x' and is recorded on the rotating drum. Show that the amplitude of motion of the machine is

$$\left| \frac{(\omega/\omega_n)^2 - 1}{(\omega/\omega_n)^2} \right|$$

times the amplitude of the recorded motion x', where $\omega_n = \sqrt{K/M}$.

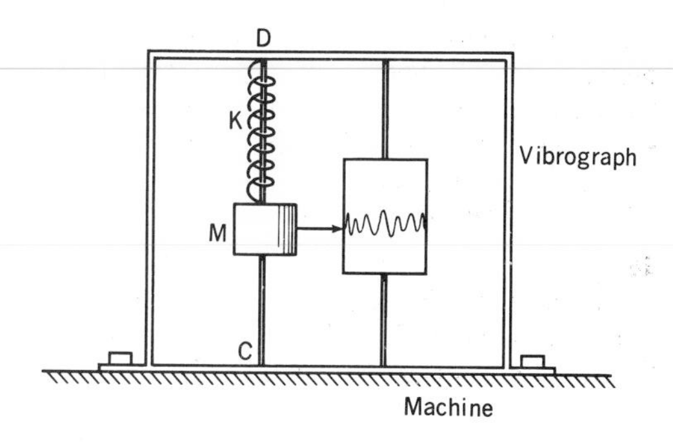

Fig. 20.72

52. [20.6] A vibrograph is attached rigidly to a diesel engine being tested for vibration amplitude. If the seismic spring-mass system has a natural frequency of 10 cycles/sec, and if the seismic mass vibrates relative to the vibrograph with an amplitude of 0.05 in. when the diesel is turning over at 1000 rpm, what is the amplitude of vibration of the diesel in the direction of the vibrograph? The seismic mass weighs 1 lb. (See Prob. 51 before doing.)

53. [20.6] Explain how you could devise an instrument that measures torsional vibrations of a shaft in a manner analogous to the way the vibrograph measures linear vibrations of a machine. Such instruments are in wide use and are called *torsiographs*. What would be the relation of the amplitude of oscillations as picked up by your apparatus to that of the shaft being measured?

54. [20.6] A block (see Fig. 20.73) is acted on by a force F given as

$$F = 20 + 5 \sin 80t$$

and is found to oscillate, after transients have died out, with an amplitude of 0.02 in. about a position 2 in. to the left of the static-equilibrium position corresponding to the condition when no force is present. What is the weight of the body?

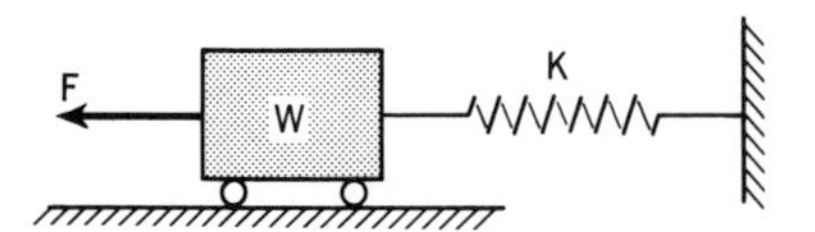

Fig. 20.73

55. [20.6] An important reason for mounting rotating and reciprocating machinery on springs is to decrease the transmission of vibration to the foundation supporting the machine. Show that the amplitude of force transmitted to the ground for such cases is given as

$$\left| \frac{1}{1 - (\omega/\omega_n)^2} \right|$$

per unit of force amplitude developed by the machine. The factor is called the *relative transmission factor*. Show that, unless the springs are soft so as to render $\omega_n < \omega/\sqrt{2}$, then the use of springs actually increases the transmission of vibratory forces to the foundation.

56. [20.6] In Example 20.8 what is the amplitude of the force transmitted to the foundation? What must K of the spring system be to decrease the amplitude by one-half?

57. [20.6] A trailer of weight W moves over a washboard road as shown in Fig. 20.74 at a constant speed U to the right. The road is approximated by a sinusoid of amplitude A and wavelength L. If the wheel B is small, the center of the wheel will have a motion x closely resembling the aforementioned sinusoid. If the trailer is connected to the wheel through a linear spring of stiffness K, formulate the steady-state equation of motion x' for the trailer. List all assumptions. What speed causes resonance?

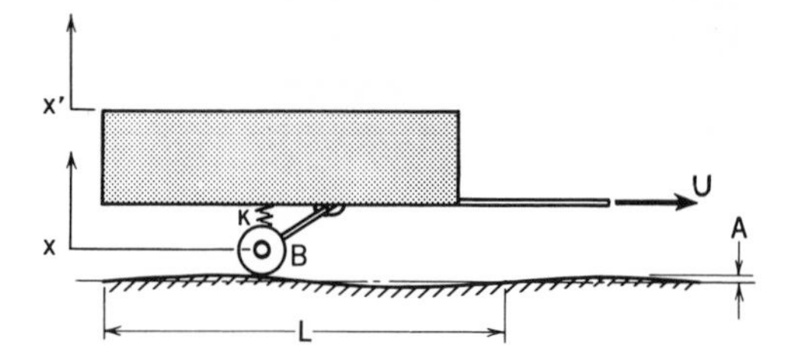

Fig. 20.74

58. [20.6] In the preceding problem compute the amplitude of motion of the trailer for the following data:

$$W = 1200 \text{ lb}$$
$$U = 10 \text{ mph}$$
$$K = 250 \text{ lb/in.}$$
$$L = 30 \text{ ft}$$
$$A = 4 \text{ in.}$$

What is the resonance speed $U_{res.}$ for the case?

59. [20.6] A machine weighing W lb contains a reciprocating mass of w lb having a vertical motion relative to the machine given approximately as $A \sin \omega t$. The machine is mounted on springs having a total spring constant K. This machine is guided so that it can move only in the vertical direction. What is the differential equation of motion for this machine? What is the formulation for the amplitude of the machine for steady-state operation?

60. [20.7] The damping constant for the body shown in Fig. 20.75 is $\frac{1}{2}$ lb/ft/sec. If at its equilibrium position the body is suddenly given a velocity of 10 ft/sec to the right, what will the frequency of its motion be? What is the position of the mass at $t = 5$ sec?

K = 2 lb/in.
M = 1 slug

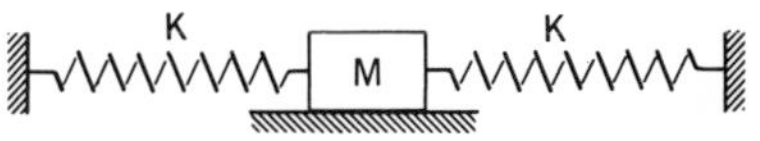

K M K

Fig. 20.75

61. [20.7] If the damping in the preceding problem is increased so that it is twice the critical damping and if the mass is released from a position 3 in. to the right of equilibrium, how far from the equilibrium position is it in 5 sec? Theoretically, does it ever reach the equilibrium position?

62. [20.7] A plot of a free damped vibration is shown in Fig. 20.76. What should the constant C_3 be in Eq. 20.35 for this motion? Show that $\ln x_1/x_2$, where x_1 and x_2 are two succeeding peaks, can be given as $(c/4m)\tau$. The expression $\ln (x_1/x_2)$ is called the *logarithmic decrement* and is used in vibration work.

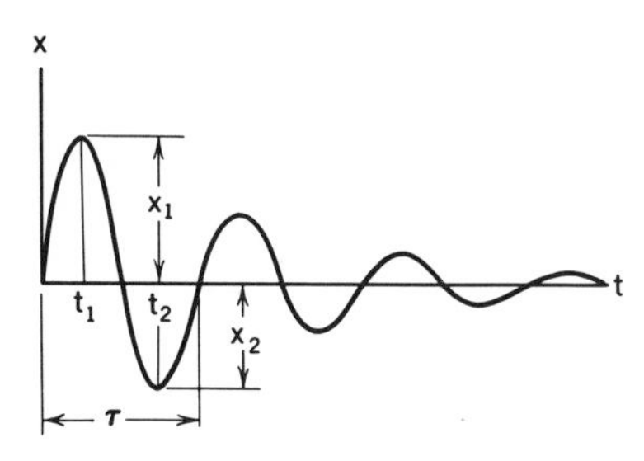

Fig. 20.76

63. [20.7] Shown in Fig. 20.77 is a body of weight W lb suspended between two springs. Two identical dashpots are shown. Each resists motion of the block at the rate of c lb/ft/sec. What is the equation of motion for the block? What is c for critical damping?

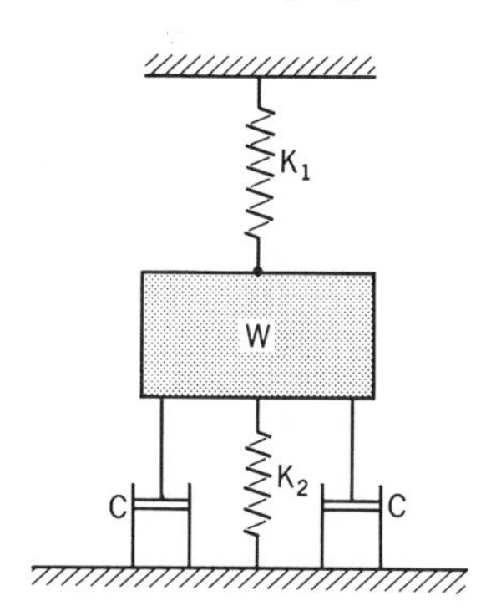

Fig. 20.77

64. [20.7] In the preceding problem the following data apply:

$$W = 100 \text{ lb}$$
$$K_1 = 50 \text{ lb/in.}$$
$$K_2 = 80 \text{ lb/in.}$$
$$c = 60 \text{ lb/ft/sec}$$

Is the system underdamped, overdamped, or critically damped? If the weight W is released 6 in. above its static-equilibrium configuration, what are the speed and position of the block after 0.1 sec? What force is transmitted to the foundation at that instant?

65. [20.7] A rod of length 7 ft and weight 50 lb is shown in the static-equilibrium position (Fig. 20.78) supported by a spring of stiffness $K = 80$ lb/in. and connected to a dashpot having a damping force c of 5 lb/ft/sec. If an impulsive torque gives the rod an angular speed clockwise of $\frac{1}{2}$ rad/sec at the position shown, what is the position of point A at $t = 0.2$ sec?

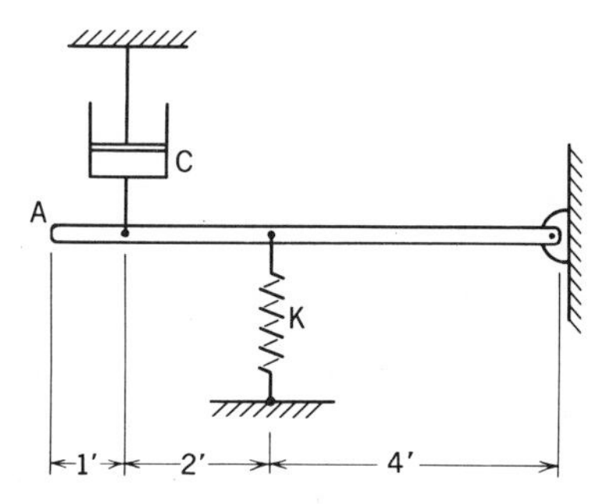

Fig. 20.78

66. [20.7] Shown in Fig. 20.79 is a rotational damper such as is used in certain meters. A disc A of diameter 6 in. rotates in a bath of oil having a viscosity of 0.020 lb-sec/ft². Compute a damping constant for rotational damping for this case. What rotational spring constant is needed for the rotating system for a critical rotational damping situation if the equivalent moment of inertia about the axis of rotation is 6 lbm-in.²? Assume linear velocity profile for the oil as discussed in Chapter 9.

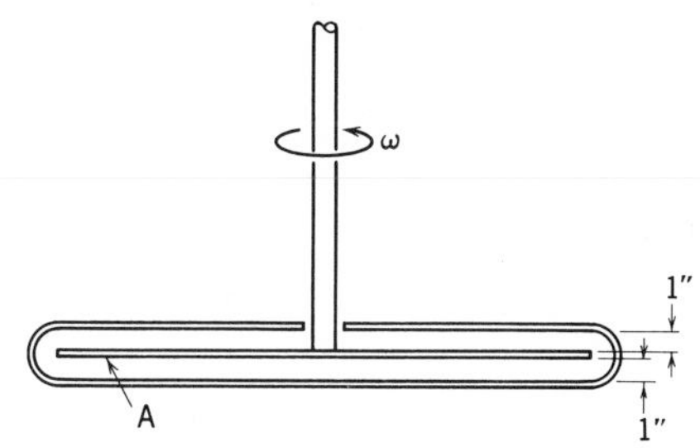

Fig. 20.79

67. [20.7] A spherical ball of weight 30 lb is shown in Fig. 20.80 on a vertical light rod welded at B to a horizontal rod. A spring of stiffness $K = 50$ lb/in. and a damper c having a value 13 lb/ft/sec are connected to the horizontal rod. If A is displaced 3 in. to the right, how long does it take for it to return to its vertical configuration?

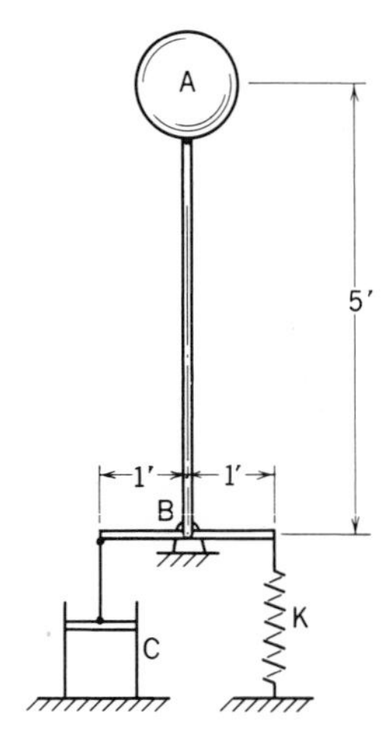

Fig. 20.80

68. [20.7] A body rests on a conveyor moving with a speed of 5 ft/sec (Fig. 20.81). If the damping constant is 2 lb/ft/sec, determine the equilibrium force in the spring. If the body is displaced 3 in. to the left from the equilibrium position, what is the time for the mass to pass through the equilibrium position again?

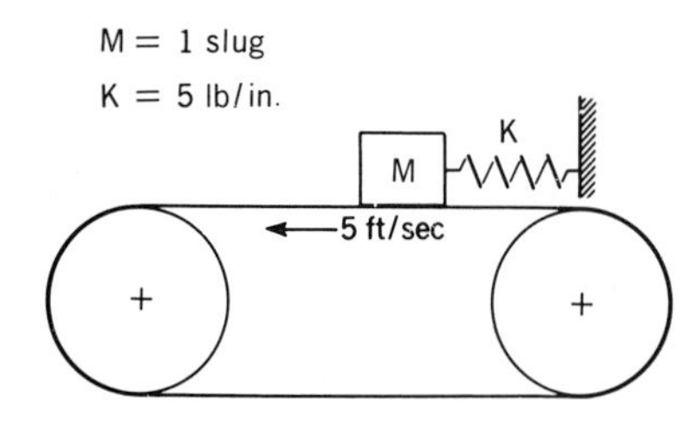

Fig. 20.81

69. [20.8] Examine the case of the mass-spring system with viscous damping for a sinusoidal forcing function given as $F_0 \sin \omega t$. Go through the steps in the text leading up to Eq. 20.41 for this case.

70. [20.8] A force $F = 8 \sin 2t$ acts on a block having a weight of 64.4 lb as shown in Fig. 20.82. A spring having stiffness K of 40 lb/ft and a dashpot having a damping factor c of 5 lb-sec/ft are connected to the body. What is the amplitude of steady-state motion for the body and what is the maximum force transmitted to the wall?

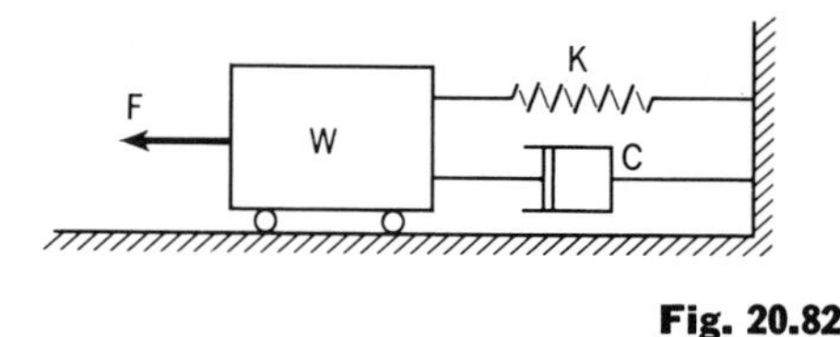

Fig. 20.82

71. [20.8] A motor is shown in Fig. 20.83 mounted on two springs of stiffness 50 lb/in. each and a dashpot having a coefficient c of 7 lb-sec/ft. The motor weighs 50 lb. The armature of the motor weighs 20 lb with a center of mass 0.2 in. from the geometric centerline. If the machine rotates at 1750 rpm, what is the amplitude of motion in the vertical direction of the motor? Determine the maximum force transmitted to the ground. [*Hint*: Consider the motion of armature and motor frame separately.]

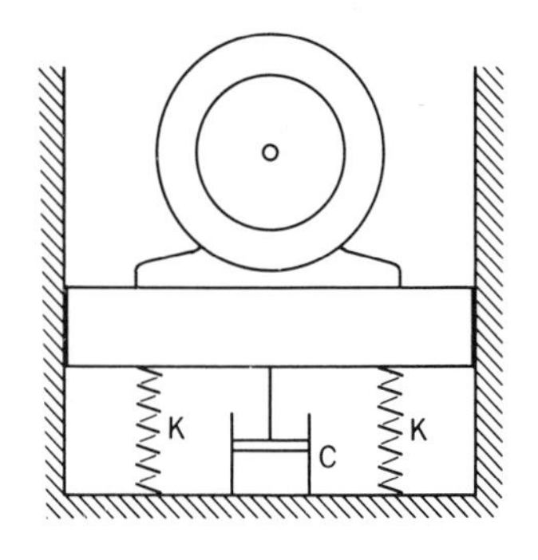

Fig. 20.83

72. [20.8] In the preceding problem, what is the resonant condition for the system? What is the amplitude of motion for this case? To what value must c be changed if the amplitude of this motor speed is to be halved?

73. [20.8] In Example 20.10 compute K for an amplitude of steady-state vibration of $\frac{1}{2}$ in.

74. [20.8] A platform weighing 50 lb deflects the spring 2 in. when placed carefully on the spring (Fig. 20.84). A motor weighing 5 lb is then clamped on top of the platform and rotates an eccentric mass m, which weighs 4 oz and is displaced 6 in. from the axis of rotation, at an angular speed of 28 rad/sec. The viscous damping present causes a resistance to the motion of the platform of 20 lb/ft/sec. What is the steady-state amplitude of the motion of the platform?

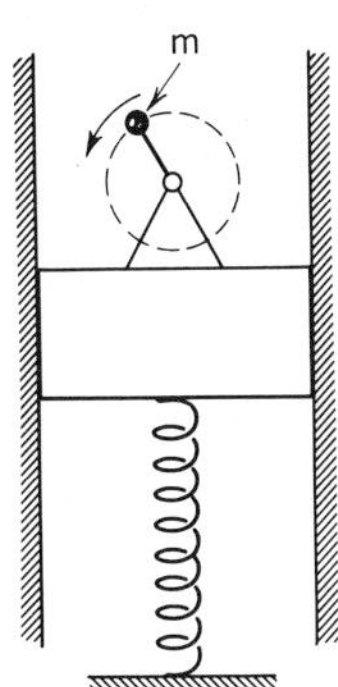

Fig. 20.84

75. [20.8] A body A in Fig. 20.85 weighing 32.2 lb is connected by a light rod to a spring of stiffness K equal to 15 lb/in. and a dashpot having a damping factor c. Point B has a given motion x' of 1.2 sin t in. If the center of A is to have an amplitude of steady-state motion of 0.8 in., what must c be?

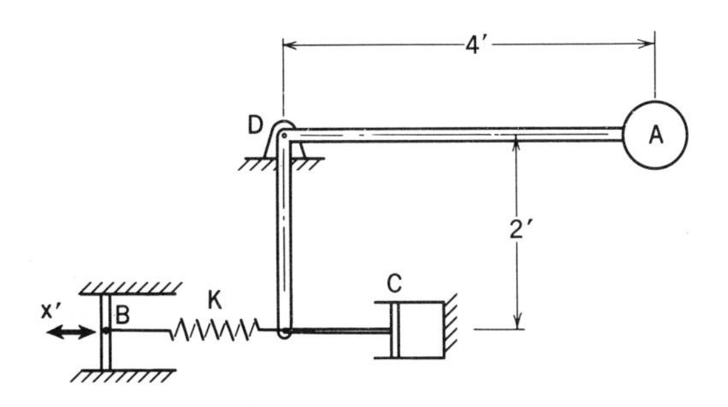

Fig. 20.85

76. [20.9] If we include the inertial effects of rod BC in Prob. 10, how many degrees of freedom does the system have? If BD weighs 10 lb, what are the differential equations of motion for the system?

77. [20.9] In Prob. 11, if we include the inertial effects of rod BC, how many degrees of freedom are there? If rod BC weighs 5 lb, set up the differential equations of motion for the system.

78. [20.9] Two bodies of equal mass, $M = 1$ slug, are attached to walls by springs having equal spring constants $K_1 = 5$ lb/in. and are connected to each other by a spring having a spring constant $K_2 = 1$ lb/in. (Fig. 20.86). If the mass on the left is released from a position $(x_1)_0 = 3$ in. at $t = 0$ with zero velocity and the mass at the right is stationary at $x_2 = 0$ at this instant, what is the position of each mass at the time $t = 5$ sec? The coordinates x_1 and x_2 are measured from the static-equilibrium positions of the body.

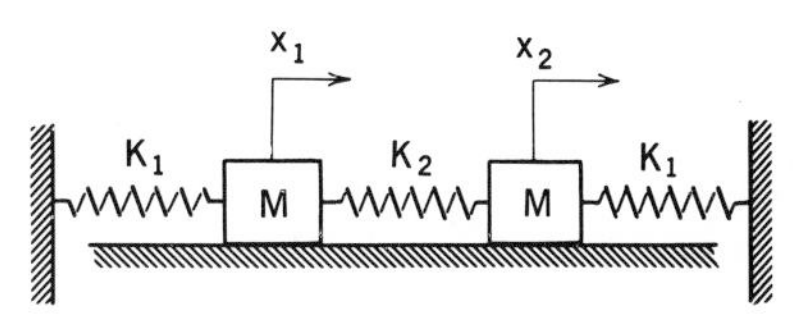

Fig. 20.86

79. [20.9] Using Fig. 20.86, let K_2 be very small compared to K_1. Assume one mass has been released at $t = 0$ from a position displaced from equilibrium with zero velocity, while the other mass is released from the equilibrium position at that instant with zero velocity. Show that one mass will have a maximum velocity while the other will have a minimum velocity and that there will be a continual transfer of kinetic energy from one mass to the other at a frequency equal to the beat frequency of the natural frequencies of the system.

80. [20.9] If one of the masses in the problem discussed in Section 20.9 is doubled, what are the natural frequencies?

81. [20.9] Set up the differential equations of motion for the identical pendulums connected by the spring having a spring constant K (Fig. 20.87). Limit your analysis to small vibrations so that the masses M can be considered as moving in a translatory manner. Neglect the mass of the pendulum rods and spring. Determine the natural frequencies and the modes.

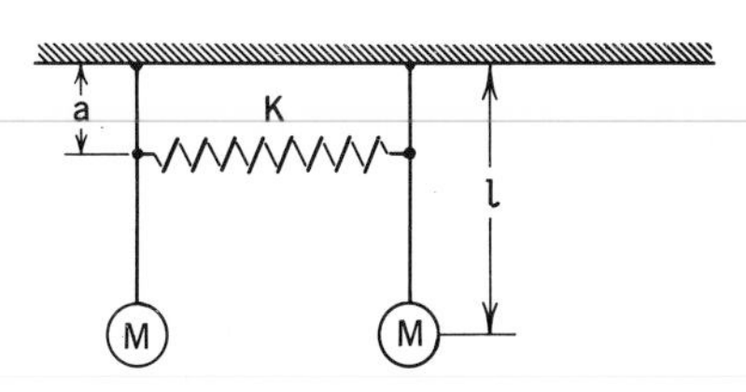

Fig. 20.87

82. [20.9] In Fig. 20.88, two identical discs are mounted on a shaft of uniform diameter. Express the equations of motion for torsional vibration of the system. What are the natural frequencies? What are the mode shapes?

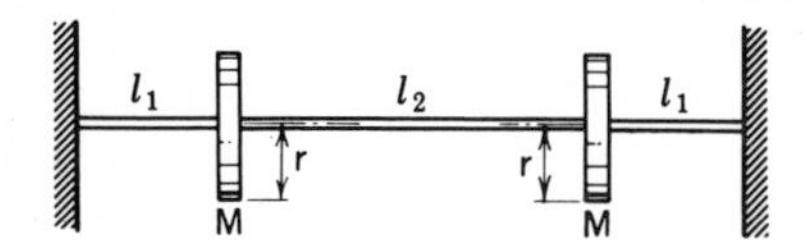

Fig. 20.88

***83.** [20.9] Shown in Fig. 20.89 are three identical masses connected by four identical springs. Write the differential equations of motion for the masses. What are the natural frequencies of oscillation? Describe the mode shapes. Neglect friction.

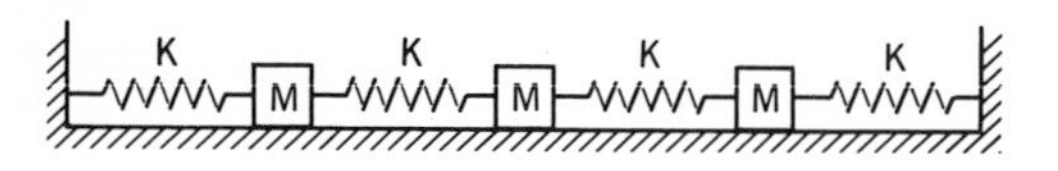

Fig. 20.89

***84.** [20.9] Formulate the differential equations of motion for the two masses M_1 and M_2 shown in Fig. 20.90. What are the natural frequencies for small vibration? The following data apply:

$$a = 1 \text{ ft}$$

$$b = 1 \text{ ft}$$

$$M_1 = 1 \text{ lbm}$$

$$M_2 = 2 \text{ lbm}$$

$$K = 5 \text{ lbm/in.}$$

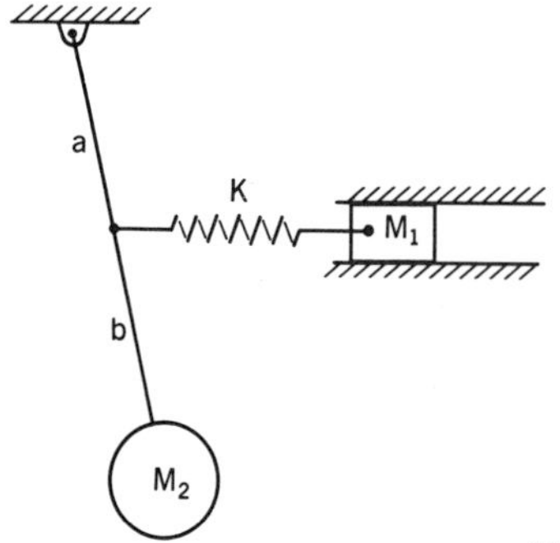

Fig. 20.90

85. [20.9] In Fig. 20.91, masses m_1 and m_2 are constrained to move along rod *cc*, which is fixed to a rotating platform. To a person on the platform, the motions of the bodies would appear as rectilinear translations. Set up differential equations giving all possible motions of the masses relative to the platform. The platform has known angular velocity and angular acceleration time variations. The static-equilibrium radial positions on m_1 and m_2 are to be taken at r_{1_0} and r_{2_0}, respectively.

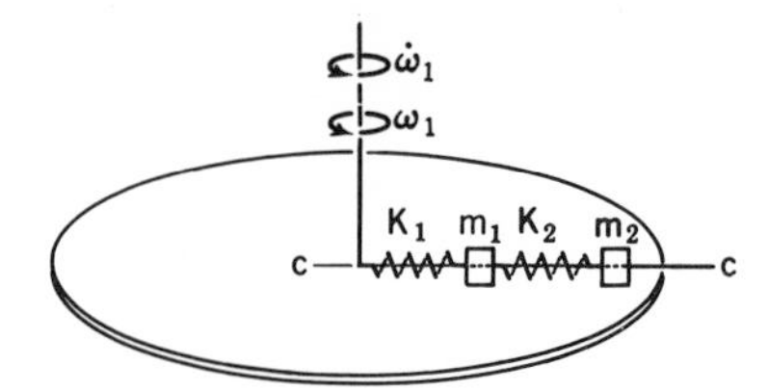

Fig. 20.91

86. [20.10] Draw the circuit analogue for the mechanical system shown in Fig. 20.92. Express the equation for the current in the loop.

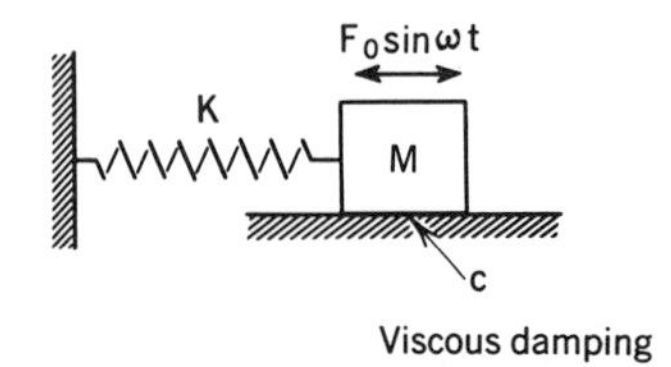

Fig. 20.92

87. [20.10] Draw the circuit analogue and express the differential equation for the current and charge (Fig. 20.93).

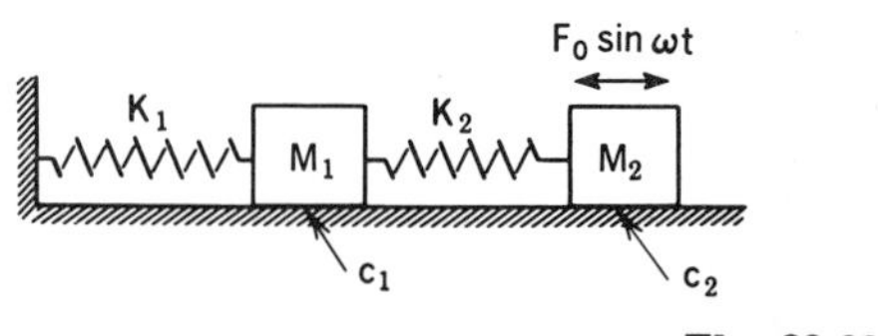

Fig. 20.93

88. [20.10] In Fig. 20.94, if the switch is closed at time $t = 0$, determine the current as a function of time. Show that the time required for the current to reach $(1 - 1/e)$ of its final value is L/R, which is called the *time constant* of the circuit.

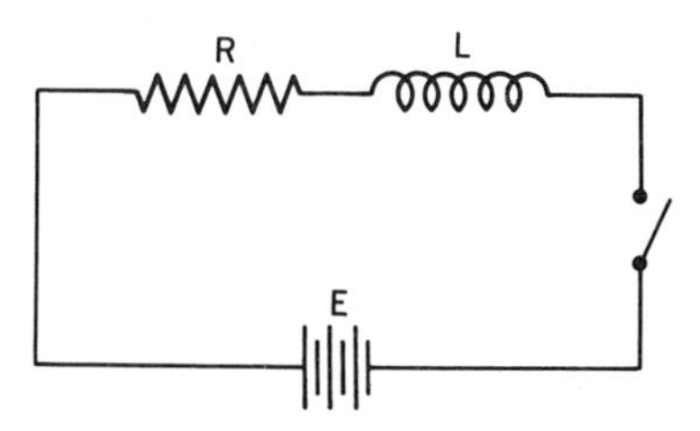

Fig. 20.94

Problems 89 and 90 are presented for students interested in D.C. analog computers.

89. [20.10] A damped, linear oscillator as shown in Fig. 20.95 is subjected to a suddenly applied, constant force, i.e.,

$$F(t) = 0 \quad \text{for} \quad t \leq 0$$

$$F(t) = F_0 \quad \text{for} \quad t > 0$$

The motion starts from rest, and the spring force is zero in the reference position.

(a) Show that the differential equation of motion and associated initial conditions are given by

$$m\ddot{x} + c\dot{x} + Kx = F(t)$$

$$x(0) = \dot{x}(0) = 0$$

(b) Show that the block diagram appropriate for a D.C. Analog Computer set-up is given in Fig. 20.96.

(c) Let $m = 1$ slug

$$K = 1 \text{ lb/ft}$$

$$c = \tfrac{1}{2} \text{ lb-sec/ft}$$

$$F_o = 60 \text{ lbs}$$

Transform the problem to machine variables, and find the dynamic response $x = x(t)$. Find $x_{\max}$. Check your answers analytically.

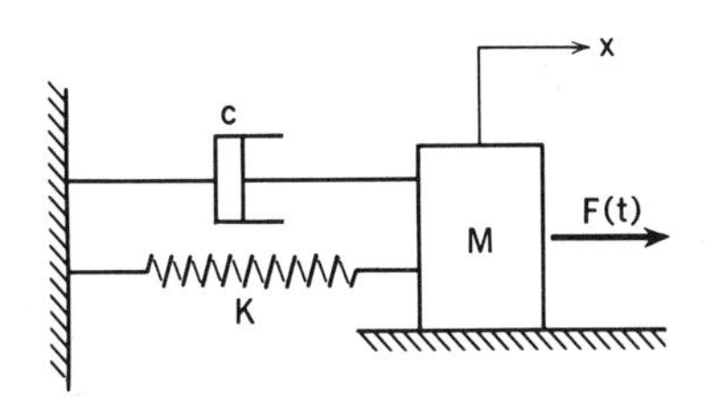

Fig. 20.95

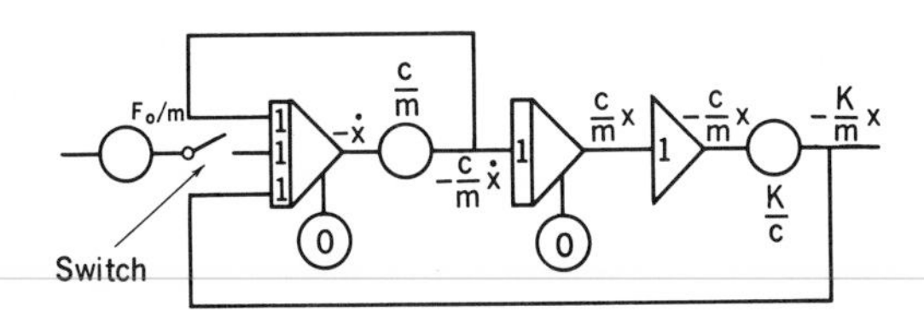

Fig. 20.96

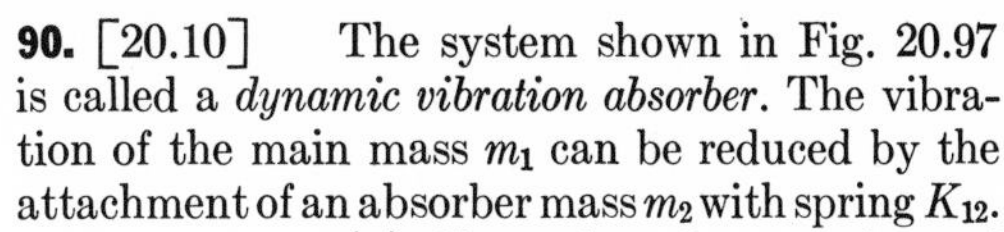

90. [20.10] The system shown in Fig. 20.97 is called a *dynamic vibration absorber*. The vibration of the main mass m_1 can be reduced by the attachment of an absorber mass m_2 with spring K_{12}.

(a) Show that the equations of motion of the system are given by

$$m_1\ddot{y}_1 = -K_1y_1 - c_1\dot{y}_1 - K_{12}(y_1 - y_2) + G\sin\omega t$$

$$m_2\ddot{y}_2 = K_{12}(y_1 - y_2)$$

(b) Show that the appropriate D.C. Analog Computer diagram is given as shown in Fig. 20.98 if:

$$m_1 = 1 \text{ slug} \qquad K_{12} = 2 \text{ lb/ft}$$

$$m_2 = \tfrac{1}{2} \text{ slug} \qquad c_1 = \tfrac{1}{2} \text{ lb-sec/ft}$$

$$K_1 = 1 \text{ lb/ft} \qquad G = 2 \text{ lb}$$

(c) Scale the problem, and set up on a D.C. Analog Computer. Show that if $\omega = 2$ rad/sec, the amplitude of the main mass m_1 is reduced to less than $\frac{1}{50}$ of the amplitude which would result without the vibration absorber.

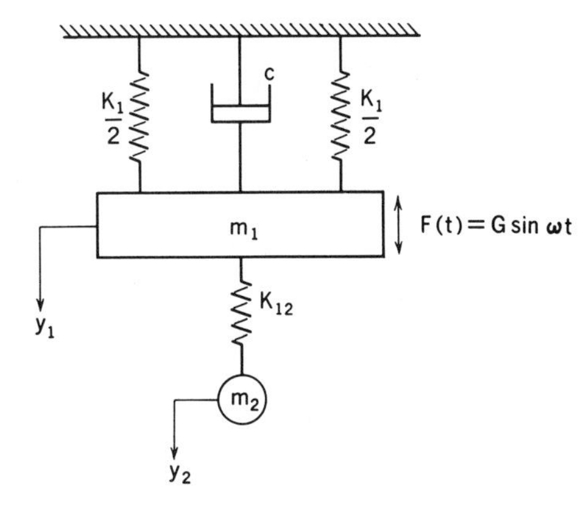

Fig. 20.97

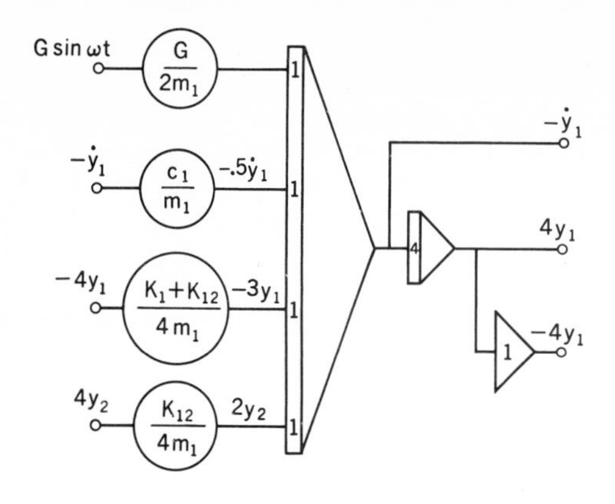

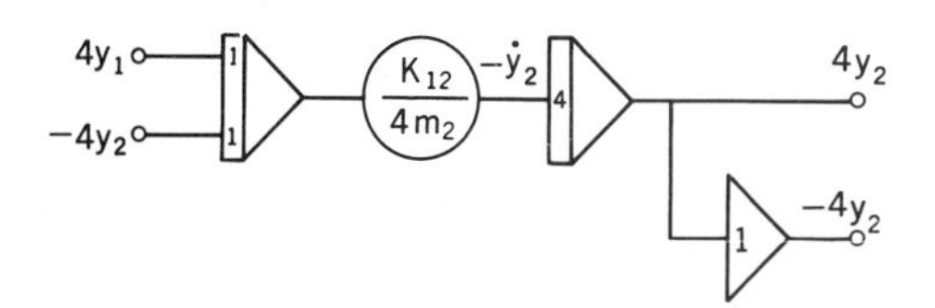

Fig. 20.98

Problems 91, 92 and 93 are presented for students interested in numerical methods and digital computers.

91. [20.10] Given a block of mass m restrained by a nonlinear spring which exerts a restoring force of the form $F(x) = -(\alpha x + \beta x^3)$. The block is subjected to an initial displacement $x(0) = x_0$ and initial velocity $\dot{x}(0) = 0$.

(a) Find a Taylor series solution for the displacement $x(t)$ in terms of x_o, m, α, β, and t. Keep terms up to and including terms of order t^5.

(b) Using the values $x_o = 1$ ft, $m = 10$ slugs, $\alpha = 10$ lb/ft, $\beta = 1$ lb/ft^3, plot the following in the interval $0 \leq t \leq \pi/2$

(1). $x(t)$ as found in part (a)

(2). $x(t)$ for a linear spring (set $\beta = 0$ in part (a) solution.)

(3). $x(t)$ for a linear spring using the exact solution to the differential equation with $\beta = 0$.

92. [20.10] A block is translating under the action of a linear restoring force and an arbitrary forcing function $(F_o)[f(t)]$. Eq. (20.21) then generalizes to

$$\frac{d^2x}{dt^2} + \frac{K}{m}x = \frac{F_o}{m}f(t)$$

(a) Obtain a complete solution to this equation for the conditions $x = x_o$ and $dx/dt = 0$ at $t = 0$. *Hint*: Use the method of variation of parameters to obtain the particular solution in terms of integrals.

(b) Consider the special case $K = 20$ lb/ft, $m = 10$ slug, $F_o = 30$ lb, $x_o = 1$ ft., and $f(t) = te^{-t}\sin t$. Evaluate the integrals obtained in (a) numerically (e.g., by Simpson's rule), and then plot $x(t)$ in the interval $0 \leq t \leq 2\pi$.

93. [20.10] Consider a block of mass m subjected to a linear restoring force and a nonlinear viscous damping force of the form $c(dx/dt)^3$. Equation (20.39) in this cane then becomes

$$\frac{d^2x}{dt^2} + \frac{c}{m}\left(\frac{dx}{dt}\right)^3 + \frac{K}{m}x = 0$$

Let $m = 10$ slugs, $c = 10$ lb/ft^3/sec^3, $K = 10$ lb/ft; and consider the initial conditions $x = 0$ and $dx/\text{dt} = 5$ ft/sec at $t = 0$. Solve this equation by some appropriate numerical procedure, and plot $x(t)$ in the interval $0 \leq t \leq 2\pi$.

Suggestion: Milne's method is a widely used numerical procedure for solving second order equations of the form

$$\ddot{x} = f(\dot{x}, x, t)$$

with initial conditions given at $t = 0$. Consult a numerical analysis text for details.

APPENDIX I

Review of Conic Sections

A *conic section* is the locus of all points whose distance from a fixed point has a constant ratio to the distances from a fixed line. The fixed point is called the *focus* (or focal point) and the line is termed the *directrix*. In Fig. I.1 we have shown point P, a directrix DD, and a focus O. For a conic section to be traced by P, it must move in a manner that keeps the ratio $r/\overline{DP}$, called the *eccentricity*, a fixed number. Clearly, for every acceptable position P there will be a mirror image position P' (see diagram) about a line normal to the directrix and going through the focal point O. Thus, the conic section will be symmetrical about axis OC.

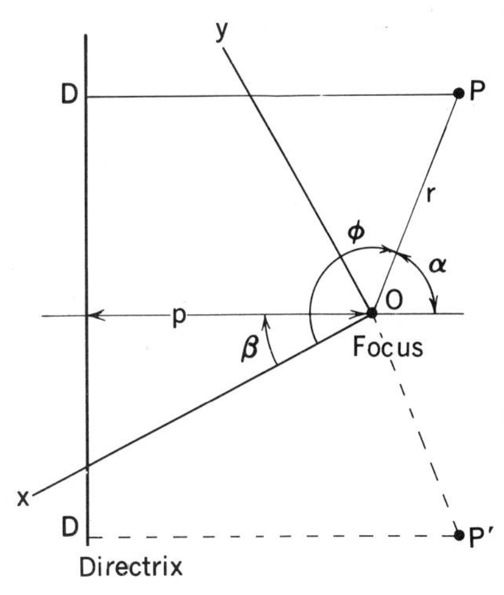

Fig. I.1

Using the letter ϵ to represent the eccentricity, we can say:

$$\frac{r}{\overline{DP}} \equiv \epsilon = \frac{r}{p + r\cos\alpha} \qquad \textbf{I.1}$$

where p is the distance from the focus to the directrix. Replacing $\cos\alpha$ by $-\cos(\phi - \beta)$, where β (see Fig. I.1) is the angle between the x axis of an arbitrary reference at O and the axis of symmetry, we then get:

$$\frac{r}{p - r\cos(\phi - \beta)} = \epsilon \qquad \textbf{I.2}$$

Now, rearranging the terms in the equation, we arrive at a standard formulation for conic sections:

$$\boxed{\frac{1}{r} = \frac{1}{\epsilon p} + \frac{1}{p}\cos(\phi - \beta)} \qquad \textbf{I.3}$$

To understand the significance of the eccentricity ϵ let us consider conic sections in terms of a reference xy where x is the axis of symmetry (that is, consider $\beta = 0$ in preceding formulations). Equation I.3 can be expressed in these rectangular coordinates in the following manner:

$$\frac{1}{\sqrt{x^2 + y^2}} = \frac{1}{\epsilon p} + \frac{1}{p}\frac{x}{\sqrt{x^2 + y^2}} \qquad \textbf{I.4}$$

Simple algebraic manipulation permits us to put the preceding equation into the following form:

$$(1 - \epsilon^2)x^2 + y^2 + 2p\epsilon^2 x - \epsilon^2 p^2 = 0 \qquad \textbf{I.5}$$

From this form we see that if $\epsilon = 1$, the coefficient of x^2 is zero and the resulting equation is that of a *parabola*. If $\epsilon < 1$, the coefficients of x^2 and y^2 are unequal in value but are both positive and so the curve represented is that of an *ellipse*. Finally, if $\epsilon > 1$, the coefficients of the squared terms are unequal and of different sign so that the curve represented is then a *hyperbola*. (You will be asked in an exercise to show why $\epsilon = 0$ corresponds to a *circular* orbit.)

If we restrict our attention to the case of an ellipse, as shown in Fig. I.2, we can compute the length of the major diameter (usually called the major axis) by solving for r from Eq. I.3 with β set equal to zero, separately for $\phi = 0$ and for $\phi = \pi$, and then adding the results Thus:

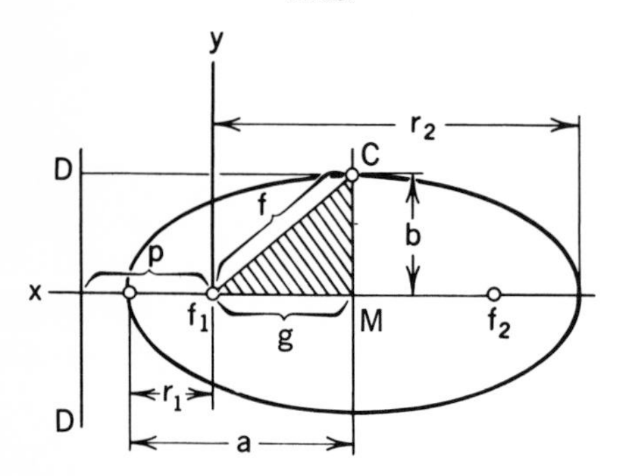

Fig. I.2

$$r_1 = \frac{\epsilon p}{1 + \epsilon}, \qquad r_2 = \frac{\epsilon p}{1 - \epsilon} \tag{I.6}$$

$$\therefore r_1 + r_2 = 2a = \epsilon p \left(\frac{1}{1 + \epsilon} + \frac{1}{1 - \epsilon} \right)$$

Solving for a, we get:

$$\boxed{a = \frac{\epsilon p}{1 - \epsilon^2}} \tag{I.7}$$

The term a is the semimajor diameter. To determine the semiminor diameter, b, we consider point C on the trajectory. Distance r_c is indicated as f in the diagram, and the distance from the focus f_1 to the center at M is g. Using the basic definition of a conic, we can say:

$$\frac{f}{\overline{DC}} = \frac{f}{p + g} = \epsilon \tag{I.8}$$

Noting the shaded right triangle in the diagram, we can write:

$$f = \sqrt{b^2 + g^2} \tag{I.9}$$

By substituting Eq. I.9 into Eq. I.8, squaring both sides, and rearranging, we get:

$$b^2 + g^2 = \epsilon^2 (p + g)^2 \tag{I.10}$$

Observing Fig. I.2 and noting Eq. I.6, we can express the distance g as follows:

$$g = a - r_1 = a - \frac{\epsilon p}{1 + \epsilon} \tag{I.11}$$

Substituting Eq. I.11 into Eq. I.10, we get:

$$b^2 + \left(a - \frac{\epsilon p}{1 + \epsilon} \right)^2 = \epsilon^2 \left(p + a - \frac{\epsilon p}{1 + \epsilon} \right)^2 \tag{I.12}$$

From Eq. I.7 we see that:

$$p = \frac{a}{\epsilon} (1 - \epsilon^2) \tag{I.13}$$

Substituting Eq. I.13 into Eq. I.12, we have:

$$b^2 + \left[a - \frac{a(1 - \epsilon^2)}{1 + \epsilon} \right]^2 = \epsilon^2 \left[\frac{a}{\epsilon} (1 - \epsilon^2) + a - \frac{a(1 - \epsilon^2)}{1 + \epsilon} \right]^2$$

Canceling terms wherever possible, we get the desired result:

$$\boxed{b = a\sqrt{1 - \epsilon^2}} \tag{I.14}$$

Finally, it can be shown by straightforward integration that the area of the ellipse is given as:

$$A = \pi ab \tag{I.15}$$

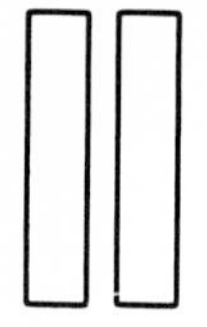

APPENDIX

Work—Kinetic Energy Relation

It is clear that the right side of Eq. 13.32 represents a change of *part* of the kinetic energy of the aggregate of particles. This part of the kinetic energy is related to the work of the external forces on a hypothetical particle having the motion of the mass center. To find the relation between the remaining part of the kinetic energy and the forces, we shall examine the energy equation for the ith particle. Starting with Newton's law, we have:

$$\boldsymbol{F}_i + \sum_{j=1}^{n} \boldsymbol{f}_{ij} = m_i \frac{d\boldsymbol{V}_i}{dt} \qquad \textbf{II.1}$$

where $\boldsymbol{f}_{ij}$ is an internal force from the jth particle onto the ith particle. Next we express the infinitesimal displacement of the ith particle in the following manner:

$$d\boldsymbol{r}_i = d\boldsymbol{r}_c + d\boldsymbol{\rho}_i \qquad \textbf{II.2}$$

where $\boldsymbol{\rho}_i$ is the displacement vector from the center of mass to the ith particle. Now we take the dot product of Eq. II.1, using $d\boldsymbol{r}_i$ for the right side and, noting Eq. II.2, using $d\boldsymbol{r}_c + d\boldsymbol{\rho}_i$ for the left side of the equation. Integrating from position 1 to position 2,

$$\int_1^2 (\boldsymbol{F}_i + \sum_{j=1}^{n} \boldsymbol{f}_{ij}) \cdot (d\boldsymbol{r}_c + d\boldsymbol{\rho}_i) = \int_1^2 \left(m_i \frac{d\boldsymbol{V}_i}{dt}\right) \cdot d\boldsymbol{r}_i \qquad \textbf{II.3}$$

It has already been shown in Section 13.1 that the right side of the above equation is simply the change in kinetic energy of the ith particle. Hence, on summing for all n particles, we see that the right side becomes the total change of kinetic energy for the aggregate of particles. Thus:

$$\sum_{i=1}^{n} \int_1^2 (\boldsymbol{F}_i + \sum_{j=1}^{n} \boldsymbol{f}_{ij}) \cdot (d\boldsymbol{r}_c + d\boldsymbol{\rho}_i) = (KE)_2 - (KE)_1 = (\Delta KE)_{1,2} \qquad \textbf{II.4}$$

Utilizing Eq. 13.30 to replace the right side, we can express this equation as follows:

$$\sum_{i=1}^{n} \int_1^2 (\boldsymbol{F}_i + \sum_{j=1}^{n} \boldsymbol{f}_{ij}) \cdot (d\boldsymbol{r}_c + d\boldsymbol{\rho}_i) = \Delta(\tfrac{1}{2}MV_c^2) + \Delta(\tfrac{1}{2}\sum_{i=1}^{n} m_i\dot{\rho}_i^2) \qquad \textbf{II.5}$$

Carrying out the dot product on the left side, we get:

$$\sum_{i=1}^{n} \int_1^2 \boldsymbol{F}_i \cdot d\boldsymbol{r}_c + \sum_{i=1}^{n} \int_1^2 \boldsymbol{F}_i \cdot d\boldsymbol{\rho}_i + \sum_{i=1}^{n} \int_1^2 \sum_{j=1}^{n} \boldsymbol{f}_{ij} \cdot d\boldsymbol{r}_c + \sum_{i=1}^{n} \int_1^2 \sum_{j=1}^{n} \boldsymbol{f}_{ij} \cdot d\boldsymbol{\rho}_i$$

$$= \Delta(\tfrac{1}{2}MV_c^2) + \Delta(\tfrac{1}{2}\sum_{i=1}^{n} m_i\dot{\rho}_i^2) \qquad \textbf{II.6}$$

It has already been shown (Eq. 13.32) that the first terms on each side of the above equation are equal to each other. Furthermore, the term:

$$\sum_{i=1}^{n} \int_1^2 \sum_{j=1}^{n} \boldsymbol{f}_{ij} \cdot d\boldsymbol{r}_c$$

may be written as

$$\int_1^2 \left(\sum_{i=1}^{n} \sum_{j=1}^{n} \boldsymbol{f}_{ij} \right) \cdot d\boldsymbol{r}_c$$

and since we have already shown in Chapter 12 that

$$\sum_{i=1}^{n} \sum_{j=1}^{n} \boldsymbol{f}_{ij} = \mathbf{0}$$

as a result of Newton's third law, it is clear that we can drop this integral. However, the integral:

$$\sum_{i=1}^{n} \int_1^2 \sum_{j=1}^{n} \boldsymbol{f}_{ij} \cdot d\boldsymbol{\varrho}_i = \int_1^2 \sum_{i=1}^{n} \sum_{j=1}^{n} \boldsymbol{f}_{ij} \cdot d\boldsymbol{\varrho}_i$$

is not necessarily zero, since you are here summing over the dot product of $\boldsymbol{f}_{ij}$ and $d\boldsymbol{\varrho}_i$ and not simply over $\boldsymbol{f}_{ij}$ as was the case for the previous integral. Now $d\boldsymbol{\varrho}_i$ can be different for each particle, and even though the condition of action equaling reaction is present, it cannot be said for the general deformable case that the work:

$$\sum_{i=1}^{n} \sum_{j=1}^{n} \boldsymbol{f}_{ij} \cdot d\boldsymbol{\varrho}_i$$

is identically zero. Thus the above equation can be written as:

$$\sum_{i=1}^{n} \int_1^2 \boldsymbol{F}_i \cdot d\boldsymbol{\varrho}_i + \sum_{i=1}^{n} \int_1^2 \sum_{j=1}^{n} \boldsymbol{f}_{ij} \cdot d\boldsymbol{\varrho}_i = \Delta\left(\tfrac{1}{2} \sum_{i=1}^{n} m_i \dot{\rho}_i^2\right) \qquad \textbf{II.7}$$

Whereas Eq. 13.32 describes the motion of the center of mass in terms of the external forces, the above equation is concerned with the motion of the particles *relative* to the center of mass in terms of both the external and internal forces.

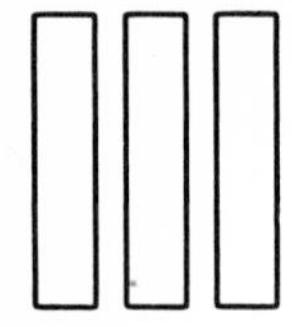

APPENDIX

Proof that Infinitesimal Rotations Are Vectors

You will recall that finite rotations did not qualify as vectors, even though they had magnitude, direction and sense, because they did not combine according to the parallelogram law. Specifically the fact that the combination of finite rotations was not commutative disqualified them as vectors. We shall here show that, in the limit, as rotations become vanishingly small they *do* combine in a commutative manner and accordingly can then be considered as vectors.

Fig. III.1

Accordingly, consider Fig. III.1 showing a rigid body with point P at position $\boldsymbol{r}$ measured from stationary reference XYZ. If the body undergoes a small but finite rotation $\Delta\phi$ about axis AA, point P goes to P' as has been in the diagram. We can express the magnitude of $\Delta\boldsymbol{r}$ between P and P' as follows:

$$|\Delta\boldsymbol{r}| \approx |\boldsymbol{r}| \sin\theta\, \Delta\phi \qquad \textbf{III.1}$$

If we assume, for the moment, that $\Delta\boldsymbol{\phi}$ is a vector having a direction along the axis of rotation consistent with the right-hand rule, we may express the above equation as a vector equation:

$$\Delta\boldsymbol{r} \approx \Delta\boldsymbol{\phi} \times \boldsymbol{r} \qquad \textbf{III.2}$$

In the limit as $\Delta\boldsymbol{\phi} \to 0$ the above relation becomes exact.

Now consider two arbitrary, small but finite rotations represented by proposed vectors $\Delta\boldsymbol{\phi}_1$ and $\Delta\boldsymbol{\phi}_2$. For the first rotation we get a displacement for point P given as:

$$\Delta\boldsymbol{r}_1 \approx \Delta\boldsymbol{\phi}_1 \times \boldsymbol{r} \qquad \textbf{III.3}$$

And for a second successive rotation we get:

$$\begin{aligned}\Delta\boldsymbol{r}_2 &\approx \Delta\boldsymbol{\phi}_2 \times (\boldsymbol{r} + \Delta\boldsymbol{r}_1)\\ &\approx \Delta\boldsymbol{\phi}_2 \times (\boldsymbol{r} + \Delta\boldsymbol{\phi}_1 \times \boldsymbol{r})\end{aligned} \qquad \textbf{III.4}$$

The total displacement for point P is then:

$$\begin{aligned}\Delta\boldsymbol{r}_1 + \Delta\boldsymbol{r}_2 &\approx \Delta\boldsymbol{\phi}_1 \times \boldsymbol{r} + \Delta\boldsymbol{\phi}_2 \times (\boldsymbol{r} + \Delta\boldsymbol{\phi}_1 \times \boldsymbol{r})\\ &\approx \Delta\boldsymbol{\phi}_1 \times \boldsymbol{r} + \Delta\boldsymbol{\phi}_2 \times \boldsymbol{r} + \Delta\boldsymbol{\phi}_2 \times (\Delta\boldsymbol{\phi}_1 \times \boldsymbol{r})\end{aligned} \qquad \textbf{III.5}$$

As the rotations become vanishingly small we can replace the approximate equality sign by an exact equality sign and we can drop the last expression in the above equation. We then have on collecting terms:

$$\Delta\boldsymbol{r}_1 + \Delta\boldsymbol{r}_2 = (\Delta\boldsymbol{\phi}_1 + \Delta\boldsymbol{\phi}_2) \times \boldsymbol{r} \qquad \textbf{III.6}$$

We see from the above equation that the total displacement of any point P for successive infinitesimal rotations is independent of the order of these rotations. Thus, superposition of vanishingly small rotations is commutative and we can now fully accept $\Delta\boldsymbol{\phi}$ as a vector in the limit.

APPENDIX

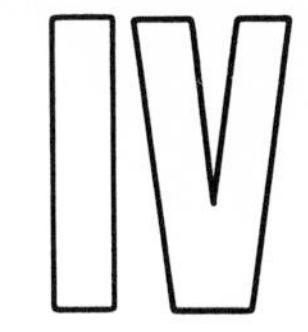

General Proof of Chasle's Theorem

In Chapter 15 we have shown, for plane motion, how a rigid body could be considered at any time to have a translational and a rotational motion, which, when superposed, give the actual motion of the body.

Let us now turn to the *general three-dimensional case*. We shall follow an argument that is similar to the one we used for the coplanar case. That is, a rigid body is shown at two positions Δt apart during a general motion. A point C is chosen in the body and a translation $\Delta \boldsymbol{R}_C$ carried out so as to bring C into the correct position C', as is shown in Fig. IV.1. We

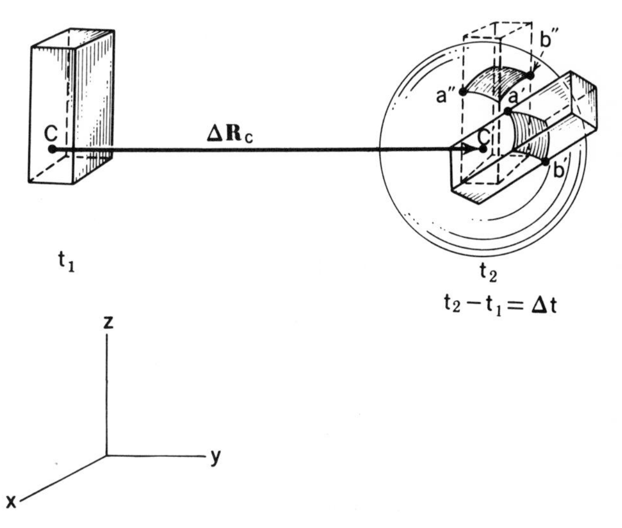

Fig. IV.1

must next prove that a simple rotation about some axis going through point C' will bring the body into the correct position (shown by solid lines) at time t_2. To do so, construct about C' a spherical surface of any convenient radius small enough to cut a portion of the body. On the region cut out by this spherical surface, select two convenient points a' and b' when the body is at the orientation corresponding to time t_2. The corresponding positions for the intermediate position (dashed lines) have been designated with double primes. Since the motion of the sets of points, a', b', C', will represent the motion of the rigid body, considerations after this will be restricted to these points.

In Fig. IV.2 we have redrawn the sphere with points a'', b'', a', b', and C'. We now draw great circles, using solid lines, from a'' to b'' and from a' to b', and, using dashed lines, we draw great circles from a'' to a' and from b'' to b'. We now pass separate planes through point C' so that they are perpendicular bisectors of great-circle arcs $a''a'$ and $b''b'$, respectively. The great-circle traces of these planes have been designated as 1 and 2 in the diagram. Consider plane 1, which forms the perpendicular bisector of arc $a''a'$. Any line in that plane would be equidistant from the points a'' and a' and, consequently, could serve as an axis of rotation so as to rotate point a'' to a'. It should be noted that the arc of motion of the point a'' on its

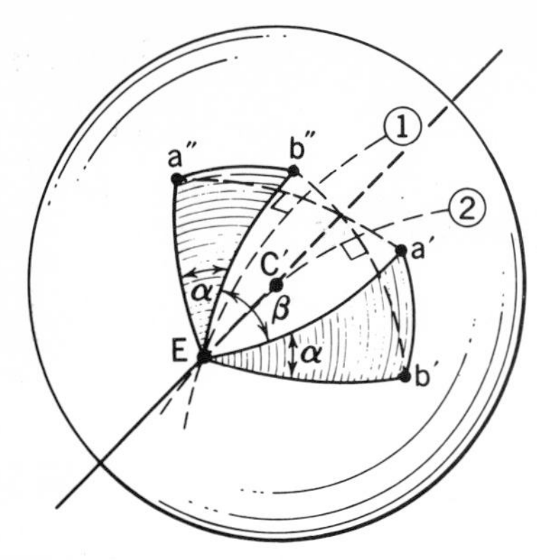

Fig. IV.2

way to a' will not, in the usual case, lie on the spherical surface we have chosen as a convenient reference. The same argument applies to lines in plane 2 serving as possible axes of rotation for the motion of point b'' going to b'. Planes 1 and 2 intersect and form a straight line from C' to a point on the spherical surface designated in the diagram as E. Thus, the line EC' can serve as an axis of rotation for point a' going to a'' and b' going to b''. If we can now show that the rotation about EC' required to get a'' to a' and the rotation about EC' required to get b'' to b' are the same, we will have demonstrated, in effect, that a pure rotation about some axis EC' will bring the body into its final position at time t_2.

To do this, connect point E with the point a'', b'', a', and b', respectively, along great circles forming two spherical triangles, as shown in Fig. IV.2. Since plane 1 is the perpendicular bisector of the great circle between a'' and a', it must be true that arcs $a''E$ and $a'E$ are equal. Similarly, arcs Eb'' and Eb' are equal. Noting that $a''b''$ and $a'b'$ are also the same, owing to the rigidity of the body, we can then see that the two spherical triangles must be congruent. The angles $\sphericalangle a''Eb''$ and $\sphericalangle a'Eb'$ are then equal and have been denoted as α. Another angle $\sphericalangle b''Ea'$ has been denoted as β. The angle of rotation about EC' needed to get a'' into its final position at time t_2 is then $\alpha + \beta$. To get b'' to b' also involves a rotation about EC' of the angle $\beta + \alpha$, as can be readily seen in the diagram. We have thus shown that a single rotation will take the body from the intermediate position, arrived at by translation, to the final position.

We then have associated with point C a displacement $\Delta \boldsymbol{R}_C$ and a rotation $\Delta\phi$ about an axis going through C'. The choice of a point other than C, such as D, would mean a different displacement, $\Delta \boldsymbol{R}_D$, but the same rotation $\Delta\phi$ about a parallel axis going through point D' rather than C'. The latter fact is true because the only difference between the intermediate positions for points C and D is a simple translation, and this would not affect in any way the angle of rotation or the direction of the axis needed to reach the same final position.

As we let the time interval approach zero, we end up with an infinitesimal displacement associated with point C and an infinitesimal rotation. Note that point C undergoes no further motion beyond that incurred during translation in the movement of the body to the final position. Therefore, we can say:

$$\lim_{\Delta t \to 0} \left(\frac{\Delta \boldsymbol{R}_C}{\Delta t} \right) = \boldsymbol{V}_C$$

where $\boldsymbol{V}_C$ is the instantaneous velocity of point C of the body. We can also say:

$$\lim_{\Delta t \to 0} \left(\frac{\Delta \phi}{\Delta t} \right) = |\,\boldsymbol{\omega}\,|$$

where $\boldsymbol{\omega}$ may be considered a free vector, since it is the instantaneous angular-velocity vector of the body for all reference points C.

From this discussion, we can conclude that the motion of a rigid body relative to a reference at any time t can be described in the following manner:

a. Choose any point C in the body.

b. Assume that the entire rigid body has the velocity $\boldsymbol{V}_C$.

c. Superpose the proper angular rotation $\boldsymbol{\omega}$ about an axis going through point C. The vector $\boldsymbol{\omega}$ at time t is independent of the reference point C.

APPENDIX

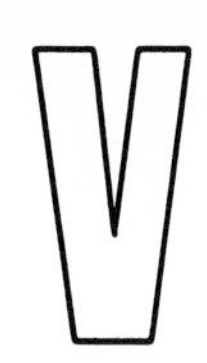

Table of Properties of Various Homogeneous Solids

$$V = abc$$

$$I_{AA} = \frac{1}{12}M(a^2 + b^2)$$

$$k_{AA} = \sqrt{\frac{a^2 + b^2}{12}}$$

$$I_{BB} = \frac{1}{12}M(b^2 + c^2)$$

$$k_{BB} = \sqrt{\frac{b^2 + c^2}{12}}$$

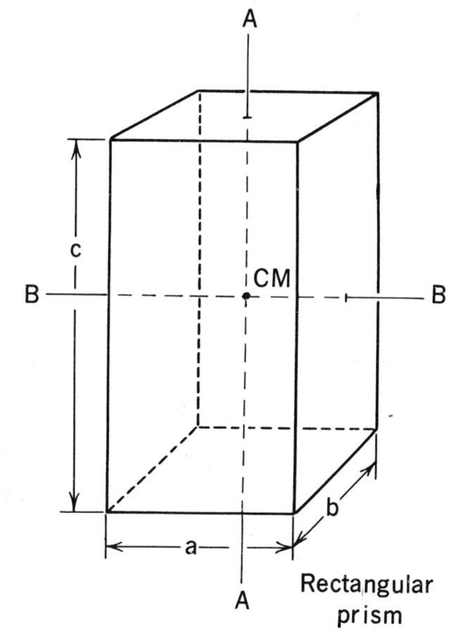

Fig. V.1

$$V = \frac{4}{3}\pi r^3$$

$$I_{AA} = \frac{2}{5}Mr^2$$

$$k_{AA} = \frac{2r}{\sqrt{10}}$$

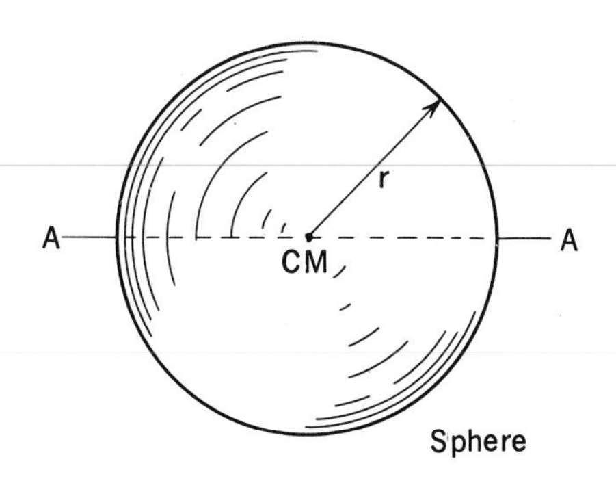

Fig. V.2

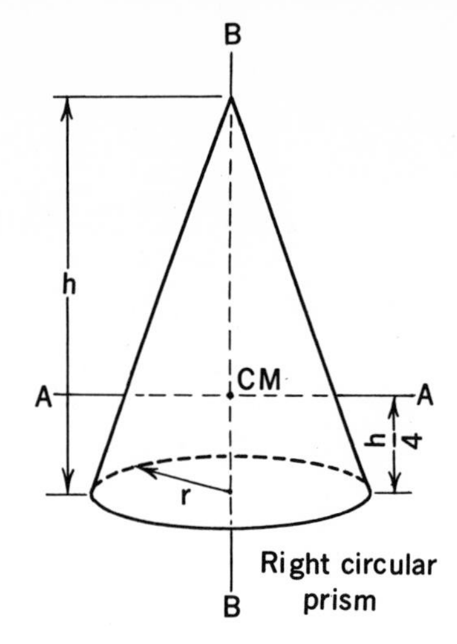

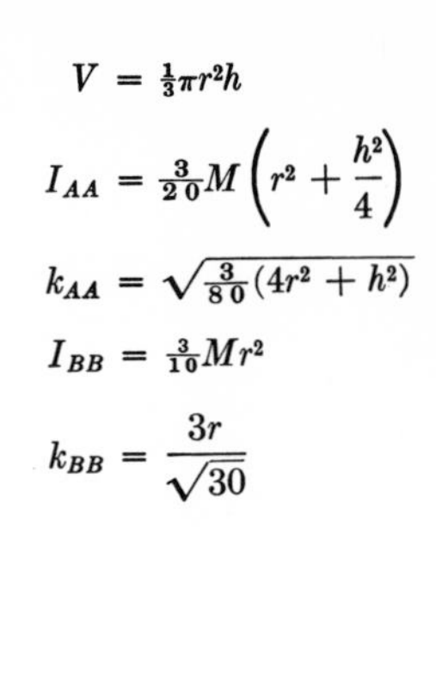

$$V = \tfrac{1}{3}\pi r^2 h$$

$$I_{AA} = \tfrac{3}{20}M\left(r^2 + \frac{h^2}{4}\right)$$

$$k_{AA} = \sqrt{\tfrac{3}{80}(4r^2 + h^2)}$$

$$I_{BB} = \tfrac{3}{10}Mr^2$$

$$k_{BB} = \frac{3r}{\sqrt{30}}$$

Fig. V.3

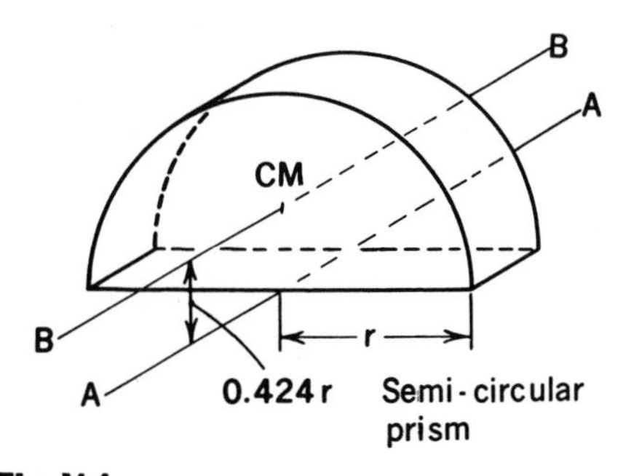

$$I_{AA} = \tfrac{1}{2}Mr^2$$

$$I_{BB} = 0.320Mr^2$$

Fig. V.4

SELECTED ANSWERS TO PROBLEMS

CHAPTER 11

2. (a) $1280t^3\boldsymbol{i} + 600t^2\boldsymbol{j} - 640t\boldsymbol{k}$
(b) $64t^5\boldsymbol{i} + 50t^4\boldsymbol{j} - 106.7t^3\boldsymbol{k} + \boldsymbol{C}$

3. $192t + 30$, $(60 - 96t)\boldsymbol{k}$,
$32t^3 + 15t^2 + C$,
$-48t\boldsymbol{i} + 96t\boldsymbol{j} +$
$(30t^2 - 16t^3)\boldsymbol{k} + \boldsymbol{C}$

4. $(10 - 6t)\boldsymbol{i} - 6t^2\boldsymbol{j}$,
$(5t^2 + t^3)\boldsymbol{i} - (\frac{1}{2}t^4 + 3t)\boldsymbol{j} -$
$6t\boldsymbol{k} + \boldsymbol{C}$, $-90t^2$,
$-60\boldsymbol{j} - (30t^4 + 18t)\boldsymbol{k} - 36t^2\boldsymbol{i}$,
$-15t^4/2 + C$,
$-(3t^4 + 18t)\boldsymbol{i} - 30t^2\boldsymbol{j} -$
$(t^6 + 3t^3)\boldsymbol{k} + \boldsymbol{C}$

8. $\boldsymbol{K} = -5313\boldsymbol{i} - 3\boldsymbol{j} - 105\boldsymbol{k}$

9. $(2t^3 + 10t)\boldsymbol{i} - 3\cos t\boldsymbol{j} +$
$2t^2\boldsymbol{k} + \boldsymbol{K}$

10. $(3\cosh 2t - 30t)\boldsymbol{i} +$
$(100t + 2\cos 3t)\boldsymbol{j} -$
$(\cos 3t + 5\cosh 2t)\boldsymbol{k} + \boldsymbol{C}$

11. $\boldsymbol{B} = 112\boldsymbol{i} + 24\boldsymbol{k}$

12. $\boldsymbol{B} = 222\boldsymbol{j} + 32\boldsymbol{k}$
$dA/dt = 120\boldsymbol{j}$

14. $\ddot{\boldsymbol{r}} = 60\boldsymbol{i} + 500\boldsymbol{j} + 10\boldsymbol{k}$ ft/sec²

15. $\boldsymbol{a}(5) = -10\boldsymbol{i} + 2.83\boldsymbol{j} - 7.91\boldsymbol{k}$

20. 54.7 miles

23. 6.62 ft/sec²

24. $\boldsymbol{a} = 10\boldsymbol{i} - 6.80\boldsymbol{j}$ ft/sec²

25. $\ddot{x} = -0.325$ ft/sec²
$\ddot{y} = -0.187$ ft/sec²

26. $\ddot{x} = -0.175$ ft/sec²
$\ddot{y} = -2.78$ ft/sec²

29. $\boldsymbol{a}_1 = 12.5\boldsymbol{j}$ ft/sec²
$\boldsymbol{a}_2 = 21.7\boldsymbol{i} - 12.5\boldsymbol{j}$ ft/sec²
$\boldsymbol{a}_3 = 0$

30. $\boldsymbol{a}_1 = 103.5\boldsymbol{i} + 215\boldsymbol{j}$ ft/sec²
$\boldsymbol{a}_2 = 1416\boldsymbol{i} - 591\boldsymbol{j}$ ft/sec²
$\boldsymbol{a}_3 = -273\boldsymbol{j}$ ft/sec²

31. $\boldsymbol{a} = -0.0222\boldsymbol{i} + 0.00074\boldsymbol{j}$

36. $\boldsymbol{a} = -0.273\boldsymbol{j} + 0.049\boldsymbol{i}$ ft/sec²

37. 16 ft/sec²

38. 56 ft/sec²

40. $a_{\min} = 1.25$ ft/sec²,
$a_{\max} = 10$ ft/sec²

41. $\boldsymbol{a} = -10.96\boldsymbol{i} - 20\boldsymbol{j} - 0.48\boldsymbol{k}$
ft/sec²

42. $\boldsymbol{\varepsilon}_0 = -0.437\boldsymbol{i} + 0.219\boldsymbol{j} +$
$0.873\boldsymbol{k}$

43. $\boldsymbol{V} = 2.93\boldsymbol{\varepsilon}_{\bar{r}} + 4.05\boldsymbol{\varepsilon}_z$ ft/sec

44. $R_{\min} = 13{,}520$ ft

46. $-150\pi^2\boldsymbol{\varepsilon}_{\bar{r}} - 73.4\boldsymbol{\varepsilon}_z$ ft/sec²

47. $-4\boldsymbol{\varepsilon}_{\bar{r}}$ ft/sec²

48. $-169\boldsymbol{\varepsilon}_{\bar{r}} + \boldsymbol{\varepsilon}_\phi + (1/48\pi)\boldsymbol{\varepsilon}_z$

49. $-140\boldsymbol{\varepsilon}_{\bar{r}} - 79.5\boldsymbol{\varepsilon}_\phi$ ft/sec²

51. $N\boldsymbol{i} - (V_0^2/A)\boldsymbol{j}$

52. $-1875\boldsymbol{\varepsilon}_{\bar{r}} - 1080\boldsymbol{\varepsilon}_\phi$ ft/sec³

54. $5\boldsymbol{\varepsilon}_t + 6\boldsymbol{\varepsilon}_n$

55. $-6\boldsymbol{\varepsilon}_{\bar{r}} + 5\boldsymbol{\varepsilon}_\phi$

73. 0.389 lb-ft

75. 65.4 lb

80. $T = (W/g)l\omega^2$
$d = g/\omega^2$

81. $\omega = 9.64$ rad/sec

82. $K = 68.2y/(y - y_0)$

83. $x = 0.403$ ft
$x = 7.66$ ft

Selected Answers to Problems

CHAPTER 12

1. 30.6 ft

4. 6.22 sec

5. 6.06 sec

6. $7.5\boldsymbol{i} + 20\boldsymbol{j} - 11.5\boldsymbol{k}$

7. $10\boldsymbol{i} + 8\boldsymbol{j} + 7\boldsymbol{k}$

9. 0.34 ft

10. 3063 ft

11. $\dot{x} = 96.7$ ft/sec
$x = 64.1$ ft

13. $x = 73{,}800$ ft; $\dot{x} = 464$ ft/sec

19. 1.072 sec

21. $\boldsymbol{V}(1) = (-1/e + 1)\boldsymbol{i} - (-4/e + 4)\boldsymbol{j} + (8e^2 - 8)\boldsymbol{k}$

22. 0.18 ft

24. 0.802 ft/sec

25. 0.822 ft/sec

37. 62.3 ft

38. 37.9 ft

42. $-0.85\boldsymbol{i} + 0.53\boldsymbol{j}$

44. 12,700 mph

45. 27.3×10^{10} ft^2/sec

46. $1/r = 0.255 \times 10^{-3} + 0.389 \times 10^{-6} \cos(\phi + 135°)$ miles^{-1}

47. 4.14×10^{23} slugs
$2.42 \times 10^{-19}\left(1 - \dfrac{14.3 \times 10^{15}}{r_0 (V_\phi)_0^2}\right)^{-1}$ %

49. $\epsilon = 0.199$; $d_{max} = 2290$ miles; 1 hr 4 min; 24,500 mph

50. 11,380 mph

51. 9410 mph; 5.42 hr; 4820 miles

53. $\Delta V = 1935$ ft/sec; 44 min

55. $\Delta V_1 = 1100$ ft/sec; $\Delta V_2 = 1000$ ft/sec

56. 194,500 mph

59. 575 hr

60. 2770 miles

61. $r_{max} = 17{,}120$ miles (pole);
$r_{max} = 30{,}900$ miles (equator)

63. 40 miles

65. 500 ft/sec

66. $100\boldsymbol{\varepsilon}_\phi - 964\boldsymbol{\varepsilon}_r$ ft/sec

68. No orbit; radius vector swings 243°.

70. $x = V_0\sqrt{2h/g}$; $t = \sqrt{2h/g}$

71. 142,000 ft

72. $d = 13$ ft

73. 77.6°

74. 71.4°

75. 2.03×10^5 ft

76. $y = 586$ ft

77. $12.4 \sin\alpha + 2.73 \sin\alpha = 3$; $\alpha = 6.3°$

78. $0.124 \sin\alpha \times [4 \times 10^4 \cos^2\alpha - 1936]^{1/2} - 2.73 \sin\alpha = 3$
$\alpha = 8.3°$; $\beta = 12.9°$

83. $y_{max} = 292$ ft; $\alpha = -9.5°$; $x = 9890$ ft

85. If $\alpha < \dfrac{GV}{g}$,

$$y_{max} = \frac{V_0\alpha_0}{G} + \frac{g}{G^2} \ln \frac{g}{g + GV_0\alpha_0}$$

93. $(27.5\boldsymbol{i} - 2.94\boldsymbol{j} + 1.06\boldsymbol{k}) \times 10^7$ newtons

94. $(22.3\boldsymbol{i} - 9.6\boldsymbol{j} + 1.602\boldsymbol{k}) \times 10^{-15}$ newtons

96. $x = 2.39 \times 10^{-5}$ cm

97. Circle in xy plane.
$R = 5.68 \times 10^{-16}$ meters

98. Speed $= \dfrac{V_0}{B_0 d}$;

$$\frac{e}{m} = -\frac{2V_0\delta}{B_0^2 ld(l + 2L)}$$

99. 0.637 cm above x axis

100. $V = ct/\sqrt{(m_0c/eE)^2 + t^2}$
$x = c\sqrt{(m_0c/eE)^2 + t^2} - \frac{m_0c^2}{eE}$

101. $x = 0;$
$y = -(Em/B^2e)\cos(eB/m)t + \frac{Em}{eB^2};$
$z = \frac{Em}{eB^2}\sin\frac{eB}{m}t - \frac{E}{B}t$

103. 1.48 cm

104. $\boldsymbol{r}_c = 3.70\boldsymbol{i} + 4.27\boldsymbol{j} + 4.35\boldsymbol{k}$ ft
$\boldsymbol{V}_c = 4.87\boldsymbol{i} + 1.305\boldsymbol{j} + 1.435\boldsymbol{k}$ ft/sec

105. $2500\boldsymbol{i} + 130.5\boldsymbol{j} - 686\boldsymbol{k}$ ft

109. $\boldsymbol{F} = -5830\boldsymbol{k}$ lb

CHAPTER 13

1. 41.2 lb
2. 34.8 ft/sec
3. 1581 ft-lb
4. 13.23 ft/sec
6. 1.465 ft/sec; $x = 1$ in.
7. 6.03 ft/sec
11. 1.52 ft
12. 5 in.
13. 1 in.
14. 1306 ft-lb
18. 3980 lb
19. 3780 lb
20. 59.1 ft/sec
21. 72.1 ft/sec
24. 9640 ft-lb
26. 0.288 ft
28. 2
30. 16,000 HP
31. 56.2 lb
32. 0.241 rev.
35. 16.35 kw
39. 60.5 sec
40. 65.5 sec
41. 17.5 ft above ground
42. 3.40 ft/sec
43. 5.53 ft/sec; $x^3 - 4x^2 - 60x - 384 = 0$
44. 9130 lb
45. 45°
46. −718 ft-lb
56. 6.72 ft/sec
57. 6.82 ft/sec
61. 27.5 ft/sec
69. 0.364 HP; 0.909 HP
70. 15.50 ft/sec
76. 9.82 ft/sec
77. $V = \sqrt{(g/L)(L^2 - a^2)}$
82. 32.9 ft-lb
83. $\frac{3}{4}MV^2$
84. 25.4 ft/sec
85. $\frac{1}{2}MV_c^2 + \frac{1}{4}[1 + (d_1/d_2)^2]MV^2$
86. 1.96%
87. 6°45′
88. $0.7\,MV_c^2$
90. 583 ft-lb
92. 265 ft-lb

CHAPTER 14

1. 2.04 sec
2. $333\boldsymbol{i} + 400\boldsymbol{j} + 4000\boldsymbol{k}$ ft/sec
3. 178.5 ft/sec
4. 1.55 sec; 0.622 sec
7. $(0.160\boldsymbol{i} - 0.180\boldsymbol{j} + 0.60\boldsymbol{k})t$
9. $-0.964\boldsymbol{i} - 0.388\boldsymbol{j} + 0.097\boldsymbol{k}$
10. 0.622 sec
13. $V = 20/\pi$ ft/sec; $t = 0.137$ sec; 9.89 lb-sec

15. 185 ft/sec

16. 3.11 ft/sec

18. 2310 lb

20. 20.6 lb

23. 7.58 sec; 13.3 sec; 5140 lb

24. 185.2 ft/sec

25. 3.11 ft/sec

26. 65.6 ft/sec

27. 100.0 ft/sec

28. 26.9 ft/sec

29. 24.8 lb

36. 77.5 lb

37. 0.179 ft

41. 10 ft

42. 3.61 ft

43. 5 lb wt, 30°; 3 lb wt, 5.5°

46. 12.05 ft-lb

48. 0.459

49. 0.773 ft

51. 1.031 ft

52. 50 ft/sec; 36.4 ft/sec

53. 3.56 ft/sec; 9.19 ft/sec

56. 400 lb-sec

57. For 5 lb wt, $y = 0.963$ ft
For 10 lb wt, $y = 0.493$ ft
(y from eq. pos. of 5 lb wt)

60. 50.5°

61. $\boldsymbol{V}_2 = -10\boldsymbol{i} - 10\boldsymbol{j} + 12\boldsymbol{k}$
$\boldsymbol{V}_3 = 8\boldsymbol{i} - 10\boldsymbol{j} + 12\boldsymbol{k}$
$\boldsymbol{V}_4 = 8\boldsymbol{i} + 8\boldsymbol{j} + 12\boldsymbol{k}$

62. xy plane: $y = 4$, $z = 3.6$
xz plane: $x = 3.2$, $z = 8.4$

63. $3.53\ mnV^2$

64. $2.97\ mnV^2$

65. $0.468\ mnV^2$

68. 5 lb

70. 26.6 ft

76. 120.1 ft/sec

79. 2050 ft/sec

80. 4040 miles

94. -20 rad/sec²

95. 1.304 rad/sec

96. $d\omega/dt = (T - 8m\omega s_2 V_1)/4m(s_1^2 + s_2^2)$

CHAPTER 15

4. $10.66\boldsymbol{i} + 7.31\boldsymbol{j} - 35.2\boldsymbol{k}$

14. $\dot{\boldsymbol{\omega}} = -0.68\boldsymbol{i} + 1.880\boldsymbol{j}$

17. $3820\boldsymbol{i}$

18. $\boldsymbol{\omega} = -7.74\boldsymbol{j}$;
$\dot{\boldsymbol{\omega}} = 15.5\boldsymbol{i} - 11.62\boldsymbol{j}$

19. $\boldsymbol{\omega} = 42.9\boldsymbol{j} - 42.9\boldsymbol{k}$

20. $\dot{\boldsymbol{\omega}} = -1345\boldsymbol{i} + 2.74\boldsymbol{j} - 2.75\boldsymbol{k}$

21. $\boldsymbol{\omega} = 18.99\boldsymbol{j} - 15.21\boldsymbol{k}$
$\dot{\boldsymbol{\omega}} = -276\boldsymbol{i}$

22. $\dot{\boldsymbol{\omega}} = -28.2\boldsymbol{i} + 3.73\boldsymbol{j} - 1.72\boldsymbol{k}$

27. $-141\boldsymbol{i} + 212\boldsymbol{j} - 50\boldsymbol{k}$ ft/sec

28. $-245\boldsymbol{i} + 210\boldsymbol{j} + 25\boldsymbol{k}$

29. $-361\boldsymbol{i} - 75\boldsymbol{j} + 250\boldsymbol{k}$ ft/sec

30. 200 ft/sec; 400 ft/sec; 200 ft/sec

34. $85.4\boldsymbol{i} - 35.4\boldsymbol{j}$ ft/sec

35. $\boldsymbol{V}_B = 20\boldsymbol{j}$ ft/sec;
$\boldsymbol{V}_D = 20\boldsymbol{j} + 20\boldsymbol{k}$ ft/sec

36. $\boldsymbol{V}_B = 5\boldsymbol{i} - 5\boldsymbol{j}$ ft/sec

37. $\boldsymbol{V}_D = -10.29\boldsymbol{i} + 6.30\boldsymbol{j}$

40. -2 ft/sec

42. $\dot{\omega}_{AB} = 16.45$ rad/sec²

44. $\omega_{GC} = 1.190$ rad/sec;
$\boldsymbol{V}_D = 5.84\boldsymbol{i} + 7.22\boldsymbol{j}$ ft/sec

46. $\boldsymbol{V}_C = -0.4\boldsymbol{i} - 11.30\boldsymbol{j}$ ft/sec;
$\boldsymbol{a}_C = -94.7\boldsymbol{i} - 154.3\boldsymbol{j}$ ft/sec

47. $\boldsymbol{V}_B = -41.2\boldsymbol{j} - 23.8\boldsymbol{k}$ ft/sec;
$\boldsymbol{\omega} = -10.35\boldsymbol{i}$ rad/sec

48. $\boldsymbol{V}_A = 80\boldsymbol{j}$ ft/sec; $\boldsymbol{\omega}_{AB} = -54.9\boldsymbol{k}$

49. $\boldsymbol{V}_B = 34.1\boldsymbol{i} - 14.14\boldsymbol{j}$ ft/sec;
$\boldsymbol{\omega}_{AB} = 2.24\boldsymbol{k}$ rad/sec

50. $\boldsymbol{a}_B = -141.4\boldsymbol{i} - 141.4\boldsymbol{j}$ ft/sec

51. $\boldsymbol{V}_B = 30.6\boldsymbol{i} - 10.6\boldsymbol{j}$ ft/sec;
$\boldsymbol{\omega}_{AB} = 2.02\boldsymbol{k}$ rad/sec

53. $0.44\boldsymbol{i}$ rad/sec²

54. $-5\boldsymbol{i} - 47\boldsymbol{j} - 17.1\boldsymbol{k}$ ft/sec

55. $50\boldsymbol{j}$ rad/sec²

56. $-20.3\boldsymbol{j} - 17\boldsymbol{k}$ ft/sec²

57. $-25\boldsymbol{i} + 900\boldsymbol{k}$ ft/sec²

60. -2.11 rad/sec

62. 4.93 ft/sec

63. 14.04 rad/sec

77. 38.0 ft/sec; 9.82 ft/sec

78. 40.6 ft/sec; 12.05 ft/sec

79. -11.80 ft/sec; 22.26 ft/sec

80. 14.72 ft/sec; 28.1 ft/sec

83. $\boldsymbol{V} = -17.32\boldsymbol{i} - 10\boldsymbol{j} - 50\boldsymbol{k}$ ft/sec
$\boldsymbol{a} = 2600\boldsymbol{i} - 173.2\boldsymbol{j} - 1732\boldsymbol{k}$ ft/sec²

84. $\boldsymbol{V} = 52.4\boldsymbol{i} - 1.25\boldsymbol{j}$ ft/sec

85. $\boldsymbol{V}_b = 5\boldsymbol{\varepsilon}_{\bar{r}} + 30\boldsymbol{\varepsilon}_\phi$ ft/sec
$\boldsymbol{a}_b = -300\boldsymbol{\varepsilon}_{\bar{r}} + 115\boldsymbol{\varepsilon}_\phi$ ft/sec
$\boldsymbol{a}_b = -115\boldsymbol{i} - 300\boldsymbol{j}$

86. $4\boldsymbol{i} + 5.6\boldsymbol{j} + 0.4\boldsymbol{k}$ ft/sec

88. $\boldsymbol{V}_{XYZ} = -47\boldsymbol{j} - 17\boldsymbol{k} - 5\boldsymbol{i}$ ft/sec

89. $\boldsymbol{V}_{XYZ} = -142\boldsymbol{j} - 17\boldsymbol{k}$ ft/sec

90. $\boldsymbol{V}_{XYZ} = 75.3\boldsymbol{i} - 2\boldsymbol{k}$ ft/sec

91. $\boldsymbol{V}_{XYZ} = 75.3\boldsymbol{i} + 10\boldsymbol{j} - 2\boldsymbol{k}$ ft/sec

92. $-37.5\boldsymbol{i}$ ft/sec

93. $(\boldsymbol{V}_c)_{XYZ} = 151.6\boldsymbol{i}$ ft/sec

95. $(\boldsymbol{V}_a)_{XYZ} = 72.3\boldsymbol{k}$ ft/sec

103. $\boldsymbol{V}_{XYZ} = 10\boldsymbol{j} - 30\boldsymbol{i}$
$\boldsymbol{a}_{XYZ} = -215\boldsymbol{i} - 299\boldsymbol{j}$

104. $\boldsymbol{V}_{XYZ} = 50\boldsymbol{i} - 5\boldsymbol{j} - 20\boldsymbol{k}$ ft/sec
$\boldsymbol{a}_{XYZ} = -100\boldsymbol{i} - 300\boldsymbol{j} - 35\boldsymbol{k}$ ft/sec²

105. $\boldsymbol{a}_{XYZ} = -50\boldsymbol{i} - 305\boldsymbol{j} - 35\boldsymbol{k}$ ft/sec²

106. 1.755 g

107. $\boldsymbol{a}_{XYZ} = -198.3\boldsymbol{i} - 10\boldsymbol{j} + 68.7\boldsymbol{k}$

108. $\boldsymbol{a}_{XYZ} = -113\boldsymbol{i} - 141.3\boldsymbol{j} - 169.8\boldsymbol{k}$ ft/sec²

110. $\boldsymbol{a}_{XYZ} = -71.6\boldsymbol{i} + 20\boldsymbol{j} - 20\boldsymbol{k}$ ft/sec²

118. $\boldsymbol{a}_{XYZ} = 3.64\boldsymbol{i} + 50.4\boldsymbol{j} - 4.13\boldsymbol{k}$ ft/sec²

120. $\omega_B = 7.3$ rad/sec;
$\omega_A = 3.48$ rad/sec

132. Axial force 4.77 lb T;
shear is $1.594\boldsymbol{i} - 0.25\boldsymbol{k}$;
moment is $1.595\boldsymbol{k} + 0.25\boldsymbol{i}$

133. $F_{\text{radial}} = 4.82$ lb

134. $T = 6.14$ lb; 20 lb-ft

135. $-4.18V_{xyz}\boldsymbol{i}$ ft/sec²

CHAPTER 16

1. $I_{yy} = \frac{1}{12}M(a^2 + b^2)$;
$I_{zz} = \frac{1}{12}M(b^2 + l^2)$
$I_{xx} = \frac{1}{12}M(a^2 + l^2)$;
$I_{xy} = 0$

2. $I_{xx} = \frac{1}{12}Ml^2$; $I_{x'x'} = \frac{1}{3}Ml^2$

3. $I_{zz} = \frac{1}{2}Mr^2$; $I_{xx} = M(\frac{1}{4}r^2 + \frac{1}{3}l^2)$

4. $I_{zz} = \frac{3}{10}Mr^2$

5. $I_{xy} = Mr^2$

6. $MR^2/2$

7. 17.2 slugs-ft²

8. $I_{xx} = 4330$ lbm-ft²
$I_{x'x'} = 15{,}330$ lbm-ft²

9. $I_{zz} = 267{,}000$ lbm-ft²
$I_{xx} = 3{,}950{,}000$ lbm-ft²

10. 17,250 lbm-ft²

11. $I_{yy} = 65.7$ lbm-ft²
$I_{yz} = 80.9$ lbm-ft²

13. $I_{yy} = 18.65$ slugs-ft²
$I_{zz} = 106.3$ slugs-ft²
$I_{xx} = 119$ slugs-ft²
$I_{xy} = 0$
$I_{yz} = -31.1$ slugs-ft²
$I_{xz} = 0$

15. $I_{xy} = -\dfrac{Mbc}{80}$

17. $10{,}856\pi$ lbm-ft²

18. $k = 2.52$ ft

19. $I_{xy} = -1328$ slugs-in.^{2}; $I_{yy} = 6660$ slugs-in.^{2}

20. $I_{yy} = 1610$ lbm-in.^{2}; $I_{xx} = 8100$ lbm-in.^{2}; $I_{xy} = 1280$ lbm-in.^{2}

21. $I_{z'z'} = 2015$ lbm-ft^2

22. $I_{x'z'} = -2800$ lbm-ft^2

23. $I_{dd} = 281$ lbm-in.^{2}

24. $I_{x'y'} = 0$

25. $I_{z'z'} = 49.2$ lbm-ft^2

27. $I_{cc} = 735$ lbm-ft^2

28. 19.1 psi

29. 3022 lbm-ft^2

30. 130 lbm-ft^2

36. 1116 psi

CHAPTER 17

2. $\boldsymbol{H} = 12\pi\boldsymbol{j} + 2.04\pi\boldsymbol{k}$ slug-ft^2/sec

4. $\boldsymbol{H} = \frac{1}{2}(Mr^2\omega_2^2)\boldsymbol{j} + M\omega_1[(3r^2 + a^2)/12 + (c + \frac{1}{2}a)^2]\boldsymbol{k}$

5. $\boldsymbol{H}_D = 1.457\boldsymbol{i} + 51.3\boldsymbol{j}$ slug-ft^2/sec

6. $\boldsymbol{H} = 1955\boldsymbol{i} + 39{,}200\boldsymbol{j}$ lbm-ft^2/sec

7. $-451\boldsymbol{i} - 768\boldsymbol{j} - 452\boldsymbol{k}$ slugs-ft^2/sec

8. $\boldsymbol{H}_c = -616\boldsymbol{i} - 274\boldsymbol{j}$ lbm-ft^2/sec

10. $\boldsymbol{H}_0 = 8.34\boldsymbol{i} + 166.6\boldsymbol{j}$ lbm-ft^2/sec

11. $\Delta\omega_1 = 1.510$ rad/sec; $\Delta\omega_2 = 0.12$ rad/sec

12. 98.2 rad/sec^2

13. 28.5 rad/sec^2

14. 390 lb

15. $A_Y = -32{,}000$; $A_X = B_X = 0$; $B_Z = 20{,}160$ lb; $A_Z = -19{,}840$ lb

16. 0.625 rad/sec^2

18. $\boldsymbol{M} = 10\boldsymbol{i} - 25\boldsymbol{k}$ lb-ft; $\dot{\omega}_1 = -10$ rad/sec^2

19. $\boldsymbol{M} = 9.25\boldsymbol{i} - 27.5\boldsymbol{k}$; $\dot{\omega}_1 = -10$ rad/sec^2

20. $-1296\boldsymbol{k}$ lb-ft

21. $\boldsymbol{M} = 2178\boldsymbol{i}$ lb-ft; $T = 25{,}000$ lb; $V = 32.2$ lb

22. $M_B = -2180$ lb-ft; $V = 32.2$ lb; $F_T = 25{,}000$ lb

24. $B_y = 29.9$ lb, $B_z = -9.32$ lb; $A_y = 23.5$ lb, $A_z = -4.68$ lb

25. $D_y = 83$ lb, $D_z = -1.432$ lb; $C_y = 276$ lb, $C_z = -4.78$ lb

26. $A_y = 17.70$ lb, $A_z = 25$ lb; $B_y = 32.3$ lb, $B_z = -25$ lb

27. $A_x = -21.8$ lb; $A_y = 100$ lb; $A_z = 0$

30. $B_X = -A_X = 27.9$ lb; $A_Y = 0$; $A_Z = B_Z = 12.5$ lb

31. $\dot{\omega} = 72.5$ rad/sec^2; $B_Z = 7.45$ lb; $A_Z = 17.55$ lb; $A_X = -B_X = -27.9$ lb

33. $-3.52\boldsymbol{k}$ rad/sec; 700 lb-ft normal to plane of OB and BC.

35. $\boldsymbol{M} = (-1470 \sin 0.419t)\boldsymbol{i} + (32{,}600 \cos 0.419t)\boldsymbol{j}$ lb-ft

37. $\theta_3 = 192.2°$; $W_3 = 1.092$ lb; $\theta_4 = 249°$; $W_4 = 1.892$ lb

38. $\theta_A = 249°$; $\theta_B = 192.2°$; $r_A = 1.260$ ft; $r_B = 1.092$ lb

39. $y_C = 5.67$ in., $z_C = 0$; $y_D = -0.67$ in., $z_D = 0$

40. $\theta_C = 180°$, $\theta_D = 0$; $W_C = -2.63$ lb, $W_D = -1.125$ lb

41. $y_C = -0.657$ ft, $y_D = -0.0938$ ft; $z_C = -0.531$ ft, $z_D = -1.594$ ft

51. 6.55 rad/sec

52. 6.68 lb

53. 3.12 rad/sec, 0.00517 sec

58. $P = 138.8$ lb

59. $N_1 = 3114$ lb, $N_2 = 1216$ lb; $f_1 = 2460$ lb, $f_2 = 963$ lb

60. 9.8 ft/sec²

61. −12.13 ft/sec², 1.04 rad/sec²

62. $F_x = 87.5$ lb, $F_y = 170$ lb

66. 3.27 ft

67. $N_A = 34.5$ lb, $N_B = 51.3$ lb

68. $N_A = 17.1$ lb, $N_B = 38.9$ lb

72. $F_a = 60.4$ lb, $F_b = 116$ lb

73. 6.46 rad/sec²

74. 8.65 ft/sec²

75. 1437 lb, 124 ft/sec²

76. 302 ft/sec

77. 26.0 ft/sec

78. 0.877 rad/sec²
1.507 lb

79. 105 rad/sec

80. 329 rad/sec

83. 4.68 ft/sec², 1.562 rad/sec²

84. $d > 2.28$ ft

86. 10.50 ft

87. 2961 lb-ft, 2690 lb-ft

88. 10.1 ft/sec²

89. 1.4 ft down conveyor; 15.2 ft down conveyor;
32.2 ft/sec²

90. 7.4 ft/sec² down incline

98. lower rod $\dot{\omega} = -6.9$ rad/sec²;
upper rod $\dot{\omega} = 4.6$ rad/sec²

99. 27.2 rad/sec²

CHAPTER 18

1. 620 ft-lb

2. 307 ft-lb

3. 7100 ft-lb

4. 60,000 ft-lb

5. 185.9 ft-lb

6. $10.68\, M_{AE} + 31.5\, M_{CD}$ ft-lb

7. 4.60 ft-lb

8. (a) 34.5 ft-lb
(b) 3.72 ft-lb

9. 12.26 ft-lb

10. 15.52 ft-lb

11. 10.34 ft-lb

12. 15.58 ft-lb

13. 661 ft-lb

14. 34.6 ft-lb

15. 44.8 ft-lb

16. 3900 ft-lb

17. 150.4 ft-lb

18. (a) 1.125 ft-lb
(b) 76.8 ft-lb

19. 5.64 ft-lb

20. 28,800 ft-lb

21. 165.2 ft-lb

22. 1,631,000 ft-lb

23. 127,800 ft-lb

24. 583 ft-lb

25. 16,100 ft-lb

26. 10,350 ft-lb

28. $\omega = \left[\dfrac{8aW_2g}{3W_1r^2 + 2W_2(r-a)^2}\right]^{1/2}$

29. 20.7 ft/sec

30. $\dot{\theta} = \left[\dfrac{4W\sin\theta - Kl(1-\cos\theta)^2}{\frac{5}{3}(W/g)l}\right]^{1/2}$

31. 3.66 rad/sec

33. $\ddot{\theta} + \dfrac{Ka^2 + (Wl/2)}{\frac{1}{3}(W/g)l^2}\,\theta = 0$

34. $\theta = 38.5°$; Max. defl. = 0.616 ft

35. (a) 6.37 ft (b) 17.68 ft

36. 5.33 ft/sec

37. 4.36 rad/sec

38. 6.30 ft/sec

39. 1.32 ft/sec

40. 2.87 rad/sec

41. 2.21 rad/sec

42. 2.64 rad/sec

50. 2.11 ft

51. 6.48 ft/sec

52. $\omega_A = 20$ rad/sec
$\omega_B = 10$ rad/sec

55. 7.59 ft/sec

56. 7.64 ft/sec

63. 3.26 ft/sec

64. 4.68 ft/sec

66. 14.5 ft/sec

67. 17.2 ft/sec

68. 0.862 rad/sec

69. 8.05 ft/sec

70. 11.72 ft/sec

CHAPTER 19

1. $l_x = 0.354l$
$l_y = -0.613l$
$l_z = 0.707l$

3. 12.80 rad/sec

7. $|\boldsymbol{M}| = 5.5$ lb-ft

8. $\dot{\psi}_{av} = 0.00205$ rad/sec

9. $\dot{\psi}_{av} = 0.00274$ rad/sec

24. 53.1 rad/sec

26. $\dot{\phi} = 2.52$ rad/sec;
$\dot{\psi} = 3.22$ rad/sec

CHAPTER 20

2. $\omega_n = 13.9$ rad/sec

3. $\omega_n = (a/b)\sqrt{(kg/W)}$ rad/sec

4. $\omega_n = \sqrt{2\mu g/L}$ rad/sec

5. Amp. $= \frac{1}{2}$ in; $\omega_n = 27.7$ rad/sec

6. $\omega_n = 21$ rad/sec;
distance = 80.0 in.

7. $K_2 = 47.5$ lb/in.
$\omega = 19.65$ rad/sec

8. 22 rad/sec

10. 2.32 rad/sec

11. 20.3 rad/sec

12. $\omega_n = \sqrt{(K/m - \omega^2)}$

13. 0.1215 ft

14. 16.05 rad/sec
87.9 rad/sec

15. 0.604 sec

16. 1.42 sec

17. $\omega_n = 181$ rad/sec; $\theta = 0.0539$ rad

18. 48.3 rad/sec

19. 0.554 cps

20. $\omega_n = 7.77$ cps; $\theta = 0.382°$

22. $(1/2\pi)\sqrt{[2r^2K/R^2(\frac{1}{2}M+W_1/g)]}$

23. 12.72 rad/sec

24. 235 rad/sec

25. 0.1220°

26. 75.0 rad/sec

27. 2.34 rad/sec

28. 0.132°

29. $k = 1.647$ ft

30. $(1/2\pi)\sqrt{3d^2g/L^2l}$

46. $\frac{1}{8}$ ft

47. 0.005ft

48. 0.0406 ft

49. 0.0264 ft

50. $\theta = C_1 \sin \sqrt{(K_T/I_{zz})}t +$
$C_2 \cos \sqrt{(K_T/I_{zz})}t$

$$\theta = \frac{AI_{zz}}{K_T - I_{zz}\omega^2} \sin \omega t$$

60. -0.0216 ft

61. 0.269×10^{-4} ft

68. 0.221 sec

74. 2.87×10^{-3} ft

80. $p_1^2 = \frac{3}{4}[(K + K_2)/M] +$
$(1/4M)(9K_2^2 + 2KK_2 + K^2)^{1/2}$

85. $\ddot{r}_1 + [(K_1/m_1) - \omega^2]r_1 +$
$(K_2/m_1)(r_1 - r_2) =$
$(K_2/m_1)(r_{1_0} - r_{2_0})$

INDEX

A

Acceleration of a particle:
  Cartesian components, 307–308
  cylindrical coordinates, 313–318
  for different references, 506–516
  path variable, 308–313
  for a single reference, 305
Accelerometer, 327
Air gun, 344
Amplitude (*see* Vibrations)
Analog computers, 731
Analog of mechanical systems, 715–716
Angle of nutation, 653–655
Angle of precession, 653–655
Angle of spin, 653–655
Angular momentum (*see* Moment of momentum)
Angular velocity, definition of, 487
Apogee, 360
Areal velocity, 354
Axis of rotation, definition of, 486

B

Balancing, 585–588
Ballistics of charged particles, 373–381
Ballistics of shells:
  with friction, 369–373
  without friction, 366–369
Binormal vector, 310
Biot-Savart law, 375
Burnout velocity, 357

C

Cathode ray tube, 376–379
Center of mass:
  definition of, 382
  energy considerations, 414–417
  motion of, 381–384
Central force motion, 351–366
  areal velocity, 354
  eccentricity, 356
  escape velocity, 359, 363
  general two-body problem, 356–357
  space mechanics, 357–366
Centrifugal force, 519
Centrifuge, 538
Chasle's theorem, 487–488
  general proof, 739–740
Circuit analog, 715–716
Coefficient of damping, 704
Coefficient of restitution, 448
Complementary solution, 347
Conic sections, 733–735
  directrix, 733
  eccentricity, 733
Conservative force field, 405–407
Coriolis' acceleration vector, 507
Coriolis' force, 517–521
Coulomb's law, 374
Critical damping constant, 706
Cycle (*see* Vibrations)
Cyclones, 520

D

D'Alembert's inertia couple, 599
D'Alembert's force, 351
D'Alembert's principle, 349–351
  for rigid bodies, 599–604
Damping coefficient, 704
Dielectric constant, 374
Differentiation of a vector, 303–305
  for arbitrary moving references, 500–502
  cylindrical coordinates, 313–318
  fixed in a moving reference, 488–493
  path coordinates, 308–313
  rectangular components, 307–308
Directrix, 733
Double-wedge airfoil, 476
Dummy indices, 554
Dynamics, definition of, 301

E

Earth satellites:
  launching of, 357–358
  trajectories, 359–360
Eccentricity, 733
Echo satellite, 477
Einstein, Albert, 438
Electric circuit analog, 715–716

Electric field, 374–375
Electrostatic potential, 407
Ellipsoid of inertia, 554–556
Energy methods:
  for a particle 398–411
  for a system of particles, 411–421
Equilibrium of a rigid body, 604
Equivalent spring constant, 346, 688
Escape velocity, 359, 363
Euler angles:
  definition of, 653–655
  need for, 653
Euler's equations, 570–572
  applications of, 572–585
  simplifications of, 589–599
  using Euler angles, 665–666

F

First-order tensor, 552
First tensor invariant, 564
Flyball governor, 323
Force:
  central, 351
  centrifugal, 519
  conservative, 405–407
  Coriolis, 518–521
  coulombic, 374
  damping, 704
  electric, 374
  gravitational, 351
  inertial, 516–517
  linear restoring, 343, 685
  magnetic, 375
Force potential, 405
Frequency (*see* Vibrations)
Friction function, 369

G

Gravitation law, 351
Gyro:
  Cardan suspension, 660
  compass, 663–665
  single-degree-of-freedom, 659–660
  two-degree-of-freedom, 660–661

H

Hamilton-Jacobi theory, 717
Hamilton's principle, 717
Harmonic motion, 344, 687
Homogeneous differential equation, 699
Homogeneous solids, table of properties, 741
Hyperion, 391

I

Impact, 447
  central impact, 448
  coefficient of restitution, 449
  line of impact, 448
  oblique central impact, 448, 450
  period of deformation, 448
  period of restitution, 449
  plane of contact, 448
Impulse of a force, 440
Impulse turbine, 505
Inertia tensor, 464
Inertial forces, 516–517
Inertial reference, 320
  definition of, 551–552
  definition of terms, 542–545
  ellipsoid of inertia, 554–556
  mass moment of inertia, 542
  mass product of inertia, 542
  parallel axis theorems, 546–548
  principal values, 554–559
  relation to area inertia terms, 545–546
  relation to stress, 541–542
  transformation equations, 548–552
  use of index notation, 552–554
Integration of a vector, 305–307
Irrotational flow, 331

J

Jellet's integrals, 684
Jupiter, 391

K

Kepler's laws, 359
Kinematics:
  definition of, 301
  instantaneous axis of rotation, 488
  of a particle, 301–325
  of a rigid body, 485–541
  rotation, 486
  translation, 485–486
Kinetic energy:
  based on center of mass, 417–421
  of a particle, 399
  relativistic form, 438
  of a rigid body, 620–626
  of a system of particles, 415–417
Kirchhoff's second law, 715

L

Lagrange multiplier, 557
Lagrange's equations, 717
Larmor radius, 381
Light, radiation pressure, 476

Linear momentum:
of a particle, 439–443
of a system of particles, 443–447
vector, 352
Line of nodes, 654
Lissajous figures, 379
Logarithmic decrement, 727
Lumped systems, 349

M

Magnetic field, 375–376
Magnetohydrodynamics, 373
Mars, 390
Mass center (*see* Center of mass)
Mass moment of inertia (*see* Inertia tensor)
Mass product of inertia (*see* Inertia tensor)
Method of undetermined coefficients, 706
Milne's method, 732
Mode shapes (*see* Vibrations)
Moment of momentum:
of a rigid body, 566–569
of a single particle, 457–459
of a system of particles, 459–466
vector, 353
Moon, 391

N

Natural frequency, 688
Newton's third law, 381
Nonhomogeneous differential equations, 699
Nutation:
angle, 655
speed, 655–656
Nutation velocity, 492

O

Oblique central impact (*see* Impact)
Orbit, for satellites, 359–360
Oscilloscope, 377–379
Osculating plane, 308

P

Parallel axis theorems, 546–548
Particle:
concept of, 302
Particular solution, 347
Path function, 399
Perfect gas:
adiabatic expansion, 344, 388
isothermal expansion, 344
Perigee, 360
Period (*see* Vibrations)
Period of deformation, 448–449
Period of restitution, 449
Phase angle (*see* Vibrations)
Phasor diagram, 585
Phasors, 686
Piecewise continuity, 339
Plane motion of rigid bodies, 590–599
Point function, 399
Power, 402–405
Precession:
angle, 655
axis of, 655
regular, 671
retrograde, 671
steady, 658
velocity, 655–656
Precession velocity, 492
Principal axes (*see* Inertia tensor)
Principal normal vector, 309

R

Radius of curvature, 309
Radius of gyration, 554
Rectilinear translation, 337
constant force, 337–339
force is function of position, 342–348
force is function of speed, 340–342
force is function of time, 339–340
several interacting particles, 349–351
Regular precession, 671
Relative motion, simple, 318–320
Relativistic kinetic energy, 438
Relativistic mass, 373
Resonance, 701
Rest mass, 373
Retrograde precession, 671
Rotation, 486
Rotation of rigid bodies, 589–590

S

Saturn, 391
Second-order tensor, 553–554
Second tensor invariant, 564
Semimajor diameter, 734
Semiminor diameter, 734
Small rotations as vectors, 738
Special theory of relativity, 373
Spin:
angle, 655
speed, 655–656
Spin velocity, 492
Spinning top, 673–678
expected nutation, 675–677
with friction, 684
precession of, 677–678
spin of, 677–678
Stabilized platform, 327
Stress ellipsoid, 555
System of particles:
center of mass, 382
Newton's law, 381–382

T

Tensor notation, 552–553
Tensors:
  definition of, 551–554
  first-order, 552
  invariants of, 564
  zero-order, 552
Terminal speed, 386
Third tensor invariant, 564
Thompson, J. J., 395
Torque-free motion, 666–673
Torsiograph, 726
Torsional spring constant, 691
Torsional vibration, 690–692
Towing tank, 400–401
Trajectory of a particle, 366
Translation, 302, 486

V

Vanguard satellite, 360
Velocity of a particle:
  involving arbitrary references, 502–508
  for a single reference, 303
Venus, 390, 391
Vibrating table, 709
Vibrations, 348, 685
  amplitude, 687
  coefficient of damping, 704
  critical damping constant, 706
  critically damped motion, 706
  cycle, 687
  dynamic vibration absorber, 731
  energy methods, 697–699
  free linear, 685–690
  free plane motion, 694
  free three-dimensional, 695
Vibrations (*cont.*)
  free torsional, 690–694
  frequency, 687
  linear restoring force with sinusoidal disturbance, 699–703
  logarithmic decrement, 727
  magnification factor, 709
  mode shapes, 714
  multidegrees of freedom 711–715
  overdamped motion, 705
  period, 687
  phase angle, 687
  relative transmission factor, 726
  simple damping, 703–706
  steady-state, 700
  torsiograph, 726
  transient, 700
  underdamped motion, 705, 706
  vibrating table, 709
  vibrograph, 725

W

Whirlpools, 520
Work-energy relations:
  for a particle, 399–400
  for a rigid body, 634–639
  for a system of particles, 311–314, 736, 737
Work-physiology, 421

Y

Young's modulus, 387

Z

Zero-order tensor, 552